Financial Aid for Persons with Disabilities and Their Families 2012 - 2014

RSP FINANCIAL AID DIRECTORIES
OF INTEREST TO PERSONS WITH
DISABILITIES & THEIR FAMILIES

College Student's Guide to Merit and Other No-Need Funding
Selected as one of the "Outstanding Titles of the Year" by *Choice,* this directory describes 1,300 no-need funding opportunities for college students. 490 pages. ISBN 1588412121. $32.50, plus $7 shipping.

Directory of Financial Aids for Women
There are 1,400+ funding programs set aside for women described in this biennial directory, which has been called "the cream of the crop" by *School Library Journal* and the "best available reference source" by *Guide to Reference.* 552 pages. ISBN 1588412164. $45, plus $7 shipping.

Financial Aid for African Americans
Nearly 1,300 funding opportunities open to African American college students, professionals, and postdoctorates are described in this award-winning directory. 490 pages. ISBN 1588412172. $42.50, plus $7 shipping.

Financial Aid for Asian Americans
This is the source to use if you are looking for funding for Asian Americans, from college-bound high school seniors to professionals and postdoctorates; more than 900 sources of free money are described here. 350 pages. ISBN 1588412180. $40, plus $7 shipping.

Financial Aid for Hispanic Americans
The 1,100 biggest and best sources of free money available to undergraduates, graduates students, professionals, and postdoctorates of Mexican, Puerto Rican, Central American, or other Latin American heritage are described here. 446 pages. ISBN 1588412199. $42.50, plus $7 shipping.

Financial Aid for Native Americans
Detailed information is provided on nearly 1,400 funding opportunities open to American Indians, Native Alaskans, and Native Pacific Islanders for college, graduate school, or professional activities. 506 pages. ISBN 1588412202. $45, plus $7 shipping.

Financial Aid for Research and Creative Activities Abroad
Described here are more than 1,000 scholarships, fellowships, grants, etc. available to support research, professional, or creative activities abroad. 422 pages. ISBN 1588412067. $45, plus $7 shipping.

Financial Aid for Study and Training Abroad
This directory, which the reviewers call "invaluable," describes nearly 1,000 financial aid opportunities available to support study abroad. 362 pages. ISBN 1588412059. $40, plus $7 shipping.

Financial Aid for Persons with Disabilities and Their Families
Formerly issued as *Financial Aid for the Disabled and Their Families,* this directory, which *Library Journal* named one of the "Best Reference Books of the Year," describes nearly 1,400 funding opportunities. 510 pages. ISBN 158841227X. $40, plus $7 shipping.

Financial Aid for Veterans, Military Personnel, and Their Families
According to *Reference Book Review,* this directory (with its 1,428 entries) is "the most comprehensive guide available on the subject." 488 pages. ISBN 1588412261. $40, plus $7 shipping.

High School Senior's Guide to Merit and Other No-Need Funding
Here's your guide to 1,100 funding programs that *never* look at income level when making awards to college-bound high school seniors. 416 pages. ISBN 1588412105. $29.95, plus $7 shipping.

How to Pay for Your Degree in Nursing
You'll find 900 scholarships, fellowships, loans, grants, and awards here that can be used for study, research, professional, or other nursing activities. 250 pages. ISBN 1588412075. $30, plus $7 shipping.

Kaplan Scholarships
Given 5 stars (highest rating) on Amazon.com, this directory identifies 3,000 of the best sources of "free" money for undergraduate students. 576 pages. ISBN 1419553089. $22.50, plus $7 shipping.

Money for Christian College Students
This is the only directory to describe 850 funding opportunities available to support Christian students working on an undergraduate or graduate degree. 264 pages. ISBN 1588412253. $30, plus $7 shipping.

Money for Graduate Students in the Social & Behavioral Sciences
Looking for money to pay for a graduate degree in the social/behavioral sciences? Here are 1,100 funding programs for you. 316 pages. ISBN 1588412016. $42.50, plus $7 shipping.

Financial Aid for Persons with Disabilities and Their Families 2012 - 2014

Thirteenth Edition

Gail A. Schlachter
R. David Weber

A Listing of Scholarships, Fellowships, Grants-in-Aid, and Other Sources of Free Money Available Primarily or Exclusively to Persons with Disabilities or Members of Their Families, Plus a Set of Six Indexes: Program Title, Sponsoring Organization, Residency, Tenability, Subject, and Deadline Date

Formerly Published as *Financial Aid for the Disabled and Their Families*

Reference Service Press
El Dorado Hills, California

Previously published as:
Financial Aid for the Disabled and Their Families

ISBN 10: 158841227X
ISBN 13: 9781588412270
ISSN: 0898-9222

10 9 8 7 6 5 4 3 2 1

Reference Service Press (RSP) began in 1977 with a single financial aid publication *(Directory of Financial Aids for Women)* and now specializes in the development of financial aid resources in multiple formats, including books, print-on-demand reports, eBooks, and online sources. Long recognized as a leader in the field, RSP has been called, by the *Simba Report on Directory Publishing,* "a true success in the world of independent directory publishers." Both Kaplan Educational Centers and Military.com have hailed RSP as "the leading authority on scholarships."

Reference Service Press
El Dorado Hills Business Park
5000 Windplay Drive, Suite 4
El Dorado Hills, CA 95762-9319
     (916) 939-9620
     Fax: (916) 939-9626
     E-mail: info@rspfunding.com
Visit our web site: www.rspfunding.com

Manufactured in the United States of America

Price: $40.00, plus $7 shipping.

ACADEMIC INSTITUTIONS, LIBRARIES, ORGANIZATIONS, AND OTHER QUANTITY BUYERS:
Discounts on this book are available for bulk purchases. Write or call for information on our discount programs.

Contents

Introduction

WHY THIS DIRECTORY IS NEEDED

With a total population of more than 50 million, the disabled constitute America's largest (and fastest growing) "minority" group. Each year, billions of dollars in financial aid are set aside to assist persons with disabilities, along with members of their families. But, how can these individuals find out about the available funding?

While numerous print and online listings have been prepared to identify and describe general financial aid opportunities (those open to all segments of society), none of those resources have ever covered more than a small portion of the programs aimed primarily or exclusively at individuals with disabilities or their family members. That's why Gail A. Schlachter and R. David Weber biennially issue *Financial Aid for Persons with Disabilities and Their Families* (formerly published as *Financial Aid for the Disabled and Their Families),* which identifies billions of dollars set aside each year specifically for members of these groups to support study, research, creative activities, travel, career development, emergencies, and much more.

WHAT'S UNIQUE ABOUT THE DIRECTORY

Financial Aid for Persons with Disabilities and Their Families is the first and only publication to identify and provide comprehensive information on the nearly 1,400 programs established to provide funding to those with physical, sensory, or other disabilities, as well as to their family members. The listings in this book cover every major field of study, are sponsored by more than 600 different private and public agencies and organizations, and are open to all levels of applicants—from high school and college students to professionals, postdoctorates, and others. And, not only does *Financial Aid for Persons with Disabilities and Their Families* provide the most comprehensive coverage of available funding, it also displays the most informative program descriptions (on the average, more than twice the detail found in any other listing).

In addition to this extensive and focused coverage, the 2012-2014 edition of the directory offers several other unique features. First, all funding described here is substantial; every program offers at least $1,000, and many award $10,000 or more. Even better, all of this is "free" money; not one dollar will ever need to be repaid (provided, of course, recipients meet the program requirements). Another plus: you can take the money awarded by these funding programs to any number of locations. Unlike other financial aid directories, which often list large numbers of scholarships available only to students enrolled at one specific school, all of the entries in this book are "portable." And, many of the programs listed here have never been covered in other financial aid directories. So, even if you have searched elsewhere, you will want to look here for new leads.

Here's another advantage: unlike other funding directories, which generally follow a straight alphabetical arrangement, this one groups entries by both type of disability (e.g., hearing impairments, visual impairments) and type of funding (e.g., scholarships, grants-in-aid)—making it easy for a user to search for appropriate programs. The same convenience is offered in the indexes, where the entries are also subdivided by disability and funding type. With this unique arrangement, users with one set of characteristics (e.g., persons with hearing impairments) will be able to find all programs set aside specifically for them—and not be distracted or have to waste time sorting through descriptions of programs intended for individuals with other types of disabilities.

In fact, everything about the directory has been designed to make your search for funding as easy as possible. You can identify programs not only by recipient group and type of funding, but also by program title, sponsoring organizations, where you live, where you want to spend the money, individual subject areas, and even deadline date (so fundseekers working within specific time constraints can locate programs that are still open). Plus, you'll find all the information you need to decide if a program is a match for you: purpose, eligibility requirements, financial data, duration, special features, limitations, number awarded, and application date. You even get fax numbers, toll-free numbers, e-mail addresses, and web site locations (when available), along with complete contact information, to make your requests for applications proceed smoothly.

Reviewers have consistently praised the unique value of *Financial Aid for Persons with Disabilities and Their Families.* For example, *Disability Resources Monthly* called the directory a "must-have." *College Financial Aid* agreed and, because of its "wealth of information," gave the directory its "four-star" (highest) rating. *American Reference Books Annual* predicted that "this directory will assuredly be a major reference tool in most libraries" and labeled it "an essential purchase." The directory has been chosen as one of the "best reference books of the year" by *Library Journal* and as one of the "outstanding reference books of the year" by the New York Public Library, which commended Reference Service Press for its "excellent contribution in an area of publishing where quality is at a premium."

WHAT'S EXCLUDED

While this book is intended to be the most comprehensive source of information on funding available to persons with disabilities and members of their families, there are some types of programs we've specifically excluded from the directory:

- *Awards open equally to all segments of the population.* Only funding opportunities open primarily or exclusively to persons with disabilities, or members of their families, are covered here. For information on unrestricted financial aid programs, see a general directory like *Kaplan Scholarships.*

- *Programs administered by individual academic institutions solely for their own students.* The directory identifies "portable" programs—ones that can be used at any number of schools. Financial aid administered by individual schools specifically for their own students is not covered. Write directly to the schools you are considering to get information on their offerings.

- *Services,* such as training and counseling, that do not involve actual financial assistance to the disabled person. To obtain information on those benefits, check with the appropriate federal, state, local, or private social service agency in your area.

- *Nonmonetary benefits,* such as special license plates for persons with disabilities. To obtain information, check with the appropriate agency in your area.

- *Money for study or research outside the United States.* Since there are comprehensive and up-to-date directories that describe the funding available for study and research abroad (particularly Reference Service Press's biennial *Financial Aid for Study and Training Abroad* and *Financial Aid for Research and Creative Activities Abroad),* only programs that support study, research, or other activities in the United States are covered here.

- *Restrictive programs,* where the funds are generally available only to a limited geographic area (specific cities or counties only), or in limited amounts (under $1,000). To get information on these more restrictive programs, contact Reference Service Press directly or access *RSP FundingFinder,* Reference Service Press's subscription-based comprehensive online funding database.

SAMPLE ENTRY

(1) **[902]**

(2) **SACKS FOR CF SCHOLARSHIPS**

(3) Boomer Esiason Foundation
c/o Jerry Cahill
483 Tenth Avenue, Suite 300
New York, NY 10018
(646) 292-7930   Fax: (646) 292-7945
E-mail: jcahill@esiason.org
Web: esiason.org/thriving-with-cf/scholarships.php

(4) **Summary** To provide financial assistance to undergraduate and graduate students who have cystic fibrosis (CF).

(5) **Eligibility** This program is open to CF patients who are working on an undergraduate or graduate degree. Applicants must submit a letter from their doctor confirming the diagnosis of CF and a list of daily medications, information on financial need, a detailed breakdown of tuition costs from their academic institution, transcripts, and a 2-page essay on 1) their post-graduation goals; and 2) the importance of compliance with CF therapies and what they practice to stay healthy. Selection is based on academic ability, character, leadership potential, community service, financial need, and adherence to daily CF therapy.

(6) **Financial data** The stipend ranges from $3,000 to $10,000. Funds are paid directly to the academic institution to assist in covering the cost of tuition and fees.

(7) **Duration** 1 year; nonrenewable.

(8) **Additional information** This program is funded by a corporate sponsor that donates $1,000 each time a quarterback is sacked on NFL Monday Night Football games.

(9) **Number awarded** 30 each year.

(10) **Deadline** January of each year.

DEFINITION

(1) **Entry number:** Consecutive number that is given to each entry and used to identify the entry in the indexes.

(2) **Program title:** Title of scholarship, fellowship, grant-in-aid, or other source of free money described in the directory.

(3) **Sponsoring organization:** Name, address, telephone number, toll-free number, fax number, e-mail address, and/or web site (when information was supplied) for the organization sponsoring the program.

(4) **Summary:** Identifies the major program requirements; read the rest of the entry for additional detail.

(5) **Eligibility:** Describes qualifications required of applicants, application procedures, and selection process.

(6) **Financial data:** Financial details of the program, including fixed sum, average amount, or range of funds offered, expenses for which funds may and may not be applied, and cash-related benefits supplied (e.g., room and board).

(7) **Duration:** Period for which support is provided; renewal prospects.

(8) **Additional information:** Any unusual (generally nonmonetary) benefits, restrictions, or requirements associated with the program.

(9) **Number awarded:** Total number of recipients each year or other specified period.

(10) **Deadline:** The month by which applications must be submitted.

- *Money that must be repaid.* The focus here is on "free money." If a program requires repayment or charges interest, it's not listed. Now you can find out about billions of dollars in aid and know (if you meet the program requirements) that not one dollar of that will ever need to be repaid.

WHAT'S UPDATED

The preparation of each new edition of *Financial Aid for Persons with Disabilities and Their Families* involves extensive updating and revision. To insure that the information included is both reliable and current, the editors at Reference Service Press 1) reviewed and updated all relevant programs covered in the previous edition of the directory, 2) collected information on all programs open to persons with disabilities and their families that were added to Reference Service Press' funding database since the last edition of the directory, and then 3) searched extensively for new program leads in a variety of sources, including printed directories, news reports, journals, newsletters, house organs, annual reports, and sites on the Internet. Our policy is to write program descriptions only from information supplied in print or online by the sponsoring organization (no information is ever taken from secondary sources). If that information could not be found, we sent up to four letters or e-mails (followed by up to three telephone inquiries, if necessary) to those sponsors. Despite our best efforts, however, some sponsors still failed to respond and, as a result, their programs are not included in this edition of the directory.

The 2012-2014 edition of the directory completely revises and updates the earlier biennial edition. Programs that have ceased operations have been dropped. Profiles of continuing programs have been rewritten to reflect operations in 2012-2014; nearly 75% of these programs reported substantive changes in their locations, requirements (particularly application deadline), or benefits since 2010. In addition, hundreds of new entries have been added to the program section of the directory. The resulting list describes the nearly 1,400 biggest and best sources of free money available to persons with disabilities or members of their families, including scholarships, fellowships, and grants-in-aid.

HOW THE DIRECTORY IS ORGANIZED

Financial Aid for Persons with Disabilities and Their Families is divided into two separate sections: 1) a descriptive list of financial aid programs designed primarily or exclusively for persons with disabilities and their families and 2) a set of six indexes, each designed to target available funding.

Financial Aid Available to Persons with Disabilities and Their Families.   The first section of the directory describes 1,383 funding opportunities aimed primarily or exclusively at persons with disabilities and members of their families. Entries in this section are grouped into the following six chapters, to make it easy to search for funding intended for members of specific disability groups (the list is based on a condensation of the disability categories established in Public Law 94-142, the Education for All Handicapped Children Act):

Any Disability: Funding for persons with any disability (programs that do not specify or restrict the type of eligible disability).

Visual Disabilities: Funding for individuals who have visual impairments (are partially sighted or blind), with or without correction.

Hearing Disabilities: Funding established specifically for individuals who have difficulty in receiving linguistic information, with or without amplification.

Physical/Orthopedic Disabilities: Funding established specifically for individuals with 1) a severe physical/orthopedic impairment caused by birth defects, diseases or disorders (e.g., multiple sclerosis), or other causes (e.g., accidents, amputations); or 2) a severe, chronic disability that was manifested before age 22 (e.g., spina bifida).

Other Disabilities/Disorders: Funding established specifically for individuals who have a communication disorder (such as stuttering or voice impairment), have a learning disability (including such conditions as brain injury and dyslexia), are emotionally disturbed, or have other chronic or acute health problems, such as cancer, tuberculosis, or hemophilia.

Families of the Disabled: Funding established specifically for the children, stepchildren, adopted children, grandchildren, parents, siblings, and other dependents or family members of persons with disabilities.

To make it easy to target available funding, each of these six chapters is then further divided into three main type-of-funding categories:

Scholarships: "Free" money available to support study or research at the undergraduate level in the United States. Usually no return of service or repayment is required.

Fellowships: "Free" money available to support graduate, postgraduate, or postdoctoral study, research, or other activities in the United States. Usually no return of service or repayment is required.

Grants-in-Aid: Funding intended to assist with personal needs, including emergency situations, property and income tax liabilities, assistive technology, and the adaptation of housing and vehicles.

Within each of these categories, entries are arranged alphabetically by program title. Some programs supply assistance to more than one specific group or supply more than one type of assistance, so those are listed in all relevant subsections. For example, since the Steven M. Perez Foundation Scholarships are for students who have survived leukemia or lost a family member to cancer, the program is described in both the Other Disabilities/Disorders *and* Families of the Disabled chapters. Similarly, the Spina Bifida Association of Illinois Scholarships are open to students with spina bifida at the undergraduate and graduate school level, so the program entry is included in both the Scholarships *and* Fellowships sections of the Physical/Orthopedic chapter.

We have designed each program profile to include information, when available, on program title, organization address, telephone number, fax and toll-free numbers, e-mail address, web site, purpose, eligibility, money awarded, duration, special features, limitations, number of awards, and application deadline (refer to the sample on page 7).

Each of the entries in the directory has been written using information provided by the sponsoring organizations (in print or online) through the first half of 2012.

Indexes. To help you find the aid you need, we have constructed six indexes; these will let you access the listings by program title, sponsoring organization, residency, tenability, subject focus, and deadline date. These indexes use a word-by-word alphabetical arrangement. Note: numbers in the index refer to entry numbers, not to page numbers, in the book.

Program Title Index. If you know the name of a particular funding program and want to find out where it is covered in the directory, use the Program Title Index. To assist you in your search, every program is listed by all its known names, former names, and abbreviations. Since one program can be listed in more than one category (e.g., a program providing assistance to persons with disabilities *and* to members of their family for either undergraduate *or* graduate study would be listed in four places), each entry number in the index has been coded to indicate both availability groups (e.g., families of the disabled) and funding types (e.g., scholarship). By using this coding system, readers can easily identify the programs that match their financial needs and eligibility characteristics.

Sponsoring Organization Index. This index provides an alphabetical listing of the 600+ organizations sponsoring financial aid programs represented in the first part of the directory. As in the Program Title Index, entry numbers have been coded to indicate both recipient group and funding type.

Residency Index. Some programs listed in this book are restricted to persons with disabilities or their families in a particular state or region. Others are open to these individuals wherever they live. This index helps you identify programs available only to residents in your area as well as programs that have no residency requirements. To assist you further, we've also indicated the types of funding and intended recipient groups for the programs open to residents in each of the areas listed in the index.

Tenability Index. This index identifies the geographic locations where the funding described in the directory may be used. Index entries (city, county, state, region) are arranged alphabetically and subdivided by funding type and recipient group. Use this index when you or your family members are looking for money to support research, study, or other activities in a particular geographic area.

Subject Index. This index allows the reader to use more than 250 subject headings to access the financial aid programs designed primarily or exclusively for persons with disabilities and members of their families listed in the first part of the directory. Extensive "see" and "see also" references facilitate the search for appropriate financial aid programs.

Calendar Index. Since most financial aid programs have specific deadline dates, some may have closed by the time you begin to look for funding. You can use the Calendar Index to determine which programs are still open. This index is arranged by recipient group and divided by funding type (e.g., scholarships, grants-in-aid) and month during which the deadline falls. Filing dates can and quite often do vary from year to year; consequently, this index should be used only as a guide for deadlines beyond 2014.

HOW TO USE THE DIRECTORY

Here are some tips to help you get the most out of the funding opportunities listed in this edition of *Financial Aid for Persons with Disabilities and Their Families.*

To Locate Funding Available to Individuals with Various Types of Disabilities. To bring programs with similar eligibility requirements together, the directory is organized into six type-of-disability chapters: Any Disability; Visual Disabilities; Hearing Disabilities; Physical/Orthopedic Disabilities; Other Disabilities/Disorders; and Families of the Disabled. If you have a disability, be sure to check not only the chapter that relates directly to you (e.g., Hearing Disabilities) but also the Any Disability chapter, where programs that do not specify or restrict the type of eligible disabilities are listed.

To Locate Programs Offering a Particular Type of Assistance. If you are looking for programs offering a particular type of funding (e.g., a scholarship for undergraduate courses, a grant-in-aid for emergency situations), turn to the appropriate chapter in the first part (e.g., Any Disability, Families of the Disabled) and read through all the entries in the category that interests you (e.g., scholarships). Since programs with multiple purposes are listed in every appropriate location, each of the three type-of-funding sections functions as a self-contained entity. Because of that, you can browse through any of the sections in the directory without first consulting an index.

To Find Information on a Particular Financial Aid Program. If you know the name of a particular financial aid program, the type of funding offered by the program, and the intended recipients, then go directly to the appropriate category in the first section of the directory, where you will find the program profiles arranged alphabetically by title. But be careful: program titles can be misleading. For example, The Air Force Health Professions Scholarship Program is available only to graduate students and therefore is listed under Fellowships not Scholarships. If you are looking for a specific program and do not find it in the section you have checked, be sure to refer to the Program Title Index to see if it is covered elsewhere. To save time, always check the Program Title Index first if you know the name of a specific award but are not sure under which category it would be listed.

To Locate Programs Sponsored by a Particular Organization. The Sponsoring Organization Index makes it easy to determine groups that provide financial assistance to persons with disabilities and their families, or to identify specific financial aid programs offered by a particular organization. Each entry number in this index is coded to identify funding type and recipient group, so that you can quickly target appropriate entries.

To Browse Quickly Through the Listings. Turn to the type of funding and recipient categories that interest you and read the "Summary" paragraph in each entry. In seconds, you'll know if this is an opportunity that might apply to you. If it is, read the rest of the information in the entry to make sure you meet all of the program requirements before writing or going online for an application form. Please, save your time and energy. Don't apply if you don't qualify!

To Locate Programs Open to Residents of or Tenable in a Particular Area. The Residency Index identifies financial aid programs open to persons with disabilities or their family members who reside in a particular state, region, or country. The Tenability Index shows where the money can be spent. In both indexes, "see" and "see also" references are used liberally, to help you find the funding that's right for you, and index entries for a particular geographic area are divided by both funding type and recipient group. When using these indexes, always check the listings under the term "United States," since the programs indexed there have no geographic restrictions and can be used in any area.

To Locate Financial Aid Programs for Persons with Disabilities and Their Families in a Particular Subject Area. Turn to the Subject Index first if you are interested in identifying financial aid programs for individuals with disabilities or their family members that focus on a particular subject area. To help you target your search, the recipient group (e.g., hearing disabilities) and types of funding (scholarships, fellowships, grants-in-aid) are clearly identified. Extensive cross-references are provided.

To Locate Financial Aid Programs for Persons with Disabilities and Their Families by Deadline Date. If you are working with specific time constraints and want to weed out the financial aid programs whose filing dates you won't be able to meet, turn first to the Calendar Index and check the program references listed under the funding type, recipient group, and month of interest to you. Note: not all sponsoring organizations supplied deadline information; those programs are listed under the "Deadline not specified" entries in the index. To identify every relevant financial aid program, regardless of filing dates, read through all the entries in each of the recipient chapters (e.g., Any Disability) and funding categories that apply.

To Locate Financial Aid Programs Open to All Segments of the Population. Only programs available specifically to individuals with disabilities or their family members are listed in this publication. However, there are thousands of other programs open equally to all segments of the population for which persons with disabilities and their families could apply. To identify those general programs, talk to your local librarian or financial aid officer, look at the RSP print resources listed opposite the title page in this directory, or see if your library subscribes to *RSP FundingFinder,* Reference Service Press' interactive online funding database (or, go online to www.rspfunding.com/esubscriptions.html).

PLANS TO UPDATE THE DIRECTORY

This volume, covering 2012-2014, is the thirteenth biennial edition of *Financial Aid for Persons with Disabilities and Their Families.* The next edition will cover the years 2014-2016 and will be released in the first half of 2014.

OTHER RELATED PUBLICATIONS

In addition to *Financial Aid for Persons with Disabilities and Their Families,* Reference Service Press publishes several other titles for fundseekers, including *Directory of Financial Aids for Women* and *College Student's Guide to Merit and Other No-Need Funding.* For more information on these and other related publications, you can 1) write to Reference Service Press' Marketing Department at 5000 Windplay Drive, Suite 4, El Dorado Hills, CA 95762; 2) call us at (916) 939-9620; 3) send us an e-mail at info@rspfunding.com; 4) fax us at (916) 939-9626; or 5) visit us online: www.rspfunding.com.

ACKNOWLEDGEMENTS

A debt of gratitude is owed all the organizations that contributed information to this edition of *Financial Aid for Persons with Disabilities and Their Families.* Their generous cooperation has helped to make this publication a current and comprehensive survey of awards.

ABOUT THE AUTHORS

Dr. Gail A. Schlachter has worked for more than three decades as a library manager, a library educator, and an administrator of library-related publishing companies. Among the many reference books to her credit are the biennially-issued *Money for Graduate Students in the Arts & Humanities* and two award-winning bibliographic guides: *Minorities and Women: A Guide to Reference Literature in the Social Sciences* (which was chosen as an "Outstanding Reference Title of the Year" by *Choice)* and *Reference Sources in Library and Information Services* (which won the first Knowledge Industry Publications "Award for Library Literature"). She was the reference book review editor of *RQ* (now *Reference and User Services Quarterly)* for 10 years, is a past president of the American Library Association's Reference and User Services Association (RUSA, formerly RASD), is serving her fifth term on the American Library Association's governing council, and is a former editor-in-chief of *Reference and User Services Quarterly.* In recognition of her outstanding contributions to reference service, Dr. Schlachter was named the "Outstanding Alumna" by the University of Wisconsin School of Library and Information Studies and has been awarded both the Isadore Gilbert Mudge Citation and the Louis Shores/Oryx Press Award.

Dr. R. David Weber taught history and economics at Los Angeles Harbor College (in Wilmington, California) for many years and continues to teach history as an emeritus professor. During his years of full-time teaching there, and at East Los Angeles College, he directed the Honors Program and was frequently selected as the "Teacher of the Year." Dr. Weber is the author of several critically-acclaimed reference works, including *Dissertations in Urban History* and the three-volume *Energy Information Guide.* With Gail Schlachter, he is the author of Reference Service Press' *College Student's Guide to Merit and Other No-Need Funding,* which was selected by *Choice* as one of the "Outstanding Academic Titles of the Year," and a number of other award-winning financial aid titles, including *Financial Aid for Hispanic Americans,* which was named the "Editor's Choice" by *Reference Books Bulletin.*

Financial Aid Programs for Persons with Disabilities and Their Families

Any Disability ●

Visual Disabilities ●

Hearing Disabilities ●

Physical/Orthopedic Disabilities ●

Other Disabilities/Disorders ●

Families of the Disabled ●

Any Disability

Scholarships   ●

Fellowships   ●

Grants-in-Aid   ●

Described here are 323 funding opportunities that do not specify or restrict the type of eligible disability. Of these, 94 cover scholarships (to pursue study, research, or other activities on the undergraduate level in the United States); 67 describe fellowships or other awards (to support graduate or postgraduate study, research, or other activities in the United States); and 162 identify grants-in-aid (to pay for emergency situations, travel, income/property tax liabilities, the acquisition of assistive technology, or other personal needs). All of this is "free" money. Not one dollar will need to be repaid (provided, of course, that recipients meet all program requirements). If you are looking for a particular program and don't find it in this section, be sure to check the Program Title Index to see if it is covered elsewhere in the directory.

Scholarships

[1]
ACADEMY OF SPECIAL DREAMS FOUNDATION COLLEGE SCHOLARSHIP FUND

Academy of Special Dreams Foundation
115 West California Boulevard, Suite 326
Pasadena, CA 91105
E-mail: specialacademy@gmail.com
Web: www.specialacademy.org/scholarships

Summary To provide funding to college students who have a disability and are majoring in a field of art.

Eligibility This program is open to students who have a disability and are enrolled or planning to enroll full or part time at a college, university, trade school, art school, or other art degree program. Applicants must be majoring or planning to major in any field of art (e.g., design, painting, drawing, photography, sculpture, video, animation). They must be lawful residents of the United States. Along with their application, they must submit 1) a statement from their physician or other medical provider describing their disability; 2) a portfolio of at least 5 unique works of art; 3) a personal statement describing their commitment to art.

Financial data Stipends are $1,000, $500, or $250.

Duration 1 year.

Number awarded Varies each year.

Deadline Applications may be submitted at any time.

[2]
ACADEMY OF TELEVISION ARTS & SCIENCES COLLEGE TELEVISION AWARDS

Academy of Television Arts & Sciences Foundation
Attn: Education Department
5220 Lankershim Boulevard
North Hollywood, CA 91601-3109
(818) 754-2820   Fax: (818) 761-ATAS
E-mail: cta@emmys.org
Web: www.emmysfoundation.org

Summary To recognize and reward outstanding videos by disabled and other college students.

Eligibility This competition is open to undergraduate and graduate students currently enrolled at a college, university, or community college. U.S. citizenship is not required, but all applicants must be enrolled at schools in the United States. All entries must have been produced for school-related classes, groups, or projects. Competitions are held in the following categories: 1) animation (all forms); 2) children's; 3) comedy; 4) commercial; 5) documentary; 6) drama; 7) interactive media; 8) magazine; 9) music (best composition); 10) music (best use of music); 11) narrative series (comedy, drama, or webisodes); and 12) newscast. Entries in the comedy, documentary, drama, and narrative series category may not exceed 1 hour. Entries in the animation, music, children's, newscast, and magazine categories may not exceed 30 minutes. Commercial entries may not exceed 1 minute and must advertise a product or service. For the narrative series category, at least 6 episodes must have been produced and 2 episodes must be submitted. For the interactive media category, the video recording may not exceed 6 minutes in length. The children's category must be targeted for preschool through 15 years of age.

Financial data In each category, first place is $2,000, second $1,000, and third $500. In addition, first-place winners in certain categories receive film stock from Kodak Entertainment Imaging. The Loreen Arbus Focus on Disability Scholarship of $10,000 is awarded to 1) a writer, producer, or director who has a disability, 2) a producer whose work focuses on people with disabilities, or 3) a piece that features a person with a disability as a main character. The Directing Award is $1,000 and the Seymour Bricker Family Humanitarian Award of $4,000 is presented to the first-place winner from any category whose work best represents a humanitarian concern.

Duration The competition is held annually.

Additional data Excerpts from the winning films and videos are screened at the awards ceremony, known as the College Awards Gala. They are also screened at the academy's "Festival of Winners," the day after the Awards Gala. The first entry is free. Each subsequent entry requires payment of a $25 fee.

Number awarded 39 each year: 1 first-place winner, 1 second-place winner, and 1 third-place winner in each category plus the 3 special awards.

Deadline January of each year.

[3]
AMERICAN ASSOCIATION ON HEALTH AND DISABILITY SCHOLARSHIPS

American Association on Health and Disability
Attn: Scholarship Committee
110 North Washington Street, Suite 328-J
Rockville, MD 20850
(301) 545-6140, ext. 206   Fax: (301) 545-6144
E-mail: contact@aahd.us
Web: www.aahd.us

Summary To provide financial assistance to undergraduate and graduate students who have a disability, especially those studying a field related to health and disability.

Eligibility This program is open to high school graduates who have a documented disability and are enrolled in an accredited 4-year college or university as a full-time undergraduate or full- or part-time graduate student. Preference is given to students working on a degree in public health, disability studies, health promotion, or other field related to health and disability. Along with their application, they must submit a 3-page personal statement that includes a personal history, educational and career goals, extracurricular activities, and reasons why they should be selected to receive this scholarship. U.S. citizenship or permanent resident status is required.

Financial data Stipends range up to $1,000.

Duration 1 year.

Additional data This program was established in 2009.

Number awarded 2 each year.
Deadline November of each year.

[4]
ARKANSAS GOVERNOR'S COMMISSION ON PEOPLE WITH DISABILITIES SCHOLARSHIPS

Arkansas Governor's Commission on People with
  Disabilities
Attn: Scholarship Committee
26 Corporate Hill Drive
Little Rock, AR 72205
(501) 296-1637   Fax: (501) 296-1883
TDD: (501) 296-1637
Web: ace.arkansas.gov

Summary To provide financial assistance to Arkansas students with disabilities who are interested in attending college or graduate school in any state.
Eligibility This program is open to high school seniors, high school graduates, undergraduates, and graduate students who have a disability and are residents of Arkansas. Applicants must be attending or planning to attend a college or university in any state. Selection is based on a description of their disability (20 points), present and past school involvement (10 points), a brief statement on their career goals (15 points), community and volunteer activities (10 points), a brief essay on the positive or negative effects their disability has had on their life thus far (20 points), 3 letters of recommendation (10 points), and financial need (10 points).
Financial data The stipend varies, up to $1,000 per year.
Duration 1 year; recipients may reapply.
Number awarded Several each year.
Deadline February of each year.

[5]
BETTY BACON MEMORIAL SCHOLARSHIP

California Association for Postsecondary Education
  and Disability
Attn: Executive Assistant
71423 Biskra Road
Rancho Mirage, CA 92270
(760) 346-8206   Fax: (760) 340-5725
TDD: (760) 341-4084   E-mail: caped2000@aol.com
Web: www.caped.net/scholarships.html

Summary To provide funding to undergraduate and graduate students in California who have a disability.
Eligibility This program is open to students at public and private colleges and universities in California who have a disability. Undergraduates must have completed at least 6 semester credits and have a GPA of 2.5 or higher. Graduate students must have completed at least 3 semester units and have a GPA of 3.0 or higher. Along with their application, they must submit a 1-page personal letter that demonstrates their writing skills, progress towards meeting their educational and vocational goals, management of their disability, and involvement in community activities. They must also submit a recommendation from a faculty

person, verification of disability, official transcripts, proof of current enrollment, and documentation of financial need.
Financial data The stipend is $1,000.
Duration 1 year.
Number awarded 1 each year.
Deadline September of each year.

[6]
BMO CAPITAL MARKETS LIME CONNECT EQUITY THROUGH EDUCATION SCHOLARSHIPS FOR STUDENTS WITH DISABILITIES

Lime Connect, Inc.
590 Madison Avenue, 21st Floor
New York, NY 10022
(212) 521-4469   Fax: (212) 521-4099
E-mail: info@limeconnect.com
Web: www.limeconnect.com/opportunities

Summary To provide financial assistance to students with disabilities working on a bachelor's or graduate degree in a business-related field at a college or university in Canada or the United States.
Eligibility This program is open to sophomores and graduate students at 4-year colleges and universities in the United States or Canada who have a disability. International students with disabilities enrolled at universities in the United States or Canada are also eligible. Applicants must be working full time on a degree in a business-related field. Along with their application, they must submit an essay on their career goals and why they believe they should be selected to receive this scholarship. Financial need is not considered in the selection process.
Financial data The stipend is $10,000 for students at U.S. universities or $C5,000 for students at Canadian universities.
Duration 1 year.
Additional data This program is jointly sponsored by BMO Capital Markets and Lime Connect, an organization founded in 2006 to promote employment of people with disabilities. BMO Capital Markets established its Equity Through Education program in 2005 and in 2011 invited Lime Connect to administer a component of the program for students with disabilities.
Number awarded Varies each year.
Deadline May of each year.

[7]
BUILDING RURAL INITIATIVE FOR DISABLED THROUGH GROUP EFFORT (B.R.I.D.G.E.) ENDOWMENT FUND SCHOLARSHIPS

National FFA Organization
Attn: Scholarship Office
6060 FFA Drive
P.O. Box 68960
Indianapolis, IN 46268-0960
(317) 802-4419   Fax: (317) 802-5419
E-mail: scholarships@ffa.org
Web: www.ffa.org

Summary To provide funding to FFA members with disabilities who are interested in studying agriculture in college.

Eligibility This program is open to members with physical disabilities who are graduating high school seniors planning to enroll full time in college. Applicants must be interested in working on a 2- or 4-year degree in agriculture. Selection is based on academic achievement (10 points for GPA, 10 points for SAT or ACT score, 10 points for class rank), leadership in FFA activities (30 points), leadership in community activities (10 points), and participation in the Supervised Agricultural Experience (SAE) program (30 points). U.S. citizenship is required.

Financial data The stipend is $5,000.

Duration 1 year; nonrenewable.

Additional data This program is supported by the Dr. Scholl Foundation, Outdoor Advertising Association of America, and numerous individuals.

Number awarded 1 or more each year.

Deadline February of each year.

[8]
CALIFORNIA ASSOCIATION FOR POSTSECONDARY EDUCATION AND DISABILITY GENERAL EXCELLENCE SCHOLARSHIP

California Association for Postsecondary Education
  and Disability
Attn: Executive Assistant
71423 Biskra Road
Rancho Mirage, CA 92270
(760) 346-8206   Fax: (760) 340-5275
TDD: (760) 341-4084   E-mail: caped2000@aol.com
Web: www.caped.net/scholarships.html

Summary To provide financial assistance to undergraduate and graduate students in California who have a disability and can demonstrate academic achievement and involvement in community and campus activities.

Eligibility This program is open to students at public and private colleges and universities in California who have a disability. Undergraduates must have completed at least 6 semester credits and have a GPA of 2.5 or higher. Graduate students must have completed at least 3 semester units and have a GPA of 3.0 or higher. Applicants must submit a 1-page personal letter that demonstrates their writing skills, progress towards meeting their educational and vocational goals, management of their disability, and involvement in community activities. They must also submit a letter of recommendation from a faculty member, verification of disability, official transcripts, proof of current enrollment, and documentation of financial need. This award is presented to the applicant who demonstrates the highest level of academic achievement and involvement in community and campus life.

Financial data The stipend is $1,500.

Duration 1 year.

Number awarded 1 each year.

Deadline September of each year.

[9]
CALIFORNIA-HAWAII ELKS MAJOR PROJECT UNDERGRADUATE SCHOLARSHIP PROGRAM FOR STUDENTS WITH DISABILITIES

California-Hawaii Elks Association
Attn: Scholarship Committee
5450 East Lamona Avenue
Fresno, CA 93727-2224
(559) 255-4531   Fax: (559) 456-2659
Web: www.chea-elks.org/uspsd.html

Summary To provide financial assistance to residents of California and Hawaii who have a disability and are interested in attending college in any state.

Eligibility This program is open to residents of California or Hawaii who have a physical impairment, neurological impairment, visual impairment, hearing impairment, and/or speech/language disorder. Applicants must be a senior in high school, be a high school graduate, or have passed the GED test. They must be planning to attend a college, university, community college, or vocational school in any state. U.S. citizenship is required. Selection is based on financial need, GPA, severity of disability, seriousness of purpose, and depth of character. Applications are available from an Elks Lodge in California or Hawaii; students must first request an interview with the lodge's scholarship chairman, secretary, or Exalted Ruler.

Financial data The stipend is $2,000 per year for 4-year colleges or universities or $1,000 for community colleges and vocational schools.

Duration 1 year; may be renewed for up to 3 additional years or until completion of an undergraduate degree, whichever occurs first.

Number awarded 20 to 30 each year.

Deadline March of each year.

[10]
CARVER SCHOLARS PROGRAM

Roy J. Carver Charitable Trust
202 Iowa Avenue
Muscatine, IA 52761-3733
(563) 263-4010   Fax: (563) 263-1547
E-mail: info@carvertrust.org
Web: www.carvertrust.org

Summary To provide money for college to disabled and other students in Iowa who have overcome significant obstacles to attend college.

Eligibility This program is open to students attending the 3 public universities in Iowa, the 18 participating private 4-year colleges and universities in the state, or a community college in Iowa and planning to transfer to 1 of those 4-year institutions. Applicants must be sophomores seeking support for their junior year. They must present evidence of unusual social and/or other barriers to attending college full time; examples include, but are not limited to, students who 1) are from 1-parent families; 2) are attending college while working full time; 3) have social, mental, or physical disabilities; or 4) have families to support. They must have graduated from a high school in Iowa or have been residents of the state for at least 5 consecutive years immediately prior to applying, be full-time students, have at least a 2.8 GPA, be U.S. citizens, and submit a financial profile indicating insufficient personal, family, and institutional resources to pay full-time college tuition. A particular goal of the program is to assist students "who fall between the cracks of other financial aid programs." Applications must be submitted to the financial aid office at the Iowa college or university the applicant attends.

Financial data Stipends generally average $5,200 at public universities or $7,600 at private colleges in Iowa.

Duration 1 year; may be renewed 1 additional year.

Additional data This program was established in 1988.

Number awarded Varies each year; since the program's establishment, it has awarded more than 2,240 scholarships worth more than $16.8 million.

Deadline March of each year.

[11]
CATHERINE T. MURRAY MEMORIAL SCHOLARSHIP

Ocean State Center for Independent Living
Attn: Office Manager
1944 Warwick Avenue
Warwick, RI 02889
(401) 738-1013, ext. 10   Toll Free: (866) 857-1161
Fax: (401) 738-1083   TDD: (401) 738-1015
E-mail: cmckenna@oscil.org
Web: www.oscil.org/murray_scholarship.htm

Summary To provide financial assistance to residents of Rhode Island who have a disability and are interested in attending college in any state.

Eligibility This program is open to residents of Rhode Island who have a significant disability. Applicants must be enrolled or planning to enroll in an academic, trade, or vocational educational program in any state and/or to acquire assistive or adaptive equipment or devices to access such an educational opportunity. Along with their application, they must submit a 1-page essay describing their career goals and plans. Selection is based on that essay (15 points), activities (5 points), accurate completion of the application (5 points), and financial need (5 points).

Financial data The stipend is $1,000.

Duration 1 year.

Additional data This program was established in 1995.

Number awarded 1 each year.

Deadline March of each year.

[12]
CENTRAL INTELLIGENCE AGENCY UNDERGRADUATE SCHOLARSHIP PROGRAM

Central Intelligence Agency
Attn: Human Resource Management
Recruitment and Retention Center, 4B14-034 DD1
Washington, DC 20505
(703) 371-2107
Web: www.cia.gov

Summary To provide funding and work experience to high school seniors and college sophomores, especially minorities and people with disabilities, who are interested in working for the Central Intelligence Agency (CIA) after graduation from college.

Eligibility This program is open to U.S. citizens who are either high school seniors or college freshmen or sophomores. Seniors must be at least 18 years of age by April of the year they apply and have minimum scores of 1500 on the SAT (1000 on critical reading and mathematics and 500 on writing) or 21 on the ACT. College students must have a GPA of 3.0 or higher. All applicants must be able to demonstrate financial need (household income of $70,000 or less for a family of 4 or $80,000 or less for a family of 5 or more) and be able to meet the same employment standards as permanent employees of the CIA. This program was developed, in part, to assist minority and disabled students.

Financial data Scholars are provided a salary, an optional benefits package (health, dental, and vision insurance, life insurance, and retirement), and up to $18,000 per year for tuition, fees, books, and supplies. They must agree to continue employment with the CIA after college graduation for a period 1.5 times the length of their college support.

Duration 1 year; may be renewed if the student maintains a GPA of 3.0 or higher and full-time enrollment in a 4- or 5-year college program.

Additional data Scholars work each summer at a CIA facility. In addition to a salary, they receive the cost of transportation between school and the Washington, D.C. area and a housing allowance.

Number awarded Varies each year.

Deadline October of each year.

[13]
CFA INSTITUTE 11 SEPTEMBER MEMORIAL SCHOLARSHIP

CFA Institute
Attn: Research Foundation
560 Ray C. Hunt Drive
P.O. Box 2082
Charlottesville, VA 22902-2082
(434) 951-5499   Toll Free: (800) 237-8132
Fax: (434) 951-5240   E-mail: rf@cfainstitute.org
Web: www.cfainstitute.org

Summary To provide financial assistance to individuals and their families who were disabled or killed in the September 11, 2001 terrorist attacks and wish to major in business-related fields in college.

Eligibility This program is open to residents of any state or country who either 1) were permanently disabled in the attacks of September 11, 2001; or 2) are the spouses, domestic partners, or children of anyone killed or permanently disabled in the attacks. Applicants must be working full or part time on an undergraduate degree in finance, economics, accounting, or business ethics. Selection is based on demonstrated leadership and good citizenship, academic record, and financial need.

Financial data Stipends range up to $25,000 per year, depending on the need of the recipient.

Duration 1 year; renewable up to 4 additional years.

Additional data The CFA (Chartered Financial Analyst) Institute was formerly the Association for Investment Management and Research (AIMR). It lost at least 56 of its members and CFA candidates in the terrorist attacks of 11 September. This program is managed by Scholarship Management Services, a division of Scholarship America.

Number awarded Varies each year; recently, 12 of these scholarships were awarded.

Deadline May of each year.

[14]
CHIEF MASTER SERGEANTS OF THE AIR FORCE SCHOLARSHIPS

Air Force Sergeants Association
Attn: Scholarship Coordinator
5211 Auth Road
Suitland, MD 20746
(301) 899-3500 Toll Free: (800) 638-0594
Fax: (301) 899-8136 E-mail: balsobrooks@hqafsa.org
Web: www.hqafsa.org

Summary To provide financial assistance for college to the dependent children of enlisted Air Force personnel, particularly those facing special challenges.

Eligibility This program is open to the unmarried children (including stepchildren and legally adopted children) of enlisted active-duty, retired, or veteran members of the U.S. Air Force, Air National Guard, or Air Force Reserves. Applicants must be attending or planning to attend an accredited academic institution. They must have an unweighted GPA of 3.5 or higher. Along with their application, they must submit 1) a paragraph on their life objectives and what they plan to do with the education they receive; and 2) an essay on the most urgent problem facing society today. High school seniors must also submit a transcript of all high school grades and a record of their SAT or ACT scores. Selection is based on academic record, character, leadership skills, writing ability, versatility, and potential for success. Financial need is not a consideration. A unique aspect of these scholarships is that applicants may supply additional information regarding circumstances that entitle them to special consideration; examples of such circumstances include student disabilities, financial hardships, parent disabled and unable to work, parent missing in action/killed in action/prisoner of war, or other unusual extenuating circumstances.

Financial data Stipends range from $1,000 to $3,000; funds may be used for tuition, room and board, fees, books, supplies, and transportation.

Duration 1 year; may be renewed if the recipient maintains full-time enrollment.

Additional data The Air Force Sergeants Association administers this program on behalf of the Airmen Memorial Foundation. It was established in 1987 and named in honor of CMSAF Richard D. Kisling, the late third Chief Master Sergeant of the Air Force. In 1997, following the deaths of CMSAF's (Retired) Andrews and Harlow, it was

given its current name. The highest-ranked applicant receives the Paul W. Airey Memorial Scholarship.

Number awarded 1 at $3,000, 1 at $2,500, 1 at $2,000, 1 at $1,500 and 7 at $1,000. Since this program began, it has awarded more than $250,000.

Deadline March of each year.

[15]
CHRISTIAN A. HERTER MEMORIAL SCHOLARSHIP

Massachusetts Office of Student Financial Assistance
454 Broadway, Suite 200
Revere, MA 02151
(617) 391-6070 Fax: (617) 727-0667
E-mail: osfa@osfa.mass.edu
Web: www.osfa.mass.edu

Summary To provide financial assistance to disabled and other Massachusetts high school students who have overcome major adversities and plan to attend college in any state.

Eligibility This program is open to residents of Massachusetts who are attending a secondary school in grades 10-11, have a cumulative GPA of 2.5 or higher, and are planning to work full time on an undergraduate degree at an accredited institution in the United States. Applicants must be able to demonstrate 1) difficult personal circumstances in their lives (e.g., physical or mental abuse, catastrophic illness) or other personal obstacles or hardships of a societal, geographic, mental, or physical nature; 2) high financial need; and 3) strong academic promise to continue their education beyond high school at a college or university. They must be nominated by their school or a public agency. U.S. citizenship or permanent resident status is required.

Financial data Awards cover up to 50% of the student's unmet financial need.

Duration 4 years.

Additional data This program was established in 1972.

Number awarded 25 each year.

Deadline February of each year.

[16]
CINDY KOLB MEMORIAL SCHOLARSHIP

California Association for Postsecondary Education
 and Disability
Attn: Executive Assistant
71423 Biskra Road
Rancho Mirage, CA 92270
(760) 346-8206 Fax: (760) 340-5275
TDD: (760) 341-4084 E-mail: caped2000@aol.com
Web: www.caped.net/scholarships.html

Summary To provide financial assistance to students enrolled at 4-year college and universities in California who have a disability.

Eligibility This program is open to students at 4-year colleges and universities in California who have a disability. Applicants must have completed at least 6 semester credits with a GPA of 2.5 or higher. Along with their application, they must submit a 1-page personal letter that demonstrates their writing skills, progress towards meeting their educational and vocational goals, management of their disability, and involvement in community activities. They must also submit a recommendation from a faculty member, verification of disability, official transcripts, proof of current enrollment, and documentation of financial need.

Financial data The stipend is $1,000.

Duration 1 year.

Number awarded 1 each year.

Deadline September of each year.

[17]
COURAGE CENTER SCHOLARSHIP FOR PEOPLE WITH DISABILITIES

Courage Center
Attn: Vocational Services Department
3915 Golden Valley Road
Minneapolis, MN 55422
(763) 520-0553   Toll Free: (888) 8-INTAKE
Fax: (763) 520-0392   TDD: (763) 520-0245
E-mail: vocationalservices@couragecenter.org
Web: www.couragecenter.org

Summary To provide financial assistance to Minnesota residents who have a disability and are interested in attending college in any state.

Eligibility This program is open to U.S. citizens who are residents of Minnesota or have received Courage Center services. Applicants must have a sensory impairment or physical disability and a desire to gain technical expertise beyond high school. They must be attending or planning to attend a college or technical school in any state. Along with their application, they must submit a concise essay that reflects their educational aspirations, career goals, and how a scholarship will help meet their needs. Selection is based on that essay, employment history, honors and awards, leadership experience, and financial need. Graduation ranking is not considered.

Financial data The stipend is $1,000.

Duration 1 year.

Number awarded 1 or more each year.

Deadline May of each year.

[18]
DEXTER G. JOHNSON EDUCATIONAL AND BENEVOLENT TRUST GRANTS

Dexter G. Johnson Educational and Benevolent Trust
Attn: Betty Crews
P.O. Box 26663
Oklahoma City, OK 73126-0663
(405) 232-3340   Fax: (405) 232-3340

Summary To provide financial assistance for vocational training, audiological evaluations, corrective surgery, speech therapy, or medical devices to the children of residents of Oklahoma who have disabilities.

Eligibility Residents of Oklahoma with disabilities are eligible to apply for this program for their children if they need financial assistance for vocational training, audiolog-

ical evaluations, corrective surgery, speech therapy, or orthopedic or hearing aid devices.

Financial data Grants range from $70 to $2,500.

Number awarded Varies; approximately 10 each year.

Deadline Applications may be submitted at any time.

[19]
DISABILITY SCHOLARSHIPS FROM MILITARYVALOAN.COM

United States Military V.A. Loan
200 112th Avenue N.E., Suite 204
Bellevue, WA 98004
Toll Free: (888) 516-9990   Fax: (425) 454-7547
E-mail: scholarship@MilitaryVALoan.com
Web: www.militaryvaloan.com

Summary To recognize and reward, with college scholarships, high school seniors who submit outstanding essays about overcoming disability.

Eligibility This program is open to students completing study in a public high school, private high school, or home school and planning to enroll at a college or other institution of higher education. Applicants must submit an essay of 500 to 1,000 words on how they or someone they know overcame disability to do something great. They must be at least 17 years of age and have a GPA of 3.0 or higher.

Financial data The stipend is $1,000.

Duration 1 year.

Additional data A goal of this program is to increase awareness of disability, so applicants are not required to have a disability themselves.

Number awarded 1 for spring and 1 for fall.

Deadline January of each year for spring applicants; July of each year for fall applicants.

[20]
DISABLED PERSON NATIONAL SCHOLARSHIP COMPETITION

Disabled Person, Inc.
P.O. Box 260636
Encinitas, CA 92023-0636
(760) 420-1269   E-mail: info@disabledperson.com
Web: www.disabledperson.com

Summary To recognize and reward, with academic scholarships, undergraduate and graduate students who have a disability and submit outstanding essays on an assigned topic.

Eligibility This competition is open to U.S. citizens who have a disability and are enrolled as full-time undergraduate or graduate students at a college or university in the United States. High school seniors and part-time students are not eligible. Applicants must submit an essay, up to 1,000 words in length, on a topic that changes annually; recently, students were asked to write on, "Define Leadership as it relates to the disability community. Who are the top leaders within the disability community and what have they accomplished?"

Financial data The award is a $1,000 scholarship.

Duration The competition is held annually.

Number awarded 1 in the fall and 1 in the spring.

Deadline October of each year for fall; February of each year for spring.

[21]
DISABLED WAR VETERANS SCHOLARSHIPS

Armed Forces Communications and Electronics Association
Attn: AFCEA Educational Foundation
4400 Fair Lakes Court
Fairfax, VA 22033-3899
(703) 631-6138   Toll Free: (800) 336-4583, ext. 6138
Fax: (703) 631-4693
E-mail: scholarshipsinfo@afcea.org
Web: www.afcea.org/education/scholarships/military

Summary To provide financial assistance to disabled military personnel and veterans who are majoring in specified scientific fields in college.

Eligibility This program is open to active-duty service personnel and honorably discharged U.S. military veterans, Reservists, and National Guard members who are disabled because of wounds received during service in Enduring Freedom (Afghanistan) or Iraqi Freedom operations. Applicants must be enrolled full or part time at an accredited 2- or 4-year college or university or in a distance learning or online degree program. They must be working toward a degree in engineering (aerospace, computer, electrical, or systems), computer science, computer engineering technology, computer network systems, computer information systems, electronics engineering technology, mathematics, physics, information systems management, information systems security, technology management, or other field directly related to the support of U.S. intelligence or national security enterprises. Selection is based on demonstrated academic excellence, leadership, and financial need.

Financial data The stipend is $2,500.

Duration 1 year.

Number awarded 1 for spring and 1 for fall.

Deadline March of each year for fall; November for spring.

[22]
ECCLESTON-CALLAHAN SCHOLARSHIPS

Community Foundation of Central Florida
Attn: Eccleston-Callahan Memorial Fund
1411 Edgewater Drive, Suite 203
Orlando, FL 32804
(407) 872-3050   Fax: (407) 425-2990
E-mail: info@cfcflorida.org
Web: www.cfcflorida.org

Summary To provide financial assistance to students with disabilities enrolled at specified Florida colleges and universities.

Eligibility This program is open to students at designated colleges and universities in Florida who have a mental or physical disability. Applicants must be enrolled full time, have a GPA of 3.0 or higher, be younger than 21 years of age, and be able to demonstrate financial need.

Financial data The stipend is $1,000 per year.

Duration 1 year; may be renewed.

Additional data The participating institutions are the University of Florida, the University of Central Florida, Florida A&M University, Florida State University, Valencia Community College, Seminole Community College, and Orlando Tech.

Number awarded Varies each year.

Deadline April of each year.

[23]
EDWARD T. CONROY MEMORIAL SCHOLARSHIP PROGRAM

Maryland Higher Education Commission
Attn: Office of Student Financial Assistance
6 North Liberty Street, Ground Suite
Baltimore, MD 21201
(410) 767-3300   Toll Free: (800) 974-0203
Fax: (410) 332-0250   TDD: (800) 735-2258
E-mail: osfamail@mhec.state.md.us
Web: www.mhec.state.md.us

Summary To provide financial assistance for college or graduate school in Maryland to children and spouses of victims of the September 11, 2001 terrorist attacks and specified categories of veterans, public safety employees, and their children or spouses.

Eligibility This program is open to entering and continuing undergraduate and graduate students in the following categories: 1) children and surviving spouses of victims of the September 11, 2001 terrorist attacks who died in the World Trade Center in New York City, in the Pentagon in Virginia, or on United Airlines Flight 93 in Pennsylvania; 2) veterans who have, as a direct result of military service, a disability of 25% or greater and have exhausted or are no longer eligible for federal veterans' educational benefits; 3) children of armed forces members whose death or 100% disability was directly caused by military service; 4) POW/MIA veterans of the Vietnam Conflict and their children; 5) state or local public safety officers or volunteers who became 100% disabled in the line of duty; and 6) children and unremarried surviving spouses of state or local public safety employees or volunteers who died or became 100% disabled in the line of duty. The parent, spouse, veteran, POW, or public safety officer or volunteer must have been a resident of Maryland at the time of death or when declared disabled. Financial need is not considered.

Financial data The amount awarded is equal to tuition and fees at a Maryland postsecondary institution, up to $19,000, for children and spouses of the September 11 terrorist attacks or $9,000 for all other recipients.

Duration Up to 5 years of full-time study or 8 years of part-time study.

Additional data Recipients must enroll at a 2- or 4-year Maryland college or university as a full-time or part-time degree-seeking undergraduate or graduate student or attend a private career school.

Number awarded Varies each year.

Deadline July of each year.

[24]
EPA GREATER RESEARCH OPPORTUNITIES (GRO) FELLOWSHIPS FOR UNDERGRADUATE ENVIRONMENTAL STUDY

Environmental Protection Agency
Attn: National Center for Environmental Research
Ariel Rios Building
1200 Pennsylvania Avenue, N.W.
Washington, DC 20460
(202) 347-8049   Toll Free: (800) 490-9194
E-mail: boddie.georgette@epa.gov
Web: epa.gov/ncer/rfa

Summary To provide financial assistance and summer internships to undergraduates who are enrolled at colleges and universities that receive limited federal funding and who are interested in majoring in fields related to the environment.

Eligibility This program is open to U.S. citizens or permanent residents who are enrolled full time at a college or university in this country that receives less than $35 million in federal research and development expenditures. Students attending eligible institutions with significant minority enrollment (defined as Minority-Serving Institutions) are particularly encouraged to apply. Applicants must have at least 2 years remaining for completion of a bachelor's degree in an environmentally-related field, such as physics, biology, health, the social sciences, or engineering. They must be available to work as interns at an EPA facility during the summer between their junior and senior years. A goal of the program is to meet the need for scientists from diverse cultural backgrounds, so the sponsor strongly encourages women, minorities, and persons with disabilities to apply. A minimum average of "B" overall is required.

Financial data The fellowship provides up to $19,700 per year, including up to $10,000 for tuition and academic fees, a stipend of $7,200 ($200 per month for 9 months), and an expense allowance of up to $2,500 for items and activities for the direct benefit of the student's education, such as books, supplies, and travel to professional conferences and workshops. The summer internship grant is $9,500, including a stipend of $7,000 for living expenses, an allowance of $1,000 for travel to and from the site, and an allowance of $1,500 for travel while at the site.

Duration The final 2 years of baccalaureate study, including 12 weeks during the summer between those years.

Additional data This program began in 1982. It was formerly known as Culturally Diverse Academic Institutions Undergraduate Student Fellowships program and subsequently as Minority Academic Institutions Undergraduate Student Fellowships.

Number awarded Approximately 40 each year.

Deadline December of each year.

[25]
EXCEPTIONAL CIRCUMSTANCES SCHOLARSHIPS

Workforce Safety & Insurance
1600 East Century Avenue, Suite 1
P.O. Box 5585
Bismarck, ND 58506-5585
(701) 328-3826   Toll Free: (800) 440-3796
Fax: (701) 328-3820   TDD: (800) 366-6888
E-mail: ndwsi@nd.gov
Web: www.workforcesafety.com

Summary To provide financial assistance for college to injured workers in North Dakota.

Eligibility This program is open to injured workers in North Dakota who can demonstrate that a program of higher or technical education would be beneficial and appropriate because of exceptional circumstances. Applicants must have completed a rehabilitation process with Workforce Safety & Insurance (WSI) and have no outstanding litigation on any rehabilitation plan.

Financial data Up to $10,000 per year.

Duration 1 year; may be renewed up to 4 additional years, provided the recipient reapplies and maintains a satisfactory GPA.

Additional data This program was established in 1997. The sponsoring company was formerly North Dakota Workers Compensation.

Number awarded Varies each year.

Deadline Deadline not specified.

[26]
FAMILIES OF FREEDOM SCHOLARSHIP FUND

Scholarship America
Attn: Scholarship Management Services
One Scholarship Way
P.O. Box 297
St. Peter, MN 56082
(507) 931-1682   Toll Free: (877) 862-0136
Fax: (507) 931-9168
E-mail: info@familiesoffreedom.org
Web: www.familiesoffreedom.org

Summary To provide college scholarships to financially-needy individuals and the families of individuals who were victims of the terrorist attacks on September 11, 2001.

Eligibility This program is open to the individuals who were disabled as a result of the terrorist attacks on September 11, 2001 and to the relatives of those individuals who were killed or permanently disabled during the attacks. Primarily, the fund will benefit dependents (including spouses and children) of the following groups: airplane crew and passengers; World Trade Center workers and visitors; Pentagon workers and visitors; and rescue workers, including fire fighters, emergency medical personnel, and law enforcement personnel. Applicants must be enrolled or planning to enroll in an accredited U.S. 2- or 4-year college, university, or vocational/technical school. They must demonstrate financial need.

Financial data Stipends range from $1,000 to $28,000 per year, depending upon the need of the recipient. Recently, awards averaged $17,100 per academic year. Funds are distributed annually, in 2 equal installments. Checks are made payable jointly to the student and the student's school.

Duration 1 year; may be renewed.

Additional data This program was established on September 17, 2001. The fundraising goal of $100 million was reached on September 4, 2002. The fund will operate until December 31, 2030.

Number awarded This is an entitlement program; all eligible students will receive funding. Recently 1,876 students had received more than $74 million in scholarship funds, including 641 students who received more than $11 million in the most recent single year.

Deadline Applications may be submitted at any time.

[27]
FLEETWOOD MEMORIAL FOUNDATION GRANTS

Fleetwood Memorial Foundation
501 South Fielder Road
Arlington, TX 76013
(817) 825-6699 Fax: (817) 542-0839
E-mail: fleetwood@fleetwoodmemorial.org
Web: www.fleetwoodmemorial.org/form.php

Summary To provide no-strings-attached grants to injured law enforcement or fire protection personnel in Texas or to the families of deceased or disabled personnel.

Eligibility Open to certified Texas law enforcement or fire protection personnel who have been injured in the performance of their duties or to the families of personnel who were killed or permanently disabled in the performance of their duties. For the purposes of this program, "line of duty" does not automatically mean "on duty;" for example, no injuries considered Section V or strains during normal exercise, automobile accidents while going to lunch, etc. are viewed as "line of duty" by this program.

Financial data These grants, of varying amounts, are designed to provide immediate financial relief to meet unexpected expenses until insurance or more permanent sources of funds can be arranged. Grants may be used to re-educate qualified personnel if they are unable to return to their normal duties after an accident. Educational funds are also available to the dependent children of deceased or disabled peace and fire personnel as long as they attend a public junior or senior college in Texas. Those funds are intended to provide support for housing and other needs not covered by funding from the Texas Higher Education Coordinating Board.

Duration These are 1-time grants.

Number awarded Since its inception in 1974, the foundation has provided more than 500 grants to qualified recipients, totaling nearly $2 million.

Deadline Applications may be submitted at any time.

[28]
GENERATION GOOGLE SCHOLARSHIPS

Google Inc.
Attn: Scholarships94141
1600 Amphitheatre Parkway
Mountain View, CA 94043-8303
(650) 253-0000 Fax: (650) 253-0001
E-mail: generationgoogle@google.com
Web: www.google.com

Summary To provide financial assistance to disabled and other underrepresented students planning to work on a bachelor's degree in a computer-related field.

Eligibility This program is open to high school seniors planning to enroll full time at a college or university in the United States or Canada. Applicants must be members of a group underrepresented in computer science: African Americans, Hispanics, American Indians, women, or people with a disability. They must be interested in working on a bachelor's degree in computer science, computer engineering, software engineering, or a related field. Selection is based on academic achievement (GPA of 3.2 or higher), leadership, commitment to and passion for computer science and technology through involvement in their community, and financial need.

Financial data The stipend is $10,000 per year for U.S. students or $C5,000 for Canadian students.

Duration 1 year; may be renewed for up to 3 additional years or until graduation, whichever comes first.

Additional data Recipients are also invited to attend Google's Computer Science Summer Institute in either Mountain View, California or Cambridge, Massachusetts in the summer.

Number awarded Varies each year.

Deadline February of each year.

[29]
GOOGLE LIME SCHOLARSHIPS FOR STUDENTS WITH DISABILITIES

Lime Connect, Inc.
590 Madison Avenue, 21st Floor
New York, NY 10022
(212) 521-4469 Fax: (212) 521-4099
E-mail: info@limeconnect.com
Web: www.limeconnect.com

Summary To provide financial assistance to students with disabilities working on a bachelor's or graduate degree in a computer-related field at a college or university in Canada or the United States.

Eligibility This program is open to students at colleges and universities in the United States or Canada who have a disability and are entering their junior or senior year of undergraduate study or are enrolled as graduate students. International students with disabilities enrolled at universities in the United States or Canada are also eligible. Applicants must be working full time on a degree in computer science, computer engineering, or a closely-related technical field. Along with their application, they must submit 2 essays of 400 to 600 words each on 1) their academic accomplishments in terms of the technical projects on which they have worked; and 2) the issue about which they are passionate, what they have done to fulfill that passion, or what they dream of doing to fulfill it. Financial need is not considered in the selection process.

Financial data The stipend is $10,000 for students at U.S. universities or $C5,000 for students at Canadian universities.

Duration 1 year.

Additional data This program is jointly sponsored by Google and Lime Connect, an organization founded in 2006 to promote employment of people with disabilities.

Number awarded Varies each year.

Deadline February of each year.

[30]
GOVERNOR'S COALITION FOR YOUTH WITH DISABILITIES SCHOLARSHIPS

Governor's Coalition for Youth with Disabilities
P.O. Box 2485
Hartford, CT 06146-2485
(860) 263-6018   E-mail: gcydinfo@gmail.com
Web: www.gcyd.org/scholarship.html

Summary To provide financial assistance for college to Connecticut residents who have a disability.

Eligibility This program is open to seniors graduating from high schools in Connecticut who have a disability. Applicants must be planning to attend 1) a college or university in Connecticut or any other state; 2) any of the 4 campuses of the Connecticut State University System; or 3) any of the 12 Connecticut community colleges. Along with their application, they must submit an essay of 500 to 600 words describing the nature of their disability, how it has impacted their life experiences, how they will use what they have learned from those experiences, and the intended major or specific occupational skill they wish to pursue in college. Selection is based on 1) the manner in which applicants have overcome the obstacles created by their disability; 2) the degree to which they have contributed to their school and community through service, leadership, and being a positive role model; and 3) their desire for a successful career.

Financial data For students at colleges and universities nationwide, the stipend ranges up to $5,000. For students at Connecticut State Universities, the stipend is $500 per semester. For students at Connecticut community colleges, the award provides for payment of tuition and fees.

Duration 1 year. National scholarships are nonrenewable, Connecticut State University scholarships may be renewed for up to 8 semesters, and Connecticut community college scholarships may be renewed for 3 years.

Additional data This program was established in 1994 with support from the governor of Connecticut and many business, labor, and individual donors in the state.

Number awarded Varies each year; recently, 18 of these scholarships, worth $30,950, were awarded.

Deadline February of each year.

[31]
HARRY GREGG FOUNDATION GRANTS

Harry Gregg Foundation
One Verney Drive
Greenfield, NH 03047
(603) 547-3311, ext. 1490
Toll Free: (800) 394-3311, ext. 1490 (within NH)
Fax: (603) 547-6212
E-mail: hgf@crotchedmountain.org
Web: www.crotchedmountain.org

Summary To provide financial assistance for vocational education, assistive technology, or other purposes to children and adults in New Hampshire who have a disability.

Eligibility This program is open to New Hampshire residents of all ages who have physical, intellectual, or emotional disabilities. Funds may be requested for broad purposes but must specifically benefit the applicant. Examples of acceptable purposes include, but are not limited to: the costs of nonreimbursed medical or therapy treatments; specialty equipment, services, or supplies; modifications to living area, workplace, or vehicle; respite services for the recipient or care givers; costs of attending a special camp or recreational activities; and vocational education or driver training tuition assistance. Selection is based on demonstrated need for a product of service, the applicant's financial circumstances, and the ability of the foundation to help improve the quality of life of a grant recipient.

Financial data Most grants range up to $1,200.

Duration Recipients may receive a maximum of 4 grants (no more than 2 in any year).

Additional data This foundation was established in 1989. If a request is not funded, applicants may reapply 6 months later for the same or a different purpose.

Number awarded Nearly 150 each year. Since this foundation was established, it has awarded more than 6,000 grants worth more than $2 million.

Deadline March, June, September, or December.

[32]
HORATIO ALGER NATIONAL SCHOLARSHIP PROGRAM

Horatio Alger Association of Distinguished Americans, Inc.
99 Canal Center Plaza, Suite 320
Alexandria, VA 22314
(703) 684-9444   Toll Free: (866) 763-9228
Fax: (703) 548-3822
Web: www.horatioalger.org/scholarships/sp.cfm

Summary To provide financial assistance for college to disabled and other high school seniors who can demonstrate integrity and perseverance in overcoming adversity.

Eligibility This program is open to seniors at high schools in all 50 states, the District of Columbia, and Puerto Rico. Applicants must be planning to enroll at a college in any state to work on a bachelor's degree (they may begin at a 2-year college and then transfer to a 4-year institution). They must be U.S. citizens, be able to demonstrate critical financial need ($50,000 or less adjusted gross income per family), have a GPA of 2.0 or higher, and have a record of involvement in co-curricular and community activities. Along with their application, they must submit information on the adversities they have encountered. Examples of adversity include having been in foster care or a ward of the state; having been homeless; experiencing the death, incarceration, or abandonment of a parent or guardian; living in a household where alcohol or drugs are or were abused; having a physical or mental disability or serious illness; or suffering from physical or mental abuse.

Financial data   The stipend is $5,000 per year.

Duration   4 years.

Additional data   This program was established in 1984.

Number awarded   104 each year: 2 in each state, the District of Columbia, and Puerto Rico.

Deadline   October of each year.

[33]
IDAHO MINORITY AND "AT RISK" STUDENT SCHOLARSHIP

Idaho State Board of Education
Len B. Jordan Office Building
650 West State Street, Room 307
P.O. Box 83720
Boise, ID 83720-0037
(208) 332-1574   Fax: (208) 334-2632
E-mail: scholarshiphelp@osbe.idaho.gov
Web: www.boardofed.idaho.gov

Summary   To provide funding to "at risk" high school seniors in Idaho who plan to attend college in the state.

Eligibility   This program is open to residents of Idaho who are graduates of high schools in the state. Applicants must meet at least 3 of the following requirements: 1) have a disability; 2) be a member of an minority group historically underrepresented in higher education in Idaho (Native Americans, African Americans, Hispanic Americans); 3) have substantial financial need; 4) be a first-generation college student; 5) be a migrant farm worker or a dependent of a farm worker. U.S. citizenship is required.

Financial data   The maximum stipend is $3,000.

Duration   1 year; renewable up to 3 more years.

Additional data   This program was established in 1991 by the Idaho state legislature. Recipients must plan to attend or be attending 1 of 11 participating colleges and universities in the state on a full-time basis. For a list of those schools, write to the State of Idaho Board of Education.

Number awarded   Approximately 40 each year.

Deadline   Deadline not specified.

[34]
ILLINOIS MIA/POW SCHOLARSHIP

Illinois Department of Veterans' Affairs
833 South Spring Street
P.O. Box 19432
Springfield, IL 62794-9432
(217) 782-6641   Toll Free: (800) 437-9824 (within IL)
Fax: (217) 524-0344   TDD: (217) 524-4645
E-mail: webmail@dva.state.il.us
Web: www2.illinois.gov

Summary   To provide financial assistance for 1) the undergraduate education of Illinois dependents of disabled or deceased veterans or those listed as prisoners of war or missing in action, and 2) the rehabilitation or education of disabled dependents of those veterans.

Eligibility   This program is open to the spouses, natural children, legally adopted children, or stepchildren of a veteran or service member who 1) has been declared by the U.S. Department of Defense or the U.S. Department of Veterans Affairs to be permanently disabled from service-connected causes with 100% disability, deceased as the result of a service-connected disability, a prisoner of war, or missing in action, and 2) at the time of entering service was an Illinois resident or was an Illinois resident within 6 months of entering such service. Special support is available for dependents who are disabled.

Financial data   An eligible dependent is entitled to full payment of tuition and certain fees at any Illinois state-supported college, university, or community college. In lieu of that benefit, an eligible dependent who has a physical, mental, or developmental disability is entitled to receive a grant to be used to cover the cost of treating the disability at 1 or more appropriate therapeutic, rehabilitative, or educational facilities. The total benefit cannot exceed the cost of 4 years of full-time enrollment, including summer terms, at the University of Illinois.

Duration   This scholarship may be used for a period equivalent to 4 calendar years, including summer terms. Dependents have 12 years from the initial term of study to complete the equivalent of 4 calendar years. Disabled dependents who elect to use the grant for rehabilitative purposes may do so as long as the total benefit does not exceed the cost equivalent of 4 calendar years of full-time enrollment at the University of Illinois.

Additional data   An eligible child must begin using the scholarship prior to his or her 26th birthday. An eligible spouse must begin using the scholarship prior to 10 years from the effective date of eligibility (e.g., prior to August 12, 1989 or 10 years from date of disability or death).

Number awarded   Varies each year.

Deadline   Deadline not specified.

[35]
INCIGHT SCHOLARSHIPS

Incight Education
Attn: Scholarship Coordinator
310 S.W. Fourth Avenue, Suite 630
Portland, OR 97204
(971) 244-0305   Fax: (971) 244-0304
E-mail: lauren@incight.org
Web: www.incighteducation.org

Summary   To provide financial assistance for college to students who have a documented disability.

Eligibility   This program is open to students who have a documented disability or impairment, including a physical, cognitive, or learning disability. Applicants must have a GPA of 2.5 or higher and be entering or attending college as a full-time student. Along with their application, they must submit a 250-word essay on the word "handicrap," a term that the sponsoring organization feels is prevalent in the disabled and non-disabled communities and what they have done to conquer it. They must also submit 2 other 250-word essays on 1) their involvement in their community in the past and what they will continue to do in the future; and 2) other information about themselves.

Financial data   Stipends range from $500 to $2,500.

Duration   1 year; renewable up to 3 more years.

Number awarded   Up to 100 each year.

Deadline   March of each year.

[36]
JAY KAPLAN MEMORIAL SCHOLARSHIP

Vermont Student Assistance Corporation
Attn: Scholarship Programs
10 East Allen Street
P.O. Box 2000
Winooski, VT 05404-2601
(802) 654-3798   Toll Free: (888) 253-4819
Fax: (802) 654-3765 TDD: (800) 281-3341 (within VT)
E-mail: info@vsac.org
Web: services.vsac.org

Summary   To provide financial assistance to residents of Vermont, especially those with disabilities, who are interested in working on a degree in science or finance at a college in any state.

Eligibility   This program is open to residents of Vermont who are attending or planning to attend a college or university in any state. Applicants must be seeking training or education related to science or finance. Preference is given to students who have a documented disability (must submit school 504 or IEP plan). Along with their application, they must submit 1) a 100-word essay on their interest in and commitment to pursuing their chosen career or vocation; and 2) any significant barriers that limit their access to education. Selection is based on those essays, a letter of recommendation, and financial need.

Financial data   The stipend is $2,000.

Duration   1 year; nonrenewable.

Additional data   The Jay Kaplan Retirement Education Fund, Inc. established this program in 2011.

Number awarded   2 each year.

Deadline   March of each year.

[37]
JOE CLERES MEMORIAL SCHOLARSHIPS

New Outlook Pioneers
c/o Shirley Zunich, Scholarship Administrator
1801 California Street, 44th Floor
Denver, CO 80202
(303) 571-9256
E-mail: szunich@pioneersvolunteer.org
Web: www.newoutlookpioneers.org

Summary   To provide funding to students who are have a disability.

Eligibility   This program is open to students with physical or mental disabilities who are enrolled or planning to enroll in high school, college, trade school, or graduate school. Applicants or their representatives must submit a 1-page essay describing how the student has met the challenge of his or her disability, including the severity of the disability. They may also include up to 1 page of supporting documentation, but photographs, audio or videotapes, display materials, films, or scrapbooks are not considered.

Financial data   Stipends range from $500 to $2,000. Funds are paid directly to the school for tuition support.

Duration   1 year.

Additional data   This program was established in 1996 by Lucent Technologies as the New Outlook Scholarships for Students with Disabilities. The current name was adopted in 2005. New Outlook Pioneers is an affiliate of TelecomPioneers. Its members are employees and retirees of Lucent Technologies, Avaya Communication, and Agere.

Number awarded   Varies each year; recently, 22 of these scholarships were awarded: 1 at $2,000, 2 at $1,500, 5 at $1,000, 8 at $750, and 6 at $500.

Deadline   March of each year.

[38]
JOYCE WALSH JUNIOR DISABILITY AWARDS

National Federation of Music Clubs
1646 Smith Valley Road
Greenwood, IN 46142
(317) 882-4003   Fax: (317) 882-4019
E-mail: info@nfmc-music.org
Web: nfmc-music.org

Summary   To recognize and reward, with financial assistance for further study, young instrumentalists and vocalists with disabilities who are members of the National Federation of Music Clubs (NFMC).

Eligibility   This program is open to musicians (instrumentalists or vocalists) who are between 12 and 18 years of age, U.S. citizens, and junior members of the federation. Applicants must submit 1) a letter from a medical doctor stating the nature and duration of a mental or physical disability; 2) a CD, up to 10 minutes in length, of their performance of 2 selections from contrasting style periods; and 3) a recommendation from a teacher, tutor, or clergyman. Financial need is not considered.

Financial data The awards are $2,000 for first place and $1,000 for second place. In addition, regional awards are $700. All awards must be used for musical study.

Duration The awards are presented annually.

Additional data These awards are funded by the T-Shirt Project Endowment. There is a $2 entry fee.

Number awarded 7 each year: 1 first-place award, 1 second-place award, and 5 regional awards (1 in each of the 5 NFMC regions).

Deadline February of each year.

[39]
KAISER PERMANENTE COLORADO DIVERSITY SCHOLARSHIP PROGRAM

Kaiser Permanente
Attn: Physician Recruitment Services
10350 East Dakota Avenue
Denver, CO 80231-1314
(303) 344-7299   Toll Free: (866) 239-1677
Fax: (303) 344-7818
E-mail: co-diversitydevelopment@kp.org
Web: scholarselect.com

Summary To provide financial assistance to disabled and other Colorado residents who come from diverse backgrounds and are interested in working on an undergraduate or graduate degree in a health care field at a public college in the state.

Eligibility This program is open to all residents of Colorado, including those who identify as 1 or more of the following: African American, Asian Pacific, Latino, lesbian, gay, bisexual, transgender, intersex, Native American, U.S. veteran, and/or a person with a disability. Applicants must be enrolled or planning to enroll full time at a publicly-funded college, university, or technical school in Colorado as 1) a graduating high school senior with a GPA of 2.7 or higher; 2) a GED recipient with a GED score of 520 or higher; 3) an undergraduate student; or 4) a graduate or doctoral student. They must be preparing for a career in health care (e.g., athletic training, audiology, cardiovascular perfusion technology, clinical medical assisting, cytotechnology, dental assisting, dental hygiene, diagnostic medicine, dietetics, emergency medical technology, medicine, nursing, occupational therapy, pharmacy, phlebotomy, physical therapy, physician assistant, radiology, respiratory therapy, social work, sports medicine, surgical technology). Along with their application, they must submit 300-word essays on 1) a brief story from their childhood and the aspects of their experience that will contribute to their become a good health care provided; 2) what giving back to the community means to them and their experiences in community involvement that demonstrate their commitment to health care; and 3) what they consider the most pressing issue in health care today. Selection is based on academic achievement, character qualities, community outreach and volunteering, and financial need. U.S. citizenship is required.

Financial data Stipends range from $1,400 to $2,600.

Duration 1 year.

Number awarded Varies each year; recently, 17 of these scholarships were awarded.

Deadline February of each year.

[40]
LAGUNA ACOMA CONNECTIONS PROGRAM

Pueblo of Laguna
Attn: Laguna Acoma Connections
P.O. Box 550
New Laguna, NM 87038
(505) 552-0619   Fax: (505) 552-0623
E-mail: grpotter@hotmail.com
Web: www.ldoe.org/pfs_programs.html

Summary To provide vocational rehabilitation to American Indian adults with disabilities who reside on the Laguna and Acoma reservations in New Mexico.

Eligibility This program is open to residents of the Laguna and Acoma reservations who either apply directly or are referred by an agency, family member, or community member. Applicants must have a physical or mental impairment that is a barrier to employment and require services in order to prepare for, enter, or obtain employment. They must submit a Certificate of Indian Blood and (if they are receiving Supplemental Security Income) the SSI letter indicating eligibility for monthly support.

Financial data This program provides services based on individual need and interest, availability of jobs, and selection of career goals.

Duration Services are provided until the participant obtains employment.

Number awarded Varies each year.

Deadline Applications may be submitted at any time.

[41]
LYNN M. SMITH MEMORIAL SCHOLARSHIP

California Association for Postsecondary Education
   and Disability
Attn: Executive Assistant
71423 Biskra Road
Rancho Mirage, CA 92270
(760) 346-8206   Fax: (760) 340-5275
TDD: (760) 341-4084   E-mail: caped2000@aol.com
Web: www.caped.net/scholarships.html

Summary To provide financial assistance to community college students in California who have a disability.

Eligibility This program is open to students at community colleges in California who have a disability. Applicants must be preparing for a vocational career and have completed at least 6 semester credits with a GPA of 2.5 or higher. Along with their application, they must submit a 1-page personal letter that demonstrates their writing skills, progress towards meeting their educational and vocational goals, management of their disability, and involvement in community activities. They must also submit a letter of recommendation from a faculty member, verification of disability, official transcripts, proof of current enrollment, and documentation of financial need.

Financial data The stipend is $1,000.

Duration   1 year.
Number awarded   1 each year.
Deadline   September of each year.

[42]
MARINE CORPS LEAGUE SCHOLARSHIPS

Marine Corps League
Attn: National Executive Director
P.O. Box 3070
Merrifield, VA 22116-3070
(703) 207-9588   Toll Free: (800) MCL-1775
Fax: (703) 207-0047   E-mail: mcl@mcleague.org
Web: www.mcleague.org

Summary   To provide college aid to students whose parents served in the Marines and to disabled and other members of the Marine Corps League or Marine Corps League Auxiliary.

Eligibility   This program is open to 1) children of Marines who lost their lives in the line of duty; 2) spouses, children, grandchildren, great-grandchildren, and stepchildren of active Marine Corps League and/or Auxiliary members; and 3) members of the Marine Corps League and/or Marine Corps League Auxiliary who are honorably discharged and in need of rehabilitation training not provided by government programs. Applicants must be seeking further education and training as a full-time student and be recommended by the commandant of an active chartered detachment of the Marine Corps League or the president of an active chartered unit of the Auxiliary. Financial need is not considered in the selection process.

Financial data   A stipend is awarded (amount not specified). Funds are paid directly to the recipient.

Duration   1 year; may be renewed up to 3 additional years (all renewals must complete an application and attach a transcript from the college or university).

Number awarded   Varies, depending upon the amount of funds available each year.

Deadline   June of each year.

[43]
MARYLAND COMMUNITY COLLEGE TUITION WAIVER FOR STUDENTS WITH DISABILITIES

Maryland Higher Education Commission
Attn: Office of Student Financial Assistance
6 North Liberty Street, Ground Suite
Baltimore, MD 21201
(410) 767-3300   Toll Free: (800) 974-0203
Fax: (410) 332-0250   TDD: (800) 735-2258
E-mail: osfamail@mhec.state.md.us
Web: www.mhec.state.md.us

Summary   To provide financial assistance to residents of Maryland who have a disability and plan to attend a community college in the state.

Eligibility   This program is open to Maryland residents who have a disability and are receiving Supplemental Security Income (SSI) or Social Security Disability Insurance (SSDI) benefits. Applicants must be taking or planning to take credit classes at a community college in the

state; non-credit courses do not qualify. They must complete and submit a FAFSA.

Financial data   Recipients are exempt from paying tuition and mandatory fees at community colleges in Maryland for up to 12 credits per semester if they are taking classes as part of a degree or certificate program designed to lead to employment or for up to 6 credits if they are enrolled in a community college for any other reason.

Duration   1 semester; may be renewed.

Additional data   This waiver was first available in 2012.

Number awarded   Varies each year.

Deadline   February of each year.

[44]
MASSACHUSETTS REHABILITATION COMMISSION OR COMMISSION FOR THE BLIND TUITION WAIVER PROGRAM

Massachusetts Office of Student Financial Assistance
454 Broadway, Suite 200
Revere, MA 02151
(617) 391-6070   Fax: (617) 727-0667
E-mail: osfa@osfa.mass.edu
Web: www.osfa.mass.edu

Summary   To provide financial assistance for college to Massachusetts residents who are clients of specified disability agencies in the state.

Eligibility   Applicants for this assistance must be certified as clients by the Massachusetts Rehabilitation Commission or Commission for the Blind. They must have been permanent residents of Massachusetts for at least 1 year, must be U.S. citizens or permanent residents, and may not be in default on any federal student loan.

Financial data   Eligible clients are exempt from tuition payments at public colleges or universities in Massachusetts.

Duration   Up to 4 years (130 semester hours.

Additional data   Recipients may enroll either part or full time in a Massachusetts publicly-supported institution.

Number awarded   Varies each year.

Deadline   Deadline not specified.

[45]
MAYS MISSION SCHOLARSHIPS

Mays Mission for the Handicapped, Inc.
Attn: Scholarship Program
604 Colonial Drive
Heber Springs, AR 72545
(501) 362-7526   Toll Free: (888) 503-7955
Fax: (501) 362-7529   E-mail: info@maysmission.org
Web: www.maysmission.org/schol.html

Summary   To provide financial assistance to college students with significant disabilities.

Eligibility   This program is open to U.S. residents with significant physical and/or mental disabilities. Applicants must be working full time on a baccalaureate degree at a 4-year college or university. They must have a score of 18 or higher on the ACT or 870 or higher on the SAT. Along with their application, they must submit a short biography that includes their goals, aspirations, and accomplishments along with a brief description of how they have overcome their disability.

Financial data A stipend is awarded (amount not specified).

Duration 1 year; may be renewed, provided the recipient remains enrolled full time with a GPA of 2.3 or higher.

Number awarded 7 scholars are supported at a time.

Deadline June of each year.

[46]
MG EUGENE C. RENZI, USA (RET.)/MANTECH INTERNATIONAL CORPORATION TEACHER'S SCHOLARSHIP

Armed Forces Communications and Electronics
Association
Attn: AFCEA Educational Foundation
4400 Fair Lakes Court
Fairfax, VA 22033-3899
(703) 631-6138   Toll Free: (800) 336-4583, ext. 6138
Fax: (703) 631-4693
E-mail: scholarshipsinfo@afcea.org
Web: www.afcea.org

Summary To provide financial assistance to undergraduate and graduate students (especially disabled veterans) who are preparing for a career as a teacher of science and mathematics.

Eligibility This program is open to full-time sophomores, juniors, seniors, and graduate students at accredited colleges and universities in the United States. Applicants must be U.S. citizens preparing for a career as a teacher of science, mathematics, or information technology at a middle or secondary school. They must have a GPA of 3.0 or higher. In the selection process, first consideration is given to wounded or disabled veterans, then to honorably discharged veterans. Financial need is not considered.

Financial data The stipend is $2,500.

Duration 1 year.

Additional data This program was established in 2008 with support from ManTech International Corporation.

Number awarded 1 each year.

Deadline March of each year.

[47]
MICHIGAN ELKS ASSOCIATION GOLD KEY SCHOLARSHIP PROGRAM

Michigan Elks Association
c/o Brad P. Saegesser, Scholarship Committee Chair
2405 Townline Road
Tawas City, MI 48763
(989) 820-7171   E-mail: brad@idealwifi.net
Web: www.mielks.org/program/gold.html

Summary To provide financial assistance to "special needs" students in Michigan who plan to attend college in any state.

Eligibility This program is open to "special needs" students who are Michigan residents. For the purposes of

this program, "special needs" students are defined as those who are physically or mentally challenged. Applicants must be high school seniors and planning to attend an accredited college, university, trade school, or vocational school in any state. They must submit a statement on the nature and degree of their "special needs;" the school they have chosen to attend and why; their educational and career goals; how they anticipate financing school; the special equipment, devices, and/or supportive services they require; and their extracurricular activities, interests, and/or hobbies. Other required submissions include high school transcripts, a 200-word letter from their parent describing the family financial situation and the student's need for assistance, 3 letters of recommendation, and verification of "special needs" from a doctor. Sponsorship by a local Elks lodge is required.

Financial data The stipend is $2,000 per year.

Duration 1 year; renewable up to 3 more years.

Number awarded Varies each year; recently, 8 first-year, 8 second-year, 10 third-year, and 9 fourth-year scholarships were awarded.

Deadline The sponsoring lodge must forward the application to the district commissioner by November of each year.

[48]
MISSOURI PUBLIC SERVICE OFFICER OR EMPLOYEE'S CHILD SURVIVOR GRANT PROGRAM

Missouri Department of Higher Education
Attn: Student Financial Assistance
205 Jefferson Street
P.O. Box 1469
Jefferson City, MO 65102-1469
(573) 526-7958   Toll Free: (800) 473-6757
Fax: (573) 751-6635   E-mail: info@dhe.mo.gov
Web: www.dhe.mo.gov

Summary To provide financial assistance to disabled public safety officers in Missouri and the spouses and children of disabled or deceased officers who are interested in attending college in the state.

Eligibility This program is open to residents of Missouri who are 1) public safety officers who were permanently and totally disabled in the line of duty; 2) spouses of public safety officers who were killed or permanently and totally disabled in the line of duty; or 3) children of Missouri public safety officers or Department of Transportation employees who were killed or permanently and totally disabled while engaged in the construction or maintenance of highways, roads, and bridges. Applicants must be Missouri residents enrolled or accepted for enrollment as a full-time undergraduate student at a participating Missouri college or university; children must be younger than 24 years of age. Students working on a degree or certificate in theology or divinity are not eligible. U.S. citizenship or permanent resident status is required.

Financial data The maximum annual grant is the lesser of 1) the actual tuition charged at the school where the recipient is enrolled, or 2) the amount of tuition charged to a Missouri undergraduate resident enrolled full time in the same class level and in the same academic major as an applicant at the University of Missouri at Columbia.

Duration   1 year; may be renewed.

Additional data   Public safety officers include fire fighters, police officers, capitol police officers, parole officers, probation officers, state correctional employees, water safety officers, conservation officers, park rangers, and highway patrolmen.

Number awarded   Varies each year; recently, 11 students received $47,045 in support from this program.

Deadline   There is no application deadline, but early submission of the completed application is encouraged.

[49]
MOTIVATING UNDERGRADUATES IN SCIENCE AND TECHNOLOGY (MUST) SCHOLARSHIP PROGRAM

National Aeronautics and Space Administration
Attn: Vanessa R. Webbs, MUST Project Manager
NASA John H. Glenn Research Center at Lewis Field
2100 Brookpark Road, M.S. 500-107
Cleveland, OH 44135
(216) 433-3768   Fax: (216) 433-3344
E-mail: vanessa.r.webbs@nasa.gov
Web: www.nasa.gov

Summary   To provide financial assistance to disabled and other underrepresented undergraduates working on a degree in a field of science, technology, engineering, or mathematics (STEM).

Eligibility   This program is open to U.S. citizens from an underrepresented group, including women, African Americans, Hispanic Americans, Native Americans, and persons with disabilities. Applicants must be entering their sophomore or junior year at an accredited college or university in the 50 states or Puerto Rico as a full-time student. They must have a GPA of 3.0 or higher and a major in a STEM field of study.

Financial data   Stipends provide payment of 50% of the tuition and fees at the recipient's institution, to a maximum of $10,000.

Duration   1 year; may be renewed 1 additional year.

Deadline   January of each year. NASA Motivating Undergraduates in Science and Technology (MUST) Scholarship Program.

[50]
MUSICIANS WITH SPECIAL NEEDS SCHOLARSHIP

Sigma Alpha Iota Philanthropies, Inc.
One Tunnel Road
Asheville, NC 28805
(828) 251-0606   Fax: (828) 251-0644
E-mail: nh@sai-national.org
Web: www.sai-national.org

Summary   To provide financial assistance for college or graduate school to members of Sigma Alpha Iota (an organization of women musicians) who have a disability and are working on a degree in music.

Eligibility   This program is open to members of the organization who either 1) have a sensory or physical impairment and are enrolled in a graduate or undergraduate degree program in music, or 2) are preparing to become a music teacher or therapist for people with disabilities. Performance majors must submit a 15-minute DVD of their work; non-performance majors must submit evidence of work in their area of specialization, such as composition, musicology, or research.

Financial data   The stipend is $1,500.

Duration   1 year.

Number awarded   1 each year.

Deadline   March of each year.

[51]
NATIONAL ASSOCIATION FOR EQUAL OPPORTUNITY IN HIGHER EDUCATION INCLUSION SCHOLARS PROGRAM

National Association for Equal Opportunity in Higher
   Education
Attn: Inclusion Scholars Program
209 Third Street, S.E.
Washington, DC 20003
(202) 552-3300   Fax: (202) 552-3330
Web: www.nafeo.org/community/index.php

Summary   To provide financial assistance to high school seniors who have a disability and plan to attend a designated Historically Black College or University (HBCU).

Eligibility   This program is open to high school seniors who have a disability, as defined by the Americans with Disabilities Act (ADA). Applicants must be planning to enroll full time at 1 of 3 designated HBCUs (that rotate annually). Along with their application, they must submit a 500-word essay that includes what they bring that makes them a real asset to the campus, what they hope to gain from their college experience at an HBCU, and the contributions they want to make to the world.

Financial data   The stipend is $9,000 per year.

Duration   1 year; may be renewed up to 3 additional years, provided the recipient remains enrolled full time and maintains a GPA of 2.75 or higher.

Additional data   This program, which began in 2010, is sponsored by AT&T. In its inaugural year, the designated HBCUs were Bethune-Cookman College (Daytona, Florida), Morgan State University (Baltimore, Maryland), and Tennessee State University (Nashville, Tennessee).

Number awarded   1 at each designated HBCU.

Deadline   March of each year.

[52]
NATIONAL PRESS CLUB SCHOLARSHIP FOR JOURNALISM DIVERSITY

National Press Club
Attn: General Manager's Office
529 14th Street, N.W.
Washington, DC 20045
(202) 662-7599
Web: www.press.org/activities/aboutscholarship.cfm

Summary To provide funding to disabled and other high school seniors who are planning to major in journalism in college and will bring diversity to the field.

Eligibility This program is open to high school seniors who have been accepted to college and plan to prepare for a career in journalism. Applicants must submit 1) a 500-word essay explaining how they would add diversity to U.S. journalism; 2) up to 5 work samples demonstrating an ongoing interest in journalism through work on a high school newspaper or other media; 3) letters of recommendation from 3 people; 4) a copy of their high school transcript; 5) documentation of financial need; 6) a letter of acceptance from the college or university of their choice; and 7) a brief description of how they have pursued journalism in high school.

Financial data The stipend is $2,000 for the first year and $2,500 for each subsequent year. The program also provides an additional $500 book stipend, designated the Ellen Masin Persina Scholarship, for the first year.

Duration 4 years.

Additional data The program began in 1990.

Number awarded 1 each year.

Deadline February of each year.

[53]
NATIONAL SPACE GRANT COLLEGE AND FELLOWSHIP PROGRAM

National Aeronautics and Space Administration
Attn: Office of Education
300 E Street, S.W.
Mail Suite 6M35
Washington, DC 20546-0001
(202) 358-1069   Fax: (202) 358-7097
E-mail: Diane.D.DeTroye@nasa.gov
Web: www.nasa.gov

Summary To provide financial assistance to disabled and other undergraduate and graduate students interested in preparing for a career in a space-related field.

Eligibility This program is open to undergraduate and graduate students at colleges and universities that participate in the National Space Grant program of the U.S. National Aeronautics and Space Administration (NASA) through their state consortium. Applicants must be interested in a program of study and/or research in a field of science, technology, engineering, or mathematics (STEM) related to space. A specific goal of the program is to recruit and train U.S. citizens, especially underrepresented minorities, women, and persons with disabilities, for careers in aerospace science and technology. Financial need is not considered in the selection process.

Financial data Each consortium establishes the terms of the fellowship program in its state.

Additional data NASA established the Space Grant program in 1989. It operates through 52 consortia in each state, the District of Columbia, and Puerto Rico. Each consortium includes selected colleges and universities in that state as well as other affiliates from industry, museums, science centers, and state and local agencies.

Number awarded Varies each year.

Deadline Each consortium sets its own deadlines.

[54]
NAVY SUPPLY CORPS FOUNDATION NIB/NISH SCHOLARSHIPS

Navy Supply Corps Foundation
Attn: Administrator
P.O. Box 6228
Athens, GA 30604-6228
(706) 354-4111   Fax: (706) 354-0334
E-mail: foundationadmin@usnscf.com
Web: www.usnscf.com/programs/scholarships.aspx

Summary To provide money for college to blind or disabled relatives of current or former Navy Supply Corps personnel.

Eligibility This program is open to dependents (child, grandchild, or spouse) of a living or deceased regular, retired, reserve, or prior Navy Supply Corps officer, warrant officer, or enlisted personnel. Enlisted ratings that apply are AK (Aviation Storekeeper), SK (Storekeeper), MS (Mess Specialist), DK (Disbursing Clerk), SH (Ship Serviceman), LI (Lithographer), and PC (Postal Clerk). Applicants must be attending or planning to attend a 2- or 4-year accredited college on a full-time basis and have a GPA of 2.5 or higher in high school and/or college. They must be able to document blindness or severe disability. Selection is based on character, leadership, academic achievement, extracurricular activities, and financial need.

Financial data Stipends range from $1,000 to $5,000.

Duration 1 year.

Additional data This program began in 2005 with support from National Industries for the Blind (NIB) and NISH (formerly the National Industries for the Severely Handicapped).

Number awarded 1 or more each year.

Deadline March of each year.

[55]
NEW JERSEY STATE ELKS SPECIAL CHILDREN'S SCHOLARSHIP

New Jersey State Elks
Attn: Special Children's Committee
665 Rahway Avenue
P.O. Box 1596
Woodbridge, NJ 07095-1596
(732) 326-1300   E-mail: info@njelks.org
Web: www.njelks.org

Summary To provide financial assistance to high school seniors in New Jersey who have a disability and plan to attend college in any state.

Eligibility This program is open to seniors graduating from high schools in New Jersey who have a disability. Applicants must be planning to attend a college or university in any state. Selection is based on academic standing, general worthiness, and financial need. Boys and girls are judged separately.

Financial data The stipend is $2,500 per year. Funds are paid directly to the recipient's college or university.

Duration 4 years.

Number awarded 2 each year: 1 to a boy and 1 to a girl.

Deadline April of each year.

[56]
NEW YORK STATE MILITARY SERVICE RECOGNITION SCHOLARSHIPS

New York State Higher Education Services Corporation
Attn: Student Information
99 Washington Avenue
Albany, NY 12255
(518) 473-1574   Toll Free: (888) NYS-HESC
Fax: (518) 473-3749   TDD: (800) 445-5234
E-mail: webmail@hesc.com
Web: www.hesc.com

Summary To provide financial assistance to disabled veterans and the family members of deceased or disabled veterans who are residents of New York and interested in attending college in the state.

Eligibility This program is open to New York residents who served in the armed forces of the United States or state organized militia at any time on or after August 2, 1990 and became severely and permanently disabled as a result of injury or illness suffered or incurred in a combat theater or combat zone or during military training operations in preparation for duty in a combat theater or combat zone of operations. Also eligible are the children, spouses, or financial dependents of members of the armed forces of the United States or state organized militia who at any time after August 2, 1990 1) died, became severely and permanently disabled as a result of injury or illness suffered or incurred, or are classified as missing in action in a combat theater or combat zone of operations; 2) died as a result of injuries incurred in those designated areas; or 3) died or became severely and permanently disabled as a result of injury or illness suffered or incurred during military training operations in preparation for duty in a combat theater or combat zone of operations. Applicants must be attending or accepted at an approved program of study as full-time undergraduates at a public college or university or private institution in New York.

Financial data At public colleges and universities, this program provides payment of actual tuition and mandatory educational fees; actual room and board charged to students living on campus or an allowance for room and board for commuter students; and allowances for books, supplies, and transportation. At private institutions, the award is equal to the amount charged at the State University of New York (SUNY) for 4-year tuition and average mandatory fees (or the student's actual tuition and fees,

whichever is less) plus allowances for room, board, books, supplies, and transportation.

Duration This program is available for 4 years of full-time undergraduate study (or 5 years in an approved 5-year bachelor's degree program).

Number awarded Varies each year.

Deadline April of each year.

[57]
NJUA EXCELLENCE IN DIVERSITY SCHOLARSHIPS

New Jersey Utilities Association
50 West State Street, Suite 1117
Trenton, NJ 08608
(609) 392-1000   Fax: (609) 396-4231
E-mail: info@njua.com
Web: www.njua.com/html/njua_eeo_scholarship.cfm

Summary To provide financial assistance to minority, female, and disabled high school seniors in New Jersey interested in attending college in any state.

Eligibility This program is open to seniors graduating from high schools in New Jersey who are women, minorities (Black or African American, Hispanic or Latino, American Indian or Alaska Native, Asian, Native Hawaiian or Pacific Islander, or 2 or more races), and persons with disabilities. Applicants must be planning to work on a bachelor's degree at a college or university in any state. Along with their application, they must submit a 500-word essay explaining their career ambition and why they have chosen that career. Children of employees of any New Jersey Utilities Association-member company are ineligible. Selection is based on overall academic excellence and demonstrated financial need. U.S. citizenship or permanent resident status is required.

Financial data The stipend is $1,500 per year. Funds are paid to the recipient's college or university.

Duration 4 years.

Number awarded 2 each year.

Deadline March of each year.

[58]
NYS WORLD TRADE CENTER MEMORIAL SCHOLARSHIPS

New York State Higher Education Services Corporation
Attn: Student Information
99 Washington Avenue
Albany, NY 12255
(518) 473-1574   Toll Free: (888) NYS-HESC
Fax: (518) 473-3749   TDD: (800) 445-5234
E-mail: webmail@hesc.com
Web: www.hesc.com

Summary To provide financial assistance to undergraduates in New York who are survivors or victims of the terrorist attacks on September 11, 2001 or their relatives.

Eligibility This program is open to 1) the children, spouses, and financial dependents of deceased or severely and permanently disabled victims of the September 11, 2001 terrorist attacks or the subsequent rescue and recovery operations; and 2) survivors of the terrorist attacks who are severely and permanently disabled as a result of injuries sustained in the attacks or the subsequent rescue and recovery operations. Applicants must be attending or accepted at an approved program of study as full-time undergraduates at a public college or university or private institution in New York.

Financial data At public colleges and universities, this program provides payment of actual tuition and mandatory educational fees; actual room and board charged to students living on campus or an allowance for room and board for commuter students; and allowances for books, supplies, and transportation. At private institutions, the award is equal to the amount charged at the State University of New York (SUNY) for 4-year tuition and average mandatory fees (or the student's actual tuition and fees, whichever is less) plus allowances for room, board, books, supplies, and transportation.

Duration This program is available for 4 years of full-time undergraduate study (or 5 years in an approved 5-year bachelor's degree program).

Number awarded Varies each year.

Deadline April of each year.

[59]
OTTO SUSSMAN TRUST GRANTS

Otto Sussman Trust
P.O. Box 1374
Trainsmeadow Station
Flushing, NY 11370-9998

Summary To provide financial assistance to residents of selected states who are attending college or graduate school in any state and experiencing financial need because of special circumstances, such as illness or injury.

Eligibility This program is open to residents of New York, New Jersey, Oklahoma, or Pennsylvania who are currently enrolled as full-time juniors, seniors, or graduate students at a college or university in any state. Applicants must be experiencing extreme special circumstances, such as unemployment, death of a parent, or medical expenses not covered by insurance. They must have a GPA of 3.0 or higher.

Financial data The amount awarded varies, depending upon the needs of the recipient, but generally varies from $5,000 to $10,000.

Duration This is a 1-time grant.

Number awarded Varies each year.

Deadline July of each year.

[60]
PATRICIA SONNTAG MEMORIAL SCHOLARSHIP

California Association for Postsecondary Education and Disability
Attn: Executive Assistant
71423 Biskra Road
Rancho Mirage, CA 92270
(760) 346-8206   Fax: (760) 340-5275
TDD: (760) 341-4084   E-mail: caped2000@aol.com
Web: www.caped.net/scholarships.html

Summary To provide funding to students enrolled at 4-year college and universities in California who have a disability and are involved in activities or classes related to providing services to people with disabilities.

Eligibility This program is open to students at 4-year colleges and universities in California who have a disability. Applicants must have completed at least 6 semester credits with a GPA of 2.5 or higher. They must be majoring in a field related to policy formulation or service delivery to students with disabilities or be actively engaged in advocacy or leadership in campus, community, or governmental organizations that benefit individuals with disabilities, regardless of their major. Along with their application, they must submit a 1-page personal letter that demonstrates their writing skills, progress towards meeting their educational and vocational goals, management of their disability, and involvement in community activities. They must also submit a letter of recommendation from a faculty member, verification of disability, official transcripts, proof of current enrollment, and documentation of financial need.

Financial data The stipend is $1,000.

Duration 1 year.

Number awarded 1 each year.

Deadline September of each year.

[61]
PENNSYLVANIA ASSOCIATION OF MEDICAL SUPPLIERS SCHOLARSHIP

Pennsylvania Association of Medical Suppliers
777 East Park Drive, Suite 300
Harrisburg, PA 17111
(717) 909-1958   Fax: (717) 236-8767
Web: www.pamsonline.org

Summary To provide funding to high school seniors in Pennsylvania and Delaware who use home medical equipment and services to overcome a physical challenge and are interested in attending college in any state.

Eligibility This program is open to seniors graduating from high school in Pennsylvania and Delaware who are planning to enroll in a postsecondary educational program in any state. Applicants must have been successful in their educational pursuits while overcoming physical challenges with the help of home medical equipment and services (e.g., wheelchairs, respiratory devices). Along with their application, they must submit a short essay that describes their experiences with home medical equipment and how it will help them work on a college degree.

Financial data The stipend is $1,000.

Duration 1 year.
Number awarded 1 each year.
Deadline March of each year.

[62]
PLAYWRIGHT DISCOVERY AWARD

John F. Kennedy Center for the Performing Arts
Attn: Department of VSA and Accessibility
2700 F Street, N.W.
Washington, DC 20566
(202) 416-8898   Toll Free: (800) 444-1324
Fax: (202) 416-4840   TDD: (202) 416-8728
E-mail: vasinfo@kennedy-center.org
Web: www.kennedy-center.org

Summary To recognize and reward young playwrights who submit scripts that deal with disabilities.

Eligibility This program is open to U.S. citizens and permanent residents in grades 6-12 who submit an original, unproduced, and unpublished script for a 1-act play (less than 40 pages in length) that addresses the issue of disability. Applicants may or may not have a disability, but their script must examine how disability affects their lives and the lives of others. They may write from their own experience or about an experience in the life of another person or fictional character. Plays may be comedies, dramas, or even musicals.

Financial data The winners receive an award of $1,000, a trip to Washington, D.C. to attend the award presentation and see a professional production or staged reading of their play at the John F. Kennedy Center for the Performing Arts, a mentoring luncheon with distinguished members of the selection committee, and press opportunities.

Duration The competition is held annually.

Additional data The sponsor was established in 1974 as the National Committee-Arts for the Handicapped. In 1985 its name was changed to Very Special Arts and in 2010 to VSA. In 2011, it merged with the Kennedy Center's Office on Accessibility to become the Department of VSA and Accessibility at the John F. Kennedy Center for the Performing Arts.

Number awarded Up to 5 each year.

Deadline April of each year.

[63]
P.O. PISTILLI SCHOLARSHIPS

Design Automation Conference
c/o Andrew B. Kahng, Scholarship Director
University of California at San Diego-Jacobs School of Engineering
Jacobs Hall, EBU3B, Rpp, 2134
9500 Gilman Drive
La Jolla, CA 92093-0404
(858) 822-4884   Fax: (858) 534-7029
E-mail: abk@cs.ucsd.edu
Web: www.dac.com

Summary To provide funding to disabled and other high school seniors who are interested in preparing for a career in computer science or electrical engineering.

Eligibility This program is open to graduating high school seniors who are members of underrepresented groups: women, African Americans, Hispanics, Native Americans, and persons with disabilities. Applicants must be interested in preparing for a career in electrical engineering, computer engineering, or computer science. They must have at least a 3.0 GPA, have demonstrated high achievements in math and science courses, have demonstrated involvement in activities associated with the underrepresented group they represent, and be able to demonstrate significant financial need. U.S. citizenship is not required, but applicants must be U.S. residents when they apply and must plan to attend an accredited U.S. college or university. Along with their application, they must submit 3 letters of recommendation, official transcripts, ACT/SAT and/or PSAT scores, a personal statement outlining future goals and why they think they should receive this scholarship, and documentation of financial need.

Financial data Stipends are $4,000 per year. Awards are paid each year in 2 equal installments.

Duration 1 year; renewable up to 4 more years.

Additional data This program is funded by the Design Automation Conference of the Association for Computing Machinery's Special Interest Group on Design Automation.

Number awarded 2 to 7 each year.

Deadline January of each year.

[64]
PORAC SCHOLARSHIPS

Peace Officers Research Association of California
Attn: Peace Officers Research and Education
   Foundation
4010 Truxel Road
Sacramento, CA 95834-3725
(916) 928-3777   Toll Free: (800) 937-6722
Fax: (916) 928-3760   E-mail: membership@porac.org
Web: www.porac.org

Summary To provide funding to relatives of members of the Peace Officers Research Association of California (PORAC) and to members who are medically retired.

Eligibility This program is open to residents of California and Nevada who are 1) family members of law enforcement officers who have died in the line of duty; 2) dependents whose parent or legal guardian is an active PORAC member; 3) spouses and dependents of deceased PORAC members; and 4) PORAC members who have medically retired. Applicants must be enrolled or planning to enroll full-time at a college or university in any state. They may be interested in scholastic or vocational study, but they are encouraged to consider law enforcement as a career. Along with their application, they must submit a 1-page essay on "My goals, present and future: why I am applying for this scholarship and its importance to me." Selection is based on the essay, academic achievement (GPA of 2.0 or higher for dependents), school activities, community service, and financial need.

Financial data The stipend is $1,000.

Duration 1 year.

Number awarded Varies each year; recently, 16 of these scholarships were awarded.

Deadline March of each year.

[65]
POWERING EDUCATION SCHOLARSHIPS

Alpha One
127 Main Street
South Portland, ME 04106
(207) 767-2189   Toll Free: (800) 640-7200
Fax: (207) 799-8346   TDD: (207) 767-5387
E-mail: mardi@alphaonenow.org
Web: alphaonenow.com

Summary To provide financial assistance to undergraduate and graduate students in Maine who have disabilities.

Eligibility This program is open to high school seniors, undergraduates, and graduate students at schools in Maine. Applicants must have a disability. They must have a "B" average or equivalent GPA. Along with their application, they must submit a personal essay of 500 to 1,000 words on how their disability has helped shape their view of the world and themselves as a person, a letter of recommendation, and current transcripts.

Financial data The $2,000 stipend is paid directly to the recipient's institution after the first semester, provided the student earns a GPA of 2.5 or higher.

Duration 1 year.

Number awarded 3 each year.

Deadline March of each year.

[66]
REHABGYM SCHOLARSHIP

Vermont Student Assistance Corporation
Attn: Scholarship Programs
10 East Allen Street
P.O. Box 2000
Winooski, VT 05404-2601
(802) 654-3798   Toll Free: (888) 253-4819
Fax: (802) 654-3765 TDD: (800) 281-3341 (within VT)
E-mail: info@vsac.org
Web: services.vsac.org

Summary To provide financial assistance to residents of Vermont who have undergone a significant physical challenge and plan to attend college in any state.

Eligibility This scholarship is available to residents of Vermont who are attending or planning to attend a college or university in any state. Applicants must be able to demonstrate that they have undergone a significant physical challenge or illness and have met the challenge with courage and perseverance. Along with their application, they must submit 1) a 100-word essay on any significant barriers that limit their access to education, and 2) a 250-word essay on what they believe distinguishes their application from others that may be submitted. Selection is based on those essays and financial need.

Financial data The stipend is $1,000.

Duration 1 year.

Additional data This scholarship began in 2006.

Number awarded 1 each year.

Deadline March of each year.

[67]
RHODE ISLAND EDUCATIONAL BENEFITS FOR DISABLED AMERICAN VETERANS

Division of Veterans Affairs
480 Metacom Avenue
Bristol, RI 02809-0689
(401) 254-8350   Fax: (401) 254-2320
TDD: (401) 254-1345 E-mail: devangelista@dhs.ri.gov
Web: www.dhs.ri.gov

Summary To provide assistance to disabled veterans in Rhode Island who wish to pursue higher education at a public institution in the state.

Eligibility This program is open to permanent residents of Rhode Island who have been verified by the Department of Veterans Affairs (DVA) as having a disability of at least 10% resulting from military service.

Financial data Eligible veterans are entitled to take courses at any public institution of higher education in Rhode Island without the payment of tuition, exclusive of other fees and charges.

Number awarded Varies each year.

Deadline Deadline not specified.

[68]
RISING ANGUS STAR YOUTH SCHOLARSHIP

National Junior Angus Association
Attn: Angus Foundation
3201 Frederick Avenue
St. Joseph, MO 64506
(816) 383-5100   Fax: (816) 233-9703
E-mail: info@njaa.info
Web: www.angusfoundation.org

Summary To provide financial assistance to students who have been members of the National Junior Angus Association (NJAA), can demonstrate special needs, and are enrolled or planning to enroll in any field in college.

Eligibility Applicants must have been a member of the NJAA in the past and presently must be a junior, regular, or life member of the American Angus Association. They must be either a high school senior or already enrolled in college working full time on an undergraduate degree with a GPA of 2.0 or higher and younger than 25 years of age. All fields of study are eligible. Along with their application, they must submit 1) an essay that summarizes their experience and knowledge in livestock production, marketing, judging, and other aspects of the livestock industry; 2) an essay that identifies an issue of concern to the beef industry and offers their recommendation for meeting that challenge in a way that benefits beef producers; and 3) a 1-page statement of their special needs (e.g., financial need, personal and/or family hardship, physical handicap, medical disability, other extenuating circumstances).

Financial data The program provides full payment of tuition.

Duration 4 years.

Additional data   This scholarship was first awarded in 2009.

Number awarded   1 each year.

Deadline   April of each year.

[69]
SAULT TRIBE SPECIAL NEEDS SCHOLARSHIPS

Sault Tribe of Chippewa Indians
Attn: Higher Education Program-Memorial/Tributary
   Scholarships
523 Ashmun Street
Sault Ste. Marie, MI 49783
(906) 635-4944   Toll Free: (800) 793-0660
Fax: (906) 635-7785   E-mail: amatson@saulttribe.net
Web: www.saulttribe.com

Summary   To provide financial assistance for education at any level to members of the Sault Tribe of Chippewa Indians who have a disability.

Eligibility   This program is open to enrolled members of the Sault Tribe who have a documented physical or emotional disability. Applicants must be enrolled in any educational program at any level. Along with their application, they must submit a letter from themselves or a parent describing the proposed use of the funds and an itemized list of the expected costs.

Financial data   The stipend is $1,000.

Duration   1 year.

Number awarded   4 each year: 2 for students under 18 years of age and 2 for students 18 years of age or older.

Deadline   May of each year.

[70]
SCOTTS COMPANY SCHOLARS PROGRAM

Golf Course Superintendents Association of America
Attn: Environmental Institute for Golf
1421 Research Park Drive
Lawrence, KS 66049-3859
(785) 832-4445   Toll Free: (800) 472-7878, ext. 4445
Fax: (785) 832-4448   E-mail: mwright@gcsaa.org
Web: www.gcsaa.org/students/Scholarships.aspx

Summary   To provide financial assistance and summer work experience to disabled and other high school seniors and college students from diverse backgrounds, who are preparing for a career in golf management.

Eligibility   This program is open to high school seniors and college students (freshmen, sophomores, and juniors) who are interested in preparing for a career in golf management (the "green industry"). Applicants should come from diverse ethnic, cultural, or socioeconomic backgrounds, defined to include women, minorities, and people with disabilities. Selection is based on cultural diversity, academic achievement, extracurricular activities, leadership, employment potential, essay responses, and letters of recommendation. Financial need is not considered. Finalists are selected for summer internships and then compete for scholarships.

Financial data   The finalists receive a $500 award to supplement their summer internship income. Scholarship stipends are $2,500.

Duration   1 year.

Additional data   The program is funded from a permanent endowment established by Scotts Company. Finalists are responsible for securing their own internships.

Number awarded   5 finalists, of whom 2 receive scholarships, are selected each year.

Deadline   February of each year.

[71]
SOPHIA L. GOKEY SCHOLARSHIP AWARD

Sophia's Heart
Attn: Scholarships
544 East Ogden Avenue, Suite 700-262
Milwaukee, WI 53202
E-mail: info@sophiasheart.org
Web: www.sophiasheart.org

Summary   To provide financial assistance for college to disabled and other high school seniors who have been challenged with a roadblock or setback.

Eligibility   This program is open to graduating high school seniors who plan to enroll at a college or university. Applicants must have been challenged with a significant roadblock or setback, such as a disability, that could stifle their desire to pursue their dream of a higher education. They must have a GPA of 2.75 or higher. Along with their application, they must submit a 500-word essay describing the dream they are pursuing and the significant roadblock, setback, or challenge they have faced along the way. Selection is based on that essay, GPA, accomplishments in community service, and participation in extracurricular activities.

Financial data   The stipend is $1,000.

Duration   1 year.

Additional data   This program was established in 2009 in memory of Sophia L. Gokey, who died of a congenital heart condition at the age of 27.

Number awarded   1 or more each year.

Deadline   December of each year.

[72]
SOUTH DAKOTA REDUCED TUITION FOR VETERANS

South Dakota Board of Regents
Attn: Scholarship Committee
306 East Capitol Avenue, Suite 200
Pierre, SD 57501-2545
(605) 773-3455   Fax: (605) 773-2422
E-mail: info@sdbor.edu
Web: www.sdbor.edu/students/redtuit_Veterans.htm

Summary   To provide free tuition at South Dakota public colleges and universities to disabled and other selected veterans.

Eligibility   This program is open to current residents of South Dakota who have been discharged from the military forces of the United States under honorable conditions. Applicants must meet 1 of the following criteria: 1) served on active duty at any time between August 2, 1990 and March 3, 1991; 2) received an Armed Forces Expeditionary Medal, Southwest Asia Service Medal, or other U.S. campaign or service medal for participation in combat operations against hostile forces outside the boundaries of the United States: or 3) have a service-connected disability rating of at least 10%. They may not be eligible for any other educational assistance from the U.S. government. Qualifying veterans must apply for this benefit within 20 years after the date proclaimed for the cessation of hostilities or within 6 years from and after the date of their discharge from military service, whichever is later. They must be attending or planning to attend a South Dakota state-supported institution of higher education or state-supported technical or vocational school.

Financial data Eligible veterans receive a waiver of tuition. The waiver applies only to tuition, not fees.

Duration Eligible veterans are entitled to receive 1 month of tuition waiver for each month of qualifying service, from a minimum of 1 year to a maximum of 4 years.

Number awarded Varies each year.

Deadline Deadline not specified.

[73]
STAN BECK FELLOWSHIP

Entomological Society of America
Attn: Entomological Foundation
9332 Annapolis Road, Suite 210
Lanham, MD 20706-3150
(301) 459-9082   Fax: (301) 459-9084
E-mail: melodie@entfdn.org
Web: www.entfdn.org/awards_education.php

Summary To assist disabled and other "needy" students working on an undergraduate or graduate degree in entomology who are nominated by members of the Entomological Society of America (ESA).

Eligibility This program is open to students working on an undergraduate or graduate degree in entomology at a college or university in Canada, Mexico, or the United States. Candidates must be nominated by members of the society. They must be "needy" students; for the purposes of this program, need may be based on physical limitations, or economic, minority, or environmental conditions.

Financial data The stipend is $2,000 per year.

Duration 1 year; may be renewed up to 3 additional years.

Additional data This fellowship was first awarded in 1996. Recipients are expected to be present at the society's annual meeting, where the award will be presented.

Number awarded 1 each year.

Deadline June of each year.

[74]
STATE VOCATIONAL REHABILITATION SERVICES PROGRAM

Department of Education
Office of Special Education and Rehabilitative Services
Attn: Rehabilitation Services Administration
500 12th Street, S.W., Room 5032
Washington, DC 20202-2800
(202) 245-7313   Fax: (202) 245-7590
E-mail: Steven.Zwillinger@ed.gov
Web: www.ed.gov/programs/rsabvrs/index.html

Summary To provide financial assistance to individuals with disabilities for undergraduate or graduate study pursued as part of their program of vocational rehabilitation.

Eligibility To be eligible for vocational rehabilitation services, an individual must 1) have a physical or mental impairment that is a substantial impediment to employment; 2) be able to benefit in terms of employment from vocational rehabilitation services; and 3) require vocational rehabilitation services to prepare for, enter, engage in, or retain gainful employment. Priority is given to applicants with the most significant disabilities. Persons accepted for vocational rehabilitation develop an Individualized Written Rehabilitation Program (IWRP) in consultation with a counselor for the vocational rehabilitation agency in the state in which they live. The IWRP may include a program of postsecondary education, if the disabled person and counselor agree that such a program will fulfill the goals of vocational rehabilitation. In most cases, the IWRP will provide for postsecondary education only to a level at which the disabled person will become employable, but that may include graduate education if the approved occupation requires an advanced degree. Students accepted to a program of postsecondary education as part of their IWRP must apply for all available federal, state, and private financial aid.

Financial data Funding for this program is provided by the federal government through grants to state vocational rehabilitation agencies. Grants under the basic support program currently total more than $3 billion per year. States must supplement federal funding with matching funds of 21.3%. Persons who are accepted for vocational rehabilitation by the appropriate state agency receive financial assistance based on the cost of their education and other funds available to them, including their own or family contribution and other sources of financial aid. Allowable costs in most states include tuition, fees, books, supplies, room, board, transportation, personal expenses, child care, and expenses related to disability (special equipment, attendants, interpreters, or notetakers).

Duration Assistance is provided until the disabled person achieves an educational level necessary for employment as provided in the IWRP.

Additional data Information on this program is available only from state vocational rehabilitation agencies.

Number awarded Varies each year; recently, more than 1.2 million people (of whom more than 80% have significant disabilities) were participating in this program.

Deadline Deadline not specified.

[75]
STEVE FASTEAU PAST PRESIDENTS' SCHOLARSHIP

California Association for Postsecondary Education
and Disability
Attn: Executive Assistant
71423 Biskra Road
Rancho Mirage, CA 92270
(760) 346-8206   Fax: (760) 340-5275
TDD: (760) 341-4084   E-mail: caped2000@aol.com
Web: www.caped.net/scholarships.html

Summary To provide financial assistance to undergraduate and graduate students in California who have a disability and have demonstrated outstanding leadership.

Eligibility This program is open to students at public and private colleges and universities in California who have a disability. Applicants must have high academic achievement and have shown leadership and dedication to the advancement of students with disabilities in postsecondary education. Undergraduates must have completed at least 6 semester credits and have a GPA of 2.5 or higher. Graduate students must have completed at least 3 semester units and have a GPA of 3.0 or higher. Along with their application, they must submit a 1-page personal letter that demonstrates their writing skills, progress towards meeting their educational and vocational goals, management of their disability, and involvement in community activities. They must also submit a recommendation from a faculty member, verification of disability, official transcripts, proof of current enrollment, and documentation of need.

Financial data The stipend is $1,000.

Duration 1 year.

Number awarded 1 each year.

Deadline September of each year.

[76]
STUDENTS WITH DISABILITIES ENDOWED SCHOLARSHIPS HONORING ELIZABETH DALEY JEFFORDS

Vermont Student Assistance Corporation
Attn: Scholarship Programs
10 East Allen Street
P.O. Box 2000
Winooski, VT 05404-2601
(802) 654-3798   Toll Free: (888) 253-4819
Fax: (802) 654-3765 TDD: (800) 281-3341 (within VT)
E-mail: info@vsac.org
Web: services.vsac.org

Summary To provide financial assistance to high school seniors with disabilities in Vermont who are interested in enrolling at a college in any state.

Eligibility This program is open to graduating high school seniors in Vermont who have a documented disability. Applicants must be planning to attend a college or university in any state. Along with their application, they must submit documentation of their disability (school 504 or IEP plan) and a 250-word essay on what they believe distinguishes their application from others that may be submitted. Selection is based on the essay, a letter of recommendation, a personal interview, and financial need.

Financial data The stipend is $1,500.

Duration 1 year; nonrenewable.

Additional data Former Senator James M. Jeffords established this program in 2006 to honor his wife.

Number awarded 1 or more each year.

Deadline March of each year.

[77]
SUPREME EMBLEM CLUB OF THE UNITED STATES OF AMERICA GRANT-IN-AID AWARDS

Supreme Emblem Club of the United States of America
c/o Marie Crockett, Supreme Corresponding Secretary
7604 West 21st Avenue
Kennewick, WA 99338-9163
(509) 735-9675   E-mail: jomarcroc@verizon.com
Web: www.emblemclub.com

Summary To provide financial aid for college to members or the children of members of the Supreme Emblem Club of the United States of America who have a physically challenging condition.

Eligibility This program is open to high school graduates or those already in college. Applicants must be sponsored by the Emblem Club in which the student or the student's mother or grandmother is a member. They must be serious about continuing their education but, because of a physically challenging situation, are unable to meet the high criteria applied to the Emblem Club's Scholarship Program.

Financial data The amount awarded varies each year. Funds must be used for tuition, books, or fees.

Duration 1 year.

Additional data The sponsoring Emblem Club must be a current contributor to the regular scholarship fund for the applicant to be considered for an award.

Number awarded Varies each year.

Deadline March of each year.

[78]
SURVIVORS' AND DEPENDENTS' EDUCATIONAL ASSISTANCE PROGRAM

Department of Veterans Affairs
Attn: Veterans Benefits Administration
810 Vermont Avenue, N.W.
Washington, DC 20420
(202) 418-4343   Toll Free: (888) GI-BILL1
Web: www.gibill.va.gov

Summary To provide financial assistance for undergraduate or graduate study to 1) children and spouses of deceased and disabled veterans, MIAs, and POWs and 2) children and spouses who have their own disabilities.

Eligibility Eligible for this assistance are spouses and children of 1) veterans who died or are permanently and totally disabled as the result of active service in the armed forces; 2) veterans who died from any cause while rated permanently and totally disabled from a service-connected disability; 3) service members listed as missing in action or captured in the line of duty by a hostile force; 4) service members listed as forcibly detained or interned by a foreign government or power; and 5) service members who are hospitalized or receiving outpatient treatment for a service-connected permanent and total disability and are likely to be discharged for that disability. Children must be between 18 and 26 years of age, although extensions may be granted. Spouses and children over 14 years of age with physical or mental disabilities are also eligible.

Financial data Monthly stipends for study at an academic institution are $957 for full time, $718 for three-quarter time, or $476 for half-time. Other rates apply for apprenticeship and on-the-job training, farm cooperative training, and special restorative training.

Duration Up to 45 months (or the equivalent in part-time training). Spouses must complete their training within 10 years of the date they are first found eligible. For spouses of service members who died on active duty, benefits end 20 years from the date of death.

Additional data Benefits may be used to work on associate, bachelor's, or graduate degrees at colleges and universities, including independent study, cooperative training, and study abroad programs. Courses leading to a certificate or diploma from business, technical, or vocational schools may also be taken. Other eligible programs include apprenticeships, on-the-job training programs, farm cooperative courses, and correspondence courses (for spouses only). Remedial, deficiency, and refresher courses may be approved under certain circumstances.

Number awarded Varies each year.

Deadline Applications may be submitted at any time.

[79]
SWIM WITH MIKE

University of Southern California
Athletic Department
Heritage Hall
MC 0602
Los Angeles, CA 90089-0602
(213) 740-4155 Fax: (213) 740-1306
E-mail: swimwithmike@gmail.com
Web: swimwithmike.org

Summary To provide financial assistance for college or graduate school to physically challenged athletes.

Eligibility This program is open to athletes who participated in organized competitive youth, high school, or collegiate athletics and subsequently have sustained a life-changing accident or illness (e.g., paralysis, blindness, cancer, amputation, head injuries). Applicants must meet the admission standards of a 4-year or graduate-level institution of higher learning. Along with their application, they must submit a personal statement with an emphasis on their athletic history and experience and their educational goals, 3 letters of recommendation, verification of disability, and documentation of financial need.

Financial data Stipends depend on the need of the recipient.

Duration 1 year; may be renewed.

Additional data This program was established in 1981 at the University of Southern California to assist All-American swimmer Mike Nyeholt, who was paralyzed in a motorcycle accident. Since its establishment, it has provided assistance to 116 athletes at 49 universities throughout the country. Recipients are expected to participate in Swim with Mike activities and to support the organization both during and after college.

Number awarded Varies each year; recently, 50 athletes received $796,000 in scholarships.

Deadline April of each year.

[80]
TEXAS 4-H AND YOUTH DEVELOPMENT COURAGEOUS HEART SCHOLARSHIPS

Texas 4-H and Youth Development Program
Attn: Extension 4-H and Youth Development Specialist
Texas A&M University
4180 Highway 6
College Station, TX 77845
(979) 845-1212 Fax: (979) 845-6495
E-mail: texas4h@ag.tamu.edu
Web: texas4-h.tamu.edu/scholarships

Summary To provide financial assistance to high school seniors who have been active in Texas 4-H activities in spite of unforeseen obstacles related to their medical/health, family, and/or educational situation.

Eligibility This program is open to graduating seniors at high schools in Texas who have been actively participating in 4-H and plan to attend a college, university, or accredited technical school in the state. Applicants must be able to demonstrate that they have overcome extreme obstacles related to medical, family, and/or education circumstances. They must have taken and passed all necessary standardized tests for graduation and admittance to the college or university of their choice. Along with their application, they must submit a detailed narrative of the obstacles they have overcome or are in the process of overcoming, including how long they have been dealing with the obstacle, the person or persons who have helped them through their situation, and how 4-H has played a positive role in overcoming their obstacle; the narrative should include details about such family situations as care of family members, medical problems, learning disabilities, or family financial burdens. Some scholarships require a major in agriculture; others are unrestricted. U.S. citizenship is required.

Financial data The stipend is $5,000.

Duration 1 year.

Additional data Applicants for this scholarships may not also apply for scholarships offered by Texas FFA or Texas FCCLA.

Number awarded 1 or more each year.

Deadline Students submit their applications to their county extension office, which must forward them to the district extension office by February of each year.

[81]
TEXAS EXEMPTION FOR PEACE OFFICERS DISABLED IN THE LINE OF DUTY

Texas Higher Education Coordinating Board
Attn: Grants and Special Programs
1200 East Anderson Lane
P.O. Box 12788
Austin, TX 78711-2788
(512) 427-6340   Toll Free: (800) 242-3062
Fax: (512) 427-6420
E-mail: grantinfo@thecb.state.tx.us
Web: www.collegeforalltexans.com

Summary To provide educational assistance to disabled Texas peace officers.

Eligibility This program is open to Texas residents who are permanently disabled as a result of an injury suffered as a peace officer and are unable to continue employment as a peace officer because of the disability. Applicants must be planning to attend a publicly-supported college or university in Texas as an undergraduate student.

Financial data Eligible students are exempted from the payment of all dues, fees, and tuition charges at publicly-supported colleges and universities in Texas.

Duration Up to 12 semesters.

Number awarded Varies each year; recently, 31 of these exemptions were awarded.

Deadline Deadline not specified.

[82]
TEXAS MUTUAL SCHOLARSHIP PROGRAM

Texas Mutual Insurance Company
Attn: Office of the President
6210 East Highway 290
Austin, TX 78723-1098
(512) 224-3820   Toll Free: (800) 859-5995, ext. 3820
Fax: (512) 224-3889   TDD: (800) 853-5339
E-mail: information@texasmutual.com
Web: www.texasmutual.com/workers/scholarship.shtm

Summary To provide money for college to workers and their families covered by workers' compensation in Texas.

Eligibility This program is open to 1) employees who qualify for lifetime income benefits as a result of injuries suffered on the job as covered by the Texas Workers' Compensation Act; 2) unmarried children and spouses of injured workers; and 3) unmarried children and unremarried spouses of employees who died as a result of a work-related injury. Workers must be covered by the Texas Mutual Insurance Company, formerly the Texas Workers' Compensation Insurance Fund. Children must be between 16 and 25 years of age. Surviving spouses must still be eligible for workers' compensation benefits. Financial need is considered in the selection process.

Financial data Scholarships are intended to cover normal undergraduate, technical, or vocational school tuition and fees, to a maximum of $4,000 per semester. Those funds are paid directly to the college or vocational school. The cost of course-related books and fees are also reimbursed, up to a maximum of $500 per semester. Those funds are paid directly to the student.

Duration 1 year; may be renewed if the recipient maintains a GPA of 2.5 or higher.

Number awarded Varies each year.

Deadline Applications may be submitted at any time.

[83]
THEODORE R. AND VIVIAN M. JOHNSON SCHOLARSHIP PROGRAM

State University System of Florida
Attn: Office of Academic and Student Affairs
325 West Gaines Street, Suite 1614
Tallahassee, FL 32399-0400
(850) 245-0466   Fax: (850) 245-9685
E-mail: info@flbog.org
Web: www.flbog.org

Summary To provide financial assistance to Florida undergraduate students who have disabilities.

Eligibility This program is open to students with disabilities enrolled at a State University System of Florida institution. Applicants must submit an official transcript (with GPA of 2.0 or higher); documentation of financial need; and documentation of the nature and/or extent of their disability, which may be in 1 or more of the following classifications: deaf or hard of hearing; orthopedic disability; specific learning disability; psychological, emotional, or behavioral disability; autism spectrum disorder; speech/language disabilities; blind or low vision; traumatic brain injury; or other health disabilities.

Financial data The stipend depends on the availability of funds.

Duration 1 year; may be renewed if the recipient maintains a GPA of 2.0 or higher and enrolls in at least 18 credits each academic year.

Additional data This program is administered by the equal opportunity program at each of the 11 State University System of Florida 4-year institutions. Funding is provided by the Theodore R. and Vivian M. Johnson Foundation, with matching funding from the Florida Legislature.

Number awarded Several each year.

Deadline May of each year.

[84]
TROY BARBOZA EDUCATIONAL FUND

Hawai'i Community Foundation
Attn: Scholarship Department
827 Fort Street Mall
Honolulu, HI 96813
(808) 537-6333   Toll Free: (888) 731-3863
Fax: (808) 521-6286
E-mail: scholarships@hcf-hawaii.org
Web: www.hawaiicommunityfoundation.org/scholarships

Summary To provide financial assistance to disabled public employees in Hawaii or their dependents who plan to attend college in any state.

Eligibility This program is open to 1) disabled public employees in Hawaii who were injured in the line of duty; 2) dependents or other immediate family members of public employees in Hawaii who were disabled or killed in the line of duty; and 3) private citizens in Hawaii who have performed a heroic act for the protection and welfare of others. The public employee must work or have worked in a job where lives are risked for the protection and safety of others. The injury must have left the employee incapacitated or incapable or continuing in his or her profession. For private citizens, the heroic act must have occurred after October 21, 1986. Applicants must submit a short statement describing their course of study, career goals, outstanding attributes, talents, community service, family circumstances, and any other relevant information. Financial need is considered in the selection process.

Financial data The amount awarded varies, depending upon the needs of the recipient and the funds available; recently, the average value of each of the scholarships awarded by the foundation was more than $2,000.

Duration 1 year; scholarships for employees and their dependents may be renewed; scholarships for private citizens who have performed a heroic act are nonrenewable.

Additional data This program was established in 1991.

Number awarded 1 or more each year.

Deadline February of each year.

[85]
USA FUNDS ACCESS TO EDUCATION SCHOLARSHIPS

Scholarship America
Attn: Scholarship Management Services
One Scholarship Way
P.O. Box 297
St. Peter, MN 56082
(507) 931-1682   Toll Free: (800) 537-4180
Fax: (507) 931-9168
E-mail: scholarship@usafunds.org
Web: www.usafunds.org

Summary To provide financial assistance to undergraduate and graduate students, especially those who are members of ethnic minority groups or have physical disabilities.

Eligibility This program is open to high school seniors and graduates who plan to enroll or are already enrolled in full- or half-time undergraduate or full-time graduate course work at an accredited 2- or 4-year college, university, or vocational/technical school. GED recipients are also eligible. Up to 50% of the awards are targeted at students who have a documented physical disability or are a member of an ethnic minority group, including but not limited to Native Hawaiian, Alaskan Native, Black/African American, Asian, Pacific Islander, American Indian, Hispanic/Latino, or multiracial. Residents of all 50 states, the District of Columbia, Puerto Rico, Guam, the U.S. Virgin Islands, and all U.S. territories and commonwealths are eligible. Applicants must also be U.S. citizens or eligible noncitizens and come from a family with an annual adjusted gross income of $35,000 or less. In addition to financial need, selection is based on past academic performance and future potential, leadership and participation in school and community activities, work experience, career and educational aspirations and goals, and unusual personal or family circumstances.

Financial data The stipend is $1,500 per year for full-time undergraduate or graduate students or $750 per year for half-time undergraduate students. Funds are paid jointly to the student and the school.

Duration 1 year; may be renewed until the student receives a final degree or certificate or until the total award to a student reaches $6,000, whichever comes first. Renewal requires the recipient to maintain a GPA of 2.5 or higher.

Additional data This program, established in 2000, is sponsored by USA Funds.

Number awarded Varies each year; recently, a total of $3.2 million was available for this program.

Deadline February of each year.

[86]
UTAH ELKS ASSOCIATION SPECIAL NEEDS STUDENT SCHOLARSHIP AWARD

Utah Elks Association
c/o Linda Gaines, Scholarship Chair
Provo Lodge 849
1000 South University Avenue
Provo, UT 84601
(801) 796-6069
Web: www.elksinutah.org

Summary To provide financial assistance for college to high school seniors in Utah who have a disability or other special need.

Eligibility This program is open to seniors graduating from high schools in Utah who have a special need, such as a disability. Applicants must submit 1) a supporting letter from a doctor or professional person stating the nature of the special need, and 2) a 500-word essay on their career and life goals and their plan to achieve those. Selection is based on that essay, academic achievement, community service, honors and awards, leadership, and financial need. U.S. citizenship is required.

Financial data A stipend is awarded (amount not specified).

Duration 1 year.

Number awarded Varies each year, depending upon the funds available.

Deadline January of each year.

[87]
VOCATIONAL REHABILITATION AND EMPLOYMENT VETSUCCESS PROGRAM

Department of Veterans Affairs
Attn: Veterans Benefits Administration
Vocational Rehabilitation and Employment Service
810 Vermont Avenue, N.W.
Washington, DC 20420
(202) 418-4343   Toll Free: (800) 827-1000
Web: www.vba.va.gov/bin/vre/index.htm

Summary To provide funding to veterans with service-connected disabilities who need assistance to find employment or, if seriously disabled, to live independently.

Eligibility This program is open to veterans who have a service-connected disability of at least 10% or a memorandum rating of 20% or more from the Department of Veterans Affairs (VA). They must qualify for services provided by the VA VetSuccess that include assistance finding and keeping a job, including the use of special employer incentives and job accommodations; on-the-job training, apprenticeships, and non-paid work experiences; postsecondary training at a college, vocational, technical, or business school; supportive rehabilitation services such as case management, counseling, and medical referrals; independent living services for veterans unable to work due to the severity of their disabilities.

Financial data   While in training and for 2 months after, eligible disabled veterans may receive subsistence allowances in addition to their disability compensation or retirement pay. For most training programs, the current full-time monthly rate is $566.97 with no dependents, $703.28 with 1 dependent, $828.76 with 2 dependents, and $60.41 for each additional dependent; proportional rates apply for less than full-time training.

Duration   Veterans remain eligible for these services up to 12 years from either the date of separation from active military service or the date the veteran was first notified by VA of a service-connected disability rating (whichever came later).

Number awarded   Varies each year.

Deadline   Applications are accepted at any time.

[88]
VSA INTERNATIONAL YOUNG SOLOISTS AWARD

John F. Kennedy Center for the Performing Arts
Attn: Department of VSA and Accessibility
2700 F Street, N.W.
Washington, DC 20566
(202) 416-8898   Toll Free: (800) 444-1324
Fax: (202) 416-4840   TDD: (202) 416-8728
E-mail: vasinfo@kennedy-center.org
Web: www.kennedy-center.org

Summary   To recognize and reward young musicians from any country who are physically or mentally challenged.

Eligibility   This competition is open to musicians between 14 and 25 years of age who have a disability. Musical ensembles of 2 to 5 performers are also eligible if at least 1 member has a disability and all members are between 14 and 25 years of age. Applicants must be either 1) U.S. citizens or permanent residents; or 2) citizens of other countries living in the United States (as on a student visa). They may be performers in any type of music, including, but not limited to, rock, alt rock, pop, classical, country, folk, jazz, R&B/blues, hip hop, rap, Latin, and world. Along with their application, they must submit recordings of 3 musical selections (audio or video) and a 1-page personal narrative that describes why they should be selected to receive this award. Tapes are evaluated on the basis of technique, tone, intonation, rhythm, and interpretation.

Financial data   The award is $5,000. Funds must be used to assist the recipients' music career.

Duration   The competition is held annually.

Additional data   The sponsor was established in 1974 as the National Committee-Arts for the Handicapped. In 1985 its name was changed to Very Special Arts and in 2010 to VSA. In 2011, it merged with the Kennedy Center's Office on Accessibility to become the Department of VSA and Accessibility at the John F. Kennedy Center for the Performing Arts.

Number awarded   4 each year: 2 from the United States and 2 from other countries.

Deadline   January of each year.

[89]
VSA/VOLKSWAGEN GROUP OF AMERICA EXHIBITION PROGRAM

John F. Kennedy Center for the Performing Arts
Attn: Department of VSA and Accessibility
2700 F Street, N.W.
Washington, DC 20566
(202) 416-8898   Toll Free: (800) 444-1324
Fax: (202) 416-4840   TDD: (202) 416-8728
E-mail: vasinfo@kennedy-center.org
Web: www.kennedy-center.org

Summary   To recognize and reward emerging visual artists who have a disability.

Eligibility   This competition is open to visual artists between 16 and 25 years of age who have a disability. Applicants must submit samples of their work along with a brief essay on the theme "Momentum" that examines the vital creative spark behind their work. Their essays should describe the force that drives their artistic interest and informs the path they take each day as they move toward their future.

Financial data   Awards are $20,000 for the grand award, $10,000 for the first award, $6,000 for the second award, and $2,000 for each award of excellence.

Duration   The competition is held annually.

Additional data   This competition, first held in 2003, is sponsored by VSA and the Volkswagen Group of America. VSA was established in 1974 as the National Committee-Arts for the Handicapped. In 1985 its name was changed to Very Special Arts and in 2010 to VSA. In 2011, it merged with the Kennedy Center's Office on Accessibility to become the Department of VSA and Accessibility at the John F. Kennedy Center for the Performing Arts. The artwork is displayed at the S. Dillon Ripley Center of the Smithsonian Institution in the fall of each year.

Number awarded   15 each year: 1 grand award, 1 first award, 1 second award, and 12 awards of excellence.

Deadline   June of each year.

[90]
WILLIAM M. EVANS SCHOLARSHIP

Bose McKinney & Evans LLP
Attn: Scholarship Award Committee
111 Monument Circle, Suite 2700
Indianapolis, IN 46204
(317) 684-5000   Fax: (317) 684-5173
Web: www.boselaw.com

Summary To provide financial assistance to high school seniors in Indiana who are classified as special education students and who plan to attend college in any state.

Eligibility This program is open to seniors graduating from high schools in Indiana who have been classified as special education students. Applicants must be planning to attend a university, college, junior college, or vocational training program in any state. Selection is based on personal achievement, future goals, and financial need.

Financial data The stipend is $2,000.

Duration 1 year.

Additional data This program began in 1992.

Number awarded 1 each year.

Deadline March of each year.

[91]
WILLIAM MAY MEMORIAL SCHOLARSHIP

California Association for Postsecondary Education
and Disability
Attn: Executive Assistant
71423 Biskra Road
Rancho Mirage, CA 92270
(760) 346-8206   Fax: (760) 340-5275
TDD: (760) 341-4084   E-mail: caped2000@aol.com
Web: www.caped.net/scholarships.html

Summary To provide funding to college and graduate students in California who have a disability.

Eligibility This program is open to students at public and private colleges and universities in California who have a disability. Undergraduates must have completed at least 6 semester credits and have a GPA of 2.5 or higher. Graduate students must have completed at least 3 semester units and have a GPA of 3.0 or higher. Along with their application, they must submit a 1-page personal letter that demonstrates their writing skills, progress towards meeting their educational and vocational goals, management of their disability, and involvement in community activities. They must also submit a recommendation from a faculty member, verification of disability, official transcripts, proof of current enrollment, and documentation of financial need.

Financial data The stipend is $1,000.

Duration 1 year.

Number awarded 1 each year.

Deadline September of each year.

[92]
WISCONSIN TALENT INCENTIVE PROGRAM (TIP) GRANTS

Wisconsin Higher Educational Aids Board
131 West Wilson Street, Suite 902
P.O. Box 7885
Madison, WI 53707-7885
(608) 266-1665   Fax: (608) 267-2808
E-mail: colettem1.brown@wi.gov
Web: heab.state.wi.us/programs.html

Summary To provide money for college to disabled and other needy or educationally disadvantaged students in Wisconsin.

Eligibility This program is open to residents of Wisconsin entering a college or university in the state who meet the requirements of both financial need and educational disadvantage. Financial need qualifications include 1) family contribution (a dependent student whose expected parent contribution is $200 or less or an independent student whose maximum academic year contribution is $200 or less); 2) Temporary Assistance to Needy Families (TANF) or Wisconsin Works (W2) benefits (a dependent student whose family is receiving TANF or W2 benefits or an independent student who is receiving TANF or W2 benefits); or 3) unemployment (a dependent student whose parents are ineligible for unemployment compensation and have no current income from employment, or an independent student and spouse, if married, who are ineligible for unemployment compensation and have no current income from employment). Educational disadvantage qualifications include students who are 1) minorities (African American, Native American, Hispanic, or southeast Asian); 2) enrolled in a special academic support program due to insufficient academic preparation; 3) a first-generation college student (neither parent graduated from a 4-year college or university); 4) disabled according to the Department of Workforce Development, the Division of Vocational Rehabilitation, or a Wisconsin college or university that uses the Americans with Disabilities Act definition; 5) currently or formerly incarcerated in a correctional institution; or 6) from an environmental and academic background that deters the pursuit of educational plans. Students already in college are not eligible.

Financial data Stipends range up to $1,800 per year.

Duration 1 year; renewable up to 4 more years, provided the recipient continues to be a Wisconsin resident enrolled at least half time in a degree or certificate program, makes satisfactory academic progress, demonstrates financial need, and remains enrolled continuously from semester to semester and year to year. If recipients withdraw from school or cease to attend classes for any reason (other than medical necessity), they may not reapply.

Number awarded Varies each year.

Deadline Deadline not specified.

[93]
WSAJ PRESIDENTS' SCHOLARSHIP

Washington State Association for Justice
1809 Seventh Avenue, Suite 1500
Seattle, WA 98101-1328
(206) 464-1011   Fax: (206) 464-0703
E-mail: wsja@washingtonjustice.org
Web: www.washingtonjustice.org

Summary To provide financial assistance to Washington high school seniors who have a disability or have been a victim of injury and plan to attend college in any state.

Eligibility This program is open to high school seniors in Washington who are planning to work on a bachelor's degree at an institution of higher education in any state. Applicants must be able to demonstrate 1) financial need; 2) a history of achievement despite having been a victim of injury or overcoming a disability, or similar challenge; 3) a record of serving others; and 4) a commitment to apply their education toward helping others.

Financial data Stipends average $2,000. Funds are paid directly to the recipient's chosen institution of higher learning to be used for tuition, room, board, and fees.

Duration 1 year.

Additional data This fund was established in 1991 when the sponsor's name was the Washington State Trial Lawyers Association.

Number awarded 1 or more each year.

Deadline March of each year.

[94]
YELLOW RIBBON SCHOLARSHIP

Tourism Cares
Attn: Academic Scholarship Program
275 Turnpike Street, Suite 307
Canton, MA 02021
(781) 821-5990   Fax: (781) 821-8949
E-mail: scholarships@tourismcares.org
Web: www.tourismcares.org

Summary To provide money for college or graduate school to students with disabilities who are planning a career in the travel and tourism or hospitality industry.

Eligibility This program is open to citizens and permanent residents of the United States and Canada who have a physical or sensory disability. Applicants must be enrolled full time and 1) entering the second year at an accredited 2-year college; 2) entering their junior or senior year at an accredited 4-year college or university; or 3) be enrolled or entering graduate school. They must have a GPA of 2.5 or higher and be working on a degree in a travel or tourism or hospitality-related field at a college or university in Canada or the United States. Undergraduates must submit an essay on the segment of the travel and tourism or hospitality industry their current program of study emphasizes, the opportunities they are utilizing as they prepare for a career in the industry, and their academic and extracurricular activities. Graduate students must submit an essay on the changes they have observed thus far in the travel and tourism or hospitality industry, the changes they anticipate in the future of the industry, and where they see their future potential in the industry. Financial need is not considered in the selection process.

Financial data The stipend is $5,000.

Duration 1 year.

Additional data This program was established in 1993.

Number awarded 1 each year.

Deadline March of each year.

Fellowships

[95]
ACADEMIC LIBRARY ASSOCIATION OF OHIO DIVERSITY SCHOLARSHIP

Academic Library Association of Ohio
c/o Diane Kolosionek, Diversity Committee Chair
Cleveland State University, Michael Schwartz Library
2121 Euclid Avenue
RT 110D
Cleveland, OH 44115-2214
(216) 802-3358 E-mail: d.kolosionek44@csuohio.edu
Web: www.alaoweb.org

Summary To provide financial assistance to disabled and other residents of Ohio who will contribute to diversity in the profession and are working on a master's degree in library science at a school in any state.

Eligibility This program is open to residents of Ohio who are enrolled or entering an ALA-accredited program for a master's degree in library science, either on campus or via distance education. Applicants must be able to demonstrate how they will contribute to diversity in the profession, including (but not limited to) race or ethnicity, sexual orientation, life experience, physical ability, and a sense of commitment to those and other diversity issues. Along with their application, they must submit 1) a list of participation in honor societies or professional organizations, awards, scholarships, prizes, honors, or class offices; 2) a list of their community, civic, organizational, or volunteer experiences; and 3) an essay on their understanding of and commitment to diversity in libraries, including how they, as library school students and future professionals, might address the issue.

Financial data The stipend is $1,500.

Duration 1 year.

Number awarded 1 each year.

Deadline March of each year.

[96]
AMERICAN ASSOCIATION ON HEALTH AND DISABILITY SCHOLARSHIPS

American Association on Health and Disability
Attn: Scholarship Committee
110 North Washington Street, Suite 328-J
Rockville, MD 20850
(301) 545-6140, ext. 206   Fax: (301) 545-6144
E-mail: contact@aahd.us
Web: www.aahd.us

Summary To provide financial assistance to undergraduate and graduate students who have a disability, especially those studying a field related to health and disability.

Eligibility This program is open to high school graduates who have a documented disability and are enrolled in an accredited 4-year college or university as a full-time undergraduate or full- or part-time graduate student. Preference is given to students working on a degree in public health, disability studies, health promotion, or other field related to health and disability. Along with their application, they must submit a 3-page personal statement that includes a personal history, educational and career goals, extracurricular activities, and reasons why they should be selected to receive this scholarship. U.S. citizenship or permanent resident status is required.

Financial data Stipends range up to $1,000.

Duration 1 year.

Additional data This program was established in 2009.

Number awarded 2 each year.

Deadline November of each year.

[97]
ARKANSAS GOVERNOR'S COMMISSION ON PEOPLE WITH DISABILITIES SCHOLARSHIPS

Arkansas Governor's Commission on People with
  Disabilities
Attn: Scholarship Committee
26 Corporate Hill Drive
Little Rock, AR 72205
(501) 296-1637   Fax: (501) 296-1883
TDD: (501) 296-1637
Web: ace.arkansas.gov

Summary To provide financial assistance to Arkansas students with disabilities who are interested in attending college or graduate school in any state.

Eligibility This program is open to high school seniors, high school graduates, undergraduates, and graduate students who have a disability and are residents of Arkansas. Applicants must be attending or planning to attend a college or university in any state. Selection is based on a description of their disability (20 points), present and past school involvement (10 points), a brief statement on their career goals (15 points), community and volunteer activities (10 points), a brief essay on the positive or negative effects their disability has had on their life thus far (20 points), 3 letters of recommendation (10 points), and financial need (10 points).

Financial data The stipend varies, up to $1,000 per year.

Duration 1 year; recipients may reapply.

Number awarded Several each year.

Deadline February of each year.

[98]
ARTIST ENRICHMENT GRANT PROGRAM

Kentucky Foundation for Women
Heyburn Building
332 West Broadway, Suite 1215-A
Louisville, KY 40202-2184
(502) 562-0045   Toll Free: (866) 654-7564
Fax: (502) 561-0420   E-mail: info@kfw.org
Web: www.kfw.org/artenr.html

Summary To support disabled and other women in Kentucky who wish to promote positive social change through feminist expression in the arts.

Eligibility This program is open to women who have resided in Kentucky for at least 1 year and are artists at

any stage in their career able to demonstrate potential in terms of quality of work and an understanding of the power of art for social change. Applicants must be seeking funding for a range of activities, including artistic development, artist residencies, the exploration of new areas or techniques, or building a body of work. In the selection process, the following criteria are considered: artwork in the sample is strong, highly original, and reflects feminism and social change; the proposed activities will further the applicant's development as a feminist social change artist; application and work sample demonstrate applicant's understanding and practice of feminism; application and work sample demonstrate a clear understanding of the relationship between art and social change; work plan, timeline, and budget are clear, detailed, and realistic; and applicant's ability to complete the proposed activities in clearly shown. If applications are of equal artistic merit, priority is given to first-time applicants, women from rural and inner-city areas, women of color (especially African American women), lesbians, low-income women, women who did not complete high school, and women with disabilities.

Financial data Grants may range from $1,000 to $7,500, but most average between $2,000 and $4,000.

Duration Up to 1 year.

Additional data The foundation was established in 1985. Funding is not provided for general operating costs for organizations; for-profit organizations; tuition costs or living expenses while working toward a degree; endowment or capital campaigns; projects that do not focus on changing the lives of women in Kentucky; the promotion of religious doctrines; non-art related expenses, such as overdue bills or taxes; or work conducted by artists or organizations that have not resided in Kentucky for at least 1 year.

Number awarded Varies each year; recently, 45 of these grants were awarded. A total of $100,000 is available annually.

Deadline August of each year.

[99]
BAKER & DANIELS DIVERSITY SCHOLARSHIPS

Baker & Daniels LLP
Attn: Diversity and Pro Bono Coordinator
300 North Meridian Street, Suite 2700
Indianapolis, IN 46204
(317) 237-8298   Fax: (317) 237-1000
E-mail: brita.horvath@bakerd.com
Web: www.bakerdaniels.com/AboutUs/recruitment.aspx

Summary To provide financial assistance and summer work experience to disabled and other students from diverse backgrounds entering the second year of law school in Indiana.

Eligibility This program is open to residents of any state who are entering their second year at selected law schools in Indiana. Applicants must reflect diversity, defined to mean that they come from varied ethnic, racial, cultural, and lifestyle backgrounds, as well as those with disabilities or unique viewpoints. They must also be interested in a place in the sponsor's summer associate program. Along with their application, they must submit a personal statement that includes an explanation of how this scholarship would benefit them, an overview of their background and interests, an explanation of what diversity they would bring to the firm, and any other financial assistance they are receiving. Selection is based primarily on academic excellence.

Financial data The stipend is $10,000.

Duration 1 year.

Additional data The eligible law schools are those at Indiana University at Bloomington, Indiana University at Indianapolis, and the University of Notre Dame.

Number awarded 2 each year.

Deadline June of each year.

[100]
BETTY BACON MEMORIAL SCHOLARSHIP

California Association for Postsecondary Education
 and Disability
Attn: Executive Assistant
71423 Biskra Road
Rancho Mirage, CA 92270
(760) 346-8206   Fax: (760) 340-5275
TDD: (760) 341-4084   E-mail: caped2000@aol.com
Web: www.caped.net/scholarships.html

Summary To provide funding to undergraduate and graduate students in California who have a disability.

Eligibility This program is open to students at public and private colleges and universities in California who have a disability. Undergraduates must have completed at least 6 semester credits and have a GPA of 2.5 or higher. Graduate students must have completed at least 3 semester units and have a GPA of 3.0 or higher. Along with their application, they must submit a 1-page personal letter that demonstrates their writing skills, progress towards meeting their educational and vocational goals, management of their disability, and involvement in community activities. They must also submit a recommendation from a faculty person, verification of disability, official transcripts, proof of current enrollment, and documentation of financial need.

Financial data The stipend is $1,000.

Duration 1 year.

Number awarded 1 each year.

Deadline September of each year.

[101]
BIUNNO SCHOLARSHIP FOR LAW STUDENTS WITH DISABILITIES

Essex County Bar Association
Attn: Committee on the Rights of Persons with
 Disabilities
Historic Courthouse, Room B-01
470 Dr. Martin Luther King, Jr. Boulevard
Newark, NJ 07102
(973) 622-6207   Fax: (973) 622-4341
E-mail: info@EssexBar.com
Web: www.EssexBar.com

Summary To provide financial assistance to students with disabilities from New Jersey who are interested in attending a law school in any state.

Eligibility Applicants must be able to demonstrate a present and permanent physical or mental disability that substantially limits 1 or more of the major life activities (medical documentation is required); be residents of New Jersey, with preference given to Essex County residents; be attending or accepted at a law school in any state; and have earned a GPA of 3.0 or higher as an undergraduate student (if an incoming law student) or in law school. Priority is given to applicants who are planning a career in the field of advocacy for persons with disabilities. Intent may be demonstrated by completion of a course in disability law, work in a disability or disability-related clinic, or prior job experience in an advocacy field or with a public interest organization. Students who can demonstrate financial need receive priority.

Financial data Stipends range from $3,000 to $6,000. Funds are paid directly to the recipient's school or to a company providing equipment for the disabled student.

Duration 1 year.

Number awarded 1 or more each year.

Deadline May of each year.

[102]
BMO CAPITAL MARKETS LIME CONNECT EQUITY THROUGH EDUCATION SCHOLARSHIPS FOR STUDENTS WITH DISABILITIES

Lime Connect, Inc.
590 Madison Avenue, 21st Floor
New York, NY 10022
(212) 521-4469   Fax: (212) 521-4099
E-mail: info@limeconnect.com
Web: www.limeconnect.com/opportunities

Summary To provide financial assistance to students with disabilities working on a bachelor's or graduate degree in a business-related field at a college or university in Canada or the United States.

Eligibility This program is open to sophomores and graduate students at 4-year colleges and universities in the United States or Canada who have a disability. International students with disabilities enrolled at universities in the United States or Canada are also eligible. Applicants must be working full time on a degree in a business-related field. Along with their application, they must submit an essay on their career goals and why they believe they should be selected to receive this scholarship. Financial need is not considered in the selection process.

Financial data The stipend is $10,000 for students at U.S. universities or $C5,000 for students at Canadian universities.

Duration 1 year.

Additional data This program is jointly sponsored by BMO Capital Markets and Lime Connect, an organization founded in 2006 to promote employment of people with disabilities. BMO Capital Markets established its Equity Through Education program in 2005 and in 2011 invited

Lime Connect to administer a component of the program for students with disabilities.

Number awarded Varies each year.

Deadline May of each year.

[103]
CALIFORNIA ASSOCIATION FOR POSTSECONDARY EDUCATION AND DISABILITY GENERAL EXCELLENCE SCHOLARSHIP

California Association for Postsecondary Education and Disability
Attn: Executive Assistant
71423 Biskra Road
Rancho Mirage, CA 92270
(760) 346-8206   Fax: (760) 340-5275
TDD: (760) 341-4084   E-mail: caped2000@aol.com
Web: www.caped.net/scholarships.html

Summary To provide financial assistance to undergraduate and graduate students in California who have a disability and can demonstrate academic achievement and involvement in community and campus activities.

Eligibility This program is open to students at public and private colleges and universities in California who have a disability. Undergraduates must have completed at least 6 semester credits and have a GPA of 2.5 or higher. Graduate students must have completed at least 3 semester units and have a GPA of 3.0 or higher. Applicants must submit a 1-page personal letter that demonstrates their writing skills, progress towards meeting their educational and vocational goals, management of their disability, and involvement in community activities. They must also submit a letter of recommendation from a faculty member, verification of disability, official transcripts, proof of current enrollment, and documentation of financial need. This award is presented to the applicant who demonstrates the highest level of academic achievement and involvement in community and campus life.

Financial data The stipend is $1,500.

Duration 1 year.

Number awarded 1 each year.

Deadline September of each year.

[104]
CAREER DEVELOPMENT AWARD TO PROMOTE DIVERSITY IN NEUROSCIENCE RESEARCH

National Institute of Neurological Disorders and Stroke
Attn: Office of Minority Health and Research
6001 Executive Boulevard, Suite 2150
Bethesda, MD 20892-9527
(301) 496-3102   Fax: (301) 594-5929
TDD: (301) 451-0088
E-mail: jonesmiche@ninds.nih.gov
Web: www.ninds.nih.gov

Summary To provide funding to neurological research scientists who are disabled or members of other underrepresented groups who are interested in making a transition to a career as an independent investigator.

Eligibility This program is open to full-time faculty members at domestic, for-profit and nonprofit, public and private institutions, such as universities, colleges, hospitals, and laboratories. Applicants must be junior neuroscience investigators making the transition to an independent scientific career at the senior postdoctoral and junior faculty stages under the supervision of a qualified mentor. They must qualify as 1) a member of an ethnic or racial group shown to be underrepresented in health-related sciences on a national basis; 2) an individual with a disability; or 3) an individual from a disadvantaged background, including those from a low-income family and those from a social, cultural, and/or educational environment that has inhibited them from preparation for a research career. Selection is based on qualifications of the applicant, soundness of the proposed career development plan, training in the responsible conduct of research, nature and scientific/technical merit of the proposed research plan, qualifications and appropriateness of the mentor, environment and institutional commitment to the applicant's career, and strength of the description of how this award will promote diversity within the institution or in science nationally. Only U.S. citizens, nationals, and permanent residents are eligible.

Financial data Grants provide an annual award of up to $85,000 for salary and fringe benefits and an annual research allowance of up to $50,000 for direct research costs. The institution may apply for up to 8% of direct costs for facilities and administrative costs.

Duration 3 to 5 years; nonrenewable.

Additional data Recipients must devote 75% of full-time professional effort to conducting health-related research.

Number awarded Varies each year.

Deadline February, June, or October of each year.

[105]
CENTURY SCHOLARSHIP

American Library Association
Attn: ASCLA
50 East Huron Street
Chicago, IL 60611-2795
(312) 280-4395   Toll Free: (800) 545-2433, ext. 4395
Fax: (312) 280-5273   TDD: (888) 814-7692
E-mail: ascla@ala.org
Web: www.ala.org/ascla/asclaawards/asclacentury

Summary To provide financial assistance to library science students with disabilities.

Eligibility This program is open to students with disabilities who have been admitted to an ALA-accredited library school to work on a master's or doctoral degree. Applicants must submit medical documentation of their disability or disabilities and a description of the services and/or accommodations they require for their studies. U.S. or Canadian citizenship is required. Selection is based on academic excellence, leadership, professional goals, and financial need.

Financial data The stipend is $2,500; funds are to be used for services or accommodations not provided by law or by the university.

Duration 1 year.

Additional data This program began in 2000.

Number awarded 1 or more each year.

Deadline February of each year.

[106]
CHANCELLOR'S POSTDOCTORAL FELLOWSHIPS FOR ACADEMIC DIVERSITY

University of California at Berkeley
Attn: Office for Faculty Equity
200 California Hall
Berkeley, CA 94720-1500
(510) 642-1935   E-mail: admin.ofe@berkeley.edu
Web: vcei.berkeley.edu/ChancPostdocFellowship

Summary To provide an opportunity for disabled and other recent postdoctorates who will increase diversity at the University of California at Berkeley to conduct research on the campus.

Eligibility This program is open to U.S. citizens and permanent residents who received a doctorate within 3 years of the start of the fellowship. The program particularly solicits applications from individuals who are members of groups that are underrepresented in American universities (e.g., women, ethnic minorities, religious minorities, differently-abled, lesbian/gay/bisexual/transgender). Special consideration is given to applicants committed to careers in university research and teaching and whose life experience, research, or employment background will contribute significantly to academic diversity and excellence at the Berkeley campus.

Financial data The stipend is $41,496 per year (11 months, plus 1 month vacation). The award also includes health insurance, vision and dental benefits, and up to $4,000 for research-related and program travel expenses.

Duration 1 year; may be renewed 1 additional year.

Additional data Research opportunities, mentoring, and guidance are provided as part of the program.

Number awarded Varies each year; recently, 5 of these fellowships were awarded.

Deadline November of each year.

[107]
COOLEY DIVERSITY FELLOWSHIP PROGRAM

Cooley LLP
Attn: Attorney Recruiting Manager
4401 Eastgate Mall
San Diego, CA 92121-1909
(858) 550-6000
E-mail: diversityfellowship@cooley.com
Web: www.cooley.com/diversityfellowship

Summary To provide financial assistance and work experience to disabled and other law students who are committed to promoting diversity in their community and are interested in a summer associateship at an office of Cooley LLP.

Eligibility This program is open to students enrolled full time at an ABA-accredited law school and planning to graduate 2 years after applying. Applicants must submit a 3-page personal statement describing their demonstrated commitment to promoting diversity (e.g., ethnicity, gender, physical disability, and/or sexual orientation) in their community. Selection is based on undergraduate and law school academic performance, personal achievements, leadership abilities, community service, demonstrated commitment to promoting diversity, and commitment to joining Cooley's summer associate program following their second year of law school.

Financial data The award includes a stipend of $15,000 to assist with law school tuition and a paid summer associate position.

Duration 1 year.

Additional data Summer associates may work in any of the firm's offices in California (Palo Alto, San Diego, or San Francisco), Colorado (Broomfield), Massachusetts (Boston), New York (New York), Virginia (Reston), Washington (Seattle), or Washington, D.C.

Number awarded 1 or more each year.

Deadline June of each year.

[108]
DICKSTEIN SHAPIRO DIVERSITY SCHOLARSHIP

Dickstein Shapiro LLP
Attn: Director of Professional Development and
  Attorney Recruiting
1825 Eye Street, N.W.
Washington, DC 20006-5403
(202) 420-4880   Fax: (202) 420-2201
E-mail: careers@dicksteinshapiro.com
Web: www.dicksteinshapiro.com/careers/diversity

Summary To provide financial assistance and summer work experience at Dickstein Shapiro in Washington, D.C. or New York City to disabled and other diverse law students from any state.

Eligibility This program is open to second-year diverse law students, including 1) members of the lesbian, gay, bisexual, and transgender (LGBT) community; 2) members of minority ethnic and racial groups (Blacks, Hispanics and Latinos, Asians, American Indians and Native Alaskans, and Native Hawaiians and Pacific Islanders); and 3) students with disabilities. Applicants must be interested in a summer associateship with Dickstein Shapiro in Washington, D.C. or New York City. Selection is based on academic and professional experience as well as the extent to which they reflect the core values of the firm: excellence, loyalty, respect, initiative, and integrity.

Financial data The stipend is $25,000, including $15,000 upon completion of the summer associate program and $10,000 upon acceptance of a full-time offer of employment following graduation.

Duration The associateship takes place during the summer following the second year of law school and the stipend covers the third year of law school.

Additional data This program was established in 2006.

Number awarded 1 or more each year.

Deadline September of each year.

[109]
DISABLED PERSON NATIONAL SCHOLARSHIP COMPETITION

Disabled Person, Inc.
P.O. Box 260636
Encinitas, CA 92023-0636
(760) 420-1269 E-mail: info@disabledperson.com
Web: www.disabledperson.com

Summary To recognize and reward, with academic scholarships, undergraduate and graduate students who have a disability and submit outstanding essays on an assigned topic.

Eligibility This competition is open to U.S. citizens who have a disability and are enrolled as full-time undergraduate or graduate students at a college or university in the United States. High school seniors and part-time students are not eligible. Applicants must submit an essay, up to 1,000 words in length, on a topic that changes annually; recently, students were asked to write on, "Define Leadership as it relates to the disability community. Who are the top leaders within the disability community and what have they accomplished?"

Financial data The award is a $1,000 scholarship.

Duration The competition is held annually.

Number awarded 1 in the fall and 1 in the spring.

Deadline October of each year for fall; February of each year for spring.

[110]
DONALD W. BANNER DIVERSITY SCHOLARSHIP

Banner & Witcoff, Ltd.
Attn: Christopher Hummel
1100 13th Street, N.W., Suite 1200
Washington, DC 20005-4051
(202) 824-3000 Fax: (202) 824-3001
E-mail: chummel@bannerwitcoff.com
Web: www.bannerwitcoff.com

Summary To provide financial assistance to disabled and other law students who come from groups historically underrepresented in intellectual property law.

Eligibility This program is open to students enrolled in the first or second year of a J.D. program at an ABA-accredited law school in the United States. Applicants must come from a group historically underrepresented in intellectual property law; that underrepresentation may be the result of race, sex, ethnicity, sexual orientation, or disability. Selection is based on academic merit, commitment to the pursuit of a career in intellectual property law, written communication skills, oral communication skills (determined through an interview), leadership qualities, and community involvement.

Financial data The stipend is $5,000 per year.

Duration 1 year (the second or third year of law school); students who accept and successfully complete the firm's summer associate program may receive an additional $5,000 for a subsequent semester of law school.

Number awarded 2 each year.

Deadline October of each year.

[111]
EDWARD T. CONROY MEMORIAL SCHOLARSHIP PROGRAM

Maryland Higher Education Commission
Attn: Office of Student Financial Assistance
6 North Liberty Street, Ground Suite
Baltimore, MD 21201
(410) 767-3300 Toll Free: (800) 974-0203
Fax: (410) 332-0250 TDD: (800) 735-2258
E-mail: osfamail@mhec.state.md.us
Web: www.mhec.state.md.us

Summary To provide financial assistance for college or graduate school in Maryland to children and spouses of victims of the September 11, 2001 terrorist attacks and specified categories of veterans, public safety employees, and their children or spouses.

Eligibility This program is open to entering and continuing undergraduate and graduate students in the following categories: 1) children and surviving spouses of victims of the September 11, 2001 terrorist attacks who died in the World Trade Center in New York City, in the Pentagon in Virginia, or on United Airlines Flight 93 in Pennsylvania; 2) veterans who have, as a direct result of military service, a disability of 25% or greater and have exhausted or are no longer eligible for federal veterans' educational benefits; 3) children of armed forces members whose death or 100% disability was directly caused by military service; 4) POW/MIA veterans of the Vietnam Conflict and their children; 5) state or local public safety officers or volunteers who became 100% disabled in the line of duty; and 6) children and unremarried surviving spouses of state or local public safety employees or volunteers who died or became 100% disabled in the line of duty. The parent, spouse, veteran, POW, or public safety officer or volunteer must have been a resident of Maryland at the time of death or when declared disabled. Financial need is not considered.

Financial data The amount awarded is equal to tuition and fees at a Maryland postsecondary institution, up to $19,000, for children and spouses of the September 11 terrorist attacks or $9,000 for all other recipients.

Duration Up to 5 years of full-time study or 8 years of part-time study.

Additional data Recipients must enroll at a 2- or 4-year Maryland college or university as a full-time or part-time degree-seeking undergraduate or graduate student or attend a private career school.

Number awarded Varies each year.

Deadline July of each year.

[112]
FISH & RICHARDSON DIVERSITY FELLOWSHIP PROGRAM

Fish & Richardson P.C.
Attn: Recruiting Department
One Marina Park Drive
Boston, MA 02110
(617) 542-5070   Fax: (617) 542-8906
E-mail: Kiley@fr.com
Web: www.fr.com/careers/diversity

Summary To provide financial assistance for law school to disabled and other students who will contribute to diversity in the legal profession.

Eligibility This program is open to students enrolled in the first year at a law school anywhere in the country. Applicants must be African American/Black, American Indian/Alaskan, Hispanic/Latino, Native Hawaiian/Pacific Islander, Asian, 2 or more races, disabled, or openly homosexual, bisexual, and/or transgender. Along with their application, they must submit a 500-word essay describing their background, what led them to the legal field, their interest in the sponsoring law firm, and what they could contribute to its practice and the profession. They must also indicate their first 3 choices of an office of the firm where they are interested in a summer associate clerkship.

Financial data The stipend is $5,000.

Duration 1 year: the second year of law school.

Additional data Recipients are also offered a paid associate clerkship during the summer following their first year of law school at an office of the firm in the location of their choice in Atlanta, Boston, Dallas, Delaware, Houston, New York, San Diego, Silicon Valley, Twin Cities, or Washington, D.C. This program began in 2005.

Number awarded 1 or more each year.

Deadline January of each year.

[113]
GAIUS CHARLES BOLIN DISSERTATION AND POST-MFA FELLOWSHIPS

Williams College
Attn: Dean of the Faculty
Hopkins Hall, Third Floor
P.O. Box 141
Williamstown, MA 01267
(413) 597-4351   Fax: (413) 597-3553
E-mail: gburda@williams.edu
Web: dean-faculty.williams.edu/graduate-fellowships

Summary To provide financial assistance to persons with disabilities and members of other underrepresented groups who are interested in teaching courses at Williams College while working on their doctoral dissertation or building their post-M.F.A. professional portfolio.

Eligibility This program is open to members of underrepresented groups, including ethnic minorities, first-generation college students, women in predominantly male fields, and scholars with disabilities. Applicants must be 1) doctoral candidates in any field who have completed all work for a Ph.D. except for the dissertation; or 2) artists

who completed an M.F.A. degree within the past 2 years and are building their professional portfolio. They must be willing to teach a course at Williams College. Along with their application, they must submit a full curriculum vitae, a graduate school transcript, 3 letters of recommendation, a copy of their dissertation prospectus or samples of their artistic work, and a description of their teaching interests within a department or program at Williams College. U.S. citizenship or permanent resident status is required.

Financial data Fellows receive $33,000 for the academic year, plus housing assistance, office space, computer and library privileges, and a research allowance of up to $4,000.

Duration 2 years.

Additional data Bolin fellows are assigned a faculty adviser in the appropriate department. This program was established in 1985. Fellows are expected to teach a 1-semester course each year. They must be in residence at Williams College for the duration of the fellowship.

Number awarded 3 each year.

Deadline November of each year.

[114]
GEOLOGICAL SOCIETY OF AMERICA GRADUATE STUDENT RESEARCH GRANTS

Geological Society of America
Attn: Program Officer-Grants, Awards and Recognition
3300 Penrose Place
P.O. Box 9140
Boulder, CO 80301-9140
(303) 357-1028   Toll Free: (800) 472-1988, ext. 1028
Fax: (303) 357-1070   E-mail: awards@geosociety.org
Web: www.geosociety.org/grants/gradgrants.htm

Summary To provide funding to disabled and other graduate student members of the Geological Society of America (GSA) interested in conducting research at universities in the United States, Canada, Mexico, or Central America.

Eligibility This program is open to GSA members working on a master's or doctoral degree at a university in the United States, Canada, Mexico, or Central America. Applicants must be interested in conducting geological research. Minorities, women, and persons with disabilities are strongly encouraged to apply. Selection is based on the scientific merits of the proposal, the capability of the investigator, and the reasonableness of the budget.

Financial data Grants range up to $4,000 and recently averaged $2,411. Funds can be used for the cost of travel, room and board in the field, services of a technician or field assistant, funding of chemical and isotope analyses, or other expenses directly related to the fulfillment of the research contract. Support is not provided for the purchase of ordinary field equipment, for maintenance of the families of the grantees and their assistants, as reimbursement for work already accomplished, for institutional overhead, for adviser participation, or for tuition costs.

Duration 1 year.

Additional data In addition to general grants, GSA awards a number of specialized grants: the Gretchen L.

Blechschmidt Award for women (especially in the fields of biostratigraphy and/or paleoceanography); the John T. Dillon Alaska Research Award for earth science problems particular to Alaska; the Robert K. Fahnestock Memorial Award for the field of sediment transport or related aspects of fluvial geomorphology; the Lipman Research Award for volcanology and petrology; the Bruce L. "Biff" Reed Award for studies in the tectonic and magmatic evolution of Alaska; the Alexander Sisson Award for studies in Alaska and the Caribbean; the Harold T. Stearns Fellowship Award for work on the geology of the Pacific Islands and the circum-Pacific region; the Parke D. Snavely, Jr. Cascadia Research Fund Award for studies of the Pacific Northwest convergent margin; the Alexander and Geraldine Wanek Fund Award for studies of coal and petroleum; the Charles A. and June R.P. Ross Research Fund Award for stratigraphy; and the John Montagne Fund Award for quaternary geology or geomorphology research.

Number awarded Varies each year; recently, the society awarded 220 grants worth more than $530,000 through this and all of its specialized programs.

Deadline January of each year.

[115]
GOOGLE LIME SCHOLARSHIPS FOR STUDENTS WITH DISABILITIES

Lime Connect, Inc.
590 Madison Avenue, 21st Floor
New York, NY 10022
(212) 521-4469   Fax: (212) 521-4099
E-mail: info@limeconnect.com
Web: www.limeconnect.com

Summary To provide financial assistance to students with disabilities working on a bachelor's or graduate degree in a computer-related field at a college or university in Canada or the United States.

Eligibility This program is open to students at colleges and universities in the United States or Canada who have a disability and are entering their junior or senior year of undergraduate study or are enrolled as graduate students. International students with disabilities enrolled at universities in the United States or Canada are also eligible. Applicants must be working full time on a degree in computer science, computer engineering, or a closely-related technical field. Along with their application, they must submit 2 essays of 400 to 600 words each on 1) their academic accomplishments in terms of the technical projects on which they have worked; and 2) the issue about which they are passionate, what they have done to fulfill that passion, or what they dream of doing to fulfill it. Financial need is not considered in the selection process.

Financial data The stipend is $10,000 for students at U.S. universities or $C5,000 for students at Canadian universities.

Duration 1 year.

Additional data This program is jointly sponsored by Google and Lime Connect, an organization founded in 2006 to promote employment of people with disabilities.

Number awarded Varies each year.

Deadline February of each year.

[116]
GRADUATE RESEARCH FELLOWSHIP PROGRAM OF THE NATIONAL SCIENCE FOUNDATION

National Science Foundation
Directorate for Education and Human Resources
Attn: Division of Graduate Education
4201 Wilson Boulevard, Room 875S
Arlington, VA 22230
(703) 292-8694   Toll Free: (866) NSF-GRFP
Fax: (703) 292-9048   E-mail: grfp@nsf.gov
Web: www.nsf.gov

Summary To provide financial assistance to disabled and other graduate students interested in working on a master's or doctoral degree in fields supported by the National Science Foundation (NSF).

Eligibility This program is open to U.S. citizens, nationals, and permanent residents who wish to work on research-based master's or doctoral degrees in a field of science (including social science), technology, engineering, or mathematics (STEM) supported by NSF. Other work in medical, dental, law, public health, or practice-oriented professional degree programs, or in joint science-professional degree programs, such as M.D./Ph.D. and J.D./Ph.D. programs, is not eligible. Other categories of ineligible support include 1) clinical, counseling, business, or management fields; 2) education (except science and engineering education); 3) history (except the history of science); 4) social work; 5) medical sciences or research with disease-related goals, including work on the etiology, diagnosis, or treatment of physical or mental disease, abnormality, or malfunction in human beings or animals; 6) research involving animal models with disease-related goals; and 7) testing of drugs or other procedures for disease-related goals. Applications normally should be submitted during the senior year in college or in the first year of graduate study; eligibility is limited to those who have completed no more than 12 months of graduate study since completion of a baccalaureate degree. Applicants who have already earned an advanced degree in science, engineering, or medicine (including an M.D., D.D.S., or D.V.M.) are ineligible. Selection is based on 1) intellectual merit of the proposed activity (strength of the academic record, proposed plan of research, previous research experience, references, appropriateness of the choice of institution); and 2) broader impacts of the proposed activity (how well does the activity advance discovery and understanding, how well does it broaden the participation of underrepresented groups (e.g., gender, ethnicity, disability, geographic), to what extent will it enhance the infrastructure for research and education, will the results be disseminated broadly to enhance scientific and technological understanding, what may be the benefits of the proposed activity to society).

Financial data The stipend is $30,000 per year; an additional $10,500 cost-of-education allowance is provided to the recipient's institution. If a fellow affiliates with a foreign institution, tuition and fees are reimbursed to the fellow up to a maximum of $10,500 per tenure year and an additional international research travel allowance of $1,000 is provided.

Duration Up to 3 years, usable over a 5-year period.

Additional data Fellows may choose as their fellowship institution any appropriate nonprofit U.S. or foreign institution of higher education.

Number awarded Approximately 2,000 each year.

Deadline November of each year.

[117]
HARRIETT G. JENKINS PRE-DOCTORAL FELLOWSHIP PROGRAM

United Negro College Fund Special Programs
  Corporation
6402 Arlington Boulevard, Suite 600
Falls Church, VA 22042
(703) 677-3400   Toll Free: (800) 530-6232
Fax: (703) 205-7645   E-mail: portal@uncfsp.org
Web: www.uncfsp.org

Summary To provide financial assistance and work experience to women, minorities, and people with disabilities working on a graduate degree in a field of interest to the National Aeronautics and Space Administration (NASA).

Eligibility This program is open to members of groups underrepresented in science, technology, engineering, or mathematics (STEM), including women, minorities, and people with disabilities. Applicants must be full-time graduate students in a program leading to a master's or doctoral degree in a NASA-related discipline (aeronautics, aerospace engineering, astronomy, atmospheric science, bioengineering, biology, chemistry, computer science, earth sciences, engineering, environmental sciences, life sciences, materials sciences, mathematics, meteorology, neuroscience, physics, or robotics). They must be U.S. citizens and have a GPA of 3.0 or higher. Doctoral students who have advanced to candidacy are ineligible.

Financial data The stipend is $22,000 per year for doctoral fellows or $16,000 per year for master's degree students. The tuition offset is at least $8,500. Fellows who are also selected for a mini research award at a NASA Center or the Jet Propulsion Laboratory receive an additional grant of $7,000.

Duration 3 years.

Additional data This program, established in 2001, is funded by NASA and administered by the United Negro College Fund Special Programs Corporation. Fellows may also compete for a mini research award to engage in a NASA research experience that is closely aligned with the research conducted at the fellow's institution. The participating NASA facilities are Ames Research Center (Moffett Field, California), Jet Propulsion Laboratory (Pasadena, California), Dryden Flight Research Center (Edwards, California), Johnson Space Center (Houston, Texas), Stennis Space Center (Stennis Space Center, Mississippi), Marshall Space Flight Center (Marshall Space Flight Center, Alabama), Glenn Research Center (Cleve-

land, Ohio), Kennedy Space Center (Kennedy Space Center, Florida), Langley Research Center (Hampton, Virginia), and Goddard Space Flight Center (Greenbelt, Maryland).

Number awarded Approximately 20 each year.

Deadline April of each year.

[118]
JOE CLERES MEMORIAL SCHOLARSHIPS

New Outlook Pioneers
c/o Shirley Zunich, Scholarship Administrator
1801 California Street, 44th Floor
Denver, CO 80202
(303) 571-9256
E-mail: szunich@pioneersvolunteer.org
Web: www.newoutlookpioneers.org

Summary To provide funding to students who are have a disability.

Eligibility This program is open to students with physical or mental disabilities who are enrolled or planning to enroll in high school, college, trade school, or graduate school. Applicants or their representatives must submit a 1-page essay describing how the student has met the challenge of his or her disability, including the severity of the disability. They may also include up to 1 page of supporting documentation, but photographs, audio or videotapes, display materials, films, or scrapbooks are not considered.

Financial data Stipends range from $500 to $2,000. Funds are paid directly to the school for tuition support.

Duration 1 year.

Additional data This program was established in 1996 by Lucent Technologies as the New Outlook Scholarships for Students with Disabilities. The current name was adopted in 2005. New Outlook Pioneers is an affiliate of TelecomPioneers. Its members are employees and retirees of Lucent Technologies, Avaya Communication, and Agere.

Number awarded Varies each year; recently, 22 of these scholarships were awarded: 1 at $2,000, 2 at $1,500, 5 at $1,000, 8 at $750, and 6 at $500.

Deadline March of each year.

[119]
JUDD JACOBSON MEMORIAL AWARD

Courage Center
Attn: Vocational Services Department
3915 Golden Valley Road
Minneapolis, MN 55422
(763) 520-0263   Toll Free: (888) 8-INTAKE
Fax: (763) 520-0562   TDD: (763) 520-0245
E-mail: sue.warner@courage.org
Web: www.couragecenter.org

Summary To recognize and reward residents of designated states who have a disability and have established their own business.

Eligibility This award is available to residents of Iowa, Minnesota, North Dakota, South Dakota, and Wisconsin who have a physical or sensory disability. Nominees must be at least 18 years of age and have established a successful business entrepreneurial endeavor. They should be able to demonstrate entrepreneurial skill, financial need, and personal commitment, and should have received little or no public recognition.

Financial data The award is $5,000; funds must be used to further the awardee's entrepreneurial business activities.

Duration The award is presented annually.

Additional data This program was established in 1992.

Number awarded 1 each year.

Deadline May of each year.

[120]
KAISER PERMANENTE COLORADO DIVERSITY SCHOLARSHIP PROGRAM

Kaiser Permanente
Attn: Physician Recruitment Services
10350 East Dakota Avenue
Denver, CO 80231-1314
(303) 344-7299   Toll Free: (866) 239-1677
Fax: (303) 344-7818
E-mail: co-diversitydevelopment@kp.org
Web: scholarselect.com

Summary To provide financial assistance to disabled and other Colorado residents who come from diverse backgrounds and are interested in working on an undergraduate or graduate degree in a health care field at a public college in the state.

Eligibility This program is open to all residents of Colorado, including those who identify as 1 or more of the following: African American, Asian Pacific, Latino, lesbian, gay, bisexual, transgender, intersex, Native American, U.S. veteran, and/or a person with a disability. Applicants must be enrolled or planning to enroll full time at a publicly-funded college, university, or technical school in Colorado as 1) a graduating high school senior with a GPA of 2.7 or higher; 2) a GED recipient with a GED score of 520 or higher; 3) an undergraduate student; or 4) a graduate or doctoral student. They must be preparing for a career in health care (e.g., athletic training, audiology, cardiovascular perfusion technology, clinical medical assisting, cytotechnology, dental assisting, dental hygiene, diagnostic medicine, dietetics, emergency medical technology, medicine, nursing, occupational therapy, pharmacy, phlebotomy, physical therapy, physician assistant, radiology, respiratory therapy, social work, sports medicine, surgical technology). Along with their application, they must submit 300-word essays on 1) a brief story from their childhood and the aspects of their experience that will contribute to their become a good health care provided; 2) what giving back to the community means to them and their experiences in community involvement that demonstrate their commitment to health care; and 3) what they consider the most pressing issue in health care today. Selection is based on academic achievement, character qualities, community outreach and volunteering, and financial need. U.S. citizenship is required.

Financial data Stipends range from $1,400 to $2,600.

Duration 1 year.

Number awarded Varies each year; recently, 17 of these scholarships were awarded.

Deadline February of each year.

[121]
KING & SPALDING DIVERSITY FELLOWSHIP PROGRAM

King & Spalding
Attn: Diversity Fellowship Program
1180 Peachtree Street
Atlanta, GA 30309
(404) 572-4643   Fax: (404) 572-5100
E-mail: fellowship@kslaw.com
Web: www.kslaw.com

Summary To provide financial assistance and summer work experience at U.S. offices of King & Spalding to disabled and other law students who will contribute to the diversity of the legal community.

Eligibility This program is open to second-year law students who 1) come from a minority ethnic or racial group (American Indian/Alaskan Native, Asian American/Pacific Islander, Black/African American, Hispanic, or multiracial); 2) are a member of the gay, lesbian, bisexual, or transgender (GLBT) community; or 3) have a disability. Applicants must receive an offer of a clerkship at a U.S. office of King & Spalding during their second-year summer. Along with their application, they must submit a 500-word personal statement that describes their talents, qualities, and experiences and how they would contribute to the diversity of the firm.

Financial data Fellows receive a stipend of $10,000 for their second year of law school and a paid summer associate clerkship at a U.S. office of the firm during the following summer.

Duration 1 year.

Additional data The firm's U.S. offices are located in Atlanta, Charlotte, Houston, New York, San Francisco, Silicon Valley, and Washington.

Number awarded Up to 4 each year.

Deadline August of each year.

[122]
LESLIE LONDER FUND SCHOLARSHIP

American Speech-Language-Hearing Foundation
Attn: Programs Administrator
2200 Research Boulevard
Rockville, MD 20850-3289
(301) 296-8703   Fax: (301) 296-8567
E-mail: foundationprograms@asha.org
Web: www.ashfoundation.org

Summary To provide financial assistance to persons with disabilities who are interested in studying communication sciences or related programs in graduate school.

Eligibility This program is open to full-time graduate students who are enrolled in communication sciences and disorders programs, with preference given to students who have a disability. Applicants must submit an essay, up to 5 pages in length, on a topic that relates to the future of leadership in the discipline. They must also submit brief statements on the major classification that best describes their impairment and the limitations that their disability has posed. Selection is based on academic promise and outstanding academic achievement.

Financial data   The stipend is $5,000. Funds must be used for education (e.g., tuition, books, school-related living expenses), not personal or conference travel.

Duration   1 year.

Number awarded   1 each year.

Deadline   June of each year.

[123]
LOREEN ARBUS DISABILITY AWARENESS GRANTS

New York Women in Film & Television
6 East 39th Street, 12th Floor
New York, NY 10016-0870
(212) 679-0870   Fax: (212) 679-0899
E-mail: info@nywift.org
Web: www.nywift.org/article.aspx?id=LAS

Summary   To provide funding to women filmmakers who are either disabled or interested in making a film on disability issues.

Eligibility   This program is open to women who are interested in making a film of any length or genre that is already in progress. Applicants must either have a disability or be proposing to make a film about disability issues. They must submit a 2- to 4-page description of the project, a budget indicating amount raised to date, a list of key creative personnel with 1-paragraph bios, and a DVD or a link to an upload of the work-in-progress.

Financial data   The grant is $7,500. Funds may be used only completion work.

Duration   These grants are provided annually.

Number awarded   1 or more each year.

Deadline   September of each year.

[124]
MARK T. BANNER SCHOLARSHIP FOR LAW STUDENTS

Richard Linn American Inn of Court
c/o Cynthia M. Ho, Programs Chair
Loyola University School of Law
25 East Pearson Street, Room 1324
Chicago, IL 60611
(312) 915-7148
Web: www.linninn.org/marktbanner.htm

Summary   To provide financial assistance to disabled and other law students who are members of a group historically underrepresented in intellectual property law.

Eligibility   This program is open to students at ABA-accredited law schools in the United States who are members of groups historically underrepresented (by race, sex, ethnicity, sexual orientation, or disability) in intellectual property law. Applicants must submit a 1-page statement on how they have focused on ethics, civility, and professionalism and how diversity has impacted them; transcripts; a writing sample; and contact information for 3 references. Selection is based on academic merit, written and oral communication skills (determined in part through a telephone interview), leadership qualities, community involvement, and commitment to the pursuit of a career in intellectual property law.

Financial data   The stipend is $5,000.

Duration   1 year.

Number awarded   1 each year.

Deadline   November of each year.

[125]
MENTAL HEALTH DISSERTATION RESEARCH GRANT TO INCREASE DIVERSITY

National Institute of Mental Health
Attn: Division of Extramural Activities
6001 Executive Boulevard, Room 6138
Bethesda, MD 20892-9609
(301) 443-3534   Fax: (301) 443-4720
TDD: (301) 451-0088   E-mail: armstrda@mail.nih.gov
Web: www.nimh.nih.gov

Summary   To provide research funding to disabled and other doctoral candidates from underrepresented groups planning to prepare for a research career in any area relevant to mental health and/or mental disorders.

Eligibility   This program is open to doctoral candidates conducting dissertation research in a field related to mental health and/or mental disorders at a university, college, or professional school with an accredited doctoral degree granting program. Applicants must be 1) members of an ethnic or racial group that has been determined by their institution to be underrepresented in biomedical or behavioral research; 2) individuals with disabilities; or 3) individuals from socially, culturally, economically, or educationally disadvantaged backgrounds that have inhibited their ability to prepare for a career in health-related research. They must be U.S. citizens, nationals, or permanent residents.

Financial data   The stipend is $21,180. An additional grant up to $15,000 is provided for additional research expenses, fringe benefits (including health insurance), travel to scientific meetings, and research costs of the dissertation. Facilities and administrative costs are limited to 8% of modified total direct costs.

Duration   Up to 2 years; nonrenewable.

Number awarded   Varies each year.

Deadline   April, August, or December of each year.

[126]
MENTORED NEW INVESTIGATOR RESEARCH GRANTS TO PROMOTE DIVERSITY OF THE ALZHEIMER'S ASSOCIATION

Alzheimer's Association
Attn: Medical and Scientific Affairs
225 North Michigan Avenue, 17th Floor
Chicago, IL 60601-7633
(312) 335-5747   Toll Free: (800) 272-3900
Fax: (866) 699-1246   TDD: (312) 335-5886
E-mail: grantsapp@alz.org
Web: www.alz.org

Summary To provide funding for mentored research on Alzheimer's Disease to disabled and other junior investigators who will contribute to diversity in the field.

Eligibility This program is open to investigators who have less than 10 years of research experience after receipt of their terminal degree. Applicants must be proposing to conduct research with focus areas that change annually but are related to Alzheimer's Disease. They must identify a mentor who is experienced in conducting Alzheimer's and related dementia research and in mentoring investigators. Eligibility is restricted to investigators who will contribute to diversity in the field of biomedical research, including members of underrepresented racial and ethnic minority groups (African Americans, Hispanic Americans, American Indians/Alaska Natives, Native Hawaiians, and Pacific Islanders) and individuals with disabilities.

Financial data Grants up to $60,000 per year, including direct expenses and up to 10% for overhead, are available. The total award for the life of the grant may not exceed $170,000, including $150,000 for costs related to the proposed research, $10,000 to the fellow upon successful completion of the program, and $10,000 to the mentor upon successful completion of the program.

Duration Up to 3 years.

Number awarded Up to 4 of these and parallel grants are awarded each year.

Deadline Letters of intent must be submitted by the end of December of each year. Final applications are due in February.

[127]
MG EUGENE C. RENZI, USA (RET.)/MANTECH INTERNATIONAL CORPORATION TEACHER'S SCHOLARSHIP

Armed Forces Communications and Electronics
  Association
Attn: AFCEA Educational Foundation
4400 Fair Lakes Court
Fairfax, VA 22033-3899
(703) 631-6138   Toll Free: (800) 336-4583, ext. 6138
Fax: (703) 631-4693
E-mail: scholarshipsinfo@afcea.org
Web: www.afcea.org

Summary To provide financial assistance to undergraduate and graduate students (especially disabled veterans) who are preparing for a career as a teacher of science and mathematics.

Eligibility This program is open to full-time sophomores, juniors, seniors, and graduate students at accredited colleges and universities in the United States. Applicants must be U.S. citizens preparing for a career as a teacher of science, mathematics, or information technology at a middle or secondary school. They must have a GPA of 3.0 or higher. In the selection process, first consideration is given to wounded or disabled veterans, then to honorably discharged veterans. Financial need is not considered.

Financial data The stipend is $2,500.

Duration 1 year.

Additional data This program was established in 2008 with support from ManTech International Corporation.

Number awarded 1 each year.

Deadline March of each year.

[128]
MUSICIANS WITH SPECIAL NEEDS SCHOLARSHIP

Sigma Alpha Iota Philanthropies, Inc.
One Tunnel Road
Asheville, NC 28805
(828) 251-0606   Fax: (828) 251-0644
E-mail: nh@sai-national.org
Web: www.sai-national.org

Summary To provide financial assistance for college or graduate school to members of Sigma Alpha Iota (an organization of women musicians) who have a disability and are working on a degree in music.

Eligibility This program is open to members of the organization who either 1) have a sensory or physical impairment and are enrolled in a graduate or undergraduate degree program in music, or 2) are preparing to become a music teacher or therapist for people with disabilities. Performance majors must submit a 15-minute DVD of their work; non-performance majors must submit evidence of work in their area of specialization, such as composition, musicology, or research.

Financial data The stipend is $1,500.

Duration 1 year.

Number awarded 1 each year.

Deadline March of each year.

[129]
NASA GRADUATE STUDENT RESEARCHERS PROGRAM

National Aeronautics and Space Administration
Attn: Acting National GSRP Project Manager
Jet Propulsion Laboratory
4800 Oak Grove Drive
Pasadena, CA 91109-8099
(818) 354-3274   Fax: (818) 393-4977
E-mail: Linda.L.Rodgers@jpl.nasa.gov
Web: fellowships.nasaprs.com/gsrp/nav

Summary To provide funding to disabled and other graduate students interested in conducting research in fields of interest to the U.S. National Aeronautics and Space Administration (NASA).

Eligibility This program is open to full-time students enrolled or planning to enroll in an accredited graduate program at a U.S. college or university. Applicants must be citizens of the United States, sponsored by a faculty adviser or department chair, and interested in conducting research in a field of science, mathematics, or engineering related to NASA research and development. Students who are interested in becoming teaching or education administrators are also eligible. Selection is based on academic qualifications, quality of the proposed research and its relevance to NASA's program, proposed utilization of center research facilities (except for NASA headquarters), and ability of the student to accomplish the defined research. Individuals from underrepresented groups in science, technology, engineering, or mathematics (STEM) fields (African Americans, Native Americans, Alaskan Natives, Mexican Americans, Puerto Ricans, Native Pacific Islanders, women, and persons with disabilities) are strongly urged to apply.

Financial data The program provides a $20,000 student stipend, a $6,000 student travel allowance, up to $1,000 for health insurance, and a $3,000 university allowance. The student stipend may cover tuition, room and board, books, software, meal plans, school and laboratory supplies, and other related expenses. The student travel allowance may be used for national and international conferences and data collection. The university allowance is a discretionary award that typically goes to the research adviser. If the student already has health insurance, that $1,000 grant may be added to the student stipend or student travel allowance.

Duration 1 year; may be renewed for up to 1 additional year for master's degree students or 2 additional years for doctoral students.

Additional data This program was established in 1980. Students are required to participate in a 10-week research experience at NASA headquarters in Washington, D.C. or at 1 of 10 NASA centers.

Number awarded This program supports approximately 180 graduate students each year.

Deadline February of each year.

[130]
NATIONAL CANCER INSTITUTE MENTORED CLINICAL SCIENTIST RESEARCH CAREER DEVELOPMENT AWARD TO PROMOTE DIVERSITY

National Cancer Institute
Attn: Center to Reduce Cancer Health Disparities
6116 Executive Boulevard, Suite 602
Bethesda, MD 20852-8341
(301) 496-7344   Fax: (301) 435-9225
TDD: (301) 451-0088   E-mail: ojeifojo@mail.nih.gov
Web: www.cancer.gov/researchandfunding

Summary To provide funding to persons with disabilities and members of other underrepresented groups who are interested in a program of training in cancer research under the supervision of an experienced mentor.

Eligibility This program is open to U.S. citizens, nationals, and permanent residents who have a clinical doctoral degree; individuals with a Ph.D. or other doctoral degree in clinical disciplines such as clinical psychology, nursing, clinical genetics, speech-language pathology, audiology, or rehabilitation are also eligible. Candidates must be nominated by an eligible institution (e.g., a domestic, nonprofit or for-profit public or private institution, such as a university, college, hospital, or laboratory; a unit of state or local government; or an eligible agency of the federal government) on the basis of their intent to conduct a research project highly relevant to cancer biology, cancer health

disparities, etiology, pathogenesis, prevention, diagnosis, and treatment that has the potential for establishing an independent research program. They must qualify as 1) members of an ethnic or racial group shown to be underrepresented in health-related sciences on a national basis; 2) individuals with a disability; or 3) individuals from a disadvantaged background, including those from a low-income family and those from a social, cultural, and/or educational environment that has inhibited them from preparation for a research career. The mentor must be a senior or mid-level faculty member with research competence and an appreciation of the cultural, socioeconomic, and research background of the individual candidate. Selection is based on the applicant's qualifications, interests, accomplishments, motivation, and potential for a career in laboratory or field-based cancer research.

Financial data The award provides salary up to $100,000 per year plus related fringe benefits. In addition, up to $30,000 per year is provided for research development support. Facilities and administrative costs are reimbursed at 8% of modified total direct costs.

Duration Up to 5 years.

Additional data This program was originally established in 2002 as the successor of a program designated the Minorities in Clinical Oncology Program Grants. Recipients must devote at least 75% of their full-time professional effort to cancer-related research and training activities.

Number awarded Varies each year, depending on the availability of funds.

Deadline February, June, or October of each year.

[131]
NATIONAL CANCER INSTITUTE MENTORED RESEARCH SCIENTIST DEVELOPMENT AWARD TO PROMOTE DIVERSITY

National Cancer Institute
Attn: Center to Reduce Cancer Health Disparities
6116 Executive Boulevard, Suite 602
Bethesda, MD 20852-8341
(301) 496-7344   Fax: (301) 435-9225
TDD: (301) 451-0088   E-mail: ojeifojo@mail.nih.gov
Web: www.cancer.gov/researchandfunding

Summary To provide funding to disabled and other underrepresented postdoctorates who need a period of "protected time" for intensive cancer research career development under the guidance of an experienced mentor.

Eligibility This program is open to U.S. citizens, nationals, and permanent residents who have a research or health professional doctorate and have completed a mentored research training experience. Candidates must be proposing to conduct a research project to prepare for an independent research career related to cancer biology, cancer health disparities, etiology, pathogenesis, prevention, diagnosis, and/or treatment. They must be nominated by a domestic nonprofit or for-profit organization, public or private (such as a university, college, hospital, or laboratory) that can demonstrate a commitment to the promotion of diversity of their student and faculty populations. Institutions must certify that the candidate qualifies as 1) a member of an ethnic or racial group shown to be underrepresented in health-related sciences on a national basis; 2) an individual with a disability; or 3) an individual from a disadvantaged background, including those from a low-income family and those from a social, cultural, and/or educational environment that have inhibited them from preparation for a research career. The mentor must have extensive research experience and an appreciation of the background of the candidate.

Financial data The award provides salary up to $100,000 per year plus related fringe benefits. In addition, up to $30,000 per year is provided for research development support. Facilities and administrative costs are reimbursed at 8% of modified total direct costs.

Duration 3, 4, or 5 years.

Additional data Recipients must devote at least 75% of their full-time professional effort to cancer-related research and training activities.

Number awarded Varies each year.

Deadline February, June, or October of each year.

[132]
NATIONAL SPACE GRANT COLLEGE AND FELLOWSHIP PROGRAM

National Aeronautics and Space Administration
Attn: Office of Education
300 E Street, S.W.
Mail Suite 6M35
Washington, DC 20546-0001
(202) 358-1069   Fax: (202) 358-7097
E-mail: Diane.D.DeTroye@nasa.gov
Web: www.nasa.gov

Summary To provide financial assistance to disabled and other undergraduate and graduate students interested in preparing for a career in a space-related field.

Eligibility This program is open to undergraduate and graduate students at colleges and universities that participate in the National Space Grant program of the U.S. National Aeronautics and Space Administration (NASA) through their state consortium. Applicants must be interested in a program of study and/or research in a field of science, technology, engineering, or mathematics (STEM) related to space. A specific goal of the program is to recruit and train U.S. citizens, especially underrepresented minorities, women, and persons with disabilities, for careers in aerospace science and technology. Financial need is not considered in the selection process.

Financial data Each consortium establishes the terms of the fellowship program in its state.

Additional data NASA established the Space Grant program in 1989. It operates through 52 consortia in each state, the District of Columbia, and Puerto Rico. Each consortium includes selected colleges and universities in that state as well as other affiliates from industry, museums, science centers, and state and local agencies.

Number awarded Varies each year.

Deadline Each consortium sets its own deadlines.

[133]
NCI MENTORED PATIENT-ORIENTED RESEARCH CAREER DEVELOPMENT AWARD TO PROMOTE DIVERSITY

National Cancer Institute
Attn: Comprehensive Minority Biomedical Branch
6116 Executive Boulevard, Suite 7031
Bethesda, MD 20892-8350
(301) 496-7344   Fax: (301) 402-4551
TDD: (301) 451-0088   E-mail: lockeb@mail.nih.gov
Web: www.cancer.gov/researchandfunding

Summary To provide funding to disabled and other underrepresented postdoctorates who will promote diversity in the field and are interested in a program of research training in patient-oriented oncology under the supervision of an experienced mentor.

Eligibility This program is open to U.S. citizens, nationals, and permanent residents who have a health professional doctoral degree or a doctoral degree in nursing research or practice; individuals with a Ph.D. degree in clinical disciplines such as clinical psychology, clinical genetics, social work, speech-language pathology, audiology, or rehabilitation are also eligible. Candidates must be nominated by a domestic nonprofit or for-profit organization, public or private (such as a university, college, hospital, laboratory, unit of state or local government, or eligible agency of the federal government) that can demonstrate a commitment to diversification of their student and faculty populations. Institutions must certify that the candidate qualifies as 1) a member of an ethnic or racial group shown to be underrepresented in health-related sciences on a national basis; 2) an individual with a disability; or 3) an individual from a disadvantaged background, including those from a low-income family and those from a social, cultural, and/or educational environment that have inhibited them from preparation for a research career. At least 2 mentors are required: an accomplished clinical investigator and at least 1 additional mentor or adviser who is recognized as an accomplished independent basic science investigator in the proposed research area.

Financial data The award provides salary up to $100,000 per year plus related fringe benefits. In addition, up to $30,000 per year is provided for research development support. Facilities and administrative costs are reimbursed at 8% of modified total direct costs.

Duration Up to 5 years.

Additional data Recipients must devote at least 75% of their full-time professional effort to cancer-related research and training activities.

Number awarded Varies each year.

Deadline February, June, or October of each year.

[134]
NEW INVESTIGATOR RESEARCH GRANTS TO PROMOTE DIVERSITY OF THE ALZHEIMER'S ASSOCIATION

Alzheimer's Association
Attn: Medical and Scientific Affairs
225 North Michigan Avenue, 17th Floor
Chicago, IL 60601-7633
(312) 335-5747   Toll Free: (800) 272-3900
Fax: (866) 699-1246   TDD: (312) 335-5886
E-mail: grantsapp@alz.org
Web: www.alz.org

Summary To provide funding for research on Alzheimer's Disease to disabled and other junior investigators who will contribute to diversity in the field.

Eligibility This program is open to investigators who have less than 10 years of research experience after receipt of their terminal degree. Applicants must be proposing to conduct research with focus areas that change annually but are related to Alzheimer's Disease. Eligibility is restricted to investigators who will contribute to diversity in the field of biomedical research, including members of underrepresented racial and ethnic minority groups (African Americans, Hispanic Americans, American Indians/Alaska Natives, Native Hawaiians, and Pacific Islanders) and individuals with disabilities.

Financial data Grants up to $60,000 per year, including direct expenses and up to 10% for overhead costs, are available. The total award for the life of the grant may not exceed $100,000.

Duration Up to 2 years.

Number awarded Up to 4 of these and parallel grants are awarded each year.

Deadline Letters of intent must be submitted by the end of December. Final applications are due in February.

[135]
NHLBI MENTORED CAREER DEVELOPMENT AWARD TO PROMOTE FACULTY DIVERSITY/RE-ENTRY IN BIOMEDICAL RESEARCH

National Heart, Lung, and Blood Institute
Attn: Division of Cardiovascular Sciences
6701 Rockledge Drive
Bethesda, MD 20892-7936
(301) 435-0709   Fax: (301) 480-1455
E-mail: silsbeeL@nhlbi.nih.gov
Web: www.nhlbi.nih.gov/funding/inits/index.htm

Summary To provide funding to persons with disabilities and members of other underrepresented groups interested in developing into independent biomedical investigators in research areas relevant to the mission of the National Heart, Lung, and Blood Institute (NHLBI).

Eligibility This program is open to U.S. citizens, nationals, and permanent residents who are full-time non-tenured faculty members at U.S. domestic institutions of higher education and eligible agencies of the federal government; applications are especially encouraged from faculty at Historically Black Colleges and Universities (HBCUs), Tribally Controlled Colleges and Universities (TCCUs), Hispanic-Serving Institutions (HSIs), and Alaska Native and Native Hawaiian Serving Institutions. Candidates must have received, at least 2 years previously, a doctoral degree or equivalent in a basic or clinical area related to cardiovascular, pulmonary, or hematologic diseases. Applications are especially encouraged from members of a group that will promote greater diversity in scientific research, including 1) members of underrepresented racial and ethnic groups (African Americans, Hispanic Americans, Alaska Natives, American Indians, Native Hawaiians, non-Asian Pacific Islanders); 2) individuals with disabilities; and 3) individuals from disadvantaged backgrounds. Candidates who have experienced an interruption in their research careers for a period of at least 3 but no more than 8 years (e.g., starting and/or raising a family, an incapacitating illness or injury, caring for an ill immediate family member, performing military service) are also eligible. The proposed research development plan must enable the candidate to become an independent investigator in cardiovascular, pulmonary, hematologic, and sleep disorders research with either a clinical or basic science emphasis.

Financial data The grant provides salary support of up to $75,000 per year plus fringe benefits. In addition, up to $30,000 per year may be provided for research project requirements and related support (e.g., technical personnel costs, supplies, equipment, candidate travel, telephone charges, publication costs, and tuition for necessary courses). Facilities and administrative costs may be reimbursed at the rate of 8% of total direct costs.

Duration 3 to 5 years.

Additional data At least 75% of the awardee's effort must be devoted to the research program. The remainder may be devoted to other clinical and teaching pursuits that are consistent with the program goals of developing the awardee into an independent biomedical scientist or the maintenance of the teaching and/or clinical skills needed for an academic research career.

Number awarded Varies each year; recently, 8 to 10 awards were available through this program; total funding was approximately $1,200,000.

Deadline Letters of intent must be submitted by August of each year; completed applications are due in September.

[136]
NHLBI SHORT-TERM RESEARCH EDUCATION PROGRAM TO INCREASE DIVERSITY IN HEALTH-RELATED RESEARCH

National Heart, Lung, and Blood Institute
Attn: Division of Cardiovascular Diseases
6701 Rockledge Drive
Bethesda, MD 20892-7940
(301) 435-0535   Fax: (301) 480-1454
TDD: (301) 451-0088
E-mail: Commaram@nhlbi.nih.gov
Web: www.nhlbi.nih.gov/funding/inits/index.htm

Summary To provide funding to persons with disabilities and members of other underrepresented groups interested in conducting a research education program relevant to the mission of the National Heart, Lung, and Blood Institute (NHLBI).

Eligibility This program is open to principal investigators at U.S. domestic institutions (universities, colleges, hospitals, laboratories, units of state and local governments, and eligible agencies of the federal government) who are interested in conducting a research education program related to activities of NHLBI. Applications are especially encouraged from principal investigators who qualify as underrepresented: 1) a member of an ethnic or racial group shown to be underrepresented in health-related sciences on a national basis; 2) an individual with a disability; or 3) an individual from a disadvantaged background, including those from a low-income family and those from a social, cultural, and/or educational environment that has inhibited them from preparation for a research career. The proposed education program must encourage the participation of undergraduate and health professional students who are also currently underrepresented in the biomedical, clinical, and behavioral sciences. Students participating in the program are not required to be enrolled at the sponsoring institution.

Financial data Grants depend on the nature of the project and the number of student participants. Maximum total direct costs should not exceed $311,088. Compensation to participating students must conform to the established salary and wage policies of the institution. Facilities and administrative costs may be reimbursed at the rate of 8% of total direct costs.

Duration Up to 5 years.

Number awarded Up to 8 each year; a total of $900,000 is available for this program annually.

Deadline Letters of intent must be submitted by August of each year; final applications are due in September.

[137]
NINR MENTORED RESEARCH SCIENTIST DEVELOPMENT AWARD FOR UNDERREPRESENTED OR DISADVANTAGED INVESTIGATORS

National Institute of Nursing Research
Attn: Office of Extramural Programs
6701 Democracy Boulevard, Suite 710
Bethesda, MD 20892-4870
(301) 496-9558   Fax: (301) 480-8260
TDD: (301) 451-0088   E-mail: banksd@mail.nih.gov
Web: www.ninr.nih.gov

Summary To provide funding for research career development to disabled and other postdoctoral nursing investigators who are members of underrepresented or disadvantaged groups.

Eligibility This program is open to nurses who have a research or health-professional doctoral degree and are employed full time at an institution that conducts research. Applicants must qualify as an individual whose participation in scientific research will increase diversity, including 1) individuals from racial and ethnic groups that have been shown to be underrepresented in health-related science

on a national basis; 2) individuals with disabilities; and 3) individuals from disadvantaged backgrounds, including those from a family with an annual income below established levels and those from a social, cultural, or educational environment that has demonstrably and recently directly inhibited the individual from obtaining the knowledge, skills, and abilities necessary to develop and participate in a research career. They must secured the commitment of an appropriate research mentor actively involved in research relevant to the mission of the National Institute of Nursing Research (NINR). Only U.S. citizens, nationals, and permanent residents are eligible.

Financial data The grant provides up to $50,000 per year for salary and fringe benefits plus an additional $20,000 per year for research development support. Facilities and administrative costs are allowed at 8% of total direct costs.

Duration Up to 3 years.

Additional data These grants have been awarded annually since 1998. Grantees are expected to spend at least 75% of their professional effort time to the program and the other 25% to other research-related and/or teaching or clinical pursuits consistent with the objectives of the award.

Number awarded 3 to 4 new grants are awarded each year.

Deadline February, June, or October of each year.

[138]
OTTO SUSSMAN TRUST GRANTS

Otto Sussman Trust
P.O. Box 1374
Trainsmeadow Station
Flushing, NY 11370-9998

Summary To provide financial assistance to residents of selected states who are attending college or graduate school in any state and experiencing financial need because of special circumstances, such as illness or injury.

Eligibility This program is open to residents of New York, New Jersey, Oklahoma, or Pennsylvania who are currently enrolled as full-time juniors, seniors, or graduate students at a college or university in any state. Applicants must be experiencing extreme special circumstances, such as unemployment, death of a parent, or medical expenses not covered by insurance. They must have a GPA of 3.0 or higher.

Financial data The amount awarded varies, depending upon the needs of the recipient, but generally varies from $5,000 to $10,000.

Duration This is a 1-time grant.

Number awarded Varies each year.

Deadline July of each year.

[139]
PAUL G. HEARNE/AAPD LEADERSHIP AWARDS

American Association of People with Disabilities
1629 K Street, N.W., Suite 950
Washington, DC 20006
(202) 457-0046   Toll Free: (800) 840-8844
Fax: (202) 457-0473   TDD: (202) 457-0046
E-mail: awards@aapd.com
Web: www.aapd.com

Summary To recognize and reward people with disabilities who provide outstanding leadership in their communities.

Eligibility These awards are presented to emerging leaders with disabilities who demonstrate outstanding leadership while having a positive impact on the community of people with disabilities. Applicants must demonstrate 1) leadership achievements that show a positive impact on the broad community of people with disabilities or within their area of disability interest; 2) connections they have made between individuals with disabilities and others in their communities; 3) a positive vision for the disability community and a continuing commitment to their leadership activities; 4) the demonstrated ability to collaborate with other leaders, to follow when necessary, and to cultivate new leaders within their organizations and communities; and 5) potential to contribute at a national level.

Financial data The award is $10,000. Funds are intended to enable recipients to continue their leadership activities.

Duration The awards are presented annually.

Additional data The Milbank Foundation for Rehabilitation established this program in 1999. Sponsorship was assumed by the American Association of People with Disabilities (AAPD) in 2000. Funding is currently provided by the Mitsubishi Electric America Foundation. Recipients are paired with a nationally-recognized leader in the disability community who supports them through mentoring.

Number awarded Up to 3 each year.

Deadline September of each year.

[140]
PERKINS COIE DIVERSITY STUDENT FELLOWSHIPS

Perkins Coie LLP
Attn: Chief Diversity Officer
131 South Dearborn Street, Suite 1700
Chicago, IL 60603-5559
(312) 324-8593   Fax: (312) 324-9400
E-mail: TCropper@perkinscoie.com
Web: www.perkinscoie.com/diversity/Diversity.aspx

Summary To provide financial assistance to disabled and other law students who reflect the diversity of communities in the country.

Eligibility This program is open to students enrolled in the first year of a J.D. program at an ABA-accredited law school. Applicants must contribute meaningfully to the diversity of the law school student body and the legal profession. Diversity is defined broadly to include members of

racial, ethnic, disabled, and sexual orientation minority groups, as well as those who may be the first person in their family to pursue higher education. Applicants must submit a 1-page personal statement that describes their unique personal history, a legal writing sample, a current resume, and undergraduate and law school transcripts. They are not required to disclose their financial circumstances, but a demonstrated need for financial assistance may be taken into consideration.

Financial data The stipend is $7,500.

Duration 1 year.

Additional data Fellows are also offered a summer associateship at their choice of the firm's offices in Anchorage, Bellevue, Boise, Chicago, Dallas, Los Angeles, Madison, Palo Alto, Phoenix, Portland, San Diego, San Francisco, Seattle, or Washington, D.C.

Number awarded Varies each year; recently, 7 of these fellowships were awarded.

Deadline January of each year.

[141]
POSTDOCTORAL RESEARCH FELLOWSHIPS IN BIOLOGY

National Science Foundation
Directorate for Biological Sciences
Attn: Division of Biological Infrastructure
4201 Wilson Boulevard, Room 615N
Arlington, VA 22230
(703) 292-8470   Fax: (703) 292-9063
TDD: (800) 281-8749   E-mail: ckimsey@nsf.gov
Web: www.nsf.gov

Summary To provide funding for research and training in specified areas related to biology to disabled and other junior doctoral-level scientists at sites in the United States or abroad.

Eligibility This program is open to citizens, nationals, and permanent residents of the United States who are graduate students completing a Ph.D. or who have earned the degree no earlier than 12 months preceding the deadline date. Applicants must be interested in a program of research and training in either of 2 competitive areas: 1) Broadening Participation in Biology, designed to increase the diversity of scientists by providing support for research and training to biologists with disabilities and underrepresented minority (Native American, Native Pacific Islander, Alaskan Native, African American, and Hispanic) biologists; or 2) Intersections of Biology and Mathematical and Physical Sciences, for junior researchers who have conducted doctoral research in biology or physical and mathematical sciences and who present a research and training plan at the intersection of biology with mathematical and physical sciences. They may not have been a principal investigator or co-principal investigator on a federal research grant of more than $20,000. Fellowships are available to postdoctorates who are proposing a research and training plan at an appropriate nonprofit U.S. or foreign host institution (colleges and universities, government and national laboratories and facilities, and privately-sponsored nonprofit institutes and museums).

Financial data The fellowship grant is $60,000 for the first year, $63,000 for the second year, and $66,000 for the third year; that includes 1) an annual stipend of $45,000 for the first year, $48,000 for the second year, and $51,000 for the third year; 2) a research allowance of $10,000 per year paid to the fellow for materials and supplies, subscription fees, and recovery costs for databases, travel, and publication expenses; and 3) an institutional allowance of $5,000 per year for fringe benefits and expenses incurred in support of the fellow.

Duration Fellowships in the area of Broadening Participation in Biology are normally for 36 continuous months; those in the area of Intersections of Biology and Mathematical and Physical Sciences are normally for 24 months (unless the fellow spends more than 1 year at a foreign institution, in which case a third year of support at a U.S. institution may be requested).

Number awarded Approximately 15 fellowships are awarded each year.

Deadline October of each year.

[142]
POWERING EDUCATION SCHOLARSHIPS

Alpha One
127 Main Street
South Portland, ME 04106
(207) 767-2189   Toll Free: (800) 640-7200
Fax: (207) 799-8346   TDD: (207) 767-5387
E-mail: mardi@alphaonenow.org
Web: alphaonenow.com

Summary To provide financial assistance to undergraduate and graduate students in Maine who have disabilities.

Eligibility This program is open to high school seniors, undergraduates, and graduate students at schools in Maine. Applicants must have a disability. They must have a "B" average or equivalent GPA. Along with their application, they must submit a personal essay of 500 to 1,000 words on how their disability has helped shape their view of the world and themselves as a person, a letter of recommendation, and current transcripts.

Financial data The $2,000 stipend is paid directly to the recipient's institution after the first semester, provided the student earns a GPA of 2.5 or higher.

Duration 1 year.

Number awarded 3 each year.

Deadline March of each year.

[143]
PROFESSIONAL ASSOCIATES PROGRAM FOR WOMEN AND MINORITIES AT BROOKHAVEN NATIONAL LABORATORY

Brookhaven National Laboratory
Attn: Diversity Office, Human Resources Division
Building 400B
P.O. Box 5000
Upton, New York 11973-5000
(631) 344-2703   Fax: (631) 344-5305
E-mail: palmore@bnl.gov
Web: www.bnl.gov/diversity/programs.asp

Summary To provide professional experience in scientific areas at Brookhaven National Laboratory (BNL) to persons with disabilities and members of other underrepresented groups.

Eligibility This program is open to underrepresented minorities (African Americans, Hispanics, or Native Americans), people with disabilities, and women. Applicants must have earned at least a bachelor's degree and be seeking professional experience in such fields as biology, chemistry, computer science, engineering, health physics, medical research, or physics. They must plan to attend a graduate or professional school and express an interest in long-term employment at BNL. U.S. citizenship or permanent resident status is required.

Financial data Participants receive a competitive salary.

Duration 1 year.

Additional data Interns work in a goal-oriented on-the-job training program under the supervision of employees who are experienced in their areas of interest.

Number awarded Varies each year.

Deadline Applications may be submitted at any time.

[144]
RUTH L. KIRSCHSTEIN NATIONAL RESEARCH SERVICE AWARDS FOR INDIVIDUAL PREDOCTORAL FELLOWSHIPS TO PROMOTE DIVERSITY IN HEALTH-RELATED RESEARCH

National Institutes of Health
Office of Extramural Research
Attn: Grants Information
6705 Rockledge Drive, Suite 4090
Bethesda, MD 20892-7983
(301) 435-0714   Fax: (301) 480-0525
TDD: (301) 451-5936   E-mail: GrantsInfo@nih.gov
Web: grants.nih.gov

Summary To provide financial assistance to disabled and other students from underrepresented groups interested in working on a doctoral degree and preparing for a career in biomedical and behavioral research.

Eligibility This program is open to students enrolled or accepted for enrollment in a Ph.D. or equivalent research degree program; a formally combined M.D./Ph.D. program; or other combined professional doctoral/research Ph.D. program in the biomedical, behavioral, health, or clinical sciences. Students in health professional degree programs (e.g., M.D., D.O., D.D.S., D.V.M.) are not eligible.

Applicants must be 1) members of an ethnic or racial group underrepresented in biomedical or behavioral research; 2) individuals with disabilities; or 3) individuals from socially, culturally, economically, or educationally disadvantaged backgrounds that have inhibited their ability to prepare for a career in health-related research. They must be U.S. citizens, nationals, or permanent residents.

Financial data The fellowship provides an annual stipend of $21,180, a tuition and fee allowance (60% of costs up to $16,000 or 60% of costs up to $21,000 for dual degrees), and an institutional allowance of $4,200 ($3,100 at for-profit and federal institutions) for travel to scientific meetings, health insurance, and laboratory and other training expenses.

Duration Up to 5 years.

Additional data These fellowships are offered by most components of the National Institutes of Health (NIH). Contact the NIH for a list of names and telephone numbers of responsible officers at each component.

Number awarded Varies each year.

Deadline April, August, or December of each year.

[145]
SARASOTA COUNTY BAR ASSOCIATION DIVERSITY SCHOLARSHIP

Community Foundation of Sarasota County
Attn: Scholarship Manager
2635 Fruitville Road
P.O. Box 49587
Sarasota, FL 34230-6587
(941) 556-7156   Fax: (941) 556-7157
E-mail: mimi@cfsarasota.org
Web: www.cfsarasota.org/Default.aspx?tabid=363

Summary To provide financial assistance to disabled and other students from any state who are attending law school in any state, are interested in practicing in Sarasota County, Florida after graduation, and have selected characteristics that will contribute to diversity in the legal profession.

Eligibility This program is open to students currently enrolled in the first through third year of study at a law school in any state. Applicants must come from an underrepresented background, based on race, color, religion, national origin, ethnicity, age, gender, sexual orientation, physical disability, or socioeconomic status. They must first apply for and obtain a summer associateship with a private law firm or governmental agency in Sarasota County, Florida as an indication of their interest in eventually practicing law in the county. Upon completion of their summer employment, they receive this funding. Along with their application, they must submit a 250-word essay describing how their particular background would help the Sarasota County Bar Association in achieving its goal of making the local legal community more diverse. Financial need is considered in the selection process.

Financial data The stipend is at least $2,000. Funds are paid directly to the student's law school.

Duration 1 year.

Additional data This program is sponsored by the Sarasota County Bar Association and administered by the Community Foundation of Sarasota County. During their summer employment, participants are assigned an attorney mentor from the bar association Diversity Committee.

Number awarded 1 or more each year.

Deadline January of each year.

[146]
SAULT TRIBE SPECIAL NEEDS SCHOLARSHIPS

Sault Tribe of Chippewa Indians
Attn: Higher Education Program-Memorial/Tributary Scholarships
523 Ashmun Street
Sault Ste. Marie, MI 49783
(906) 635-4944   Toll Free: (800) 793-0660
Fax: (906) 635-7785   E-mail: amatson@saulttribe.net
Web: www.saulttribe.com

Summary To provide financial assistance for education at any level to members of the Sault Tribe of Chippewa Indians who have a disability.

Eligibility This program is open to enrolled members of the Sault Tribe who have a documented physical or emotional disability. Applicants must be enrolled in any educational program at any level. Along with their application, they must submit a letter from themselves or a parent describing the proposed use of the funds and an itemized list of the expected costs.

Financial data The stipend is $1,000.

Duration 1 year.

Number awarded 4 each year: 2 for students under 18 years of age and 2 for students 18 years of age or older.

Deadline May of each year.

[147]
SCIENCE GRADUATE STUDENT GRANT FUND

Foundation for Science and Disability, Inc.
Attn: Science Student Grant Committee Chair
503 N.W. 89th Street
Gainesville, FL 32607-1400
(352) 374-5774   Fax: (352) 374-5804
E-mail: rmankin1@ufl.edu
Web: www.stemd.org

Summary To provide supplemental grants to students with disabilities who are interested in working on a graduate degree in a science-related field.

Eligibility This program is open to 1) college seniors who have a disability and have been accepted to a graduate or professional school in the sciences, and 2) graduate science students who have a disability. Applicants must be U.S. citizens interested in working on a degree in an area of engineering, mathematics, medicine, science, or technology. Along with their application, they must submit an essay (about 250 words) describing professional goals and objectives, as well as the specific purpose for which the grant would be used. Selection is based on financial need, sincerity of purpose, and scholarship and/or research ability.

Financial data The grant is $1,000. Funds may be used for an assistive device or instrument, as financial support to work with a professor on an individual research project, or for some other special need.

Duration The award is granted annually.

Additional data The Foundation for Science and Disability, Inc. is an affiliate society of the American Association for the Advancement of Science.

Number awarded Varies each year.

Deadline November of each year.

[148]
SMALL GRANTS FOR CLINICAL SCIENTISTS TO PROMOTE DIVERSITY IN HEALTH-RELATED RESEARCH

National Institute of Diabetes and Digestive and Kidney Diseases
Attn: Office of Minority Health Research Coordination
6707 Democracy Boulevard, Room 653
Bethesda, MD 20892-5454
(301) 594-1932   Fax: (301) 594-9358
TDD: (301) 451-0088   E-mail: la21i@nih.gov
Web: www2.niddk.nih.gov/Funding

Summary To provide funding to disabled and other physicians from underrepresented groups who are interested in conducting a research project in fields of interest to the National Institute of Diabetes and Digestive and Kidney Diseases (NIDDK) of the National Institutes of Health.

Eligibility This program is open to investigators who 1) have a health professional doctoral degree (e.g., M.D., D.D.S., D.O., D.V.M., O.D., Psy.D., Dr.P.H.); 2) have at least 2 to 4 years of postdoctoral research experience; 3) qualify as new investigators; and 4) belong to a population group nationally underrepresented in biomedical or behavioral research, including members of designated racial and ethnic groups (e.g., African Americans, Hispanics, Native Americans, Alaska Natives, Hawaiian Natives, and non-Asian Pacific Islanders), individual with disabilities, or individuals from a disadvantaged background (defined to include those who come from a low-income family and those who come from a social, cultural, and/or educational environment that has inhibited them from obtaining the knowledge, skills, and abilities necessary to develop and participate in a research career). Applicants must be interested in conducting a research project in the area of diabetes, endocrinology, metabolism, digestive diseases, hepatology, obesity, nutrition, kidney, urology, or hematology. They must be sponsored by a domestic for-profit or nonprofit public or private institution, such as a university, college, hospital, or laboratory.

Financial data Direct costs are limited to $125,000 per year. Facilities and administrative costs are reimbursed at 8% of modified total direct costs.

Duration 3 years; nonrenewable.

Additional data This program is also supported by the Office of Dietary Supplements within NIH.

Number awarded Varies each year.

Deadline February, June, or October of each year.

[149]
STAN BECK FELLOWSHIP

Entomological Society of America
Attn: Entomological Foundation
9332 Annapolis Road, Suite 210
Lanham, MD 20706-3150
(301) 459-9082   Fax: (301) 459-9084
E-mail: melodie@entfdn.org
Web: www.entfdn.org/awards_education.php

Summary To assist disabled and other "needy" students working on an undergraduate or graduate degree in entomology who are nominated by members of the Entomological Society of America (ESA).

Eligibility This program is open to students working on an undergraduate or graduate degree in entomology at a college or university in Canada, Mexico, or the United States. Candidates must be nominated by members of the society. They must be "needy" students; for the purposes of this program, need may be based on physical limitations, or economic, minority, or environmental conditions.

Financial data The stipend is $2,000 per year.

Duration 1 year; may be renewed up to 3 additional years.

Additional data This fellowship was first awarded in 1996. Recipients are expected to be present at the society's annual meeting, where the award will be presented.

Number awarded 1 each year.

Deadline June of each year.

[150]
STATE VOCATIONAL REHABILITATION SERVICES PROGRAM

Department of Education
Office of Special Education and Rehabilitative Services
Attn: Rehabilitation Services Administration
500 12th Street, S.W., Room 5032
Washington, DC 20202-2800
(202) 245-7313   Fax: (202) 245-7590
E-mail: Steven.Zwillinger@ed.gov
Web: www.ed.gov/programs/rsabvrs/index.html

Summary To provide financial assistance to individuals with disabilities for undergraduate or graduate study pursued as part of their program of vocational rehabilitation.

Eligibility To be eligible for vocational rehabilitation services, an individual must 1) have a physical or mental impairment that is a substantial impediment to employment; 2) be able to benefit in terms of employment from vocational rehabilitation services; and 3) require vocational rehabilitation services to prepare for, enter, engage in, or retain gainful employment. Priority is given to applicants with the most significant disabilities. Persons accepted for vocational rehabilitation develop an Individualized Written Rehabilitation Program (IWRP) in consultation with a counselor for the vocational rehabilitation agency in the state in which they live. The IWRP may include a program of postsecondary education, if the disabled person and counselor agree that such a program will fulfill the goals of vocational rehabilitation. In most cases, the IWRP will provide for postsecondary education only to a level at which the disabled person will become employable, but that may include graduate education if the approved occupation requires an advanced degree. Students accepted to a program of postsecondary education as part of their IWRP must apply for all available federal, state, and private financial aid.

Financial data Funding for this program is provided by the federal government through grants to state vocational rehabilitation agencies. Grants under the basic support program currently total more than $3 billion per year. States must supplement federal funding with matching funds of 21.3%. Persons who are accepted for vocational rehabilitation by the appropriate state agency receive financial assistance based on the cost of their education and other funds available to them, including their own or family contribution and other sources of financial aid. Allowable costs in most states include tuition, fees, books, supplies, room, board, transportation, personal expenses, child care, and expenses related to disability (special equipment, attendants, interpreters, or notetakers).

Duration Assistance is provided until the disabled person achieves an educational level necessary for employment as provided in the IWRP.

Additional data Information on this program is available only from state vocational rehabilitation agencies.

Number awarded Varies each year; recently, more than 1.2 million people (of whom more than 80% have significant disabilities) were participating in this program.

Deadline Deadline not specified.

[151]
STEVE FASTEAU PAST PRESIDENTS' SCHOLARSHIP

California Association for Postsecondary Education
  and Disability
Attn: Executive Assistant
71423 Biskra Road
Rancho Mirage, CA 92270
(760) 346-8206   Fax: (760) 340-5275
TDD: (760) 341-4084   E-mail: caped2000@aol.com
Web: www.caped.net/scholarships.html

Summary To provide financial assistance to undergraduate and graduate students in California who have a disability and have demonstrated outstanding leadership.

Eligibility This program is open to students at public and private colleges and universities in California who have a disability. Applicants must have high academic achievement and have shown leadership and dedication to the advancement of students with disabilities in postsecondary education. Undergraduates must have completed at least 6 semester credits and have a GPA of 2.5 or higher. Graduate students must have completed at least 3 semester units and have a GPA of 3.0 or higher. Along with their application, they must submit a 1-page personal letter that demonstrates their writing skills, progress towards meeting their educational and vocational goals, management of their disability, and involvement in community activities. They must also submit a recommendation from a faculty member, verification of disability, offi-

cial transcripts, proof of current enrollment, and documentation of need.

Financial data The stipend is $1,000.

Duration 1 year.

Number awarded 1 each year.

Deadline September of each year.

[152]
SURVIVORS' AND DEPENDENTS' EDUCATIONAL ASSISTANCE PROGRAM

Department of Veterans Affairs
Attn: Veterans Benefits Administration
810 Vermont Avenue, N.W.
Washington, DC 20420
(202) 418-4343   Toll Free: (888) GI-BILL1
Web: www.gibill.va.gov

Summary To provide financial assistance for undergraduate or graduate study to 1) children and spouses of deceased and disabled veterans, MIAs, and POWs and 2) children and spouses who have their own disabilities.

Eligibility Eligible for this assistance are spouses and children of 1) veterans who died or are permanently and totally disabled as the result of active service in the armed forces; 2) veterans who died from any cause while rated permanently and totally disabled from a service-connected disability; 3) service members listed as missing in action or captured in the line of duty by a hostile force; 4) service members listed as forcibly detained or interned by a foreign government or power; and 5) service members who are hospitalized or receiving outpatient treatment for a service-connected permanent and total disability and are likely to be discharged for that disability. Children must be between 18 and 26 years of age, although extensions may be granted. Spouses and children over 14 years of age with physical or mental disabilities are also eligible.

Financial data Monthly stipends for study at an academic institution are $957 for full time, $718 for three-quarter time, or $476 for half-time. Other rates apply for apprenticeship and on-the-job training, farm cooperative training, and special restorative training.

Duration Up to 45 months (or the equivalent in part-time training). Spouses must complete their training within 10 years of the date they are first found eligible. For spouses of service members who died on active duty, benefits end 20 years from the date of death.

Additional data Benefits may be used to work on associate, bachelor's, or graduate degrees at colleges and universities, including independent study, cooperative training, and study abroad programs. Courses leading to a certificate or diploma from business, technical, or vocational schools may also be taken. Other eligible programs include apprenticeships, on-the-job training programs, farm cooperative courses, and correspondence courses (for spouses only). Remedial, deficiency, and refresher courses may be approved under certain circumstances.

Number awarded Varies each year.

Deadline Applications may be submitted at any time.

[153]
TEXAS LIBRARY ASSOCIATION CENTURY SCHOLARSHIP

Texas Library Association
Attn: Director of Administration
3355 Bee Cave Road, Suite 401
Austin, TX 78746-6763
(512) 328-1518   Toll Free: (800) 580-2TLA
Fax: (512) 328-8852   E-mail: tla@txla.org
Web: www.txla.org/awards

Summary To provide additional funding to students at schools of library and information studies in Texas who have received a Century Scholarship for persons with disabilities from the American Library Association (ALA).

Eligibility This program is open to recipients of ALA Century Scholarships who have a disability and are enrolled in a master's degree program in library and information studies at a Texas university. Applicants must be members of the Texas Library Association (TLA) and agree to work for 2 years in a Texas library following completion of their master's degree requirements.

Financial data The stipend is $2,000.

Duration 1 year.

Number awarded 1 or more each year.

Deadline January of each year.

[154]
TRANSITION CAREER DEVELOPMENT AWARD TO PROMOTE DIVERSITY

National Cancer Institute
Attn: Center to Reduce Cancer Health Disparities
6116 Executive Boulevard, Suite 602
Bethesda, MD 20852-8341
(301) 496-8589   Fax: (301) 435-9225
TDD: (301) 451-0088   E-mail: walia@mail.nih.gov
Web: www.cancer.gov/researchandfunding

Summary To provide funding to disabled and other underrepresented scientists who are establishing an independent research and academic career in cancer research.

Eligibility This program is open to U.S. citizens, nationals, and permanent residents who have earned a terminal clinical or research doctorate and intend to conduct a research project highly relevant to cancer biology, cancer health disparities, etiology, pathogenesis, prevention, diagnosis, and treatment that has the potential for establishing an independent research program. Candidates must be sponsored by a domestic, nonprofit or for-profit organization, public or private (such as a university, college, hospital, laboratory, unit of state or local government, or eligible agency of the federal government) that can demonstrate a commitment to the promotion of diversity in their student and faculty populations. They must qualify as a member of a group underrepresented in biomedical research, defined as members of a particular ethnic, racial, or other group determined by their institution to be underrepresented in biomedical, behavioral, clinical, or social sciences, e.g., first-generation college students or

graduates, socio-economically disadvantaged persons, or persons with disabilities.

Financial data The award provides salary up to $100,000 per year plus related fringe benefits. In addition, up to $50,000 per year is provided for research support costs. Facilities and administrative costs are reimbursed at 8% of modified total direct costs.

Duration Up to 3 years.

Additional data Recipients must devote at least 75% of their full-time professional effort to cancer-related research and peer review activities. The remaining 25% can be divided among other activities only if they are consistent with the program goals, i.e., the candidate's development into an independent investigator.

Number awarded Approximately 10 each year.

Deadline February, June, or October of each year.

[155]
UNIVERSITY OF CALIFORNIA PRESIDENT'S POSTDOCTORAL FELLOWSHIP PROGRAM FOR ACADEMIC DIVERSITY

University of California at Berkeley
Attn: Office of Equity and Inclusion
102 California Hall
Berkeley, CA 94720-1508
(510) 643-6566   E-mail: kadkinson@berkeley.edu
Web: www.ucop.edu/acadadv/ppfp

Summary To provide an opportunity to conduct research at campuses of the University of California to disabled and other recent postdoctorates who are committed to careers in university teaching and research and who will contribute to diversity in the field.

Eligibility This program is open to U.S. citizens or permanent residents who have a Ph.D. from an accredited university. Applicants must be proposing to conduct research at a branch of the university under the mentorship of a faculty or laboratory sponsor. Preference is given to applicants 1) with the potential to bring to their academic careers the critical perspective that comes from their nontraditional educational background or their understanding of the experiences of groups historically underrepresented in higher education; 2) who have the communications skill and cross-cultural abilities to maximize effective collaboration with a diverse cross-section of the academic community; 3) who have demonstrated significant academic achievement by overcoming barriers such as economic, social, or educational disadvantage; and 4) who have the potential to contribute to higher education through their understanding of the barriers facing women, domestic minorities, students with disabilities, and other members of groups underrepresented in higher education careers, as evidenced by life experiences and educational background.

Financial data The stipend ranges from $40,000 to $50,000, depending on the field and level of experience. The program also offers health benefits and up to $4,000 for supplemental and research-related expenses.

Duration Appointments are for 1 academic year, with possible renewal for a second year.

Additional data   Research may be conducted at any of the University of California's 10 campuses (Berkeley, Davis, Irvine, Los Angeles, Merced, Riverside, San Diego, San Francisco, Santa Barbara, or Santa Cruz). The program provides mentoring and guidance in preparing for an academic career. This program was established in 1984 to encourage applications from minority and women scholars in fields where they were severely underrepresented; it is now open to all qualified candidates who are committed to university careers in research, teaching, and service that will enhance the diversity of the academic community at the university.

Number awarded   15 to 20 each year.

Deadline   November of each year.

[156]
USA FUNDS ACCESS TO EDUCATION SCHOLARSHIPS

Scholarship America
Attn: Scholarship Management Services
One Scholarship Way
P.O. Box 297
St. Peter, MN 56082
(507) 931-1682   Toll Free: (800) 537-4180
Fax: (507) 931-9168
E-mail: scholarship@usafunds.org
Web: www.usafunds.org

Summary   To provide financial assistance to undergraduate and graduate students, especially those who are members of ethnic minority groups or have physical disabilities.

Eligibility   This program is open to high school seniors and graduates who plan to enroll or are already enrolled in full- or half-time undergraduate or full-time graduate course work at an accredited 2- or 4-year college, university, or vocational/technical school. GED recipients are also eligible. Up to 50% of the awards are targeted at students who have a documented physical disability or are a member of an ethnic minority group, including but not limited to Native Hawaiian, Alaskan Native, Black/African American, Asian, Pacific Islander, American Indian, Hispanic/Latino, or multiracial. Residents of all 50 states, the District of Columbia, Puerto Rico, Guam, the U.S. Virgin Islands, and all U.S. territories and commonwealths are eligible. Applicants must also be U.S. citizens or eligible noncitizens and come from a family with an annual adjusted gross income of $35,000 or less. In addition to financial need, selection is based on past academic performance and future potential, leadership and participation in school and community activities, work experience, career and educational aspirations and goals, and unusual personal or family circumstances.

Financial data   The stipend is $1,500 per year for full-time undergraduate or graduate students or $750 per year for half-time undergraduate students. Funds are paid jointly to the student and the school.

Duration   1 year; may be renewed until the student receives a final degree or certificate or until the total award to a student reaches $6,000, whichever comes first.

Renewal requires the recipient to maintain a GPA of 2.5 or higher.

Additional data   This program, established in 2000, is sponsored by USA Funds.

Number awarded   Varies each year; recently, a total of $3.2 million was available for this program.

Deadline   February of each year.

[157]
VOCATIONAL REHABILITATION AND EMPLOYMENT VETSUCCESS PROGRAM

Department of Veterans Affairs
Attn: Veterans Benefits Administration
Vocational Rehabilitation and Employment Service
810 Vermont Avenue, N.W.
Washington, DC 20420
(202) 418-4343   Toll Free: (800) 827-1000
Web: www.vba.va.gov/bin/vre/index.htm

Summary   To provide funding to veterans with service-connected disabilities who need assistance to find employment or, if seriously disabled, to live independently.

Eligibility   This program is open to veterans who have a service-connected disability of at least 10% or a memorandum rating of 20% or more from the Department of Veterans Affairs (VA). They must qualify for services provided by the VA VetSuccess that include assistance finding and keeping a job, including the use of special employer incentives and job accommodations; on-the-job training, apprenticeships, and non-paid work experiences; post-secondary training at a college, vocational, technical, or business school; supportive rehabilitation services such as case management, counseling, and medical referrals; independent living services for veterans unable to work due to the severity of their disabilities.

Financial data   While in training and for 2 months after, eligible disabled veterans may receive subsistence allowances in addition to their disability compensation or retirement pay. For most training programs, the current full-time monthly rate is $566.97 with no dependents, $703.28 with 1 dependent, $828.76 with 2 dependents, and $60.41 for each additional dependent; proportional rates apply for less than full-time training.

Duration   Veterans remain eligible for these services up to 12 years from either the date of separation from active military service or the date the veteran was first notified by VA of a service-connected disability rating (whichever came later).

Number awarded   Varies each year.

Deadline   Applications are accepted at any time.

[158]
VSA INTERNATIONAL YOUNG SOLOISTS AWARD

John F. Kennedy Center for the Performing Arts
Attn: Department of VSA and Accessibility
2700 F Street, N.W.
Washington, DC 20566
(202) 416-8898   Toll Free: (800) 444-1324
Fax: (202) 416-4840   TDD: (202) 416-8728
E-mail: vasinfo@kennedy-center.org
Web: www.kennedy-center.org

Summary To recognize and reward young musicians from any country who are physically or mentally challenged.

Eligibility This competition is open to musicians between 14 and 25 years of age who have a disability. Musical ensembles of 2 to 5 performers are also eligible if at least 1 member has a disability and all members are between 14 and 25 years of age. Applicants must be either 1) U.S. citizens or permanent residents; or 2) citizens of other countries living in the United States (as on a student visa). They may be performers in any type of music, including, but not limited to, rock, alt rock, pop, classical, country, folk, jazz, R&B/blues, hip hop, rap, Latin, and world. Along with their application, they must submit recordings of 3 musical selections (audio or video) and a 1-page personal narrative that describes why they should be selected to receive this award. Tapes are evaluated on the basis of technique, tone, intonation, rhythm, and interpretation.

Financial data The award is $5,000. Funds must be used to assist the recipients' music career.

Duration The competition is held annually.

Additional data The sponsor was established in 1974 as the National Committee-Arts for the Handicapped. In 1985 its name was changed to Very Special Arts and in 2010 to VSA. In 2011, it merged with the Kennedy Center's Office on Accessibility to become the Department of VSA and Accessibility at the John F. Kennedy Center for the Performing Arts.

Number awarded 4 each year: 2 from the United States and 2 from other countries.

Deadline January of each year.

[159]
VSA/VOLKSWAGEN GROUP OF AMERICA EXHIBITION PROGRAM

John F. Kennedy Center for the Performing Arts
Attn: Department of VSA and Accessibility
2700 F Street, N.W.
Washington, DC 20566
(202) 416-8898   Toll Free: (800) 444-1324
Fax: (202) 416-4840   TDD: (202) 416-8728
E-mail: vasinfo@kennedy-center.org
Web: www.kennedy-center.org

Summary To recognize and reward emerging visual artists who have a disability.

Eligibility This competition is open to visual artists between 16 and 25 years of age who have a disability. Applicants must submit samples of their work along with a brief essay on the theme "Momentum" that examines the vital creative spark behind their work. Their essays should describe the force that drives their artistic interest and informs the path they take each day as they move toward their future.

Financial data Awards are $20,000 for the grand award, $10,000 for the first award, $6,000 for the second award, and $2,000 for each award of excellence.

Duration The competition is held annually.

Additional data This competition, first held in 2003, is sponsored by VSA and the Volkswagen Group of America. VSA was established in 1974 as the National Committee-Arts for the Handicapped. In 1985 its name was changed to Very Special Arts and in 2010 to VSA. In 2011, it merged with the Kennedy Center's Office on Accessibility to become the Department of VSA and Accessibility at the John F. Kennedy Center for the Performing Arts. The artwork is displayed at the S. Dillon Ripley Center of the Smithsonian Institution in the fall of each year.

Number awarded 15 each year: 1 grand award, 1 first award, 1 second award, and 12 awards of excellence.

Deadline June of each year.

[160]
WILLIAM MAY MEMORIAL SCHOLARSHIP

California Association for Postsecondary Education and Disability
Attn: Executive Assistant
71423 Biskra Road
Rancho Mirage, CA 92270
(760) 346-8206   Fax: (760) 340-5275
TDD: (760) 341-4084   E-mail: caped2000@aol.com
Web: www.caped.net/scholarships.html

Summary To provide funding to college and graduate students in California who have a disability.

Eligibility This program is open to students at public and private colleges and universities in California who have a disability. Undergraduates must have completed at least 6 semester credits and have a GPA of 2.5 or higher. Graduate students must have completed at least 3 semester units and have a GPA of 3.0 or higher. Along with their application, they must submit a 1-page personal letter that demonstrates their writing skills, progress towards meeting their educational and vocational goals, management of their disability, and involvement in community activities. They must also submit a recommendation from a faculty member, verification of disability, official transcripts, proof of current enrollment, and documentation of financial need.

Financial data The stipend is $1,000.

Duration 1 year.

Number awarded 1 each year.

Deadline September of each year.

[161]
YELLOW RIBBON SCHOLARSHIP

Tourism Cares
Attn: Academic Scholarship Program
275 Turnpike Street, Suite 307
Canton, MA 02021
(781) 821-5990   Fax: (781) 821-8949
E-mail: scholarships@tourismcares.org
Web: www.tourismcares.org

Summary To provide money for college or graduate school to students with disabilities who are planning a career in the travel and tourism or hospitality industry.

Eligibility This program is open to citizens and permanent residents of the United States and Canada who have a physical or sensory disability. Applicants must be enrolled full time and 1) entering the second year at an accredited 2-year college; 2) entering their junior or senior year at an accredited 4-year college or university; or 3) be enrolled or entering graduate school. They must have a GPA of 2.5 or higher and be working on a degree in a travel or tourism or hospitality-related field at a college or university in Canada or the United States. Undergraduates must submit an essay on the segment of the travel and tourism or hospitality industry their current program of study emphasizes, the opportunities they are utilizing as they prepare for a career in the industry, and their academic and extracurricular activities. Graduate students must submit an essay on the changes they have observed thus far in the travel and tourism or hospitality industry, the changes they anticipate in the future of the industry, and where they see their future potential in the industry. Financial need is not considered in the selection process.

Financial data The stipend is $5,000.

Duration 1 year.

Additional data This program was established in 1993.

Number awarded 1 each year.

Deadline March of each year.

Grants-in-Aid

[162]
ABLE TRUST GRANT PROGRAM FOR INDIVIDUALS

Able Trust
Attn: Grant Proposal
3320 Thomasville Road, Suite 200
Tallahassee, FL 32308
(850) 224-4493 Toll Free: (888) 838-ABLE (within FL)
Fax: (850) 224-4496   TDD: (850) 224-4493
E-mail: info@abletrust.org
Web: www.abletrust.org/grant

Summary To provide funding for projects related to employment to Florida residents with disabilities.

Eligibility Individual applicants must be Florida residents who have a documented disability recognized under the Americans with Disabilities Act and are not currently active clients receiving services from an applicable state agency. Applicants must be able to demonstrate that they need emergency on-the-job accommodations to accept an employment offer or to retain or receive a promotion at their current employment. Priority is given to projects with direct employment placement outcomes during the grant time period. Proposals are not accepted if they include funds for vehicles, property, building improvements, capital campaigns, endowments, fellowships, scholarships, travel grants, tuition, small business start-ups, lobbying, medical items, or incurred debt.

Financial data Grants are typically around $2,500.

Duration 1 year; recipients may reapply.

Additional data The Able Trust also makes grants to Florida not-for-profit agencies serving citizens with disabilities in the state. It is also designated as the Florida Governor's Alliance for the Employment of Citizens with Disabilities. Not more than 1 proposal from the same individual will be considered at any 1 time.

Number awarded Varies each year.

Deadline Proposals may be submitted at any time.

[163]
ACCESS FOR ATHLETES GRANTS

Challenged Athletes Foundation
Attn: Program Manager
9591 Waples Street
San Diego, CA 92121
(858) 866-0959   Fax: (858) 866-0958
E-mail: caf@challengedathletes.org
Web: www.challengedathletes.org

Summary To provide funding to disabled athletes for travel, coaching, or equipment.

Eligibility This program is open to athletes of any age with a permanent physical disability that is recognized by the International Paralympic Committee. Applicants must need funding for 1 of 3 categories: 1) equipment, for wheelchairs, prosthetics, or other assistive devices; 2) training, for club or gym dues or membership fees, team or association dues or membership fees, or coaching or training expense; or 3) competition, for travel, entry fees, or other costs to participate in a recognized event. They may apply for only 1 category per year. Along with their application, they must submit information on their short- and long-term goals in the sport of their choice, how this grant will help them reach their goal, their motto or words to live by, a list of their volunteer or community service work, and documentation of financial need.

Financial data Grants generally are limited to $2,500.

Duration 1 or 2 years (equipment grants are considered 2-year grants). Recipients may reapply.

Additional data This foundation was established, in 1994, to raise funds for triathlete Jim MacLaren, who became a quadriplegic while competing.

Number awarded Varies each year; recently, 812 grants, with a value greater than $1.3 million, were awarded.

Deadline November of each year.

[164]
ALABAMA AD VALOREM TAX EXEMPTION FOR SPECIALLY ADAPTED HOUSES

Alabama Department of Revenue
Attn: Property Tax Division
Gordon Persons Building
50 North Ripley Street, Room 4126
P.O. Box 327210
Montgomery, AL 36132-7210
(334) 242-1525
Web: www.ador.state.al.us

Summary To provide a property tax exemption to the owners of specially adapted housing (housing adapted for disabled veterans) in Alabama.

Eligibility The home of any veteran which is or was acquired pursuant to the provisions of Public Law 702, 80th Congress (specially adapted housing grants for veterans) as amended (38 USC) will be exempted from ad valorem taxation if the house is owned and occupied by the veteran or the veteran's unremarried widow(er).

Financial data Qualifying houses are exempt from all ad valorem taxation.

Duration This exemption continues as long as the qualifying veteran or the unremarried widow(er) resides in the house.

Number awarded Varies each year.

Deadline Deadline not specified.

[165]
ALABAMA COUNTY HOMESTEAD EXEMPTIONS

Alabama Department of Revenue
Attn: Property Tax Division
Gordon Persons Building
50 North Ripley Street, Room 4126
P.O. Box 327210
Montgomery, AL 36132-7210
(334) 242-1525
Web: www.ador.state.al.us

Summary To exempt disabled, blind, and elderly residents of Alabama from ad valorem property taxes imposed by counties.

Eligibility Residents of Alabama are eligible to apply if they are over the age of 65 and have a net annual income of $12,000 or less for income tax purposes for the preceding year; or are retired due to permanent and total disability, regardless of age; or are blind, regardless of age or retirement status.

Financial data Qualifying residents are exempt from ad valorem property taxes levied by counties, including taxes levied for school districts, to a maximum of $5,000 in assessed value, or 160 acres in area.

Duration 1 year; this exemption will be granted as long as the resident continues to meet the eligibility requirements.

Number awarded Varies each year.

Deadline Deadline not specified.

[166]
ALABAMA MILITARY RETIREE INCOME TAX EXEMPTION

Alabama Department of Revenue
Attn: Income Tax Division
Gordon Persons Building
50 North Ripley Street, Room 4212
P.O. Box 327410
Montgomery, AL 36132-7410
(334) 242-1105   Fax: (334) 242-0064
E-mail: erohelpdesk@revenue.state.al.us
Web: www.ador.state.al.us

Summary To exempt a portion of the income of disabled and other veterans and their survivors from taxation in Alabama.

Eligibility Eligible are Alabama recipients of regular military retired pay or military survivors benefits. Recipients of benefits paid by the U.S. Department of Veterans Affairs (including disability retirement payments) are also eligible for this exemption.

Financial data All income received as military retired pay, veterans' disability payment, or military survivors benefits is exempt from state, county, or municipal income taxation.

Duration The exemption continues as long as the recipient resides in Alabama.

Deadline Deadline not specified.

[167]
ALABAMA PRINCIPAL RESIDENCE EXEMPTION

Alabama Department of Revenue
Attn: Property Tax Division
Gordon Persons Building
50 North Ripley Street, Room 4126
P.O. Box 327210
Montgomery, AL 36132-7210
(334) 242-1525
Web: www.ador.state.al.us

Summary To exempt disabled and elderly residents of Alabama from ad valorem property taxes imposed by the state.

Eligibility Residents of Alabama are eligible to apply if they are 1) over the age of 65 or totally disabled; and 2) have a net annual income of $7,500 or less for income tax purposes for the preceding year. They must own and occupy as their principal residence a single-family home with up to 160 adjacent acres.

Financial data Qualifying residents are exempt from all ad valorem property taxes levied by the state on their principal residence.

Duration 1 year; this exemption will be granted as long as the resident continues to meet the eligibility requirements.
Number awarded Varies each year.
Deadline Deadline not specified.

[168]
ALABAMA STATE HOMESTEAD EXEMPTIONS

Alabama Department of Revenue
Attn: Property Tax Division
Gordon Persons Building
50 North Ripley Street, Room 4126
P.O. Box 327210
Montgomery, AL 36132-7210
(334) 242-1525
Web: www.ador.state.al.us

Summary To exempt disabled, blind, and elderly residents of Alabama from ad valorem property taxes imposed by the state.
Eligibility Residents of Alabama are eligible to apply if they are 1) over the age of 65; 2) retired due to permanent and total disability, regardless of age; or 3) blind, regardless of age or retirement status.
Financial data Qualifying residents are exempt from all ad valorem property taxes levied by the state, up to 160 acres in area.
Duration 1 year; this exemption is granted as long as the resident continues to meet the eligibility requirements.
Number awarded Varies each year.
Deadline Deadline not specified.

[169]
ALASKA PROPERTY TAX EXEMPTION

Division of Community and Regional Affairs
Attn: Office of the State Assessor
550 West Seventh Avenue, Suite 1790
Anchorage, AK 99501-3510
(907) 269-4605   Fax: (907) 269-4539
E-mail: Steve.VanSant@alaska.gov
Web: www.commerce.state.ak.us/dcra/osa/taxfacts.htm

Summary To exempt from taxation the property owned by veterans with disabilities in Alaska.
Eligibility This exemption is available to veterans in Alaska who have a disability that was incurred or aggravated in the line of duty and that has been rated as 50% or more by the military service or the U.S. Department of Veterans Affairs. Applicants must own and occupy real property that is their primary residence and permanent place of abode. Senior citizens who are 65 years of age or older are also eligible for this exemption.
Financial data Qualified veterans are exempt from taxation on the first $150,000 of assessed valuation on real property.
Duration The exemption continues as long as the veteran with a disability resides in Alaska.
Additional data Applications may be obtained from the local assessor's office. Since 1986, the cost of this program has exceeded the funding available for it. As a result, recipients may be granted a prorated level of payments.

Number awarded Varies each year; recently, more than 27,000 disabled veterans and senior citizens received an average exemption of $1,839 on their property, which had an average assessed value of $135,420.
Deadline Applications may be submitted at any time.

[170]
AMTRAK DISABLED TRAVELERS DISCOUNT

National Railroad Passenger Corporation
Attn: Office of Amtrak Access
60 Massachusetts Avenue, N.E.
Washington, DC 20002
Toll Free: (800) USA-RAIL   TDD: (800) 523-6590
Web: www.amtrak.com

Summary To provide financial assistance to people with disabilities who travel by rail.
Eligibility Travelers with disabilities are eligible for a discount if they present appropriate identification, which may be in the form of a card issued by a handicapped organization, such as the American Foundation for the Blind, or a local, state, or federal government agency. A letter from a physician certifying that the passenger has an impairment that limits ability to use Amtrak services is also acceptable.
Financial data Travelers with disabilities are entitled to 15% off the lowest available fare (regular, discounted, 1-way, round-trip). Children (aged 2 through 11) with disabilities pay one half of the disabled adult fare. Any adult companion may accompany a passenger with a mobility impairment at 15% off the regular fare.
Additional data The discounted fares have no holiday or length of stay restrictions. Information on other special services provided for disabled rail travelers is also available from Amtrak's Office of Customer Relations. No discount is provided on club car seats or sleeping space charges.
Number awarded There is no limit; all eligible travelers are granted discounts.
Deadline Applications may be submitted at any time.

[171]
ARIZONA PROPERTY TAX EXEMPTION FOR WIDOWS, WIDOWERS, AND DISABLED PERSONS

Arizona Department of Revenue
Attn: Property Tax Division
1600 West Monroe Street
Phoenix, AZ 85007-2650
(602) 716-6843
E-mail: taxpayerassistance@azdor.gov
Web: www.azdor.gov

Summary To exempt a portion of the property of widow(er)s and disabled people from property taxes in Arizona.
Eligibility This exemption is available to residents of Arizona who are widows, widowers, or permanently and totally disabled. Their total income must be less than $25,000 if no children reside with them or less than

$30,000 if 1 or more of their children who are younger than 18 years of age or also disabled live with them.

Financial data The exemption is $3,000, if the person's total assessment does not exceed $20,000. No exemption is available if the person's total assessment exceeds $20,000.

Duration The exemption continues as long as the recipient resides in Arizona.

Deadline Deadline not specified.

[172]
ARKANSAS DISABLED VETERANS PROPERTY TAX EXEMPTION

Arkansas Assessment Coordination Department
1614 West Third Street
Little Rock, AR 72201-1815
(501) 324-9240   Fax: (501) 324-9242
E-mail: dasbury@acd.state.ar.us
Web: www.arkansas.gov/acd

Summary To exempt from taxation the property owned by blind or disabled veterans, surviving spouses, and minor dependent children in Arkansas.

Eligibility This program is open to disabled veterans in Arkansas who have been awarded special monthly compensation by the U.S. Department of Veterans Affairs and who have 1) the loss of or the loss of use of 1 or more limbs, 2) total blindness in 1 or both eyes, or 3) total and permanent disability. The benefit also extends to veterans' unremarried surviving spouses and their minor children.

Financial data Qualifying veterans (or their unremarried widows or dependent children) are exempt from payment of all state taxes on their homestead and personal property.

Duration This exemption continues as long as the qualifying veteran (or dependent) resides in Arkansas.

Number awarded Varies each year.

Deadline Applications may be submitted at any time.

[173]
ARKANSAS INCOME TAX EXEMPTIONS FOR MILITARY COMPENSATION AND DISABILITY PAY

Arkansas Department of Finance and Administration
Attn: Office of Income Tax Administration
Joel Ledbetter Building, Room 2300
1816 West Seventh Street
P.O. Box 3628
Little Rock, AR 72203-3628
(501) 682-1100   Fax: (501) 682-7692
E-mail: individual.income@dfa.arkansas.gov
Web: www.dfa.arkansas.gov

Summary To exempt a portion of the income of military personnel and disabled veterans from state income taxes in Arkansas.

Eligibility Eligible are residents of Arkansas receiving military compensation or military disability income.

Financial data The first $9,000 of U.S. military compensation pay or military disability income is exempt from state income taxation.

Duration The exemptions continue as long as the recipient resides in Arkansas.

Deadline Deadline not specified.

[174]
ARKANSAS INCOME TAX EXEMPTIONS FOR RETIREMENT AND DISABILITY PAY

Arkansas Department of Finance and Administration
Attn: Office of Income Tax Administration
Joel Ledbetter Building, Room 2300
1816 West Seventh Street
P.O. Box 3628
Little Rock, AR 72203-3628
(501) 682-1100   Fax: (501) 682-7692
E-mail: individual.income@dfa.arkansas.gov
Web: www.dfa.arkansas.gov

Summary To exempt a portion of the income from retirement or disability plans from state income taxes in Arkansas.

Eligibility Eligible are residents of Arkansas receiving income from retirement or disability plans. Surviving spouses also qualify for the exemption.

Financial data Exempt from state income taxation is the first $6,000 in disability pay, retired pay, or survivors benefits. Any resident who receives both military retirement or disability pay and other retirement or disability benefits is entitled to only a single $6,000 deduction. Surviving spouses are also limited to a single $6,000 exemption. Military retirees may adjust their figures if the payment includes survivor's benefit payments; the amount of adjustment must be listed on the income statement, and supporting documentation must be submitted with the return.

Duration The exemption continues as long as the recipient resides in Arkansas.

Deadline Deadline not specified.

[175]
ARKANSAS SALES TAX EXEMPTION FOR ADAPTIVE MEDICAL EQUIPMENT

Arkansas Department of Finance and Administration
Attn: Sales and Use Tax Section
Joel Ledbetter Building, Suite 2350
1816 West Seventh Street
P.O. Box 1272
Little Rock, AR 72203-1272
(501) 682-7104   Fax: (501) 682-7904
E-mail: sales.tax@dfa.arkansas.gov
Web: www.dfa.arkansas.gov

Summary To exempt adaptive equipment from sales tax in Arkansas.

Eligibility Rental, sale, or repair of adaptive and disposable medical equipment in Arkansas qualifies for this exemption. Adaptive equipment includes wheelchairs, leg braces, raised toilet seats, wheelchair batteries, grab bars and hand rails, automobile hand controls, Braille writers, hearing aids, and other equipment used by people with disabilities.

Financial data Qualified equipment is exempt from payment of all sales tax.

Additional data This exemption does not apply to equipment purchased by physicians, hospitals, nursing homes, or long-term care facilities for use by their patients or residents.

Deadline Deadline not specified.

[176]
ARTISTS' FELLOWSHIP FINANCIAL ASSISTANCE

Artists' Fellowship, Inc.
47 Fifth Avenue
New York, NY 10003
(212) 255-7740, ext. 216
E-mail: info@artistsfellowship.org
Web: www.artistsfellowship.com/financial.html

Summary To provide emergency assistance to professional fine artists.

Eligibility This assistance is available to professional fine artists who are facing emergency needs because of health-related issues, accidents, financial crises, or bereavement. Support is not provided for study, projects, art supplies, school, travel, or exhibitions. Only fine artists (e.g., painting, sculpture, graphics) are eligible; performance artists, commercial artists, commercial photographers, filmmakers, crafts persons, and hobbyists do not qualify.

Financial data The amount of the grant depends on the need of the artist.

Duration Most grants are 1-time only, but many infirmed artists receive continuing support.

Number awarded Between 65 and 75 artists receive assistance from this program each year.

Deadline Applications may be submitted at any time.

[177]
CALIFORNIA DISABLED VETERAN EXEMPTION FROM THE IN LIEU TAX FEE FOR A MANUFACTURED HOME OR MOBILEHOME

Department of Housing and Community Development
Attn: Registration and Titling
1800 Third Street
P.O. Box 2111
Sacramento, CA 95812-2111
(916) 323-9224   Toll Free: (800) 952-8356
Web: www.hcd.ca.gov

Summary To provide a special property tax exemption to blind or disabled California veterans and/or their spouses who own and occupy a mobile home.

Eligibility This program is open to disabled veterans and/or their spouses in California who have a manufactured home or mobile home as their principal place of residence. Veterans must be disabled as a result of injury or disease incurred in military service and have been a resident of California 1) at the time of entry into the service and be blind, or have lost the use of 1 or more limbs, or be totally disabled; 2) on November 7, 1972 and be blind in both eyes, or have lost the use of 2 or more limbs; or 3) on January 1, 1975 and be totally disabled. The spouses and unremarried surviving spouses of those disabled veterans are also eligible.

Financial data The exemption applies to the first $20,000 of the assessed market value of the manufactured home or mobile home. Veterans and/or spouses whose income falls below a specified level are entitled to an additional $10,000 exemption. The amount of the exemption is 100% if the home is owned by a veteran only, a veteran and spouse, or a spouse only; 50% if owned by a veteran and another person other than a spouse or by a spouse and another person other than the veteran; 67% if owned by a veteran, the spouse, and another person; 34% if owned by a veteran and 2 other people other than a spouse or by a spouse and 2 other people; 50% if owned by a veteran, the spouse, and 2 other people; or 25% if owned by a veteran and 3 other people or by a spouse and 3 other people.

Duration The exemption is available annually as long as the applicant meets all requirements.

Number awarded Varies each year.

Deadline Deadline not specified.

[178]
CALIFORNIA PROPERTY TAX EXEMPTIONS FOR VETERANS

California Department of Veterans Affairs
Attn: Division of Veterans Services
1227 O Street, Room 101
P.O. Box 942895
Sacramento, CA 94295
(916) 653-2573   Toll Free: (877) 741-8532
Fax: (916) 653-2563   TDD: (800) 324-5966
Web: www.cdva.ca.gov/VetServices/Benefits.aspx

Summary To exempt a portion of the property of blind or disabled veterans in California and their spouses from taxation.

Eligibility This exemption is available to homeowners in California who are wartime veterans in receipt of service-connected disability compensation that is 1) at the totally disabled rate, 2) for loss or loss of use of 2 or more limbs, or 3) for blindness. Unremarried surviving spouses, including registered domestic partners, of veterans who are in receipt of service-connected death benefits are also eligible.

Financial data For veterans and spouses whose total household income from all sources is greater than $51,669 per year, up to $115,060 of the assessed value of a home is exempt from taxation. For veterans and spouses whose total household income from all sources is less than $51,669 per year, up to $172,592 of the assessed value of a home is exempt from taxation.

Duration The exemption is available as long as the veteran or spouse owns a home in California.

Additional data Information is available from the local county assessor's office in each California county.

Number awarded Varies each year.

Deadline Applications may be submitted at any time.

[179]
CARNEGIE FUND FOR AUTHORS GRANTS-IN-AID

Carnegie Fund for Authors
c/o W.L. Rothenberg
One Old Country Road, Suite 113
Carle Place, NY 11514
(516) 877-2141　　　　　Fax: (516) 743-6595

Summary To provide emergency financial assistance to authors or their family members who have experienced an illness or injury.

Eligibility Authors who have had at least 1 book published are eligible to apply for financial assistance if they or their spouses/dependents have suffered financial problems because of an injury or illness. To qualify for assistance, the author's book must have earned reader acceptance and should have been listed in a standard reference book (e.g., *Books in Print*). Authors whose books have not been listed in a standard source must submit a copy of the qualifying publication when applying.

Financial data The amount awarded ranges from $500 to $1,500, depending upon the needs of the recipient.

Duration This is a 1-time award.

Number awarded Varies each year.

Deadline Applications may be submitted at any time.

[180]
CATHERINE T. MURRAY MEMORIAL SCHOLARSHIP

Ocean State Center for Independent Living
Attn: Office Manager
1944 Warwick Avenue
Warwick, RI 02889
(401) 738-1013, ext. 10　　Toll Free: (866) 857-1161
Fax: (401) 738-1083　　　TDD: (401) 738-1015
E-mail: cmckenna@oscil.org
Web: www.oscil.org/murray_scholarship.htm

Summary To provide financial assistance to residents of Rhode Island who have a disability and are interested in attending college in any state.

Eligibility This program is open to residents of Rhode Island who have a significant disability. Applicants must be enrolled or planning to enroll in an academic, trade, or vocational educational program in any state and/or to acquire assistive or adaptive equipment or devices to access such an educational opportunity. Along with their application, they must submit a 1-page essay describing their career goals and plans. Selection is based on that essay (15 points), activities (5 points), accurate completion of the application (5 points), and financial need (5 points).

Financial data The stipend is $1,000.

Duration 1 year.

Additional data This program was established in 1995.

Number awarded 1 each year.

Deadline March of each year.

[181]
CHILDREN OF FALLEN SOLDIERS RELIEF FUND FINANCIAL ASSISTANCE GRANTS

Children of Fallen Soldiers Relief Fund
P.O. Box 3968
Gaithersburg, MD 20885-3968
(301) 685-3421　　　　Toll Free: (866) 96-CFSRF
Fax: (301) 630-0592　　E-mail: grants@cfsrf.org
Web: www.cfsrf.org

Summary To provide personal financial assistance to veterans severely disabled during service in Iraq or Afghanistan and to the families of military personnel killed or severely disabled in those countries.

Eligibility This program is open to 1) veterans severely disabled as a result of service in Operation Iraqi Freedom or Operation Enduring Freedom; and 2) the spouses and children of military personnel killed or severely disabled during that service. Applicants must submit a 1-page statement describing their reason for requesting funds, the amount requested, the specified purpose to which the funds will be applied, a breakdown of monthly income and expenses, 2 recent months of bank statements, and current bills that are in arrears.

Financial data Grants have ranged from $1,650 to $16,916, depending on the need of the recipient.

Duration These are 1-time grants.

Additional data This organization was founded in 2003.

Number awarded Varies each year; since the organization was founded, it has awarded 18 of these financial assistance grants.

Deadline Applications may be submitted at any time.

[182]
CHILDREN OF WOMEN VIETNAM VETERANS ALLOWANCE

Department of Veterans Affairs
Attn: Veterans Benefits Administration
810 Vermont Avenue, N.W.
Washington, DC 20420
(202) 418-4343　　　　Toll Free: (888) 820-1756
Web: www1.va.gov

Summary To provide support to children of female Vietnam veterans who have birth defects.

Eligibility This program is open to biological children of female veterans who served in the Republic of Vietnam and were conceived after the date the veteran first served, which must have been between February 28, 1961 and May 7, 1975. Applicants must have certain birth defects identified as resulting in permanent physical or mental disability. Conditions that are a family disorder, a birth-related injury, or a fetal or neonatal infirmity with well-established causes are not included.

Financial data Support depends on the degree of disability. The monthly rate for children at the first level is $136, at the second level $297, at the third level $1,020, or at the fourth level $1,739.

Additional data Applications are available from the nearest VA medical center. Recipients are also entitled to vocational training and medical treatment.

Number awarded Varies each year.

Deadline Applications are accepted at any time.

[183]
CHILDREN WITH SPECIAL NEEDS FUND GRANTS

Michigan Department of Community Health
Attn: Children with Special Needs Fund
Lewis Cass Building, Sixth Floor
320 South Walnut
P.O. Box 30479
Lansing, MI 48909-7979
(517) 241-7420   Toll Free: (800) 359-3722
Fax: (517) 335-8055   TDD: (866) 501-5656
E-mail: csnfund@michigan.gov
Web: www.michigan.gov/csnfund

Summary To provide funding for special equipment to children with disabilities in Michigan.

Eligibility This program is open to children in Michigan who are younger than 21 years of age and enrolled in (or medically eligible to enroll in) Children's Special Health Care Services of the Department of Community Health. Applicants must be able to demonstrate a need for the following special equipment: van lifts and tiedowns, wheelchair ramps into homes, air conditioners, electrical service upgrades necessitated by the eligible child's medical equipment, or therapeutic specialty tricycles. Along with their application, they must submit a completed financial assessment, a letter of medical necessity from the child's physician, documentation that other sources (e.g., insurance companies, professional organizations, local service groups and charities, churches) have been contacted for assistance, and 3 bids or quotes for the equipment or services being requested. Only families with income below specified levels ($54,451 for a family of 1, rising to $130,851 for a family of 5) are eligible.

Financial data The amount of the grant depends on the income of the family. The lowest level is up to $27,225 for a family of 1, rising to $65,425 for a family of 5. At that income level, maximum grants are $6,000 for van lifts, $500 to replace a wheelchair tie-down system, $3,000 for home wheelchair ramps, $500 for air conditioners, $1,000 for electrical system upgrades, or $1,500 for therapeutic specialty tricycles. Families with higher incomes (up to the specified maximum) are eligible for smaller grants.

Duration These are 1-time grants.

Additional data This program was established in 1944 by a donation of Dow Chemical Company stock from James T. Pardee, a founder of that company. Although the program is administered by the state of Michigan, all funding is provided by the return on that donation and subsequent private support.

Number awarded Varies each year.

Deadline Applications may be submitted at any time.

[184]
CHRYSLER AUTOMOBILITY PROGRAM

Chrysler Corporation
Attn: Automobility Program
P.O. Box 5080
Troy, MI 48007-5080
Toll Free: (800) 255-9877   Fax: (904) 828-6717
TDD: (800) 922-3826   E-mail: rebates@chrysler.com
Web: www.chryslergroupllc.com

Summary To provide a cash reimbursement for the cost of installing adaptive driving aids on new purchases from Chrysler Motors.

Eligibility Eligible for this rebate are purchasers of new Chrysler Motors cars, trucks, or vans that require adaptive driving aids or conversion equipment for users with disabilities.

Financial data Conversions to Dodge, Chrysler, Jeep, Ram, and Fiat models are reimbursed up to $1,000. Running boards qualify for maximum reimbursement of $400 and alerting devices for $200.

Additional data Applications for reimbursement are submitted through the dealer from whom the vehicle was originally purchased. Only retail purchases and leases of new Chrysler Motors vehicles qualify for this program. The reimbursement applies only to equipment installed by converters in the after market, not to factory installed equipment of any kind.

Deadline The conversion process must be completed within 6 months of vehicle purchase or lease. Reimbursement claims must be submitted within 60 days after completion of the conversion.

[185]
COLONIAL CHAPTER PARALYZED VETERANS ASSOCIATION ASSISTANCE

Paralyzed Veterans of America-Colonial Chapter
111 East Scotland Drive
Bear, DE 19701
(302) 365-5670   Toll Free: (877) 280-4581
Fax: (302) 365-5679   E-mail: office@colonialPVA.org
Web: www.colonialpva.org/programs/prosthetics.php

Summary To provide funding for the purchase of equipment or other aids for people with disabilities in Delaware, Maryland, New Jersey, and southeastern Pennsylvania.

Eligibility This program is open to people with disabilities who live in Delaware, Maryland, New Jersey, or southeastern Pennsylvania. Applicants do not need to be veterans and assistance is not limited by age or type of disability. They must be interested in purchasing equipment (e.g., ramps, prostheses, wheelchairs) or other assistance (e.g., van adaptations, home modifications).

Financial data The maximum award is about $1,500.

Number awarded Varies each year.

Deadline Applications may be submitted at any time.

[186]
COLORADO PENSION/ANNUITY SUBTRACTION

Colorado Department of Revenue
Attn: Taxpayer Service Division
1375 Sherman Street, Room 242A
Denver, CO 80261-0005
(303) 232-2446   Toll Free: (800) 811-0172
Web: www.colorado.gov

Summary To exempt a portion of the pensions or annuities of veterans, people with disabilities, and other persons over the age of 55 from state income taxation in Colorado.

Eligibility This exemption is available to taxpayers over the age of 55 who are classified as Colorado residents for purposes of state income taxation, and to beneficiaries (such as a widowed spouse or orphan child) who are receiving a pension or annuity because of the death of the person who earned the pension. To qualify, the payment must be a retirement benefit that arose from an employer/employee relationship, service in the uniformed services of the United States, or contributions to a retirement plan that are deductible for federal income tax purposes. Disability retirement payments received by persons 55 years of age or older also qualify.

Financial data For retirees who are at least 65 years of age, up to $24,000 of qualified pension or retirement income may be excluded from income for purposes of Colorado state taxation. For persons who are at least 55 but under 65 years of age, up to $20,000 of qualified pension or retirement income may be excluded.

Duration The exclusion continues as long as the recipient resides in Colorado.

Additional data Disability retirement payments received by persons under 55 years of age do not qualify for the pension exclusion.

Deadline Deadline not specified.

[187]
COLORADO PROPERTY TAX EXEMPTION FOR DISABLED VETERANS

Division of Veterans Affairs
1355 South Colorado Boulevard, Building C, Suite 113
Denver, CO 80220
(303) 343-1268   Fax: (303) 343-7238
Web: www.dmva.state.co.us/page/va/prop_tax

Summary To provide a partial exemption of taxes on property owned by disabled veterans or their spouses in Colorado.

Eligibility This exemption is open to veterans who reside in Colorado and have been rated 100% permanent and total service-connected disabled by the U.S. Department of Veterans Affairs. Applicants must have been honorably discharged and must own property in Colorado which they use as their primary residence. The exemption also applies to members of the National Guard or Reserves who sustained their injury during a period in which they were called to active duty, property owned by a veteran's spouse if both occupy the property as their primary residence, and property owned by a trust or other legal entity if the veteran or spouse is a major of the trust or other legal entity, the property was transferred solely for estate planning purposes, and the veteran or spouse would otherwise be the owner of record.

Financial data For qualifying veterans, 50% of the first $200,000 of actual value of the primary residence is exempted from taxes.

Duration The exemption continues as long as the veteran resides in the property.

Additional data This program was approved by Colorado voters in 2006.

Number awarded Varies each year.

Deadline Applications must be submitted by June of the year for which the exemption is requested.

[188]
COMBAT-RELATED SPECIAL COMPENSATION

Department of Defense
Attn: Defense Finance and Accounting Service
U.S. Military Annuitant Pay
P.O. Box 7131
London, KY 40742-7131
Toll Free: (877) 327-4457   Fax: (800) 982-8459
Web: www.dfas.mil

Summary To provide supplemental compensation to military retirees who are receiving disability pay from the U.S. Department of Veterans Affairs (VA).

Eligibility This program is open to retirees from the U.S. uniformed services who 1) are entitled to and/or receiving military retired pay; 2) are rated at least 10% disabled by the U.S. Department of Veterans Affairs (VA); 3) are a Reservist at least 60 years of age or retired under Temporary Early Retirement Authorization (TERA); and 4) waive their VA pay from their retired pay. Applicants must have a disability rating of 10% or higher, be drawing retirement pay, and be receiving VA disability that is not just service-connected but also combat-related, including injuries incurred as a direct result of armed conflict, hazardous duty, an instrumentality of war, or simulated war. Spouses and other dependents are not eligible for this program.

Financial data Qualified veterans receive compensation that depends on their combat-related disability rating (which may differ from their VA service-connected disability rating). They continue to receive their full military retirement pay (unlike VA disability compensation, which acts as an offset for an equivalent reduction in military retirement pay). The compensation is non-taxable.

Duration This compensation is payable for the life of the veteran.

Additional data The Combat-Related Special Compensation Program (CRSC I) began in June, 2003. The program was revised to offer compensation to a larger group of retirees and CRSC II began in January, 2004. Another revision in January, 2008 again expanded eligibility requirements. Military retirees, including those from the other uniformed services (Coast Guard, National Oceanic and Atmospheric Administration, and Public Health Service) must apply through the armed forces branch in which they served.

Number awarded Varies each year. Currently, more than 50,000 retirees are receiving payments of more than $59 million per month.

Deadline Applications may be submitted at any time.

[189]
CONNECTICUT DISABLED TAX RELIEF PROGRAM

Office of Policy and Management
Attn: Intergovernmental Policy Division
450 Capitol Avenue
Hartford, CT 06106-1308
(860) 418-6406   Toll Free: (800) 286-2214 (within CT)
Fax: (860) 418-6493   TDD: (860) 418-6456
E-mail: patrick.j.sullivan@ct.gov
Web: www.ct.gov

Summary To exempt disabled residents of Connecticut from a portion of their personal property taxes.

Eligibility Eligible to apply for this exemption are Connecticut residents who are rated as totally and permanently disabled by the U.S. Social Security Administration. If they never engaged in employment covered by Social Security, they are also eligible if they have become qualified for permanent and total disability benefits under any federal, state, or local government retirement or disability plan. An additional exemption may be available to residents whose total adjusted gross income is less than $32,300 if unmarried or $39,500 if married.

Financial data The basic state exemption is $1,000 of assessed valuation. Municipalities may elect to provide an additional exemption of $1,000 to residents whose income is less than the qualifying level.

Duration 1 year; exemptions continue as long as the eligible resident lives in Connecticut.

Number awarded Varies each year; recently, a total of 12,713 residents received property tax exemptions through this program.

Deadline Applications for the additional municipality exemption must be submitted to the assessor's office of the town or residence by September of every other year.

[190]
CONNECTICUT ELDERLY AND DISABLED HOMEOWNERS TAX RELIEF PROGRAM

Office of Policy and Management
Attn: Intergovernmental Policy Division
450 Capitol Avenue
Hartford, CT 06106-1308
(860) 418-6406   Toll Free: (800) 286-2214 (within CT)
Fax: (860) 418-6493   TDD: (860) 418-6456
E-mail: patrick.j.sullivan@ct.gov
Web: www.ct.gov

Summary To provide a credit to elderly and disabled residents of Connecticut for a portion of their real property taxes.

Eligibility Eligible to apply for this relief are Connecticut residents who are 1) over 65 years of age, or 2) rated as totally and permanently disabled by the U.S. Social Security Administration. If they never engaged in employment covered by Social Security, they are also eligible if they have become qualified for permanent and total disability benefits under any federal, state, or local government retirement or disability plan. Applicants must have total adjusted gross income less than $32,300 if unmarried or $39,500 if married. The credit applies to property owned by the applicant and located on a "standard building lot," including residences, mobile homes, life care facilities, modular homes, condominiums, and dwellings on leased land.

Financial data The credit depends on the income of the recipient, to a maximum of $1,250 for married homeowners or $1,000 for unmarried homeowners.

Duration 1 year; the credit is available as long as the eligible homeowner lives in Connecticut.

Number awarded Varies each year; recently, a total of 38,992 homeowners received property tax credits through this program.

Deadline Applications must be submitted to the assessor's office of the town or residence by May of every other year.

[191]
CONNECTICUT SOLDIERS', SAILORS' AND MARINES' FUND

Connecticut Department of Veterans' Affairs
Attn: Soldiers', Sailors' and Marines' Fund
864 Wethersfield Avenue
Hartford, CT 06114-3184
(860) 296-0719   Toll Free: (800) 491-4941 (within CT)
Fax: (860) 296-0820
E-mail: john.monahan@po.state.ct.us
Web: www.state.ct.us/ssmf

Summary To provide temporary financial assistance to needy Connecticut veterans.

Eligibility This program is open to veterans who were honorably discharged after at least 90 days of service during specified periods of war time and are currently residents of Connecticut. Applicants must be able to demonstrate need for the following types of assistance: medical expenses; emergent dental care; prescription medications; eye examinations and purchase of eyeglasses; audiological evaluations and hearing aids; assistance with rental payments or mortgage interest payments; utilities (including gas, water, electric, and fuel oil); funeral expenses; or durable medical equipment. Support is not provided for payment of taxes; payment of insurance premiums (except medical insurance); purchase of real estate or payments of principal on mortgages; payment of telephone or cable bills; purchase of equities, bonds, or mutual funds; alimony or child support payments; payment of personal debts, credit card bills, past-due bills, loans, or other obligations; or purchase of furniture, automobiles, or other capital goods.

Financial data The fund provides payments in the form of short-term grants.

Duration The funds are provided for emergency situations only; the program does not assist with ongoing financial needs.

Additional data This program, established in 1919, is subsidized by the state of Connecticut but administered by the American Legion of Connecticut.

Number awarded Varies each year.

Deadline Applications may be submitted at any time.

[192]
CONNECTICUT VETERANS' ADDITIONAL EXEMPTION TAX RELIEF PROGRAM

Office of Policy and Management
Attn: Intergovernmental Policy Division
450 Capitol Avenue
Hartford, CT 06106-1308
(860) 418-6278   Toll Free: (800) 286-2214 (within CT)
Fax: (860) 418-6493   TDD: (860) 418-6456
E-mail: leeann.graham@ct.gov
Web: www.ct.gov

Summary To exempt disabled veterans and their surviving spouses who are residents of Connecticut from a portion of their personal property taxes.

Eligibility Eligible to apply for this exemption are Connecticut veterans who are rated as disabled by the U.S. Department of Veterans Affairs (VA). Unremarried surviving spouses of qualified veterans are also eligible. An additional exemption may be available to veterans and spouses whose total adjusted gross income is less than $32,300 if unmarried or $39,500 if married. If the veteran is rated as 100% disabled by the U.S. Department of Veterans Affairs (VA), the maximum income levels are $18,000 if unmarried or $21,000 if married.

Financial data The amount of the exemption depends on the level of the VA disability rating: for 10% to 25%, it is $1,500; for more than 25% to 50%, $2,000; for more than 50% to 75%, $2,500; for more than 75% and for veterans older than 65 years of age with any level of disability, $3,000. Municipalities may elect to provide an additional exemption, equal to twice the amount provided, to veterans and spouses whose income is less than the qualifying level. For veterans and spouses who do not meet the income requirement, the additional exemption from participating municipalities is equal to 50% of the basic state exemption.

Duration 1 year; exemptions continue as long as the eligible resident lives in Connecticut.

Number awarded Varies each year; recently, a total of 19,669 veterans received property tax exemptions through this and other programs in Connecticut.

Deadline Applications for the additional municipality exemption must be submitted to the assessor's office of the town of residence by September of every other year.

[193]
DEATH PENSION FOR SURVIVORS OF VETERANS

Department of Veterans Affairs
Attn: Veterans Benefits Administration
810 Vermont Avenue, N.W.
Washington, DC 20420
(202) 418-4343   Toll Free: (800) 827-1000
Web: www.vba.va.gov/bln/21/pension/spousepen.htm

Summary To provide pensions to disabled and other spouses and children of deceased veterans with wartime service.

Eligibility This program is open to surviving spouses and unmarried children of deceased veterans who were discharged under conditions other than dishonorable and who had at least 90 days of active military service, at least 1 day of which was during a period of war. Veterans who enlisted after September 7, 1980 generally had to have served at least 24 months or the full period for which they were called to active duty. The countable income of spouses and children must be below specified limits.

Financial data Currently, the maximum annual pension rate is $8,219 for a surviving spouse without dependent children or $10,759 for a surviving spouse with 1 dependent child. Other rates apply to surviving spouses in need of regular aid and attendance, surviving spouses permanently housebound without dependent children, and surviving children who are living alone.

Duration For surviving spouse: until remarriage. For surviving unmarried child: until the age of 18, or 23 if attending a VA-approved school. For surviving child with disability: as long as the condition exists or until marriage.

Number awarded Varies each year.

Deadline Applications may be submitted at any time.

[194]
DELAWARE INCOME TAX EXCLUSION FOR DISABLED AND ELDERLY PERSONS

Division of Revenue
Attn: Office of Personal Income Taxes
Carvel State Office Building
820 North French Street
P.O. Box 8763
Wilmington, DE 19899-8763
(302) 577-8170   E-mail: Personaltax@state.de.us
Web: revenue.delaware.gov

Summary To provide a partial exemption from state income taxation to people with disabilities and those over the age of 60 in Delaware.

Eligibility This exemption is available to residents of Delaware who are 60 years of age or over or totally and permanently disabled. Married applicants filing a joint return must have a combined earned income of less than $5,000 and total gross income less than $20,000; applicants who are single or married and filing a separate return must have earned income of less than $2,500 and total gross income less than $10,000.

Financial data Married residents filing a joint return are entitled to exempt $4,000 from their gross income for purposes of state income taxation; single residents and married residents filing a separate return are entitled to exclude $2,000 from their gross income.

Duration The exemption continues as long as the recipient remains a resident of Delaware for state income tax purposes.

Number awarded Varies each year.

Deadline Deadline not specified.

[195]
DEXTER G. JOHNSON EDUCATIONAL AND BENEVOLENT TRUST GRANTS

Dexter G. Johnson Educational and Benevolent Trust
Attn: Betty Crews
P.O. Box 26663
Oklahoma City, OK 73126-0663
(405) 232-3340   Fax: (405) 232-3340

Summary To provide financial assistance for vocational training, audiological evaluations, corrective surgery, speech therapy, or medical devices to the children of residents of Oklahoma who have disabilities.

Eligibility Residents of Oklahoma with disabilities are eligible to apply for this program for their children if they need financial assistance for vocational training, audiological evaluations, corrective surgery, speech therapy, or orthopedic or hearing aid devices.

Financial data Grants range from $70 to $2,500.

Number awarded Varies; approximately 10 each year.

Deadline Applications may be submitted at any time.

[196]
DISABILITY PENSION PROGRAM FOR VETERANS

Department of Veterans Affairs
Attn: Veterans Benefits Administration
810 Vermont Avenue, N.W.
Washington, DC 20420
(202) 418-4343   Toll Free: (800) 827-1000
Web: www.vba.va.gov/bin/21/compensation/index.htm

Summary To provide a pension to disabled or elderly veterans who served during war time.

Eligibility This program is open to veterans who were discharged under conditions other than dishonorable and who had at least 90 days of active military service, at least 1 day of which was during a period of war. They must be permanently and totally disabled or older than 65 years of age. Veterans who enlisted after September 7, 1980 generally had to have served at least 24 months or the full period for which they were called to active duty. The countable income of veterans must be below specified limits.

Financial data The pension program pays the difference, in 12 monthly installments, between countable income and the specified income level. Currently, those limits are the following: veteran with no dependents, $12,256; veteran with 1 dependent, $16,051; veteran in need of regular aid and attendance with no dependents, $20,447; veteran in need of regular aid and attendance with 1 dependent, $24,239; veteran permanently housebound without dependents, $14,978; veteran permanently

housebound with 1 dependent, $18,773; 2 veterans married to each other, $16,051; increase for each additional dependent child, $2,093.

Duration The pension is paid for the life of the recipient.

Number awarded Varies each year.

Deadline Applications are accepted at any time.

[197]
DISTRICT OF COLUMBIA DISABILITY INCOME TAX EXCLUSION

Office of Tax and Revenue
Attn: Customer Service Center
1101 Fourth Street, S.W., Suite W270
Washington, DC 20024
(202) 727-4TAX   Fax: (202) 442-6304
E-mail: taxhelp@dc.gov
Web: otr.cfo.dc.gov/otr/site/default.asp

Summary To exclude a portion of the disability pay received by residents of the District of Columbia from local income taxation.

Eligibility This exclusion is available to residents of the District of Columbia who retired on disability and were permanently and totally disabled when they retired. Applicants must have received disability pay and did not elect to treat that income as a pension for federal purposes. They must be younger than 65 years of age.

Financial data Up to $5,200 per year of disability pay may be excluded from income for purposes of District taxation. The amount of the exclusion is reduced by the excess of the person's federal adjusted gross income over $15,000.

Duration The exclusion continues as long as the recipient resides in the District of Columbia.

Number awarded Varies each year.

Deadline The exclusion is claimed as part of the local income return, due in April of each year.

[198]
EAGLES MEMORIAL FOUNDATION MEDICAL ASSISTANCE

Fraternal Order of Eagles
Attn: Eagles Memorial Foundation
1623 Gateway Circle South
Grove City, OH 43123
(614) 883-2200   Fax: (613) 883-2201
E-mail: memorialfoundation@foe.com
Web: www.foe.com

Summary To provide medical assistance for the children of deceased members of the Fraternal Order of Eagles who died in action.

Eligibility Applicants must be the minor (under 18 years of age), unmarried children of a deceased parent who was a member of the Fraternal Order of Eagles or its Ladies Auxiliary at the time of death; the member must have died from injuries or diseases incurred or aggravated in the line of duty while serving 1) in the armed forces of the United States or Canada; 2) as volunteer law enforcement officers in the United States; 3) as volunteer fire fighters; or 4) as volunteer emergency medical service officers.

Financial data Benefits up to $10,000 are provided to eligible recipients for doctor, dentist, and hospital bills; the cost of eyeglasses, drugs, and medical and dental devices (including orthodontia); and psychiatric care.

Duration The total benefit is a lifetime payment to each recipient.

Additional data Benefits are not paid for any injury or illness resulting from the unlawful use of drugs, the excessive use of alcohol, the commission or attempt to commit a crime, or any self-inflicted injury.

Number awarded Varies each year.

Deadline Deadline not specified.

[199]
ELSIE S. BELLOWS FUND GRANTS

United Cerebral Palsy
Attn: Bellows Fund
1825 K Street, N.W., Suite 600
Washington, DC 20006
(202) 776-0406   Toll Free: (800) USA-5UCP
Fax: (202) 776-0414   TDD: (202) 973-7197
E-mail: info@ucp.org
Web: www.ucp.org

Summary To provide funding to individuals with disabilities interested in purchasing assistive technology equipment.

Eligibility This program is open to individuals with disabilities who are represented by a local affiliate of United Cerebral Palsy (UCP). Applicants must be interested in purchasing assistive technology devices, such as wheelchairs (manual or electric), augmentative communication devices, environmental controls, computer equipment, lifts, or hearing aids. Funding is not available for automobiles, evaluations or other assistive technology services, or furniture and appliances that are not adapted. The individuals must have exhausted all governmental and personal financial resources available to them. Applications must be submitted on their behalf by a local UCP affiliate.

Financial data Grants depend on the availability of funds and the cost of the proposed assistive technology purchase. Each UCP chapter is allocated between $2,250 and $3,750 for its grants.

Duration These are 1-time grants.

Additional data This program was established in 1995.

Number awarded Varies each year; recently, approximately $273,000 was available for these grants.

Deadline Applications may be submitted at any time.

[200]
FALLEN PATRIOT FUND GRANTS

Fallen Patriot Fund
c/o Bank of America Private Bank
TX1-492-19-09
P.O. Box 832409
Dallas, TX 75283-2409
(214) 658-7125   Fax: (214) 696-6310
E-mail: info@fallenpatriotfund.org
Web: www.fallenpatriotfund.org

Summary To provide personal financial assistance to veterans disabled as a result of combat in Iraq and to spouses and children of military personnel injured or killed in action in Iraq.

Eligibility This program is open to 1) veterans who were wounded in combat in support of Operation Iraqi Free, have been medically discharged from military service, received a disability rating from the U.S. Department of Veterans Affairs of 75% or greater, and can demonstrate dire financial hardship; 2) spouses of military personnel injured or killed in action in support of Operation Iraqi Freedom who can demonstrate dire financial hardship; and 3) children under 18 years of age of military personnel injured or killed in action in support of Operation Iraqi Freedom. Applicants who are currently enrolled as full-time undergraduate or vocational school students must demonstrate that all funds will be used to meet basic living expenses, not educational expenses. Graduate students, spouses who have received SGLI life insurance benefits, parents of military personnel injured or killed in action in support of Operation Iraqi Freedom, children over 18 years of age, and children or spouses of deceased military personnel whose death was a result of suicide are all ineligible. All applicants must state the nature of their financial hardship and how the money will be spent if a grant is provided.

Financial data The maximum grant is $3,000.

Duration Each disabled veteran or surviving spouse is limited to a total of 3 separate grants.

Additional data This program was established by the Mark Cuban Foundation.

Number awarded Varies each year; since the program was established, it has awarded more than $4.8 million in grants.

Deadline Applications may be submitted at any time.

[201]
FEDERAL INCOME TAX CREDIT FOR THE ELDERLY OR THE DISABLED

Internal Revenue Service
1111 Constitution Avenue, N.W.
Washington, DC 20224
Toll Free: (800) TAX-FORM
Web: www.irs.gov

Summary To provide a federal income tax credit for certain elderly and disabled citizens.

Eligibility Eligible for this credit are U.S. citizens or residents who are either 1) 65 years of age or older or 2) under 65 and retired on permanent and total disability, not yet of mandatory retirement age, and receiving taxable disability benefits. Beneficiaries of this credit must also have adjusted gross income below certain levels depending on their filing status: $17,500 for single, head of household, or qualifying widow(er) with dependent child filers; $20,000 for married taxpayers filing a joint return if only 1 spouse is elderly or disabled; $25,000 for married taxpayers filing a joint return if both spouses qualify as elderly or disabled; or $12,500 for married taxpayers filing a separate return who did not live with their spouse at any time during the year. Alternatively, taxpayers also qualify if the total of their nontaxable Social Security and other nontaxable pension(s) is less than $5,000 for single, head of household, or qualifying widow(er) with dependent child filers; $5,000 for married taxpayers filing a joint return if only 1 spouse is elderly or disabled; $7,500 for married taxpayers filing a joint return if both spouses qualify as elderly or disabled; or $3,750 for married taxpayers filing a separate return who did not live with their spouse at any time during the year.

Financial data　The amount of this credit is calculated on the basis of the filing status and income of the recipient.

Duration　1 year; must reapply each year.

Number awarded　Varies each year.

Deadline　This credit is applied to the qualifying tax filers' federal income tax return, which is due in April of each year.

[202]
FLEETWOOD MEMORIAL FOUNDATION GRANTS

Fleetwood Memorial Foundation
501 South Fielder Road
Arlington, TX 76013
(817) 825-6699　　　　　　Fax: (817) 542-0839
E-mail: fleetwood@fleetwoodmemorial.org
Web: www.fleetwoodmemorial.org/form.php

Summary　To provide no-strings-attached grants to injured law enforcement or fire protection personnel in Texas or to the families of deceased or disabled personnel.

Eligibility　Open to certified Texas law enforcement or fire protection personnel who have been injured in the performance of their duties or to the families of personnel who were killed or permanently disabled in the performance of their duties. For the purposes of this program, "line of duty" does not automatically mean "on duty;" for example, no injuries considered Section V or strains during normal exercise, automobile accidents while going to lunch, etc. are viewed as "line of duty" by this program.

Financial data　These grants, of varying amounts, are designed to provide immediate financial relief to meet unexpected expenses until insurance or more permanent sources of funds can be arranged. Grants may be used to re-educate qualified personnel if they are unable to return to their normal duties after an accident. Educational funds are also available to the dependent children of deceased or disabled peace and fire personnel as long as they attend a public junior or senior college in Texas. Those funds are intended to provide support for housing and other needs not covered by funding from the Texas Higher Education Coordinating Board.

Duration　These are 1-time grants.

Number awarded　Since its inception in 1974, the foundation has provided more than 500 grants to qualified recipients, totaling nearly $2 million.

Deadline　Applications may be submitted at any time.

[203]
FLORIDA DISABLED VETERANS' PROPERTY TAX DISCOUNT ON HOMESTEAD PROPERTY

Florida Department of Revenue
Attn: Taxpayer Services
5050 West Tennessee Street
Tallahassee, FL 32399-0100
(850) 617-8600　　　　　Toll Free: (800) 352-3671
E-mail: EMailDOR@dor.state.fl.us
Web: www.myflorida.com

Summary　To provide elderly disabled veterans with a partial exemption from taxation on their homesteads in Florida.

Eligibility　This exemption is available to Florida residents who have real estate that they own and use as a homestead. Applicants must be at least 65 years of age and honorably-discharged veterans who have a service-related permanent disability as rated by the U.S. Department of Veterans Affairs (VA). They must have been a resident of Florida at the time they entered the military.

Financial data　Qualifying veterans are entitled to a percentage discount on their property taxes equal to the percentage disability rating as determined by VA. This discount is in addition to any other exemptions for which the homestead owner is eligible (e.g., senior citizen, disabled veteran, regular homestead).

Duration　The exemption applies as long as the taxpayer owns the property in Florida.

Additional data　This program began in 2007. Initial applications should be made in person at the appropriate county property appraiser's office.

Number awarded　Varies each year.

Deadline　Applications must be submitted by February of the year for which the exemption is sought.

[204]
FLORIDA PROPERTY TAX DISABILITY EXEMPTION FOR EX-SERVICE MEMBERS

Florida Department of Revenue
Attn: Taxpayer Services
5050 West Tennessee Street
Tallahassee, FL 32399-0100
(850) 617-8600　　　　　Toll Free: (800) 352-3671
E-mail: EMailDOR@dor.state.fl.us
Web: www.myflorida.com

Summary　To exempt a portion of the value of property owned by disabled veterans in Florida.

Eligibility　This exemption is available to veterans who have at least a 10% disability as a result of wartime or other service-connected events and are Florida residents owning taxable property.

Financial data　The exemption applies to $5,000 of the value of the property.

Duration　The exemption applies as long as the taxpayer owns the property in Florida.

Additional data　Initial applications should be made in person at the county property appraiser's office.

Number awarded   Varies each year.

Deadline   Applications must be submitted by February of the year for which the exemption is sought.

[205]
FLORIDA SERVICE-CONNECTED TOTAL AND PERMANENT DISABILITY PROPERTY TAX EXEMPTION

Florida Department of Revenue
Attn: Taxpayer Services
5050 West Tennessee Street
Tallahassee, FL 32399-0100
(850) 617-8600   Toll Free: (800) 352-3671
E-mail: EMailDOR@dor.state.fl.us
Web: www.myflorida.com

Summary   To exempt from property taxation real estate owned by disabled veterans and their surviving spouses.

Eligibility   This exemption is available to Florida residents who have real estate that they own and use as a homestead. Applicants must be honorably-discharged veterans who have a total and permanent disability or require a wheelchair for mobility as a result of their military service. Under certain circumstances, the benefit of this exemption can carry over to a surviving spouse.

Financial data   All real estate used and owned as a homestead, less any portion used for commercial purposes, is exempt from taxation.

Duration   The exemption applies as long as the taxpayer owns the property in Florida.

Additional data   Initial applications should be made in person at the appropriate county property appraiser's office.

Number awarded   Varies each year.

Deadline   Applications must be submitted by February of the year for which the exemption is sought.

[206]
GEORGIA HOMESTEAD TAX EXEMPTION FOR DISABLED VETERANS

Georgia Department of Revenue
Attn: Property Tax Division
4245 International Parkway, Suite A
Hapeville, GA 30354-3918
(404) 968-0707   Fax: (404) 968-0778
E-mail: Local.Government.Services@dor.ga.gov
Web: etax.dor.ga.gov

Summary   To exempt from property taxation a portion of the value of homesteads owned by disabled veterans in Georgia and their families.

Eligibility   This program is open to residents of Georgia who qualify as a 100% disabled veteran under any of several provisions of state law. Surviving spouses and minor children are also eligible. Applicants must actually occupy a homestead and use it as their legal residence for all purposes.

Financial data   The first $50,000 of assessed valuation of the homestead owned by disabled veterans or their family members is exempt from property taxes for state, county, municipal, and school purposes.

Duration   The exemption remains in effect as long as the veteran or family member owns and resides in the homestead.

Number awarded   Varies each year.

Deadline   Applications must be filed with local tax officials by February of each year.

[207]
GEORGIA INCOME TAX EXEMPTION FOR DISABLED PERSONS

Georgia Department of Revenue
Attn: Taxpayer Services Division
1800 Century Boulevard, Room 8300
Atlanta, GA 30345-3205
(404) 417-2400   Toll Free: (877) GADOR-11
Fax: (404) 417-2439   TDD: (404) 417-4302
E-mail: taxpayer.services@dor.ga.gov
Web: etax.dor.ga.gov/IndTax_TSD.aspx

Summary   To exempt a portion of the retirement income of persons with disabilities from state income taxation in Georgia.

Eligibility   Eligible are persons classified as residents of Georgia for the purpose of state income taxation who are permanently and totally disabled (regardless of age).

Financial data   Up to $35,000 of retirement income received by people with disabilities is exempt from state income taxation.

Duration   The exemption continues as long as the recipient resides in Georgia.

Deadline   Deadline not specified.

[208]
GOTTLIEB FOUNDATION EMERGENCY GRANTS

Adolph and Esther Gottlieb Foundation, Inc.
Attn: Grants Manager
380 West Broadway
New York, NY 10012-5115
(212) 226-0581   Fax: (212) 226-0584
E-mail: sross@gottliebfoundation.org
Web: www.gottliebfoundation.org

Summary   To provide emergency financial assistance to artists.

Eligibility   This program is open to painters, sculptors, and printmakers who have been working at their art in a mature phase for at least 10 years. Applicants must be facing financial need due to an imminent and unforeseen catastrophic situation, as from a fire, flood, or medical emergency situation. The program does not consider requests for dental work, chronic situations, capital improvements, projects of any kind, or situations resulting from general indebtedness or lack of employment.

Financial data   Grants to the artists range from $1,000 to $10,000; the average award is $4,000.

Duration   These are 1-time grants.

Number awarded   Varies each year.

Deadline   Applications may be submitted at any time.

[209]
GRANTS FOR ACCESSIBILITY

Corporation for Independent Living
157 Charter Oak Avenue, Third Floor
Hartford, CT 06106
(860) 563-6011   Fax: (860) 563-2562
E-mail: access@cilhomes.org
Web: www.cilhomes.org/accessolutions.html

Summary To provide grants to low- or moderate-income residents of Connecticut who have a disability (as well as their parents) and need to modify their existing housing.

Eligibility Eligible to participate in this program are Connecticut residents who have a specified disability: people in wheelchairs, the deaf or hearing impaired, the blind or visually impaired, and people who have multiple sclerosis, cerebral palsy, traumatic brain injury, or any other physical disability). Applicants must own their homes and have a total household income at or below 80% of median income. Also eligible are homeowner parents of a child who is physically disabled and tenants who have the landlord's written consent to make accessibility renovations. Applicants must have total household income that is less than 80% of the state median. Grant funds may be used to purchase and install fixtures and improvements required to improve accessibility and/or usability of a residential dwelling in Connecticut.

Financial data Grants range from $5,000 to $50,000. Initially, a full lien is placed against the recipient's home. Total lien amounts are reduced automatically by 10% every year. At the end of 10 years, the grant is forgiven in full and the lien is removed.

Additional data Funding for this program, which began in 1984, is provided by the Connecticut Department of Economic and Community Development.

Number awarded Varies each year. Since the program began, more than 1,500 individuals have received grants.

Deadline Applications may be submitted at any time.

[210]
HARRY GREGG FOUNDATION GRANTS

Harry Gregg Foundation
One Verney Drive
Greenfield, NH 03047
(603) 547-3311, ext. 1490
Toll Free: (800) 394-3311, ext. 1490 (within NH)
Fax: (603) 547-6212
E-mail: hgf@crotchedmountain.org
Web: www.crotchedmountain.org

Summary To provide financial assistance for vocational education, assistive technology, or other purposes to children and adults in New Hampshire who have a disability.

Eligibility This program is open to New Hampshire residents of all ages who have physical, intellectual, or emotional disabilities. Funds may be requested for broad purposes but must specifically benefit the applicant. Examples of acceptable purposes include, but are not limited to: the costs of nonreimbursed medical or therapy treatments; specialty equipment, services, or supplies; modifi-cations to living area, workplace, or vehicle; respite services for the recipient or care givers; costs of attending a special camp or recreational activities; and vocational education or driver training tuition assistance. Selection is based on demonstrated need for a product of service, the applicant's financial circumstances, and the ability of the foundation to help improve the quality of life of a grant recipient.

Financial data Most grants range up to $1,200.

Duration Recipients may receive a maximum of 4 grants (no more than 2 in any year).

Additional data This foundation was established in 1989. If a request is not funded, applicants may reapply 6 months later for the same or a different purpose.

Number awarded Nearly 150 each year. Since this foundation was established, it has awarded more than 6,000 grants worth more than $2 million.

Deadline March, June, September, or December.

[211]
HAWAII GRANTS FOR SPECIAL HOUSING FOR DISABLED VETERANS

Office of Veterans Services
Attn: Veterans Services Coordinator
459 Patterson Road
E-Wing, Room 1-A103
Honolulu, HI 96819-1522
(808) 433-0420   Fax: (808) 433-0385
E-mail: ovs@ovs.hawaii.gov
Web: hawaii.gov

Summary To provide grants to disabled veterans in Hawaii for purchasing or remodeling a home.

Eligibility This program is open to totally disabled veterans in Hawaii. Applicants must be proposing to purchase or remodel a home to improve handicapped accessibility.

Financial data Grants up to $5,000 are available.

Duration These are 1-time grants.

Deadline Deadline not specified.

[212]
HAWAII INCOME TAX EXEMPTION FOR DISABLED RESIDENTS

Department of Taxation
Attn: Taxpayer Services Branch
425 Queen Street
P.O. Box 259
Honolulu, HI 96809-0259
(808) 587-4242   Toll Free: (800) 222-3229
Fax: (808) 587-1488   TDD: (808) 587-1418
Web: hawaii.gov/tax

Summary To exempt a portion of the income of blind, deaf, and other disabled residents from state income tax in Hawaii.

Eligibility Eligible for this exemption are 1) blind residents whose central visual acuity does not exceed 20/200 in the better eye with corrective lenses or whose visual acuity is greater than 20/200 but is accompanied by a limitation in the field of vision such that the widest diameter of the visual field subtends an angle no greater than 20 degrees; 2) deaf residents whose average loss in the speech frequencies in the better ear is 82 decibels A.S.A. or worse; or 3) totally disabled residents (physically or mentally) who are unable to engage in any substantial gainful business or occupation (a person whose gross income exceeds $30,000 per year is assumed to be engaged in a substantial gainful business or occupation).

Financial data The maximum exemptions from state income tax are as follows: single disabled resident, $7,000; disabled husband and wife, $14,000; disabled husband or wife, with non-disabled spouse under 65, $8,040; disabled husband or wife, with non-disabled spouse 65 years of age or older, $9,080.

Duration The exemption continues as long as the recipient resides in Hawaii.

Additional data Residents who claim this special exemption are not eligible to claim additional exemptions for their children or other dependents.

Deadline Deadline not specified.

[213]
HAWAII PROPERTY TAX EXEMPTIONS FOR DISABLED VETERANS

Office of Veterans Services
Attn: Veterans Services Coordinator
459 Patterson Road
E-Wing, Room 1-A103
Honolulu, HI 96819-1522
(808) 433-0420　　　　　　　　Fax: (808) 433-0385
E-mail: ovs@ovs.hawaii.gov
Web: hawaii.gov

Summary To exempt the homes of disabled veterans and surviving spouses in Hawaii from real estate taxation.

Eligibility This program is open to totally disabled veterans in Hawaii and their surviving spouses.

Financial data The real property owned and occupied as a home is exempt from taxation.

Duration The exemption applies as long as the disabled veteran or his/her widow(er) resides in Hawaii.

Deadline Deadline not specified.

[214]
HOPE FOR THE WARRIORS IMMEDIATE NEEDS GRANTS

Hope for the Warriors
Attn: Immediate Needs
1335 Western Boulevard, Suite E
Jacksonville, NC 28546-5539
(910) 938-1817　　　　　　　Toll Free: (877) 246-7349
E-mail: imn@hopeforthewarriors.org
Web: www.hopeforthewarriors.org/immneeds.html

Summary To provide funding for immediate needs to disabled military personnel, veterans, and their families.

Eligibility This assistance is available to wounded service members and their families. Applicants must need assistance to meet such immediate needs as travel to bedside where the government does not provide assistance, rental cars, lodging, groceries, gas, furniture, child

care, essentials of daily living (e.g., rent and utilities), or items that assist and/or supplement programs at military treatment facilities and Veterans Administration polytrauma units.

Financial data The amount of the grant depends on the need of the recipient. Payment is always made to a third party.

Duration Applicants may apply once a year.

Number awarded Varies each year.

Deadline Applications may be submitted at any time.

[215]
IDAHO CIRCUIT BREAKER PROPERTY TAX REDUCTION

Idaho State Tax Commission
Attn: Public Information Office
800 Park Boulevard, Plaza IV
P.O. Box 36
Boise, ID 83722-0410
(208) 334-7736　　　　　　　Toll Free: (800) 972-7660
TDD: (800) 377-3529
E-mail: pamela.waters@tax.idaho.com
Web: tax.idaho.gov/i-1052.cfm

Summary To reduce a portion of the property tax of disabled, blind, and other veterans and other disabled or elderly residents of Idaho.

Eligibility Eligible for this property tax reduction are residents of Idaho who own and live in a primary residence in the state and have an annual income of $28,000 or less (after deducting designated forms of income, including compensation received by a veteran from the U.S. Department of Veterans Affairs for a 40% to 100% service-connected disability). Applicants must be in 1 or more of the following categories: disabled (as recognized by an appropriate federal agency), blind, former prisoner of war or hostage, veteran with at least 10% service-connected disability or receiving a VA pension for a nonservice-connected disability, 65 years of age or older, widow(er) of any age, or fatherless or motherless child under 18 years of age.

Financial data The maximum amount of reduction is the lesser of $1,320 or the actual taxes on the recipient's qualifying home. The minimum reduction is the lesser of $100 or the actual taxes on the home.

Duration Applications for this reduction must be submitted each year.

Additional data All recipients of this reduction automatically receive Idaho's Homeowner's Exemption, which reduces the taxable value of the home (excluding land) by 50% or $75,000, whichever is less. Solid waste, irrigation, or other fees charged by some counties are not taxes and cannot be reduced by this program.

Number awarded Varies each year.

Deadline April of each year.

[216]
IDAHO RETIREMENT BENEFITS DEDUCTION

Idaho State Tax Commission
Attn: Public Information Office
800 Park Boulevard, Plaza IV
P.O. Box 36
Boise, ID 83722-0410
(208) 334-7660   Toll Free: (800) 972-7660
TDD: (800) 377-3529
Web: tax.idaho.gov/i-1039.cfm

Summary To deduct the retirement and disability income of certain residents from state income tax in Idaho.

Eligibility Eligible for this deduction are full-year residents of Idaho who are age 65 or older, or disabled and age 62 and older, and who are receiving the following annuities and benefits: 1) retirement annuities paid by the United States to a retired civil service employee or the unremarried widow of the employee; 2) retirement benefits paid from the firemen's retirement fund of the state of Idaho to a retired fireman or the unremarried widow of a retired fireman; 3) retirement benefits paid from the policeman's retirement fund of a city within Idaho to a retired policeman or the unremarried widow of a retired policeman; or 4) retirement benefits paid by the United States to a retired member of the U.S. military service or the unremarried widow of those veterans.

Financial data The amount of retirement or disability benefits may be deducted from taxable state income in Idaho, to a maximum deduction of $41,814 for married couples or $27,876 for single persons.

Duration 1 year; must reapply each year.

Number awarded Varies each year.

Deadline April of each year.

[217]
IDAHO WAR VETERAN'S EMERGENCY GRANT PROGRAM

Idaho Division of Veterans Services
Attn: Office of Veterans Advocacy
444 Fort Street
Boise, ID 83702
(208) 577-2300   Fax: (208) 577-2333
E-mail: info@veterans.idaho.gov
Web: www.veterans.idaho.gov/Veterans_Advocacy.aspx

Summary To provide emergency assistance to disabled veterans, wartime veterans, and their families in Idaho.

Eligibility Eligible for these grants are veterans who had at least 90 days of honorable wartime military service and entered the military from Idaho or lived within the state for at least 5 years. Veterans with a service-connected disability are eligible with earlier separation. Surviving spouses and dependent children are also eligible. Applicants must be current residents of Idaho in need of assistance because of a major catastrophe (e.g., natural disaster or death of a spouse or child), loss of job because of a disability, or other extreme financial emergency (e.g., cut-off notice from a utility company, eviction notice from a

landlord, arrears payment notice from the lien holder of a home).

Financial data The maximum amount available under this program is $1,000, issued in small incremental grants.

Duration The limit of $1,000 applies for the lifetime of each veteran or his/her family.

Additional data This program was established by the Idaho legislature in lieu of granting a wartime bonus to Idaho veterans.

Number awarded Varies each year.

Deadline Deadline not specified.

[218]
ILLINOIS DISABLED PERSONS' HOMESTEAD EXEMPTION

Illinois Department of Revenue
101 West Jefferson Street
P.O. Box 19044
Springfield, IL 62794-9044
(217) 782-3336   Toll Free: (800) 732-8866
TDD: (800) 544-5304
Web: www.revenue.state.il.us

Summary To reduce the value for property taxation of homesteads owned by disabled residents of Illinois.

Eligibility This exemption is available to residents of Illinois who own a homestead in the state as their primary residence. Applicants must have a verified disability.

Financial data Qualifying homeowners receive a $2,000 reduction in the equalized assessed value (EAV) of their property.

Duration Homeowners must file an annual application to continue to receive this exemption.

Additional data This program was established in 2007.

Deadline Deadline not specified.

[219]
ILLINOIS DISABLED VETERANS' HOMESTEAD EXEMPTION

Illinois Department of Revenue
101 West Jefferson Street
P.O. Box 19044
Springfield, IL 62794-9044
(217) 782-3336   Toll Free: (800) 732-8866
TDD: (800) 544-5304
Web: www.revenue.state.il.us

Summary To exempt a portion of the value of specially adapted housing owned by disabled veterans and their spouses in Illinois for purposes of property taxation.

Eligibility This exemption applies to housing owned and used by disabled veterans and their unmarried surviving spouses. The housing must have been purchased or constructed with funds provided by the U.S. Department of Veterans Affairs (VA) as part of a program of specially adapted housing for disabled veterans. The exemption is also available to disabled veterans and spouses who live in mobile homes. They may not utilize this exemption and either the Disabled Persons' Homestead Exemption or the Disabled Veterans Standard Homestead Exemption.

Financial data The exemption provides a reduction of $70,000 in the assessed value of the homestead.

Duration Veterans must file an annual application to continue to receive this exemption.

Deadline Deadline not specified.

[220]
ILLINOIS DISABLED VETERANS' STANDARD HOMESTEAD EXEMPTION

Illinois Department of Revenue
101 West Jefferson Street
P.O. Box 19044
Springfield, IL 62794-9044
(217) 782-3336   Toll Free: (800) 732-8866
TDD: (800) 544-5304
Web: www.revenue.state.il.us

Summary To reduce the value for property taxation of homesteads owned by disabled veterans in Illinois.

Eligibility This exemption is available to veterans who own or lease a single-family residence in Illinois and are liable for payment of property taxes. Applicants must have a service-connected disability verified by the U.S. Department of Veterans Affairs of at least 50%. They may not utilize this exemption and either the Disabled Persons' Homestead Exemption or the Disabled Veterans Homestead Exemption.

Financial data Veterans whose disability is rated as at least 50% but less than 70% receive a $2,500 reduction in the equalized assessed value (EAV) of their property. Veterans whose disability is rated as at least 70% receive a $5,000 reduction in the EAV of their property.

Duration Veterans must file an annual application to continue to receive this exemption.

Additional data This program was established in 2007.

Deadline Deadline not specified.

[221]
ILLINOIS INCOME TAX SUBTRACTION FOR GOVERNMENT RETIREES

Illinois Department of Revenue
101 West Jefferson Street
P.O. Box 19044
Springfield, IL 62794-9044
(217) 782-3336   Toll Free: (800) 732-8866
TDD: (800) 544-5304
Web: www.revenue.state.il.us

Summary To exempt the retirement and disability income of veterans and other government employees from state taxation in Illinois.

Eligibility This exemption applies to the income received from government retirement and disability plans, including military plans.

Financial data All government retirement and disability income of eligible residents is exempt from state income taxation.

Duration The exemption continues as long as the recipient resides in Illinois.

Deadline Deadline not specified.

[222]
INDIANA DISABILITY RETIREMENT INCOME TAX DEDUCTION

Indiana Department of Revenue
Attn: Taxpayer Services Division
Indiana Government Center North
100 North Senate Avenue
Indianapolis, IN 46204-2253
(317) 232-2240   TDD: (317) 232-4952
E-mail: individualtaxassistance@dor.in.gov
Web: www.in.gov/dor

Summary To exempt a portion of the disability income of Indiana residents from state taxation.

Eligibility This exclusion is available to residents of Indiana who retired on disability and were permanently and totally disabled when they retired. Applicants must have received disability pay and did not elect to treat that income as a pension for federal purposes. They must be younger than 65 years of age.

Financial data Up to $5,200 per year of disability pay may be excluded from income for purposes of state taxation. The amount of the exclusion is reduced by the excess of the person's federal adjusted gross income over $15,000.

Duration The exclusion is available as long as the recipient resides in Indiana.

Deadline Deadline not specified.

[223]
INDIANA PROPERTY TAX DEDUCTION FOR BLIND OR DISABLED PERSONS

Department of Local Government Finance
Indiana Government Center North, Room N1058(B)
100 North Senate Avenue
Indianapolis, IN 46201
(317) 232-3777   Toll Free: (888) 739-9826
Fax: (317) 232-8779
E-mail: PropertyTaxInfo@dlgf.in.gov
Web: www.in.gov/dlgf

Summary To exempt Indiana residents who are blind or disabled from a portion of their property tax.

Eligibility Eligible for this program are Indiana residents who are blind or disabled and receive less than $17,000 in annual taxable income. A blind person is defined as an individual who has vision in the better eye with correcting glasses of 20/200 or less, or a disqualifying visual field defect as determined upon examination by a designated ophthalmologist or optometrist. A disabled person is defined as an individual unable to engage in any substantial gainful activity by reason of a medically determinable physical or mental impairment that can be expected to result in death or has lasted and can be expected to last for at least 12 continuous months.

Financial data The maximum property tax deduction is $12,480.

Duration This deduction may be taken annually, as long as the Indiana resident meets the requirements of the program.

Additional data Property taxes are administered by individual counties in Indiana. Further information is available from county tax assessors.

Number awarded Varies each year.

Deadline Applications must be filed during the 12 months before May of each year for which the individual wishes to obtain the deduction.

[224]
INDIANA PROPERTY TAX DEDUCTIONS FOR DISABLED VETERANS

Department of Local Government Finance
Indiana Government Center North, Room N1058(B)
100 North Senate Avenue
Indianapolis, IN 46201
(317) 232-3777   Fax: (317) 232-8779
E-mail: PropertyTaxInfo@dlgf.in.gov
Web: www.in.gov/dlgf

Summary To exempt disabled Indiana veterans and their spouses from a portion of their property taxes.

Eligibility This program is open to the following categories of veterans who are residents of Indiana: 1) served honorably at least 90 days and are either totally disabled (the disability does not need to be service connected) or are at least 62 years of age and have at least a 10% service-connected disability; 2) served honorably during war time and have at least a 10% service-connected disability; or 3) served honorably during war time and either have a 100% service-connected disability or are at least 62 years of age and have at least a 10% service-connected disability. A statutory disability rating for pulmonary tuberculosis does not qualify. A disability incurred during Initial Active Duty for Training (IADT) with the National Guard or Reserves is eligible only if the disability occurred from an event during the period of active duty and that duty was performed during wartime. Surviving spouses of those 3 categories of veterans are also eligible.

Financial data Property tax exemptions are $12,480 for veterans and spouses in the first category (only if the assessed value of the combined real and personal property owned by the veteran or spouse does not exceed $143,160), $24,960 in the second category, or $37,440 in the third category; there is no limit on the value of the property owned by a surviving spouse).

Duration 1 year; may be renewed as long as the eligible veteran or surviving unremarried spouse owns and occupies the primary residence in Indiana.

Number awarded Varies each year.

Deadline Applications must be submitted no later than May of each year.

[225]
INJURED MARINE SEMPER FI GRANTS

Injured Marine Semper Fi Fund
c/o Wounded Warrior Center
Building H49
P.O. Box 555193
Camp Pendleton, CA 92055-5193
(760) 725-3680   Fax: (760) 725-3685
E-mail: info@semperfifund.org
Web: semperfifund.org/assistance

Summary To provide supplemental assistance to Marines injured in combat and their families.

Eligibility This program is open to Marines injured in post-9/11 combat operations or facing a life-threatening illness and their families. Members of the Army, Air Force, Coast Guard, and Navy who served in support of Marine forces are also eligible. Applicants must need financial assistance to deal with such needs as family support (e.g., travel and lodging, costs of hospitalization and rehabilitation, mortgages, car payments, utilities, grocery bills), adaptive housing support, adaptive transportation, or specialized and adaptive equipment.

Financial data Funds are available for such expenses as child care, travel expenses for families, and other necessities. Assistance is also available for the purchase of adaptive transportation, home modifications, and specialized equipment such as wheelchairs, audio/visual equipment for the blind, and software for traumatic brain injuries.

Duration Grants are provided as needed.

Additional data This fund was established in 2004 by a small group of Marine Corps spouses.

Number awarded Varies each year. Since this program was established, it has awarded more than 38,000 grants worth more than $57 million.

Deadline Applications may be submitted at any time.

[226]
IOWA DISABILITY INCOME TAX EXCLUSION

Iowa Department of Revenue
Attn: Taxpayer Services
Hoover State Office Building
1305 East Walnut
P.O. Box 10457
Des Moines, IA 50306-0457
(515) 281-3114   Toll Free: (800) 367-3388 (within IA)
Fax: (515) 242-6487   E-mail: idr@iowa.gov
Web: www.iowa.gov/tax

Summary To exclude a portion of the disability income of residents of Iowa from state income taxation.

Eligibility This exclusion is available to residents of Iowa who retired on disability and were permanently and totally disabled when they retired. Applicants must have received disability pay and did not elect to treat that income as a pension for federal purposes. They must be younger than 65 years of age.

Financial data Up to $5,200 per year of disability pay may be excluded from income for purposes of state taxation. The amount of the exclusion is reduced by the excess of the person's federal adjusted gross income over $15,000.

Duration The exclusion continues until the recipient reaches the age of 65 years.

Number awarded Varies each year.

Deadline Deadline not specified.

[227]
IOWA DISABLED AND SENIOR CITIZENS PROPERTY TAX CREDIT

Iowa Department of Revenue
Attn: Property Tax Division
Hoover State Office Building
1305 East Walnut
P.O. Box 10469
Des Moines, IA 50306-0469
(515) 281-4040   Toll Free: (800) 367-3388 (within IA)
Fax: (515) 242-6487   E-mail: idr@iowa.gov
Web: www.iowa.gov/tax/taxlaw/PropertyTaxCredits.html

Summary To provide a property tax credit to residents of Iowa who have a disability or are elderly.

Eligibility This credit is available to residents of Iowa who are either totally disabled and over 18 years of age or 65 years of age or older. Applicants must have household income less than $20,906 per year.

Financial data Eligible residents receive a percentage credit on their property taxes that depends on their household income: from $0.00 to $10,769.99: 100%; from 10,770 to $12,036.99: 85%; from 12,037 to 13,303.99: 70%, from $13,304 to 15,837.99: 50%; from 15,838 to $18,371.99: 35%; or from $18,372 to $20,905.99: 25%.

Duration The credit continues as long as the recipient remains a resident of Iowa and owns a homestead subject to property taxation.

Number awarded Varies each year; recently, the total value of credits extended through this program was more than $23 million.

Deadline Claims must be filed with the county treasurer by the end of May of each year. The treasurer may extend the filing deadline to the end of September, or the Director of Revenue may extend the filing deadline to the end of December.

[228]
IOWA PENSION/RETIREMENT INCOME EXCLUSION

Iowa Department of Revenue
Attn: Taxpayer Services
Hoover State Office Building
1305 East Walnut
P.O. Box 10457
Des Moines, IA 50306-0457
(515) 281-3114   Toll Free: (800) 367-3388 (within IA)
Fax: (515) 242-6487   E-mail: idr@iowa.gov
Web: www.iowa.gov/tax

Summary To exempt a portion of the income received by disabled and other retirees in Iowa, as well as their surviving spouses, from state taxation.

Eligibility This exemption applies to the retirement income of residents of Iowa who are 1) 55 years of age or older, 2) disabled, or 3) a surviving spouse or a survivor having an insurable interest in an individual who would have qualified from the exclusion on the basis of age or disability.

Financial data For joint filers, the exclusion is the lesser of $12,000 or the taxable amount of the retirement income; for all other statuses of filers, each eligible taxpayer can claim as an exemption the lesser of $6,000 or the taxable amount of the retirement income.

Duration The exemption continues as long as the recipient remains a resident of Iowa for state income tax purposes.

Number awarded Varies each year.

Deadline Deadline not specified.

[229]
KANSAS DISABLED ACCESS INCOME TAX CREDIT

Kansas Department of Revenue
Attn: Taxpayer Assistance Center
Robert B. Docking State Office Building
915 S.W. Harrison Street
Topeka, KS 66612-1712
(785) 368-8222   Toll Free: (877) 526-7738
Fax: (785) 291-3614   TDD: (785) 296-6461
Web: www.ksrevenue.org/taxcredits-disabled.htm

Summary To provide an income tax credit to individual and business taxpayers in Kansas who incur certain expenditures to make their property accessible to people with disabilities.

Eligibility This credit is available to state income taxpayers in Kansas who make buildings or facilities accessible and usable by persons with disabilities in conformity with the Americans with Disabilities Act of 1990. The credit applies to the taxpayer's principal dwelling or the principal dwelling of a lineal ascendant or descendant, including construction of a small barrier-free living unit attached to the principal dwelling. The only expenditures that qualify for this credit are those that are specifically intended to 1) make an existing facility accessible to people with disabilities; 2) remove existing architectural barriers; or 3) modify or adapt an existing facility or piece of equipment in order to employ people with disabilities.

Financial data For individuals, the amount of the credit depends on adjusted gross income and the amount of the expenditure, ranging from 100% of the expenditure for incomes less than $25,000, to 50% for incomes greater than $45,000 but less than $55,000; persons with incomes greater than $55,000 do not qualify for the credit; the maximum individual credit is $9,000. For businesses, the credit is 50% of the amount of the expenditure, to a maximum of $10,000.

Duration This is a 1-time credit.

Number awarded Varies each year.

Deadline Claims are filed with the state income tax return, due in April.

[230]
KANSAS INTANGIBLES TAX SENIOR CITIZEN OR DISABILITY EXEMPTION

Kansas Department of Revenue
Attn: Taxpayer Assistance Center
Robert B. Docking State Office Building
915 S.W. Harrison Street
Topeka, KS 66612-1712
(785) 368-8222   Toll Free: (877) 526-7738
Fax: (785) 291-3614   TDD: (785) 296-6461
Web: www.ksrevenue.org/perstaxtypeint.htm

Summary To exempt a portion of the income received by elderly, blind, or disabled residents in Kansas from the intangibles tax.

Eligibility This exemption applies to residents of local areas in Kansas that levy an intangibles tax on gross earnings received from such property as savings accounts, stocks, bonds, accounts receivable, and mortgages. Applicants must 1) be disabled, blind, or 60 years of age or older and 2) have a household income of $20,000 or less.

Financial data Qualified residents are entitled to exempt from their intangibles income an amount that depends on their income. If total household income is $15,000 or less, the exemption is $5,000. For incomes between $15,000 and $20,000, the exemption is calculated as the difference between $5,000 and the amount of the income over $15,000.

Duration This benefit continues as long as the recipient remains a resident of the Kansas locality that imposes an intangibles tax.

Number awarded Varies each year.

Deadline Deadline not specified.

[231]
KANSAS STATE DEAF-BLIND FUND

Kansas State Department of Education
Special Education Services
Attn: Kansas State Deaf-Blind Fund
120 S.E. Tenth Avenue
Topeka, KS 66612-1182
(785) 296-2515   Toll Free: (800) 203-9462
Fax: (785) 296-6715   TDD: (785) 296-2515
E-mail: jhoughton@ksde.org
Web: www.ksde.org/Default.aspx?tabid=2322

Summary To provide supplementary financial assistance to deaf-blind or severely disabled students in Kansas.

Eligibility Applications may be submitted by school personnel for students in Kansas (up to the age of 21) who are deaf-blind and/or have severe multiple disabilities. Approval for funding is granted on a first-come, first-served basis for the following areas: 1) assistive technology that enables a student with dual sensory impairments and with severe disabilities to participate more fully in an educational program (e.g., computers, adaptive equipment, eyeglasses, hearing aids, computer peripherals, augmentative communication devices, microswitches, software); 2) consultation; 3) evaluation for the cost of vision and/or hearing evaluations for students who are

suspected of being deaf-blind, or a vision, hearing, or educational evaluation for recertification purposes; or 4) other costs associated with additional items or expenses that reflect best educational or effective practices, such as expenses involved in providing community activities. Applicants must provide documentation that other funding sources have been approached and that costs do not exceed the amount local education agencies are able to provide out of federal, state, or local funds. Priority candidates are students who have current deaf-blind certification, deaf-blind children from birth through 2 years of age, students who are exiting state hospital schools and returning to their home district, students who have a suspected vision loss and documented hearing loss and are in need of an evaluation, and students who have a suspected hearing loss and documented vision loss and are in need of an evaluation.

Financial data Eligible students are awarded up to $3,000 per year.

Duration 1 year; may be renewed.

Number awarded Varies each year; recently, 76 students received $108,160 in funding from this program. Grants provided $107,555 for assistive technology and $605 for consultants.

Deadline May of each year.

[232]
KENTUCKY HOMESTEAD EXEMPTION PROGRAM

Kentucky Department of Revenue
Attn: Office of Property Evaluation
501 High Street
P.O. Box 1202
Frankfort, KY 40602-1202
(502) 564-7237   Fax: (502) 564-8368
E-mail: wayne.gunnell@ky.gov
Web: revenue.ky.gov/Property+Tax

Summary To exempt a portion of the value of real estate owned by elderly and disabled residents of Kentucky from property taxation.

Eligibility This exemption applies to owners of real estate in Kentucky who are either 65 years of age or older or totally disabled. The property must be owned, occupied, and maintained by the taxpayer as a personal residence.

Financial data Up to $34,000 of the value of real estate is exempt from property taxation.

Duration The exemption continues as long as the recipient resides in Kentucky.

Deadline Deadline not specified.

[233]
LONGSHORE AND HARBOR WORKERS' COMPENSATION PROGRAM

Department of Labor
Employment Standards Administration
Office of Workers' Compensation Programs
Attn: Division of Longshore and Harbor Workers'
  Compensation
200 Constitution Avenue, N.W., Room C4315
Washington, DC 20210
(202) 693-0038   Toll Free: (800) 638-7072
Fax: (202) 693-1380   TDD: (800) 326-2577
Web: www.dol.gov/dol/topic/workcomp/index.htm

Summary To provide benefits to maritime workers disabled or killed during the course of employment and to their spouses.

Eligibility This program is open to longshoremen, harbor workers, and other maritime workers who are injured during the course of employment; by extension, various other classes of private industry workers (including workers engaged in the extraction of natural resources on the outer continental shelf, employees of defense contractors overseas, and employees at post exchanges on military bases) are also eligible if they become disabled for work-related causes. In addition, survivor benefits are provided if the work-related injury causes the employee's death.

Financial data The compensation for disability is 66 2/3% of the employee's average weekly wage, with a minimum of 50% of the national average weekly wage (NAWW) and a maximum of 200% of the NAWW. In a recent year, the Department of Labor calculated the NAWW as $647.60, so the minimum weekly disability payment was $323.80 and the maximum was $1,295.20. Death benefits are equivalent to the average weekly wage of the deceased employee, with a minimum equivalent to 100% of the NAWW and a maximum equivalent to 200% of the NAWW.

Duration Benefits are paid as long as the worker remains disabled; death benefits are paid for the life of the qualified survivor.

Additional data This program also provides medical benefits and rehabilitation services to qualifying longshoremen, harbor workers, and other workers.

Number awarded Varies; more than 15,000 maritime workers recently received compensation and medical benefits through this program.

Deadline Deadline not specified.

[234]
LOUISIANA DISABILITY INCOME EXCLUSION

Louisiana Department of Revenue
Attn: Individual Income Tax
P.O. Box 201
Baton Rouge, LA 70821
(225) 219-0102
Web: www.revenue.louisiana.gov

Summary To exclude a portion of disability income from state taxation in Louisiana.

Eligibility This exclusion is available to residents of Louisiana who receive income for a permanent total disability.

Financial data Up to $6,000 of disability income may be excluded from income for state taxation purposes.

Duration The exclusion is available as long as the recipient remains a resident of Louisiana for state income tax purposes and receives disability income.

Number awarded Varies each year.

Deadline Deadline not specified.

[235]
MAINE PROPERTY TAX EXEMPTIONS FOR VETERANS

Maine Revenue Services
Attn: Property Tax Division
P.O. Box 9106
Augusta, ME 04332-9106
(207) 287-2013   Fax: (207) 287-6396
E-mail: prop.tax@maine.gov
Web: www.maine.gov

Summary To exempt the estates of disabled Maine veterans and selected family members from property taxation.

Eligibility Eligible for this program are veterans who served during World War I, World War II, the Korean campaign, the Vietnam war, the Persian Gulf war, or other recognized service periods, are legal residents of Maine, and are either older than 62 years of age or are receiving a pension or compensation from the U.S. government for total disability (whether service connected or not). Vietnam veterans must have served 180 days on active duty unless discharged earlier for a service-connected disability. The exemption also includes 1) property held in joint tenancy with the veterans' spouses, and 2) property of unremarried widow(er)s, minor children, and parents of deceased veterans, if those dependents are receiving a pension or compensation from the U.S. government.

Financial data Estates of disabled veterans and eligible dependents, including both real and personal property, are exempt up to $6,000 of just valuation. For veterans and dependents who served in war time prior to World War II, estates up to $7,000 are exempt.

Duration Veterans, spouses, unremarried widow(er)s, and mothers are eligible for this exemption throughout their lifetimes; minor children of veterans are eligible until they reach the age of 18.

Number awarded Varies each year.

Deadline When an eligible person first submits an application, the proof of entitlement must reach the assessors of the local municipality prior to the end of March. Once eligibility has been established, notification need not be repeated in subsequent years.

[236]
MARYLAND PENSION EXCLUSION FOR DISABLED AND ELDERLY RESIDENTS

Comptroller of Maryland
Attn: Revenue Administration Division
80 Calvert Street
Annapolis, MD 21411
(410) 260-7980
Toll Free: (800) MD-TAXES (within MD)
Fax: (410) 974-3456   TDD: (410) 260-7157
E-mail: taxhelp@comp.state.md.us
Web: individuals.marylandtaxes.com

Summary   To exempt a portion of the income of disabled and elderly residents (and selected spouses) from state income taxation in Maryland.

Eligibility   Eligible are Maryland residents who receive income from a pension, annuity, or endowment from an employee retirement system and who are at least 65 years of age or classified as totally disabled; spouses of disabled persons also qualify. The disability must be a mental or physical impairment that prevents the person from engaging in gainful activity and that is expected to be of long, continuing, or indefinite duration (or to result in death).

Financial data   Persons with disabilities, who have a spouse who is totally disabled, or who are 65 years of age or older may exclude from state taxation up to $26,300 of income received as a pension, annuity, or endowment.

Duration   The exemption continues as long as the recipient resides in Maryland.

Deadline   Deadline not specified.

[237]
MARYLAND PROPERTY TAX EXEMPTION FOR DISABLED VETERANS AND SURVIVING SPOUSES

Maryland Department of Assessments and Taxation
Attn: Property Taxes
301 West Preston Street
Baltimore, MD 21201-2395
(410) 767-1184   Toll Free: (888) 246-5941
TDD: (800) 735-2258
Web: www.dat.state.md.us/sdatweb/exempt.html

Summary   To exempt the homes of disabled veterans and their surviving spouses from property taxation in Maryland.

Eligibility   This exemption is available to armed services veterans with a permanent service-connected disability rated 100% by the U.S. Department of Veterans Affairs who own a dwelling house in Maryland. Unremarried surviving spouses are also eligible.

Financial data   The dwelling houses of eligible veterans and surviving spouses are exempt from real property taxes.

Duration   The exemption is available as long as the veteran or surviving spouse owns the dwelling house in Maryland.

Number awarded   Varies each year.

Deadline   Applications may be submitted at any time.

[238]
MASSACHUSETTS PROPERTY TAX EXEMPTION FOR VETERANS AND THEIR FAMILIES

Massachusetts Department of Revenue
Attn: Division of Local Services
100 Cambridge Street
Boston, MA 02114
(617) 626-2386   Fax: (617) 626-2330
Web: www.mass.gov/dor/all-taxes/excise-and-property

Summary   To provide a property tax exemption to blind, disabled, and other veterans (and their families) in Massachusetts.

Eligibility   This program is open to veterans who are residents of Massachusetts, were residents for at least 6 months prior to entering the service, have been residents for at least 5 consecutive years, and are occupying property as their domicile. Applicants must have an ownership interest in the domicile that ranges from $2,000 to $10,000, depending on the category of exemption. Veterans must have been discharged under conditions other than dishonorable. Several categories of veterans and their families qualify: 1) veterans who have a service-connected disability rating of 10% or more; veterans who have been awarded the Purple Heart; Gold Star mothers and fathers; and surviving spouses of eligible veterans who do not remarry; 2) veterans who suffered, in the line of duty, the loss or permanent loss of use of 1 foot, 1 hand, or 1 eye; veterans who received the Congressional Medal of Honor, Distinguished Service Cross, Navy Cross, or Air Force Cross; and their spouses or surviving spouses; 3) veterans who suffered, in the line of duty, the loss or permanent loss of use of both feet, both hands, or both eyes; and their spouses or surviving spouses; 4) veterans who suffered total disability in the line of duty and received assistance in acquiring specially adapted housing, which they own and occupy as their domicile; and their spouses or surviving spouses; 5) unremarried surviving spouses of military personnel who died due to injury or disease from being in a combat zone, or are missing and presumed dead due to combat; 6) veterans who suffered total disability in the line of duty and are incapable of working; and their spouses or surviving spouses; and 7) veterans who are certified by the Veterans Administration as paraplegic and their surviving spouses.

Financial data   Qualified veterans and family members are entitled to an annual exemption from their taxes for the different categories: 1), $400; 2), $750; 3), $1,250; 4), $1,500; 5), total exemption for 5 years after death, and up to $2,500 after 5 years; 6), $1,000; or 7), total.

Duration   The exemptions are provided each year that the veteran or unremarried surviving spouse lives in Massachusetts and owns the property as a domicile.

Additional data   Applications are available from local assessor's offices.

Number awarded   Varies each year.

Deadline   Applications must be filed with the local assessor by December of each year.

[239]
MASSACHUSETTS VETERANS ANNUITY PROGRAM

Department of Veterans' Services
Attn: Annuities
600 Washington Street, Seventh Floor
Boston, MA 02111
(617) 210-5480   Fax: (617) 210-5755
E-mail: mdvs@vet.state.ma.us
Web: www.mass.gov/veterans

Summary   To provide an annuity to blind or disabled veterans from Massachusetts and to the parents and spouses of deceased military personnel.

Eligibility   This program is open to 1) veterans who are blind, double amputee, paraplegic, or have a 100% service-connected disability; 2) the parents of military personnel who died of service-connected causes; and 3) the unremarried spouses of military personnel who died of service-connected causes. Veterans must have been residents of Massachusetts at the time of entry into military service who served during specified wartime periods and received other than a dishonorable discharge. All applicants must currently be residents of Massachusetts.

Financial data   Recipients are entitled to an annuity of $2,000 per year.

Duration   The annuity is paid as long as the recipient continues to reside in Massachusetts.

Deadline   Deadline not specified.

[240]
MEDICARE DME PROGRAM

Centers for Medicare & Medicaid Services
Attn: Medicare
7500 Security Boulevard
Baltimore, MD 21244-1850
Toll Free: (800) 772-1213   TDD: (800) 325-0778
Web: www.medicare.gov

Summary   To enable Medicare recipients to acquire durable medical equipment (DME), such as wheelchairs, walkers, hospital beds, and oxygen equipment prescribed for home use by a doctor.

Eligibility   People are eligible for Medicare if they or a spouse worked for at least 40 quarters in Medicare-covered employment, are at least 65 years old, and are U.S. citizens or permanent residents. Part A helps pay for care in a hospital, a skilled nursing facility, or home and hospice care (including DME). Part B helps pay for doctors, outpatient hospital care, and other medical services, such as DME.

Financial data   Most people do not pay a monthly Part A premium because they or their spouses have 40 or more quarters of Medicare-covered employment. To participate in Part B, a monthly premium (currently $99.90 for individuals with incomes less than $85,000, rising to $319.70 for individuals with incomes greater than $214,000), is required, as are a $140 annual deductible and a 20% coinsurance rate. Medicare carriers do not pay the entire bill for DME. Instead, they determine an allowable charge (based on the actual charge) and the prevailing charge in a geographic area. The regional Medicare carrier pays 80% of the allowable amount; the remainder is paid by the beneficiary or another third party.

Additional data   DME is defined as medical equipment that is ordered by a doctor for use in the home. These items must be reuseable.

Number awarded   Varies each year.

Deadline   Applications may be submitted at any time.

[241]
MICHIGAN HOMESTEAD PROPERTY TAX CREDIT FOR VETERANS AND BLIND PEOPLE

Michigan Department of Treasury
Attn: Homestead Exemption
Treasury Building
430 West Allegan Street
Lansing, MI 48922
(517) 636-4486   TDD: (800) 649-3777
E-mail: treasIndTax@michigan.gov
Web: www.michigan.gov/taxes

Summary   To provide an income tax credit to disabled and other veterans, military personnel, their spouses, blind people, and their surviving spouses in Michigan.

Eligibility   Eligible to apply are residents of Michigan who are 1) blind and own their homestead; 2) a veteran with a service-connected disability or his/her surviving spouse; 3) a surviving spouse of a veteran deceased in service; 4) a pensioned veteran, a surviving spouse of those veterans, or an active military member, all of whose household income is less than $7,500; or 5) a surviving spouse of a non-disabled or non-pensioned veteran of the Korean War, World War II, or World War I whose household income is less than $7,500. All applicants must own or rent a home in Michigan, have been a Michigan resident for at least 6 months during the year in which application is made, and fall within qualifying income levels (up to $82,650 in household income).

Financial data   The maximum credit, applied to state income taxes, is $1,200. The exact amount varies. For homeowners, the credit depends on the state equalized value of the homestead and on an allowance for filing category. For renters, 20% of the rent is considered property tax eligible for credit.

Duration   1 year; eligibility must be established each year.

Number awarded   Varies each year.

Deadline   April of each year.

[242]
MICHIGAN HOMESTEAD PROPERTY TAX EXEMPTION FOR SPECIALLY ADAPTED HOUSING

Michigan Department of Treasury
Attn: Homestead Exemption
Treasury Building
430 West Allegan Street
Lansing, MI 48922
(517) 373-3200   TDD: (800) 649-3777
E-mail: treasPtd2@michigan.gov
Web: www.michigan.gov/taxes

Summary   To exempt specially adapted housing occupied as homesteads by disabled veterans and their unremarried spouses from property taxation in Michigan.

Eligibility   This exemption is available to Michigan residents who are disabled veterans living in specially adapted housing that they acquired with financial assistance from the U.S. Department of Veterans Affairs (VA). If the veteran has died, the exemption continues for the unremarried surviving spouse.

Financial data   All taxes on qualified housing are cancelled.

Duration   This exemption continues as long as the disabled veteran or unremarried surviving spouse owns the property in Michigan and, in the case of surviving spouses, remains unmarried.

Number awarded   Varies each year.

Deadline   Deadline not specified.

[243]
MICHIGAN INCOME TAX EXEMPTION FOR PEOPLE WITH DISABILITIES

Michigan Department of Treasury
Attn: Income Tax
Treasury Building
430 West Allegan Street
Lansing, MI 48922
(517) 373-3200   TDD: (800) 649-3777
E-mail: treasIndTax@michigan.gov
Web: www.michigan.gov/taxes

Summary   To exempt a portion of the income of deaf, blind, and disabled residents of Michigan from state income taxation.

Eligibility   Eligible for this exemption are residents of Michigan who 1) receive messages through a sense other than hearing, such as lip reading or sign language; 2) have vision in their better eye of 20/200 or less with corrective lenses or peripheral field of vision of 20 degrees or less; or 3) are hemiplegic, paraplegic, quadriplegic, or totally and permanently disabled.

Financial data   Qualifying people with disabilities receive an exemption of $2,400 from their adjusted gross income for purposes of state taxation.

Duration   The exemption continues as long as the recipient resides in Michigan.

Deadline   Deadline not specified.

[244]
MICHIGAN VETERANS TRUST FUND EMERGENCY GRANTS

Department of Military and Veterans Affairs
Attn: Michigan Veterans Trust Fund
2500 South Washington Avenue
Lansing, MI 48913-5101
(517) 373-3130   E-mail: dutchera@michigan.gov
Web: www.michigan.gov

Summary   To provide temporary financial assistance to disabled and other Michigan veterans and their families who are facing personal emergencies.

Eligibility   Eligible for this assistance are veterans and their families residing in Michigan who are temporarily unable to provide the basic necessities of life. Support is not provided for long-term problems or chronic financial difficulties. The qualifying veteran must have been discharged under honorable conditions with at least 180 days of active wartime service or have been separated as a result of a physical or mental disability incurred in the line of duty.

Financial data   No statutory limit exists on the amount of assistance that may be provided; a local board in each Michigan county determines if the applicant is genuinely needy and the amount of assistance to be awarded.

Duration   This assistance is provided to meet temporary needs only.

Number awarded   Varies each year.

Deadline   Applications may be submitted at any time.

[245]
MINNESOTA INCOME TAX SUBTRACTION FOR THE ELDERLY OR DISABLED

Minnesota Department of Revenue
Attn: Individual Income Tax Division
600 North Robert Street
Mail Station 5510
St. Paul, MN 55146-5510
(651) 296-3781   Toll Free: (800) 652-9094 (within MN)
E-mail: indinctax@state.mn.us
Web: www.taxes.state.mn.us

Summary   To exempt from state taxation a portion of the income received by residents of Minnesota who are disabled or elderly.

Eligibility   This exemption is available to residents of Minnesota who are either 65 years of age or older or permanently and totally disabled and receiving disability income from the Social Security Administration or U.S. Department of Veterans Affairs. Their adjusted gross income must be less than $42,000 if married filing a joint return and both spouses qualify, $38,500 if married filing a joint return and 1 spouse qualifies, $21,000 if married filing a separate return, or $33,700 if filing single, head of household, or qualifying widow(er).

Financial data   Qualified taxpayers are entitled to subtract from their income for purposes of Minnesota state taxation $18,000 if married filing a joint return and both spouses qualify, $14,500 if married filing a joint return and 1 spouse qualifies, $9,000 if married filing a separate return, or $14,500 if filing single, head of household, or qualifying widow(er).

Duration   This exemption is available as long as the tax-payer resides in Minnesota.

Number awarded   Varies each year.

Deadline   Income tax returns must be submitted by April of each year.

[246]
MINNESOTA MARKET VALUE EXCLUSION FOR DISABLED VETERANS

Minnesota Department of Revenue
Attn: Property Tax Division
600 North Robert Street
Mail Station 3340
St. Paul, MN 55146-3340
(651) 556-6087
Web: www.taxes.state.mn.us

Summary   To exclude from property taxation a portion of the value of homesteads owned by disabled veterans, family caregivers, and surviving spouses in Minnesota.

Eligibility   This exclusion is available to owners of homesteads in Minnesota who are veterans who have a service-connected disability rated at least at 70% by the U.S. Department of Veterans Affairs. If a disabled veteran has died (or was killed in action without becoming disabled), the surviving spouse is eligible for the exclusion. If a veteran meets the disability qualification but does not own homestead property, the homestead of the veteran's primary family caregiver, if any, is eligible for the exclusion for that veteran.

Financial data   For veterans with a service-connected of 70% or more (and their surviving spouses or primary family caregivers), $150,000 of the market value of the homestead is excluded from property taxation. For veterans with a total (100%) and permanent service-connected disability (and their surviving spouses or primary family caregivers), $300,000 of the market value of the homestead is excluded from property taxation.

Duration   This exclusion is available as long as the veteran, surviving spouse, or primary family caregiver owns the homestead and meets the eligibility requirements.

Additional data   This exclusion was established by the Minnesota legislature for veterans in 2008 and expanded to included surviving spouses and primary family caregivers in 2011.

Deadline   Applications must be submitted by June of each year.

[247]
MINNESOTA STATE SOLDIERS ASSISTANCE PROGRAM

Minnesota Department of Veterans Affairs
Veterans Service Building
20 West 12th Street, Room 206C
St. Paul, MN 55155-2006
(651) 757-1556   Toll Free: (888) LINK-VET
Fax: (651) 296-3954
E-mail: kathy.schwartz@state.mn.us
Web: www.mdva.state.mn.us/SSAP/index.htm

Summary   To provide emergency financial assistance to disabled veterans and their families in Minnesota.

Eligibility   This assistance is available to veterans who are unable to work because of a temporary disability (from service-connected or other causes). Their dependents and survivors are also eligible. Applicants must also meet income and asset guidelines and be residents of Minnesota.

Financial data   The maximum grant is $1,500. Funds may be used to pay for food and shelter, utility bills, and emergency medical treatment (including optical and dental benefits).

Duration   This is a short-term program, with benefits payable up to 6 months only. If the veteran's disability is expected to be long term in nature or permanent, the department may continue to provide assistance while application is made for long-term benefits, such as Social Security disability or retirement benefits.

Number awarded   Varies each year. A total of $1.4 million is available for this program annually.

Deadline   Applications may be submitted at any time.

[248]
MISSISSIPPI AD VALOREM TAX EXEMPTION FOR DISABLED VETERANS

Mississippi State Veterans Affairs Board
3466 Highway 80
P.O. Box 5947
Pearl, MS 39288-5947
(601) 576-4850   Toll Free: (877) 203-5632
Fax: (601) 576-4868
Web: www.vab.ms.gov

Summary   To exempt the property of disabled veterans from ad valorem taxation in Mississippi.

Eligibility   This exemption applies to homesteads owned by American veterans in Mississippi who were honorably discharged. Applicants must have a 100% permanent service-connected disability.

Financial data   All qualifying homesteads of $7,500 or less in assessed value are exempt from ad valorem taxation.

Duration   This exemption applies as long as the disabled veteran owns the homestead in Mississippi.

Number awarded   Varies each year.

Deadline   Deadline not specified.

[249]
MISSISSIPPI HOMESTEAD TAX EXEMPTION FOR THE DISABLED

Mississippi Department of Revenue
Attn: Property Tax Division
P.O. Box 1033
Jackson, MS 39215-1033
(601) 923-7618   Fax: (601) 923-7637
Web: www.dor.ms.gov/taxareas/property/main.html

Summary To exempt from property taxes a portion of the value of homesteads owned by people with disabilities and blind people in Mississippi.

Eligibility Eligible for this exemption are residents of Mississippi who are totally disabled or legally blind and own a homestead that they occupy as a home. Disability and blindness are defined according to federal Social Security regulations.

Financial data The exemption covers the first $7,500 of assessed value of the property (or $75,000 true value).

Duration The exemption continues as long as the disabled or blind person resides in Mississippi.

Number awarded Varies each year.

Deadline The first time an exemption is requested, it must be submitted before the end of March of that year. Subsequently, most Mississippi counties do not require renewal filing unless the disable person's homestead status changes.

[250]
MISSOURI INCOME TAX DEDUCTION FOR THE BLIND AND DISABLED

Missouri Department of Revenue
Attn: Taxation Division
301 West High Street, Room 330
P.O. Box 2200
Jefferson City, MO 65105-2200
(573) 751-3505   Toll Free: (800) 877-6881
Fax: (573) 751-2195   TDD: (800) 735-2966
E-mail: income@dor.mo.gov
Web: dor.mo.gov/personal

Summary To provide an additional income tax deduction to blind and disabled people in Missouri.

Eligibility This deduction is available to all residents of Missouri who are legally classified as blind or 100% disabled.

Financial data Blind and disabled residents are entitled to deduct an additional $1,200 from their income for taxation purposes.

Duration This deduction is available as long as the recipient remains a resident of Missouri for state income tax purposes.

Number awarded Varies each year.

Deadline Deadline not specified.

[251]
MISSOURI SENIOR CITIZEN, DISABLED VETERAN, AND DISABLED PERSON PROPERTY TAX CREDIT CLAIM

Missouri Department of Revenue
Attn: Taxation Division
301 West High Street, Room 330
P.O. Box 2800
Jefferson City, MO 65105-2800
(573) 751-3505   Toll Free: (800) 877-6881
Fax: (573) 751-2195   TDD: (800) 735-2966
E-mail: PropertyTaxCredit@dor.mo.gov
Web: dor.mo.gov/personal

Summary To provide a property tax credit to low-income disabled veterans, senior citizens, and other persons with disabilities or their spouses in Missouri.

Eligibility This program is open to residents of Missouri (or their spouses) whose net household income does not exceed certain limits ($27,500 per year if they rented or did not own and occupy their home for the entire year, $30,000 if they owned and occupied their home for the entire year) and have paid property tax or rent on their homestead during the tax year. Applicants must be 1) 65 years of age or older, 2) classified by the U.S. Department of Veterans Affairs as a 100% service-connected disabled veteran, 3) 60 years of age or older and receiving surviving spouse Society Security benefits, or 4) 100% disabled.

Financial data The tax credit depends on the claimant's income and amount paid in property taxes or rent, up to a maximum of $1,100 per year for property tax or $750 per year for rent.

Duration The tax credit is available annually.

Number awarded Varies each year.

Deadline Eligible veterans, people with disabilities, and senior citizens may claim this credit when they file their state income tax return, in April of each year.

[252]
MONTANA DISABILITY INCOME EXCLUSION

Montana Department of Revenue
Attn: Individual Income Tax
125 North Roberts, Third Floor
P.O. Box 5805
Helena, MT 59604-5805
(406) 444-6900   Toll Free: (866) 859-2254
Fax: (406) 444-6642   TDD: (406) 444-2830
Web: mt.gov/revenue

Summary To provide a state income tax exclusion to residents of Montana who receive disability payments.

Eligibility Eligible are all persons considered Montana residents for purposes of state income taxation who are receiving disability payments. They must be under 65 years of age, be retired on disability, be permanently and totally disabled, and not have chosen to treat their disability income as a pension or annuity.

Financial data Eligible residents may exclude up to $5,200 a year of disability payments.

Duration The exclusion continues as long as the recipient resides in Montana and receives disability payments.

Deadline Deadline not specified.

[253]
MONTANA DISABLED AMERICAN VETERAN PROPERTY TAX BENEFIT

Montana Department of Revenue
Attn: Property Tax
125 North Roberts, Third Floor
P.O. Box 5805
Helena, MT 59604-5805
(406) 444-6900   Toll Free: (866) 859-2254
Fax: (406) 444-1505   TDD: (406) 444-2830
Web: mt.gov/revenue

Summary To reduce the property tax rate in Montana for disabled veterans and their surviving spouses.

Eligibility This benefit is available to residents of Montana who own and occupy property in the state. Applicants must have been honorably discharged from active service in the armed forces and be currently rated 100% disabled or compensated at the 100% disabled rate because of a service-connected disability. They must have an adjusted gross income less than $53,867 if married or $46,685 if single. Also eligible are unremarried surviving spouses with an adjusted gross income less than $40,700 whose spouse was a veteran with a 100% service-connected disability or compensation at the 100% disabled rate at the time of death, died while on active duty, or died of a service-connected disability.

Financial data Qualifying veterans and surviving spouses are entitled to a reduction in local property taxes on their residence, 1 attached or detached garage, and up to 1 acre of land. The amount of the reduction depends on the status of the applicant (married, single, or surviving spouse) and adjusted gross income, but ranges from 50% to 100%.

Duration The reduction continues as long as the recipient resides in Montana and owns and occupies property used as a primary residence.

Number awarded Varies each year.

Deadline Applications must be filed with the local Department of Revenue Office by April of each year.

[254]
MUSICIANS FOUNDATION FINANCIAL ASSISTANCE

Musicians Foundation, Inc.
875 Sixth Avenue, Suite 2303
New York, NY 10001
(212) 239-9137   Fax: (212) 239-9138
E-mail: info@musiciansfoundation.org
Web: www.musiciansfoundation.org

Summary To provide emergency assistance to disabled and other professional musicians (and their family members) who need assistance for living, medical, or related expenses.

Eligibility Eligible to apply for this assistance are professional musicians who are working in the United States, regardless of their genre. Applicants must need financial assistance because of their age, illness, disability, or other misfortune. Their family members may also apply.

Financial data The amount awarded varies, depending upon the needs of the recipient. Funds are to be used to meet current living, medical, and related costs.

Duration These are generally 1-time awards.

Additional data This foundation was incorporated in 1914. The foundation does not award scholarships, loans, or composition grants.

Number awarded Varies each year.

Deadline Applications may be submitted at any time.

[255]
NATIONAL VACCINE INJURY COMPENSATION PROGRAM

Health Resources and Services Administration
Bureau of Health Professions
Attn: Division of Vaccine Injury Compensation
5600 Fishers Lane, Room 11C-26
Rockville, MD 20857
(301) 443-2703   Toll Free: (800) 338-2382
Fax: (301) 443-3354   E-mail: jceresa@hrsa.gov
Web: www.hrsa.gov/vaccinecompensation

Summary To provide compensate individuals and/or the family of those individuals who became injured or died as a result of adverse vaccine or toxoid reactions for vaccines administered after October 1, 1988.

Eligibility The vaccines and toxoids covered under the compensation law are: diphtheria and tetanus toxoids and pertussis vaccine (DTP); measles, mumps, and rubella (MMR); oral poliovirus vaccine (OPV) and inactivated poliovirus vaccine (IPV); hepatitis A vaccine; hepatitis B vaccine; haemophilus influenza type b vaccine; human papillomavirus; influenza (TIV or LAIV); varicella vaccine; rotavirus vaccine; and pneumococcal conjugate vaccines. No petition may be filed under this program if a civil action is pending for damages related to the vaccine injury or if damages were awarded by a court or in a settlement of a civil action against the vaccine manufacturer or administrator. Applicants must file a petition with the U.S. Court of Federal Claims. In the case of an injury, the effects must have continued at least 6 months after vaccine administration and the claim must be filed within 36 months after the first symptoms appeared. In the case of a death, the claim must be filed within 24 months of the death and within 48 months after the onset of the vaccine-related injury from which the death occurred. Medical documentation must be provided. The court will make a decision based on the individual's health prior to administering the vaccine, the type of vaccine and date given, and the date of onset and extent of injury occurring after receiving the vaccine.

Financial data For vaccine-related injury, the program provides reasonable compensation for past and future unreimbursable medical, custodial care, and/or rehabilitation costs; $250,000 maximum for actual and projected pain and suffering and/or emotional distress; lost earnings; and reasonable attorneys' fees and costs. For vaccine-related death, the program provides $250,000 compensation to the estate of the deceased and reasonable attorneys' fees and costs.

Duration Benefits can be awarded for the recipient's lifetime.

Additional data This program, begun in 1988, is jointly administered by the U.S. Department of Health and Human Services, Court of Federal Claims, and Department of Justice. Information on the rules of the court, including requirements for filing a petition, is available from Court of Federal Claims. The deadline has passed for filing claims for conditions that resulted from a vaccine administered prior to October 1, 1988 (the effective date of the National Childhood Vaccine Injury Act).

Number awarded Varies each year. Recently, the program awarded nearly $218 million to 250 patients.

Deadline In the case of a disability/injury, the residual effects or complications must have continued for at least 6 months after the vaccine was administered before a petition can be filed. In addition, in the case of a disability/injury, the claim must be filed within 36 months after the first symptoms appear. In the case of death, the claim must be filed within 24 months of the death and within 48 months after the appearance of the first symptoms of the disability/injury from which the death occurred.

[256]
NATIVE DAUGHTERS OF THE GOLDEN WEST CHILDREN'S FOUNDATION GRANTS

Native Daughters of the Golden West
Attn: Children's Foundation
543 Baker Street
San Francisco, CA 94117-1405
(415) 563-9091   Toll Free: (800) 994-NDGW
Fax: (415) 563-5230   E-mail: ndgwgpo@att.net
Web: www.ndgw.org/child_found.htm

Summary To provide funding for special needs of young people with disabilities in California.

Eligibility This program is open to children in California from infancy to 18 years of age who have a disability for which they need special assistance, such as braces, a wheelchair, artificial limbs, speech correction lessons, sight-saving books, hospitalization, nursing care, special medicines, operations, hearing aids, therapy, or glasses. Applications may be submitted by the child's parents, members of the Native Daughters of the Golden West, doctors, dentists, orthodontists, nurses, or any other person who has reason to know of the child's need. The application must include information about the family's financial circumstances; a statement from medical professionals giving a diagnosis, prognosis, and statement of the charges to be incurred; information about the child, including strengths, likes, achievements; a statement of how the child will benefit personally from receiving the requested grant; and (if the child is able) a personal statement from the child. Emergency grants are available for children requiring immediate treatment during periods between meetings of the selection committee.

Financial data Grants depend on the need of the recipient and the cost of the service to be provided. Funding is limited to $6,000 for van lifts, $1,000 for orthodontia, or $500 for emergency grants. All funds are paid directly to the service provider and not to the parent or guardian.

Duration Support may be provided until the recipient reaches 18 years of age.

Additional data All services must be administered within California and supplies purchased through vendors in the state.

Number awarded Varies each year.

Deadline Applications may be submitted at any time.

[257]
NEVADA DISABLED VETERAN'S TAX EXEMPTION

Nevada Office of Veterans Services
Attn: Executive Director
5460 Reno Corporate Drive
Reno, NV 89511
(775) 688-1653   Toll Free: (866) 630-8387
Fax: (775) 688-1656
Web: veterans.nv.gov/veteran_benefits.html

Summary To exempt from taxation in Nevada a portion of the property owned by disabled veterans or their surviving spouses.

Eligibility This program is open to veterans who are residents of Nevada and have incurred a service-connected disability of 60% or more. Applicants must have received an honorable separation from military service. The widow(er) of a disabled veteran, who was eligible at the time of death, may also be eligible for this benefit.

Financial data Veterans and widow(er)s are entitled to exempt from taxation a portion of their property's assessed value. The amount depends on the extent of the disability and the year filed; it ranges from $6,250 to $20,000 and doubles over a 4-year period.

Duration Disabled veterans and their widow(er)s are entitled to this exemption as long as they live in Nevada.

Additional data Disabled veterans and widow(er)s are able to split their exemption between vehicle taxes and/or property taxes. Further information is available at local county assessors' offices.

Number awarded Varies each year.

Deadline Deadline not specified.

[258]
NEW HAMPSHIRE DISABLED PROPERTY TAX EXEMPTION

New Hampshire Department of Revenue
  Administration
109 Pleasant Street
Concord, NH 03301
(603) 271-2191   Fax: (603) 271-6121
TDD: (800) 735-2964
Web: revenue.nh.gov

Summary To provide disabled residents of New Hampshire with a partial exemption from real estate taxes.

Eligibility Residents of New Hampshire are covered by this program if they are eligible for benefits to the disabled from the U.S. Social Security Administration, own and occupy their primary residence in New Hampshire, and live in a municipality that has chosen through a referendum vote to grant an exemption to the disabled. Their income and assets may not exceed specified limits; the current income limit is $13,400 for single applicants or $20,400 for married applicants, and the current asset limit is $35,000, excluding the residence. Towns may set higher limits.

Financial data The amount of the exemption (and the allowable level of income and assets) is determined by a vote of the municipality.

Duration 1 year; this exemption will be continued as long as the recipient meets the eligibility requirements.

Number awarded Varies each year; recently, 1,600 of these exemptions were granted, enabling New Hampshire residents with disabilities to save $2,967,093 in property taxes.

Deadline The original application for a permanent tax credit must be submitted by April.

[259]
NEW HAMPSHIRE INTEREST AND DIVIDEND TAX EXEMPTION FOR PEOPLE WITH DISABILITIES

New Hampshire Department of Revenue
Administration
109 Pleasant Street
Concord, NH 03301
(603) 271-2191 Fax: (603) 271-6121
TDD: (800) 735-2964
Web: revenue.nh.gov

Summary To provide disabled residents of New Hampshire with a partial exemption from taxes on interest and dividend income.

Eligibility This exemption is available to residents of New Hampshire who have a disability, are unable to work, are younger than 65 years of age, and pay taxes on income from interest and dividends.

Financial data Qualifying residents receive an exemption of $1,200 from interest and dividend income.

Duration 1 year; this exemption will be continued as long as the recipient meets the eligibility requirements.

Number awarded Varies each year.

Deadline The application for this exemption is included with the interest and dividend income tax form, due in April of each year.

[260]
NEW HAMPSHIRE PROPERTY TAX EXEMPTION FOR IMPROVEMENTS TO ASSIST PERSONS WITH DISABILITIES

New Hampshire Department of Revenue
Administration
109 Pleasant Street
Concord, NH 03301
(603) 271-2191 Fax: (603) 271-6121
TDD: (800) 735-2964
Web: revenue.nh.gov

Summary To exempt from real estate taxes any home improvements made to assist disabled residents in New Hampshire.

Eligibility This program is open to residents of New Hampshire who own residential real estate where they reside and to which they have made improvements to assist a person with a disability who also resides on such real estate.

Financial data The value of such improvements is deducted from the assessed value of the residential real estate.

Duration 1 year; this exemption will be continued as long as the recipient meets the eligibility requirements.

Number awarded Varies each year.

Deadline The original application for a permanent tax credit must be submitted by April.

[261]
NEW HAMPSHIRE SERVICE-CONNECTED TOTAL AND PERMANENT DISABILITY TAX CREDIT

New Hampshire Department of Revenue
Administration
109 Pleasant Street
Concord, NH 03301
(603) 271-2191 Fax: (603) 271-6121
TDD: (800) 735-2964
Web: revenue.nh.gov

Summary To provide property tax credits in New Hampshire to disabled veterans or their surviving spouses.

Eligibility Eligible for this tax credit are honorably discharged veterans residing in New Hampshire who 1) have a total and permanent service-connected disability, or 2) are a double amputee or paraplegic because of a service-connected disability. Unremarried surviving spouses of qualified veterans are also eligible.

Financial data Qualifying disabled veterans and surviving spouses receive an annual credit of $700 for property taxes on residential property. In addition, individual towns in New Hampshire may adopt a local option to increase the dollar amount credited to disabled veterans, to a maximum of $2,000.

Duration 1 year; once the credit has been approved, it is automatically renewed for as long as the qualifying person owns the same residence in New Hampshire.

Number awarded Varies each year.

Deadline The original application for a permanent tax credit must be submitted by April.

[262]
NEW JERSEY HOMESTEAD REBATE FOR THE ELDERLY AND DISABLED

New Jersey Division of Taxation
Attn: Technical Information Branch
50 Barrack Street
P.O. Box 281
Trenton, NJ 08695-0281
(609) 292-6400　　　　　Toll Free: (888) 238-1233
TDD: (800) 286-6613　E-mail: taxation@tax.state.nj.us
Web: www.state.nj.us

Summary　To refund a portion of property taxes paid by residents of New Jersey, especially those who are disabled elderly.

Eligibility　This rebate is available to all residents of New Jersey, but separate provisions apply to those who are permanently and totally disabled or 65 years of age or older. Applicants must own and occupy a home in New Jersey that is their principal residence and have qualifying income of $150,000 or less. Tenants who rent are no longer eligible.

Financial data　The rebate depends on income. For homeowners with income less than $100,000, the rebate is equal to 10% of the taxes paid in 2006, to a maximum of $1,000. For homeowners with income from $100,000 to $150,000, the rebate is equal to 5% of the taxes paid in 2006, to a maximum of $500.

Duration　The rebate is available as long as the person remains a New Jersey resident.

Additional data　This program was established in 2007 as a replacement for the New Jersey FAIR Rebate Program.

Number awarded　Varies each year.

Deadline　Senior and disabled homeowners must file their applications by October of each year.

[263]
NEW JERSEY INCOME TAX EXCLUSIONS FOR PERSONS WITH DISABILITIES

New Jersey Division of Taxation
Attn: Technical Information Branch
50 Barrack Street
P.O. Box 281
Trenton, NJ 08695-0281
(609) 292-6400　　　　　Toll Free: (800) 323-4400
TDD: (800) 286-6613　E-mail: taxation@tax.state.nj.us
Web: www.state.nj.us/treasury/taxation/prntgit.shtml

Summary　To exclude from income taxation in New Jersey certain benefits received by veterans and other persons with disabilities.

Eligibility　Residents of New Jersey with disabilities are entitled to this exclusion if they are receiving benefits from public agencies, including compensation from the U.S. Department of Veterans Affairs for permanent and total disability or from the state of New Jersey for temporary disability.

Financial data　Disability payments are excluded from income for state taxation purposes.

Duration　The exclusion applies as long as the individual receives qualifying disability payments.

Number awarded　Varies each year.

Deadline　Deadline not specified.

[264]
NEW JERSEY INCOME TAX EXEMPTIONS FOR THE BLIND AND DISABLED

New Jersey Division of Taxation
Attn: Technical Information Branch
50 Barrack Street
P.O. Box 281
Trenton, NJ 08695-0281
(609) 292-6400　　　　　Toll Free: (800) 323-4400
TDD: (800) 286-6613　E-mail: taxation@tax.state.nj.us
Web: www.state.nj.us/treasury/taxation/prntgit.shtml

Summary　To provide an income tax exemption in New Jersey to blind and disabled people.

Eligibility　Residents of New Jersey who are blind or disabled are entitled to this exemption.

Financial data　Each blind or disabled person is entitled to an exemption of $1,000 from income for taxation purposes.

Duration　The exemption continues as long as the qualifying condition persists and the person remains a New Jersey resident.

Number awarded　Varies each year.

Deadline　Deadline not specified.

[265]
NEW JERSEY PENSION EXCLUSION

New Jersey Division of Taxation
Attn: Technical Information Branch
50 Barrack Street
P.O. Box 281
Trenton, NJ 08695-0281
(609) 292-6400　　　　　Toll Free: (800) 323-4400
TDD: (800) 286-6613　E-mail: taxation@tax.state.nj.us
Web: www.state.nj.us/treasury/taxation/prntgit.shtml

Summary　To exclude from taxation a portion of the retirement income of elderly and disabled residents of New Jersey.

Eligibility　Residents of New Jersey who are permanently and totally disabled or 62 years of age or older may exclude all or a portion of pension and annuity income from taxable income. They must have gross income (before subtracting any pension exclusion) of $100,000 or less.

Financial data　The annual exclusion is $20,000 for a married couple filing jointly, $10,000 for a married person filing separately, or $15,000 for a single individual, head of household, or qualifying widow(er).

Duration　The exclusion continues as long as the person remains a New Jersey resident.

Number awarded　Varies each year.

Deadline　Deadline not specified.

[266]
NEW JERSEY PROPERTY TAX DEDUCTION

New Jersey Division of Taxation
Attn: Technical Information Branch
50 Barrack Street
P.O. Box 281
Trenton, NJ 08695-0281
(609) 292-6400   Toll Free: (800) 323-4400
TDD: (800) 286-6613 E-mail: taxation@tax.state.nj.us
Web: www.state.nj.us/treasury/taxation/prntgit.shtml

Summary To exclude from income taxation a portion of the property taxes paid by blind, disabled, and other residents of New Jersey.

Eligibility This deduction is available to residents of New Jersey whose income is greater than $20,000 (or $10,000 if single or married filing separately). It is also available to residents, regardless of income, who are 1) blind, 2) permanently and totally disabled, or 3) 65 years of age or older. Applicants must either own the home in which they reside or rent a dwelling with its own separate kitchen and bath facilities.

Financial data Qualified residents are entitled to deduct from their income (for state taxation purposes) 100% of their property taxes, to a maximum of $10,000. For renters, 18% of their rent is considered the equivalent of property taxes and may be deducted to a maximum of $10,000.

Duration The deduction continues as long as the person remains a New Jersey resident.

Additional data This program began in 1996. Taxpayers may not claim both the property tax deduction and the property tax credit; they may claim whichever is most beneficial, but only the deduction or the credit.

Number awarded Varies each year.

Deadline The deduction is claimed as part of the annual income tax return, due in April of each year.

[267]
NEW JERSEY PROPERTY TAX EXEMPTION FOR DISABLED VETERANS OR SURVIVING SPOUSES

New Jersey Division of Taxation
Attn: Technical Information Branch
50 Barrack Street
P.O. Box 281
Trenton, NJ 08695-0281
(609) 292-6400   Toll Free: (800) 323-4400
TDD: (800) 286-6613 E-mail: taxation@tax.state.nj.us
Web: www.state.nj.us/treasury/taxation/otherptr.shtml

Summary To provide a real estate tax exemption to New Jersey veterans with disabilities and certain surviving widow(er)s.

Eligibility This exemption is available to New Jersey residents who have been honorably discharged with active wartime service in the U.S. armed forces and have been certified by the U.S. Department of Veterans Affairs as totally and permanently disabled as a result of wartime service-connected conditions. Unremarried surviving spouses and civil union partners of eligible disabled veterans or of certain wartime servicepersons who died on active duty are also entitled to this exemption. Applicants must be the full owner of and a permanent resident in the dwelling house for which the exemption is claimed.

Financial data A 100% exemption from locally-levied real estate taxes is provided.

Duration 1 year; the exemption continues as long as the eligible veteran remains a resident of New Jersey.

Additional data This program is administered by the local tax assessor or collector. Veterans who are denied exemptions have the right to appeal the decision to their county and state governments.

Number awarded Varies each year.

Deadline Applications may be submitted at any time.

[268]
NEW JERSEY PROPERTY TAX REIMBURSEMENT

New Jersey Division of Taxation
Attn: Technical Information Branch
50 Barrack Street
P.O. Box 281
Trenton, NJ 08695-0281
(609) 292-6400   Toll Free: (800) 882-6597
TDD: (800) 286-6613 E-mail: taxation@tax.state.nj.us
Web: www.state.nj.us/treasury/taxation/propfrez.shtml

Summary To reimburse residents of New Jersey who are disabled or elderly for the increase in property taxes due on their home.

Eligibility This reimbursement is available to residents of New Jersey who are either 1) 65 years of age or older, or 2) receiving federal Social Security disability benefits. Applicants must have lived in New Jersey continuously for at least 10 years and have owned and lived in their home (or have leased a site in a mobile home park on which they have placed a manufactured or mobile home that they own) for at least 3 years. Their annual income must be $70,000 or less. They must have paid the full amount of property taxes due on their home for the past 2 years.

Financial data Qualifying homeowners are entitled to reimbursement of all property taxes they have paid in excess of the base year (the first year in which they met all the eligibility requirements).

Duration The reimbursement is available as long as the person remains a New Jersey resident and meets eligibility requirements.

Number awarded Varies each year.

Deadline May of each year.

[269]
NEW MEXICO DISABLED VETERAN PROPERTY TAX EXEMPTION

New Mexico Department of Veterans' Services
Attn: Benefits Division
407 Galisteo Street, Room 142
P.O. Box 2324
Santa Fe, NM 87504-2324
(505) 827-6374   Toll Free: (866) 433-VETS
Fax: (505) 827-6372
E-mail: alan.martinez@state.nm.us
Web: www.dvs.state.nm.us/benefits.html

Summary   To exempt disabled veterans and their spouses from payment of property taxes in New Mexico.
Eligibility   This exemption is available to veterans who are rated 100% service-connected disabled by the U.S. Department of Veterans Affairs, are residents of New Mexico, and own a primary residence in the state. Also eligible are qualifying veterans' unremarried surviving spouses, if they are New Mexico residents and continue to own the residence.
Financial data   Veterans and surviving spouses are exempt from payment of property taxes in New Mexico.
Duration   1 year; continues until the qualifying veteran or spouse no longer live in the residence.
Number awarded   Varies each year.
Deadline   Deadline not specified.

[270]
NEW YORK ALTERNATIVE PROPERTY TAX EXEMPTIONS FOR VETERANS

New York State Department of Taxation and Finance
Attn: Office of Real Property Tax Services
W.A. Harriman Campus
Building 8, Sixth Floor
Albany, NY 12227
(518) 486-4403   Fax: (518) 486-7754
Web: www.orps.state.ny.us

Summary   To provide disabled and other wartime veterans and their spouses who are residents of New York with a partial exemption from property taxes.
Eligibility   This program is open to veterans who served during specified periods of war time. Applicants must have been discharged under honorable conditions; additional benefits are available to those who served in a combat zone and to those who have a service-connected disability. The legal title to the property must be in the name of the veteran or the spouse of the veteran or both, or the unremarried surviving spouse of a deceased veteran. The property must be used exclusively for residential purposes. This program is only available in counties, cities, towns, and villages in New York that have opted to participate.
Financial data   This program provides an exemption of 15% of the assessed valuation of the property, to a basic maximum of $12,000 per year; local governments may opt for reduced maximums of $9,000 or $6,000, or for increased maximums of $15,000 to $36,000. For combat-zone veterans, an additional 10% of the assessed valua-

tion is exempt, to a basic maximum of $8,000 per year; local governments may opt for a reduced maximum of $6,000 or $4,000, or for increased maximums of $10,000 to $24,000. For disabled veterans, the exemption is the percentage of assessed value equal to half of the service-connected disability rating, to a basic maximum of $40,000 per year; local governments may opt for a reduced maximum of $30,000 or $20,000, or for increased maximums of $50,000 to $120,000. At its option, New York City and other high appreciation municipalities may use the following increased maximum exemptions: war veteran, $54,000; combat-zone veteran, $36,000; disabled veteran, $180,000.
Duration   This exemption is available annually.
Number awarded   Varies each year.
Deadline   Applications must be filed with the local assessor by "taxable status date;" in most towns, that is the end of February.

[271]
NEW YORK COLD WAR VETERANS PROPERTY TAX EXEMPTIONS

New York State Department of Taxation and Finance
Attn: Office of Real Property Tax Services
W.A. Harriman Campus
Building 8, Sixth Floor
Albany, NY 12227
(518) 486-4403   Fax: (518) 486-7754
Web: www.orps.state.ny.us

Summary   To provide disabled and other New York veterans who served during the Cold War and their spouses with a partial exemption from property taxes.
Eligibility   This program is open to veterans who served during the Cold War, defined as September 2, 1945 to December 26, 1991. Applicants must have been discharged under honorable conditions; additional benefits are available to those who have a service-connected disability. The legal title to the property must be in the name of the veteran or the spouse of the veteran or both, or the unremarried surviving spouse of a deceased veteran. The property must be used exclusively for residential purposes. This program is only available in counties, cities, towns, and villages in New York that have opted to participate.
Financial data   Local governments may opt to grant exemptions of 15% or 10%. For the 15% option, the basic maximum exemption is $12,000 per year; local governments may opt for reduced maximums of $9,000 or $6,000, or for increased maximums of $15,000 to $36,000. For the 10% option, the basic maximum exemption is $8,000 per year; local governments may opt for a reduced maximum of $6,000 or $4,000, or for increased maximums of $10,000 to $24,000. For disabled veterans, the exemption is the percentage of assessed value equal to half of the service-connected disability rating, to a basic maximum of $40,000 per year; local governments may opt for a reduced maximum of $30,000 or $20,000, or for increased maximums of $50,000 to $120,000. At its option, New York City and other high appreciation municipalities may use the following increased maximum exemp-

tions: 15% option, $54,000; 10% option, $36,000; disabled veteran, $180,000.

Duration This exemption is available annually.

Number awarded Varies each year.

Deadline Applications must be filed with the local assessor by "taxable status date;" in most towns, that is the end of February.

[272]
NEW YORK STATE DISABILITY INCOME EXCLUSION

New York State Department of Taxation and Finance
W.A. Harriman Campus
Tax and Finance Building
Albany, NY 12227-0001
(518) 438-8581 Toll Free: (800) 225-5829 (within NY)
Web: www.tax.ny.gov

Summary To exclude disability pay from state income taxation in New York.

Eligibility Eligible are persons who are considered residents of New York for state income taxation purposes and who are receiving any form of disability retirement pay. Applicants must be permanently and totally disabled and not yet 65 years of age.

Financial data Eligible residents may exclude either their actual weekly disability pay or $100 per week ($5,200 per year), whichever is less. The amount of the exclusion is reduced by the amount that the applicant's federal adjusted gross income exceeds $15,000, so no exclusion is available if that exceeds $20,200 and 1 person could take the exclusion or $25,400 if both spouses could take the exclusions.

Duration The exclusion is provided as long as the recipient remains a resident of New York.

Number awarded Varies each year.

Deadline Deadline not specified.

[273]
NORTH CAROLINA PROPERTY TAX RELIEF FOR DISABLED VETERANS

North Carolina Department of Revenue
Attn: Property Tax Division
501 North Wilmington Street
P.O. Box 871
Raleigh, NC 27602
(919) 733-7711   Fax: (919) 733-1821
Web: www.dornc.com/taxes/property/index.html

Summary To provide property tax relief to disabled North Carolina veterans.

Eligibility Disabled veterans who are residents of North Carolina are eligible for these programs. They must own 1) a vehicle that is altered with special equipment to accommodate a service-connected disability; or 2) specially adapted housing purchased with the assistance of the U.S. Department of Veterans Affairs.

Financial data Qualifying vehicles are exempt from personal property taxes. Qualifying housing is eligible for an exemption on the first $45,000 in assessed value of the

housing and land that is owned and used as a residence by the disabled veteran.

Duration The exemptions continue as long as the eligible veteran is a resident of North Carolina.

Number awarded Varies each year.

Deadline Deadline not specified.

[274]
NORTH CAROLINA PROPERTY TAX RELIEF FOR ELDERLY AND PERMANENTLY DISABLED PERSONS

North Carolina Department of Revenue
Attn: Property Tax Division
501 North Wilmington Street
P.O. Box 871
Raleigh, NC 27602
(919) 733-7711   Fax: (919) 733-1821
Web: www.dornc.com/taxes/property/index.html

Summary To provide property tax relief to elderly and disabled North Carolina residents.

Eligibility This program is open to residents of North Carolina who 1) are permanently and totally disabled or at least 65 years of age, and 2) have an income of less than $27,100. Applicants must own and occupy real property as their permanent residence.

Financial data Qualified owners are exempt from taxation on 50% of the appraised value of their property or $25,000, whichever is greater.

Duration The exemptions continue as long as the eligible property owner is a resident of North Carolina.

Number awarded Varies each year.

Deadline Applications must be submitted by May of each year.

[275]
NORTH DAKOTA HOMESTEAD CREDIT FOR SENIOR CITIZENS OR DISABLED PERSONS

Office of State Tax Commissioner
State Capitol Building
600 East Boulevard Avenue, Department 127
Bismarck, ND 58505-0599
(701) 328-7088   Toll Free: (877) 328-7088
Fax: (701) 328-3700   TDD: (800) 366-6888
E-mail: taxinfo@state.nd.us
Web: www.nd.gov/tax/property

Summary To provide property tax credits for disabled or senior citizen residents of North Dakota.

Eligibility To qualify for this program, applicants must be residents of North Dakota and either totally and permanently disabled (regardless of age) or at least 65 years of age. For spouses who are living together, only 1 can apply for the credit. Applicants must reside in the property for which the credit is claimed. Their income cannot exceed $26,000 and their aggregate assets cannot exceed $75,000 (excluding the first unencumbered $100,000 of market value of their homestead).

Financial data The credit depends on the income of the taxpayer, ranging from 20% (or a maximum of $900) for people with incomes from $24,001 to $26,000, to 100%

(or a maximum of $4,500) for people with incomes up to $18,000.

Duration Once approved, the deduction continues as long as the recipient meets the qualification requirements.

Additional data No person whose homestead is a farm structure exempt from taxation can qualify to receive this property tax credit.

Number awarded Varies each year.

Deadline Applications must be submitted in January of the year for which the property tax credit is requested.

[276]
NORTH DAKOTA PROPERTY TAX CREDIT FOR DISABLED VETERANS

Office of State Tax Commissioner
State Capitol Building
600 East Boulevard Avenue, Department 127
Bismarck, ND 58505-0599
(701) 328-7088   Toll Free: (877) 328-7088
Fax: (701) 328-3700   TDD: (800) 366-6888
E-mail: taxinfo@state.nd.us
Web: www.nd.gov/tax/property

Summary To provide property tax credits to disabled North Dakota veterans and their surviving spouses.

Eligibility This property tax credit is available to honorably-discharged veterans who have more than a 50% service-connected disability as certified by the U.S. Department of Veterans Affairs. Applicants must own and occupy a homestead according to state law. Unremarried surviving spouses are also eligible. If a disabled veteran co-owns the property with someone other than a spouse, the credit is limited to the disabled veteran's interest in the fixtures, buildings, and improvements of the homestead.

Financial data The credit is applied against the first $120,000 of true and full valuation of the fixtures, buildings, and improvements of the homestead, to a maximum amount calculated by multiplying $120,000 by the percentage of the disabled veteran's disability compensation rating for service-connected disabilities.

Duration 1 year; renewable as long as qualified individuals continue to reside in North Dakota and live in their homes.

Number awarded Varies each year.

Deadline Applications may be submitted to the county auditor at any time.

[277]
NORTH DAKOTA PROPERTY TAX EXEMPTION FOR VETERANS WHO LIVE IN SPECIALLY ADAPTED HOUSING

Office of State Tax Commissioner
State Capitol Building
600 East Boulevard Avenue, Department 127
Bismarck, ND 58505-0599
(701) 328-7088   Toll Free: (877) 328-7088
Fax: (701) 328-3700   TDD: (800) 366-6888
E-mail: taxinfo@state.nd.us
Web: www.nd.gov/tax/property

Summary To provide property tax exemptions to North Dakota veterans and their surviving spouses who have been awarded specially adapted housing.

Eligibility This exemption is available to paraplegic disabled veterans of the U.S. armed forces or any veteran who has been awarded specially adapted housing by the U.S. Department of Veterans Affairs. The paraplegic disability does not have to be service connected. The unremarried surviving spouses of such deceased veterans are also eligible. Income and assets are not considered in determining eligibility for the exemption.

Financial data The maximum benefit may not exceed $5,400 taxable value, because the exemption is limited to the first $120,000 of true and full value of fixtures, buildings, and improvements.

Duration 1 year; renewable as long as qualified individuals reside in North Dakota and live in their homes.

Number awarded Varies each year.

Deadline Applications may be submitted to the county auditor at any time.

[278]
NURSES HOUSE FINANCIAL ASSISTANCE

Nurses House, Inc.
c/o Veronica M. Driscoll Center for Nursing
2113 Western Avenue, Suite 2
Guilderland, NY 12084-9559
(518) 456-7858   Fax: (518) 452-3760
E-mail: mail@NursesHouse.org
Web: www.NursesHouse.org

Summary To provide temporary financial assistance to nurses who are unable to meet current living expenses because of disability or other causes.

Eligibility Assistance is provided to registered nurses who need temporary financial assistance because of disability, illness, or injury. Applicants must need funding for such needs as rent or mortgage payments, food, utilities, telephone, or health insurance. Requests for assistance can be made by the nurse, a colleague, a friend, or other source.

Financial data The amount of assistance offered depends on need of the recipient.

Duration These are intended as short-term grants to tide the nurse over a temporary crisis or need.

Additional data Nurses House was established in 1922 when Emily Bourne donated $300,000 to purchase a 10-acre estate on Long Island to serve as a rest home for nurses. In 1959, the property was sold and proceeds were invested to provide income for the services of Nurses House. The name has been retained and nurses receiving assistance are still called guests.

Number awarded Varies each year; recently, more than $100,000 in grants were awarded.

Deadline Applications may be submitted at any time.

[279]
OHIO HOMESTEAD EXEMPTION FOR SENIOR CITIZENS, DISABLED PERSONS AND SURVIVING SPOUSES

Ohio Department of Taxation
Attn: Tax Equalization Division
P.O. Box 530
Columbus, OH 43216-0530
(614) 466-5744 Toll Free: (800) 282-1780 (within OH)
Fax: (614) 752-9822
Web: tax.ohio.gov

Summary To exempt a portion of the value of homesteads owned by senior citizens and disabled persons (and their surviving spouses) from property taxation in Ohio.

Eligibility This exemption is available to residents of Ohio who are 65 years of age or older or who have a total and permanent disability. Applicants must own and occupy their home as their principal place of residence. Surviving spouses of persons who were receiving the exemption at the time of their death are also eligible if they were at least 59 years of age on the date of the decedent's death. There is no income limitation.

Financial data Qualifying homeowners may exempt up to $25,000 from the assessed value of their home for purposes of property taxation.

Duration The exemption is available as long as the recipient resides in Ohio and owns his or her home.

Number awarded Varies each year.

Deadline Applications must be submitted to the county auditor by May of each year.

[280]
OHIO INCOME TAX DEDUCTION FOR DISABILITY BENEFITS

Ohio Department of Taxation
Attn: Individual Income Tax
30 East Broad Street
P.O. Box 530
Columbus, OH 43216-0530
(614) 433-5817 Toll Free: (800) 282-1780 (within OH)
Fax: (614) 433-7771
Web: tax.ohio.gov

Summary To deduct disability benefits from state income taxation in Ohio.

Eligibility This deduction is available to residents of Ohio who are receiving benefits from an employee's disability plan paid as the result of a permanent physical or mental disability. Payments that otherwise qualify as retirement or pension benefits, temporary wage continuation plans, and payments for temporary illnesses or injuries do not qualify.

Financial data All payments for permanent disability are excluded from income for purposes of Ohio state taxation.

Duration The exclusion is available as long as the recipient resides in Ohio and receives eligible disability payments.

Number awarded Varies each year.

Deadline Deadline not specified.

[281]
OHIO VETERANS BONUS

Ohio Department of Veterans Services
Attn: Veterans Bonus Program
P.O. Box 373
Sandusky, OH 44871
Toll Free: (877) OHIO-VET
Web: veteransbonus.ohio.gov/odvs_web

Summary To provide a bonus to disabled and other Ohio veterans and active-duty service members who served during the Persian Gulf War, Afghanistan, or Iraq and their family members.

Eligibility This bonus is available to current residents of Ohio who were also residents of the state when they began active-duty military service, including as a member of a Reserve component or the Ohio National Guard. Applicants must have served at least 90 days or be currently serving in the U.S. armed forces during the periods of the Persian Gulf War (August 2, 1990 through March 3, 1991), the war in Afghanistan (October 7, 2001 through the present), or the war in Iraq (March 19, 2003 through the present). If no longer serving, they must have received an honorable discharge. Additional bonuses are available to of 1) veterans who were medically discharged or retired because of combat-related disabilities sustained in the Persian Gulf, Afghanistan, or Iraq; and 2) veterans who were declared Missing in Action (MIA) or Prisoner of War (POW) or (if the veteran is deceased) their family members. Also eligible are family members (in order of preference: spouses, children, parents) 1) veterans who have died but whose death was not a result of injuries or illness sustained in the Persian Gulf, Afghanistan, or Iraq; or 2) veterans who died as a result of injuries or illness sustained in the Persian Gulf, Afghanistan, or Iraq.

Financial data The bonus for veterans and military personnel who served in the Persian Gulf, Afghanistan, or Iraq is $100 per month of service, to a maximum of $1,000; the bonus for veterans and military personnel who served during the specified time periods but elsewhere in the world is $50 per month of service, to a maximum of $500; veterans who were medically discharged or retired because of combat-related disabilities are eligible for an in-theater bonus of $1,000 (regardless of time served in-theater) plus $50 per month for non-theater service time, to a maximum benefit of $1,500; veterans who were declared MIA or POW or family members are eligible for a bonus of $5,000; families of deceased veterans whose death was not a result of injuries or illness are eligible for the same bonus that the veteran would have received if still living, to a maximum of $1,500; families of veterans who died as a result of injuries or illness are eligible for a bonus of $5,000.

Duration These are 1-time bonuses.

Number awarded Varies each year.

Deadline Applications may be submitted at any time. For veterans and current military members who served during the wars in Afghanistan or Iraq, applications must be submitted within 3 years after the President has officially proclaimed the end of those hostilities.

[282]
OHIO VETERANS' FINANCIAL ASSISTANCE

Ohio Department of Veterans Services
77 South High Street, Seventh Floor
Columbus, OH 43215
(614) 644-0898   Toll Free: (888) DVS-OHIO
Fax: (614) 728-9498   E-mail: ohiovet@dvs.ohio.gov
Web: dvs.ohio.gov

Summary   To provide emergency aid to Ohio veterans, military personnel, and their dependents who, because of disability or disaster, are in financial need.

Eligibility   This assistance is available to veterans and active-duty members of the U.S. armed forces, as well as their spouses, surviving spouses, dependent parents, minor children, and wards. Applicants must have been residents of the Ohio county in which they are applying for at least 3 months. They must be able to demonstrate need for relief because of sickness, accident, or destitution.

Financial data   The amount granted varies, depending on the needs of the recipient.

Duration   These are emergency funds only and are not designed to be a recurring source of income.

Additional data   These grants are made by the various county veterans services offices in Ohio.

Number awarded   Varies each year.

Deadline   Applications may be submitted at any time.

[283]
OKLAHOMA DISABILITY DEDUCTION

Oklahoma Tax Commission
Attn: Income Tax
2501 North Lincoln Boulevard
Oklahoma City, OK 73194-0009
(405) 521-3160   Toll Free: (800) 522-8165 (within OK)
Fax: (405) 522-0063   E-mail: otcmaster@tax.ok.gov
Web: www.tax.ok.gov/incometax.html

Summary   To provide an income tax deduction to Oklahoma residents with disabilities who incur expenses for modifying facilities.

Eligibility   This deduction is available to Oklahoma residents who have a physical disability that constitutes a substantial handicap to employment. Applicants must have incurred expenses to modify a motor vehicle, home, or workplace necessary to compensate for the disability.

Financial data   All expenses allowed by the Social Security Administration may be deducted from income for purposes of Oklahoma taxation.

Duration   The deduction may be taken in any year when qualifying expenses are incurred.

Deadline   Income tax returns must be filed by April of each year.

[284]
OKLAHOMA FINANCIAL ASSISTANCE PROGRAM

Oklahoma Department of Veterans Affairs
Veterans Memorial Building
2311 North Central Avenue
P.O. Box 53067
Oklahoma City, OK 73152
(405) 521-3684   Fax: (405) 521-6533
E-mail: mspear@odva.state.ok.us
Web: www.ok.gov

Summary   To provide emergency aid to Oklahoma veterans and their families who, because of disability or disaster, are in financial need.

Eligibility   This program is open to veterans with at least 90 days of wartime service (unless discharged earlier because of a service-connected disability) and an honorable discharge who are current residents of Oklahoma and have resided in the state for at least 1 year immediately preceding the date of application. Applicants must be seeking assistance because of an interruption or loss of job and income resulting from illness, injury, or disaster (such as loss of home due to fire, floor, or storm). Widow(er)s and minor children may also qualify for the benefit.

Financial data   The amount of the grant depends on the need of the recipient.

Duration   The grant is available only on a 1-time basis.

Additional data   No financial assistance will be granted when regular monetary benefits are being received from other state agencies. The funds cannot be used for old debts, car payments, or medical expenses.

Number awarded   Varies each year.

Deadline   Applications must be submitted to the local post or chapter of a veterans services organization for initial approval or disapproval. They may be submitted at any time during the year.

[285]
OKLAHOMA PROPERTY TAX EXEMPTION FOR DISABLED VETERANS

Oklahoma Tax Commission
Attn: Ad Valorem Division
2501 North Lincoln Boulevard
P.O. Box 269060
Oklahoma City, OK 73126-9060
(405) 319-8200   Toll Free: (800) 522-8165 (within OK)
Fax: (405) 522-0166   E-mail: otcmaster@tax.ok.gov
Web: www.tax.ok.gov/adval.html

Summary   To exempt the property of disabled veterans and their surviving spouses from taxation in Oklahoma.

Eligibility   This program is available to Oklahoma residents who are veterans honorably discharged from a branch of the armed forces or the Oklahoma National Guard. Applicants must have a 100% permanent disability sustained through military action or accident or resulting from a disease contracted while in active service; the disability must be certified by the U.S. Department of Veterans Affairs. They must own property that qualifies for the

Oklahoma homestead exemption. Surviving spouses of qualified veterans are also eligible.

Financial data Qualified veterans and surviving spouses are eligible for exemption of the taxes on the full fair cash value of their homestead.

Duration The exemption is available as long as the veteran or surviving spouse resides in Oklahoma and owns a qualifying homestead.

Additional data This exemption was first available in 2006.

Deadline Deadline not specified.

[286]
OPERATION FAMILY FUND FINANCIAL ASSISTANCE

Operation Family Fund
P.O. Box 837
Ridgecrest, CA 93556
(760) 793-0053   Fax: (888) 851-1456
E-mail: support@operatonfamilyfund.org
Web: operationfamilyfund.org

Summary To provide personal assistance to military and civilian personnel and the families of those personnel who died or were severely disabled as a result of service as a result of the Global War on Terror.

Eligibility This assistance is available to military and civilian personnel and their families who died or were severely disabled as a result of Operations Enduring or Iraqi Freedom, either domestically or abroad. Civilians must have been serving officially as an employee of the U.S. government or contractor to the U.S. government. Applicants must be seeking funding for such short- and long-term living needs as food; rent or utilities; emergency transportation; vehicle repair; funeral expenses; medical and dental expenses; assistance with a home, rental, lease, or purchase; home improvements; or assistance with the purchase, rent, or lease of a vehicle. Grants are approved to applicants in the following priority order: 1) member injured because of a hostile action and have a Department of Veterans Affairs (VA) disability rating of 50% or higher; 2) member injured because of an accident while serving in Iraq or Afghanistan and have a VA disability rating of 50% or higher; 3) member who has post-traumatic stress disorder with a VA disability rating of 50% or higher as a result of serving in Iraq or Afghanistan; 4) member who has other service-connected injuries caused in support of the Global War on Terror and a VA disability rating of 50% or higher; 5) member in any of the prior categories but still in the medical board process with a pending VA disability rating; 6) child (under 22 years of age) and/or spouse of a military member killed in action who did not receive government death benefit or SGLA; and 7) second requests.

Financial data Most grants are at least $1,000 but less than $10,000.

Duration These are 1-time grants; renewals may be approved if funding is available.

Number awarded Varies each year; since this organization began, it has awarded more than 385 grants.

Deadline Applications may be submitted at any time.

[287]
OPERATION HOMEFRONT GRANTS

Operation Homefront
8930 Fourwinds Drive, Suite 340
San Antonio, TX 78239
(210) 659-7756   Toll Free: (800) 722-6098
Fax: (210) 566-7544
Web: www.operationhomefront.net

Summary To provide assistance to military families and wounded personnel who face financial difficulties related to service.

Eligibility This program is open to 1) veterans who are disabled as a result of service-connected injuries and their families; and 2) other military families who face financial needs because of the hardships associated with military service. Examples of financial needs include food assistance, auto repair, moving assistance, transitional family housing, vision care, child and dependent care, critical baby needs, travel and transportation, home repair, and essential home items.

Financial data The amounts of the grants vary, depending on the need of the applicant. Recently, average grants were $100 to families for critical baby items, $161 for food assistance, $300 to assist in paying utilities, or $1,117 to help with rent or mortgage payments.

Duration This are 1-time grants.

Additional data This program began in 2002.

Number awarded Varies each year; since the foundation was established, it has awarded $128 million to support more than 400,000 families and personnel.

Deadline Applications may be submitted at any time.

[288]
OPERATION REBOUND GRANTS

Challenged Athletes Foundation
Attn: Program Manager
9591 Waples Street
San Diego, CA 92121
(858) 866-0959   Fax: (858) 866-0958
E-mail: caf@challengedathletes.org
Web: www.challengedathletes.org

Summary To provide funding to veterans and September 11 first responders who became disabled as a result of service and wish to participate in athletic activities.

Eligibility This program is open to 1) veterans and service members who suffered a permanent physical disability (such as loss of a limb(s), sight, or spinal cord injury, in the Global War on Terror; and 2) law enforcement personnel, fire fighters, and others who were the first to respond to the September 11, 2001 attacks and became disabled as a result. Applicants must need funding for 1 of 3 categories: 1) equipment, for wheelchairs, prosthetics, or other assistive devices; 2) training, for club or gym dues or membership fees, team or association dues or membership fees, or coaching or training expense; or 3) competition, for travel, entry fees, or other costs to participate in a recognized event. They may apply for only 1 category per year. Along with their application, they must submit a brief autobiography with their personal and athletic goals, a brief summary of their military or law enforcement history, a statement on how they are planning to raise awareness for "Operation Rebound" and the Challenged Athletes Foundation, and documentation of financial need.

Financial data Grant amounts depend on the documented need of the applicant.

Duration These are 1-time grants. Recipients may reapply.

Additional data This program was established for veterans in 2004 and expanded to include first responders in 2008.

Number awarded Varies each year.

Deadline Applications may be submitted at any time, but they must be received at least 90 days prior to the date needed.

[289]
OPERATION SECOND CHANCE FAMILY ASSISTANCE GRANTS

Operation Second Chance
Attn: President
22708 Birchcrest Lane
P.O. Box 461
Clarksburg, MD 20871
Toll Free: (888) OSC-4VET
E-mail: assistance@operationsecondchance.org
Web: www.operationsecondchance.org

Summary To provide assistance for payment of ordinary living expenses to disabled veterans and military personnel and their families.

Eligibility This assistance is available to disabled veterans and military personnel who are within 18 months of their injury or are currently receiving care at a military health care facility and have an expected or adjudicated disability rating of 70% or higher. Their family members are also eligible. Applicants must be seeking funding for payment of rent or mortgages, utility bills, child care during illness or injury, or housing and/or airfare for a family member to assist an injured or recovering member.

Financial data The amount of the grant depends on the need of the recipient.

Duration These are 1-time grants.

Number awarded Varies each year.

Deadline Applications may be submitted at any time.

[290]
OREGON INCOME TAX CREDIT FOR THE ELDERLY OR DISABLED

Oregon Department of Revenue
Revenue Building
955 Center Street, N.E.
Salem, OR 97310-2555
(503) 378-4988 Toll Free: (800) 356-4222 (within OR)
Fax: (503) 945-8738
TDD: (800) 886-7204 (within OR)
Web: www.oregon.gov/DOR/PERTAX/index.shtml

Summary To provide an income tax credit to Oregon residents who are elderly or disabled.

Eligibility This credit is available to taxpayers in Oregon who qualify for the federal elderly or disabled income tax credit. Taxpayers may claim this credit or the retirement income credit, but not both in the same year.

Financial data The credit is equal to 40% of the federal credit.

Duration The credit continues as long as the recipient resides in Oregon.

Additional data People who claim this credit may not also claim the retirement income credit.

Deadline Credits are filed with state income tax returns in April of each year.

[291]
OREGON PROPERTY TAX DEFERRAL FOR DISABLED AND SENIOR CITIZENS

Oregon Department of Revenue
Attn: Property Tax Division
Revenue Building
955 Center Street, N.E.
Salem, OR 97310-2555
(503) 378-4988 Toll Free: (800) 356-4222 (within OR)
Fax: (503) 945-8738
TDD: (800) 886-7204 (within OR)
Web: www.oregon.gov/DOR/PTD/property.shtml

Summary To enable blind, disabled, and elderly Oregon residents to defer payment of their property taxes.

Eligibility This program is open to residents of Oregon who are determined to be eligible to receive or are receiving federal Social Security benefits due to disability or blindness. Applicants must own a residence, have net worth less than $500,000, and have a total household income less than $39,500.

Financial data The state pays all taxes on the property to the county but places a lien on the property and charges 6% compound interest per year on the deferred taxes. The lien and interest become due and payable when the disabled person or senior citizen sells the property or changes its ownership, moves permanently from the property (unless for medical reasons), or dies.

Duration 1 year; the deferment is automatically renewed as long as the property owner lives in the residence.

Number awarded   Varies each year; recently, 712 blind and disabled residents of Oregon were participating in this program.

Deadline   Applications for new deferrals must be filed in the appropriate county assessor's office by April of each year.

[292]
OREGON PROPERTY TAX EXEMPTION FOR VETERANS WITH DISABILITIES AND THEIR SPOUSES

Oregon Department of Revenue
Attn: Property Tax Division
Revenue Building
955 Center Street, N.E.
Salem, OR 97310-2555
(503) 378-4988   Toll Free: (800) 356-4222 (within OR)
Fax: (503) 945-8738
TDD: (800) 886-7204 (within OR)
Web: www.oregon.gov/DOR/PTD/exemptions.shtml

Summary   To exempt disabled Oregon veterans and their spouses from a portion of their property taxes.

Eligibility   Qualifying veterans are those who received a discharge or release under honorable conditions after service of either 1) 90 consecutive days during World War I, World War II, or the Korean Conflict; or 2) 210 consecutive days after January 31, 1955. Eligible individuals must meet 1 of these conditions: 1) a war veteran who is officially certified by the U.S. Department of Veterans Affairs (VA) or any branch of the U.S. armed forces as having disabilities of 40% or more; 2) a war veteran who is certified each year by a licensed physician as being 40% or more disabled and has total gross income that is less than 185% of the federal poverty level; or 3) a war veteran's surviving spouse who has not remarried, even if the veteran's spouse was not disabled or did not take advantage of the exemption if disabled. Recipients of this exemption must own and live on a property in Oregon.

Financial data   The exemption is $17,911 of the homestead property's real market value.

Duration   1 year; may be renewed as long as the eligible veteran or surviving unremarried spouse owns and occupies the primary residence.

Number awarded   Varies each year.

Deadline   This exemption is not automatic. Applications must be submitted by March of each year.

[293]
OREGON PROPERTY TAX EXEMPTION FOR VETERANS WITH SERVICE-CONNECTED DISABILITIES AND THEIR SPOUSES

Oregon Department of Revenue
Attn: Property Tax Division
Revenue Building
955 Center Street, N.E.
Salem, OR 97310-2555
(503) 378-4988   Toll Free: (800) 356-4222 (within OR)
Fax: (503) 945-8738
TDD: (800) 886-7204 (within OR)
Web: www.oregon.gov/DOR/PTD/exemptions.shtml

Summary   To exempt Oregon veterans with service-connected disabilities and their spouses from a portion of their property taxes.

Eligibility   Qualifying veterans are those who received a discharge or release under honorable conditions after service of either 1) 90 consecutive days during World War I, World War II, or the Korean Conflict; or 2) 210 consecutive days after January 31, 1955. Eligible individuals must meet 1 of these conditions: 1) a war veteran who is certified by the U.S. Department of Veterans Affairs (VA) or any branch of the U.S. armed forces as having service-connected disabilities of 40% or more; or 2) a surviving spouse of a war veteran who died because of service-connected injury or illness or who received at least 1 year of this exemption. Recipients of this exemption must own and live on a property in Oregon.

Financial data   The exemption is $21,493 of the homestead property's real market value.

Duration   1 year; may be renewed as long as the eligible veterans or surviving spouse owns and occupies the primary residence.

Number awarded   Varies each year.

Deadline   This exemption is not automatic. Applications must be submitted by March of each year.

[294]
PENNSYLVANIA DISABLED VETERANS REAL ESTATE TAX EXEMPTION

Office of the Deputy Adjutant General for Veterans
   Affairs
Building S-0-47, FTIG
Annville, PA 17003-5002
(717) 865-8907
Toll Free: (800) 54 PA VET (within PA)
Fax: (717) 861-8589   E-mail: RA-VA-Info@pa.gov
Web: www.dmva.state.pa.us

Summary   To exempt blind and disabled Pennsylvania veterans and their unremarried surviving spouses from all state real estate taxes.

Eligibility   Eligible to apply for this exemption are honorably-discharged veterans who are residents of Pennsylvania and who are blind, paraplegic, or 100% disabled from a service-connected disability sustained during wartime military service. The dwelling must be owned by the veteran solely or jointly with a spouse, and financial need for the exemption must be determined by the State Veterans'

Commission. Veterans whose income is less than $81,340 per year are presumed to have financial need; veterans with income greater than $81,340 must document need. Upon the death of the veteran, the tax exemption passes on to the veteran's unremarried surviving spouse.

Financial data　This program exempts the principal residence (and the land on which it stands) from all real estate taxes.

Duration　The exemption continues as long as the eligible veteran or unremarried widow resides in Pennsylvania.

Number awarded　Varies each year.

Deadline　Deadline not specified.

[295]
RAILROAD RETIREMENT DISABILITY ANNUITY

Railroad Retirement Board
Attn: Office of Public Affairs
844 North Rush Street
Chicago, IL 60611-2092
(312) 751-4777　　　　Toll Free: (877) 772-5772
Fax: (312) 751-7154　　　TDD: (312) 751-4701
Web: www.rrb.gov

Summary　To provide an annuity to railroad workers with disabilities and their families.

Eligibility　The Railroad Retirement Board provides annuities for 2 types of disability. Eligible for total disability are regular employees of companies covered by the Railroad Retirement Act (railroads engaged in interstate commerce and certain of their subsidiaries, railroad associations, and national railway labor organizations) who are totally disabled for all regular work and have at least 10 years of creditable railroad service; credit for a month of railroad service is given for every month in which an employee had some compensated service for at least 1 day, but the 120 service months need not be consecutive. The other type of disability, occupational disability, is available to employees who have at least 20 years of service, or who are 60 years of age or older and have at least 10 years of service, and are permanently disabled from their regular railroad occupation. Survivor benefits are available to widows, widowers, unmarried children, and, in certain cases, parents, remarried widow(er)s, grandchildren, and surviving divorced spouses. For widow(er)s of workers with disabilities, annuities are payable at the age of 60; widow(er)s who are permanently and totally disabled are eligible if they are between the ages of 50 and 59 and the disability began within 7 years after the employee's death; widow(er)s of any age are eligible if they are caring for a child of the deceased employee under the age of 18 or a child with a disability of any age who became disabled before age 22. Unmarried children (or grandchildren if both parents are deceased) are eligible for survivor benefits if they are under the age of 18, or are still enrolled full time in an elementary or secondary school, or become totally and permanently disabled before age 22. Parents over the age of 60 who were dependent on the employee for at least half of the parent's support also qualify for survivor benefits. Surviving divorced spouses qualify if they were married to the employee for at least 10 years and are 60 years of age or older (50 or older if disabled), or if they are still caring for a child of the employee under 16 years of age or disabled. Remarried widow(er)s retain eligibility if they remarry after age 60 (after age 50 if disabled).

Financial data　Benefits are based on months of service and earnings credits. Recently, the average monthly annuity paid to employees retired with disabilities was $2,221, for spouses and divorced spouses it was $817, for disabled widows and widowers it was $1,108, for widowed mothers and fathers it was $1,653, for remarried widows and widowers it was $896, for divorced widows and widowers it was $880, and for children it was $937.

Duration　Disability annuities are paid until the employee dies or recovers from the disability; survivor annuities are paid until death or, in the case of able-bodied children, until age 18 or graduation from high school.

Additional data　Employees who are disabled from their regular railroad occupation may work in another job and earn up to $700 per month or $8,400 per year without loss of any railroad retirement disability benefits. A 5-month waiting period beginning with the month after the month of the onset of disability is required before disability annuity payments can begin.

Number awarded　Varies each year; recently, the number of employees retired with disabilities was 83,517, and disabled widows and widowers 4,251.

Deadline　Deadline not specified.

[296]
SCIENCE GRADUATE STUDENT GRANT FUND

Foundation for Science and Disability, Inc.
Attn: Science Student Grant Committee Chair
503 N.W. 89th Street
Gainesville, FL 32607-1400
(352) 374-5774　　　　　　Fax: (352) 374-5804
E-mail: rmankin1@ufl.edu
Web: www.stemd.org

Summary　To provide supplemental grants to students with disabilities who are interested in working on a graduate degree in a science-related field.

Eligibility　This program is open to 1) college seniors who have a disability and have been accepted to a graduate or professional school in the sciences, and 2) graduate science students who have a disability. Applicants must be U.S. citizens interested in working on a degree in an area of engineering, mathematics, medicine, science, or technology. Along with their application, they must submit an essay (about 250 words) describing professional goals and objectives, as well as the specific purpose for which the grant would be used. Selection is based on financial need, sincerity of purpose, and scholarship and/or research ability.

Financial data　The grant is $1,000. Funds may be used for an assistive device or instrument, as financial support to work with a professor on an individual research project, or for some other special need.

Duration　The award is granted annually.

Additional data The Foundation for Science and Disability, Inc. is an affiliate society of the American Association for the Advancement of Science.

Number awarded Varies each year.

Deadline November of each year.

[297]
SINGERS' FINANCIAL AID

Society of Singers
Attn: Human Services Department
26500 Agoura Road 102-554
Calabasas, CA 91302
(818) 995-7100, ext. 104   Toll Free: (866) 767-7671
Fax: (818) 995-7466   E-mail: help@singers.org
Web: www.singers.org/programs.html

Summary To provide assistance to professional singers who are facing medical or other crises.

Eligibility This program is open to professional singers who have derived their primary income from singing for 5 years or more. Applicants must have financial needs resulting from medical, personal, or family crises. They must submit 5 years of career documentation, copies of bills for which help is needed, diagnosis letter and treatment plan from primary physicians or dentists with costs estimates or bills, and documentation of financial need.

Financial data Grants are paid directly to creditors to provide for such needs as rent, utilities, medical and/or dental expenses, substance abuse rehabilitation, psychotherapy, or HIV/AIDS treatment. Support is not provided for credit card debts, tax debts, loans, voice lessons, demos, headshots, or other music projects.

Duration These are 1-time grants.

Number awarded Varies each year.

Deadline Applications may be submitted at any time.

[298]
SOCIAL SECURITY DISABILITY INSURANCE (SSDI) BENEFITS

Social Security Administration
6401 Security Boulevard
Baltimore, MD 21235-0001
(410) 594-1234   Toll Free: (800) 772-1213
TDD: (800) 325-0778
Web: www.ssa.gov

Summary To provide monthly benefits to workers and their families if the worker becomes disabled or blind.

Eligibility This program defines disabled people as those who are unable to do any kind of work for which they are suited and whose disability has lasted or is expected to last for at least a year or to result in death. Blind people qualify if their vision cannot be corrected to better than 20/200 in their better eye or if their visual field is 20 degrees or less, even with corrective lenses. Family members who are eligible include 1) unmarried children, including adopted children and, in some cases, stepchildren and grandchildren who are under 18 years of age (19 if still in high school full time); 2) unmarried children, over 18 years of age, if they have a disability that started before age 22; and 3) spouses who are 62 years of age or older, or of any age if caring for a child of the disabled worker who is under 16 years of age or disabled. For deceased workers, disabled widow(er)s 50 years of age or older are also eligible. Applicants must also have worked long enough and recently enough under Social Security in order to qualify. Workers who become disabled before the age of 24 need 6 credits in the 3-year period ending when the disability begins; workers who become disabled between the ages of 24 and 31 must have credit for having worked half the time between the age of 21 and the date of disability; workers 31 years of age or older at the time of disability must have earned as many total credits as needed for retirement (from 20 credits if disabled at age 31 through 42 to 40 credits if disabled at age 62 or older) and must have earned at least 20 of the credits in the 10 years immediately before becoming disabled. An exception applies to blind workers who need no recent credit but may have earned the required credit any time after 1936.

Financial data The amount of the monthly benefit depends on several factors, including the worker's age at the time of disability, the number of dependents, and the amount of earnings on which Social Security taxes have been paid. Recently, the average monthly benefit was $1,110.70 for disabled workers, $298.60 for spouses of disabled workers, and $330.70 for children of disabled workers.

Duration For a disabled or blind person, whether a worker, widow, widower, surviving divorced spouse, or person over the age of 18 who became disabled before the age of 22, monthly benefits continue until the person is no longer disabled or dies. For a dependent spouse, benefits are paid until the worker is no longer disabled or dies. For a dependent child, the benefits continue until the child marries or reaches the age of 18 (19 if still enrolled as a full-time high school student).

Additional data Disabled workers may test their ability to return to work for a trial work period of up to 9 months, during which time they receive full SSDI benefits. At the end of that period, a decision is made as to whether or not they are able to engage in substantial gainful activity. Persons who find that they cannot continue substantial gainful employment continue to receive SSDI benefits without interruption. Persons who can engage in substantial gainful activity receive benefits for an additional 3 months after which payments cease. Several factors are considered to determine if the person can engage in substantial gainful employment, but the most important is income; for disabled people the amount is $1,000 a month gross wages and for blind people the income is $1,640 monthly.

Number awarded Varies; recently, approximately 8,630,000 disabled workers were receiving SSDI monthly benefits, along with 163,000 spouses and 1,897,000 children.

Deadline Deadline not specified.

[299]
SOUTH CAROLINA HOMESTEAD EXEMPTION PROGRAM

South Carolina Department of Revenue
301 Gervais Street
P.O. Box 125
Columbia, SC 29214
(803) 898-5680   Toll Free: (800) 763-1295
Fax: (803) 898-5822   E-mail: MillerC@sctax.org
Web: www.sctax.org

Summary To provide a homestead exemption to South Carolina residents who are elderly, disabled, or blind, and their widow(er)s.

Eligibility Legal residents of South Carolina who own a house or mobile home are eligible for this exemption if they are 65 years of age or older, totally and permanently disabled, or legally blind. Spouses of deceased persons who were eligible also qualify to receive the exemption as long as they remain unmarried.

Financial data The first $50,000 of the fair market value of the qualified applicant's home is exempted from property taxes. The exemption is from county, municipal, school, and special assessment real estate property taxes.

Duration The exemption continues as long as the homeowners live in their primary residence in South Carolina.

Additional data This program, established in 1972, is administered by county auditors.

Number awarded Varies each year.

Deadline Persons applying for this exemption for the first time must do so prior to July of each year; subsequently, no re-application is necessary unless the title or use of the property changes.

[300]
SOUTH CAROLINA PERMANENT DISABILITY RETIREMENT INCOME TAX EXCLUSION

South Carolina Department of Revenue
301 Gervais Street
P.O. Box 125
Columbia, SC 29214
(803) 898-5000   Toll Free: (800) 763-1295
Fax: (803) 898-5822
Web: www.sctax.org

Summary To exempt the retirement income received by people with total and permanent disabilities from state taxation in South Carolina.

Eligibility This exemption is available to residents of South Carolina who are permanently and totally disabled and who are also unable to be gainfully employed. People who are receiving disability income from 1 job but are able to perform another job are not eligible for this exclusion.

Financial data Qualified permanent disability retirement income is exempt from state income taxation in South Carolina.

Duration The exemption continues as long as the recipient resides in South Carolina and receives the specified disability retirement income.

Number awarded Varies each year.

Deadline Deadline not specified.

[301]
SOUTH CAROLINA PROPERTY TAX EXEMPTION FOR DISABLED VETERANS, LAW ENFORCEMENT OFFICERS, AND FIREFIGHTERS

South Carolina Department of Revenue
Attn: Property Division
301 Gervais Street
P.O. Box 125
Columbia, SC 29214
(803) 898-5480   Fax: (803) 898-5822
Web: www.sctax.org

Summary To exempt the residence of disabled South Carolina veterans, law enforcement officers, fire fighters, their unremarried widow(er)s, and others from property taxation.

Eligibility This exemption is available to owners of homes in South Carolina who are veterans of the U.S. armed forces, former law enforcement officers, or former fire fighters (including volunteer fire fighters). Applicants must be permanently and totally disabled from service-connected causes. The exemption is also available to qualified surviving spouses (defined to include unremarried spouses of disabled veterans, law enforcement officers, and fire fighters, as well as surviving spouses of service members killed in the line of duty, law enforcement officers who died in the line of duty, and fire fighters who died in the line of duty).

Financial data The exemption applies to all taxes on 1 house and a lot (not to exceed 1 acre).

Duration The exemption extends as long as the veteran, law enforcement officer, or fire fighter resides in the house, or as long as the spouse of a deceased veteran, service member, law enforcement officer, or fire fighter remains unmarried and resides in the original house or a single new dwelling.

Number awarded Varies each year.

Deadline Applications may be submitted at any time.

[302]
SOUTH DAKOTA SALES AND PROPERTY TAX REFUND FOR SENIOR AND DISABLED CITIZENS

South Dakota Department of Revenue and Regulation
Attn: Special Tax Division
445 East Capitol Avenue
Pierre, SD 57501-3185
(605) 773-3311   Toll Free: (800) TAX-9188
Fax: (605) 773-6729   E-mail: specialt@state.sd.us
Web: www.state.sd.us

Summary To provide a partial refund of sales taxes to elderly and disabled residents (including disabled veterans) in South Dakota.

Eligibility This program is open to residents of South Dakota who either have a qualified disability or are 66 years of age or older. Applicants must live alone and have a yearly income of less than $10,250 or live in a household whose members' combined income is less than $13,250. Veterans must have a disability of 60% or greater. Other people with disabilities must have been qualified to receive Social Security disability benefits or Supplemental Security Income disability benefits.

Financial data Qualified residents are entitled to a refund of a portion of the sales or property taxes they paid during the preceding calendar year.

Duration Residents of South Dakota are entitled to this refund annually.

Additional data This program has been in effect since 1974. South Dakotans are not entitled to both a sales tax refund and a property tax refund in the same year. The state will calculate both refunds and pay the amount that is greater.

Number awarded Varies each year.

Deadline June of each year.

[303]
TENNESSEE PROPERTY TAX RELIEF FOR DISABLED AND ELDERLY HOMEOWNERS

Tennessee Comptroller of the Treasury
Attn: Property Tax Relief Program
James K. Polk State Office Building
505 Deaderick Street, Room 1700
Nashville, TN 37243-1402
(615) 747-8858   Fax: (615) 532-3866
E-mail: kim.darden@cot.tn.gov
Web: www.comptroller1.state.tn.us/pa/patxr.asp

Summary To provide property tax relief for elderly and disabled homeowners in Tennessee.

Eligibility This exemption is offered to residents of Tennessee who own and live in their home and are either 1) 65 years of age or older, or 2) totally and permanently disabled as rated by the Social Security Administration or other qualified agency. To qualify, the combined income of all owners of the property cannot exceed $26,830.

Financial data The amount of the relief depends on the property assessment and the tax rate in the city or county where the beneficiary lives. The maximum market value on which tax relief is calculated is $25,000.

Duration 1 year; may be renewed as long as the qualified Tennessee resident owns and occupies the primary residence.

Number awarded Varies each year.

Deadline Deadline not specified.

[304]
TENNESSEE PROPERTY TAX RELIEF FOR DISABLED VETERANS AND THEIR SPOUSES

Tennessee Comptroller of the Treasury
Attn: Property Tax Relief Program
James K. Polk State Office Building
505 Deaderick Street, Room 1700
Nashville, TN 37243-1402
(615) 747-8858   Fax: (615) 532-3866
E-mail: kim.darden@cot.tn.gov
Web: www.comptroller1.state.tn.us/pa/patxr.asp

Summary To provide property tax relief to blind and disabled veterans and their spouses in Tennessee.

Eligibility This exemption is offered to veterans or their surviving unremarried spouses who are residents of Tennessee and own and live in their home in the state. The veteran must have served in the U.S. armed forces and 1) have acquired, as a result of such service, a disability from paraplegia, permanent paralysis of both legs and lower part of the body resulting from traumatic injury, disease to the spinal cord or brain, legal blindness, or loss or loss of use of both legs or arms from any service-connected cause; 2) have been rated by the U.S. Department of Veterans Affairs (VA) as 100% permanently disabled as a result of service as a prisoner of war for at least 5 months; or 3) have been rated by the VA as 100% permanently and totally disabled from any other service-connected cause. Unremarried spouses of deceased veterans are also eligible if 1) the veteran was receiving tax relief as a disabled veteran before death; 2) death resulted from a service-connected, combat-related cause, or killed in action; or 3) death resulted from being deployed, away from any home base of training, and in support of combat operations.

Financial data The amount of the relief depends on the property assessment and the tax rate in the city or county where the beneficiary lives. The maximum market value on which tax relief is calculated is $175,000.

Duration 1 year; may be renewed as long as the eligible veteran or surviving unremarried spouse owns and occupies the primary residence.

Number awarded Varies each year.

Deadline Deadline not specified.

[305]
TEXAS PROPERTY TAX EXEMPTION FOR DISABLED VETERANS AND THEIR FAMILIES

Texas Veterans Commission
P.O. Box 12277
Austin, TX 78711-2277
(512) 463-5538
Toll Free: (800) 252-VETS (within TX)
Fax: (512) 475-2395   E-mail: info@tvc.state.tx.us
Web: texas-veterans.com/claims/property-tax-exemption

Summary To extend property tax exemptions on the appraised value of their property to blind, disabled, and other Texas veterans and their surviving family members.

Eligibility Eligible veterans must be Texas residents rated at least 10% service-connected disabled. Surviving spouses and children of eligible veterans are also covered by this program.

Financial data For veterans in Texas whose disability is rated as 10% through 29%, the first $5,000 of the appraised property value is exempt from taxation; veterans rated as 30% through 49% disabled are exempt from the first $7,500 of appraised value; those with a 50% through 69% disability are exempt from the first $10,000 of appraised value; the exemption applies to the first $12,000 of appraised value for veterans with disabilities rated as 70% to 99%; veterans rated as 100% disabled are exempt from 100% of the appraised value of their property. A veteran whose disability is 10% or more and who is 65 years or older is entitled to exemption of the first $12,000 of appraised property value. A veteran whose disability consists of the loss of use of 1 or more limbs, total blindness in 1 or both eyes, or paraplegia is exempt from the first $12,000 of the appraised value. The unremarried surviving spouse of a deceased veteran who died on active duty and who, at the time of death had a compensable disability and was entitled to an exemption, is entitled to the same exemption. The surviving spouse of a person who died on active duty is entitled to exemption of the first $5,000 of appraised value of the spouse's property; they are also eligible for the 100% exemption. A surviving child of a person who dies on active duty is entitled to exemption of the first $5,000 of appraised value of the child's property, as long as the child is unmarried and under 21 years of age.

Duration　1 year; may be renewed as long as the eligible veteran (or unremarried surviving spouse or child) owns and occupies the primary residence in Texas.

Additional data　This program is administered at the local level by the various taxing authorities.

Number awarded　Varies each year.

Deadline　April of each year.

[306]
THE 9-11 HELPAMERICA FOUNDATION ASSISTANCE

The 9-11 HelpAmerica Foundation
14147 Hawthorne Boulevard
Hawthorne, CA 90250
(310) 355-0266
Web: www.911helpamerica.com

Summary　To provide support to veterans wounded in Iraq or Afghanistan and to families of veterans and military personnel wounded or killed in combat.

Eligibility　This assistance is available to 1) veterans disabled as a result of service in Operation Iraqi Freedom or Operation Enduring Freedom; and 2) families of veterans and military personnel injured or killed in those operations. Applicants must need general financial assistance to help meet special circumstances, especially those associated with the death or disability of the veteran or military service member.

Financial data　The amount of the support depends on the need of the recipient.

Duration　Support is provided for up to 18 months.

Additional data　This foundation was established in October, 2001.

Number awarded　Varies; in a recent year, 20 disabled veterans or survivors received support from this foundation.

Deadline　Applications may be submitted at any time.

[307]
TROOPS-TO-TEACHERS PROGRAM

Defense Activity for Non-Traditional Education Support
Attn: Troops to Teachers
6490 Sauffley Field Road
Pensacola, FL 32509-5243
(850) 452-1242　　　　　　Toll Free: (800) 231-6242
Fax: (850) 452-1096　　　　E-mail: ttt@navy.mil
Web: www.dantes.doded.mil

Summary　To provide a bonus to disabled and other veterans and military personnel interested in a second career as a public school teacher.

Eligibility　This program is open to 1) active-duty military personnel who are retired, have an approved date of retirement within 1 year, or separated on or after January 8, 2002 for physical disability; 2) members of a Reserve component who are retired, currently serving in the Selected Reserve with 10 or more years of credible service and commit to serving an additional 3 years, separated on or after January 8, 2002 due to a physical disability, or transitioned from active duty on or after January 8, 2002 after at least 6 years on active duty and commit to 3 years with a Selected Reserve unit. Applicants must have a baccalaureate or advanced degree, the equivalent of 1 year of college with 6 years of work experience in a vocational or technical field, or meet state requirements for vocational/technical teacher referral. A bonus is available to applicants who are willing to accept employment as a teacher in 1) a school district that has at least 10% of the students from families living below the poverty level, and 2) at a specific school within the district where at least 50% of the students are eligible for the free or reduced cost lunch program or where at least 13.5% of the students have disabilities. A stipend is available to applicants who are willing to accept employment as a teacher at 1) any school within a "high need" district that has at least 20% of the students from families living below the poverty level; or 2) at a specific school where at least 50% of the students are eligible for the free or reduced cost lunch program or at least 13.5% of the students have disabilities, as long as that school is in a district that has between 10% and 20% of students who come from poverty-level families. Preference is given to applicants interested in teaching mathematics, science, or special education.

Financial data　A bonus of $10,000 is awarded to recipients who agree to teach for 3 years in a school that serves a high percentage of students from low-income families. A stipend of $5,000 is awarded to recipients who agree to teach for 3 years in a school located in a "high-need" district; stipend funds are intended to help pay for teacher certification costs.

Duration　The bonuses are intended as 1-time grants.

Additional data　This program was established in 1994 by the Department of Defense (DoD). In 2000, program oversight and funding were transferred to the U.S. Department of Education, but DoD continues to operate the program. The No Child Left Behind Act of 2001 provided for continuation of the program.

Number awarded Varies each year.
Deadline Deadline not specified.

[308]
UTAH DISABLED VETERAN PROPERTY TAX ABATEMENT

Utah Department of Veteran's Affairs
Attn: Director
550 Foothill Boulevard, Room 202
Salt Lake City, UT 84108
(801) 326-2372   Toll Free: (800) 894-9497 (within UT)
Fax: (801) 326-2369   E-mail: veterans@utah.gov
Web: veterans.utah.gov

Summary To exempt a portion of the property of disabled veterans and their families in Utah from taxation.

Eligibility This program is available to residents of Utah who are disabled veterans or their unremarried widow(er)s or minor orphans. The disability must be at least 10% and incurred as the result of injuries in the line of duty.

Financial data The exemption is based on the disability rating of the veteran, to a maximum of $232,312 for a 100% disability. The exemption for veterans with lesser disabilities is equal to $232,312 times the percentage of their disability.

Duration This benefit is available as long as the disabled veteran or family members reside in Utah.

Deadline Tax exemption applications must be filed with the county government of residence by August of the initial year; once eligibility has been established, reapplication is not required.

[309]
UTAH VETERAN'S PROPERTY TAX EXEMPTION

Utah State Tax Commission
Attn: Property Tax Division
210 North 1950 West
Salt Lake City, UT 84134
(801) 297-3600   Toll Free: (800) 662-4335, ext. 3600
Fax: (801) 297-7699   TDD: (801) 297-2020
E-mail: propertytax@utah.gov
Web: propertytax.utah.gov

Summary To exempt from taxation a portion of the real and tangible property of disabled veterans and their families in Utah.

Eligibility This exemption is available to property owners in Utah who are veterans with a disability of at least 10% incurred in the line of duty, along with their unremarried surviving spouses or minor orphans. First year applications must be accompanied by proof of military service and proof of disability or death.

Financial data Veterans with a 100% disability are entitled to a full current-year exemption (recently, that was $237,949). Veterans with disabilities rated at a smaller percentage are entitled to that percentage of the current year exemption amount. Survivors are entitled to the same percentage as if the veteran were still living.

Duration The exemption is available each year the beneficiary owns property in Utah.

Number awarded Varies each year.

Deadline Applications must be submitted by August of each year.

[310]
VERMONT PROPERTY TAX EXEMPTION FOR DISABLED VETERANS

Vermont Department of Taxes
Attn: Property Valuation and Review Division
P.O. Box 1577
Montpelier, VT 05601-1577
(802) 828-2865   Toll Free: (866) 828-2865 (within VT)
Fax: (802) 828-2824
Web: www.state.vt.us/tax/pvrmilitary.shtml

Summary To exempt disabled Vermont veterans and their dependents from the payment of at least a portion of the state's property tax.

Eligibility Entitled to a property tax exemption are veterans of any war (or their spouses, widow(er)s, or children) who are receiving wartime disability compensation for at least a 50% disability, wartime death compensation, wartime dependence and indemnity compensation, or pension for disability paid through any military department or the Department of Veterans Affairs. Unremarried widow(er)s of previously qualified veterans are also entitled to the exemption whether or not they are receiving government compensation or a pension.

Financial data Up to $10,000 of the assessed value of real and personal property belonging to eligible veterans or their unremarried widow(er)s is exempt from taxation; individual towns may increase the exemption to as much as $40,000.

Duration 1 year; may be renewed as long as the eligible veteran or widow(er) continues to be the owner/occupant of the residence and lives in Vermont.

Additional data Only 1 exemption may be allowed on a property.

Number awarded Varies each year.

Deadline April of each year.

[311]
VETERANS DISABILITY COMPENSATION

Department of Veterans Affairs
Attn: Veterans Benefits Administration
810 Vermont Avenue, N.W.
Washington, DC 20420
(202) 418-4343   Toll Free: (800) 827-1000
Web: www.vba.va.gov/bin/21/compensation/index.htm

Summary To provide monthly compensation to veterans who have a disability that occurred or was made worse during military service.

Eligibility Disabled persons who are eligible for compensation under this program are those whose disability resulted from injury or disease incurred or aggravated during active service in the U.S. armed forces in the line of duty during wartime or peacetime service. They must have been discharged or separated under other than dishonorable conditions.

Financial data Disabled veterans who are found to be eligible for disability compensation are entitled to monthly payments, depending on the degree of disability as determined by the Department of Veterans Affairs. Recent monthly rates for veterans living alone with no dependents ranged from $127 for 10% disability to $2,769 for 100% disability. Veterans whose service-connected disabilities are rated at 30% or more are entitled to additional allowances for dependent children, spouses, and/or parents. The additional amount is determined according to the number of dependents and the degree of disability. In addition, a veteran whose disability is rated at 30% or more and whose spouse is in need of the aid and attendance of another person may receive an additional amount.

Duration Compensation continues as long as the veteran remains disabled.

Additional data In addition to monthly compensation under this program, disabled veterans may also be entitled to prosthetic appliances if they are receiving treatment in a facility under the direct jurisdiction of the Department of Veterans Affairs (VA), or outpatient care under certain specified conditions. Blind veterans are eligible for various aids and services, including adjustment to blindness training, home improvements and structural alterations, low vision aids and training in their use, guide dogs, and material for the blind from the Library of Congress. Former prisoners of war who were incarcerated for at least 30 days and have at least a 10% disability are entitled to a presumption of service connection. Persian Gulf veterans who suffer from chronic disabilities resulting from undiagnosed illnesses may receive disability compensation.

Number awarded Varies each year.

Deadline Applications are accepted at any time.

[312]
VETERANS SPECIAL MONTHLY COMPENSATION

Department of Veterans Affairs
Attn: Veterans Benefits Administration
810 Vermont Avenue, N.W.
Washington, DC 20420
(202) 418-4343   Toll Free: (800) 827-1000
Web: www1.va.gov

Summary To provide monthly compensation to veterans who have a disability that exceeds the 100% combined degree compensation or that results from special circumstances.

Eligibility This assistance is available to honorably-discharged veterans who have service-connected disabilities that have resulted in anatomical loss or loss of use of 1 hand, 1 foot, both buttocks, 1 or more creative organs, blindness of 1 eye having only light perception, deafness of both ears, having absence of air and bone conduction, complete organic aphonia with constant inability to communicate by speech, or (in the case of a female veteran) loss of 25% or more of tissue from a single breast or both

breasts. Additional assistance is available to veterans who are permanently bedridden or so helpless as to be in need of regular aid and attendance. A special allowance is also available to veterans who have a spouse determined to require regular aid and attendance.

Financial data Disabled veterans who are found to be eligible for special compensation are entitled to monthly payments, depending on the nature of the disability and the type and number of dependents. Recent monthly rates ranged from $3,100 to $7,925 for veterans living alone with no dependents, from $3,255 to $8,080 for a veteran and spouse, from $3,368 to $8,193 for a veteran with spouse and 1 child, from $3,204 to $8,029 for a veteran and 1 child, $77 for each additional child under 18 years of age, and $248 for each additional child over 18 years of age and enrolled in school. Other rates are available for veterans who live with 1 or more parents. In addition, a veteran whose spouse is in need of the aid and attendance of another person may receive an additional $141.

Duration Compensation continues as long as the veteran remains disabled.

Number awarded Varies each year.

Deadline Applications are accepted at any time.

[313]
VIRGINIA LIVABLE HOME TAX CREDIT

Virginia Department of Taxation
Attn: Tax Credit Unit
1957 Westmoreland Street
P.O. Box 715
Richmond, VA 23218-0715
(804) 786-2992   Fax: (804) 786-2800
Web: www.tax.virginia.gov

Summary To provide an income tax credit to residents of Virginia who wish to install accessibility features in a home to accommodate disabled individuals.

Eligibility This credit is available to residents of Virginia who either 1) purchase a new residence that has universal visibility or accessibility features, or 2) retrofit a residence to improve accessibility or provide universal visitability. New residences must include the 3 features of universal visitability (at least 1 zero-step entrance, an accessible bathroom on the same floor as the zero-step entrance, and doors with at least 32 inches of clear width and hallways of at least 36 inches of clear width to the accessible bathroom and eating area). Retrofitting of an existing residential unit must include at least 1 accessibility feature, lifts, or elevators and meet the requirements of an existing standard or provide sensory modifications.

Financial data The credit is $5,000 for the purchase of a new residence or 50% of the cost of retrofitting activities, up to $5,000.

Additional data This program was formerly known as the Virginia Home Accessibility Features for the Disabled Credit.

Number awarded Varies each year. The Department of Taxation is allowed to grant up to $1 million in these credits each year; if the total amount of applications for credits exceeds that sum, the Virginia Department of

Housing and Community Development prorates the amounts of credits among the eligible applicants.

Deadline Applications must be submitted by February of each year.

[314]
VIRGINIA TAX EXEMPTION FOR DISABILITY INCOME

Virginia Department of Taxation
Attn: Office of Customer Services
1957 Westmoreland Street
P.O. Box 1115
Richmond, VA 23218-1115
(804) 367-8031   Fax: (804) 254-6113
E-mail: TaxIndReturns@tax.virginia.gov
Web: www.tax.virginia.gov

Summary To exempt from state income taxation a portion of the disability income of Virginia residents.

Eligibility This exemption is available to residents of Virginia who receive income for permanent and total disability.

Financial data Qualified taxpayers are entitled to exempt up to $20,000 from their income for purposes of state taxation in Virginia.

Duration The exemption is available as long as the taxpayer lives and earns disability income in Virginia.

Number awarded Varies each year.

Deadline The request for an exemption is filed with the state income tax return in April of each year.

[315]
VOCATIONAL REHABILITATION AND EMPLOYMENT VETSUCCESS PROGRAM

Department of Veterans Affairs
Attn: Veterans Benefits Administration
Vocational Rehabilitation and Employment Service
810 Vermont Avenue, N.W.
Washington, DC 20420
(202) 418-4343   Toll Free: (800) 827-1000
Web: www.vba.va.gov/bin/vre/index.htm

Summary To provide funding to veterans with service-connected disabilities who need assistance to find employment or, if seriously disabled, to live independently.

Eligibility This program is open to veterans who have a service-connected disability of at least 10% or a memorandum rating of 20% or more from the Department of Veterans Affairs (VA). They must qualify for services provided by the VA VetSuccess that include assistance finding and keeping a job, including the use of special employer incentives and job accommodations; on-the-job training, apprenticeships, and non-paid work experiences; post-secondary training at a college, vocational, technical, or business school; supportive rehabilitation services such as case management, counseling, and medical referrals; independent living services for veterans unable to work due to the severity of their disabilities.

Financial data While in training and for 2 months after, eligible disabled veterans may receive subsistence allowances in addition to their disability compensation or retire-

ment pay. For most training programs, the current full-time monthly rate is $566.97 with no dependents, $703.28 with 1 dependent, $828.76 with 2 dependents, and $60.41 for each additional dependent; proportional rates apply for less than full-time training.

Duration Veterans remain eligible for these services up to 12 years from either the date of separation from active military service or the date the veteran was first notified by VA of a service-connected disability rating (whichever came later).

Number awarded Varies each year.

Deadline Applications are accepted at any time.

[316]
WASHINGTON PROPERTY TAX ASSISTANCE PROGRAM FOR WIDOWS OR WIDOWERS OF VETERANS

Washington State Department of Revenue
Attn: Property Tax Division
P.O. Box 47471
Olympia, WA 98504-7471
(360) 534-1410   Toll Free: (800) 647-7706
TDD: (360) 705-6718
Web: dor.wa.gov

Summary To exempt from taxation in Washington a portion of the assessed valuation of property owned by senior citizens or people with disabilities who are widow(er)s of veterans.

Eligibility This exemption is available to residents of Washington who are either 62 years of age or older or who have a disability that prevents them from being gainfully employed and is expected to last for at least 12 months. Applicants must be the unmarried widow or widower of a veteran who 1) died as a result of a service-connected disability; 2) was 100% disabled for 10 years prior to his or her death; 3) was a former prisoner of war and rated as 100% disabled for at least 1 year prior to death; or 4) died in active duty or in active training status. They must own property that they use as their principal home for at least 6 months of the year; mobile homes may qualify as a residence even if its owner does not own the land where it is located. Their annual disposable income may not exceed $40,000 per year.

Financial data The exemption is $100,000 of the home's assessed value if disposable income is $30,000 or less, $75,000 if disposable income is $30,001 to $35,000, or $50,000 if disposable income is $35,001 to $40,000.

Duration The exemption is available as long as the widow or widower meets the eligibility requirements.

Additional data This program offered assistance beginning with the 2006 tax year.

Number awarded Varies each year.

Deadline 30 days before taxes are due.

[317]
WASHINGTON PROPERTY TAX EXEMPTIONS FOR SENIOR CITIZENS AND DISABLED PERSONS

Washington State Department of Revenue
Attn: Property Tax Division
P.O. Box 47471
Olympia, WA 98504-7471
(360) 534-1410   Toll Free: (800) 647-7706
TDD: (360) 705-6718
Web: dor.wa.gov

Summary To exempt a portion of the property owned by senior citizens and people with disabilities, including their surviving spouses, from taxation in Washington.

Eligibility This exemption is available to residents of Washington who are 1) unable to work because of a disability, 2) veterans with a 100% service-connected disability, 3) at least 61 years of age, or 4) a surviving spouse at least 57 years of age of a person who was approved for this exemption. Applicants must own property that they use as their principal home for at least 6 months of the year; mobile homes may qualify as a residence even if its owner does not own the land where it is located. Their annual disposable income may not exceed $35,000 per year.

Financial data Property owners whose annual income is $25,000 or less are exempt from regular property taxes on the first $60,000 or 60% of their home's assessed value, whichever is greater. Property owners whose annual income is between $25,001 and $30,000 are exempt from regular property taxes on $50,000 or 35% of the assessed value, whichever is greater, not to exceed $70,000 or the assessed value. Property owners whose annual income is $35,000 or less are exempt from all levies that have been approved by voters in excess of regular property taxes.

Duration The exemption is available as long as the property owner meets the eligibility requirements.

Number awarded Varies each year.

Deadline Applications for each year are due by December of the preceding year.

[318]
WEST VIRGINIA HOMESTEAD EXEMPTION

West Virginia State Tax Department
Attn: Property Tax Division
1124 Smith Street
P.O. Box 2389
Charleston, WV 25328-2389
(304) 558-3940
Toll Free: (800) WVA-TAXS (within WV)
Fax: (304) 558-1843   TDD: (800) 282-9833
Web: www.wva.state.wv.us

Summary To provide a partial exemption of property taxes on residences owned by disabled or elderly persons and retired veterans in West Virginia.

Eligibility Eligible for this exemption are single-family residences owned and occupied by any person who is permanently and totally disabled or at least 65 years old.

Applicants must have been West Virginia residents for 2 consecutive calendar years prior to the tax year to which the exemption relates. Members of the U.S. military forces who maintain West Virginia as their state of residence throughout military service and return to the state to purchase a homestead upon retirement or separation from the military because of permanent and total disability are considered to meet the residency requirement and also qualify for this exemption.

Financial data The exemption applies to the first $20,000 of the total assessed value of eligible property.

Duration The exemption continues as long as the eligible property is owned and occupied by the qualifying person in West Virginia.

Additional data Applications for this program are submitted to the office of the county assessor in each West Virginia county.

Number awarded Varies each year.

Deadline Individuals with disabilities apply for this exemption during July, August, or September of any year. Once they have filed for the exemption, they do not need to refile in subsequent years if they sign a statement that they will notify the assessor within 30 days if they cease to be eligible for the exemption on the basis of disability.

[319]
WEST VIRGINIA SENIOR CITIZEN OR DISABILITY INCOME TAX EXEMPTION

West Virginia State Tax Department
Attn: Taxpayer Services Division
P.O. Box 3784
Charleston, WV 25337-3784
(304) 558-3333 Toll Free: (800) 982-8297 (within WV)
Fax: (304) 558-3269   TDD: (800) 282-9833
Web: www.wva.state.wv.us/wvtax/default.aspx

Summary To provide income tax exemptions for West Virginia residents with disabilities and their surviving spouses.

Eligibility Residents of West Virginia who are totally and permanently disabled (or 65 years of age or older) are eligible for this income tax exemption. Surviving spouses of eligible residents are also entitled to the exemption.

Financial data Qualifying taxpayers may deduct from state income taxation up to $8,000 for a single return or a maximum of $8,000 per person for a joint return.

Duration The exemption continues as long as the eligible resident (or his/her spouse) remains a resident of West Virginia.

Deadline Deadline not specified.

[320]
WISCONSIN DISABILITY INCOME EXCLUSION

Wisconsin Department of Revenue
Attn: Individual Income Tax
2135 Rimrock Road
P.O. Box 59
Madison, WI 53785-0001
(608) 266-2486   Fax: (608) 267-0834
E-mail: income@revenue.wi.gov
Web: www.revenue.wi.gov

Summary To exclude from state income taxation a portion of the disability income received by residents of Wisconsin.

Eligibility This exclusion is available to residents of Wisconsin who are younger than 65 years of age but who are retired on permanent and total disability.

Financial data Up to $5,200 per year may be excluded from income for purposes of state taxation. The exclusion is reduced by any income over $15,000 per year. Generally, no exclusion is left if income is greater than $20,200 if 1 person could take the exclusion or $25,400 if both husband and wife could take the exclusion.

Duration The exclusion is available as long as the recipient resides in Wisconsin.

Number awarded Varies each year.

Deadline Income tax returns must be filed by April of each year.

[321]
WISCONSIN VETERANS AND SURVIVING SPOUSES PROPERTY TAX CREDIT

Wisconsin Department of Revenue
Attn: Homestead Credit
2135 Rimrock Road
P.O. Box 34
Madison, WI 53786-0001
(608) 266-8641   Fax: (608) 267-1030
E-mail: homestd@revenue.wi.gov
Web: www.revenue.wi.gov/individuals/military.html

Summary To provide an income tax credit to disabled Wisconsin veterans and their surviving spouses equal to the amount of property taxes they pay.

Eligibility This credit is available to Wisconsin veterans who served on active duty under honorable conditions in the U.S. armed forces and have resided in Wisconsin for any consecutive 5-year period after entry into active duty. Applicants must have either a service-connected disability rating of 100% or a 100% disability rating based on individual unemployability. Also eligible are unremarried surviving spouses of such disabled veterans and of members of the National Guard or a Reserve component of the U.S. armed forces who were residents of Wisconsin and died in the line of duty while on active or inactive duty for training purposes.

Financial data Eligible veterans and surviving spouses are entitled to an income tax credit equal to the amount of property taxes they pay on their principal residence.

Duration The credit is available as long as the recipient resides in Wisconsin.

Number awarded Varies each year.

Deadline Income tax returns must be filed by April of each year.

[322]
WRITERS EMERGENCY ASSISTANCE FUND

American Society of Journalists and Authors
Attn: Charitable Trust
1501 Broadway, Suite 403
New York, NY 10036
(212) 997-0947   Fax: (212) 937-2315
E-mail: weaf@asja.org
Web: www.asja.org/weaf.php

Summary To assist professional freelance writers who are in financial need because of a disability or other causes.

Eligibility This program is open to established freelance nonfiction writers who, because of advancing age, illness, disability, or extraordinary professional crisis, are unable to work. Applicants need not be members of the American Society of Journalists and Authors, but they must establish a record of past professional freelance writing over a sustained period of years. They must be 60 years of age or older, be so disabled that their normal writing capacity has been severely diminished, or (regardless of age or disability) be caught up in a professional crisis (such as a lawsuit) where a grant would help. Grants are not available to beginning freelancers seeking funds for writing projects nor for works-in-progress of any kind.

Financial data Awards depend on the need of the recipient and the availability of funds.

Duration A recipient may apply for an additional grant at the end of a 12-month period.

Additional data Applications may be submitted by either the applicant or a nominator on the applicant's behalf. This program, established in 1982, was formerly known as the Llewellyn Miller Fund.

Number awarded Varies each year. Since the program began, it has issued more than 160 grants with a total value of approximately $400,000.

Deadline Applications may be submitted at any time.

[323]
WYOMING VETERANS PROPERTY TAX EXEMPTION

Wyoming Department of Revenue
Attn: Property Tax Relief Program
122 West 25th Street, Second Floor West
Cheyenne, WY 82002-0110
(307) 777-7320   Fax: (307) 777-7527
E-mail: DirectorOfRevenue@wy.gov
Web: revenue.state.wy.us

Summary To provide a partial tax exemption on the property owned by disabled and other veterans and their surviving spouses in Wyoming.

Eligibility This program is open to honorably-discharged veterans who were Wyoming residents at the time they entered military service and have resided in Wyoming for 3 years prior to applying for this exemption.

Applicants must have served during specified periods of war time or have received an armed forces expeditionary medal or other authorized service or campaign medal for service in an armed conflict in a foreign country. Surviving spouses of qualified veterans are also eligible. The exemption applies to county fees only, not state fees.

Financial data Veterans and spouses may exempt $3,000 in assessed value of property from taxation per year. Disabled veterans are entitled to additional exemptions that depend on the level of their disability, to a maximum of $2,000 for a 100% disability.

Duration Veterans and spouses are entitled to use these exemptions as long as they reside in Wyoming and own the property as their principal residence.

Number awarded Varies each year.

Deadline Applicants must advise their county assessor of their intent to use the exemption by May of each year.

Visual Disabilities

Scholarships   •

Fellowships   •

Grants-in-Aid   •

Described here are 266 funding opportunities available to individuals who have visual impairments (are partially sighted or blind), with or without correction. Of these, 127 cover scholarships (to pursue study, research, or other activities on the undergraduate level in the United States); 69 describe fellowships or other awards (to support graduate or postgraduate study, research, or other activities in the United States); and 70 identify grants-in-aid (to pay for emergency situations, travel, income/property tax liabilities, the acquisition of assistive technology, or other personal needs). All of this is "free" money. Not one dollar will need to be repaid (provided, of course, that recipients meet all program requirements). If you are looking for a particular program and don't find it in this section, be sure to check the Program Title Index to see if it is covered elsewhere in the directory.

Scholarships

[324]
ALLEN-SPRINKLE MEMORIAL GIFT

National Federation of the Blind of West Virginia
c/o Andy Baughman, Scholarship Committee Chair
220 Buena Vista Avenue
Clarksburg, MD 26301
(301) 622-9626   E-mail: andybob@frontier.com
Web: www.nfbwv.org

Summary To provide financial assistance to legally blind residents of West Virginia who are interested in attending college or graduate school in any state.

Eligibility This program is open to legally blind residents of Virginia who are graduating high school seniors, undergraduates, or graduate students. Applicants must be enrolled or planning to enroll full time at an accredited college, university, postsecondary vocational institute, or graduate school in any state. Along with their application, they must submit 2 letters of recommendation, transcripts, verification of blindness, and a personal letter that includes the kinds of things that interest them, their goals and aspirations, and how this scholarship would help them. Selection is based on academic excellence, community service, and financial need.

Financial data The stipend is $1,000.

Duration 1 year.

Additional data The winner is expected to attend the sponsor's annual convention.

Number awarded 1 each year.

Deadline May of each year.

[325]
AMERICAN COUNCIL OF THE BLIND OF COLORADO SCHOLARSHIPS

American Council of the Blind of Colorado
Attn: Executive Director
1536 Wynkoop Street, Suite 201
Denver, CO 80202
(303) 831-0117   Toll Free: (888) 775-2221
Fax: (303) 454-3378 E-mail: barbara.boyer@acbco.org
Web: www.acbco.org/programs/scholarships

Summary To provide money for college or graduate school in any state to blind students from Colorado.

Eligibility This program is open to legally blind students who are residents of Colorado and U.S. citizens. Applicants must be working on an undergraduate (academic, vocational, or certificate) or graduate (master's or doctoral) degree at a college or university in any state. A cumulative GPA of 3.3 or higher is generally required, but extenuating circumstances may be considered. Along with their application, they must submit a 750-word statement describing their educational, career, and personal goals. Financial need is also considered in the selection process.

Financial data The stipend is $2,500. Funds are paid directly to the recipient's college or university.

Duration 1 year.

Number awarded 4 each year.

Deadline February of each year.

[326]
AMERICAN COUNCIL OF THE BLIND OF MINNESOTA SCHOLARSHIPS

American Council of the Blind of Minnesota
Attn: Scholarship Committee
P.O. Box 7341
Minneapolis, MN 55407
(612) 501-1431   E-mail: jsilvers03@comcast.net
Web: www.acb.org/minnesota/Scholarship.html

Summary To provide financial assistance to blind and visually impaired residents of Minnesota who are interested in attending college or graduate school in any state.

Eligibility This program is open to residents of Minnesota who are blind or visually impaired. Applicants may be either high school seniors entering their first year of postsecondary study or students in their second year or above of undergraduate or graduate study in any state. Along with their application, they must submit 2 essays of 500 words each on 1) a situation in which they solved a problem or broke down a blindness-related barrier in order to meet an academic requirement, and 2) a pair of instances in which they would have advocated for their own needs or the needs of others. Selection is based on the essays, extracurricular activities, transcripts, and recommendations.

Financial data The stipend is $1,000.

Duration 1 year.

Number awarded 2 each year: 1 to a high school senior entering college and 1 to a student already enrolled in a postsecondary educational program.

Deadline June of each year.

[327]
AMERICAN COUNCIL OF THE BLIND OF TEXAS SCHOLARSHIPS

American Council of the Blind of Texas
c/o Joyce Watson, Scholarship Chair
4631 Connorvale Road
Houston, TX 77039-3514
(281) 449-0915   E-mail: jwatson2670@sbcglobal.net
Web: acbtexas.org/financial.htm

Summary To provide financial assistance to blind and visually impaired residents of Texas who are interested in attending college in any state.

Eligibility This program is open to residents of Texas who can document legal or total blindness. Applicants must be enrolled or planning to enroll at a college, university, or vocational/trade school in any state. They must have a GPA of 3.0 or higher. Along with their application, they must submit documentation of financial need, transcripts, a copy of their acceptance letter (if not yet attending college), 2 to 3 letters of recommendation not more than 12 months old, and a 1- to 2-page autobiography, including information on their family, hobbies, activities, community service, and educational and career goals.

Selection is based on career goals, academic achievement, and letters of recommendation.

Financial data Stipends range from $250 to $1,000 per year. Funds may be used for any educational purpose, including tuition, books, housing, and transportation.

Duration 1 year; recipients may reapply.

Number awarded Varies each year; recently, 5 of these scholarships were awarded.

Deadline June of each year.

[328]
ARKANSAS COUNCIL OF THE BLIND SCHOLARSHIPS

Arkansas Council of the Blind
Attn: Education Committee
P.O. Box 4166
Little Rock, AR 72214-4166
(501) 223-9090   Toll Free: (800) 562-6101
E-mail: arkansas_acb@yahoo.com

Summary To provide funding to blind residents of Arkansas interested in attending college in any state.

Eligibility This program is open to residents of Arkansas who are blind. Applicants must be attending or planning to attend a college or university in any state.

Financial data The stipend is $1,000.

Duration 1 year.

Number awarded 3 each year.

Deadline March of each year.

[329]
ARNOLD SADLER MEMORIAL SCHOLARSHIP

American Council of the Blind
Attn: Coordinator, Scholarship Program
2200 Wilson Boulevard, Suite 650
Arlington, VA 22201
(202) 467-5081   Toll Free: (800) 424-8666
Fax: (703) 465-5085   E-mail: info@acb.org
Web: www.acb.org/scholarship

Summary To provide financial assistance to undergraduate or graduate students who are blind and are interested in studying in a field of service to persons with disabilities.

Eligibility This program is open to undergraduate and graduate students in rehabilitation, education, law, or other fields of service to persons with disabilities. Applicants must be legally blind in both eyes. Along with their application, they must submit verification of legal blindness in both eyes; SAT, ACT, GRE, or similar scores; information on extracurricular activities (including involvement in the American Council of the Blind); employment record; and a 500-word autobiographical sketch that includes their personal goals, strengths, weaknesses, hobbies, honors, achievements, and reasons for choice of field or courses of study. Financial need is not considered. A cumulative GPA of 3.3 or higher is generally required.

Financial data The stipend is $1,500.

Duration 1 year.

Additional data This scholarship is funded by the Arnold Sadler Memorial Scholarship Fund. Scholarship winners are expected to attend the council's annual conference; the council will cover all reasonable expenses.

Number awarded 1 each year.

Deadline February of each year.

[330]
ASSOCIATION OF BLIND CITIZENS SCHOLARSHIPS

Association of Blind Citizens
P.O. Box 246
Holbrook, MA 02343
(781) 961-1023   Fax: (781) 961-0004
E-mail: scholarship@blindcitizens.org
Web: www.blindcitizens.org/abc_scholarship.htm

Summary To provide financial assistance to residents of designated states who are blind or visually impaired and interested in attending college in any state.

Eligibility This program is open to high school seniors, high school graduates, and currently-enrolled college students who are residents of California, Connecticut, Florida, Massachusetts, New Hampshire, or Rhode Island. Applicants must be blind or visually impaired and interested in working on a college (2- or 4-year) degree in any state. They must be legal U.S. residents. Along with their application, they must submit an autobiography, indicating how the scholarship award would help them achieve their goal of attending college or a recognized vocational program; a high school or college transcript; a certificate of legal blindness or a letter from their ophthalmologist; and 2 letters of reference. The highest ranked applicant receives the Reggie Johnson Memorial Scholarship.

Financial data Stipends are $2,000 or $1,000. Funds may be used to pay for tuition, living expenses, or related expenses resulting from vision impairment.

Duration 1 year.

Number awarded 4 each year: 1 at $2,000 (the Reggie Johnson Memorial Scholarship) and 3 at $1,000.

Deadline April of each year.

[331]
BAY STATE COUNCIL OF THE BLIND SCHOLARSHIP

American Council of the Blind
Attn: Coordinator, Scholarship Program
2200 Wilson Boulevard, Suite 650
Arlington, VA 22201
(202) 467-5081   Toll Free: (800) 424-8666
Fax: (703) 465-5085   E-mail: info@acb.org
Web: www.acb.org/scholarship

Summary To provide financial assistance for college to blind students from Massachusetts.

Eligibility This program is open to legally blind students who are residents of Massachusetts or attending college in the state. Applicants must submit verification of legal blindness in both eyes; SAT or ACT scores; information on extracurricular activities (including involvement in the American Council of the Blind); employment record; and a

500-word autobiographical sketch that includes their personal goals, strengths, weaknesses, hobbies, honors, achievements, and reasons for choice of field or courses of study. Financial need is not considered. A cumulative GPA of 3.3 or higher is generally required.

Financial data The stipend is $1,000.

Duration 1 year.

Additional data This scholarship is sponsored by the Bay State Council of the Blind, an affiliate of the American Council of the Blind. Scholarship winners are expected to attend the council's annual conference; the council will cover all reasonable expenses.

Number awarded 1 each year.

Deadline February of each year.

[332]
BEVERLY PROWS MEMORIAL SCHOLARSHIP

National Federation of the Blind of Washington
Attn: Scholarship Chair
P.O. Box 2516
Seattle, WA 98111
(425) 823-6380   E-mail: president@nfbw.org
Web: www.nfbw.org/programs.html

Summary To provide money for undergraduate or graduate study in any state to blind students in Washington.

Eligibility This program is open to legally blind residents of Washington state who are working on or planning to work on a full-time college or graduate degree at a school in any state. Applicants must submit a list of honors and awards they have received, information on their community service involvement, high school and/or college transcripts, and 3 letters of reference.

Financial data The stipend is $3,000.

Duration 1 year; recipients may reapply.

Additional data This scholarship was first awarded in 1991. Winners must attend the state convention of the National Federation of the Blind of Washington to accept the award; convention expenses are covered.

Number awarded 1 each year.

Deadline August of each year.

[333]
BILL TOMLIN SCHOLARSHIP AWARD

Association for Education and Rehabilitation of the
   Blind and Visually Impaired-Arkansas Chapter
c/o Sharon Niemczyk
Dr. Martin Luther King Elementary
905 M.L. King Drive
Little Rock, AR 72202-3632
(501) 447-5100   E-mail: sharon.niemczyk@lrsd.org
Web: ar.aerbvi.org/awards.htm

Summary To provide financial assistance to blind and visually impaired residents of Arkansas interested in attending college in any state.

Eligibility This program is open to residents of Arkansas who are blind or visually impaired and enrolled or planning to enroll in a postsecondary educational or vocational training program in any state. Applicants must submit an autobiography of 1 to 2 pages that includes their personal goals, perceived strengths and needs, hobbies, honors, extracurricular activities, and achievements. Selection is based on the autobiography, 2 recommendations, and transcripts.

Financial data The stipend is $1,000. Funds may be used for the purchase of textbooks, specialized materials, or adaptive equipment.

Duration 1 year.

Number awarded 1 or more each year.

Deadline March of each year.

[334]
BONNIE AND ERICH OHLENDORF AWARD

Connecticut Institute for the Blind
Attn: Vice President for Development
120 Holcomb Street
Hartford, CT 06112-1589
(860) 242-2274   Fax: (860) 242-3103
TDD: (860) 286-3113   E-mail: info@ciboakhill.org
Web: www.ciboakhill.org/ways_to_give/donor.asp

Summary To provide funding to Connecticut high school seniors who are legally blind and interested in attending college in any state.

Eligibility This program is open to seniors graduating from high schools in Connecticut who are legally blind. Applicants must be planning to enroll in a postsecondary educational institution in any state. They must be able to demonstrate financial need. Along with their application, they must submit answers to questions about their major accomplishments, who or what has helped them in their accomplishments, the extracurricular activities (including sports) in which they were involved in high school, their involvement in their community, their goals for the next 5 years, how an award would help them achieve their goals, how they will be financing their college education, and why they feel they should be considered for an award.

Financial data A stipend is awarded (amount not specified).

Duration 1 year.

Additional data This program was established in 2000. The Connecticut Institute for the Blind, doing business as Oak Hill, also operates independent living facilities in West Hartford and Wethersfield for blind, visually impaired, and disabled individuals.

Number awarded 1 each year.

Deadline December of each year.

[335]
CALIFORNIA COUNCIL OF THE BLIND SCHOLARSHIPS

California Council of the Blind
Attn: Executive Office
1510 J Street, Suite 125
Sacramento, CA 95814
(916) 441-2100   Toll Free: (800) 221-6359 (within CA)
Fax: (916) 441-2188   E-mail: ccotb@ccbnet.org
Web: www.ccbnet.org/scholar.htm

Summary To provide money for undergraduate or graduate study in any state to blind people in California.

Eligibility Applicants must be legally blind residents of California who are enrolled or planning to enroll full time at an accredited college or university at either the undergraduate or graduate level. The school may be in any state. Along with their application, they must submit a 200-word statement on their purpose in undertaking college work and their vocational goals. Selection is based on academic achievement and financial need.

Financial data The amount of the assistance depends on the availability of funds and the needs of the applicant.

Duration 1 year; may be renewed. For graduate students, support is limited to 2 years of work for a master's degree or 3 years for a Ph.D.

Number awarded Varies each year.

Deadline June of each year.

[336]
CHARLES AND MELVA T. OWEN MEMORIAL SCHOLARSHIPS

National Federation of the Blind
Attn: Scholarship Committee
200 East Wells Street
Baltimore, MD 21230
(410) 659-9314, ext. 2415   Fax: (410) 685-5653
E-mail: scholarships@nfb.org
Web: www.nfb.org/nfb/scholarship_program.asp

Summary To provide funding to entering or continuing undergraduate or graduate students who are blind.

Eligibility This program is open to legally blind students who are working on or planning to work full time on an undergraduate or graduate degree. Scholarships, however, are not awarded for the study of religion or solely to further general or cultural education; the academic program should be directed towards attaining financial independence. Along with their application, they must submit transcripts, standardized test scores, proof of legal blindness, 2 letters of recommendation, and a letter of endorsement from their National Federation of the Blind state president or designee. Selection is based on academic excellence, service to the community, and financial need.

Financial data Stipends are $10,000 or $3,000.

Duration 1 year; recipients may resubmit applications up to 2 additional years.

Additional data Scholarships are awarded at the federation convention in July. Recipients must attend the convention at federation expense; that funding is in addition to the scholarship grant.

Number awarded 1 at $10,000 and 1 at $3,000.

Deadline March of each year.

[337]
CHICAGO LIGHTHOUSE SCHOLARSHIPS

Chicago Lighthouse for People Who Are Blind or
  Visually Impaired
Attn: Scholarship Program Coordinator
1850 West Roosevelt Road
Chicago, IL 60608-1298
(312) 666-1331   Fax: (312) 243-8539
TDD: (312) 666-8874
E-mail: scholarships@chicagolighthouse.org
Web: chicagolighthouse.org

Summary To provide funding to blind or visually impaired college and graduate students, especially those from Illinois and states close to Chicago.

Eligibility This program is open to undergraduate and graduate students who are legally blind, totally blind, visually impaired, or multi-disabled and attending or planning to attend an accredited college, university, or community college. Students from throughout the country are eligible, but preference is given to residents of Illinois and the greater Chicago area (southern Wisconsin and northwestern Indiana) and to those attending school in Illinois. Along with their application, they must submit an essay about their visual impairment, background, educational and career goals, and how this scholarship will help achieve those goals. Selection is based on academic achievement, career goal, extracurricular activities, character, and personal and family financial need.

Financial data Stipends range up to $5,000.

Duration 1 year; a small number of the awards may be renewed up to 3 additional years.

Additional data This program includes the Mary Kathryn and Michael Panitch Scholarships. This program was established in 2004 and limited to students from the Chicago area. Recently, it has begun to accept applications from students living in other areas.

Number awarded Varies each year; recently, 14 of these scholarships were awarded.

Deadline March of each year.

[338]
CHRISTIAN RECORD SERVICES SCHOLARSHIPS

Christian Record Services
4444 South 52nd Street
P.O. Box 6097
Lincoln, NE 68506-0097
(402) 488-0981   Fax: (402) 488-7582
E-mail: info@christianrecord.org
Web: services.christianrecord.org

Summary To provide money for college to blind students.

Eligibility Applicants must be legally blind and attending or planning to attend college full time on the undergraduate level to secure training that will result in independence and self-support. Financial need is considered in the selection process. U.S. citizenship is required.

Financial data A stipend is awarded (amount not specified).

Duration 1 year; may be renewed.

Additional data Christian Record Services is operated for the benefit of the general public by the General Conference of Seventh-Day Adventists, 6840 Eastern Avenue, N.W., Washington, DC 20012.

Number awarded Varies each year; recently, 10 of these scholarships were awarded.

Deadline March of each year.

[339]
CHRISTINE H. EIDE MEMORIAL SCHOLARSHIP AWARD

Lighthouse International
Attn: New York Lighthouse Vision Rehabilitation
  Services
111 East 59th Street
New York, NY 10022-1202
(212) 821-9428   Toll Free: (800) 829-0500
Fax: (212) 821-9703   TDD: (212) 821-9713
E-mail: gobando@lighthouse.org
Web: www.lighthouse.org

Summary To provide funding to legally blind high school seniors, recent graduates, undergraduates, or graduate students.

Eligibility This program is open to legally blind graduating high school seniors, recent graduates, current undergraduates, or current graduate students. Applicants must be enrolled or planning to enroll full time at an accredited college or university in 1 of the 50 states, the District of Columbia, or a U.S. territory. Along with their application, they must submit on essay of 1 to 3 pages on 1) their career objectives and career plans upon completion of their educational program; 2) why they chose this school to meet their vocational objectives; 3) how they plan to use the scholarship funds; and 4) (for renewal applicants) how the scholarship benefited their education. Financial need is not considered in the selection process.

Financial data The stipend is $500 per semester ($1,000 per year).

Duration 1 semester; may be renewed 1 additional semester.

Additional data This program was established in 1967.

Number awarded Varies each year.

Deadline August of each year for fall semester; December of each year for spring semester.

[340]
COLLEGE-BOUND AWARD OF LIGHTHOUSE INTERNATIONAL

Lighthouse International
Attn: Scholarship and Career Awards
111 East 59th Street
New York, NY 10022-1202
(212) 821-9428   Toll Free: (800) 829-0500
Fax: (212) 821-9703   TDD: (212) 821-9713
E-mail: sca@lighthouse.org
Web: www.lighthouse.org/services-and-assistance

Summary To provide financial assistance to legally blind high school seniors who plan to attend college.

Eligibility This program is open to high school seniors or recent high school graduates now planning to begin college who are legally blind and U.S. citizens. Applicants must be planning to attend an accredited college or university in 1 of the 50 states, the District of Columbia, or a U.S. territory. Along with their application, they must submit essays of 400 to 600 words on 1) their academic focus and extracurricular activities and what inspires their interest in each area; 2) their passion and how they express that passion; 3) key academic and personal accomplishments and the challenges they overcome to be successful; and 4) how this scholarship will support their academic and/or career development. Selection is based on academic and personal achievements; financial need is not considered.

Financial data The stipend is $10,000.

Duration 1 year.

Number awarded 2 each year.

Deadline January of each year.

[341]
DALE M. SCHOETTLER SCHOLARSHIP FOR VISUALLY IMPAIRED STUDENTS

California State University
CSU Foundation
Attn: Director, Foundation Programs and Services
401 Golden Shore, Sixth Floor
Long Beach, CA 90802-4210
(562) 951-4768   E-mail: abrown@calstate.edu
Web: www.calstate.edu/foundation/scholarship.shtml

Summary To provide financial assistance to undergraduate and graduate students with visual impairments at campuses of the California State University (CSU) system.

Eligibility This program is open to full-time undergraduate and graduate students enrolled at CSU campuses who have been declared visually impaired or legally blind. Applicants must have a cumulative GPA of 2.8 or higher.

Financial data The stipend is $6,000.

Duration 1 year.

Number awarded 1 or more each year.

Deadline Deadline not specified.

[342]
DAVID NEWMEYER SCHOLARSHIP

American Council of the Blind of Ohio
Attn: Executive Director
P.O. Box 307128
Gahanna, OH 43230-7128
(614) 221-6688 Toll Free: (800) 835-2226 (within OH)
E-mail: mary.hiland@wowway.com
Web: www.acbohio.org

Summary To provide financial assistance to entering or continuing Ohio undergraduate students who are blind.

Eligibility This program is open to 1) residents of Ohio who are high school seniors or current college students, and 2) students at colleges and universities in Ohio. Applicants must be legally blind and working on or planning to work on an undergraduate degree in any field. Along with their application, they must submit transcripts (must have a GPA of 3.0 or higher), a certificate of legal blindness, and an essay of 250 to 500 words on their career objectives, future plans, personal goals, other academic or personal qualities, and why they believe they are qualified to receive this scholarship. Financial need is not the sole factor considered in the selection process.

Financial data　The stipend is $2,000 per year.

Duration　1 year; recipients may reapply.

Additional data　Winners are required to attend the Saturday morning business meeting and Sunday breakfast of the sponsor's annual convention; a stipend for meals and workshops is provided.

Number awarded　1 each year.

Deadline　August of each year.

[343]
DELTA GAMMA FOUNDATION FLORENCE MARGARET HARVEY MEMORIAL SCHOLARSHIP

American Foundation for the Blind
Attn: Scholarship Committee
2 Penn Plaza, Suite 1102
New York, NY 10121
(212) 502-7661　　　　　　Toll Free: (800) AFB-LINE
Fax: (888) 545-8331　　　　　E-mail: afbinfo@afb.net
Web: www.afb.org/Section.asp?Documentid=2962

Summary　To provide financial assistance to blind undergraduate and graduate students who wish to study in the field of rehabilitation and/or education of the blind.

Eligibility　This program is open to legally blind juniors, seniors, or graduate students. U.S. citizenship is required. Applicants must be studying in the field of rehabilitation and/or education of visually impaired and blind persons. Along with their application, they must submit 200-word essays on 1) their past and recent achievements and accomplishments; 2) their intended field of study and why they have chosen it; and 3) the role their visual impairment has played in shaping their life. Financial need is considered in the selection process.

Financial data　The stipend is $1,000.

Duration　1 year.

Additional data　This scholarship is supported by the Delta Gamma Foundation and administered by the American Foundation for the Blind.

Number awarded　1 each year.

Deadline　April of each year.

[344]
DELTA GAMMA FOUNDATION/RUTH BILLOW MEMORIAL EDUCATION FUND

Delta Gamma Foundation
Attn: Director, Service for Sight
3250 Riverside Drive
P.O. Box 21397
Columbus, OH 43221-0397
(614) 481-8169　　　　　　Toll Free: (800) 644-5414
Fax: (614) 481-0133
E-mail: fngrants@deltagamma.org
Web: www.deltagamma.org

Summary　To provide financial assistance to undergraduate or graduate members of Delta Gamma sorority who are visually impaired or preparing for a career in working with the visually impaired.

Eligibility　This program is open to undergraduate and graduate members of the sorority who are either 1) blind or visually impaired; or 2) pursuing professional training in areas related to working with persons who are blind or visually impaired or in sight preservation. Applicants must be pursuing a program of postsecondary education in the United States or Canada.

Financial data　The stipend is $1,000 for undergraduates or $2,500 for graduate students.

Duration　1 year or more.

Number awarded　2 each year: 1 to an undergraduate and 1 to a graduate student.

Deadline　Applications may be submitted at any time.

[345]
DR. MAE DAVIDOW MEMORIAL SCHOLARSHIP

American Council of the Blind
Attn: Coordinator, Scholarship Program
2200 Wilson Boulevard, Suite 650
Arlington, VA 22201
(202) 467-5081　　　　　　Toll Free: (800) 424-8666
Fax: (703) 465-5085　　　　　E-mail: info@acb.org
Web: www.acb.org/scholarship

Summary　To provide financial assistance for college to blind students from Pennsylvania.

Eligibility　This program is open to legally blind students who are residents of Pennsylvania or attending college in the state. Applicants must submit verification of legal blindness in both eyes; SAT or ACT scores; information on extracurricular activities (including involvement in the American Council of the Blind); employment record; and a 500-word autobiographical sketch that includes their personal goals, strengths, weaknesses, hobbies, honors, achievements, and reasons for choice of field or courses of study. Financial need is not considered. A cumulative GPA of 3.3 or higher is generally required.

Financial data　The stipend is $1,500.

Duration　1 year.

Additional data　This scholarship is sponsored by the Pennsylvania Council of the Blind, an affiliate of the American Council of the Blind. Scholarship winners are expected to attend the council's annual conference; the council will cover all reasonable expenses.

Number awarded 1 each year.

Deadline February of each year.

[346]
DR. S. BRADLEY BURSON MEMORIAL SCHOLARSHIP

American Council of the Blind
Attn: Coordinator, Scholarship Program
2200 Wilson Boulevard, Suite 650
Arlington, VA 22201
(202) 467-5081 Toll Free: (800) 424-8666
Fax: (703) 465-5085 E-mail: info@acb.org
Web: www.acb.org/scholarship

Summary To provide financial assistance to blind students who are working on an undergraduate or graduate degree in designated fields of science.

Eligibility This program is open to undergraduate or graduate students working on a degree in the "pure" sciences (i.e., biology, chemistry, physics, and engineering, but not computer science). Applicants must be legally blind in both eyes. Along with their application, they must submit verification of legal blindness in both eyes; SAT, ACT, GRE, or similar scores; information on extracurricular activities (including involvement in the American Council of the Blind); employment record; and a 500-word autobiographical sketch that includes their personal goals, strengths, weaknesses, hobbies, honors, achievements, and reasons for choice of field or courses of study. A cumulative GPA of 3.3 or higher is generally required. Financial need is not considered in the selection process.

Financial data The stipend is $1,000.

Duration 1 year.

Additional data Scholarship winners are expected to attend the council's annual conference; the council will cover all reasonable expenses.

Number awarded 1 each year.

Deadline February of each year.

[347]
DUANE BUCKLEY MEMORIAL SCHOLARSHIP

American Council of the Blind
Attn: Coordinator, Scholarship Program
2200 Wilson Boulevard, Suite 650
Arlington, VA 22201
(202) 467-5081 Toll Free: (800) 424-8666
Fax: (703) 465-5085 E-mail: info@acb.org
Web: www.acb.org/scholarship

Summary To provide financial assistance for college to blind high school seniors.

Eligibility This program is open to graduating high school seniors who are legally blind in both eyes. Applicants must submit verification of legal blindness in both eyes; SAT or ACT scores; information on extracurricular activities (including involvement in the American Council of the Blind); employment record; and a 500-word autobiographical sketch that includes their personal goals, strengths, weaknesses, hobbies, honors, achievements,

and reasons for choice of field or courses of study. A cumulative GPA of 3.3 or higher is generally required. Financial need is not considered in the selection process.

Financial data The stipend is $1,000.

Duration 1 year.

Additional data Scholarship winners are expected to attend the council's annual conference; the council will cover all reasonable expenses.

Number awarded 1 each year.

Deadline February of each year.

[348]
EDUCATION FOR LIFE COLLEGE SCHOLARSHIPS

The See the Future Fund
P.O. Box 63022
Colorado Springs, CO 80962-3022
(719) 471-3200 Fax: (719) 471-3210
E-mail: twtheune@prodigy.net
Web: seethefuture.org

Summary To provide financial assistance to blind or visually impaired residents of Colorado who are interested in attending college or graduate school in any state.

Eligibility This program is open to residents of Colorado who meet standards of blindness or visual impairment. Applicants must be enrolled full time at a postsecondary program in any state as 1) a freshman entering an academic program; 2) a sophomore, junior, or senior in an academic program; 3) a graduate student in an academic program; or 4) a student in a vocational/technical school or community college. Selection is based on academic achievement, service, and financial need.

Financial data Stipends are $3,000, $2,500, or $2,000 per year. Funds are paid directly to the institution as payment for tuition, fees, books, room, and board.

Duration 2 or 4 years.

Additional data This program began in 1998.

Number awarded Varies each year; recently, the program offered 1 scholarship at $3,000 per year for 4 years, 1 at $2,500 per year for 4 years, 1 at $2,000 per year for 4 years, and 3 at $2,000 per year for 2 years.

Deadline February of each year.

[349]
EMIL A. HONKA SCHOLARSHIPS

Montana Association for the Blind
7 West Sixth Street, Suite E
P.O. Box 465
Helena, MT 59624
(406) 442-9411 Fax: (406) 442-1612
E-mail: lglueckert@milp.us

Summary To provide financial assistance to blind residents of Montana who are attending college or graduate school in any state.

Eligibility This program is open to residents of Montana who are blind or have a prognosis of serious vision loss and are working on an undergraduate or graduate degree in any field at a college or university in any state. Applicants must have completed at least 1 semester or quarter and have a GPA of 2.5 or higher. Selection is based primarily on financial need.

Financial data The stipend is $1,000 per year.

Duration 1 year; recipients may reapply.

Additional data Recipients must attend the annual convention of the sponsoring organization to accept their award; expenses to attend the convention are reimbursed.

Number awarded 2 each year.

Deadline January of each year.

[350]
EMMA SKOGEN SCHOLARSHIP

North Dakota Association of the Blind
c/o Tracy Wicken, Scholarship Committee Chair
733 Dawn Circle
Grand Forks, ND 58203
E-mail: trwicken@nd.gov
Web: www.ndab.org/Skogen.htm

Summary To provide financial assistance for vocational school to blind students in North Dakota.

Eligibility This program is open to North Dakota residents who are blind or visually impaired and attending a vocational or trade school. Applicants must provide information on what they plan to study, where, and when; their long-term career goals; and their financial need. Selection is based on clarity of study plan, long-term career goals, GPA, letter of recommendation, extracurricular involvements, and financial need.

Financial data The stipend is $1,000.

Duration 1 year.

Additional data This program was established in 2004.

Number awarded 1 each year.

Deadline March of each year.

[351]
ESTHER V. TAYLOR SCHOLARSHIPS

Kansas Association for the Blind and Visually Impaired
603 S.W. Topeka Boulevard, Suite 304B
Topeka, KS 66603
(785) 235-8990   Toll Free: (800) 749-1499 (within KS)
E-mail: kabvi@att.net
Web: www.kabvi.com/Scholarship%20Opportunity.html

Summary To provide financial assistance to residents of Kansas who are blind or visually impaired and interested in attending college in any state.

Eligibility This program is open to blind and visually impaired residents of Kansas who are attending or planning to attend a college, university, or technical school in any state. Applicants must submit an autobiographical sketch that includes their goals, strengths, weaknesses, hobbies, honors, activities, and achievements. Need is considered in the selection process.

Financial data The stipend is $1,000.

Duration 1 year.

Number awarded 2 each year.

Deadline April of each year.

[352]
EUNICE FIORITO MEMORIAL SCHOLARSHIP

American Council of the Blind
Attn: Coordinator, Scholarship Program
2200 Wilson Boulevard, Suite 650
Arlington, VA 22201
(202) 467-5081   Toll Free: (800) 424-8666
Fax: (703) 465-5085   E-mail: info@acb.org
Web: www.acb.org/scholarship

Summary To provide funding to undergraduate or graduate students who are blind and are interested in studying in a field of advocacy or service for persons with disabilities.

Eligibility This program is open to undergraduate and graduate students in rehabilitation, education, law, or other fields of service or advocacy for persons with disabilities. Applicants must be legally blind in both eyes. Along with their application, they must submit verification of legal blindness in both eyes; SAT, ACT, GRE, or similar scores; information on extracurricular activities (including involvement in the American Council of the Blind); employment record; and a 500-word autobiographical sketch that includes their personal goals, strengths, weaknesses, hobbies, honors, achievements, and reasons for choice of field or courses of study. A cumulative GPA of 3.3 or higher is generally required. Financial need is not considered in the selection process. Preference is given to students with little or no vision.

Financial data The stipend is $2,000.

Duration 1 year.

Additional data Scholarship winners are expected to attend the council's annual conference; the council will cover all reasonable expenses.

Number awarded 1 each year.

Deadline February of each year.

[353]
FERDINAND TORRES SCHOLARSHIP

American Foundation for the Blind
Attn: Scholarship Committee
2 Penn Plaza, Suite 1102
New York, NY 10121
(212) 502-7661   Toll Free: (800) AFB-LINE
Fax: (888) 545-8331   E-mail: afbinfo@afb.net
Web: www.afb.org/Section.asp?Documentid=2962

Summary To provide financial assistance for college or graduate school to blind students, especially immigrants and those from New York City.

Eligibility Applicants must be legally blind and reside in the United States, although U.S. citizenship is not necessary. They must present evidence of economic need, legal blindness, and acceptance into a full-time undergraduate or graduate program. Preference is given to new immigrants and residents of New York City. Along with their application, they must submit 200-word essays on 1) their past and recent achievements and accomplishments; 2) their intended field of study and why they have chosen it; 3) the role their visual impairment has played in shaping their life; and 4) their financial need, how they would use the scholarship if they receive it, and (for immigrants) their country of origin and their reasons for coming here.

Financial data The stipend is $3,500.

Duration 1 year.

Number awarded 1 each year.

Deadline April of each year.

[354]
FLORIDA CHAIRSCHOLARS PROGRAM

ChairScholars Foundation, Inc.
16101 Carencia Lane
Odessa, FL 33556-3278
(813) 926-0544   Toll Free: (888) 926-0544
Fax: (813) 920-7661
E-mail: chairscholars@tampabay.rr.com
Web: www.chairscholars.org/florida.html

Summary To provide funding to students in Florida with specified disabilities who plan to attend college in the state.

Eligibility This program is open to residents of Florida who are enrolled in grades 7-11 at a public school and have a serious physical disability. Qualifying disabilities include cerebral palsy, muscular dystrophy, spinal muscular atrophy, amputations, congenital missing or shortened limbs, multiple sclerosis, profound deafness, hearing impairments requiring FM modulator, blindness, various forms of cancer, any condition that permanently places the student in a wheelchair, or other illnesses, diseases, or conditions that severely impair mobility or motor skills. Applicants must have at least a "B" average and be able to demonstrate significant financial need (annual income less than $20,137 for a family of 1, rising to $69,616 for a family of 8). They must be planning to attend a college, university, community college, or vocational school in the state. Along with their application, they must submit a 1-page essay outlining how they became physically challenged, how their situation has affected them or their family, their family situation, things they like to do, why they need this scholarship, and their goals and dreams for the future.

Financial data The awards provide full payment of tuition at any public college, university, or community college, or vocational school in Florida.

Duration Up to 4 years.

Additional data This program began in 1996. Recipients are provided with a mentor until they graduate from high school. They must sign a "contract" pledging to remain drug and crime free.

Number awarded Varies each year; recently, 24 of these scholarships were awarded. Since the program was established, it has awarded 502 scholarships.

Deadline January of each year.

[355]
FLOYD CALLWARD MEMORIAL SCHOLARSHIP

National Federation of the Blind of New Hampshire
c/o Cassandra McNabb, President
12 Sumner Street, Apartment A
Keene, NH 03431
(603) 357-4080   E-mail: cemcnabb21@yahoo.com

Summary To provide funding to blind students in New Hampshire who are interested in working on a college or graduate degree in any state.

Eligibility This program is open to legally blind and totally blind residents of New Hampshire who are attending or planning to attend college or graduate school in any state. Applicants may be attending college immediately after high school, returning to college at a later age, attending graduate or professional school, or enrolled in postsecondary vocational training. Along with their application, they must submit 1) a letter describing what they have done to deal with situations involving their blindness, their personal goals and aspirations, and how the scholarship will help them; 2) 2 letters of recommendation; 3) high school or college transcripts; 4) a list of honors and awards; and 5) information on community service and volunteer work. There are no restrictions on level, gender, or field of study. Financial need is not considered.

Financial data The stipend is $1,000. The funds may be used to purchase education-related equipment or services or to defray the costs of tuition, board, and other school fees.

Duration 1 year.

Additional data This program was established in 1990.

Number awarded 1 or more each year.

Deadline October of each year.

[356]
FLOYD QUALLS MEMORIAL SCHOLARSHIPS

American Council of the Blind
Attn: Coordinator, Scholarship Program
2200 Wilson Boulevard, Suite 650
Arlington, VA 22201
(202) 467-5081   Toll Free: (800) 424-8666
Fax: (703) 465-5085   E-mail: info@acb.org
Web: www.acb.org/scholarship

Summary To provide funding to entering and continuing college and graduate students who are blind.

Eligibility This program is open to legally blind students in 4 categories: entering freshmen in academic programs, undergraduates (sophomores, juniors, and seniors) in academic programs, graduate students in academic programs, and vocational school students or students working on an associate's degree from a community college. Applicants must submit verification of legal blindness in both eyes; SAT, ACT, GRE, or similar scores; information on extracurricular activities (including involvement in the American Council of the Blind); employment record; and a 500-word autobiographical sketch that includes their personal goals, strengths, weaknesses, hobbies, honors, achievements, and reasons for choice of field or courses of study. Financial need is not considered. A cumulative GPA of 3.3 or higher is generally required.

Financial data The stipend is $2,500.

Duration 1 year.

Additional data Scholarship winners are expected to attend the council's annual conference; the council will cover all reasonable expenses.

Number awarded 1 in each of the 4 categories.

Deadline February of each year.

[357]
FRED SCHEIGERT SCHOLARSHIPS

Council of Citizens with Low Vision International
c/o American Council of the Blind
2200 Wilson Boulevard, Suite 650
Arlington, VA 22201
(202) 467-5081   Toll Free: (800) 733-2258
Fax: (703) 465-5085   E-mail: scholarship@cclvi.org
Web: www.cclvi.org/schguide.htm

Summary To provide funding to entering and continuing undergraduate and graduate students with low vision.

Eligibility This program is open to full-time undergraduate and graduate students who have been certified by an ophthalmologist as having low vision (acuity of 20/70 or worse in the better seeing eye with best correction or side vision with a maximum diameter of no greater than 30 degrees). Applicants may be entering freshmen, undergraduates, or graduate students. They must have a GPA of 3.2 or higher and a record of involvement in their school and/or local community.

Financial data The stipend is $3,000.

Duration 1 year.

Number awarded 3 each year: 1 each to an entering freshman, undergraduate, and graduate student.

Deadline February of each year.

[358]
FRIENDS IN ART SCHOLARSHIP

Friends in Art
c/o Nancy Pendegraph, President
2331 Poincianna Street
Huntsville, AL 35801
E-mail: nansong@knology.net
Web: www.friendsinart.com/scholarship.htm

Summary To provide financial assistance to blind students who are majoring or planning to major in fields related to the arts.

Eligibility This program is open to blind and visually impaired high school seniors and college students who are majoring or planning to major in music, art, drama, or creative writing. Applicants must be residents of North America. Music students must submit a tape with their performance of a fast piece and a slow piece; art students must submit 10 slides of their work; drama students must submit a tape with a dramatic presentation and a comic presentation; creative writing students must submit examples of their work. Selection is based on achievement, talent, and excellence in the arts.

Financial data The stipend is $1,500.

Duration 1 year.

Additional data This program began in 1999.

Number awarded 1 each year.

Deadline May of each year.

[359]
GAYLE M. KRAUSE-EDWARDS SCHOLARSHIP

Florida Council for the Blind
c/o Wanda L. Stokley, Education and Leadership
  Committee
111 Ponce De Leon
Tallahassee, FL 32305-3403
(850) 309-0821 E-mail: wandastokley@centurylink.net
Web: www.fcb.org/scholapp-info.htm

Summary To provide funding to blind residents of Florida who are attending college in any state and can demonstrate outstanding academic and leadership achievements.

Eligibility This program is open to blind residents of Florida who have completed at least 1 semester at a college or university in any state. Applicants must have a GPA of 3.2 or higher and be able to demonstrate outstanding academic and leadership achievements. Along with their application, they must submit a narrative statement on their vocational objectives and outlook for employment in their chosen field. Financial need is not considered.

Financial data The stipend is $2,000.

Duration 1 year.

Number awarded 1 each year.

Deadline March of each year.

[360]
GEORGIA COUNCIL OF THE BLIND SCHOLARSHIPS

Georgia Council of the Blind
850 Gaines School Road
Athens, GA 30605
(706) 208-7132   Toll Free: (888) 519-3988
E-mail: gcbfyi@yahoo.com
Web: www.georgiacounciloftheblind.org

Summary To provide funding to students in Georgia who plan to attend college or graduate school in any state and are either legally blind or have legally blind parents.

Eligibility This program is open to residents of Georgia who are either 1) legally blind students, or 2) sighted students financially dependent on legally blind parents. Applicants must be enrolled or accepted for enrollment at a vocational/technical school, a 2- or 4-year college, or a master's or doctoral program in any state. All fields of study are eligible. Selection is based on academic transcripts, 2 letters of recommendation, a 1-page typed statement of the applicant's educational goals, an audio cassette recording of the applicant reading the goals statement, extracurricular activities, and financial need.

Financial data Stipends range up to $1,000 per year.

Duration 1 year; recipients may reapply.

Additional data This program began in 1988.

Number awarded 1 or more each year.

Deadline June of each year.

[361]
GLADYS C. ANDERSON MEMORIAL SCHOLARSHIP

American Foundation for the Blind
Attn: Scholarship Committee
2 Penn Plaza, Suite 1102
New York, NY 10121
(212) 502-7661   Toll Free: (800) AFB-LINE
Fax: (888) 545-8331   E-mail: afbinfo@afb.net
Web: www.afb.org/Section.asp?Documentid=2962

Summary To provide financial assistance to legally blind women who are studying classical or religious music on the undergraduate or graduate school level.

Eligibility This program is open to women who are legally blind, U.S. citizens, and enrolled in an undergraduate or graduate degree program in classical or religious music. Along with their application, they must submit 200-word essays on 1) their past and recent achievements and accomplishments; 2) their intended field of study and why they have chosen it; and 3) the role their visual impairment has played in shaping their life. They must also submit a sample performance tape or CD of up to 30 minutes. Financial need is considered in the selection process.

Financial data The stipend is $1,000.

Duration 1 academic year.

Number awarded 1 each year.

Deadline April of each year.

[362]
GREATER FORT WORTH CHAPTER ACB OF TEXAS SCHOLARSHIP

American Council of the Blind of Texas-Greater Fort
  Worth Chapter
c/o Heidi Swan, Scholarship Chair
2101 Mayfield Villa Drive, Apartment 6103
Arlington, TX 76014-3592
(817) 466-0046 E-mail: fr1end2servant@sbcglobal.net
Web: acb-fw.org/scholarship.html

Summary To provide funding to blind Texas residents interested in attending college in any state.

Eligibility This program is open to residents of Texas who can document legal or total blindness. Applicants must be accepted for admission or currently enrolled at a college or vocational/trade school in any state. They must have a GPA of 3.0 or higher. Along with their application, they must submit an autobiography of 1 to 2 pages that includes family, hobbies, activities, community service, and educational and career goals. Selection is based on academic achievement, community service, and need.

Financial data A stipend is awarded (amount not specified).

Duration 1 year.

Additional data This scholarship was first awarded in 2011.

Number awarded 1 or more each year.

Deadline June of each year.

[363]
GUILDSCHOLAR PROGRAM

Jewish Guild for the Blind
Attn: GuildScholar Program
15 West 65th Street
New York, NY 10023
(212) 769-7801   Toll Free: (800) 284-4422
Fax: (212) 769-6266   E-mail: guildscholar@jgb.org
Web: www.jgb.org/guildscholar.asp?GS=TRue

Summary To provide financial assistance for college to blind high school seniors.

Eligibility This program is open to college-bound high school seniors who can document legal blindness. Applicants must submit copies of school transcripts and SAT or ACT scores, proof of U.S. citizenship, 3 letters of recommendation, proof of legal blindness, a 500-word personal statement describing their educational and personal goals, a 500-word essay describing the influence of an outstanding teacher on their education, and documentation of financial need (if they wish that to be considered).

Financial data The stipend ranges up to $15,000.

Duration 1 year.

Additional data This program was established in 2004.

Number awarded 12 to 16 each year.

Deadline June of each year (the end of the junior year of high school).

[364]
HANK HOFSTETTER OPPORTUNITY GRANTS

American Council of the Blind of Indiana
c/o James R. Durst
Indiana School for the Blind and Visually Impaired
7725 North College Avenue
Indianapolis, IN 46240
Web: acb-indiana.org/3/miscellaneous8.htm

Summary To provide funding to Indiana residents who are blind and need materials or equipment to continue their education or meet other goals.

Eligibility This fund is open to certified legally blind Indiana residents who are unable to obtain funding through other means. Applicants must need funding for an activity, materials, and/or equipment that will enhance their educational, entrepreneurial, or vocational aims. Along with their application, they must submit a 1-page statement on why they should be considered for a grant, a list of other options they have already tried, and a reference letter.

Financial data The amount awarded varies, depending upon the needs of the recipient. A total of $1,000 is available annually.

Number awarded 1 each year.

Deadline Requests may be submitted at any time but should be received at least 90 days prior to the need.

[365]
HARRY G. STARR ENDOWED SCHOLARSHIP

Lighthouse International
Attn: Scholarship and Career Awards
111 East 59th Street
New York, NY 10022-1202
(212) 821-9428   Toll Free: (800) 829-0500
Fax: (212) 821-9703   TDD: (212) 821-9713
E-mail: sca@lighthouse.org
Web: www.lighthouse.org

Summary To provide financial assistance to legally blind high school seniors, recent graduates, undergraduates, or graduate students.

Eligibility This program is open to legally blind U.S. citizens who are graduating high school seniors, recent graduates, current undergraduates, or current graduate students. Applicants must be attending or planning to attend an accredited college or university in 1 of the 50 states, the District of Columbia, or a U.S. territory. Along with their application, they must submit essays of 400 to 600 words on 1) their academic focus and extracurricular activities and what inspires their interest in each area; 2) their passion and how they express that passion; 3) key academic and personal accomplishments and the challenges they overcome to be successful; and 4) how this scholarship will support their academic and/or career development. Selection is based on academic and personal achievements; financial need is not considered.

Financial data The stipend is $10,000.

Duration 1 year.

Additional data This award was first presented in 2008.

Number awarded 1 each year.

Deadline January of each year.

[366]
HARRY LUDWIG MEMORIAL SCHOLARSHIP

Oregon Student Access Commission
Attn: Grants and Scholarships Division
1500 Valley River Drive, Suite 100
Eugene, OR 97401-2146
(541) 687-7395   Toll Free: (800) 452-8807, ext. 7395
Fax: (541) 687-7414   TDD: (800) 735-2900
E-mail: awardinfo@osac.state.or.us
Web: www.oregonstudentaid.gov/scholarships.aspx

Summary To provide financial assistance to residents of Oregon who are visually impaired and are interested in attending college or graduate school in the state.

Eligibility This program is open to residents of Oregon who are visually impaired (have residual acuity of 20/70 or less in the better eye with correction, or their visual field is restricted to 20 degrees or less in the better eye). Applicants must be enrolled or planning to enroll as full-time undergraduate or graduate students in Oregon.

Financial data Stipends for scholarships offered by the Oregon Student Access Commission (OSAC) range from $200 to $10,000 but recently averaged $2,300.

Duration 1 year.

Additional data This program is administered by the OSAC with funds provided by the Oregon Community Foundation.

Number awarded Varies each year; recently, 7 of these scholarships were awarded.

Deadline February of each year.

[367]
HAWAII ASSOCIATION OF THE BLIND SCHOLARSHIP

Hawaii Association of the Blind
Attn: Scholarship Committee
1255 Nuuanu Avenue, Number 1102
Honolulu, HI 96817
(808) 521-6213   E-mail: toyamaj005@hawaii.rr.com
Web: www.acb.org/hawaii/scholarship.htm

Summary To provide financial assistance to blind residents of Hawaii who plan to attend college in any state.

Eligibility This program is open to Hawaii residents who meet the legal definition of blindness or visual impairment. Applicants must be members of the American Council of the Blind but may not be members of any other national organization for the blind. They must submit high school and/or college transcripts, 2 letters of reference, and a 2-page letter describing their educational goals.

Financial data Stipends are at least $500 per semester ($1,000 per year).

Duration 1 year.

Number awarded 1 or more each year.

Deadline May of each year for fall semester; November of each year for spring semester.

[368]
HAZEL TEN BROEK MEMORIAL SCHOLARSHIP

National Federation of the Blind of Washington
Attn: Scholarship Chair
P.O. Box 2516
Seattle, WA 98111
(425) 823-6380   E-mail: president@nfbw.org
Web: www.nfbw.org/programs.html

Summary To provide funding for college or graduate studies in any state to blind students in Washington.

Eligibility This program is open to legally blind residents of Washington state who are working on or planning to work on a full-time college or graduate degree at a school in any state. Applicants must submit a list of honors and awards they have received, information on their community service involvement, high school and/or college transcripts, and 3 letters of reference.

Financial data The stipend is $2,000.

Duration 1 year.

Additional data This scholarship was first awarded in 1996. Winners must attend the state convention of the National Federation of the Blind of Washington to accept the award; convention expenses are covered.

Number awarded 1 each year.

Deadline August of each year.

[369]
ITALIAN CATHOLIC FEDERATION GIFTS OF LOVE FOR SPECIAL PEOPLE

Italian Catholic Federation
8393 Capwell Drive, Suite 110
Oakland, CA 94621
(510) 633-9058   Toll Free: (888) ICF-1924
Fax: (510) 633-9758   E-mail: info@icf.org
Web: www.icf.org/charitable.html

Summary To provide funding to individuals who have specific disabilities and need additional training or instruction.

Eligibility This program is open to 1) individuals who have a disability and desire formal training or instruction in a particular vocation, academic, athletic, or artistic field; 2) qualified instructors on behalf of an individual with a disability who exhibits a particular skill to be developed and who desires formal instruction or training; or 3) adults with custodial responsibility for, and on behalf of, an individual with a disability who exhibits a particular skill to be developed and who desires formal instruction or training. The program defines individuals with a disability as those who have mental retardation, hearing impairments, speech and language impairments, visual impairments, emotional disturbances, orthopedic impairments, autism, traumatic brain injury, other health impairments, specific learning disabilities, or multiple disabilities who, because of their needs, require special education or related services. Financial need is considered in the selection process.

Financial data A stipend is awarded (amount not specified).

Duration These are 1-time grants.

Number awarded Varies each year.

Deadline Deadline not specified.

[370]
JAMES DOYLE CASE MEMORIAL SCHOLARSHIPS

Mississippi Council of the Blind
c/o Kenneth Maddox
217 Taylor Street
Jackson, MS 39216
Web: www.acb.org/mcb

Summary To provide financial assistance to legally blind residents of Mississippi and their children who plan to attend college or graduate school in any state.

Eligibility This program is open to residents of Mississippi who are legally blind or the children of at least 1 legally blind parent. Applicants must be enrolled or accepted for enrollment in an undergraduate or graduate program in any state and carrying or planning to carry at least 12 academic hours. Along with their application, they must submit a 2-page autobiographical sketch, transcripts, standardized test scores (ACT or SAT for undergraduates; GRE, MCAT, LSAT, etc. for graduate students), 2 letters of recommendation, proof of acceptance from a postsecondary school, and verification of blindness of the qualifying person (applicant or parent).

Financial data The stipend is $1,500 per year.

Duration 4 years.

Number awarded 2 each year.

Deadline February of each year.

[371]
JAMES F. NELSON, JR. SCHOLARSHIPS

National Federation of the Blind of Virginia
Attn: Scholarship Committee
3230 Grove Avenue
Richmond, VA 23221
(703) 319-9226   E-mail: corbbo@gmail.com
Web: www.nfbv.org

Summary To provide financial assistance for college to blind students from Virginia.

Eligibility This program is open to legally blind students who are either residents of Virginia or enrolled full time at a college or university in the state. Applicants may be graduating high school seniors or current college students. Along with their application, they must submit 250-word essays on 1) their most notable quality; 2) their attitude about blindness; 3) how they have demonstrated leadership ability; 4) what the selection committee needs to know about them; and 5) the 2 questions they most want to ask the scholarship committee and why. Selection is based on academics, service, and leadership potential.

Financial data The stipend is $1,500.

Duration 1 year.

Number awarded 3 each year.

Deadline September of each year.

[372]
JAMES R. OLSEN MEMORIAL SCHOLARSHIP

American Council of the Blind
Attn: Coordinator, Scholarship Program
2200 Wilson Boulevard, Suite 650
Arlington, VA 22201
(202) 467-5081   Toll Free: (800) 424-8666
Fax: (703) 465-5085   E-mail: info@acb.org
Web: www.acb.org/scholarship

Summary To provide financial assistance to outstanding blind college students.

Eligibility This program is open to legally blind students enrolling or continuing in an undergraduate program. Applicants must submit verification of legal blindness in both eyes; SAT or ACT scores; information on extracurricular activities (including involvement in the American Council of the Blind); employment record; and a 500-word autobiographical sketch that includes their personal goals, strengths, weaknesses, hobbies, honors, achievements, and reasons for choice of field or courses of study. A cumulative GPA of 3.3 or higher is generally required. Financial need is not considered in the selection process.

Financial data The stipend is at least $1,000.

Duration 1 year.

Additional data Scholarship winners are expected to attend the council's annual conference; the council will cover all reasonable expenses.

Number awarded 1 each year.

Deadline February of each year.

[373]
JENNICA FERGUSON MEMORIAL SCHOLARSHIP OF OHIO

National Federation of the Blind of Ohio
c/o Barbara Pierce, Scholarship Committee Chair
237 Oak Street
Oberlin, OH 44074-1517
(440) 775-2216 E-mail: bpierce@nfb.org
Web: www.nfbohio.org

Summary To provide financial assistance to blind residents of Ohio who are interested in working on an undergraduate or graduate degree at a school in any state.

Eligibility This program is open to residents of Ohio who are legally blind. Applicants must be attending or planning to attend an accredited institution of higher education in any state as a full-time undergraduate or graduate student. Along with their application, they must submit 2 letters of recommendation, current transcripts, a letter about themselves that includes how they have dealt with their blindness and their hopes and dreams, and a letter from an officer of the National Federation of the Blind of Ohio indicating that they have discussed their scholarship application with that officer. Selection is based on academic excellence, community service, and financial need.

Financial data The stipend is $1,500.

Duration 1 year.

Number awarded 1 each year.

Deadline April of each year.

[374]
JOHN A. COCCOMO, SR. AWARDS

Connecticut Institute for the Blind
Attn: Vice President for Development
120 Holcomb Street
Hartford, CT 06112-1589
(860) 242-2274 Fax: (860) 242-3103
TDD: (860) 286-3113 E-mail: info@ciboakhill.org
Web: www.ciboakhill.org/ways_to_give/donor.asp

Summary To provide financial assistance for college to Connecticut high school seniors who are legally blind.

Eligibility This program is open to seniors graduating from high schools in Connecticut who are legally blind. Applicants must be planning to enroll in a postsecondary educational institution. They must be able to demonstrate financial need. Along with their application, they must submit answers to questions about their major accomplishments, who or what has helped them in their accomplishments, the extracurricular activities (including sports) in which they were involved in high school, their involvement in their community, their goals for the next 5 years, how an award would help them achieve their goals, how they will be financing their college education, and why they feel they should be considered for an award.

Financial data A stipend is awarded (amount not specified).

Duration 1 year.

Additional data This program was established in 1993. The Connecticut Institute for the Blind, doing business as Oak Hill, also operates independent living facilities in West Hartford and Wethersfield for blind, visually impaired, and disabled individuals.

Number awarded 1 or more each year.

Deadline December of each year.

[375]
JOHN HEBNER MEMORIAL SCHOLARSHIP

American Council of the Blind
Attn: Coordinator, Scholarship Program
2200 Wilson Boulevard, Suite 650
Arlington, VA 22201
(202) 467-5081 Toll Free: (800) 424-8666
Fax: (703) 465-5085 E-mail: info@acb.org
Web: www.acb.org/scholarship

Summary To provide funding for college to blind or visually impaired students who are also employed full time.

Eligibility This program is open to blind or visually impaired students who are employed full time. Applicants must submit verification of legal blindness in both eyes; SAT or ACT scores; information on extracurricular activities (including involvement in the American Council of the Blind); employment record; and a 500-word autobiographical sketch that includes their personal goals, strengths, weaknesses, hobbies, honors, achievements, and reasons for choice of field or courses of study. A cumulative GPA of 3.3 or higher is generally required. Financial need is not considered in the selection process.

Financial data The stipend is at least $1,000.

Duration 1 year.

Number awarded 1 each year.

Deadline February of each year.

[376]
JOHN T. MCCRAW SCHOLARSHIPS

National Federation of the Blind of Maryland
c/o Melissa Riccobono, President
1026 East 36th Street
Baltimore, MD 21218
(410) 645-0632 E-mail: president@nfbmd.org
Web: www.nfbmd.org/students.html

Summary To provide financial assistance for college to blind students from Maryland.

Eligibility This program is open to legally blind students who are residents of Maryland or enrolled full time at a university, 2- or 4-year college, or vocational/technical school in the state. Applicants must be able to demonstrate academic achievement and community involvement. Along with their application, they must submit 2 letters of recommendation, a current transcript, and a statement that describes the honors they have received, what they have done to deal with situations involving their blindness, what they are like as a person, their goals and aspirations, and how this scholarship will help them.

Financial data The stipend is either $2,000 or $1,500.

Duration 1 year; recipients may reapply.

Additional data A special scholarship may be awarded to former McCraw Scholarship recipients. To apply for this special scholarship, former recipients must still meet all of the requirements for the scholarship program and submit a new application. Recipients must attend the sponsor's annual convention; financial assistance to attend the convention may be provided if the recipient needs and requests it (this is in addition to the scholarship grant).

Number awarded 1 at $2,000 and 1 at $1,500.

Deadline April of each year.

[377]
JOSEPH ROEDER ASSISTIVE TECHNOLOGY SCHOLARSHIP

National Industries for the Blind
Attn: Scholarship Program
1310 Braddock Place
Alexandria, VA 22314-1691
(703) 310-0343 E-mail: kgallagher@nib.org
Web: www.nib.org/content/scholarship-application

Summary To provide funding to blind upper-division and graduate students preparing for a career in assistive technology.

Eligibility This program is open to blind college juniors, seniors, and graduate students working on a degree in computer science, information systems, or a related field to prepare for a career in assistive technology. Applicants must submit information about their work experience, community activities, years of experience using a screen reader, years of experience using a text magnification program, the adaptive technology they use, and an essay of 200 to 300 words on their career history and future career goals.

Financial data The stipend is $2,500.

Duration 1 year.

Additional data This scholarship was first awarded in 2011.

Number awarded 1 each year.

Deadline July of each year.

[378]
JUDY VAN NOSTRAND ARTS AWARD

Lighthouse International
Attn: Scholarship and Career Awards
111 East 59th Street
New York, NY 10022-1202
(212) 821-9428 Toll Free: (800) 829-0500
Fax: (212) 821-9703 TDD: (212) 821-9713
E-mail: sca@lighthouse.org
Web: www.lighthouse.org

Summary To provide financial assistance to legally blind high school seniors, recent graduates, undergraduates, or graduate students who are interested in working on a degree in the arts.

Eligibility This program is open to legally blind U.S. citizens who are graduating high school seniors, recent graduates, current undergraduates, or current graduate students. Applicants must be attending or planning to attend an accredited college or university in 1 of the 50 states, the District of Columbia, or a U.S. territory. They must be working on or planning to work on a degree in the arts (including graphic arts, music, visual arts, and writing). Along with their application, they must submit essays of 400 to 600 words on 1) their academic focus and extra-curricular activities and what inspires their interest in each area; 2) their passion and how they express that passion; 3) key academic and personal accomplishments and the challenges they overcome to be successful; and 4) how this scholarship will support their academic and/or career development. Selection is based on academic and personal achievements; financial need is not considered.

Financial data The stipend is $10,000.

Duration 1 year.

Number awarded 1 each year.

Deadline January of each year.

[379]
KANE SEE THE FUTURE FULL-RIDE TUITION SCHOLARSHIPS

The See the Future Fund
P.O. Box 63022
Colorado Springs, CO 80962-3022
(719) 471-3200 Fax: (719) 471-3210
E-mail: twtheune@prodigy.net
Web: seethefuture.org

Summary To provide financial assistance to blind or visually impaired high school seniors in Colorado who are planning to attend designated universities in the state.

Eligibility This program is open to seniors graduating from high schools in Colorado who meet standards of blindness or visual impairment. Applicants must be planning to enroll at the Colorado University campuses in Boulder, Colorado Springs, or Denver. They must 1) have a GPA of 3.4 or higher; 2) have taken at least 1 Advanced Placement (AP) or International Baccalaureate (IB) class during their junior or senior year and earned a grade of "A" or "B"; and 3) have an ACT composite score of at least 25. Selection is based on merit.

Financial data Stipends provide for full payment of tuition and fees at the designated Colorado University campuses and a grant of $1,500 for purchase of books.

Duration 1 year.

Additional data This program is sponsored by the Kane Foundation.

Number awarded Up to 2 each year.

Deadline February of each year.

[380]
KELLIE CANNON MEMORIAL SCHOLARSHIP

American Council of the Blind
Attn: Coordinator, Scholarship Program
2200 Wilson Boulevard, Suite 650
Arlington, VA 22201
(202) 467-5081 Toll Free: (800) 424-8666
Fax: (703) 465-5085 E-mail: info@acb.org
Web: www.acb.org/scholarship

Summary To provide funding to students who are blind and interested in preparing for a career in the computer field.
Eligibility This program is open to high school seniors, high school graduates, and college students who are blind and interested in majoring in computer information systems or data processing. Applicants must submit verification of legal blindness in both eyes; SAT or ACT scores; information on extracurricular activities (including involvement in the American Council of the Blind); employment record; and a 500-word autobiographical sketch that includes their personal goals, strengths, weaknesses, hobbies, honors, achievements, and reasons for choice of field or courses of study. A cumulative GPA of 3.3 or higher is generally required. Need is not considered in the selection process, but the severity of the applicant's visual impairment and study methods are taken into account.
Financial data The stipend is $1,000.
Duration 1 year.
Additional data This program is sponsored by Blind Information Technology Specialists (BITS), Inc., a special interest affiliate of the American Council of the Blind. Scholarship winners are expected to attend the council's annual conference; the council will cover all reasonable expenses.
Number awarded 1 each year.
Deadline February of each year.

[381]
KENNETH JERNIGAN SCHOLARSHIP

National Federation of the Blind
Attn: Scholarship Committee
200 East Wells Street
Baltimore, MD 21230
(410) 659-9314, ext. 2415   Fax: (410) 685-5653
E-mail: scholarships@nfb.org
Web: www.nfb.org/nfb/scholarship_program.asp

Summary To provide financial assistance to entering or continuing undergraduate and graduate blind students.
Eligibility This program is open to legally blind students who are working on or planning to work full time on an undergraduate or graduate degree. Along with their application, they must submit transcripts, standardized test scores, proof of legal blindness, 2 letters of recommendation, and a letter of endorsement from their National Federation of the Blind state president or designee. Selection is based on academic excellence, service to the community, and financial need.
Financial data The stipend is $12,000.
Duration 1 year; recipients may resubmit applications up to 2 additional years.
Additional data Scholarships are awarded at the federation convention in July. Recipients must attend the convention at federation expense; that funding is in addition to the scholarship grant. This scholarship is given by the American Action Fund for Blind Children and Adults, a nonprofit organization that assists blind people.
Number awarded 1 each year.
Deadline March of each year.

[382]
KENNETH TIEDE MEMORIAL SCHOLARSHIPS

National Federation of the Blind of Kansas
c/o Dianne Hemphill, Scholarship Chair
600 North Bel Rue Street
Derby, KS 67037-7300
(316) 201-1323   E-mail: diannehemphill@cox.net
Web: www.nfbks.org/conventions/scholarships.shtml

Summary To provide money for college or graduate school to blind students from Kansas.
Eligibility This program is open to legally blind undergraduate and graduate students who are residents of Kansas or attending or planning to attend a college, university, or technical school in the state. Applicants must have a GPA of 2.5 or higher. They must be able to attend the state convention of the National Federation of the Blind of Kansas. Selection is based on academic excellence, community service, and financial need.
Financial data Stipends range from $1,500 to $2,500.
Duration 1 year.
Number awarded Up to 5 each year.
Deadline May of each year.

[383]
LANCASTER SCHOLARSHIP

Susquehanna Foundation for the Blind
244 North Queen Street
Lancaster, PA 17603
(717) 291-5951
Web: www.sabvi.org/Grants%20and%20Scholarships

Summary To provide financial assistance to Pennsylvania residents who are legally blind veterans and interested in working on a degree at any level at a college in any state.
Eligibility This program is open to veterans who are residents of Pennsylvania and legally blind. Applicants must be attending or planning to attend an institution of higher education at any level in any state. Along with their application, they must submit a brief description of their career goal. Need is considered in the selection process.
Financial data The stipend is $1,000 per year.
Duration 1 year; renewable up to 3 more years.
Number awarded 1 or more each year.
Deadline January of each year.

[384]
LARRY STREETER MEMORIAL SCHOLARSHIP

National Federation of the Blind
Attn: Scholarship Committee
200 East Wells Street
Baltimore, MD 21230
(410) 659-9314, ext. 2415   Fax: (410) 685-5653
E-mail: scholarships@nfb.org
Web: www.nfb.org/nfb/scholarship_program.asp

Summary To provide funding to blind students working on an college or graduate degree in any field.
Eligibility This program is open to legally blind students who are working on or planning to work full time on an

undergraduate or graduate degree in any field. Applicants must be attempting to "elevate their quality of life, equipping them to be active, productive participants in their family, community, and the workplace." Along with their application, they must submit transcripts, standardized test scores, proof of legal blindness, 2 letters of recommendation, and a letter of endorsement from their National Federation of the Blind state president or designee. Selection is based on academic excellence, service to the community, and financial need.

Financial data The stipend is $3,000.

Duration 1 year; recipients may resubmit applications up to 2 additional years.

Additional data This program began in 2011. Scholarships are awarded at the federation convention in July. Recipients must attend the convention at federation expense; that funding is in addition to the scholarship grant.

Number awarded 1 each year.

Deadline March of each year.

[385]
LAVELLE FUND FOR THE BLIND SCHOLARSHIPS

Lavelle Fund for the Blind, Inc.
Attn: Scholarship Program Coordinator
307 West 38th Street, Suite 2010
New York, NY 10018
(212) 668-9801   Fax: (212) 668-9803
E-mail: lmamrosh@lavellefund.org
Web: www.lavellefund.org/lfb_scholarship_program.html

Summary To provide financial assistance to blind residents of the New York tri-state region who are attending designated colleges in the New York City area.

Eligibility This program is open to residents of Connecticut, New Jersey, and New York who are legally blind or severely visually impaired. Applicants must be working on or planning to work full time on an undergraduate or graduate degree at 1 of 8 designated colleges and universities in the New York City area. They must be able to demonstrate financial need.

Financial data Stipends range up to $15,000 per year, depending on the need of the recipient. Funds are paid directly to the college or university the recipient attends.

Duration 1 year; renewable up to 3 more years.

Additional data The participating schools are Dominican College, Fordham University (graduate study only), Manhattanville College, Marist College, Marymount Manhattan College, St. John's University (graduate study only), St. Thomas Aquinas College, and Seton Hall University.

Number awarded Varies each year.

Deadline Deadline not specified.

[386]
LHB INDUSTRIES CONTINUING EDUCATION PROGRAM

Lighthouse for the Blind
Attn: Continuing Education Program
10440 Trenton Avenue
St. Louis, MO 63132-1223
(314) 423-4333, ext. 132   Toll Free: (800) 542-3697
Fax: (314) 423-0139
E-mail: ayorke@lhbindustries.com
Web: www.lhbindustries.com

Summary To provide funding for continuing education to legally blind residents of Missouri and western Illinois.

Eligibility This program is open to legally blind residents of Missouri and the surrounding counties of western Illinois. Also eligible are the sighted children of legally blind employees of the St. Louis Lighthouse for the Blind (LHB). Applicants must be enrolled full time in elementary, middle, high school, college, or trade school. They must be interested in a program of continuing education that may include adaptive equipment (to facilitate education), college tuition, or training that enables an individual to succeed in academic endeavors. Selection is based on merit, demonstrated achievement, ambition, drive, dedication, volunteer record, and demonstrated leadership.

Financial data Grants range from $250 to $6,000 per year.

Duration 1 year; may be renewed, provided the recipient maintains a GPA of 2.0 or higher.

Number awarded Varies each year.

Deadline Applications may be submitted at any time; grants are awarded on a first-come, first-served basis.

[387]
LIONS CLUBS SUPPORT SERVICES FOR THE BLIND AND VISUALLY IMPAIRED

Lions Clubs International
Attn: Program Development Department
300 West 22nd Street
Oak Brook, IL 60523-8842
(630) 571-5466, ext. 316   Fax: (630) 571-1692
E-mail: programs@lionsclubs.org
Web: www.lionsclubs.org

Summary To provide college scholarships and other assistance (transportation, assistive technology, Braille products, etc.) to blind people.

Eligibility These programs are open to blind people and others involved in service to the blind. Applicants may be seeking support for the following activities: scholarships for the blind and visually impaired, medical research, assistive technology grants, independent mobility, transportation, reading materials and aids, audio products, Braille products, and other aids.

Financial data The amount of this assistance varies.

Additional data Support is provided by local Lions Clubs. Requests sent to the international office are referred to the appropriate district governor, who then sends the inquiries to an appropriate club within the district. No funds are available from the office of Lions Clubs International.

Deadline Deadline not specified.

[388]
MARY P. OENSLAGER SCHOLASTIC ACHIEVEMENT AWARDS

Learning Ally
Attn: Training and Support Center
20 Roszel Road
Princeton, NJ 08540
(609) 243-7087   Toll Free: (800) 221-4792
Fax: (609) 987-8116
E-mail: mGreenwald@LearningAlly.org
Web: www.learningally.org/awards

Summary To recognize and reward the outstanding academic achievements of blind college seniors and graduate students.

Eligibility To be eligible for this award, candidates must 1) be legally blind; 2) have received, or will receive, a bachelor's, master's, or doctoral degree from a 4-year accredited college or university in the United States or its territories during the year the award is given; 3) have an overall academic average of 3.0 or higher; and 4) have been registered members of Learning Ally for at least 1 year. Selection is based on academic excellence, leadership, and service to others.

Financial data Top winners receive $6,000 each, special honors winners $3,000 each, and honors winners $1,000 each.

Duration The awards are presented annually.

Additional data These awards are named for the founder of the program who established it in 1959 and endowed it with a gift of $1 million in 1990. Learning Ally was formerly named Recording for the Blind and Dyslexic.

Number awarded 9 each year: 3 top winners, 3 special honors winners, and 3 honors winners.

Deadline March of each year.

[389]
MARY ZOE ALLEE SCHOLARSHIP

Wyoming Council of the Blind
c/o Betty Matthews
374 West Alger, Apartment A
Sheridan, WY 82801
E-mail: bettymatt88@bresnan.net
Web: www.wycb.info/scholarship.html

Summary To provide financial assistance to blind residents of Wyoming who are interested in attending college or graduate school in any state.

Eligibility This program is open to residents of Wyoming who are legally blind or visually impaired. Applicants must be entering or enrolled at a vocational training program, college, university, community college, or graduate school in any state. Along with their application, they must submit a 2-page autobiographical sketch that includes their goals, strengths, weaknesses, hobbies, honors, achievements, the field of study they have chosen, and the reason why they have chosen it. Financial need is not con-

sidered in the selection process. Leading candidates are interviewed.

Financial data The stipend is $1,000.

Duration 1 year.

Number awarded 1 each year.

Deadline April of each year.

[390]
MASSACHUSETTS REHABILITATION COMMISSION OR COMMISSION FOR THE BLIND TUITION WAIVER PROGRAM

Massachusetts Office of Student Financial Assistance
454 Broadway, Suite 200
Revere, MA 02151
(617) 391-6070   Fax: (617) 727-0667
E-mail: osfa@osfa.mass.edu
Web: www.osfa.mass.edu

Summary To provide financial assistance for college to Massachusetts residents who are clients of specified disability agencies in the state.

Eligibility Applicants for this assistance must be certified as clients by the Massachusetts Rehabilitation Commission or Commission for the Blind. They must have been permanent residents of Massachusetts for at least 1 year, must be U.S. citizens or permanent residents, and may not be in default on any federal student loan.

Financial data Eligible clients are exempt from tuition payments at public colleges or universities in Massachusetts.

Duration Up to 4 years (130 semester hours.

Additional data Recipients may enroll either part or full time in a Massachusetts publicly-supported institution.

Number awarded Varies each year.

Deadline Deadline not specified.

[391]
MAX EDELMAN SCHOLARSHIP

American Council of the Blind of Ohio
Attn: Executive Director
P.O. Box 307128
Gahanna, OH 43230-7128
(614) 221-6688   Toll Free: (800) 835-2226 (within OH)
E-mail: mary.hiland@wowway.com
Web: www.acbohio.org

Summary To provide financial assistance to entering or continuing undergraduate students in Ohio who are blind.

Eligibility This program is open to 1) residents of Ohio who are high school seniors or current college students, and 2) students at colleges and universities in Ohio. Applicants must be legally blind and working on or planning to work on an undergraduate degree in any field. Along with their application, they must submit transcripts (must have a GPA of 3.0 or higher), a certificate of legal blindness, and an essay of 250 to 500 words on their career objectives, future plans, personal goals, other academic or personal qualities, and why they believe they are qualified to receive this scholarship. Financial need is not the only factor considered in the selection process.

Financial data The stipend is $2,000 per year.

Duration 1 year; recipients may reapply.

Additional data Winners are required to attend the Saturday morning business meeting and Sunday breakfast of the sponsor's annual convention; a stipend for meals and workshops is provided.

Number awarded 1 each year.

Deadline August of each year.

[392]
MCGREGOR SCHOLARSHIP PROGRAM

Iowa Braille School
Attn: Scholarship Committee
1002 G Avenue
Vinton, IA 52349
(319) 472-5221, ext. 1105
Toll Free: (800) 645-4579 (within IA)
Fax: (319) 472-4371
E-mail: mcgregorscholar@iowa-braille.k12.ia.us
Web: www.iowa-braille.k12.ia.us

Summary To provide financial assistance for college to Iowa residents who are blind.

Eligibility This program is open to residents of Iowa who became blind or visually impaired prior to reaching the age of 21. Applicants must be graduating high school seniors, high school graduates, or GED recipients who are within 8 years of high school graduation or receipt of the GED. They must be enrolled or planning to enroll full time at an accredited college, university, or vocational school in any state and have a GPA of 2.5 or higher. Along with their application, they must submit an autobiography (300 to 500 words) that includes a statement of their goals and how this scholarship will help them achieve them.

Financial data The stipend is $2,500 per year.

Duration 1 year; may be renewed if the recipient maintains a GPA of 2.5 or higher.

Additional data Information on this program is available from the Teachers of the Visually Impaired throughout Iowa, the Iowa Department for the Blind, and the Iowa Braille School.

Number awarded Varies each year; recently, 7 of these scholarships were awarded.

Deadline April of each year.

[393]
MICHAEL J. MCGOWAN LEADERSHIP SCHOLARSHIP AWARD

National Organization for Albinism and
  Hypopigmentation
Attn: Scholarship Committee
P.O. Box 959
East Hampstead, NH 03826-0959
(603) 887-2310   Toll Free: (800) 473-2310
Fax: (800) 648-2310
E-mail: scholarship@albinism.org
Web: www.albinism.org/noahprojects.html

Summary To provide financial assistance to undergraduate students with albinism.

Eligibility This program is open to students with albinism who are enrolled or planning to enroll in an undergraduate program at an institution of higher education in the United States or Canada. Applicants must submit a 500-word essay on their leadership potential, extracurricular involvement, academic achievement, educational background, and vocational goals; an eye report documenting a diagnosis of albinism; at least 2 letters of recommendation; an academic transcript (including SAT/ACT scores, if applicable); and a letter of acceptance of proof of enrollment from an institution of higher learning.

Financial data The stipend is $3,000.

Duration 1 year.

Additional data Albinism frequently leads to vision difficulties. This program began in 2008.

Number awarded 1 each year.

Deadline April of each year.

[394]
MISSOURI COUNCIL OF THE BLIND SCHOLARSHIPS

Missouri Council of the Blind
5453 Chippewa Street
St. Louis, MO 63109-1635
(314) 832-7172 Toll Free: (800) 342-5632 (within MO)
Fax: (314) 832-7796   E-mail: aa@moblind.org
Web: www.moblind.org

Summary To provide financial assistance for college or graduate school to blind students in Missouri.

Eligibility This program is open to Missouri residents who are high school or college graduates, legally blind, and in good academic standing. Applicants must be working on or planning to work on an undergraduate or graduate degree. They should have a specific goal in mind and that goal should be realistically within reach.

Financial data A stipend is awarded (amount not specified).

Duration 1 year; may be renewed if the recipient maintains a GPA of 2.0 or higher.

Number awarded Varies each year; recently, 14 of these scholarships were awarded.

Deadline April of each year.

[395]
MISSOURI REHABILITATION SERVICES FOR THE BLIND

Missouri Department of Social Services
Attn: Family Support Division
615 Howerton Court
P.O. Box 2320
Jefferson City, MO 65102-2320
(573) 751-4249   Fax: (573) 751-4984
TDD: (800) 735-2966
Web: www.dss.mo.gov/fsd/rsb

Summary To provide support to blind and visually impaired Missouri residents engaged in rehabilitation training, including enrollment at a college or university.

Eligibility This program is open to residents of Missouri who qualify as visually impaired, ranging from those who cannot read regular print to those who are totally blind. Applicants must be engaged in a program of vocational rehabilitation, including full-time enrollment at a college or university in Missouri or another state.

Financial data A range of support services are available. For college students, that includes transportation; housing and maintenance (up to the cost of double occupancy dormitory charges at the University of Missouri at Columbia); books, equipment, tools, and supplies; reader service; and interpreter service for deaf-blind persons.

Duration Qualified blind people are eligible for this assistance as long as they are attending college.

Number awarded Varies each year.

Deadline Deadline not specified.

[396]
MOUSE HOLE SCHOLARSHIPS

Blind Mice, Inc.
16810 Pinemoor Way
Houston, TX 77058
(713) 893-7277   E-mail: blindmicemart@att.net
Web: www.blindmicemegamall.com

Summary To provide financial assistance for college to blind students and the children of blind parents.

Eligibility This program is open to visually impaired students and to sighted students who have visually impaired parents. Applicants must be high school seniors or graduates who have never been enrolled in college. Along with their application, they must submit an essay, between 4 and 15 pages in length, on a topic that changes annually; recently, students were asked to speculate on what their life will be like in 10 years. Essays are judged on originality, creativity, grammar, spelling, and the judge's overall impression of the applicant.

Financial data Stipends are $2,000 for the winner and $1,000 for the first runner-up.

Duration 1 year.

Additional data These scholarships were first awarded in 2003. The winner receives the Antonia M. Derks Memorial Scholarship and the first runner-up receives the Kelsey Campbell Memorial Scholarship.

Number awarded 2 each year.

Deadline May of each year.

[397]
NATIONAL FEDERATION OF THE BLIND OF ARIZONA SCHOLARSHIP

National Federation of the Blind of Arizona
c/o Marcus Schmidt, Scholarship Committee Chair
3202 West Muriel Drive
Phoenix, AZ 85053
(602) 942-0181   E-mail: nfbazwest@gmail.com
Web: www.az.nfb.org/node/36

Summary To provide financial assistance for college or graduate school to blind residents of Arizona.

Eligibility This program is open to residents of Arizona who are legally blind in both eyes and currently attending high school or college. Applicants must be enrolled or planning to enroll as a full-time undergraduate or graduate

student at a college or university in any state. Along with their application, they must submit a 1,000-word essay about themselves, including their most notable qualities, their attitude about blindness, their community involvement, and their demonstrated leadership ability. High school seniors must also submit SAT or ACT scores.

Financial data The stipend is $1,000.

Duration 1 year.

Number awarded 1 each year.

Deadline May of each year.

[398]
NATIONAL FEDERATION OF THE BLIND OF CALIFORNIA SCHOLARSHIPS

National Federation of the Blind of California
c/o Mary Willows, President
39481 Gallaudet Drive, Apartment 127
Fremont, CA 94538
(510) 248-0100   Toll Free: (877) 558-6524
E-mail: mwillows@sbcglobal.net
Web: sixdots.org/category/grants-and-scholarships

Summary To provide financial assistance to blind residents of California interested in attending college or graduate school in any state.

Eligibility This program is open to residents of California who are legally blind. Applicants must be enrolled or planning to enroll as a full-time student in an undergraduate or graduate degree program in any state. They must have a GPA of 3.0 or higher. Along with their application, they must submit a 500-word statement on their educational and career goals, their involvement in the blindness community, the alternative techniques they use to do their school work (e.g., Braille, large print, recording, adapted computer), and any rehabilitation services they are receiving.

Financial data Stipends range from $2,000 to $5,000.

Duration 1 year.

Additional data This program includes the following named awards: the Gerald Drake Memorial Scholarship, the LaVyrl "Pinky" Johnson Memorial Scholarship, the Julie Landucci Scholarship, and the Lawrence "Muzzy" Marcelino Memorial Scholarship.

Number awarded Several each year.

Deadline September of each year.

[399]
NATIONAL FEDERATION OF THE BLIND OF COLORADO SCHOLARSHIP

National Federation of the Blind of Colorado
Attn: Scholarship Committee
2233 West Shepperd Avenue
Littleton, CO 80120-2038
(303) 778-1130   Toll Free: (800) 401-4NFB
Fax: (303) 778-1598   E-mail: nfbco@nfbco.org
Web: www.nfbco.org

Summary To provide financial assistance to legally blind residents of Colorado who are interested in attending college in any state.

Eligibility This program is open to legally blind residents of Colorado who are enrolled or planning to enroll as a full-time student at a college or university in any state (except for 1 scholarship reserved for an applicant who is employed full time and studying part time). Applicants must submit 2 letters of recommendation, current transcripts, a personal letter that describes their best qualities, and a letter from a state officer of the National Federation of the Blind of Colorado indicating that they have discussed their scholarship application with that officer. Selection is based on academic excellence, service to the community, and financial need.

Financial data Stipend range from $800 to $6,000.

Duration 1 year; recipients may reapply.

Number awarded Varies each year; a total of $15,000 is available for this program annually.

Deadline April of each year.

[400]
NATIONAL FEDERATION OF THE BLIND OF CONNECTICUT SCHOLARSHIPS

National Federation of the Blind of Connecticut
477 Connecticut Boulevard, Suite 217
East Hartford, CT 06108
(860) 289-1971   E-mail: info@nfbct.org
Web: www.nfbct.org/html/schform.htm

Summary To provide financial assistance for college or graduate school to blind students from Connecticut.

Eligibility This program is open to full-time undergraduate and graduate students who are legally blind. Applicants must be residents of Connecticut or attending school in the state. Along with their application, they must submit 2 letters of recommendation, academic transcripts, a description of their career goals and how this scholarship might help them achieve those, and a letter from a state officer of the National Federation of the Blind of Connecticut confirming that they have discussed their application with him or her. Selection is based on academic excellence, service to the community, and financial need.

Financial data Stipends are $8,000, $4,000, or $3,000.

Duration 1 year.

Additional data This program consists of the following named awards: the C. Rodney Demarest Memorial Scholarship ($3,000), the Howard E. May Memorial Scholarship ($6,000), the Jonathan May Memorial Scholarship ($5,000), and the Mary Main Memorial Scholarship ($4,000). The latter 3 programs are supported by the John A. Coccomo, Sr. Foundation. Recipients are expected to attend the annual convention of the National Federation of the Blind of Connecticut.

Number awarded 4 each year.

Deadline September of each year.

[401]
NATIONAL FEDERATION OF THE BLIND OF IDAHO SCHOLARSHIPS

National Federation of the Blind of Idaho
c/o Elsie Dickerson, President
211 N 70 E
Malad City, ID 83252-1209
(208) 766-2266   E-mail: elsiedickerson@ymail.com
Web: www.nfbidaho.org/scholarships.html

Summary To provide financial assistance for college to blind residents of Idaho.

Eligibility This program is open to blind residents of Idaho who are enrolled or planning to enroll in college. Selection is based on academic achievement, community service, and financial need.

Financial data Stipends are either $1,000 or $500.

Duration 1 year.

Additional data The $1,000 scholarship is sponsored by Weyerhaeuser Foundation.

Number awarded 1 at $1,000 and 1 at $500.

Deadline March of each year.

[402]
NATIONAL FEDERATION OF THE BLIND OF ILLINOIS SCHOLARSHIPS

National Federation of the Blind of Illinois
c/o Deborah Kent Stein, Scholarship Committee Chair
5817 North Nina Avenue
Chicago, IL 60631
(773) 631-1093   E-mail: dkent5817@att.net
Web: www.nfbofillinois.org/?page_id=97

Summary To provide financial assistance for college or graduate school to blind students in Illinois.

Eligibility This program is open to legally blind full-time undergraduate and graduate students. Applicants must be residents of Illinois or attending a college or university in the state. Along with their application, they must submit a personal essay that describes their strengths, achievements, and aspirations; what is important to them; who they hope to become; if a particular person or experience has changed their life; how their blindness has affected them; and how they handle blindness at school, on the job, and in interpersonal relationships. Selection is based on academic excellence and service to the community.

Financial data Stipends range from $1,250 to $2,000.

Duration 1 year; recipients may reapply.

Additional data This program consists of the following named awards: the Peter Grunwald Scholarship (1 awarded at $2,000), the Mary MacDill Napheide Scholarships (2 awarded at $1,500 each), and the Kenneth Jernigan Scholarships (2 awarded at $1,250 each).

Number awarded 5 each year.

Deadline March of each year.

[403]
NATIONAL FEDERATION OF THE BLIND OF KENTUCKY SCHOLARSHIPS

National Federation of the Blind of Kentucky
c/o Cathy Jackson, President
210 Cambridge Drive
Louisville, KY 40214
(502) 366-2317   E-mail: president@nfbky.org
Web: www.nfbky.org/scholarship.php

Summary To provide financial assistance for college to blind students from Kentucky.

Eligibility This program is open to legally blind and visually impaired students attending or planning to attend a postsecondary institution. Applicants must be residents of Kentucky or attending a college or university in the state. They must be eligible for services from the Kentucky Office for the Blind. Along with their application, they must submit a 2-page letter describing how the scholarship will help them achieve their career goals; how they are involved in their community, organizations, and other activities; any honors, awards, or special recognition they have received; and how they would like to be involved in the National Federation of the Blind of Kentucky.

Financial data The stipend is $1,000.

Duration 1 year.

Additional data This program includes the following named awards: the Allen Scholarship and the Emerson Foulke Memorial Scholarship. Finalists are required to attend and participate in the annual convention of the National Federation of the Blind of Kentucky; travel, hotel accommodations, registration fees, and banquet tickets are provided.

Number awarded Varies each year; recently, 3 of these scholarships were awarded.

Deadline May of each year.

[404]
NATIONAL FEDERATION OF THE BLIND OF LOUISIANA SCHOLARSHIPS

National Federation of the Blind of Louisiana
c/o Joshua Boudreaux, Scholarship Committee Chair
Louisiana Center for the Blind
101 South Trenton Street
Ruston, LA 71270
(318) 251-2891   Toll Free: (800) 234-4166 (within LA)
Fax: (318) 251-0109
E-mail: jboudreau@lcb-ruston.com
Web: www.nfbla.org/pages/scholarships.html

Summary To provide funding to blind Louisiana residents interested in attending college in any state.

Eligibility This program is open to residents of Louisiana who are legally blind. Applicants must be enrolled or planning to enroll in a full-time postsecondary program of study or training at an accredited college, university, or trade/technical school in any state. Selection is based on academic excellence, leadership ability, service to the community, and financial need.

Financial data Stipends range from $500 to $1,500.

Duration 1 year; recipients may reapply.

Additional data Recipients must attend the annual convention of the National Federation of the Blind of Louisiana. Convention expenses are covered.

Number awarded Varies each year.

Deadline February of each year.

[405]
NATIONAL FEDERATION OF THE BLIND OF MINNESOTA SCHOLARSHIP

National Federation of the Blind of Minnesota
c/o Jennifer Dunnam, President
100 East 22nd Street
Minneapolis, MN 55404
(612) 872-9363
E-mail: jennifer.dunnam1829@gmail.com
Web: members.tcq.net/nfbmn/students/scholarship.htm

Summary To provide funding to blind residents of Minnesota who are interested in attending college in the state.

Eligibility This program is open to residents of Minnesota who are blind or visually impaired. Applicants must be attending or planning to attend a college, university, or technical school in the state. Along with their application, they must submit a personal letter on their goals and academic and community activities, official transcripts, and 2 letters of recommendation. Selection is based on scholastic excellence and community and campus service.

Financial data The stipend is $1,500 or $1,000.

Duration 1 year.

Additional data The recipient must attend the national convention of the National Federation of the Blind; all expenses are paid.

Number awarded 1 at $1,500 and 1 at $1,000.

Deadline April of each year.

[406]
NATIONAL FEDERATION OF THE BLIND OF MISSISSIPPI SCHOLARSHIPS

National Federation of the Blind of Mississippi
c/o Linda Howard, Scholarship Committee Chair
104 Derby Drive
Madison, MS 39110-8038
(601) 209-4557
Web: nfbofmississippi.org

Summary To provide financial assistance to blind residents of Mississippi who are interested in attending college in any state.

Eligibility This program is open to residents of Mississippi who are legally blind and attending or planning to attend a college or university in any state. Applicants must submit their SAT or ACT scores, a list of honors and awards, information on their community service, and a personal letter about themselves that conveys their best qualities. Selection is based on academic excellence, community service, and financial need.

Financial data A stipend is awarded (amount not specified).

Duration 1 year.

Number awarded 1 or more each year.

Deadline January of each year.

[407]
NATIONAL FEDERATION OF THE BLIND OF NEBRASKA SCHOLARSHIP

National Federation of the Blind of Nebraska
c/o Shane Buresh, Scholarship Committee Chair
6210 Walker Avenue
Lincoln, NE 68507-2468
(402) 465-5468   E-mail: scholarship@ne.nfb.org
Web: www.ne.nfb.org/scholarship_app

Summary To provide financial assistance to blind residents of Nebraska who plan to attend college in any state.

Eligibility This program is open to residents of Nebraska who are blind and attending or planning to attend a postsecondary institution in any state. Applicants must submit a letter that describes their educational plans, vocational goals, and awards. Their letter should also explain how they deal with situations involving their blindness and how the scholarship will help them.

Financial data The maximum stipend is $1,000.

Duration 1 year.

Number awarded 5 each year: the sponsor awards 1 scholarship at $1,000; other scholarships are presented by its Lincoln and Omaha chapters and by the Nebraska Association of Blind Students.

Deadline September of each year.

[408]
NATIONAL FEDERATION OF THE BLIND OF NEVADA SCHOLARSHIP

National Federation of the Blind of Nevada
c/o Rena Smith, President
1344 North Jones Boulevard
Las Vegas, NV 89108
(702) 228-4217   E-mail: realhappygirl1@gmail.com
Web: nfbnevada.org

Summary To provide financial assistance to members of the National Federation of the Blind (NFB) in Nevada who are interested in attending college in any state.

Eligibility This program is open to residents of Nevada who are legally blind and graduating high school seniors or students currently enrolled at a college, university, or trade school in any state. Applicants must be NFB members. Along with their application, they must submit a letter explaining their reasons for applying for the scholarship, 3 letters of reference (including 1 from an officer in the NFB), and their most recent transcript.

Financial data The stipend is $1,250.

Duration 1 year.

Additional data This scholarship was first awarded in 2011. Recipients are required to attend the NFB of Nevada state convention.

Number awarded 1 each year.

Deadline October of each year.

[409]
NATIONAL FEDERATION OF THE BLIND OF NEW JERSEY SCHOLARSHIPS

National Federation of the Blind of New Jersey
c/o Jerilyn Higgins, Scholarship Chair
2 Old Farm Road
Verona, NJ 07044-1726
(973) 239-8874   Toll Free: (866) 632-1940
E-mail: jdhiggins3@verizon.net
Web: www.nfbnj.org/scholarships.php

Summary To provide financial assistance to entering and continuing undergraduate and graduate students from New Jersey who are blind.

Eligibility This program is open to legally blind students who are working on or planning to work full time on an undergraduate or graduate degree. Applicants must be residents of New Jersey or attending school in the state. Along with their application, they must submit a personal letter, 2 letters of recommendation, transcripts, and a letter of endorsement from an officer of the National Federation of the Blind of New Jersey. Selection is based on academic excellence, service to the community, and financial need.

Financial data A stipend is awarded (amount not specified).

Duration 1 year.

Number awarded 1 or more each year.

Deadline March of each year.

[410]
NATIONAL FEDERATION OF THE BLIND OF NEW YORK SCHOLARSHIPS

National Federation of the Blind of New York State, Inc.
P.O. Box 205666 Sunset Station
Brooklyn, NY 11220
(718) 567-7821   Fax: (718) 765-1843
E-mail: office@nfbny.org
Web: www.nfbny.org/Scholsrships.htm

Summary To provide financial assistance to blind residents of New York who are interested in attending college or graduate school in any state.

Eligibility This program is open to residents of New York who are legally blind. Applicants must be entering or enrolled in a degree program at the undergraduate, graduate, or postgraduate level at a school in any state. Along with their application, they must submit a 500-word essay explaining their goals, attitudes, and approach to living with blindness.

Financial data A stipend is awarded (amount not specified).

Duration 1 year.

Additional data This program includes the following named awards: the Gisela Distal Memorial Scholarship and the Maryanne Swaton Memorial Scholarship.

Number awarded At least 3 each year.

Deadline October of each year.

[411]
NATIONAL FEDERATION OF THE BLIND OF OHIO SCHOLARSHIP

National Federation of the Blind of Ohio
c/o Barbara Pierce, Scholarship Committee Chair
237 Oak Street
Oberlin, OH 44074-1517
(440) 775-2216   E-mail: bpierce@nfb.org
Web: www.nfbohio.org

Summary To provide financial assistance to blind residents of Ohio who are interested in working on an undergraduate or graduate degree at a school in any state.

Eligibility This program is open to residents of Ohio who are legally blind. Applicants must be attending or planning to attend an accredited institution of higher education as a full-time undergraduate or graduate student. Along with their application, they must submit 2 letters of recommendation, current transcripts, a letter about themselves that includes how they have dealt with their blindness and their hopes and dreams, and a letter from an officer of the National Federation of the Blind of Ohio indicating that they have discussed their scholarship application with that officer. Selection is based on academic excellence, community service, and financial need.

Financial data The stipend is $1,000.

Duration 1 year.

Number awarded 1 each year.

Deadline April of each year.

[412]
NATIONAL FEDERATION OF THE BLIND OF OREGON SCHOLARSHIPS

National Federation of the Blind of Oregon
c/o Art Stevenson, President
1616 Fifth Street N.E.
Salem, OR 97303
(503) 585-4318   Toll Free: (800) 422-7093 (within OR)
E-mail: artds55@comcast.net
Web: www.nfb-oregon.org/scholarship.php

Summary To provide financial assistance for college or graduate school to blind residents of Oregon.

Eligibility This program is open to blind residents of Oregon who are working on or planning to work on an undergraduate or graduate degree at a college or university in the state. Applicants must be enrolled full time or enrolled part time and working full time. Along with the application, they must submit a personal letter that includes what they consider their best qualities and the techniques and approaches they practice concerning their blindness. Selection is based on academic excellence, community service, and financial need.

Financial data Stipends are either $1,500 or $1,000.

Duration 1 year.

Number awarded 1 at $1,500 and 2 at $1,000.

Deadline March of each year.

[413]
NATIONAL FEDERATION OF THE BLIND OF PENNSYLVANIA SCHOLARSHIPS

National Federation of the Blind of Pennsylvania
Attn: Scholarship Committee
42 South 15th Street, Suite 222
Philadelphia, PA 19102
(215) 988-0888   E-mail: zrb5030@psu.edu
Web: students.nfbp.org

Summary To provide financial assistance to blind residents of Pennsylvania who are interested in attending college in any state.

Eligibility This program is open to residents of Pennsylvania who are legally blind. Applicants must be enrolled or planning to enroll full time at a college or university in any state. Along with their application, they must submit a personal letter about themselves, especially the techniques and approaches they use to overcome blindness. Selection is based on academic excellence, community service, and financial need.

Financial data The stipend is $1,000.

Duration 1 year.

Number awarded 2 each year.

Deadline August of each year.

[414]
NATIONAL FEDERATION OF THE BLIND OF SOUTH CAROLINA SCHOLARSHIPS

National Federation of the Blind of South Carolina
Attn: Scholarship Committee
119 South Kilbourne Road
Columbia, SC 29205
(803) 254-3777   Fax: (803) 252-5655
E-mail: nfbsc@sc.rr.com
Web: www.nfbsc.net/scholarship.html

Summary To provide financial assistance for college to legally blind students from South Carolina.

Eligibility This program is open to legally blind undergraduates who are residents of South Carolina or attending a college or university in the state. Applicants must submit 2 letters of recommendation, a current transcript, ACT and/or SAT test scores (high school seniors only), and a 250-word personal letter explaining their reasons for applying for a scholarship and how it will assist them to achieve a professional goal. Selection is based on academic excellence, community service, and financial need.

Financial data A stipend is awarded (amount not specified).

Duration 1 year.

Additional data Winners are required to attend the annual convention of the National Federation of the Blind of South Carolina at the federation's expense.

Number awarded 1 or more each year.

Deadline May of each year.

[415]
NATIONAL FEDERATION OF THE BLIND OF TEXAS MERIT SCHOLARSHIPS

National Federation of the Blind of Texas
Attn: Scholarship Committee
314 East Highland Mall Boulevard, Suite 253
Austin, TX 78752
(512) 323-5444   Toll Free: (866) 636-3289
Fax: (512) 420-8160
E-mail: nfbtscholarship@gmail.com
Web: www.nfbtx.org/scholarships

Summary To provide funding to blind residents of Texas who are interested in attending college in any state.

Eligibility This program is open to blind residents of Texas who are enrolled or planning to enroll full time at a college or university in any state. Applicants must submit proof of legal blindness, a current transcript, a 2-page personal letter, and 2 letters of recommendation. Selection is based on academics, community service, and need.

Financial data Stipends are $1,500 or $1,000 per year.

Duration 1 year; recipients may reapply.

Additional data This program includes 1 scholarship sponsored by the Houston chapter of the National Federation of the Blind of Texas.

Number awarded 1 at $1,500 and 2 at $1,000.

Deadline July of each year.

[416]
NATIONAL FEDERATION OF THE BLIND SCHOLARSHIPS

National Federation of the Blind
Attn: Scholarship Committee
200 East Wells Street
Baltimore, MD 21230
(410) 659-9314, ext. 2415   Fax: (410) 685-5653
E-mail: scholarships@nfb.org
Web: www.nfb.org/nfb/scholarship_program.asp

Summary To provide financial assistance for college or graduate school to blind students.

Eligibility This program is open to legally blind students who are working on or planning to work on an undergraduate or graduate degree. In general, full-time enrollment is required, although 1 scholarship may be awarded to a part-time student who is working full time. Along with their application, they must submit transcripts, standardized test scores, proof of legal blindness, 2 letters of recommendation, and a letter of endorsement from their National Federation of the Blind state president or designee. Selection is based on academic excellence, service to the community, and financial need.

Financial data Stipends are $7,000, $5,000, or $3,000.

Duration 1 year; recipients may resubmit applications up to 2 additional years.

Additional data Scholarships are awarded at the federation convention in July. Recipients must attend the convention at federation expense; that funding is in addition to the scholarship grant.

Number awarded 26 each year: 2 at $7,000, 4 at $5,000, and 20 at $3,000.

Deadline March of each year.

[417]
NAVY SUPPLY CORPS FOUNDATION NIB/NISH SCHOLARSHIPS

Navy Supply Corps Foundation
Attn: Administrator
P.O. Box 6228
Athens, GA 30604-6228
(706) 354-4111   Fax: (706) 354-0334
E-mail: foundationadmin@usnscf.com
Web: www.usnscf.com/programs/scholarships.aspx

Summary To provide money for college to blind or disabled relatives of current or former Navy Supply Corps personnel.

Eligibility This program is open to dependents (child, grandchild, or spouse) of a living or deceased regular, retired, reserve, or prior Navy Supply Corps officer, warrant officer, or enlisted personnel. Enlisted ratings that apply are AK (Aviation Storekeeper), SK (Storekeeper), MS (Mess Specialist), DK (Disbursing Clerk), SH (Ship Serviceman), LI (Lithographer), and PC (Postal Clerk). Applicants must be attending or planning to attend a 2- or 4-year accredited college on a full-time basis and have a GPA of 2.5 or higher in high school and/or college. They must be able to document blindness or severe disability. Selection is based on character, leadership, academic achievement, extracurricular activities, and financial need.

Financial data Stipends range from $1,000 to $5,000.

Duration 1 year.

Additional data This program began in 2005 with support from National Industries for the Blind (NIB) and NISH (formerly the National Industries for the Severely Handicapped).

Number awarded 1 or more each year.

Deadline March of each year.

[418]
NFBCT-COCCOMO QUARTERLY GRANTS

National Federation of the Blind of Connecticut
Attn: Quarterly Grant Committee
477 Connecticut Boulevard, Suite 217
East Hartford, CT 06108
(860) 289-1971   E-mail: info@nfbct.org
Web: www.nfbct.org/html/coccomo.htm

Summary To provide funding to blind people in Connecticut interested in a program of training, employment, independent living, or technological advancement.

Eligibility This assistance is available to residents of Connecticut who meet the state's definition of legal blindness. Applicants must be seeking support for activities in the areas of training, employment, independent living, or technological advancement. A wide range of requests are considered, including a talking watch, a computer system, a note taker (such as a Braille Note or Braille Lite), payment assistance for postsecondary part-time course work, or even a new suit for the sake of maximizing impressions on job interviews. Along with their application, they must submit a statement about themselves, their goals, and how the requested product or service will enhance their daily life and/or career aspirations.

Financial data   The amount awarded depends on the nature of the request.

Duration   These are 1-time grants. Recipients are eligible for a second grant 2 years after receiving the first grant.

Additional data   This program is supported by the John A. Coccomo, Sr. Foundation and administered by the National Federation of the Blind of Connecticut (NFBCT).

Number awarded   Varies each year.

Deadline   February, May, August, or November of each year.

[419]
NIB GRANT M. MACK MEMORIAL SCHOLARSHIP

American Council of the Blind
Attn: Coordinator, Scholarship Program
2200 Wilson Boulevard, Suite 650
Arlington, VA 22201
(202) 467-5081   Toll Free: (800) 424-8666
Fax: (703) 465-5085   E-mail: info@acb.org
Web: www.acb.org/scholarship

Summary   To provide financial assistance to blind students who are working on an undergraduate or graduate degree in business or management.

Eligibility   This program is open to undergraduate and graduate students working on a degree in business or management. Applicants must submit verification of legal blindness in both eyes; SAT, ACT, GMAT, or similar scores; information on extracurricular activities (including involvement in the American Council of the Blind); employment record; and a 500-word autobiographical sketch that includes their personal goals, strengths, weaknesses, hobbies, honors, achievements, and reasons for choice of field or courses of study. A cumulative GPA of 3.3 or higher is generally required. Financial need is not considered in the selection process. U.S. citizenship or permanent resident status is required.

Financial data   The stipend is $2,000.

Duration   1 year.

Additional data   This scholarship is sponsored by National Industries for the Blind (NIB) in honor of a dedicated leader of the American Council of the Blind. Scholarship winners are expected to attend the council's annual conference; the council will cover all reasonable expenses.

Number awarded   1 each year.

Deadline   February of each year.

[420]
NORA WEBB-MCKINNEY SCHOLARSHIP

American Council of the Blind of Ohio
Attn: Executive Director
P.O. Box 307128
Gahanna, OH 43230-7128
(614) 221-6688   Toll Free: (800) 835-2226 (within OH)
E-mail: mary.hiland@wowway.com
Web: www.acbohio.org

Summary   To provide financial assistance to Ohio students who are interested in working on an undergraduate or graduate degree involving service to blind people.

Eligibility   This program is open to 1) residents of Ohio who are high school seniors or current undergraduate or graduate students; and 2) undergraduate and graduate students from any state enrolled at colleges and universities in Ohio. Applicants must be interested in working on or planning to work on a degree in a field related to blindness (e.g., special education, rehabilitation teaching or counseling, orientation and mobility, or a concentration on programs serving people who are blind). They may be blind or sighted. Along with their application, they must submit transcripts (must have a GPA of 3.0 or higher) and an essay of 250 to 500 words on their career objectives, future plans, personal goals, other academic or personal qualities, and why they believe they are qualified to receive this scholarship. Financial need is not the sole factor considered in the selection process.

Financial data   The stipend is $2,000 per year.

Duration   1 year; recipients may reapply.

Additional data   Winners are required to attend the Saturday morning business meeting and Sunday breakfast of the sponsor's annual convention; a stipend for meals and workshops is provided.

Number awarded   1 each year.

Deadline   August of each year.

[421]
NORTH CAROLINA COUNCIL OF THE BLIND SCHOLARSHIP

North Carolina Council of the Blind
408 Ward Street
Graham, NC 27253
(336) 222-1050   Toll Free: (800) 344-7113 (within NC)
E-mail: nccb2020@bellsouth.net
Web: www.nccouncileftheblind.org/Topics.html

Summary   To provide financial assistance to blind and visually impaired North Carolina residents who are interested in attending college in any state.

Eligibility   This program is open to blind and visually impaired residents of North Carolina who are high school seniors or students currently enrolled at a college or vocational school in any state. Applicants must complete an application form and submit 2 character reference letters, a transcript of courses completed, and a brief biographical statement. Need is considered in the selection process.

Financial data   The stipend is $1,500.

Duration   1 year.

Number awarded 4 each year.

Deadline April of each year.

[422]
NORTH DAKOTA ASSOCIATION OF THE BLIND SCHOLARSHIPS

North Dakota Association of the Blind
c/o Tracy Wicken, Scholarship Committee Chair
733 Dawn Circle
Grand Forks, ND 58203
E-mail: trwicken@nd.gov
Web: www.ndab.org/Scholarship.html

Summary To provide funding to blind students in North Dakota who are attending college in any state.

Eligibility This program is open to North Dakota residents who have a visual impairment that cannot be corrected with prescription glasses and are attending an institution of higher education in any state. Applicants for the $1,000 scholarship must be full-time students and have a GPA of 2.5 or higher; applicants for the $500 scholarships may be part-time students. Along with their application, they must submit 2 letters of recommendation, transcripts, a family financial aid statement, and an essay that describes their vocational interests, how the scholarship will help them, their goals and aspirations, and what they have done to deal with situations involving their visual impairment. Selection is based on academic excellence, financial need, and service to the community.

Financial data Stipends are $1,000 or $500.

Duration 1 year.

Additional data This program was established in 1990.

Number awarded 1 at $1,000 and 2 at $500.

Deadline March of each year.

[423]
ONKYO BRAILLE ESSAY CONTEST

National Federation of the Blind
Attn: Trisha Tatam
200 East Wells Street
Baltimore, MD 21230
(410) 659-9314, ext. 2510   Fax: (410) 685-5653
E-mail: ttatam@nfb.org
Web: www.nfb.org

Summary To recognize and reward outstanding essays by blind people from around the world on the impact of Braille on their lives.

Eligibility This competition is open to individuals who are blind and live in any country. Entries may be submitted in the junior group, for 25 years of age and under, or the senior group, for 26 years of age and older. Candidates must submit an essay, from 800 to 1,000 words, on 1 of the following topics: 1) how they acquire knowledge and information through Braille or audio devices; 2) how blind persons can become independent by learning Braille or music; or 3) their individual concept about world peace from the viewpoint of persons with disabilities. Essays must be written in English or their native language, in Braille, and completely original. Selection is based on the essay's pertinence to the selected topic, impact and cred-

ibility of the experiences described, accuracy and neatness in using Braille, and style and language skills.

Financial data The Otsuki Award is $2,000, Excellent Work Awards are $1,000, and Fine Work Awards are $500.

Duration The competition is held annually.

Additional data This competition was established in 2003 by the Onkyo Corporation of Japan and the Braille Mainichi. In the United States, the National Federation of the Blind administers the contest on behalf of the North America-Caribbean Region of the World Blind Union.

Number awarded 7 each year: the Otsuki Award (awarded to the outstanding essay from either the senior or the junior group), 2 Excellent Work Awards (1 each for the senior and the junior group), and 4 Fine Work Awards (2 each for the senior and the junior group).

Deadline April of each year.

[424]
OREGON COUNCIL OF THE BLIND SCHOLARSHIPS

American Council of the Blind
Attn: Coordinator, Scholarship Program
2200 Wilson Boulevard, Suite 650
Arlington, VA 22201
(202) 467-5081   Toll Free: (800) 424-8666
Fax: (703) 465-5085   E-mail: info@acb.org
Web: www.acb.org/scholarship

Summary To provide financial assistance for college to blind students, especially those from Oregon.

Eligibility This program is open to legally blind students who are entering or attending college. Preference is given to residents of Oregon, but if no students from that state apply, residents of other states are considered. Applicants must submit verification of legal blindness in both eyes; SAT or ACT scores; information on extracurricular activities (including involvement in the American Council of the Blind); employment record; and a 500-word autobiographical sketch that includes their personal goals, strengths, weaknesses, hobbies, honors, achievements, and reasons for choice of field or courses of study. A cumulative GPA of 3.3 or higher is generally required. Financial need is not considered in the selection process.

Financial data The stipend is $2,500.

Duration 1 year.

Additional data Funding for this scholarship is provided by the Oregon Council of the Blind, an affiliate of the American Council of the Blind. Scholarship winners are expected to attend the council's annual conference; the council will cover all reasonable expenses.

Number awarded 2 each year.

Deadline February of each year.

[425]
PAUL AND ELLEN RUCKES SCHOLARSHIP

American Foundation for the Blind
Attn: Scholarship Committee
2 Penn Plaza, Suite 1102
New York, NY 10121
(212) 502-7661   Toll Free: (800) AFB-LINE
Fax: (888) 545-8331   E-mail: afbinfo@afb.net
Web: www.afb.org/Section.asp?Documentid=2962

Summary To provide financial assistance to legally blind students who wish to work on a graduate or undergraduate degree in engineering or computer, physical, or life sciences.

Eligibility This program is open to legally blind undergraduate or graduate students who are U.S. citizens working or planning to work full time on a degree in engineering or the computer, physical, or life sciences. Along with their application, they must submit 200-word essays on 1) their past and recent achievements; 2) their intended field of study and why they chose it; and 3) the role their visual impairment has played in shaping their life. Financial need is considered in the selection process.

Financial data The stipend is $1,000.

Duration 1 year.

Number awarded 1 each year.

Deadline April of each year.

[426]
PETER LINDH SCHOLARSHIP

Association for Education and Rehabilitation of the
  Blind and Visually Impaired-Georgia Chapter
c/o Mike Muchow
3354 Chestnut Woods Circle
Doraville, GA 30340
E-mail: michaelmuchow@yahoo.com
Web: www.gaaer.org/home/peter-lindh-scholarship

Summary To provide financial assistance to residents of Georgia who are legally blind and interested in attending college or graduate school in any state.

Eligibility This program is open to legally blind residents of Georgia who are attending or planning to attend a college, university, junior college, or graduate school in any state. Applicants must submit a letter about themselves that includes their goals and aspirations, why they feel they deserve this scholarship, how it will help them, and how they would use the money. Selection is based on academics; neither college level nor financial need is considered.

Financial data The stipend is $1,000.

Duration 1 year.

Number awarded 1 each year.

Deadline August of each year.

[427]
POULSON FAMILY SCHOLARSHIPS

Utah Council of the Blind
c/o Leslie Gertsch, Executive Director
1301 West 500 South
Woods Cross, UT 84087-2224
(801) 292-1156   Fax: (801) 292-6046
E-mail: lgertsch@comcast.net
Web: www.utahcounciloftheblind.org

Summary To provide financial assistance to members of the Utah Council of the Blind (UCB) who plan to attend college or graduate school in the state.

Eligibility This program is open to UCB members who are entering or enrolled as an undergraduate or graduate student at a college or university in Utah. Applicants must be blind or visually impaired, defined as having a visual acuity of less than 20/70, a visual field not exceeding 30 degrees, or a functional visual impairment of similar degree in the best eye with best correction. Along with their application, they must submit an autobiographical sketch that includes their personal goals, strengths, weaknesses, hobbies, honors, achievements, the course of study they are pursuing, and why they have chosen it. Financial need is not considered. Interviews may be held.

Financial data The stipend is at least $1,000.

Duration 1 year; may be renewed.

Number awarded Varies each year; recently, 5 of these scholarships were awarded.

Deadline April of each year.

[428]
RED ROSE SCHOLARSHIP

Susquehanna Foundation for the Blind
244 North Queen Street
Lancaster, PA 17603
(717) 291-5951
Web: www.sabvi.org/Grants%20and%20Scholarships

Summary To provide financial assistance to legally blind Pennsylvania residents who are interested in working on an undergraduate degree at a college in any state.

Eligibility This program is open to residents of Pennsylvania who are legally blind. Applicants must be high school seniors or graduates planning to attend a 2- or 4-year college or university in any state. Along with their application, they must submit a brief description of their career goal. Financial need is considered in the selection process.

Financial data The stipend is $1,500 per year.

Duration 2 years; may be renewed another 2 years by students at 4-year institutions.

Number awarded 1 or more each year.

Deadline January of each year.

[429]
RICHARD BENNET OF MAINE SCHOLARSHIP

American Council of the Blind
Attn: Coordinator, Scholarship Program
2200 Wilson Boulevard, Suite 650
Arlington, VA 22201
(202) 467-5081   Toll Free: (800) 424-8666
Fax: (703) 465-5085   E-mail: info@acb.org
Web: www.acb.org/scholarship

Summary To provide financial assistance for college to blind students from Maine.

Eligibility This program is open to legally blind students who are residents of Maine or attending college in the state. Applicants must submit verification of legal blindness in both eyes; SAT or ACT scores; information on extracurricular activities (including involvement in the American Council of the Blind); employment record; and a 500-word autobiographical sketch that includes their personal goals, strengths, weaknesses, hobbies, honors, achievements, and reasons for choice of field or courses of study. A cumulative GPA of 3.3 or higher is generally required. Financial need is not considered.

Financial data The stipend is $1,000.

Duration 1 year.

Additional data This scholarship is sponsored by the American Council of the Blind of Maine, an affiliate of the American Council of the Blind. Scholarship winners are expected to attend the council's annual conference; the council will cover all reasonable expenses.

Number awarded 1 each year.

Deadline February of each year.

[430]
R.L. GILLETTE SCHOLARSHIPS

American Foundation for the Blind
Attn: Scholarship Committee
2 Penn Plaza, Suite 1102
New York, NY 10121
(212) 502-7661   Toll Free: (800) AFB-LINE
Fax: (888) 545-8331   E-mail: afbinfo@afb.net
Web: www.afb.org/Section.asp?Documentid=2962

Summary To provide financial assistance to legally blind undergraduate women who are studying literature or music.

Eligibility This program is open to women who are legally blind, U.S. citizens, and enrolled full time in a 4-year baccalaureate degree program in literature or music. Along with their application, they must submit 200-word essays on 1) their past and recent achievements and accomplishments; 2) their intended field of study and why they have chosen it; and 3) the role their visual impairment has played in shaping their life. They must also submit a sample performance tape or CD (not to exceed 30 minutes) or a creative writing sample. Financial need is considered in the selection process.

Financial data The stipend is $1,000.

Duration 1 academic year.

Number awarded 2 each year.

Deadline April of each year.

[431]
ROBERT AND HAZEL STALEY MEMORIAL SCHOLARSHIP

National Federation of the Blind of North Carolina
c/o Julius Locklear
3102 Kings Court, Apartment A
Raleigh, NC 27606
(910) 740-1129   E-mail: Jrl006@bellsouth.net
Web: www.nfbofnc.org

Summary To provide financial assistance to undergraduate and graduate students from North Carolina who are blind and interested in attending college or graduate school in any state.

Eligibility This program is open to legally blind residents of North Carolina who are attending or planning to attend a college or university in any state. Applicants must be working on or planning to work on an undergraduate or graduate degree. Along with their application, they must submit 2 letters of recommendation, a current transcript, and a letter of introduction about themselves that includes their likes and dislikes, how their blindness has affected them, the honors and awards they have received, and their school and extracurricular activities. Selection is based on academics, community service, and financial need.

Financial data The stipend is $1,500. Funds may be used for the purchase of equipment, reader services, transportation, or other services or materials necessary to accomplish the recipient's educational objectives. They are not intended to offset support provided by state or federal agencies.

Duration 1 year.

Additional data Recipients must attend the sponsor's annual convention, at federation expense, where they receive their awards.

Number awarded Up to 2 each year.

Deadline June of each year.

[432]
ROSS N. AND PATRICIA PANGERE FOUNDATION SCHOLARSHIPS

American Council of the Blind
Attn: Coordinator, Scholarship Program
2200 Wilson Boulevard, Suite 650
Arlington, VA 22201
(202) 467-5081   Toll Free: (800) 424-8666
Fax: (703) 465-5085   E-mail: info@acb.org
Web: www.acb.org/scholarship

Summary To provide funding to blind students working on a college or graduate degree in business.

Eligibility This program is open to undergraduate and graduate students working on a degree in business. Applicants must submit verification of legal blindness in both eyes; SAT, ACT, GMAT, or similar scores; information on extracurricular activities (including involvement in the American Council of the Blind); employment record; and a 500-word autobiographical sketch that includes their personal goals, strengths, weaknesses, hobbies, honors, achievements, and reasons for choice of field or courses of study. A cumulative GPA of 3.3 or higher is generally required. Need is not considered in the selection process.

Financial data The stipend is $2,500.

Duration 1 year.

Additional data This program is funded by the Ross N. and Patricia Pangere Foundation. Scholarship winners are expected to attend the council's annual conference; the council will cover all reasonable expenses.

Number awarded 2 each year.

Deadline February of each year.

[433]
RUDOLPH DILLMAN MEMORIAL SCHOLARSHIP

American Foundation for the Blind
Attn: Scholarship Committee
2 Penn Plaza, Suite 1102
New York, NY 10121
(212) 502-7661   Toll Free: (800) AFB-LINE
Fax: (888) 545-8331   E-mail: afbinfo@afb.net
Web: www.afb.org/Section.asp?Documentid=2962

Summary To provide funding to legally blind college or graduate students studying in the field of rehabilitation and/or education of visually impaired and blind persons.

Eligibility This program is open to legally blind U.S. citizens who have been accepted to an accredited undergraduate or graduate training program within the broad field of rehabilitation and/or education of blind and visually impaired persons. Along with their application, they must submit 200-word essays on 1) their past and recent achievements and accomplishments; 2) their intended field of study and why they have chosen it; and 3) the role their visual impairment has played in shaping their life. Financial need is considered for 1 of the scholarships.

Financial data The stipend is $2,500 per year.

Duration 1 year; previous recipients may not reapply.

Number awarded 4 each year: 3 without consideration to financial need and 1 based on financial need.

Deadline April of each year.

[434]
SOUTH DAKOTA REDUCED TUITION FOR VISUAL IMPAIRMENT

South Dakota Board of Regents
Attn: Scholarship Committee
306 East Capitol Avenue, Suite 200
Pierre, SD 57501-2545
(605) 773-3455   Fax: (605) 773-2422
E-mail: info@sdbor.edu
Web: www.sdbor.edu

Summary To provide waiver of tuition and fees to South Dakota residents with a visual impairment who are interested in attending college or graduate school in the state.

Eligibility This program is open to visually impaired residents of South Dakota who can meet the entrance requirements for admission to a postsecondary educational institution (including graduate school and medical school) under the supervision of the state board of regents. For purposes of the program, "visual impairment"

means that the person cannot, with use of correcting glasses, see sufficiently well to perform ordinary activities for which eyesight is essential. This program does not extend to visually impaired persons who are entitled to receive tuition and fee support from the state's department of vocational rehabilitation.

Financial data Qualified applicants receive a total waiver of standard tuition and fees.

Duration Benefits are provided until the recipient has earned 225 semester hours of credit or the equivalent.

Additional data Applicants should contact the financial aid director at the South Dakota college or university they plan to attend, not the sponsor. The exemption from charges does not apply if a course is repeated because of unsatisfactory performance within the student's control.

Deadline Deadline not specified.

[435]
SUSQUEHANNA FOUNDATION FOR THE BLIND TRUSTEES' SCHOLARSHIP

Susquehanna Foundation for the Blind
244 North Queen Street
Lancaster, PA 17603
(717) 291-5951
Web: www.sabvi.org/Grants%20and%20Scholarships

Summary To provide financial assistance to legally blind Pennsylvania residents who are interested in working on an undergraduate or graduate degree or other academic program at a school in any state.

Eligibility This program is open to residents of Pennsylvania who are legally blind. Applicants must be working on an undergraduate or graduate degree or other specialized program intended to generate upward mobility in employment. Along with their application, they must submit a brief description of their career goal. Financial need is considered in the selection process.

Financial data A stipend is awarded (amount not specified).

Duration 1 year.

Number awarded 1 or more each year.

Deadline January of each year.

[436]
SYDE HURDUS PRESIDENT'S AWARD

Lighthouse International
Attn: Scholarship and Career Awards
111 East 59th Street
New York, NY 10022-1202
(212) 821-9428   Toll Free: (800) 829-0500
Fax: (212) 821-9703   TDD: (212) 821-9713
E-mail: sca@lighthouse.org
Web: www.lighthouse.org

Summary To provide financial assistance to legally blind high school seniors, recent graduates, undergraduates, or graduate students.

Eligibility This program is open to legally blind U.S. citizens who are graduating high school seniors, recent graduates, current undergraduates, or current graduate students. Applicants must be attending or planning to attend an accredited college or university in 1 of the 50 states, the District of Columbia, or a U.S. territory. Along with their application, they must submit essays of 400 to 600 words on 1) their academic focus and extracurricular activities and what inspires their interest in each area; 2) their passion and how they express that passion; 3) key academic and personal accomplishments and the challenges they overcome to be successful; and 4) how this scholarship will support their academic and/or career development. Selection is based on academic and personal achievements; financial need is not considered.

Financial data The stipend is $10,000.

Duration 1 year.

Number awarded 1 each year.

Deadline January of each year.

[437]
TAER STUDENT WITH A VISUAL IMPAIRMENT SCHOLARSHIP

Texas Association for Education and Rehabilitation of the Blind and Visually Impaired
c/o Michael Munro
Stephen F. Austin State University
Department of Human Services
Teacher Preparation-Visual Impairment
P.O. Box 13019
Nacogdoches, TX 75962
(936) 468-1036   Fax: (936) 468-1342
E-mail: munromicha@sfasu.edu
Web: www.txaer.org

Summary To provide financial assistance to residents of Texas who have a visual impairment and are interested in attending college in any state.

Eligibility This program is open to residents of Texas who have a visual impairment and are enrolled or planning to enroll at a college or university in any state. Applicants must be able to demonstrate financial need. Along with their application, they must submit a letter regarding the goal of their education.

Financial data The stipend is $1,000.

Duration 1 year.

Number awarded 1 or more each year.

Deadline February of each year.

[438]
TERESA BLESSING SCHOLARSHIP

Florida Council for the Blind
c/o Wanda L. Stokley, Education and Leadership Committee
111 Ponce De Leon
Tallahassee, FL 32305-3403
(850) 309-0821 E-mail: wandastokley@centurylink.net
Web: www.fcb.org/scholapp-info.htm

Summary To provide funding to blind high school seniors in Florida who plan to attend college in any state and can demonstrate academic and leadership excellence.

Eligibility This program is open to seniors graduating from high schools in Florida who are legally blind and

planning to attend a college or university in any state. Applicants must have a GPA of 3.0 or higher and be able to demonstrate academic and leadership excellence. Along with their application, they must submit a narrative statement on their vocational objectives and outlook for employment in their chosen field. Financial need is not considered in the selection process.

Financial data The stipend is $1,000.

Duration 1 year.

Number awarded 1 each year.

Deadline March of each year.

[439]
TEXAS BLIND/DEAF STUDENT EXEMPTION PROGRAM

Texas Higher Education Coordinating Board
Attn: Grants and Special Programs
1200 East Anderson Lane
P.O. Box 12788
Austin, TX 78711-2788
(512) 427-6340   Toll Free: (800) 242-3062
Fax: (512) 427-6420
E-mail: grantinfo@thecb.state.tx.us
Web: www.collegeforalltexans.com

Summary To provide a tuition exemption to blind and/or deaf residents of Texas.

Eligibility This program is open to Texas residents who can present certification from the Department of Assistive and Rehabilitative Services of their deafness or blindness. Applicants must present to the registrar of a public college or university in Texas a copy of their high school transcript, a letter of recommendation, proof that they have met all admission requirements, and a statement of purpose that indicates the certificate, degree program, or professional enhancement that they intend to pursue.

Financial data Eligible students are exempted from the payment of all dues, fees, and tuition charges at publicly-supported colleges and universities in Texas.

Duration Up to 8 semesters.

Number awarded Varies each year; recently, nearly 3,500 students received support through this program.

Deadline Deadline not specified.

[440]
TIMOTHY TURPIN SCHOLARSHIP

Florida Council for the Blind
c/o Wanda L. Stokley, Education and Leadership Committee
111 Ponce De Leon
Tallahassee, FL 32305-3403
(850) 309-0821 E-mail: wandastokley@centurylink.net
Web: www.fcb.org/scholapp-info.htm

Summary To provide financial assistance to blind high school seniors in Florida who plan to attend college in any state to study a field that will increase advancement potential in their chosen field.

Eligibility This program is open to residents of Florida who are legally blind and enrolled or planning to enroll at a college or university in any state. Applicants must have a

GPA of 3.0 or higher. They must intend to work on a degree that will increase advancement potential in their chosen field. Along with their application, they must submit a narrative statement on their vocational objectives and outlook for employment in their chosen field. Financial need is not considered in the selection process.

Financial data   The stipend is $1,000.

Duration   1 year.

Number awarded   1 each year.

Deadline   March of each year.

[441]
UNDERGRADUATE AWARD OF LIGHTHOUSE INTERNATIONAL

Lighthouse International
Attn: Scholarship and Career Awards
111 East 59th Street
New York, NY 10022-1202
(212) 821-9428   Toll Free: (800) 829-0500
Fax: (212) 821-9703   TDD: (212) 821-9713
E-mail: sca@lighthouse.org
Web: www.lighthouse.org

Summary   To provide financial assistance to legally blind students working on an undergraduate degree.

Eligibility   This program is open to undergraduate students who are legally blind and U.S. citizens. Applicants must be attending an accredited college or university in 1 of the 50 states, the District of Columbia, or a U.S. territory. Along with their application, they must submit essays of 400 to 600 words on 1) their academic focus and extracurricular activities and what inspires their interest in each area; 2) their passion and how they express that passion; 3) key academic and personal accomplishments and the challenges they overcome to be successful; and 4) how this scholarship will support their academic and/or career development. Selection is based on academic and personal achievements; financial need is not considered.

Financial data   The stipend is $10,000.

Duration   1 year.

Number awarded   1 each year.

Deadline   January of each year.

[442]
VISUAL AID VOLUNTEERS OF FLORIDA SCHOLARSHIPS

Visual Aid Volunteers of Florida
c/o Lynnette Taylor, Scholarship Committee
1423 Marlee Road
Switzerland, FL 32259-8847
(904) 287-1275   E-mail: dandltaylor@att.net
Web: www.vavf.org

Summary   To provide financial assistance to blind residents of Florida who are interested in attending college.

Eligibility   This program is open to seniors graduating from high schools in Florida who are blind and planning to attend college in any state. As part of their application, students must submit a statement of career goals, a list of extracurricular activities, 3 recommendations, and a paper

(1 print page or 2 Braille pages) about themselves and how this scholarship will make a difference to them.

Financial data   A stipend is awarded (amount not specified).

Duration   1 year.

Number awarded   Varies each year; recently, 6 of these scholarships were awarded.

Deadline   March of each year.

[443]
WALTER YOUNG MEMORIAL SCHOLARSHIP

California Association for Postsecondary Education
  and Disability
Attn: Executive Assistant
71423 Biskra Road
Rancho Mirage, CA 92270
(760) 346-8206   Fax: (760) 340-5275
TDD: (760) 341-4084   E-mail: caped2000@aol.com
Web: www.caped.net/scholarships.html

Summary   To provide funding to blind and visually impaired college and graduate students in California.

Eligibility   This program is open to blind and visually impaired students at public and private colleges and universities in California. Undergraduates must have completed at least 6 semester credits and have a GPA of 2.5 or higher. Graduate students must have completed at least 3 semester units and have a GPA of 3.0 or higher. Along with their application, they must submit a 1-page personal letter that demonstrates their writing skills, progress towards meeting their educational and vocational goals, management of their disability, and involvement in community activities. They must also submit a letter of recommendation from a faculty member, verification of disability, official transcripts, proof of current enrollment, and documentation of financial need.

Financial data   The stipend is $1,000.

Duration   1 year.

Number awarded   1 each year.

Deadline   September of each year.

[444]
WASHINGTON COUNCIL OF THE BLIND SCHOLARSHIPS

Washington Council of the Blind
c/o Tim McCorcle, Scholarship Committee Chair
2253 N.E. 54th Street
Seattle, WA 98105-3213
Toll Free: (206) 522-5850
E-mail: t.mccorcle@comcast.net
Web: www.wcbinfo.org

Summary   To provide financial aid to blind students in Washington who plan to attend college or graduate school in any state.

Eligibility   This program is open to blind residents of Washington state who are enrolled or planning to enroll at an accredited college, university, vocational school, or graduate school in any state. Applicants must submit a 1,000-word statement of their reasons for applying for this scholarship and how it will assist them to achieve their goals. The statement should include a brief description of their background, education, work experience, economic status, strengths, weaknesses, and personal goals for the next 5 to 10 years. Interviews are required.

Financial data The stipend ranges up to $4,000.

Duration 1 year.

Number awarded 1 or more each year.

Deadline July of each year.

[445]
W.B. TAYLOR MEMORIAL SCHOLARSHIP

National Federation of the Blind of Texas
Attn: Scholarship Committee
314 East Highland Mall Boulevard, Suite 253
Austin, TX 78752
(512) 323-5444   Toll Free: (866) 636-3289
Fax: (512) 420-8160
E-mail: nfbtscholarship@gmail.com
Web: www.nfbtx.org/scholarships

Summary To provide funding to blind Texas residents interested in attending college in any state.

Eligibility This program is open to blind residents of Texas who are enrolled or planning to enroll full time at a college or university in any state. Applicants must submit proof of legal blindness, a current transcript, a 2-page personal letter, and 2 recommendations. Selection is based on academic excellence, community service, and need.

Financial data The stipend is $2,000 per year.

Duration 1 year; recipients may reapply.

Number awarded 1 each year.

Deadline July of each year.

[446]
WHITE CANE SCHOLARSHIP

Lions of Michigan
Attn: Scholarship Committee
5730 Executive Drive
Lansing, MI 48911
(517) 887-6640   Fax: (517) 887-6642
E-mail: lions@lionsofmi.com
Web: www.lionsofmi.com

Summary To provide financial assistance to residents of Michigan who are legally blind and interested in attending college in any state.

Eligibility This program is open to residents of Michigan who are legally blind and attending or planning to attend an accredited trade or business school, college, or university in any state. Applicants must have a GPA of 2.5 or higher. Along with their application, they must submit an essay explaining why they deserve this scholarship. Financial need is not considered in the selection process.

Financial data The stipend is $3,000.

Duration 1 year.

Number awarded 1 each year.

Deadline December of each year.

[447]
WILLIAM G. COREY MEMORIAL SCHOLARSHIP

American Council of the Blind
Attn: Coordinator, Scholarship Program
2200 Wilson Boulevard, Suite 650
Arlington, VA 22201
(202) 467-5081   Toll Free: (800) 424-8666
Fax: (703) 465-5085   E-mail: info@acb.org
Web: www.acb.org/scholarship

Summary To provide money for college to blind undergraduate and graduate students from Pennsylvania.

Eligibility This program is open to legally blind undergraduate and graduate students who are residents of Pennsylvania or attending college in the state. Applicants must submit verification of legal blindness in both eyes; SAT, ACT, GRE, or similar scores; information on extracurricular activities (including involvement in the American Council of the Blind); employment record; and a 500-word autobiographical sketch that includes their personal goals, strengths, weaknesses, hobbies, honors, achievements, and reasons for choice of field or courses of study. A cumulative GPA of 3.3 or higher is generally required. Financial need is not considered in the selection process.

Financial data The stipend is $1,500.

Duration 1 year.

Additional data Scholarship winners are expected to attend the council's annual conference; the council will cover all reasonable expenses.

Number awarded 1 each year.

Deadline February of each year.

[448]
WILLIAM L. RITCHIE LEARNING THROUGH LISTENING AWARD

Learning Ally
Attn: Training and Support Center
20 Roszel Road
Princeton, NJ 08540
(609) 243-7087   Toll Free: (800) 221-4792
Fax: (609) 987-8116
E-mail: mGreenwald@LearningAlly.org
Web: www.learningally.org/awards

Summary To recognize and reward high school students who live in the Washington, D.C. metropolitan area and have a learning disability or visual impairment.

Eligibility This award is available to students currently enrolled in a public, private, or parochial high school (or home school) in Washington, D.C.; the Virginia counties of Arlington, Fairfax, Fauquier, Loudoun, or Prince William; the Virginia cities of Alexandria or Fairfax; or the Maryland counties of Anne Arundel, Frederick, Howard, Montgomery, or Prince Georges. Applicants must 1) have a learning disability or visual impairment; and 2) have been registered members of Learning Ally for at least 1 year. The award is presented to the student who, "through persistence and determination, has overcome obstacles to accomplish his or her goals."

Financial data The award is $1,000.

Duration The award is presented annually.

Additional data Learning Ally was formerly named Recording for the Blind and Dyslexic.

Number awarded 1 each year.

Deadline March of each year.

[449]
WISCONSIN COUNCIL OF THE BLIND AND VISUALLY IMPAIRED SCHOLARSHIPS

Wisconsin Council of the Blind and Visually Impaired
Attn: Scholarship Committee
754 Williamson Street
Madison, WI 53703
(608) 255-1166   Toll Free: (800) 783-5213
Fax: (608) 255-3301   E-mail: info@wcblind.org
Web: www.wcblind.org

Summary To provide funding to blind students from Wisconsin who are planning to attend college in the state.

Eligibility This program is open to legally blind residents of Wisconsin who are enrolled or entering college or vocational school in the state. Applicants must have a GPA of 2.5 or higher. They must be able to identify goals for the future, including eventual employment. Full-time enrollment is required, although part-time students may be eligible if they verify their courses and schedules.

Financial data The stipend is $1,500.

Duration 1 year.

Number awarded Varies each year; recently, 9 of these scholarships were awarded.

Deadline September of each year.

[450]
WISCONSIN HEARING AND VISUALLY HANDICAPPED STUDENT GRANT PROGRAM

Wisconsin Higher Educational Aids Board
131 West Wilson Street, Suite 902
P.O. Box 7885
Madison, WI 53707-7885
(608) 266-0888   Fax: (608) 267-2808
E-mail: cindy.cooley@wisconsin.gov
Web: heab.state.wi.us/programs.html

Summary To provide funding for undergraduate study to Wisconsin residents who are legally deaf or blind.

Eligibility This program is open to Wisconsin residents who can submit evidence of a severe or profound hearing or visual impairment certified by a medical examiner. Applicants must be enrolled at least half time at a branch of the University of Wisconsin, a technical college in the state, a Wisconsin independent college or university, a tribal college in the state, or an institution out of state that specializes in the training of deaf, hard of hearing, or visually handicapped students or that offers a program of study not offered by a Wisconsin institution. Financial need is considered in the selection process.

Financial data Grants range from $250 to $1,800.

Duration 1 year; may be renewed up to 4 additional years.

Number awarded Varies each year.

Deadline Deadline not specified.

Fellowships

[451]
ALLEN-SPRINKLE MEMORIAL GIFT

National Federation of the Blind of West Virginia
c/o Andy Baughman, Scholarship Committee Chair
220 Buena Vista Avenue
Clarksburg, MD 26301
(301) 622-9626   E-mail: andybob@frontier.com
Web: www.nfbwv.org

Summary To provide financial assistance to legally blind residents of West Virginia who are interested in attending college or graduate school in any state.

Eligibility This program is open to legally blind residents of Virginia who are graduating high school seniors, undergraduates, or graduate students. Applicants must be enrolled or planning to enroll full time at an accredited college, university, postsecondary vocational institute, or graduate school in any state. Along with their application, they must submit 2 letters of recommendation, transcripts, verification of blindness, and a personal letter that includes the kinds of things that interest them, their goals and aspirations, and how this scholarship would help them. Selection is based on academic excellence, community service, and financial need.

Financial data The stipend is $1,000.

Duration 1 year.

Additional data The winner is expected to attend the sponsor's annual convention.

Number awarded 1 each year.

Deadline May of each year.

[452]
AMERICAN COUNCIL OF THE BLIND OF COLORADO SCHOLARSHIPS

American Council of the Blind of Colorado
Attn: Executive Director
1536 Wynkoop Street, Suite 201
Denver, CO 80202
(303) 831-0117   Toll Free: (888) 775-2221
Fax: (303) 454-3378 E-mail: barbara.boyer@acbco.org
Web: www.acbco.org/programs/scholarships

Summary To provide money for college or graduate school in any state to blind students from Colorado.

Eligibility This program is open to legally blind students who are residents of Colorado and U.S. citizens. Applicants must be working on an undergraduate (academic, vocational, or certificate) or graduate (master's or doctoral) degree at a college or university in any state. A cumulative GPA of 3.3 or higher is generally required, but extenuating circumstances may be considered. Along with their application, they must submit a 750-word statement describing their educational, career, and personal goals. Financial need is also considered in the selection process.

Financial data The stipend is $2,500. Funds are paid directly to the recipient's college or university.

Duration 1 year.

Number awarded 4 each year.

Deadline February of each year.

[453]
AMERICAN COUNCIL OF THE BLIND OF MINNESOTA SCHOLARSHIPS

American Council of the Blind of Minnesota
Attn: Scholarship Committee
P.O. Box 7341
Minneapolis, MN 55407
(612) 501-1431   E-mail: jsilvers03@comcast.net
Web: www.acb.org/minnesota/Scholarship.html

Summary To provide financial assistance to blind and visually impaired residents of Minnesota who are interested in attending college or graduate school in any state.

Eligibility This program is open to residents of Minnesota who are blind or visually impaired. Applicants may be either high school seniors entering their first year of postsecondary study or students in their second year or above of undergraduate or graduate study in any state. Along with their application, they must submit 2 essays of 500 words each on 1) a situation in which they solved a problem or broke down a blindness-related barrier in order to meet an academic requirement, and 2) a pair of instances in which they would have advocated for their own needs or the needs of others. Selection is based on the essays, extracurricular activities, transcripts, and recommendations.

Financial data The stipend is $1,000.

Duration 1 year.

Number awarded 2 each year: 1 to a high school senior entering college and 1 to a student already enrolled in a postsecondary educational program.

Deadline June of each year.

[454]
ARNOLD SADLER MEMORIAL SCHOLARSHIP

American Council of the Blind
Attn: Coordinator, Scholarship Program
2200 Wilson Boulevard, Suite 650
Arlington, VA 22201
(202) 467-5081   Toll Free: (800) 424-8666
Fax: (703) 465-5085   E-mail: info@acb.org
Web: www.acb.org/scholarship

Summary To provide financial assistance to undergraduate or graduate students who are blind and are interested in studying in a field of service to persons with disabilities.

Eligibility This program is open to undergraduate and graduate students in rehabilitation, education, law, or other fields of service to persons with disabilities. Applicants must be legally blind in both eyes. Along with their application, they must submit verification of legal blind-

ness in both eyes; SAT, ACT, GRE, or similar scores; information on extracurricular activities (including involvement in the American Council of the Blind); employment record; and a 500-word autobiographical sketch that includes their personal goals, strengths, weaknesses, hobbies, honors, achievements, and reasons for choice of field or courses of study. Financial need is not considered. A cumulative GPA of 3.3 or higher is generally required.

Financial data The stipend is $1,500.

Duration 1 year.

Additional data This scholarship is funded by the Arnold Sadler Memorial Scholarship Fund. Scholarship winners are expected to attend the council's annual conference; the council will cover all reasonable expenses.

Number awarded 1 each year.

Deadline February of each year.

[455]
BEVERLY PROWS MEMORIAL SCHOLARSHIP

National Federation of the Blind of Washington
Attn: Scholarship Chair
P.O. Box 2516
Seattle, WA 98111
(425) 823-6380   E-mail: president@nfbw.org
Web: www.nfbw.org/programs.html

Summary To provide money for undergraduate or graduate study in any state to blind students in Washington.

Eligibility This program is open to legally blind residents of Washington state who are working on or planning to work on a full-time college or graduate degree at a school in any state. Applicants must submit a list of honors and awards they have received, information on their community service involvement, high school and/or college transcripts, and 3 letters of reference.

Financial data The stipend is $3,000.

Duration 1 year; recipients may reapply.

Additional data This scholarship was first awarded in 1991. Winners must attend the state convention of the National Federation of the Blind of Washington to accept the award; convention expenses are covered.

Number awarded 1 each year.

Deadline August of each year.

[456]
BLIND EDUCATOR OF THE YEAR AWARD

National Federation of the Blind
Attn: Director of Community Relations
200 East Wells Street
Baltimore, MD 21230
(410) 659-9314, ext. 272   Fax: (410) 685-5653
E-mail: CommunityRelations@nfb.org
Web: www.nfb.org

Summary To recognize and reward outstanding blind educators.

Eligibility Candidates for this award must be distinguished educators who have contributed to the nation. All candidates must be blind. The recipient is chosen to symbolize the best in teaching and the best in service to the blind.

Financial data The award is $1,000.

Duration The award is presented annually.

Additional data This award was established in 1986. Honorees must be present at the annual convention of the National Federation of the Blind.

Number awarded 1 each year.

Deadline Nominations must be submitted by April of each year.

[457]
CALIFORNIA COUNCIL OF THE BLIND SCHOLARSHIPS

California Council of the Blind
Attn: Executive Office
1510 J Street, Suite 125
Sacramento, CA 95814
(916) 441-2100   Toll Free: (800) 221-6359 (within CA)
Fax: (916) 441-2188   E-mail: ccotb@ccbnet.org
Web: www.ccbnet.org/scholar.htm

Summary To provide money for undergraduate or graduate study in any state to blind people in California.

Eligibility Applicants must be legally blind residents of California who are enrolled or planning to enroll full time at an accredited college or university at either the undergraduate or graduate level. The school may be in any state. Along with their application, they must submit a 200-word statement on their purpose in undertaking college work and their vocational goals. Selection is based on academic achievement and financial need.

Financial data The amount of the assistance depends on the availability of funds and the needs of the applicant.

Duration 1 year; may be renewed. For graduate students, support is limited to 2 years of work for a master's degree or 3 years for a Ph.D.

Number awarded Varies each year.

Deadline June of each year.

[458]
CHARLES AND MELVA T. OWEN MEMORIAL SCHOLARSHIPS

National Federation of the Blind
Attn: Scholarship Committee
200 East Wells Street
Baltimore, MD 21230
(410) 659-9314, ext. 2415   Fax: (410) 685-5653
E-mail: scholarships@nfb.org
Web: www.nfb.org/nfb/scholarship_program.asp

Summary To provide funding to entering or continuing undergraduate or graduate students who are blind.

Eligibility This program is open to legally blind students who are working on or planning to work full time on an undergraduate or graduate degree. Scholarships, however, are not awarded for the study of religion or solely to further general or cultural education; the academic program should be directed towards attaining financial independence. Along with their application, they must submit transcripts, standardized test scores, proof of legal blindness, 2 letters of recommendation, and a letter of endorsement from their National Federation of the Blind

state president or designee. Selection is based on academic excellence, service to the community, and financial need.

Financial data Stipends are $10,000 or $3,000.

Duration 1 year; recipients may resubmit applications up to 2 additional years.

Additional data Scholarships are awarded at the federation convention in July. Recipients must attend the convention at federation expense; that funding is in addition to the scholarship grant.

Number awarded 1 at $10,000 and 1 at $3,000.

Deadline March of each year.

[459]
CHICAGO LIGHTHOUSE SCHOLARSHIPS

Chicago Lighthouse for People Who Are Blind or
  Visually Impaired
Attn: Scholarship Program Coordinator
1850 West Roosevelt Road
Chicago, IL 60608-1298
(312) 666-1331   Fax: (312) 243-8539
TDD: (312) 666-8874
E-mail: scholarships@chicagolighthouse.org
Web: chicagolighthouse.org

Summary To provide funding to blind or visually impaired college and graduate students, especially those from Illinois and states close to Chicago.

Eligibility This program is open to undergraduate and graduate students who are legally blind, totally blind, visually impaired, or multi-disabled and attending or planning to attend an accredited college, university, or community college. Students from throughout the country are eligible, but preference is given to residents of Illinois and the greater Chicago area (southern Wisconsin and northwestern Indiana) and to those attending school in Illinois. Along with their application, they must submit an essay about their visual impairment, background, educational and career goals, and how this scholarship will help achieve those goals. Selection is based on academic achievement, career goal, extracurricular activities, character, and personal and family financial need.

Financial data Stipends range up to $5,000.

Duration 1 year; a small number of the awards may be renewed up to 3 additional years.

Additional data This program includes the Mary Kathryn and Michael Panitch Scholarships. This program was established in 2004 and limited to students from the Chicago area. Recently, it has begun to accept applications from students living in other areas.

Number awarded Varies each year; recently, 14 of these scholarships were awarded.

Deadline March of each year.

[460]
CHRISTINE H. EIDE MEMORIAL SCHOLARSHIP AWARD

Lighthouse International
Attn: New York Lighthouse Vision Rehabilitation
  Services
111 East 59th Street
New York, NY 10022-1202
(212) 821-9428   Toll Free: (800) 829-0500
Fax: (212) 821-9703   TDD: (212) 821-9713
E-mail: gobando@lighthouse.org
Web: www.lighthouse.org

Summary To provide funding to legally blind high school seniors, recent graduates, undergraduates, or graduate students.

Eligibility This program is open to legally blind graduating high school seniors, recent graduates, current undergraduates, or current graduate students. Applicants must be enrolled or planning to enroll full time at an accredited college or university in 1 of the 50 states, the District of Columbia, or a U.S. territory. Along with their application, they must submit on essay of 1 to 3 pages on 1) their career objectives and career plans upon completion of their educational program; 2) why they chose this school to meet their vocational objectives; 3) how they plan to use the scholarship funds; and 4) (for renewal applicants) how the scholarship benefited their education. Financial need is not considered in the selection process.

Financial data The stipend is $500 per semester ($1,000 per year).

Duration 1 semester; may be renewed 1 additional semester.

Additional data This program was established in 1967.

Number awarded Varies each year.

Deadline August of each year for fall semester; December of each year for spring semester.

[461]
DALE M. SCHOETTLER SCHOLARSHIP FOR VISUALLY IMPAIRED STUDENTS

California State University
CSU Foundation
Attn: Director, Foundation Programs and Services
401 Golden Shore, Sixth Floor
Long Beach, CA 90802-4210
(562) 951-4768   E-mail: abrown@calstate.edu
Web: www.calstate.edu/foundation/scholarship.shtml

Summary To provide financial assistance to undergraduate and graduate students with visual impairments at campuses of the California State University (CSU) system.

Eligibility This program is open to full-time undergraduate and graduate students enrolled at CSU campuses who have been declared visually impaired or legally blind. Applicants must have a cumulative GPA of 2.8 or higher.

Financial data The stipend is $6,000.

Duration 1 year.

Number awarded 1 or more each year.

Deadline Deadline not specified.

[462]
DELTA GAMMA FOUNDATION FLORENCE MARGARET HARVEY MEMORIAL SCHOLARSHIP

American Foundation for the Blind
Attn: Scholarship Committee
2 Penn Plaza, Suite 1102
New York, NY 10121
(212) 502-7661   Toll Free: (800) AFB-LINE
Fax: (888) 545-8331   E-mail: afbinfo@afb.net
Web: www.afb.org/Section.asp?Documentid=2962

Summary To provide financial assistance to blind undergraduate and graduate students who wish to study in the field of rehabilitation and/or education of the blind.

Eligibility This program is open to legally blind juniors, seniors, or graduate students. U.S. citizenship is required. Applicants must be studying in the field of rehabilitation and/or education of visually impaired and blind persons. Along with their application, they must submit 200-word essays on 1) their past and recent achievements and accomplishments; 2) their intended field of study and why they have chosen it; and 3) the role their visual impairment has played in shaping their life. Financial need is considered in the selection process.

Financial data The stipend is $1,000.

Duration 1 year.

Additional data This scholarship is supported by the Delta Gamma Foundation and administered by the American Foundation for the Blind.

Number awarded 1 each year.

Deadline April of each year.

[463]
DELTA GAMMA FOUNDATION/RUTH BILLOW MEMORIAL EDUCATION FUND

Delta Gamma Foundation
Attn: Director, Service for Sight
3250 Riverside Drive
P.O. Box 21397
Columbus, OH 43221-0397
(614) 481-8169   Toll Free: (800) 644-5414
Fax: (614) 481-0133
E-mail: fngrants@deltagamma.org
Web: www.deltagamma.org

Summary To provide financial assistance to undergraduate or graduate members of Delta Gamma sorority who are visually impaired or preparing for a career in working with the visually impaired.

Eligibility This program is open to undergraduate and graduate members of the sorority who are either 1) blind or visually impaired; or 2) pursuing professional training in areas related to working with persons who are blind or visually impaired or in sight preservation. Applicants must be pursuing a program of postsecondary education in the United States or Canada.

Financial data The stipend is $1,000 for undergraduates or $2,500 for graduate students.

Duration 1 year or more.

Number awarded   2 each year: 1 to an undergraduate and 1 to a graduate student.
Deadline   Applications may be submitted at any time.

[464]
DR. S. BRADLEY BURSON MEMORIAL SCHOLARSHIP

American Council of the Blind
Attn: Coordinator, Scholarship Program
2200 Wilson Boulevard, Suite 650
Arlington, VA 22201
(202) 467-5081   Toll Free: (800) 424-8666
Fax: (703) 465-5085   E-mail: info@acb.org
Web: www.acb.org/scholarship

Summary   To provide financial assistance to blind students who are working on an undergraduate or graduate degree in designated fields of science.
Eligibility   This program is open to undergraduate or graduate students working on a degree in the "pure" sciences (i.e., biology, chemistry, physics, and engineering, but not computer science). Applicants must be legally blind in both eyes. Along with their application, they must submit verification of legal blindness in both eyes; SAT, ACT, GRE, or similar scores; information on extracurricular activities (including involvement in the American Council of the Blind); employment record; and a 500-word autobiographical sketch that includes their personal goals, strengths, weaknesses, hobbies, honors, achievements, and reasons for choice of field or courses of study. A cumulative GPA of 3.3 or higher is generally required. Financial need is not considered in the selection process.
Financial data   The stipend is $1,000.
Duration   1 year.
Additional data   Scholarship winners are expected to attend the council's annual conference; the council will cover all reasonable expenses.
Number awarded   1 each year.
Deadline   February of each year.

[465]
EDUCATION FOR LIFE COLLEGE SCHOLARSHIPS

The See the Future Fund
P.O. Box 63022
Colorado Springs, CO 80962-3022
(719) 471-3200   Fax: (719) 471-3210
E-mail: twtheune@prodigy.net
Web: seethefuture.org

Summary   To provide financial assistance to blind or visually impaired residents of Colorado who are interested in attending college or graduate school in any state.
Eligibility   This program is open to residents of Colorado who meet standards of blindness or visual impairment. Applicants must be enrolled full time at a postsecondary program in any state as 1) a freshman entering an academic program; 2) a sophomore, junior, or senior in an academic program; 3) a graduate student in an academic program; or 4) a student in a vocational/technical school

or community college. Selection is based on academic achievement, service, and financial need.
Financial data   Stipends are $3,000, $2,500, or $2,000 per year. Funds are paid directly to the institution as payment for tuition, fees, books, room, and board.
Duration   2 or 4 years.
Additional data   This program began in 1998.
Number awarded   Varies each year; recently, the program offered 1 scholarship at $3,000 per year for 4 years, 1 at $2,500 per year for 4 years, 1 at $2,000 per year for 4 years, and 3 at $2,000 per year for 2 years.
Deadline   February of each year.

[466]
EMIL A. HONKA SCHOLARSHIPS

Montana Association for the Blind
7 West Sixth Street, Suite E
P.O. Box 465
Helena, MT 59624
(406) 442-9411   Fax: (406) 442-1612
E-mail: lglueckert@milp.us

Summary   To provide financial assistance to blind residents of Montana who are attending college or graduate school in any state.
Eligibility   This program is open to residents of Montana who are blind or have a prognosis of serious vision loss and are working on an undergraduate or graduate degree in any field at a college or university in any state. Applicants must have completed at least 1 semester or quarter and have a GPA of 2.5 or higher. Selection is based primarily on financial need.
Financial data   The stipend is $1,000 per year.
Duration   1 year; recipients may reapply.
Additional data   Recipients must attend the annual convention of the sponsoring organization to accept their award; expenses to attend the convention are reimbursed.
Number awarded   2 each year.
Deadline   January of each year.

[467]
EUNICE FIORITO MEMORIAL SCHOLARSHIP

American Council of the Blind
Attn: Coordinator, Scholarship Program
2200 Wilson Boulevard, Suite 650
Arlington, VA 22201
(202) 467-5081   Toll Free: (800) 424-8666
Fax: (703) 465-5085   E-mail: info@acb.org
Web: www.acb.org/scholarship

Summary   To provide funding to undergraduate or graduate students who are blind and are interested in studying in a field of advocacy or service for persons with disabilities.
Eligibility   This program is open to undergraduate and graduate students in rehabilitation, education, law, or other fields of service or advocacy for persons with disabilities. Applicants must be legally blind in both eyes. Along with their application, they must submit verification of legal blindness in both eyes; SAT, ACT, GRE, or similar scores; information on extracurricular activities (including involve-

ment in the American Council of the Blind); employment record; and a 500-word autobiographical sketch that includes their personal goals, strengths, weaknesses, hobbies, honors, achievements, and reasons for choice of field or courses of study. A cumulative GPA of 3.3 or higher is generally required. Financial need is not considered in the selection process. Preference is given to students with little or no vision.

Financial data The stipend is $2,000.

Duration 1 year.

Additional data Scholarship winners are expected to attend the council's annual conference; the council will cover all reasonable expenses.

Number awarded 1 each year.

Deadline February of each year.

[468]
FERDINAND TORRES SCHOLARSHIP

American Foundation for the Blind
Attn: Scholarship Committee
2 Penn Plaza, Suite 1102
New York, NY 10121
(212) 502-7661   Toll Free: (800) AFB-LINE
Fax: (888) 545-8331   E-mail: afbinfo@afb.net
Web: www.afb.org/Section.asp?Documentid=2962

Summary To provide financial assistance for college or graduate school to blind students, especially immigrants and those from New York City.

Eligibility Applicants must be legally blind and reside in the United States, although U.S. citizenship is not necessary. They must present evidence of economic need, legal blindness, and acceptance into a full-time undergraduate or graduate program. Preference is given to new immigrants and residents of New York City. Along with their application, they must submit 200-word essays on 1) their past and recent achievements and accomplishments; 2) their intended field of study and why they have chosen it; 3) the role their visual impairment has played in shaping their life; and 4) their financial need, how they would use the scholarship if they receive it, and (for immigrants) their country of origin and their reasons for coming here.

Financial data The stipend is $3,500.

Duration 1 year.

Number awarded 1 each year.

Deadline April of each year.

[469]
FLOYD CALLWARD MEMORIAL SCHOLARSHIP

National Federation of the Blind of New Hampshire
c/o Cassandra McNabb, President
12 Sumner Street, Apartment A
Keene, NH 03431
(603) 357-4080   E-mail: cemcnabb21@yahoo.com

Summary To provide funding to blind students in New Hampshire who are interested in working on a college or graduate degree in any state.

Eligibility This program is open to legally blind and totally blind residents of New Hampshire who are attend-

ing or planning to attend college or graduate school in any state. Applicants may be attending college immediately after high school, returning to college at a later age, attending graduate or professional school, or enrolled in postsecondary vocational training. Along with their application, they must submit 1) a letter describing what they have done to deal with situations involving their blindness, their personal goals and aspirations, and how the scholarship will help them; 2) 2 letters of recommendation; 3) high school or college transcripts; 4) a list of honors and awards; and 5) information on community service and volunteer work. There are no restrictions on level, gender, or field of study. Financial need is not considered.

Financial data The stipend is $1,000. The funds may be used to purchase education-related equipment or services or to defray the costs of tuition, board, and other school fees.

Duration 1 year.

Additional data This program was established in 1990.

Number awarded 1 or more each year.

Deadline October of each year.

[470]
FLOYD QUALLS MEMORIAL SCHOLARSHIPS

American Council of the Blind
Attn: Coordinator, Scholarship Program
2200 Wilson Boulevard, Suite 650
Arlington, VA 22201
(202) 467-5081   Toll Free: (800) 424-8666
Fax: (703) 465-5085   E-mail: info@acb.org
Web: www.acb.org/scholarship

Summary To provide funding to entering and continuing college and graduate students who are blind.

Eligibility This program is open to legally blind students in 4 categories: entering freshmen in academic programs, undergraduates (sophomores, juniors, and seniors) in academic programs, graduate students in academic programs, and vocational school students or students working on an associate's degree from a community college. Applicants must submit verification of legal blindness in both eyes; SAT, ACT, GRE, or similar scores; information on extracurricular activities (including involvement in the American Council of the Blind); employment record; and a 500-word autobiographical sketch that includes their personal goals, strengths, weaknesses, hobbies, honors, achievements, and reasons for choice of field or courses of study. Financial need is not considered. A cumulative GPA of 3.3 or higher is generally required.

Financial data The stipend is $2,500.

Duration 1 year.

Additional data Scholarship winners are expected to attend the council's annual conference; the council will cover all reasonable expenses.

Number awarded 1 in each of the 4 categories.

Deadline February of each year.

[471]
FRED SCHEIGERT SCHOLARSHIPS

Council of Citizens with Low Vision International
c/o American Council of the Blind
2200 Wilson Boulevard, Suite 650
Arlington, VA 22201
(202) 467-5081   Toll Free: (800) 733-2258
Fax: (703) 465-5085   E-mail: scholarship@cclvi.org
Web: www.cclvi.org/schguide.htm

Summary   To provide funding to entering and continuing undergraduate and graduate students with low vision.

Eligibility   This program is open to full-time undergraduate and graduate students who have been certified by an ophthalmologist as having low vision (acuity of 20/70 or worse in the better seeing eye with best correction or side vision with a maximum diameter of no greater than 30 degrees). Applicants may be entering freshmen, undergraduates, or graduate students. They must have a GPA of 3.2 or higher and a record of involvement in their school and/or local community.

Financial data   The stipend is $3,000.

Duration   1 year.

Number awarded   3 each year: 1 each to an entering freshman, undergraduate, and graduate student.

Deadline   February of each year.

[472]
GEORGIA COUNCIL OF THE BLIND SCHOLARSHIPS

Georgia Council of the Blind
850 Gaines School Road
Athens, GA 30605
(706) 208-7132   Toll Free: (888) 519-3988
E-mail: gcbfyi@yahoo.com
Web: www.georgiacounciloftheblind.org

Summary   To provide funding to students in Georgia who plan to attend college or graduate school in any state and are either legally blind or have legally blind parents.

Eligibility   This program is open to residents of Georgia who are either 1) legally blind students, or 2) sighted students financially dependent on legally blind parents. Applicants must be enrolled or accepted for enrollment at a vocational/technical school, a 2- or 4-year college, or a master's or doctoral program in any state. All fields of study are eligible. Selection is based on academic transcripts, 2 letters of recommendation, a 1-page typed statement of the applicant's educational goals, an audio cassette recording of the applicant reading the goals statement, extracurricular activities, and financial need.

Financial data   Stipends range up to $1,000 per year.

Duration   1 year; recipients may reapply.

Additional data   This program began in 1988.

Number awarded   1 or more each year.

Deadline   June of each year.

[473]
GLADYS C. ANDERSON MEMORIAL SCHOLARSHIP

American Foundation for the Blind
Attn: Scholarship Committee
2 Penn Plaza, Suite 1102
New York, NY 10121
(212) 502-7661   Toll Free: (800) AFB-LINE
Fax: (888) 545-8331   E-mail: afbinfo@afb.net
Web: www.afb.org/Section.asp?Documentid=2962

Summary   To provide financial assistance to legally blind women who are studying classical or religious music on the undergraduate or graduate school level.

Eligibility   This program is open to women who are legally blind, U.S. citizens, and enrolled in an undergraduate or graduate degree program in classical or religious music. Along with their application, they must submit 200-word essays on 1) their past and recent achievements and accomplishments; 2) their intended field of study and why they have chosen it; and 3) the role their visual impairment has played in shaping their life. They must also submit a sample performance tape or CD of up to 30 minutes. Financial need is considered in the selection process.

Financial data   The stipend is $1,000.

Duration   1 academic year.

Number awarded   1 each year.

Deadline   April of each year.

[474]
HARRY G. STARR ENDOWED SCHOLARSHIP

Lighthouse International
Attn: Scholarship and Career Awards
111 East 59th Street
New York, NY 10022-1202
(212) 821-9428   Toll Free: (800) 829-0500
Fax: (212) 821-9703   TDD: (212) 821-9713
E-mail: sca@lighthouse.org
Web: www.lighthouse.org

Summary   To provide financial assistance to legally blind high school seniors, recent graduates, undergraduates, or graduate students.

Eligibility   This program is open to legally blind U.S. citizens who are graduating high school seniors, recent graduates, current undergraduates, or current graduate students. Applicants must be attending or planning to attend an accredited college or university in 1 of the 50 states, the District of Columbia, or a U.S. territory. Along with their application, they must submit essays of 400 to 600 words on 1) their academic focus and extracurricular activities and what inspires their interest in each area; 2) their passion and how they express that passion; 3) key academic and personal accomplishments and the challenges they overcome to be successful; and 4) how this scholarship will support their academic and/or career development. Selection is based on academic and personal achievements; financial need is not considered.

Financial data   The stipend is $10,000.

Duration   1 year.

Additional data This award was first presented in 2008.

Number awarded 1 each year.

Deadline January of each year.

[475]
HARRY LUDWIG MEMORIAL SCHOLARSHIP

Oregon Student Access Commission
Attn: Grants and Scholarships Division
1500 Valley River Drive, Suite 100
Eugene, OR 97401-2146
(541) 687-7395   Toll Free: (800) 452-8807, ext. 7395
Fax: (541) 687-7414   TDD: (800) 735-2900
E-mail: awardinfo@osac.state.or.us
Web: www.oregonstudentaid.gov/scholarships.aspx

Summary To provide financial assistance to residents of Oregon who are visually impaired and are interested in attending college or graduate school in the state.

Eligibility This program is open to residents of Oregon who are visually impaired (have residual acuity of 20/70 or less in the better eye with correction, or their visual field is restricted to 20 degrees or less in the better eye). Applicants must be enrolled or planning to enroll as full-time undergraduate or graduate students in Oregon.

Financial data Stipends for scholarships offered by the Oregon Student Access Commission (OSAC) range from $200 to $10,000 but recently averaged $2,300.

Duration 1 year.

Additional data This program is administered by the OSAC with funds provided by the Oregon Community Foundation.

Number awarded Varies each year; recently, 7 of these scholarships were awarded.

Deadline February of each year.

[476]
HAZEL TEN BROEK MEMORIAL SCHOLARSHIP

National Federation of the Blind of Washington
Attn: Scholarship Chair
P.O. Box 2516
Seattle, WA 98111
(425) 823-6380   E-mail: president@nfbw.org
Web: www.nfbw.org/programs.html

Summary To provide funding for college or graduate studies in any state to blind students in Washington.

Eligibility This program is open to legally blind residents of Washington state who are working on or planning to work on a full-time college or graduate degree at a school in any state. Applicants must submit a list of honors and awards they have received, information on their community service involvement, high school and/or college transcripts, and 3 letters of reference.

Financial data The stipend is $2,000.

Duration 1 year.

Additional data This scholarship was first awarded in 1996. Winners must attend the state convention of the National Federation of the Blind of Washington to accept the award; convention expenses are covered.

Number awarded 1 each year.

Deadline August of each year.

[477]
HOLLY ELLIOTT AND LAUREL GLASS SCHOLARSHIP ENDOWMENT

United Methodist Higher Education Foundation
Attn: Scholarships Administrator
60 Music Square East, Suite 350
P.O. Box 340005
Nashville, TN 37203-0005
(615) 649-3990   Toll Free: (800) 811-8110
Fax: (615) 649-3980
E-mail: umhefscholarships@umhef.org
Web: www.umhef.org/receive.php

Summary To provide financial assistance to students at United Methodist seminaries who are deaf or deaf-blind.

Eligibility This program is open to students enrolled full time at United Methodist theological schools who are culturally deaf, orally deaf, deafened, late deafened, deaf-blind, or hard of hearing. Applicants must have a GPA of 3.0 or higher and be preparing for specialized ministries in the church, including (but not limited to) those wishing to become ordained. They must have been active, full members of a United Methodist Church for at least 1 year prior to applying. Financial need and U.S. citizenship or permanent resident status are required.

Financial data The stipend is at least $1,000 per year.

Duration 1 year; nonrenewable.

Additional data This program was established in 2004.

Number awarded 1 each year.

Deadline February of each year.

[478]
JAMES DOYLE CASE MEMORIAL SCHOLARSHIPS

Mississippi Council of the Blind
c/o Kenneth Maddox
217 Taylor Street
Jackson, MS 39216
Web: www.acb.org/mcb

Summary To provide financial assistance to legally blind residents of Mississippi and their children who plan to attend college or graduate school in any state.

Eligibility This program is open to residents of Mississippi who are legally blind or the children of at least 1 legally blind parent. Applicants must be enrolled or accepted for enrollment in an undergraduate or graduate program in any state and carrying or planning to carry at least 12 academic hours. Along with their application, they must submit a 2-page autobiographical sketch, transcripts, standardized test scores (ACT or SAT for undergraduates; GRE, MCAT, LSAT, etc. for graduate students), 2 letters of recommendation, proof of acceptance from a postsecondary school, and verification of blindness of the qualifying person (applicant or parent).

Financial data The stipend is $1,500 per year.

Duration 4 years.

Number awarded 2 each year.
Deadline February of each year.

[479]
JENNICA FERGUSON MEMORIAL SCHOLARSHIP OF OHIO

National Federation of the Blind of Ohio
c/o Barbara Pierce, Scholarship Committee Chair
237 Oak Street
Oberlin, OH 44074-1517
(440) 775-2216   E-mail: bpierce@nfb.org
Web: www.nfbohio.org

Summary To provide financial assistance to blind residents of Ohio who are interested in working on an undergraduate or graduate degree at a school in any state.

Eligibility This program is open to residents of Ohio who are legally blind. Applicants must be attending or planning to attend an accredited institution of higher education in any state as a full-time undergraduate or graduate student. Along with their application, they must submit 2 letters of recommendation, current transcripts, a letter about themselves that includes how they have dealt with their blindness and their hopes and dreams, and a letter from an officer of the National Federation of the Blind of Ohio indicating that they have discussed their scholarship application with that officer. Selection is based on academic excellence, community service, and financial need.

Financial data The stipend is $1,500.

Duration 1 year.

Number awarded 1 each year.

Deadline April of each year.

[480]
JOANN FISCHER SCHOLARSHIP

American Council of the Blind of Ohio
Attn: Executive Director
P.O. Box 307128
Gahanna, OH 43230-7128
(614) 221-6688 Toll Free: (800) 835-2226 (within OH)
E-mail: mary.hiland@wowway.com
Web: www.acbohio.org

Summary To provide financial assistance to Ohio graduate students who are blind.

Eligibility This program is open to 1) residents of Ohio who are currently enrolled as graduate students, and 2) graduate students at colleges and universities in Ohio. Applicants must be legally blind and working on or planning to work on a degree in any field. Along with their application, they must submit transcripts (must have a GPA of 3.0 or higher), a certificate of legal blindness, and an essay of 250 to 500 words on their career objectives, future plans, personal goals, other academic or personal qualities, and why they believe they are qualified to receive this scholarship. Financial need is not the sole factor considered in the selection process.

Financial data The stipend is $2,500 per year.

Duration 1 year; recipients may reapply.

Additional data Winners are required to attend the Saturday morning business meeting and Sunday breakfast of the sponsor's annual convention; a stipend for meals and workshops is provided.

Number awarded 1 each year.

Deadline August of each year.

[481]
JOSEPH ROEDER ASSISTIVE TECHNOLOGY SCHOLARSHIP

National Industries for the Blind
Attn: Scholarship Program
1310 Braddock Place
Alexandria, VA 22314-1691
(703) 310-0343   E-mail: kgallagher@nib.org
Web: www.nib.org/content/scholarship-application

Summary To provide funding to blind upper-division and graduate students preparing for a career in assistive technology.

Eligibility This program is open to blind college juniors, seniors, and graduate students working on a degree in computer science, information systems, or a related field to prepare for a career in assistive technology. Applicants must submit information about their work experience, community activities, years of experience using a screen reader, years of experience using a text magnification program, the adaptive technology they use, and an essay of 200 to 300 words on their career history and future career goals.

Financial data The stipend is $2,500.

Duration 1 year.

Additional data This scholarship was first awarded in 2011.

Number awarded 1 each year.

Deadline July of each year.

[482]
JUDY VAN NOSTRAND ARTS AWARD

Lighthouse International
Attn: Scholarship and Career Awards
111 East 59th Street
New York, NY 10022-1202
(212) 821-9428   Toll Free: (800) 829-0500
Fax: (212) 821-9703   TDD: (212) 821-9713
E-mail: sca@lighthouse.org
Web: www.lighthouse.org

Summary To provide financial assistance to legally blind high school seniors, recent graduates, undergraduates, or graduate students who are interested in working on a degree in the arts.

Eligibility This program is open to legally blind U.S. citizens who are graduating high school seniors, recent graduates, current undergraduates, or current graduate students. Applicants must be attending or planning to attend an accredited college or university in 1 of the 50 states, the District of Columbia, or a U.S. territory. They must be working on or planning to work on a degree in the arts (including graphic arts, music, visual arts, and writing). Along with their application, they must submit essays of 400 to 600 words on 1) their academic focus and extracurricular activities and what inspires their interest in each area; 2) their passion and how they express that passion; 3) key academic and personal accomplishments and the challenges they overcome to be successful; and 4) how this scholarship will support their academic and/or career development. Selection is based on academic and personal achievements; financial need is not considered.

Financial data The stipend is $10,000.

Duration 1 year.

Number awarded 1 each year.

Deadline January of each year.

[483]
KENNETH JERNIGAN SCHOLARSHIP

National Federation of the Blind
Attn: Scholarship Committee
200 East Wells Street
Baltimore, MD 21230
(410) 659-9314, ext. 2415   Fax: (410) 685-5653
E-mail: scholarships@nfb.org
Web: www.nfb.org/nfb/scholarship_program.asp

Summary To provide financial assistance to entering or continuing undergraduate and graduate blind students.

Eligibility This program is open to legally blind students who are working on or planning to work full time on an undergraduate or graduate degree. Along with their application, they must submit transcripts, standardized test scores, proof of legal blindness, 2 letters of recommendation, and a letter of endorsement from their National Federation of the Blind state president or designee. Selection is based on academic excellence, service to the community, and financial need.

Financial data The stipend is $12,000.

Duration 1 year; recipients may resubmit applications up to 2 additional years.

Additional data Scholarships are awarded at the federation convention in July. Recipients must attend the convention at federation expense; that funding is in addition to the scholarship grant. This scholarship is given by the American Action Fund for Blind Children and Adults, a nonprofit organization that assists blind people.

Number awarded 1 each year.

Deadline March of each year.

[484]
KENNETH TIEDE MEMORIAL SCHOLARSHIPS

National Federation of the Blind of Kansas
c/o Dianne Hemphill, Scholarship Chair
600 North Bel Rue Street
Derby, KS 67037-7300
(316) 201-1323   E-mail: diannehemphill@cox.net
Web: www.nfbks.org/conventions/scholarships.shtml

Summary To provide money for college or graduate school to blind students from Kansas.

Eligibility This program is open to legally blind undergraduate and graduate students who are residents of Kansas or attending or planning to attend a college, university, or technical school in the state. Applicants must have a GPA of 2.5 or higher. They must be able to attend the state convention of the National Federation of the Blind of Kan-

sas. Selection is based on academic excellence, community service, and financial need.

Financial data Stipends range from $1,500 to $2,500.

Duration 1 year.

Number awarded Up to 5 each year.

Deadline May of each year.

[485]
LANCASTER SCHOLARSHIP

Susquehanna Foundation for the Blind
244 North Queen Street
Lancaster, PA 17603
(717) 291-5951
Web: www.sabvi.org/Grants%20and%20Scholarships

Summary To provide financial assistance to Pennsylvania residents who are legally blind veterans and interested in working on a degree at any level at a college in any state.

Eligibility This program is open to veterans who are residents of Pennsylvania and legally blind. Applicants must be attending or planning to attend an institution of higher education at any level in any state. Along with their application, they must submit a brief description of their career goal. Need is considered in the selection process.

Financial data The stipend is $1,000 per year.

Duration 1 year; renewable up to 3 more years.

Number awarded 1 or more each year.

Deadline January of each year.

[486]
LARRY STREETER MEMORIAL SCHOLARSHIP

National Federation of the Blind
Attn: Scholarship Committee
200 East Wells Street
Baltimore, MD 21230
(410) 659-9314, ext. 2415   Fax: (410) 685-5653
E-mail: scholarships@nfb.org
Web: www.nfb.org/nfb/scholarship_program.asp

Summary To provide funding to blind students working on an college or graduate degree in any field.

Eligibility This program is open to legally blind students who are working on or planning to work full time on an undergraduate or graduate degree in any field. Applicants must be attempting to "elevate their quality of life, equipping them to be active, productive participants in their family, community, and the workplace." Along with their application, they must submit transcripts, standardized test scores, proof of legal blindness, 2 letters of recommendation, and a letter of endorsement from their National Federation of the Blind state president or designee. Selection is based on academic excellence, service to the community, and financial need.

Financial data The stipend is $3,000.

Duration 1 year; recipients may resubmit applications up to 2 additional years.

Additional data This program began in 2011. Scholarships are awarded at the federation convention in July. Recipients must attend the convention at federation expense; that funding is in addition to the scholarship grant.

Number awarded 1 each year.

Deadline March of each year.

[487]
LAVELLE FUND FOR THE BLIND SCHOLARSHIPS

Lavelle Fund for the Blind, Inc.
Attn: Scholarship Program Coordinator
307 West 38th Street, Suite 2010
New York, NY 10018
(212) 668-9801   Fax: (212) 668-9803
E-mail: lmamrosh@lavellefund.org
Web: www.lavellefund.org/lfb_scholarship_program.html

Summary To provide financial assistance to blind residents of the New York tri-state region who are attending designated colleges in the New York City area.

Eligibility This program is open to residents of Connecticut, New Jersey, and New York who are legally blind or severely visually impaired. Applicants must be working on or planning to work full time on an undergraduate or graduate degree at 1 of 8 designated colleges and universities in the New York City area. They must be able to demonstrate financial need.

Financial data Stipends range up to $15,000 per year, depending on the need of the recipient. Funds are paid directly to the college or university the recipient attends.

Duration 1 year; renewable up to 3 more years.

Additional data The participating schools are Dominican College, Fordham University (graduate study only), Manhattanville College, Marist College, Marymount Manhattan College, St. John's University (graduate study only), St. Thomas Aquinas College, and Seton Hall University.

Number awarded Varies each year.

Deadline Deadline not specified.

[488]
LINWOOD WALKER SCHOLARSHIP

American Council of the Blind of Ohio
Attn: Executive Director
P.O. Box 307128
Gahanna, OH 43230-7128
(614) 221-6688   Toll Free: (800) 835-2226 (within OH)
E-mail: mary.hiland@wowway.com
Web: www.acbohio.org

Summary To provide financial assistance to blind Ohio graduate students in service-related fields.

Eligibility This program is open to 1) residents of Ohio who are currently enrolled as graduate students, and 2) graduate students at colleges and universities in Ohio. Applicants must be legally blind and working on or planning to work on a degree in a service-related field (e.g., teaching, health care, public administration). Along with their application, they must submit transcripts (must have a GPA of 3.0 or higher), a certificate of legal blindness, and an essay of 250 to 500 words on their career objectives, future plans, personal goals, other academic or per-

sonal qualities, and why they believe they are qualified to receive this scholarship. Financial need is not the sole factor considered in the selection process.

Financial data The stipend is $2,500 per year.

Duration 1 year; recipients may reapply.

Additional data Winners are required to attend the Saturday morning business meeting and Sunday breakfast of the sponsor's annual convention; a stipend for meals and workshops is provided.

Number awarded 1 each year.

Deadline August of each year.

[489]
LIONS CLUBS SUPPORT SERVICES FOR THE BLIND AND VISUALLY IMPAIRED

Lions Clubs International
Attn: Program Development Department
300 West 22nd Street
Oak Brook, IL 60523-8842
(630) 571-5466, ext. 316   Fax: (630) 571-1692
E-mail: programs@lionsclubs.org
Web: www.lionsclubs.org

Summary To provide college scholarships and other assistance (transportation, assistive technology, Braille products, etc.) to blind people.

Eligibility These programs are open to blind people and others involved in service to the blind. Applicants may be seeking support for the following activities: scholarships for the blind and visually impaired, medical research, assistive technology grants, independent mobility, transportation, reading materials and aids, audio products, Braille products, and other aids.

Financial data The amount of this assistance varies.

Additional data Support is provided by local Lions Clubs. Requests sent to the international office are referred to the appropriate district governor, who then sends the inquiries to an appropriate club within the district. No funds are available from the office of Lions Clubs International.

Deadline Deadline not specified.

[490]
MARY P. OENSLAGER SCHOLASTIC ACHIEVEMENT AWARDS

Learning Ally
Attn: Training and Support Center
20 Roszel Road
Princeton, NJ 08540
(609) 243-7087   Toll Free: (800) 221-4792
Fax: (609) 987-8116
E-mail: mGreenwald@LearningAlly.org
Web: www.learningally.org/awards

Summary To recognize and reward the outstanding academic achievements of blind college seniors and graduate students.

Eligibility To be eligible for this award, candidates must 1) be legally blind; 2) have received, or will receive, a bachelor's, master's, or doctoral degree from a 4-year accredited college or university in the United States or its territories during the year the award is given; 3) have an overall academic average of 3.0 or higher; and 4) have been registered members of Learning Ally for at least 1 year. Selection is based on academic excellence, leadership, and service to others.

Financial data Top winners receive $6,000 each, special honors winners $3,000 each, and honors winners $1,000 each.

Duration The awards are presented annually.

Additional data These awards are named for the founder of the program who established it in 1959 and endowed it with a gift of $1 million in 1990. Learning Ally was formerly named Recording for the Blind and Dyslexic.

Number awarded 9 each year: 3 top winners, 3 special honors winners, and 3 honors winners.

Deadline March of each year.

[491]
MARY ZOE ALLEE SCHOLARSHIP

Wyoming Council of the Blind
c/o Betty Matthews
374 West Alger, Apartment A
Sheridan, WY 82801
E-mail: bettymatt88@bresnan.net
Web: www.wycb.info/scholarship.html

Summary To provide financial assistance to blind residents of Wyoming who are interested in attending college or graduate school in any state.

Eligibility This program is open to residents of Wyoming who are legally blind or visually impaired. Applicants must be entering or enrolled at a vocational training program, college, university, community college, or graduate school in any state. Along with their application, they must submit a 2-page autobiographical sketch that includes their goals, strengths, weaknesses, hobbies, honors, achievements, the field of study they have chosen, and the reason why they have chosen it. Financial need is not considered in the selection process. Leading candidates are interviewed.

Financial data The stipend is $1,000.

Duration 1 year.

Number awarded 1 each year.

Deadline April of each year.

[492]
MISSOURI COUNCIL OF THE BLIND SCHOLARSHIPS

Missouri Council of the Blind
5453 Chippewa Street
St. Louis, MO 63109-1635
(314) 832-7172 Toll Free: (800) 342-5632 (within MO)
Fax: (314) 832-7796   E-mail: aa@moblind.org
Web: www.moblind.org

Summary To provide financial assistance for college or graduate school to blind students in Missouri.

Eligibility This program is open to Missouri residents who are high school or college graduates, legally blind, and in good academic standing. Applicants must be working on or planning to work on an undergraduate or gradu-

ate degree. They should have a specific goal in mind and that goal should be realistically within reach.

Financial data A stipend is awarded (amount not specified).

Duration 1 year; may be renewed if the recipient maintains a GPA of 2.0 or higher.

Number awarded Varies each year; recently, 14 of these scholarships were awarded.

Deadline April of each year.

[493]
NATIONAL FEDERATION OF THE BLIND OF ARIZONA SCHOLARSHIP

National Federation of the Blind of Arizona
c/o Marcus Schmidt, Scholarship Committee Chair
3202 West Muriel Drive
Phoenix, AZ 85053
(602) 942-0181   E-mail: nfbazwest@gmail.com
Web: www.az.nfb.org/node/36

Summary To provide financial assistance for college or graduate school to blind residents of Arizona.

Eligibility This program is open to residents of Arizona who are legally blind in both eyes and currently attending high school or college. Applicants must be enrolled or planning to enroll as a full-time undergraduate or graduate student at a college or university in any state. Along with their application, they must submit a 1,000-word essay about themselves, including their most notable qualities, their attitude about blindness, their community involvement, and their demonstrated leadership ability. High school seniors must also submit SAT or ACT scores.

Financial data The stipend is $1,000.

Duration 1 year.

Number awarded 1 each year.

Deadline May of each year.

[494]
NATIONAL FEDERATION OF THE BLIND OF CALIFORNIA SCHOLARSHIPS

National Federation of the Blind of California
c/o Mary Willows, President
39481 Gallaudet Drive, Apartment 127
Fremont, CA 94538
(510) 248-0100   Toll Free: (877) 558-6524
E-mail: mwillows@sbcglobal.net
Web: sixdots.org/category/grants-and-scholarships

Summary To provide financial assistance to blind residents of California interested in attending college or graduate school in any state.

Eligibility This program is open to residents of California who are legally blind. Applicants must be enrolled or planning to enroll as a full-time student in an undergraduate or graduate degree program in any state. They must have a GPA of 3.0 or higher. Along with their application, they must submit a 500-word statement on their educational and career goals, their involvement in the blindness community, the alternative techniques they use to do their school work (e.g., Braille, large print, recording, adapted computer), and any rehabilitation services they are receiving.

Financial data Stipends range from $2,000 to $5,000.

Duration 1 year.

Additional data This program includes the following named awards: the Gerald Drake Memorial Scholarship, the LaVyrl "Pinky" Johnson Memorial Scholarship, the Julie Landucci Scholarship, and the Lawrence "Muzzy" Marcelino Memorial Scholarship.

Number awarded Several each year.

Deadline September of each year.

[495]
NATIONAL FEDERATION OF THE BLIND OF CONNECTICUT SCHOLARSHIPS

National Federation of the Blind of Connecticut
477 Connecticut Boulevard, Suite 217
East Hartford, CT 06108
(860) 289-1971   E-mail: info@nfbct.org
Web: www.nfbct.org/html/schform.htm

Summary To provide financial assistance for college or graduate school to blind students from Connecticut.

Eligibility This program is open to full-time undergraduate and graduate students who are legally blind. Applicants must be residents of Connecticut or attending school in the state. Along with their application, they must submit 2 letters of recommendation, academic transcripts, a description of their career goals and how this scholarship might help them achieve those, and a letter from a state officer of the National Federation of the Blind of Connecticut confirming that they have discussed their application with him or her. Selection is based on academic excellence, service to the community, and financial need.

Financial data Stipends are $8,000, $4,000, or $3,000.

Duration 1 year.

Additional data This program consists of the following named awards: the C. Rodney Demarest Memorial Scholarship ($3,000), the Howard E. May Memorial Scholarship ($6,000), the Jonathan May Memorial Scholarship ($5,000), and the Mary Main Memorial Scholarship ($4,000). The latter 3 programs are supported by the John A. Coccomo, Sr. Foundation. Recipients are expected to attend the annual convention of the National Federation of the Blind of Connecticut.

Number awarded 4 each year.

Deadline September of each year.

[496]
NATIONAL FEDERATION OF THE BLIND OF ILLINOIS SCHOLARSHIPS

National Federation of the Blind of Illinois
c/o Deborah Kent Stein, Scholarship Committee Chair
5817 North Nina Avenue
Chicago, IL 60631
(773) 631-1093   E-mail: dkent5817@att.net
Web: www.nfbofillinois.org/?page_id=97

Summary To provide financial assistance for college or graduate school to blind students in Illinois.

Eligibility This program is open to legally blind full-time undergraduate and graduate students. Applicants must be residents of Illinois or attending a college or university in the state. Along with their application, they must submit a personal essay that describes their strengths, achievements, and aspirations; what is important to them; who they hope to become; if a particular person or experience has changed their life; how their blindness has affected them; and how they handle blindness at school, on the job, and in interpersonal relationships. Selection is based on academic excellence and service to the community.

Financial data Stipends range from $1,250 to $2,000.

Duration 1 year; recipients may reapply.

Additional data This program consists of the following named awards: the Peter Grunwald Scholarship (1 awarded at $2,000), the Mary MacDill Napheide Scholarships (2 awarded at $1,500 each), and the Kenneth Jernigan Scholarships (2 awarded at $1,250 each).

Number awarded 5 each year.

Deadline March of each year.

[497]
NATIONAL FEDERATION OF THE BLIND OF NEW JERSEY SCHOLARSHIPS

National Federation of the Blind of New Jersey
c/o Jerilyn Higgins, Scholarship Chair
2 Old Farm Road
Verona, NJ 07044-1726
(973) 239-8874   Toll Free: (866) 632-1940
E-mail: jdhiggins3@verizon.net
Web: www.nfbnj.org/scholarships.php

Summary To provide financial assistance to entering and continuing undergraduate and graduate students from New Jersey who are blind.

Eligibility This program is open to legally blind students who are working on or planning to work full time on an undergraduate or graduate degree. Applicants must be residents of New Jersey or attending school in the state. Along with their application, they must submit a personal letter, 2 letters of recommendation, transcripts, and a letter of endorsement from an officer of the National Federation of the Blind of New Jersey. Selection is based on academic excellence, service to the community, and financial need.

Financial data A stipend is awarded (amount not specified).

Duration 1 year.

Number awarded 1 or more each year.

Deadline March of each year.

[498]
NATIONAL FEDERATION OF THE BLIND OF NEW YORK SCHOLARSHIPS

National Federation of the Blind of New York State, Inc.
P.O. Box 205666 Sunset Station
Brooklyn, NY 11220
(718) 567-7821   Fax: (718) 765-1843
E-mail: office@nfbny.org
Web: www.nfbny.org/Scholsrships.htm

Summary To provide financial assistance to blind residents of New York who are interested in attending college or graduate school in any state.
Eligibility This program is open to residents of New York who are legally blind. Applicants must be entering or enrolled in a degree program at the undergraduate, graduate, or postgraduate level at a school in any state. Along with their application, they must submit a 500-word essay explaining their goals, attitudes, and approach to living with blindness.
Financial data A stipend is awarded (amount not specified).
Duration 1 year.
Additional data This program includes the following named awards: the Gisela Distal Memorial Scholarship and the Maryanne Swaton Memorial Scholarship.
Number awarded At least 3 each year.
Deadline October of each year.

[499]
NATIONAL FEDERATION OF THE BLIND OF OHIO SCHOLARSHIP

National Federation of the Blind of Ohio
c/o Barbara Pierce, Scholarship Committee Chair
237 Oak Street
Oberlin, OH 44074-1517
(440) 775-2216   E-mail: bpierce@nfb.org
Web: www.nfbohio.org

Summary To provide financial assistance to blind residents of Ohio who are interested in working on an undergraduate or graduate degree at a school in any state.
Eligibility This program is open to residents of Ohio who are legally blind. Applicants must be attending or planning to attend an accredited institution of higher education as a full-time undergraduate or graduate student. Along with their application, they must submit 2 letters of recommendation, current transcripts, a letter about themselves that includes how they have dealt with their blindness and their hopes and dreams, and a letter from an officer of the National Federation of the Blind of Ohio indicating that they have discussed their scholarship application with that officer. Selection is based on academic excellence, community service, and financial need.
Financial data The stipend is $1,000.
Duration 1 year.
Number awarded 1 each year.
Deadline April of each year.

[500]
NATIONAL FEDERATION OF THE BLIND OF OREGON SCHOLARSHIPS

National Federation of the Blind of Oregon
c/o Art Stevenson, President
1616 Fifth Street N.E.
Salem, OR 97303
(503) 585-4318 Toll Free: (800) 422-7093 (within OR)
E-mail: artds55@comcast.net
Web: www.nfb-oregon.org/scholarship.php

Summary To provide financial assistance for college or graduate school to blind residents of Oregon.
Eligibility This program is open to blind residents of Oregon who are working on or planning to work on an undergraduate or graduate degree at a college or university in the state. Applicants must be enrolled full time or enrolled part time and working full time. Along with the application, they must submit a personal letter that includes what they consider their best qualities and the techniques and approaches they practice concerning their blindness. Selection is based on academic excellence, community service, and financial need.
Financial data Stipends are either $1,500 or $1,000.
Duration 1 year.
Number awarded 1 at $1,500 and 2 at $1,000.
Deadline March of each year.

[501]
NATIONAL FEDERATION OF THE BLIND SCHOLARSHIPS

National Federation of the Blind
Attn: Scholarship Committee
200 East Wells Street
Baltimore, MD 21230
(410) 659-9314, ext. 2415   Fax: (410) 685-5653
E-mail: scholarships@nfb.org
Web: www.nfb.org/nfb/scholarship_program.asp

Summary To provide financial assistance for college or graduate school to blind students.
Eligibility This program is open to legally blind students who are working on or planning to work on an undergraduate or graduate degree. In general, full-time enrollment is required, although 1 scholarship may be awarded to a part-time student who is working full time. Along with their application, they must submit transcripts, standardized test scores, proof of legal blindness, 2 letters of recommendation, and a letter of endorsement from their National Federation of the Blind state president or designee. Selection is based on academic excellence, service to the community, and financial need.
Financial data Stipends are $7,000, $5,000, or $3,000.
Duration 1 year; recipients may resubmit applications up to 2 additional years.
Additional data Scholarships are awarded at the federation convention in July. Recipients must attend the convention at federation expense; that funding is in addition to the scholarship grant.
Number awarded 26 each year: 2 at $7,000, 4 at $5,000, and 20 at $3,000.
Deadline March of each year.

[502]
NIB GRANT M. MACK MEMORIAL SCHOLARSHIP

American Council of the Blind
Attn: Coordinator, Scholarship Program
2200 Wilson Boulevard, Suite 650
Arlington, VA 22201
(202) 467-5081   Toll Free: (800) 424-8666
Fax: (703) 465-5085   E-mail: info@acb.org
Web: www.acb.org/scholarship

Summary To provide financial assistance to blind students who are working on an undergraduate or graduate degree in business or management.

Eligibility This program is open to undergraduate and graduate students working on a degree in business or management. Applicants must submit verification of legal blindness in both eyes; SAT, ACT, GMAT, or similar scores; information on extracurricular activities (including involvement in the American Council of the Blind); employment record; and a 500-word autobiographical sketch that includes their personal goals, strengths, weaknesses, hobbies, honors, achievements, and reasons for choice of field or courses of study. A cumulative GPA of 3.3 or higher is generally required. Financial need is not considered in the selection process. U.S. citizenship or permanent resident status is required.

Financial data The stipend is $2,000.

Duration 1 year.

Additional data This scholarship is sponsored by National Industries for the Blind (NIB) in honor of a dedicated leader of the American Council of the Blind. Scholarship winners are expected to attend the council's annual conference; the council will cover all reasonable expenses.

Number awarded 1 each year.

Deadline February of each year.

[503]
NORA WEBB-MCKINNEY SCHOLARSHIP

American Council of the Blind of Ohio
Attn: Executive Director
P.O. Box 307128
Gahanna, OH 43230-7128
(614) 221-6688   Toll Free: (800) 835-2226 (within OH)
E-mail: mary.hiland@wowway.com
Web: www.acbohio.org

Summary To provide financial assistance to Ohio students who are interested in working on an undergraduate or graduate degree involving service to blind people.

Eligibility This program is open to 1) residents of Ohio who are high school seniors or current undergraduate or graduate students; and 2) undergraduate and graduate students from any state enrolled at colleges and universities in Ohio. Applicants must be interested in working on or planning to work on a degree in a field related to blindness (e.g., special education, rehabilitation teaching or counseling, orientation and mobility, or a concentration on programs serving people who are blind). They may be blind or sighted. Along with their application, they must submit transcripts (must have a GPA of 3.0 or higher) and an essay of 250 to 500 words on their career objectives, future plans, personal goals, other academic or personal qualities, and why they believe they are qualified to receive this scholarship. Financial need is not the sole factor considered in the selection process.

Financial data The stipend is $2,000 per year.

Duration 1 year; recipients may reapply.

Additional data Winners are required to attend the Saturday morning business meeting and Sunday breakfast of the sponsor's annual convention; a stipend for meals and workshops is provided.

Number awarded 1 each year.

Deadline August of each year.

[504]
ONKYO BRAILLE ESSAY CONTEST

National Federation of the Blind
Attn: Trisha Tatam
200 East Wells Street
Baltimore, MD 21230
(410) 659-9314, ext. 2510   Fax: (410) 685-5653
E-mail: ttatam@nfb.org
Web: www.nfb.org

Summary To recognize and reward outstanding essays by blind people from around the world on the impact of Braille on their lives.

Eligibility This competition is open to individuals who are blind and live in any country. Entries may be submitted in the junior group, for 25 years of age and under, or the senior group, for 26 years of age and older. Candidates must submit an essay, from 800 to 1,000 words, on 1 of the following topics: 1) how they acquire knowledge and information through Braille or audio devices; 2) how blind persons can become independent by learning Braille or music; or 3) their individual concept about world peace from the viewpoint of persons with disabilities. Essays must be written in English or their native language, in Braille, and completely original. Selection is based on the essay's pertinence to the selected topic, impact and credibility of the experiences described, accuracy and neatness in using Braille, and style and language skills.

Financial data The Otsuki Award is $2,000, Excellent Work Awards are $1,000, and Fine Work Awards are $500.

Duration The competition is held annually.

Additional data This competition was established in 2003 by the Onkyo Corporation of Japan and the Braille Mainichi. In the United States, the National Federation of the Blind administers the contest on behalf of the North America-Caribbean Region of the World Blind Union.

Number awarded 7 each year: the Otsuki Award (awarded to the outstanding essay from either the senior or the junior group), 2 Excellent Work Awards (1 each for the senior and the junior group), and 4 Fine Work Awards (2 each for the senior and the junior group).

Deadline April of each year.

[505]
PAUL AND ELLEN RUCKES SCHOLARSHIP

American Foundation for the Blind
Attn: Scholarship Committee
2 Penn Plaza, Suite 1102
New York, NY 10121
(212) 502-7661   Toll Free: (800) AFB-LINE
Fax: (888) 545-8331   E-mail: afbinfo@afb.net
Web: www.afb.org/Section.asp?Documentid=2962

Summary To provide financial assistance to legally blind students who wish to work on a graduate or undergraduate degree in engineering or computer, physical, or life sciences.

Eligibility This program is open to legally blind undergraduate or graduate students who are U.S. citizens working or planning to work full time on a degree in engineering or the computer, physical, or life sciences. Along with their application, they must submit 200-word essays on 1) their past and recent achievements; 2) their intended field of study and why they chose it; and 3) the role their visual impairment has played in shaping their life. Financial need is considered in the selection process.

Financial data The stipend is $1,000.

Duration 1 year.

Number awarded 1 each year.

Deadline April of each year.

[506]
PETER LINDH SCHOLARSHIP

Association for Education and Rehabilitation of the Blind and Visually Impaired-Georgia Chapter
c/o Mike Muchow
3354 Chestnut Woods Circle
Doraville, GA 30340
E-mail: michaelmuchow@yahoo.com
Web: www.gaaer.org/home/peter-lindh-scholarship

Summary To provide financial assistance to residents of Georgia who are legally blind and interested in attending college or graduate school in any state.

Eligibility This program is open to legally blind residents of Georgia who are attending or planning to attend a college, university, junior college, or graduate school in any state. Applicants must submit a letter about themselves that includes their goals and aspirations, why they feel they deserve this scholarship, how it will help them, and how they would use the money. Selection is based on academics; neither college level nor financial need is considered.

Financial data The stipend is $1,000.

Duration 1 year.

Number awarded 1 each year.

Deadline August of each year.

[507]
POULSON FAMILY SCHOLARSHIPS

Utah Council of the Blind
c/o Leslie Gertsch, Executive Director
1301 West 500 South
Woods Cross, UT 84087-2224
(801) 292-1156   Fax: (801) 292-6046
E-mail: lgertsch@comcast.net
Web: www.utahcounciloftheblind.org

Summary To provide financial assistance to members of the Utah Council of the Blind (UCB) who plan to attend college or graduate school in the state.

Eligibility This program is open to UCB members who are entering or enrolled as an undergraduate or graduate student at a college or university in Utah. Applicants must be blind or visually impaired, defined as having a visual acuity of less than 20/70, a visual field not exceeding 30 degrees, or a functional visual impairment of similar degree in the best eye with best correction. Along with their application, they must submit an autobiographical sketch that includes their personal goals, strengths, weaknesses, hobbies, honors, achievements, the course of study they are pursuing, and why they have chosen it. Financial need is not considered. Interviews may be held.

Financial data The stipend is at least $1,000.

Duration 1 year; may be renewed.

Number awarded Varies each year; recently, 5 of these scholarships were awarded.

Deadline April of each year.

[508]
ROBERT AND HAZEL STALEY MEMORIAL SCHOLARSHIP

National Federation of the Blind of North Carolina
c/o Julius Locklear
3102 Kings Court, Apartment A
Raleigh, NC 27606
(910) 740-1129   E-mail: Jrl006@bellsouth.net
Web: www.nfbofnc.org

Summary To provide financial assistance to undergraduate and graduate students from North Carolina who are blind and interested in attending college or graduate school in any state.

Eligibility This program is open to legally blind residents of North Carolina who are attending or planning to attend a college or university in any state. Applicants must be working on or planning to work on an undergraduate or graduate degree. Along with their application, they must submit 2 letters of recommendation, a current transcript, and a letter of introduction about themselves that includes their likes and dislikes, how their blindness has affected them, the honors and awards they have received, and their school and extracurricular activities. Selection is based on academics, community service, and financial need.

Financial data The stipend is $1,500. Funds may be used for the purchase of equipment, reader services, transportation, or other services or materials necessary to accomplish the recipient's educational objectives. They are not intended to offset support provided by state or federal agencies.

Duration 1 year.

Additional data Recipients must attend the sponsor's annual convention, at federation expense, where they receive their awards.

Number awarded Up to 2 each year.

Deadline June of each year.

[509]
ROSS N. AND PATRICIA PANGERE FOUNDATION SCHOLARSHIPS

American Council of the Blind
Attn: Coordinator, Scholarship Program
2200 Wilson Boulevard, Suite 650
Arlington, VA 22201
(202) 467-5081   Toll Free: (800) 424-8666
Fax: (703) 465-5085   E-mail: info@acb.org
Web: www.acb.org/scholarship

Summary To provide funding to blind students working on a college or graduate degree in business.

Eligibility This program is open to undergraduate and graduate students working on a degree in business. Applicants must submit verification of legal blindness in both eyes; SAT, ACT, GMAT, or similar scores; information on extracurricular activities (including involvement in the American Council of the Blind); employment record; and a 500-word autobiographical sketch that includes their personal goals, strengths, weaknesses, hobbies, honors, achievements, and reasons for choice of field or courses of study. A cumulative GPA of 3.3 or higher is generally required. Need is not considered in the selection process.

Financial data The stipend is $2,500.

Duration 1 year.

Additional data This program is funded by the Ross N. and Patricia Pangere Foundation. Scholarship winners are expected to attend the council's annual conference; the council will cover all reasonable expenses.

Number awarded 2 each year.

Deadline February of each year.

[510]
ROY JOHNSON SCHOLARSHIPS

Roy Johnson Scholarship Trust Fund
Attn: James S. Buscetta, Trustee
Michigan Commission for the Blind
201 North Washington Square, Second Floor
P.O. Box 30652
Lansing, MI 48909
(517) 373-2062   Toll Free: (800) 292-4200
Fax: (517) 335-5140   TDD: (517) 373-4025

Summary To provide tuition assistance to residents of any state who are blind and interested in working on a graduate degree in Michigan.

Eligibility This program is open to blind people (regardless of sex, race, color, religion, or age) who have received a bachelor's degree from an accredited college or university in the United States. Applicants must be working on or planning to work on a graduate degree at an institution in Michigan. Both college seniors and currently-enrolled graduate students are eligible. For the purposes of this award, a "blind person" means an individual who has a visual acuity of 20/200 or less in the better eye with correction, or has a limitation of vision such that the widest diameter of the visual field subtends an angular distance of not greater than 20 degrees. Factors considered in the selection process: financial need, scholastic record, recommendations, and applicant's plans for graduate education.

Financial data Stipends range from $250 to $1,000. Funds may be used to cover tuition, room and board, or reader services.

Duration 1 year.

Additional data Funds must be used to pursue graduate studies at an accredited college in Michigan.

Number awarded Varies each year; recently, 13 of these scholarships were awarded.

Deadline May of each year.

[511]
RUDOLPH DILLMAN MEMORIAL SCHOLARSHIP

American Foundation for the Blind
Attn: Scholarship Committee
2 Penn Plaza, Suite 1102
New York, NY 10121
(212) 502-7661   Toll Free: (800) AFB-LINE
Fax: (888) 545-8331   E-mail: afbinfo@afb.net
Web: www.afb.org/Section.asp?Documentid=2962

Summary To provide funding to legally blind college or graduate students studying in the field of rehabilitation and/or education of visually impaired and blind persons.

Eligibility This program is open to legally blind U.S. citizens who have been accepted to an accredited undergraduate or graduate training program within the broad field of rehabilitation and/or education of blind and visually impaired persons. Along with their application, they must submit 200-word essays on 1) their past and recent achievements and accomplishments; 2) their intended field of study and why they have chosen it; and 3) the role their visual impairment has played in shaping their life. Financial need is considered for 1 of the scholarships.

Financial data The stipend is $2,500 per year.

Duration 1 year; previous recipients may not reapply.

Number awarded 4 each year: 3 without consideration to financial need and 1 based on financial need.

Deadline April of each year.

[512]
SOUTH DAKOTA REDUCED TUITION FOR VISUAL IMPAIRMENT

South Dakota Board of Regents
Attn: Scholarship Committee
306 East Capitol Avenue, Suite 200
Pierre, SD 57501-2545
(605) 773-3455   Fax: (605) 773-2422
E-mail: info@sdbor.edu
Web: www.sdbor.edu

Summary To provide waiver of tuition and fees to South Dakota residents with a visual impairment who are interested in attending college or graduate school in the state.
Eligibility This program is open to visually impaired residents of South Dakota who can meet the entrance requirements for admission to a postsecondary educational institution (including graduate school and medical school) under the supervision of the state board of regents. For purposes of the program, "visual impairment" means that the person cannot, with use of correcting glasses, see sufficiently well to perform ordinary activities for which eyesight is essential. This program does not extend to visually impaired persons who are entitled to receive tuition and fee support from the state's department of vocational rehabilitation.
Financial data Qualified applicants receive a total waiver of standard tuition and fees.
Duration Benefits are provided until the recipient has earned 225 semester hours of credit or the equivalent.
Additional data Applicants should contact the financial aid director at the South Dakota college or university they plan to attend, not the sponsor. The exemption from charges does not apply if a course is repeated because of unsatisfactory performance within the student's control.
Deadline Deadline not specified.

[513]
SUSQUEHANNA FOUNDATION FOR THE BLIND TRUSTEES' SCHOLARSHIP

Susquehanna Foundation for the Blind
244 North Queen Street
Lancaster, PA 17603
(717) 291-5951
Web: www.sabvi.org/Grants%20and%20Scholarships

Summary To provide financial assistance to legally blind Pennsylvania residents who are interested in working on an undergraduate or graduate degree or other academic program at a school in any state.
Eligibility This program is open to residents of Pennsylvania who are legally blind. Applicants must be working on an undergraduate or graduate degree or other specialized program intended to generate upward mobility in employment. Along with their application, they must submit a brief description of their career goal. Financial need is considered in the selection process.
Financial data A stipend is awarded (amount not specified).
Duration 1 year.
Number awarded 1 or more each year.
Deadline January of each year.

[514]
SUSQUEHANNA POST-GRADUATE SCHOLARSHIP

Susquehanna Foundation for the Blind
244 North Queen Street
Lancaster, PA 17603
(717) 291-5951
Web: www.sabvi.org/Grants%20and%20Scholarships

Summary To provide financial assistance to legally blind Pennsylvania residents who are interested in working on a graduate degree at a school in any state to prepare for a career in rehabilitation services for people who are blind.
Eligibility This program is open to residents of Pennsylvania who are legally blind. Applicants must be interested in working on a graduate degree in a professional field serving people who are blind (e.g., rehabilitation teaching, orientation and mobility instruction, teacher of the visually impaired). Along with their application, they must submit a brief description of their career goal. Financial need is considered in the selection process.
Financial data The stipend is $3,000 per year.
Duration 2 years.
Number awarded 1 or more each year.
Deadline January of each year.

[515]
SYDE HURDUS PRESIDENT'S AWARD

Lighthouse International
Attn: Scholarship and Career Awards
111 East 59th Street
New York, NY 10022-1202
(212) 821-9428   Toll Free: (800) 829-0500
Fax: (212) 821-9703   TDD: (212) 821-9713
E-mail: sca@lighthouse.org
Web: www.lighthouse.org

Summary To provide financial assistance to legally blind high school seniors, recent graduates, undergraduates, or graduate students.
Eligibility This program is open to legally blind U.S. citizens who are graduating high school seniors, recent graduates, current undergraduates, or current graduate students. Applicants must be attending or planning to attend an accredited college or university in 1 of the 50 states, the District of Columbia, or a U.S. territory. Along with their application, they must submit essays of 400 to 600 words on 1) their academic focus and extracurricular activities and what inspires their interest in each area; 2) their passion and how they express that passion; 3) key academic and personal accomplishments and the challenges they overcome to be successful; and 4) how this scholarship will support their academic and/or career development. Selection is based on academic and personal achievements; financial need is not considered.
Financial data The stipend is $10,000.
Duration 1 year.
Number awarded 1 each year.
Deadline January of each year.

[516]
TRINKA DAVIS GRADUATE AWARD

Lighthouse International
Attn: Scholarship and Career Awards
111 East 59th Street
New York, NY 10022-1202
(212) 821-9428   Toll Free: (800) 829-0500
Fax: (212) 821-9703   TDD: (212) 821-9713
E-mail: sca@lighthouse.org
Web: www.lighthouse.org

Summary To provide financial assistance to legally blind students working on a graduate degree.

Eligibility This program is open to graduate students who are legally blind and U.S. citizens. Applicants must be attending an accredited college or university in 1 of the 50 states, the District of Columbia, or a U.S. territory. Along with their application, they must submit essays of 400 to 600 words on 1) their academic focus and extracurricular activities and what inspires their interest in each area; 2) their passion and how they express that passion; 3) key academic and personal accomplishments and the challenges they overcome to be successful; and 4) how this scholarship will support their academic and/or career development. Selection is based on academic and personal achievements; financial need is not considered.

Financial data The stipend is $10,000.

Duration 1 year.

Number awarded 1 each year.

Deadline January of each year.

[517]
WALTER YOUNG MEMORIAL SCHOLARSHIP

California Association for Postsecondary Education
  and Disability
Attn: Executive Assistant
71423 Biskra Road
Rancho Mirage, CA 92270
(760) 346-8206   Fax: (760) 340-5275
TDD: (760) 341-4084   E-mail: caped2000@aol.com
Web: www.caped.net/scholarships.html

Summary To provide funding to blind and visually impaired college and graduate students in California.

Eligibility This program is open to blind and visually impaired students at public and private colleges and universities in California. Undergraduates must have completed at least 6 semester credits and have a GPA of 2.5 or higher. Graduate students must have completed at least 3 semester units and have a GPA of 3.0 or higher. Along with their application, they must submit a 1-page personal letter that demonstrates their writing skills, progress towards meeting their educational and vocational goals, management of their disability, and involvement in community activities. They must also submit a letter of recommendation from a faculty member, verification of disability, official transcripts, proof of current enrollment, and documentation of financial need.

Financial data The stipend is $1,000.

Duration 1 year.

Number awarded 1 each year.

Deadline September of each year.

[518]
WASHINGTON COUNCIL OF THE BLIND SCHOLARSHIPS

Washington Council of the Blind
c/o Tim McCorcle, Scholarship Committee Chair
2253 N.E. 54th Street
Seattle, WA 98105-3213
Toll Free: (206) 522-5850
E-mail: t.mccorcle@comcast.net
Web: www.wcbinfo.org

Summary To provide financial aid to blind students in Washington who plan to attend college or graduate school in any state.

Eligibility This program is open to blind residents of Washington state who are enrolled or planning to enroll at an accredited college, university, vocational school, or graduate school in any state. Applicants must submit a 1,000-word statement of their reasons for applying for this scholarship and how it will assist them to achieve their goals. The statement should include a brief description of their background, education, work experience, economic status, strengths, weaknesses, and personal goals for the next 5 to 10 years. Interviews are required.

Financial data The stipend ranges up to $4,000.

Duration 1 year.

Number awarded 1 or more each year.

Deadline July of each year.

[519]
WILLIAM G. COREY MEMORIAL SCHOLARSHIP

American Council of the Blind
Attn: Coordinator, Scholarship Program
2200 Wilson Boulevard, Suite 650
Arlington, VA 22201
(202) 467-5081   Toll Free: (800) 424-8666
Fax: (703) 465-5085   E-mail: info@acb.org
Web: www.acb.org/scholarship

Summary To provide money for college to blind undergraduate and graduate students from Pennsylvania.

Eligibility This program is open to legally blind undergraduate and graduate students who are residents of Pennsylvania or attending college in the state. Applicants must submit verification of legal blindness in both eyes; SAT, ACT, GRE, or similar scores; information on extracurricular activities (including involvement in the American Council of the Blind); employment record; and a 500-word autobiographical sketch that includes their personal goals, strengths, weaknesses, hobbies, honors, achievements, and reasons for choice of field or courses of study. A cumulative GPA of 3.3 or higher is generally required. Financial need is not considered in the selection process.

Financial data The stipend is $1,500.

Duration 1 year.

Additional data Scholarship winners are expected to attend the council's annual conference; the council will cover all reasonable expenses.
Number awarded 1 each year.
Deadline February of each year.

Grants-in-Aid

[520]
ALABAMA COUNTY HOMESTEAD EXEMPTIONS

Alabama Department of Revenue
Attn: Property Tax Division
Gordon Persons Building
50 North Ripley Street, Room 4126
P.O. Box 327210
Montgomery, AL 36132-7210
(334) 242-1525
Web: www.ador.state.al.us

Summary To exempt disabled, blind, and elderly residents of Alabama from ad valorem property taxes imposed by counties.
Eligibility Residents of Alabama are eligible to apply if they are over the age of 65 and have a net annual income of $12,000 or less for income tax purposes for the preceding year; or are retired due to permanent and total disability, regardless of age; or are blind, regardless of age or retirement status.
Financial data Qualifying residents are exempt from ad valorem property taxes levied by counties, including taxes levied for school districts, to a maximum of $5,000 in assessed value, or 160 acres in area.
Duration 1 year; this exemption will be granted as long as the resident continues to meet the eligibility requirements.
Number awarded Varies each year.
Deadline Deadline not specified.

[521]
ALABAMA PERSONAL PROPERTY TAX EXEMPTION FOR THE BLIND

Alabama Department of Revenue
Attn: Property Tax Division
Gordon Persons Building
50 North Ripley Street, Room 4126
P.O. Box 327210
Montgomery, AL 36132-7210
(334) 242-1525
Web: www.ador.state.al.us

Summary To exempt blind residents of Alabama from taxation on a portion of their personal property.
Eligibility Residents of Alabama are eligible for this personal property tax exemption if they are legally defined as blind.

Financial data Up to $12,000 of personal property is exempt from taxation.
Duration 1 year; this exemption will be granted as long as the resident continues to meet the eligibility requirements.
Number awarded Varies each year.
Deadline Deadline not specified.

[522]
ALABAMA STATE HOMESTEAD EXEMPTIONS

Alabama Department of Revenue
Attn: Property Tax Division
Gordon Persons Building
50 North Ripley Street, Room 4126
P.O. Box 327210
Montgomery, AL 36132-7210
(334) 242-1525
Web: www.ador.state.al.us

Summary To exempt disabled, blind, and elderly residents of Alabama from ad valorem property taxes imposed by the state.
Eligibility Residents of Alabama are eligible to apply if they are 1) over the age of 65; 2) retired due to permanent and total disability, regardless of age; or 3) blind, regardless of age or retirement status.
Financial data Qualifying residents are exempt from all ad valorem property taxes levied by the state, up to 160 acres in area.
Duration 1 year; this exemption is granted as long as the resident continues to meet the eligibility requirements.
Number awarded Varies each year.
Deadline Deadline not specified.

[523]
AMERICAN COUNCIL OF THE BLIND OF OREGON GRANT-IN-AID

American Council of the Blind of Oregon
c/o Bev Rushing, Secretary
4730 Auburn Road, Space 52
Salem, OR 97301
(503) 362-4151   E-mail: b.rushing@juno.com
Web: www.acboforegon.org/grants.html

Summary To provide funding for special purposes or purchase of equipment to blind residents of Oregon.
Eligibility This program is open to blind residents of Oregon who are either registered with the Oregon Commission for the Blind or can provide proof of legal blindness. Applicants must submit an statement of 25 to 50 words on the purpose of the proposed grant. If the application is for an equipment grant, they must provide an indication of the item's cost and name of the company from which the equipment is to be purchased. They must also include a 50- to 75-word narrative about themselves.
Financial data The amount of the grant depends on the nature of the application.
Duration 1 year.
Additional data The American Council of the Blind of Oregon is legally incorporated as the Oregon Council of the Blind.

Number awarded Varies each year.

Deadline Applications may be submitted at any time; decisions are made quarterly.

[524]
ARIZONA INCOME TAX EXEMPTION FOR THE BLIND

Arizona Department of Revenue
1600 West Monroe Street
Phoenix, AZ 85007-2650
(602) 542-3572   Toll Free: (800) 352-4090 (within AZ)
TDD: (602) 542-4021
Web: www.azdor.gov

Summary To exempt a portion of the income of blind people from state income taxes in Arizona.

Eligibility This exemption is available to blind residents of Arizona who meet a legal definition of blindness.

Financial data Exempt from state income taxation is $1,500 of the income of blind people.

Duration The exemption continues as long as the recipient resides in Arizona.

Deadline Deadline not specified.

[525]
ARKANSAS DISABLED VETERANS PROPERTY TAX EXEMPTION

Arkansas Assessment Coordination Department
1614 West Third Street
Little Rock, AR 72201-1815
(501) 324-9240   Fax: (501) 324-9242
E-mail: dasbury@acd.state.ar.us
Web: www.arkansas.gov/acd

Summary To exempt from taxation the property owned by blind or disabled veterans, surviving spouses, and minor dependent children in Arkansas.

Eligibility This program is open to disabled veterans in Arkansas who have been awarded special monthly compensation by the U.S. Department of Veterans Affairs and who have 1) the loss of or the loss of use of 1 or more limbs, 2) total blindness in 1 or both eyes, or 3) total and permanent disability. The benefit also extends to veterans' unremarried surviving spouses and their minor children.

Financial data Qualifying veterans (or their unremarried widows or dependent children) are exempt from payment of all state taxes on their homestead and personal property.

Duration This exemption continues as long as the qualifying veteran (or dependent) resides in Arkansas.

Number awarded Varies each year.

Deadline Applications may be submitted at any time.

[526]
ASSOCIATION OF BLIND CITIZENS ASSISTIVE TECHNOLOGY FUND

Association of Blind Citizens
P.O. Box 246
Holbrook, MA 02343
(781) 961-1023   Fax: (781) 961-0004
E-mail: atf@blindcitizens.org
Web: www.blindcitizens.org/assistive_tech.htm

Summary To provide funding to blind people interested in purchasing adaptive devices or software.

Eligibility This program is open to legally blind residents of the United States. Applicants must be interested in purchasing a technology product that will improve their employment opportunities, increase their level of independence, and enhance their overall quality of life. They must have a family income of less than $50,000 per year and cash assets of less than $20,000. The products covered by this program must retail for at least $200 but no more than $6,000. Applicants must include a 500-word description of the device and how it will help them achieve employment or increase their independence.

Financial data Grants cover 50% of the retail price of adaptive devices or software.

Duration These are 1-time grants.

Number awarded Varies each year.

Deadline June or December of each year.

[527]
CALIFORNIA DISABLED VETERAN EXEMPTION FROM THE IN LIEU TAX FEE FOR A MANUFACTURED HOME OR MOBILEHOME

Department of Housing and Community Development
Attn: Registration and Titling
1800 Third Street
P.O. Box 2111
Sacramento, CA 95812-2111
(916) 323-9224   Toll Free: (800) 952-8356
Web: www.hcd.ca.gov

Summary To provide a special property tax exemption to blind or disabled California veterans and/or their spouses who own and occupy a mobile home.

Eligibility This program is open to disabled veterans and/or their spouses in California who have a manufactured home or mobile home as their principal place of residence. Veterans must be disabled as a result of injury or disease incurred in military service and have been a resident of California 1) at the time of entry into the service and be blind, or have lost the use of 1 or more limbs, or be totally disabled; 2) on November 7, 1972 and be blind in both eyes, or have lost the use of 2 or more limbs; or 3) on January 1, 1975 and be totally disabled. The spouses and unremarried surviving spouses of those disabled veterans are also eligible.

Financial data The exemption applies to the first $20,000 of the assessed market value of the manufactured home or mobile home. Veterans and/or spouses whose income falls below a specified level are entitled to an additional $10,000 exemption. The amount of the exemption is 100% if the home is owned by a veteran only, a veteran and spouse, or a spouse only; 50% if owned by a veteran and another person other than a spouse or by a spouse and another person other than the veteran; 67% if owned by a veteran, the spouse, and another person; 34% if owned by a veteran and 2 other people other than a spouse or by a spouse and 2 other people; 50% if owned by a veteran, the spouse, and 2 other people; or 25% if owned by a veteran and 3 other people or by a spouse and 3 other people.

Duration The exemption is available annually as long as the applicant meets all requirements.

Number awarded Varies each year.

Deadline Deadline not specified.

[528]
CALIFORNIA PROPERTY TAX EXEMPTIONS FOR VETERANS

California Department of Veterans Affairs
Attn: Division of Veterans Services
1227 O Street, Room 101
P.O. Box 942895
Sacramento, CA 94295
(916) 653-2573   Toll Free: (877) 741-8532
Fax: (916) 653-2563   TDD: (800) 324-5966
Web: www.cdva.ca.gov/VetServices/Benefits.aspx

Summary To exempt a portion of the property of blind or disabled veterans in California and their spouses from taxation.

Eligibility This exemption is available to homeowners in California who are wartime veterans in receipt of service-connected disability compensation that is 1) at the totally disabled rate, 2) for loss or loss of use of 2 or more limbs, or 3) for blindness. Unremarried surviving spouses, including registered domestic partners, of veterans who are in receipt of service-connected death benefits are also eligible.

Financial data For veterans and spouses whose total household income from all sources is greater than $51,669 per year, up to $115,060 of the assessed value of a home is exempt from taxation. For veterans and spouses whose total household income from all sources is less than $51,669 per year, up to $172,592 of the assessed value of a home is exempt from taxation.

Duration The exemption is available as long as the veteran or spouse owns a home in California.

Additional data Information is available from the local county assessor's office in each California county.

Number awarded Varies each year.

Deadline Applications may be submitted at any time.

[529]
CONNECTICUT REAL ESTATE TAX EXEMPTION FOR DISABLED VETERANS

Office of Policy and Management
Attn: Intergovernmental Policy Division
450 Capitol Avenue
Hartford, CT 06106-1308
(860) 418-6278   Toll Free: (800) 286-2214 (within CT)
Fax: (860) 418-6493   TDD: (860) 418-6456
E-mail: leeann.graham@ct.gov
Web: www.ct.gov

Summary To exempt disabled or blind Connecticut veterans and their surviving spouses from the payment of a portion of their local property taxes.

Eligibility There are 2 categories of Connecticut veterans who qualify for exemptions from their dwelling house and the lot on which it is located: 1) those with major service-connected disabilities (paraplegia or osteochondritis resulting in permanent loss of the use of both legs or permanent paralysis of both legs and lower parts of the body; hemiplegia with permanent paralysis of 1 leg and 1 arm or either side of the body resulting from injury to the spinal cord, skeletal structure, or brain, or from disease of the spinal cord not resulting from syphilis; total blindness; amputation of both arms, both legs, both hands or both feet, or the combination of a hand and a foot; sustained through enemy action or resulting from an accident occurring or disease contracted in such active service) and 2) those with less severe disabilities (loss of use of 1 arm or 1 leg because of service-connected injuries). Surviving unremarried spouses of eligible deceased veterans are entitled to the same exemption as would have been granted to the veteran, as long as they continue to be the legal owner/occupier of the exempted residence. An additional exemption is available to veterans and spouses whose total adjusted gross income is less than $32,300 if unmarried or $39,500 if married. If the veteran is rated as 100% disabled by the U.S. Department of Veterans Affairs (VA), the maximum income levels are $18,000 if unmarried or $21,000 if married.

Financial data Veterans in the first category receive an exemption from local property taxation of $10,000 of assessed valuation. Veterans in the second category receive exemptions of $5,000 of assessed valuation. For veterans whose income is less than the specified levels, additional exemptions of $20,000 for the first category or $10,000 for the second category are available from municipalities that choose to participate. For veterans whose income exceeds the specified levels, the additional exemption from participating municipalities is $5,000 for the first category or $2,500 for the second category. Connecticut municipalities may also elect to exempt from taxation specially adapted housing acquired or modified by a veteran under the provisions of Section 801 of Title 38 of the United States Code.

Duration 1 year; exemptions continue as long as the eligible resident (or surviving spouse) owns/occupies the primary residence and lives in Connecticut.

Number awarded Varies each year; recently, a total of 19,669 veterans received property tax exemptions through this and other programs in Connecticut.

Deadline Applications for the additional municipality exemption must be submitted to the assessor's office of the town or residence by September of every other year.

[530]
CONNECTICUT TAX RELIEF PROGRAM FOR BLIND PEOPLE

Office of Policy and Management
Attn: Intergovernmental Policy Division
450 Capitol Avenue
Hartford, CT 06106-1308
(860) 418-6322 Toll Free: (800) 286-2214 (within CT)
Fax: (860) 418-6493 TDD: (860) 418-6456
E-mail: ronald.madrid@ct.gov
Web: www.ct.gov/opm/site/default.asp

Summary To exempt blind residents of Connecticut from a portion of their personal property taxes.

Eligibility Eligible to apply for this exemption are Connecticut residents who are blind. An additional exemption may be available to blind residents whose total adjusted gross income is less than $32,300 if unmarried or $39,500 if married.

Financial data The basic state exemption is $3,000 of assessed valuation. Municipalities may elect to provide an additional exemption of $2,000 to blind residents whose income is less than the qualifying level.

Duration 1 year; exemptions continue as long as the eligible resident lives in Connecticut.

Number awarded Varies each year.

Deadline Applications for the additional municipality exemption must be submitted to the assessor's office of the town of residence by September of every other year.

[531]
DELAWARE INCOME TAX DEDUCTION FOR BLIND AND ELDERLY PERSONS

Division of Revenue
Attn: Office of Personal Income Taxes
Carvel State Office Building
820 North French Street
P.O. Box 8763
Wilmington, DE 19899-8763
(302) 577-8170 E-mail: Personaltax@state.de.us
Web: revenue.delaware.gov

Summary To provide a deduction from state income taxation to blind people and those over the age of 65 in Delaware.

Eligibility This deduction is available to residents of Delaware who are 1) 65 years of age or older or 2) blind.

Financial data Taxpayers are entitled to an additional standard deduction of $2,500 if they are blind or older than 65. For blind people older than 65, the additional standard deduction is $5,000.

Duration The deduction continues as long as the recipient remains a resident of Delaware for state income tax purposes.

Number awarded Varies each year.

Deadline Deadline not specified.

[532]
DISTRICT OF COLUMBIA INCOME TAX EXEMPTION FOR THE BLIND

Office of Tax and Revenue
Attn: Customer Service Center
1101 Fourth Street, S.W., Suite W270
Washington, DC 20024
(202) 727-4TAX Fax: (202) 442-6304
E-mail: taxhelp@dc.gov
Web: otr.cfo.dc.gov/otr/site/default.asp

Summary To exempt a portion of the income of blind people from local income taxation in the District of Columbia.

Eligibility This exemption is available to residents of the District of Columbia who are blind.

Financial data Blind residents are entitled to an exemption of $1,675 from their income for local tax purposes in the District of Columbia.

Duration The exemption continues as long as the recipient resides in the District of Columbia.

Number awarded Varies each year.

Deadline The exemption is claimed as part of the local income return, due in April of each year.

[533]
FEDERAL INCOME TAX DEDUCTION FOR THE BLIND AND ELDERLY

Internal Revenue Service
1111 Constitution Avenue, N.W.
Washington, DC 20224
Toll Free: (800) TAX-FORM
Web: www.irs.gov

Summary To exempt a portion of the income of blind and elderly citizens from federal income tax liability.

Eligibility Eligible for these deduction are tax filers who are legally blind and/or over the age of 65, and whose spouses are legally blind and/or over the age of 65. The deductions are in addition to the standard deductions for taxpayers who do not itemize their deductions. Taxpayers who itemize deductions do not qualify for these additional deductions.

Financial data Each deduction is $1,450 for taxpayers filing as single; for married taxpayers (whether filing jointly or separately), heads of household, and qualifying widow(er)s, each deduction is $1,150; 1 deduction is allowed for each individual who is either blind and/or over the age of 65.

Duration 1 year; must reapply each year.

Number awarded Varies each year.

Deadline This deduction is taken on the qualifying tax filer's federal income tax return, which is due in April of each year.

[534]
FLORIDA PROPERTY TAX EXEMPTION FOR TOTALLY AND PERMANENTLY DISABLED PERSONS

Florida Department of Revenue
Attn: Taxpayer Services
5050 West Tennessee Street
Tallahassee, FL 32399-0100
(850) 617-8600　　　　Toll Free: (800) 352-3671
E-mail: EMailDOR@dor.state.fl.us
Web: www.myflorida.com

Summary To exempt from property taxation real estate owned by blind or disabled people in Florida.

Eligibility This exemption is available to Florida residents who have real estate that they own and use as a homestead. Applications are accepted from 2 categories of residents: 1) those who are quadriplegic (regardless of income); or 2) those who are paraplegic or hemiplegic, have another total and permanent disability that requires use of a wheelchair for mobility, or are legally blind, and have an income below a specified limit that changes annually (recently, it was $25,544 per year).

Financial data All real estate used and owned as a homestead, less any portion used for commercial purposes, is exempt from taxation.

Duration The exemption applies as long as the taxpayer owns the property in Florida.

Additional data Initial applications should be made in person at the appropriate county property appraiser's office.

Number awarded Varies each year.

Deadline Applications must be submitted by February of the year for which the exemption is sought.

[535]
GEORGIA INCOME TAX DEDUCTION FOR THE BLIND

Georgia Department of Revenue
Attn: Taxpayer Services Division
1800 Century Boulevard, N.E., Room 8300
Atlanta, GA 30345-3205
(404) 417-2400　　　　Toll Free: (877) GADOR-11
Fax: (404) 417-2439　　　　TDD: (404) 417-4302
E-mail: taxpayer.services@dor.ga.gov
Web: etax.dor.ga.gov/IndTax_TSD.aspx

Summary To provide a deduction from state income taxation to blind people in Georgia.

Eligibility Eligible are persons classified as residents of Georgia for the purpose of state income taxation who are blind.

Financial data Qualified blind residents are entitled to a deduction of $1,300 from their state income taxation.

Duration The deduction continues as long as the recipient resides in Georgia.

Deadline Deadline not specified.

[536]
HANK HOFSTETTER OPPORTUNITY GRANTS

American Council of the Blind of Indiana
c/o James R. Durst
Indiana School for the Blind and Visually Impaired
7725 North College Avenue
Indianapolis, IN 46240
Web: acb-indiana.org/3/miscellaneous8.htm

Summary To provide funding to Indiana residents who are blind and need materials or equipment to continue their education or meet other goals.

Eligibility This fund is open to certified legally blind Indiana residents who are unable to obtain funding through other means. Applicants must need funding for an activity, materials, and/or equipment that will enhance their educational, entrepreneurial, or vocational aims. Along with their application, they must submit a 1-page statement on why they should be considered for a grant, a list of other options they have already tried, and a reference letter.

Financial data The amount awarded varies, depending upon the needs of the recipient. A total of $1,000 is available annually.

Number awarded 1 each year.

Deadline Requests may be submitted at any time but should be received at least 90 days prior to the need.

[537]
HAWAII INCOME TAX EXEMPTION FOR DISABLED RESIDENTS

Department of Taxation
Attn: Taxpayer Services Branch
425 Queen Street
P.O. Box 259
Honolulu, HI 96809-0259
(808) 587-4242　　　　Toll Free: (800) 222-3229
Fax: (808) 587-1488　　　　TDD: (808) 587-1418
Web: hawaii.gov/tax

Summary To exempt a portion of the income of blind, deaf, and other disabled residents from state income tax in Hawaii.

Eligibility Eligible for this exemption are 1) blind residents whose central visual acuity does not exceed 20/200 in the better eye with corrective lenses or whose visual acuity is greater than 20/200 but is accompanied by a limitation in the field of vision such that the widest diameter of the visual field subtends an angle no greater than 20 degrees; 2) deaf residents whose average loss in the speech frequencies in the better ear is 82 decibels A.S.A. or worse; or 3) totally disabled residents (physically or mentally) who are unable to engage in any substantial gainful business or occupation (a person whose gross income exceeds $30,000 per year is assumed to be engaged in a substantial gainful business or occupation).

Financial data The maximum exemptions from state income tax are as follows: single disabled resident, $7,000; disabled husband and wife, $14,000; disabled husband or wife, with non-disabled spouse under 65,

$8,040; disabled husband or wife, with non-disabled spouse 65 years of age or older, $9,080.

Duration The exemption continues as long as the recipient resides in Hawaii.

Additional data Residents who claim this special exemption are not eligible to claim additional exemptions for their children or other dependents.

Deadline Deadline not specified.

[538]
IDAHO CIRCUIT BREAKER PROPERTY TAX REDUCTION

Idaho State Tax Commission
Attn: Public Information Office
800 Park Boulevard, Plaza IV
P.O. Box 36
Boise, ID 83722-0410
(208) 334-7736   Toll Free: (800) 972-7660
TDD: (800) 377-3529
E-mail: pamela.waters@tax.idaho.com
Web: tax.idaho.gov/i-1052.cfm

Summary To reduce a portion of the property tax of disabled, blind, and other veterans and other disabled or elderly residents of Idaho.

Eligibility Eligible for this property tax reduction are residents of Idaho who own and live in a primary residence in the state and have an annual income of $28,000 or less (after deducting designated forms of income, including compensation received by a veteran from the U.S. Department of Veterans Affairs for a 40% to 100% service-connected disability). Applicants must be in 1 or more of the following categories: disabled (as recognized by an appropriate federal agency), blind, former prisoner of war or hostage, veteran with at least 10% service-connected disability or receiving a VA pension for a nonservice-connected disability, 65 years of age or older, widow(er) of any age, or fatherless or motherless child under 18 years of age.

Financial data The maximum amount of reduction is the lesser of $1,320 or the actual taxes on the recipient's qualifying home. The minimum reduction is the lesser of $100 or the actual taxes on the home.

Duration Applications for this reduction must be submitted each year.

Additional data All recipients of this reduction automatically receive Idaho's Homeowner's Exemption, which reduces the taxable value of the home (excluding land) by 50% or $75,000, whichever is less. Solid waste, irrigation, or other fees charged by some counties are not taxes and cannot be reduced by this program.

Number awarded Varies each year.

Deadline April of each year.

[539]
IDAHO INCOME TAX DEDUCTION FOR THE BLIND AND THEIR WIDOW(ER)S

Idaho State Tax Commission
Attn: Public Information Office
800 Park Boulevard, Plaza IV
P.O. Box 36
Boise, ID 83722-0410
(208) 334-7660   Toll Free: (800) 972-7660
TDD: (800) 377-3529
Web: tax.idaho.gov/i-1039.cfm

Summary To exempt a portion of the income of blind or elderly residents from state income tax in Idaho.

Eligibility Eligible for this deduction are blind residents of Idaho and residents over the age of 65.

Financial data Single individuals and heads of households who are blind or elderly receive an additional $1,450 standard deduction; married individuals who are blind or elderly receive an additional $1,150 standard deduction.

Duration 1 year; must reapply each year.

Number awarded Varies each year.

Deadline April of each year.

[540]
ILLINOIS INCOME TAX EXEMPTION FOR THE BLIND

Illinois Department of Revenue
101 West Jefferson Street
P.O. Box 19044
Springfield, IL 62794-9044
(217) 782-3336   Toll Free: (800) 732-8866
TDD: (800) 544-5304
Web: www.revenue.state.il.us

Summary To provide an income tax deduction to blind people in Illinois.

Eligibility Legally blind residents of Illinois are entitled to take this deduction from their state income tax.

Financial data The deduction is $1,000.

Duration The deduction continues as long as the recipient resides in Illinois.

Deadline Deadline not specified.

[541]
INDIANA INCOME TAX EXEMPTION FOR THE BLIND

Indiana Department of Revenue
Attn: Taxpayer Services Division
Indiana Government Center North
100 North Senate Avenue
Indianapolis, IN 46204-2253
(317) 232-2240   TDD: (317) 232-4952
E-mail: individualtaxassistance@dor.in.gov
Web: www.in.gov/dor

Summary To exempt a portion of the income of blind people from state taxation in Indiana.

Eligibility Eligible are residents of Indiana who are legally blind.

Financial data An additional exemption of $1,000 from the income for state income taxation in Indiana is allowed.

Duration The exemption continues as long as the recipient resides in Indiana.

Deadline Deadline not specified.

[542]
INDIANA PROPERTY TAX DEDUCTION FOR BLIND OR DISABLED PERSONS

Department of Local Government Finance
Indiana Government Center North, Room N1058(B)
100 North Senate Avenue
Indianapolis, IN 46201
(317) 232-3777   Toll Free: (888) 739-9826
Fax: (317) 232-8779
E-mail: PropertyTaxInfo@dlgf.in.gov
Web: www.in.gov/dlgf

Summary To exempt Indiana residents who are blind or disabled from a portion of their property tax.

Eligibility Eligible for this program are Indiana residents who are blind or disabled and receive less than $17,000 in annual taxable income. A blind person is defined as an individual who has vision in the better eye with correcting glasses of 20/200 or less, or a disqualifying visual field defect as determined upon examination by a designated ophthalmologist or optometrist. A disabled person is defined as an individual unable to engage in any substantial gainful activity by reason of a medically determinable physical or mental impairment that can be expected to result in death or has lasted and can be expected to last for at least 12 continuous months.

Financial data The maximum property tax deduction is $12,480.

Duration This deduction may be taken annually, as long as the Indiana resident meets the requirements of the program.

Additional data Property taxes are administered by individual counties in Indiana. Further information is available from county tax assessors.

Number awarded Varies each year.

Deadline Applications must be filed during the 12 months before May of each year for which the individual wishes to obtain the deduction.

[543]
KANSAS INTANGIBLES TAX SENIOR CITIZEN OR DISABILITY EXEMPTION

Kansas Department of Revenue
Attn: Taxpayer Assistance Center
Robert B. Docking State Office Building
915 S.W. Harrison Street
Topeka, KS 66612-1712
(785) 368-8222   Toll Free: (877) 526-7738
Fax: (785) 291-3614   TDD: (785) 296-6461
Web: www.ksrevenue.org/perstaxtypeint.htm

Summary To exempt a portion of the income received by elderly, blind, or disabled residents in Kansas from the intangibles tax.

Eligibility This exemption applies to residents of local areas in Kansas that levy an intangibles tax on gross earnings received from such property as savings accounts, stocks, bonds, accounts receivable, and mortgages. Applicants must 1) be disabled, blind, or 60 years of age or older and 2) have a household income of $20,000 or less.

Financial data Qualified residents are entitled to exempt from their intangibles income an amount that depends on their income. If total household income is $15,000 or less, the exemption is $5,000. For incomes between $15,000 and $20,000, the exemption is calculated as the difference between $5,000 and the amount of the income over $15,000.

Duration This benefit continues as long as the recipient remains a resident of the Kansas locality that imposes an intangibles tax.

Number awarded Varies each year.

Deadline Deadline not specified.

[544]
KANSAS STATE DEAF-BLIND FUND

Kansas State Department of Education
Special Education Services
Attn: Kansas State Deaf-Blind Fund
120 S.E. Tenth Avenue
Topeka, KS 66612-1182
(785) 296-2515   Toll Free: (800) 203-9462
Fax: (785) 296-6715   TDD: (785) 296-2515
E-mail: jhoughton@ksde.org
Web: www.ksde.org/Default.aspx?tabid=2322

Summary To provide supplementary financial assistance to deaf-blind or severely disabled students in Kansas.

Eligibility Applications may be submitted by school personnel for students in Kansas (up to the age of 21) who are deaf-blind and/or have severe multiple disabilities. Approval for funding is granted on a first-come, first-served basis for the following areas: 1) assistive technology that enables a student with dual sensory impairments and with severe disabilities to participate more fully in an educational program (e.g., computers, adaptive equipment, eyeglasses, hearing aids, computer peripherals, augmentative communication devices, microswitches, software); 2) consultation; 3) evaluation for the cost of vision and/or hearing evaluations for students who are suspected of being deaf-blind, or a vision, hearing, or educational evaluation for recertification purposes; or 4) other costs associated with additional items or expenses that reflect best educational or effective practices, such as expenses involved in providing community activities. Applicants must provide documentation that other funding sources have been approached and that costs do not exceed the amount local education agencies are able to provide out of federal, state, or local funds. Priority candidates are students who have current deaf-blind certification, deaf-blind children from birth through 2 years of age, students who are exiting state hospital schools and returning to their home district, students who have a suspected vision loss and documented hearing loss and are in need of an evaluation, and students who have a suspected hearing loss and documented vision loss and are in need of an evaluation.

Financial data Eligible students are awarded up to $3,000 per year.

Duration 1 year; may be renewed.

Number awarded Varies each year; recently, 76 students received $108,160 in funding from this program. Grants provided $107,555 for assistive technology and $605 for consultants.

Deadline May of each year.

[545]
LIONS CLUBS SUPPORT SERVICES FOR THE BLIND AND VISUALLY IMPAIRED

Lions Clubs International
Attn: Program Development Department
300 West 22nd Street
Oak Brook, IL 60523-8842
(630) 571-5466, ext. 316   Fax: (630) 571-1692
E-mail: programs@lionsclubs.org
Web: www.lionsclubs.org

Summary To provide college scholarships and other assistance (transportation, assistive technology, Braille products, etc.) to blind people.

Eligibility These programs are open to blind people and others involved in service to the blind. Applicants may be seeking support for the following activities: scholarships for the blind and visually impaired, medical research, assistive technology grants, independent mobility, transportation, reading materials and aids, audio products, Braille products, and other aids.

Financial data The amount of this assistance varies.

Additional data Support is provided by local Lions Clubs. Requests sent to the international office are referred to the appropriate district governor, who then sends the inquiries to an appropriate club within the district. No funds are available from the office of Lions Clubs International.

Deadline Deadline not specified.

[546]
MAINE INCOME TAX DEDUCTION FOR THE BLIND

Maine Revenue Services
Attn: Income/Estate Tax Division
P.O. Box 9107
Augusta, ME 04332-9107
(207) 626-8475   Fax: (207) 624-9694
E-mail: income.tax@maine.gov
Web: www.maine.gov

Summary To deduct a portion of the income of blind and elderly Maine residents from income taxation.

Eligibility Eligible for this deduction are inhabitants of Maine who are legally blind as determined by the Department of Human Services.

Financial data For single and head of household taxpayers, the deduction is $1,450 if the individual is 65 or over or blind, or $2,900 if the individual is both 65 or over

and blind. For married taxpayers, the deduction is $1,150 for each spouse who is 65 or over or blind.

Duration Eligible blind residents qualify for this deduction as long as they reside in Maine.

Number awarded Varies each year.

Deadline The deduction is included along with the state income tax forms, filed in April of each year.

[547]
MAINE PROPERTY TAX EXEMPTION FOR THE BLIND

Maine Revenue Services
Attn: Property Tax Division
P.O. Box 9106
Augusta, ME 04332-9106
(207) 287-2013   Fax: (207) 287-6396
E-mail: prop.tax@maine.gov
Web: www.maine.gov

Summary To exempt the estates of blind Maine residents from property taxation.

Eligibility Eligible for this program are inhabitants of Maine who are legally blind as determined by the Department of Human Services.

Financial data The exemption is equal to $4,000 times the certified ratio.

Duration Eligible blind residents qualify for this exemption as long as they own residential property in Maine.

Number awarded Varies each year.

Deadline When an eligible person first submits an application, the proof of entitlement must reach the assessors of the local municipality prior to the end of March. Once eligibility has been established, notification need not be repeated in subsequent years.

[548]
MARYLAND INCOME TAX EXEMPTION FOR READERS FOR BLIND RESIDENTS

Comptroller of Maryland
Attn: Revenue Administration Division
80 Calvert Street
Annapolis, MD 21411
(410) 260-7980
Toll Free: (800) MD-TAXES (within MD)
Fax: (410) 974-3456   TDD: (410) 260-7157
E-mail: taxhelp@comp.state.md.us
Web: individuals.marylandtaxes.com

Summary To exempt from state income taxation in Maryland a portion of the expenses incurred by blind people for a reader.

Eligibility Eligible are Maryland residents who 1) are blind and pay for the use of a reader; or 2) are employers and pay for a reader for a blind employee.

Financial data Blind people may exclude up to $5,000 of expenses incurred for a reader from state income taxation. Employers may exclude up to $1,000 of expenses incurred for a reader for a blind employee.

Duration The exclusion continues as long as the recipient resides in Maryland and utilizes the services of a reader.

Deadline Deadline not specified.

[549]
MARYLAND PROPERTY TAX EXEMPTION FOR BLIND PERSONS

Maryland Department of Assessments and Taxation
Attn: Property Taxes
301 West Preston Street
Baltimore, MD 21201-2395
(410) 767-1184   Toll Free: (888) 246-5941
TDD: (800) 735-2258
Web: www.dat.state.md.us/sdatweb/exempt.html

Summary To exempt the homes of blind people and their surviving spouses from property taxation in Maryland.

Eligibility This exemption is available to residents of Maryland who have a central visual acuity of 20/200 or less in the better eye. Applicants must own a dwelling house in Maryland. Surviving spouses of deceased blind people are also eligible for the exemption.

Financial data The dwelling houses of eligible blind people and their surviving spouses is exempt from $15,000 of assessment on their dwelling house for purposes of real property taxes.

Duration The exemption is available as long as the blind person or surviving spouse owns the dwelling house in Maryland.

Number awarded Varies each year.

Deadline Applications may be submitted at any time.

[550]
MASSACHUSETTS INCOME TAX EXEMPTION FOR BLIND PEOPLE

Massachusetts Department of Revenue
Attn: Personal Income Tax
P.O. Box 7010
Boston, MA 02204
(617) 887-MDOR
Toll Free: (800) 392-6089 (within MA)
Fax: (617) 887-1900
Web: www.mass.gov

Summary To exempt a portion of the income received by blind people from state income taxation in Massachusetts.

Eligibility Eligible for this exemption are residents of Massachusetts who are classified as legally blind.

Financial data Blind persons in Massachusetts are entitled to exempt $2,200 from their income for purposes of state income taxation.

Duration The benefit continues as long as the recipient remains a resident of Massachusetts for state income tax purposes.

Number awarded Varies each year.

Deadline Deadline not specified.

[551]
MASSACHUSETTS PROPERTY TAX EXEMPTION FOR VETERANS AND THEIR FAMILIES

Massachusetts Department of Revenue
Attn: Division of Local Services
100 Cambridge Street
Boston, MA 02114
(617) 626-2386   Fax: (617) 626-2330
Web: www.mass.gov/dor/all-taxes/excise-and-property

Summary To provide a property tax exemption to blind, disabled, and other veterans (and their families) in Massachusetts.

Eligibility This program is open to veterans who are residents of Massachusetts, were residents for at least 6 months prior to entering the service, have been residents for at least 5 consecutive years, and are occupying property as their domicile. Applicants must have an ownership interest in the domicile that ranges from $2,000 to $10,000, depending on the category of exemption. Veterans must have been discharged under conditions other than dishonorable. Several categories of veterans and their families qualify: 1) veterans who have a service-connected disability rating of 10% or more; veterans who have been awarded the Purple Heart; Gold Star mothers and fathers; and surviving spouses of eligible veterans who do not remarry; 2) veterans who suffered, in the line of duty, the loss or permanent loss of use of 1 foot, 1 hand, or 1 eye; veterans who received the Congressional Medal of Honor, Distinguished Service Cross, Navy Cross, or Air Force Cross; and their spouses or surviving spouses; 3) veterans who suffered, in the line of duty, the loss or permanent loss of use of both feet, both hands, or both eyes; and their spouses or surviving spouses; 4) veterans who suffered total disability in the line of duty and received assistance in acquiring specially adapted housing, which they own and occupy as their domicile; and their spouses or surviving spouses; 5) unremarried surviving spouses of military personnel who died due to injury or disease from being in a combat zone, or are missing and presumed dead due to combat; 6) veterans who suffered total disability in the line of duty and are incapable of working; and their spouses or surviving spouses; and 7) veterans who are certified by the Veterans Administration as paraplegic and their surviving spouses.

Financial data Qualified veterans and family members are entitled to an annual exemption from their taxes for the different categories: 1), $400; 2), $750; 3), $1,250; 4), $1,500; 5), total exemption for 5 years after death, and up to $2,500 after 5 years; 6), $1,000; or 7), total.

Duration The exemptions are provided each year that the veteran or unremarried surviving spouse lives in Massachusetts and owns the property as a domicile.

Additional data Applications are available from local assessor's offices.

Number awarded Varies each year.

Deadline Applications must be filed with the local assessor by December of each year.

[552]
MASSACHUSETTS VETERANS ANNUITY PROGRAM

Department of Veterans' Services
Attn: Annuities
600 Washington Street, Seventh Floor
Boston, MA 02111
(617) 210-5480   Fax: (617) 210-5755
E-mail: mdvs@vet.state.ma.us
Web: www.mass.gov/veterans

Summary   To provide an annuity to blind or disabled veterans from Massachusetts and to the parents and spouses of deceased military personnel.

Eligibility   This program is open to 1) veterans who are blind, double amputee, paraplegic, or have a 100% service-connected disability; 2) the parents of military personnel who died of service-connected causes; and 3) the unremarried spouses of military personnel who died of service-connected causes. Veterans must have been residents of Massachusetts at the time of entry into military service who served during specified wartime periods and received other than a dishonorable discharge. All applicants must currently be residents of Massachusetts.

Financial data   Recipients are entitled to an annuity of $2,000 per year.

Duration   The annuity is paid as long as the recipient continues to reside in Massachusetts.

Deadline   Deadline not specified.

[553]
MICHIGAN HOMESTEAD PROPERTY TAX CREDIT FOR VETERANS AND BLIND PEOPLE

Michigan Department of Treasury
Attn: Homestead Exemption
Treasury Building
430 West Allegan Street
Lansing, MI 48922
(517) 636-4486   TDD: (800) 649-3777
E-mail: treasIndTax@michigan.gov
Web: www.michigan.gov/taxes

Summary   To provide an income tax credit to disabled and other veterans, military personnel, their spouses, blind people, and their surviving spouses in Michigan.

Eligibility   Eligible to apply are residents of Michigan who are 1) blind and own their homestead; 2) a veteran with a service-connected disability or his/her surviving spouse; 3) a surviving spouse of a veteran deceased in service; 4) a pensioned veteran, a surviving spouse of those veterans, or an active military member, all of whose household income is less than $7,500; or 5) a surviving spouse of a non-disabled or non-pensioned veteran of the Korean War, World War II, or World War I whose household income is less than $7,500. All applicants must own or rent a home in Michigan, have been a Michigan resident for at least 6 months during the year in which application is made, and fall within qualifying income levels (up to $82,650 in household income).

Financial data   The maximum credit, applied to state income taxes, is $1,200. The exact amount varies. For homeowners, the credit depends on the state equalized value of the homestead and on an allowance for filing category. For renters, 20% of the rent is considered property tax eligible for credit.

Duration   1 year; eligibility must be established each year.

Number awarded   Varies each year.

Deadline   April of each year.

[554]
MICHIGAN INCOME TAX EXEMPTION FOR PEOPLE WITH DISABILITIES

Michigan Department of Treasury
Attn: Income Tax
Treasury Building
430 West Allegan Street
Lansing, MI 48922
(517) 373-3200   TDD: (800) 649-3777
E-mail: treasIndTax@michigan.gov
Web: www.michigan.gov/taxes

Summary   To exempt a portion of the income of deaf, blind, and disabled residents of Michigan from state income taxation.

Eligibility   Eligible for this exemption are residents of Michigan who 1) receive messages through a sense other than hearing, such as lip reading or sign language; 2) have vision in their better eye of 20/200 or less with corrective lenses or peripheral field of vision of 20 degrees or less; or 3) are hemiplegic, paraplegic, quadriplegic, or totally and permanently disabled.

Financial data   Qualifying people with disabilities receive an exemption of $2,400 from their adjusted gross income for purposes of state taxation.

Duration   The exemption continues as long as the recipient resides in Michigan.

Deadline   Deadline not specified.

[555]
MISSISSIPPI HOMESTEAD TAX EXEMPTION FOR THE DISABLED

Mississippi Department of Revenue
Attn: Property Tax Division
P.O. Box 1033
Jackson, MS 39215-1033
(601) 923-7618   Fax: (601) 923-7637
Web: www.dor.ms.gov/taxareas/property/main.html

Summary   To exempt from property taxes a portion of the value of homesteads owned by people with disabilities and blind people in Mississippi.

Eligibility   Eligible for this exemption are residents of Mississippi who are totally disabled or legally blind and own a homestead that they occupy as a home. Disability and blindness are defined according to federal Social Security regulations.

Financial data   The exemption covers the first $7,500 of assessed value of the property (or $75,000 true value).

Duration   The exemption continues as long as the disabled or blind person resides in Mississippi.

Number awarded Varies each year.

Deadline The first time an exemption is requested, it must be submitted before the end of March of that year. Subsequently, most Mississippi counties do not require renewal filing unless the disable person's homestead status changes.

[556]
MISSISSIPPI INCOME TAX EXEMPTION FOR THE BLIND

Mississippi Department of Revenue
Attn: Individual Income Tax Division
P.O. Box 1033
Jackson, MS 39215-1033
(601) 923-7089　　　　　　　Fax: (601) 923-7039
Web: www.dor.ms.gov/taxareas/individ/main.htm

Summary To exempt a portion of the income of blind people and their spouses from state income tax liability in Mississippi.

Eligibility Eligible for this exemption are residents of Mississippi who have been declared legally blind and their spouses.

Financial data The exemption is $1,500.

Duration The exemption continues as long as the blind person resides in Mississippi.

Number awarded Varies each year.

Deadline The exemption must be requested on the resident's state income tax return, which is due in April.

[557]
MISSOURI BLIND PENSION

Missouri Department of Social Services
Attn: Family Support Division
615 Howerton Court
P.O. Box 2320
Jefferson City, MO 65102-2320
(573) 751-4249　　　　　　　Fax: (573) 751-4984
TDD: (800) 735-2966
Web: www.dss.mo.gov/fsd/blindp.htm

Summary To provide assistance to blind residents of Missouri who are not eligible for other support.

Eligibility This program is open to blind (vision less than 5/200) residents of Missouri who are 18 years of age or older; do not own real or personal property worth more than $20,000 (excluding the value of the home used as a residence); have not given away, sold, or transferred real or personal property in order to be eligible; are of good moral character; have no sighted spouse living in Missouri who can provide support; do not publicly solicit alms; are not residents of a public, private, or endowed institution except a public medical institution; are willing to have medical treatment or an operation to cure blindness (unless 75 years of age or older); and are ineligible for federal Supplemental Security Income and Missouri Supplemental Aid to the Blind.

Financial data Eligible individuals receive a monthly cash grant of up to $651 and state-funded Mo HealthNet coverage.

Duration Qualified blind people are eligible for this assistance as long as they reside in Missouri.

Number awarded Varies each year.

Deadline Deadline not specified.

[558]
MISSOURI COUNCIL OF THE BLIND SPECIAL SERVICES PROGRAM

Missouri Council of the Blind
5453 Chippewa Street
St. Louis, MO 63109-1635
(314) 832-7172　Toll Free: (800) 342-5632 (within MO)
Fax: (314) 832-7796　　　　　E-mail: aa@moblind.org
Web: www.moblind.org/programs/special_services

Summary To provide funding for emergency purposes to blind residents of Missouri.

Eligibility This program is open to residents of Missouri who are legally blind and need emergency funds. Applicants need not be members of the Missouri Council of the Blind.

Financial data The amount of the grant depends on the need of the recipient and the availability of funds.

Duration Grants are limited to 1 per household within a 3-year period.

Number awarded Varies each year.

Deadline Applications may be submitted at any time.

[559]
MISSOURI INCOME TAX DEDUCTION FOR THE BLIND AND DISABLED

Missouri Department of Revenue
Attn: Taxation Division
301 West High Street, Room 330
P.O. Box 2200
Jefferson City, MO 65105-2200
(573) 751-3505　　　　　Toll Free: (800) 877-6881
Fax: (573) 751-2195　　　　TDD: (800) 735-2966
E-mail: income@dor.mo.gov
Web: dor.mo.gov/personal

Summary To provide an additional income tax deduction to blind and disabled people in Missouri.

Eligibility This deduction is available to all residents of Missouri who are legally classified as blind or 100% disabled.

Financial data Blind and disabled residents are entitled to deduct an additional $1,200 from their income for taxation purposes.

Duration This deduction is available as long as the recipient remains a resident of Missouri for state income tax purposes.

Number awarded Varies each year.

Deadline Deadline not specified.

[560]
MISSOURI SUPPLEMENTAL AID TO THE BLIND

Missouri Department of Social Services
Attn: Family Support Division
615 Howerton Court
P.O. Box 2320
Jefferson City, MO 65102-2320
(573) 751-4249   Fax: (573) 751-4984
TDD: (800) 735-2966
Web: www.dss.mo.gov/fsd/sblind.htm

Summary   To provide supplemental income to blind residents of Missouri.

Eligibility   This program is open to blind (vision less than 5/200) residents of Missouri who are 18 years of age or older; are single and do not own real and personal property worth more than $2,000, or, if married and living with a spouse, do not own real and personal property worth more than $4,000 (the residence, clothing, furniture, household equipment, personal jewelry, or any property used directly by the blind person in earning a living are not included in that valuation); do not have parents living in Missouri or a sighted spouse who can provide support; do not publicly solicit alms; are not residents of a public, private, or endowed institution except a public medical institution; are in need of assistance because of insufficient income to meet basic needs; are U.S. citizens or eligible qualified noncitizens; and are required to apply for federal Supplemental Security Income.

Financial data   Eligible individuals receive a monthly cash grant of up to $651 and state-funded Mo HealthNet coverage.

Duration   Qualified blind people are eligible for this assistance as long as they reside in Missouri.

Number awarded   Varies each year.

Deadline   Deadline not specified.

[561]
MONTANA INCOME TAX EXEMPTION FOR THE BLIND

Montana Department of Revenue
Attn: Individual Income Tax
125 North Roberts, Third Floor
P.O. Box 5805
Helena, MT 59604-5805
(406) 444-6900   Toll Free: (866) 859-2254
Fax: (406) 444-6642   TDD: (406) 444-2830
Web: mt.gov/revenue

Summary   To provide a state income tax exemption to blind residents of Montana and their spouses.

Eligibility   Eligible are all persons considered Montana residents for purposes of state income taxation who are blind or whose spouse is blind.

Financial data   Blind people and their spouses may claim an additional exemption of $2,190 from their income for state taxation purposes.

Duration   The exemption continues as long as the recipient resides in Montana.

Deadline   Deadline not specified.

[562]
NEBRASKA INCOME TAX EXEMPTION FOR THE BLIND

Nebraska Department of Revenue
301 Centennial Mall South
P.O. Box 94818
Lincoln, NE 68509-4818
(402) 471-5729
Toll Free: (800) 742-7474 (within NE and IA)
Web: www.revenue.ne.gov

Summary   To exempt a portion of the income of blind people from state taxation in Nebraska.

Eligibility   This exemption is available to residents of Nebraska who are blind. Applicants must be claiming the state standard deduction on their annual state income tax return.

Financial data   Blind taxpayers may add $1,150 to their standard deduction if they are married or $1,450 if they are single or head of household.

Duration   The exemption is available annually.

Number awarded   Varies each year.

Deadline   Exemption claims are included with the state income tax return, due in April of each year.

[563]
NEW HAMPSHIRE BLIND PROPERTY TAX EXEMPTION

New Hampshire Department of Revenue
  Administration
109 Pleasant Street
Concord, NH 03301
(603) 271-2191   Fax: (603) 271-6121
TDD: (800) 735-2964
Web: revenue.nh.gov

Summary   To provide blind residents of New Hampshire with a partial exemption from real estate taxes.

Eligibility   Residents of New Hampshire are covered by this program if they are blind, own and occupy their primary residence in New Hampshire, and live in a municipality that has chosen through a referendum vote to grant an exemption to the legally blind.

Financial data $15,000 of the value of the residential real estate is exempted from taxation for qualifying residents. Towns may exempt any amount they determine is appropriate to address significant increases in property values.

Duration   1 year; this exemption will be continued as long as the recipient meets the eligibility requirements.

Number awarded   Varies each year; recently, 794 of these exemption were granted, enabling blind New Hampshire residents to save $740,466 in property taxes.

Deadline   The original application for a permanent tax credit must be submitted by April.

[564]
NEW HAMPSHIRE INTEREST AND DIVIDEND TAX EXEMPTION FOR BLIND PEOPLE

New Hampshire Department of Revenue
  Administration
109 Pleasant Street
Concord, NH 03301
(603) 271-2191 Fax: (603) 271-6121
TDD: (800) 735-2964
Web: revenue.nh.gov

Summary To provide blind residents of New Hampshire with a partial exemption from taxes on interest and dividend income.

Eligibility This exemption is available to residents of New Hampshire who are blind, regardless of age, and pay taxes on income from interest and dividends.

Financial data Qualifying residents receive an exemption of $1,200 from interest and dividend income.

Duration 1 year; this exemption will be continued as long as the recipient meets the eligibility requirements.

Number awarded Varies each year.

Deadline The application for this exemption is included with the interest and dividend income tax form, due in April of each year.

[565]
NEW HAMPSHIRE PROPERTY TAX EXEMPTION FOR CERTAIN DISABLED VETERANS

New Hampshire Department of Revenue
  Administration
109 Pleasant Street
Concord, NH 03301
(603) 271-2191 Fax: (603) 271-6121
TDD: (800) 735-2964
Web: revenue.nh.gov

Summary To exempt from taxation certain property owned by New Hampshire blind and other disabled veterans or their surviving spouses.

Eligibility Eligible for this exemption are New Hampshire residents who are honorably discharged veterans with a total and permanent service-connected disability that involves double amputation of the upper or lower extremities or any combination thereof, paraplegia, or blindness of both eyes with visual acuity of 5/200 or less. Applicants or their surviving spouses must own a specially adapted homestead that has been acquired with the assistance of the U.S. Department of Veterans Affairs.

Financial data Qualifying disabled veterans and surviving spouses are exempt from all taxation on their specially adapted homestead.

Duration 1 year; once the credit has been approved, it is automatically renewed as long as the qualifying person owns the same residence in New Hampshire.

Number awarded Varies each year.

Deadline The original application for a permanent tax credit must be submitted by April.

[566]
NEW JERSEY INCOME TAX EXEMPTIONS FOR THE BLIND AND DISABLED

New Jersey Division of Taxation
Attn: Technical Information Branch
50 Barrack Street
P.O. Box 281
Trenton, NJ 08695-0281
(609) 292-6400 Toll Free: (800) 323-4400
TDD: (800) 286-6613 E-mail: taxation@tax.state.nj.us
Web: www.state.nj.us/treasury/taxation/prntgit.shtml

Summary To provide an income tax exemption in New Jersey to blind and disabled people.

Eligibility Residents of New Jersey who are blind or disabled are entitled to this exemption.

Financial data Each blind or disabled person is entitled to an exemption of $1,000 from income for taxation purposes.

Duration The exemption continues as long as the qualifying condition persists and the person remains a New Jersey resident.

Number awarded Varies each year.

Deadline Deadline not specified.

[567]
NEW JERSEY PROPERTY TAX DEDUCTION

New Jersey Division of Taxation
Attn: Technical Information Branch
50 Barrack Street
P.O. Box 281
Trenton, NJ 08695-0281
(609) 292-6400 Toll Free: (800) 323-4400
TDD: (800) 286-6613 E-mail: taxation@tax.state.nj.us
Web: www.state.nj.us/treasury/taxation/prntgit.shtml

Summary To exclude from income taxation a portion of the property taxes paid by blind, disabled, and other residents of New Jersey.

Eligibility This deduction is available to residents of New Jersey whose income is greater than $20,000 (or $10,000 if single or married filing separately). It is also available to residents, regardless of income, who are 1) blind, 2) permanently and totally disabled, or 3) 65 years of age or older. Applicants must either own the home in which they reside or rent a dwelling with its own separate kitchen and bath facilities.

Financial data Qualified residents are entitled to deduct from their income (for state taxation purposes) 100% of their property taxes, to a maximum of $10,000. For renters, 18% of their rent is considered the equivalent of property taxes and may be deducted to a maximum of $10,000.

Duration The deduction continues as long as the person remains a New Jersey resident.

Additional data This program began in 1996. Taxpayers may not claim both the property tax deduction and the property tax credit; they may claim whichever is most beneficial, but only the deduction or the credit.

Number awarded Varies each year.

Deadline The deduction is claimed as part of the annual income tax return, due in April of each year.

[568]
NEW MEXICO TAX EXEMPTION FOR THE BLIND AND ELDERLY

New Mexico Taxation and Revenue Department
Attn: Personal Income Tax Division
1100 South St. Francis Drive
P.O. Box 25122
Santa Fe, NM 87504-5122
(505) 827-0700
Web: www.tax.newmexico.gov

Summary To exempt a portion of the income of New Mexico residents who are blind or over the age of 65, and their surviving spouses, from state income tax liability.

Eligibility This exemption is available to residents of New Mexico who are 65 years of age or older or who are blind.

Financial data The income exemption ranges from $1,000 to $8,000, depending on filing status and income. The maximum income that still qualifies for an exemption is $25,500 for married individuals filing separate returns, $51,000 for heads of household, surviving spouses, and married individuals filing joint returns, or $28,500 for single individuals.

Duration The exemption continues as long as the qualifying resident remains in the state.

Number awarded Varies each year.

Deadline The qualifying resident claims the exemption on the New Mexico state income tax return, which is due in April.

[569]
NEW YORK STATE BLIND ANNUITY

New York State Division of Veterans' Affairs
5 Empire State Plaza, Suite 2836
Albany, NY 12223-1551
(518) 486-3602
Toll Free: (888) VETS-NYS (within NY)
Fax: (518) 473-0379 E-mail: dvainfo@veterans.ny.gov
Web: veterans.ny.gov/state-benefits.html

Summary To provide an annuity to blind wartime veterans and their surviving spouses in New York.

Eligibility This benefit is available to veterans who served on active duty during specified periods of war. Applicants must 1) meet the New York standards of blindness; 2) have received an honorable or general discharge, or a discharge other than for dishonorable service; and 3) be now, and continue to be, residents of and continuously domiciled in New York. The annuity is also payable to unremarried spouses of deceased veterans who were receiving annuity payments (or were eligible to do so) at the time of their death, and are residents of and continuously domiciled in New York.

Financial data The annuity is currently $1,220.76 per year.

Number awarded Varies each year.

Deadline Deadline not specified.

[570]
NFBCT-COCCOMO QUARTERLY GRANTS

National Federation of the Blind of Connecticut
Attn: Quarterly Grant Committee
477 Connecticut Boulevard, Suite 217
East Hartford, CT 06108
(860) 289-1971 E-mail: info@nfbct.org
Web: www.nfbct.org/html/coccomo.htm

Summary To provide funding to blind people in Connecticut interested in a program of training, employment, independent living, or technological advancement.

Eligibility This assistance is available to residents of Connecticut who meet the state's definition of legal blindness. Applicants must be seeking support for activities in the areas of training, employment, independent living, or technological advancement. A wide range of requests are considered, including a talking watch, a computer system, a note taker (such as a Braille Note or Braille Lite), payment assistance for postsecondary part-time course work, or even a new suit for the sake of maximizing impressions on job interviews. Along with their application, they must submit a statement about themselves, their goals, and how the requested product or service will enhance their daily life and/or career aspirations.

Financial data The amount awarded depends on the nature of the request.

Duration These are 1-time grants. Recipients are eligible for a second grant 2 years after receiving the first grant.

Additional data This program is supported by the John A. Coccomo, Sr. Foundation and administered by the National Federation of the Blind of Connecticut (NFBCT).

Number awarded Varies each year.

Deadline February, May, August, or November of each year.

[571]
NORTH DAKOTA PROPERTY TAX EXEMPTION FOR THE BLIND

Office of State Tax Commissioner
State Capitol Building
600 East Boulevard Avenue, Department 127
Bismarck, ND 58505-0599
(701) 328-7088 Toll Free: (877) 328-7088
Fax: (701) 328-3700 TDD: (800) 366-6888
E-mail: taxinfo@state.nd.us
Web: www.nd.gov/tax/property

Summary To provide partial tax exemption in North Dakota to blind persons and their spouses.

Eligibility Blind persons are defined as those who are totally blind, who have visual acuity of not more than 20/200 in the better eye with correction, or whose vision is limited in field so that the widest diameter subtends an angle no greater than 20 degrees. Eligible for this exemption is property that is owned by a blind person, by the spouse of a blind person, or jointly by a blind person and a spouse. The property that is exempt includes the entire building classified as residential, and owned and occupied as a residence by a person who qualifies, as long as the building contains no more than 2 apartments or rental units that are leased.

Financial data The exemption applies to all or any part of fixtures, building, and improvements upon any nonfarm-land up to a taxable valuation of $7,200.

Duration The exemption continues as long as the blind person resides in the home in North Dakota.

Number awarded Varies each year.

Deadline Deadline not specified.

[572]
OAK HILL LEGACY FUND GRANTS

Connecticut Institute for the Blind
Attn: Legacy Fund
120 Holcomb Street
Hartford, CT 06112-1589
(860) 242-2274   Fax: (860) 242-3103
TDD: (860) 286-3113   E-mail: info@ciboakhill.org
Web: www.ciboakhill.org

Summary To provide funding to blind Connecticut residents for projects that increase their options for independence.

Eligibility This program is open to residents of Connecticut whose vision is no more than 20/200 after correction. Preference is given to Oak Hill School graduates and former students and to others who demonstrate financial need. Applicants must be seeking funding for activities or equipment that will increase employment opportunities, enhance work productivity, or assist them in becoming more independent and for which other funding is not available. They must have applied to the state Board of Education and Services for the Blind (BESB) for funding and been denied. Along with their application, they must submit a brief description of their past and current activities and accomplishments, their need for this item or activity, what the item or activity will enable them to accomplish, a certificate of blindness or other documentation from a physician confirming legal blindness, information on financial need, and a copy of a letter from the BESB indicating why they have denied the applicant's request.

Financial data Grants range from $50 to $2,500.

Duration These are 1-time awards. They may be renewed upon reapplication but only 1 grant will be awarded in any 12-month period.

Additional data The Connecticut Institute for the Blind, doing business as Oak Hill, also operates independent living facilities in West Hartford and Wethersfield for blind, visually impaired, and disabled individuals. Grants are not intended to provide ongoing support.

Number awarded Varies each year.

Deadline January, April, July, or October of each year.

[573]
OKLAHOMA INCOME TAX EXEMPTION FOR THE BLIND

Oklahoma Tax Commission
Attn: Income Tax
2501 North Lincoln Boulevard
Oklahoma City, OK 73194-0009
(405) 521-3160   Toll Free: (800) 522-8165 (within OK)
Fax: (405) 522-0063   E-mail: otcmaster@tax.ok.gov
Web: www.tax.ok.gov/incometax.html

Summary To exempt a portion of the income of blind people and their spouses in Oklahoma from state taxation.

Eligibility This exemption is available to residents of Oklahoma and their spouses who are legally blind.

Financial data Each qualifying resident is entitled to claim an additional exemption of $1,000.

Duration The exemption is available as long as the recipient resides in Oklahoma.

Deadline Deadline not specified.

[574]
OREGON INCOME TAX DEDUCTION FOR THE BLIND

Oregon Department of Revenue
Revenue Building
955 Center Street, N.E.
Salem, OR 97310-2555
(503) 378-4988   Toll Free: (800) 356-4222 (within OR)
Fax: (503) 945-8738
TDD: (800) 886-7204 (within OR)
Web: www.oregon.gov/DOR/PERTAX/index.shtml

Summary To enable blind residents of Oregon to deduct a portion of their income from state taxation.

Eligibility This deduction is available to blind taxpayers in Oregon who utilize the standard deduction for their income taxes.

Financial data The additional deduction is $1,200 for single people and heads of households. It is $1,000 for married people filing jointly or separately and for qualifying widow(er)s.

Duration The deduction continues as long as the recipient resides in Oregon.

Deadline Deductions are filed with state income tax returns in April of each year.

[575]
OREGON PROPERTY TAX DEFERRAL FOR DISABLED AND SENIOR CITIZENS

Oregon Department of Revenue
Attn: Property Tax Division
Revenue Building
955 Center Street, N.E.
Salem, OR 97310-2555
(503) 378-4988   Toll Free: (800) 356-4222 (within OR)
Fax: (503) 945-8738
TDD: (800) 886-7204 (within OR)
Web: www.oregon.gov/DOR/PTD/property.shtml

Summary   To enable blind, disabled, and elderly Oregon residents to defer payment of their property taxes.

Eligibility   This program is open to residents of Oregon who are determined to be eligible to receive or are receiving federal Social Security benefits due to disability or blindness. Applicants must own a residence, have net worth less than $500,000, and have a total household income less than $39,500.

Financial data   The state pays all taxes on the property to the county but places a lien on the property and charges 6% compound interest per year on the deferred taxes. The lien and interest become due and payable when the disabled person or senior citizen sells the property or changes its ownership, moves permanently from the property (unless for medical reasons), or dies.

Duration   1 year; the deferment is automatically renewed as long as the property owner lives in the residence.

Number awarded   Varies each year; recently, 712 blind and disabled residents of Oregon were participating in this program.

Deadline   Applications for new deferrals must be filed in the appropriate county assessor's office by April of each year.

[576]
PENNSYLVANIA BLIND VETERANS PENSION

Office of the Deputy Adjutant General for Veterans
  Affairs
Building S-0-47, FTIG
Annville, PA 17003-5002
(717) 865-8911
Toll Free: (800) 54 PA VET (within PA)
Fax: (717) 861-8589   E-mail: RA-VA-Info@pa.gov
Web: www.dmva.state.pa.us

Summary   To provide financial assistance to blind residents of Pennsylvania who lost their sight while serving in the U.S. armed forces.

Eligibility   Persons who have 3/60 or 10/200 or less normal vision are eligible if they are honorably-discharged veterans and were residents of Pennsylvania when they joined the U.S. armed forces. Their blindness must have resulted from a service-connected injury or disease.

Financial data   The pension is $150 per month.

Duration   The pension is awarded for the life of the veteran.

Number awarded   Varies each year.

Deadline   Applications may be submitted at any time.

[577]
PENNSYLVANIA DISABLED VETERANS REAL ESTATE TAX EXEMPTION

Office of the Deputy Adjutant General for Veterans
  Affairs
Building S-0-47, FTIG
Annville, PA 17003-5002
(717) 865-8907
Toll Free: (800) 54 PA VET (within PA)
Fax: (717) 861-8589   E-mail: RA-VA-Info@pa.gov
Web: www.dmva.state.pa.us

Summary   To exempt blind and disabled Pennsylvania veterans and their unremarried surviving spouses from all state real estate taxes.

Eligibility   Eligible to apply for this exemption are honorably-discharged veterans who are residents of Pennsylvania and who are blind, paraplegic, or 100% disabled from a service-connected disability sustained during wartime military service. The dwelling must be owned by the veteran solely or jointly with a spouse, and financial need for the exemption must be determined by the State Veterans' Commission. Veterans whose income is less than $81,340 per year are presumed to have financial need; veterans with income greater than $81,340 must document need. Upon the death of the veteran, the tax exemption passes on to the veteran's unremarried surviving spouse.

Financial data   This program exempts the principal residence (and the land on which it stands) from all real estate taxes.

Duration   The exemption continues as long as the eligible veteran or unremarried widow resides in Pennsylvania.

Number awarded   Varies each year.

Deadline   Deadline not specified.

[578]
RHODE ISLAND INCOME TAX DEDUCTION FOR THE BLIND

Rhode Island Division of Taxation
One Capitol Hill
Providence, RI 02908-5806
(401) 574-8829   TDD: (401) 574-8934
E-mail: txassist@tax.state.ri.gov
Web: www.tax.ri.gov

Summary   To increase the standard deduction from the income of blind people from state taxation in Rhode Island.

Eligibility   This additional deduction is available to residents of Rhode Island who are blind. Applicants must utilize the standard deduction schedule.

Financial data   Blind taxpayers are entitled to deduct an additional $3,500 from their income for purposes of state taxation in Rhode Island.

Duration   The deduction is available annually.

Number awarded   Varies each year.

Deadline   Deduction claims are included with the state income tax return, due in April of each year.

[579]
RUTH BILLOW MEMORIAL PERSONAL AID

Delta Gamma Foundation
Attn: Director, Service for Sight
3250 Riverside Drive
P.O. Box 21397
Columbus, OH 43221-0397
(614) 481-8169   Toll Free: (800) 644-5414
Fax: (614) 481-0133
E-mail: fngrants@deltagamma.org
Web: www.deltagamma.org

Summary To provide financial assistance to members of Delta Gamma sorority who are in need because of their visual impairment or that of a family member.

Eligibility This program is open to members of the sorority who require assistance 1) in order to restore or retain their sight; or 2) because of their responsibilities directly related to dependents who are blind or visually impaired. Applicants must be residents of the United States or Canada.

Financial data The amount awarded varies, depending upon individual circumstances.

Duration 1 year or more.

Number awarded Varies each year.

Deadline Applications may be submitted at any time.

[580]
SENTINELS OF FREEDOM SCHOLARSHIPS

Sentinels of Freedom
P.O. Box 1316
San Ramon, CA 94583
(925) 380-6342   Fax: (925) 867-1078
E-mail: info@sentinelsoffreedom.org
Web: www.sentinelsoffreedom.org

Summary To provide funding to veterans and current military personnel who became blind, deaf, or disabled as a result of injuries sustained in the line of duty on or after September 11, 2001.

Eligibility This program is open to members of the U.S. Air Force, Army, Coast Guard, Marines, or Navy who sustained injuries in the line of duty on or after September 11, 2001. Applicants must be rated as 60% or more disabled as a result of 1 or more of the following conditions: amputation, blindness, deafness, paraplegia, severe burns, limited traumatic brain injury (TBI), or limited post-traumatic stress disorder (PTSD); other severe injuries may be considered on a case-by-case basis. They must complete an interview process and demonstrate that they have the skills, experience, and attitude that lead to employment.

Financial data Assistance is available for the following needs: housing (adapted for physical needs if necessary), new furniture and other household supplies, career-placement assistance and training, new adaptive vehicles, educational opportunities in addition to the new GI Bill, or financial and personal mentorship.

Duration Assistance may be provided for up to 4 years.

Additional data The first assistance granted by this program was awarded in 2004.

Number awarded Varies each year. Since the program was established, it has supported 84 current and former service members.

Deadline Applications may be submitted at any time.

[581]
SOCIAL SECURITY DISABILITY INSURANCE (SSDI) BENEFITS

Social Security Administration
6401 Security Boulevard
Baltimore, MD 21235-0001
(410) 594-1234   Toll Free: (800) 772-1213
TDD: (800) 325-0778
Web: www.ssa.gov

Summary To provide monthly benefits to workers and their families if the worker becomes disabled or blind.

Eligibility This program defines disabled people as those who are unable to do any kind of work for which they are suited and whose disability has lasted or is expected to last for at least a year or to result in death. Blind people qualify if their vision cannot be corrected to better than 20/200 in their better eye or if their visual field is 20 degrees or less, even with corrective lenses. Family members who are eligible include 1) unmarried children, including adopted children and, in some cases, stepchildren and grandchildren who are under 18 years of age (19 if still in high school full time); 2) unmarried children, over 18 years of age, if they have a disability that started before age 22; and 3) spouses who are 62 years of age or older, or of any age if caring for a child of the disabled worker who is under 16 years of age or disabled. For deceased workers, disabled widow(er)s 50 years of age or older are also eligible. Applicants must also have worked long enough and recently enough under Social Security in order to qualify. Workers who become disabled before the age of 24 need 6 credits in the 3-year period ending when the disability begins; workers who become disabled between the ages of 24 and 31 must have credit for having worked half the time between the age of 21 and the date of disability; workers 31 years of age or older at the time of disability must have earned as many total credits as needed for retirement (from 20 credits if disabled at age 31 through 42 to 40 credits if disabled at age 62 or older) and must have earned at least 20 of the credits in the 10 years immediately before becoming disabled. An exception applies to blind workers who need no recent credit but may have earned the required credit any time after 1936.

Financial data The amount of the monthly benefit depends on several factors, including the worker's age at the time of disability, the number of dependents, and the amount of earnings on which Social Security taxes have been paid. Recently, the average monthly benefit was $1,110.70 for disabled workers, $298.60 for spouses of disabled workers, and $330.70 for children of disabled workers.

Duration For a disabled or blind person, whether a worker, widow, widower, surviving divorced spouse, or person over the age of 18 who became disabled before the age of 22, monthly benefits continue until the person is no longer disabled or dies. For a dependent spouse, benefits are paid until the worker is no longer disabled or dies. For a dependent child, the benefits continue until the child marries or reaches the age of 18 (19 if still enrolled as a full-time high school student).

Additional data Disabled workers may test their ability to return to work for a trial work period of up to 9 months, during which time they receive full SSDI benefits. At the end of that period, a decision is made as to whether or not they are able to engage in substantial gainful activity. Persons who find that they cannot continue substantial gainful employment continue to receive SSDI benefits without interruption. Persons who can engage in substantial gainful activity receive benefits for an additional 3 months after which payments cease. Several factors are considered to determine if the person can engage in substantial gainful employment, but the most important is income; for disabled people the amount is $1,000 a month gross wages and for blind people the income is $1,640 monthly.

Number awarded Varies; recently, approximately 8,630,000 disabled workers were receiving SSDI monthly benefits, along with 163,000 spouses and 1,897,000 children.

Deadline Deadline not specified.

[582]
SOUTH CAROLINA HOMESTEAD EXEMPTION PROGRAM

South Carolina Department of Revenue
301 Gervais Street
P.O. Box 125
Columbia, SC 29214
(803) 898-5680   Toll Free: (800) 763-1295
Fax: (803) 898-5822   E-mail: MillerC@sctax.org
Web: www.sctax.org

Summary To provide a homestead exemption to South Carolina residents who are elderly, disabled, or blind, and their widow(er)s.

Eligibility Legal residents of South Carolina who own a house or mobile home are eligible for this exemption if they are 65 years of age or older, totally and permanently disabled, or legally blind. Spouses of deceased persons who were eligible also qualify to receive the exemption as long as they remain unmarried.

Financial data The first $50,000 of the fair market value of the qualified applicant's home is exempted from property taxes. The exemption is from county, municipal, school, and special assessment real estate property taxes.

Duration The exemption continues as long as the homeowners live in their primary residence in South Carolina.

Additional data This program, established in 1972, is administered by county auditors.

Number awarded Varies each year.

Deadline Persons applying for this exemption for the first time must do so prior to July of each year; subsequently, no re-application is necessary unless the title or use of the property changes.

[583]
SPECIAL HOUSING ADAPTATIONS GRANTS

Department of Veterans Affairs
Attn: Specially Adapted Housing
810 Vermont Avenue, N.W.
Washington, DC 20420
(202) 461-9546   Toll Free: (800) 827-1000
Web: www.benefits.va.gov/homeloans/sah_info.asp

Summary To provide grants to certain disabled or blind veterans or service members who wish to make adaptations to their home to meet their needs.

Eligibility These grants are available to veterans and service members who are entitled to compensation for permanent and total service-connected disability due to: 1) blindness in both eyes with 5/200 visual acuity or less; 2) the anatomical loss or loss of use of both hands; or 3) a severe burn injury. Applicants must be planning to 1) adapt a house which they plan to purchase and in which they intend to reside; 2) adapt a house which a member of their family plans to purchase and in which they intend to reside; 3) adapt a house which they already own and in which they intend to reside; 4) adapt a house which is already owned by a member of their family in which they intend to reside; or 5) purchase a house that has already been adapted with special features that are reasonably necessary because of their disability and in which they intend to reside.

Financial data Eligible veterans and service members are entitled to grants up to $12,756 to adapt a house.

Duration Eligible veterans and service members are entitled to up to 3 usages of these grants.

Number awarded Varies each year.

Deadline Applications are accepted at any time.

[584]
SPECIALLY ADAPTED HOUSING GRANTS

Department of Veterans Affairs
Attn: Specially Adapted Housing
810 Vermont Avenue, N.W.
Washington, DC 20420
(202) 461-9546   Toll Free: (800) 827-1000
Web: www.homeloans.va.gov/sah.htm

Summary To provide loans, grants, and loan guaranties to blind and disabled veterans and service members for a home specially adapted to their needs.

Eligibility These grants are available to veterans and service members who are entitled to compensation for permanent and total service-connected disability due to: 1) the loss or loss of use of both lower extremities, such as to preclude locomotion without the aid of braces, crutches, canes, or a wheelchair; or 2) blindness in both eyes, having only light perception, plus loss or loss of use of 1 lower extremity; 3) a loss or loss of use of 1 lower extremity together with residuals of organic disease or injury or the loss or loss of use of 1 upper extremity, such as to preclude locomotion without resort to braces, canes, crutches, or a wheelchair; 4) the loss or loss of use of both upper extremities, so as to preclude use of the arms at or above the elbows; or 5) a severe burn injury. Applicants must be planning to 1) construct a home on land to be acquired for that purpose; 2) build a home on land already owned if it is suitable for specially adapted housing; 3) remodel an existing home if it can be made suitable for specially adapted housing, or 4) apply funds against the unpaid principle mortgage balance of a specially adapted home that has already been acquired.

Financial data The U.S. Department of Veterans Affairs (VA) may approve a grant of not more than 50% of the cost of building, buying, or remodeling homes for eligible veterans, or paying indebtedness on such homes already acquired, up to a maximum grant of $63,780. Eligible veterans with available loan guarantee entitlements may also obtain a guaranteed loan from the VA to supplement the grant to acquire a specially adapted home. If private financing is not available, the VA may make a direct loan up to $33,000 to cover the difference between the total cost of the home and the grant.

Duration This is a 1-time grant, guaranteed loan, or direct loan.

Additional data Veterans who receive a specially adapted housing grant may be eligible for Veterans Mortgage Life Insurance.

Number awarded Varies each year.

Deadline Applications are accepted at any time.

[585]
SUPPLEMENTAL SECURITY INCOME (SSI)

Social Security Administration
6401 Security Boulevard
Baltimore, MD 21235-0001
(410) 594-1234   Toll Free: (800) 772-1213
TDD: (800) 325-0778
Web: www.socialsecurity.gov/ssi/index.htm

Summary To provide monthly payments to disabled, blind, deaf, and elderly people who have limited income and resources.

Eligibility This assistance is available to U.S. citizens and certain categories of aliens who are 65 years of age or older, blind, or disabled. A person 18 years of age or older is considered disabled if a physical or mental impairment prevents him or her from doing any substantial gainful work and is expected to last for at least 12 months or to result in death. Children under the age of 18 are considered disabled if they have a physical or mental impairment that is comparable in severity to a disability that would prevent an adult from working and is expected to last at least 12 months or result in death. Children with certain conditions are automatically disabled and eligible for these benefits; the conditions include HIV infection, blindness, deafness, cerebral palsy, Down syndrome, muscular dystrophy, significant mental deficiency, diabetes (with amputation of 1 foot), amputation of 2 limbs, or amputation of leg at the hip. Regardless of age, a person whose vision is no better than 20/200 or who has a limited visual field of 20 degrees or less with the best corrective eyeglasses is considered blind; individuals with visual impairments not severe enough to meet the definition of blindness still may qualify as disabled persons. Applicants must have limited income and limited resources (less than $2,000 for an individual or $3,000 for a couple); items excluded from resources include the home used as a principal place of residence, personal and household goods, life insurance with face value of $1,500 or less, a car, burial plots for individuals and immediate family members, and burial funds up to $1,500.

Financial data The basic monthly payment is $698 for an eligible individual or $1,048 for an eligible individual with an eligible spouse. Many states add money to that basic payment. SSI recipients may also be eligible for food stamps and other nutrition programs.

Duration Assistance is provided as long as the recipient remains blind or disabled and in financial need.

Additional data Although SSI is administered through the Social Security Administration, it is not financed by Social Security taxes. Financing of SSI is provided through general funds of the U.S. Treasury. Recipients of SSI need not have been employed or paid Social Security taxes, but they may be eligible for both SSI and Social Security. Disabled and blind applicants for SSI are referred to their state vocational rehabilitation agency to determine their eligibility for a program of vocational rehabilitation. Disabled drug addicts or alcoholics are referred for appropriate treatment if it is available at an approved facility or institution.

Number awarded Recently, approximately 8,164,000 people (including 6,981,000 who were blind and disabled) were receiving SSI benefits, including 1,294,000 under 18 years of age, 4,806,000 who were 18 to 64 years of age, and 2,064,000 who were 65 or older.

Deadline Deadline not specified.

[586]
TENNESSEE INCOME TAX EXEMPTION FOR BLIND RESIDENTS

Tennessee Department of Revenue
Andrew Jackson State Office Building
500 Deaderick Street
Nashville, TN 37242-1099
(615) 253-0600   Toll Free: (800) 342-1003 (within TN)
Fax: (615) 253-3580   E-mail: tn.revenue@state.tn.us
Web: www.tennessee.gov/revenue

Summary To exempt from state taxation the dividend and interest income of blind residents of Tennessee.

Eligibility This exemption applies to income received by blind residents of Tennessee as 1) dividends from stock, investment trusts, and mutual funds; and 2) interest from bonds, notes, and mortgages. As defined by this program, blindness means that vision does not exceed 20/200 in the better eye with correcting lenses or that the widest diameter of the visual field subtends an angle no greater than 20 degrees.

Financial data All dividend and interest income is exempt from taxation if the recipient meets the definition of blindness. However, when taxable interest/dividend income is received jointly by a blind person and a sighted spouse, only one half of the jointly received income is exempted from taxation. The sighted spouse is entitled only to a $1,250 exemption.

Duration The exemption continues as long as the recipient meets the definition of blindness and resides in Tennessee.

Deadline Deadline not specified.

[587]
TENNESSEE PROPERTY TAX RELIEF FOR DISABLED VETERANS AND THEIR SPOUSES

Tennessee Comptroller of the Treasury
Attn: Property Tax Relief Program
James K. Polk State Office Building
505 Deaderick Street, Room 1700
Nashville, TN 37243-1402
(615) 747-8858   Fax: (615) 532-3866
E-mail: kim.darden@cot.tn.gov
Web: www.comptroller1.state.tn.us/pa/patxr.asp

Summary To provide property tax relief to blind and disabled veterans and their spouses in Tennessee.

Eligibility This exemption is offered to veterans or their surviving unremarried spouses who are residents of Tennessee and own and live in their home in the state. The veteran must have served in the U.S. armed forces and 1) have acquired, as a result of such service, a disability from paraplegia, permanent paralysis of both legs and lower part of the body resulting from traumatic injury, disease to the spinal cord or brain, legal blindness, or loss or loss of use of both legs or arms from any service-connected cause; 2) have been rated by the U.S. Department of Veterans Affairs (VA) as 100% permanently disabled as a result of service as a prisoner of war for at least 5 months; or 3) have been rated by the VA as 100% permanently and totally disabled from any other service-connected cause. Unremarried spouses of deceased veterans are also eligible if 1) the veteran was receiving tax relief as a disabled veteran before death; 2) death resulted from a service-connected, combat-related cause, or killed in action; or 3) death resulted from being deployed, away from any home base of training, and in support of combat operations.

Financial data The amount of the relief depends on the property assessment and the tax rate in the city or county where the beneficiary lives. The maximum market value on which tax relief is calculated is $175,000.

Duration 1 year; may be renewed as long as the eligible veteran or surviving unremarried spouse owns and occupies the primary residence.

Number awarded Varies each year.

Deadline Deadline not specified.

[588]
TEXAS PROPERTY TAX EXEMPTION FOR DISABLED VETERANS AND THEIR FAMILIES

Texas Veterans Commission
P.O. Box 12277
Austin, TX 78711-2277
(512) 463-5538
Toll Free: (800) 252-VETS (within TX)
Fax: (512) 475-2395   E-mail: info@tvc.state.tx.us
Web: texas-veterans.com/claims/property-tax-exemption

Summary To extend property tax exemptions on the appraised value of their property to blind, disabled, and other Texas veterans and their surviving family members.

Eligibility Eligible veterans must be Texas residents rated at least 10% service-connected disabled. Surviving spouses and children of eligible veterans are also covered by this program.

Financial data For veterans in Texas whose disability is rated as 10% through 29%, the first $5,000 of the appraised property value is exempt from taxation; veterans rated as 30% through 49% disabled are exempt from the first $7,500 of appraised value; those with a 50% through 69% disability are exempt from the first $10,000 of appraised value; the exemption applies to the first $12,000 of appraised value for veterans with disabilities rated as 70% to 99%; veterans rated as 100% disabled are exempt from 100% of the appraised value of their property. A veteran whose disability is 10% or more and who is 65 years or older is entitled to exemption of the first $12,000 of appraised property value. A veteran whose disability consists of the loss of use of 1 or more limbs, total blindness in 1 or both eyes, or paraplegia is exempt from the first $12,000 of the appraised value. The unremarried surviving spouse of a deceased veteran who died on active duty and who, at the time of death had a compensable disability and was entitled to an exemption, is entitled to the same exemption. The surviving spouse of a person who died on active duty is entitled to exemption of the first $5,000 of appraised value of the spouse's property; they are also eligible for the 100% exemption. A surviving child of a person who dies on active duty is entitled to exemption of the first $5,000 of appraised value of the child's property, as long as the child is unmarried and under 21 years of age.

Duration 1 year; may be renewed as long as the eligible veteran (or unremarried surviving spouse or child) owns and occupies the primary residence in Texas.

Additional data This program is administered at the local level by the various taxing authorities.

Number awarded Varies each year.

Deadline April of each year.

[589]
UTAH BLIND PROPERTY TAX EXEMPTION

Utah State Tax Commission
Attn: Property Tax Division
210 North 1950 West
Salt Lake City, UT 84134
(801) 297-3600   Toll Free: (800) 662-4335, ext. 3600
Fax: (801) 297-3699   TDD: (801) 297-2020
E-mail: propertytax@utah.gov
Web: propertytax.utah.gov

Summary   To exempt from taxation a portion of the real and tangible property of blind people and their families in Utah.

Eligibility   This exemption is available to legally blind property owners in Utah, along with their unremarried surviving spouses or minor orphans. First-year applications must be accompanied by a signed statement from an ophthalmologist and, if appropriate, a death certificate.

Financial data   The first $11,500 of the taxable value of real and tangible personal property is exempt from taxation.

Duration   The exemption is available each year the beneficiary owns property in Utah.

Number awarded   Varies each year.

Deadline   Applications must be submitted by August of each year.

Hearing Disabilities

Scholarships ●

Fellowships ●

Grants-in-Aid ●

Described here are 45 funding opportunities available to individuals who have difficulty in receiving linguistic information, with or without amplification. Of these, 18 cover scholarships (to pursue study, research, or other activities on the undergraduate level in the United States); 13 describe fellowships or grants (to support graduate or postgraduate study, research, or other activities in the United States); and 14 identify grants-in-aid (to pay for emergency situations, travel, income/property tax liabilities, the acquisition of assistive technology, or other personal needs). All of this is "free" money. Not one dollar will need to be repaid (provided, of course, that recipients meet all program requirements). If you are looking for a particular program and don't find it in this section, be sure to check the Program Title Index to see if it is covered elsewhere in the directory.

Scholarships

[590]
ALEXANDER GRAHAM BELL COLLEGE SCHOLARSHIP AWARDS PROGRAM

Alexander Graham Bell Association for the Deaf and
  Hard of Hearing
Attn: College Scholarship Program
3417 Volta Place, N.W.
Washington, DC 20007-2778
(202) 337-5220   Fax: (202) 337-8314
TDD: (202) 337-5221   E-mail: financialaid@agbell.org
Web: nc.agbell.org/page.aspx?pid=493

Summary   To provide financial assistance to undergraduate students with moderate to profound hearing loss.

Eligibility   This program is open to full-time undergraduate students who have been diagnosed with a moderate to profound bilateral hearing loss prior to their fourth birthday (hearing loss averages 60dB or greater in the better ear in the speech frequencies of 500, 1000, and 2000 Hz). Applicants must be committed to using spoken language as their primary mode of communication. They must be accepted or enrolled at a mainstream college or university and have a GPA of 3.25 or higher. Along with their application, they must submit a 1-page essay on 1 of the following topics: 1) if they could invent or improve upon a product, what it would be and why; 2) if they could change 1 thing to improve society on a local or global level, what it would be and why; or 3) their goals and the impact they hope to have over the course of their life. Financial need is not considered in the selection process.

Financial data   Stipends range from $1,000 to $10,000.

Duration   1 year; may be renewed 1 additional year.

Additional data   This program includes the following named awards: the Allie Raney Hunt Scholarship, the Bennion Family Scholarship, the Deaf and Hard of Hearing Section Scholarship Fund, the Elsie M. Bell Grosvenor Scholarship Awards, the Federation of Jewish Women's Organization Scholarship, the Herbert P. Feibelman, Jr. Scholarship, the Ladies' Auxiliary National Rural Letter Carriers Scholarship, the Louis DiCarlo Scholarship, the Lucille B. Abt Scholarships, the Robert H. Weitbrecht Scholarship, the Samuel M. and Gertrude G. Levy Scholarship Fund, the Volta Scholarship Fund, and the Walter W. and Thelma C. Hissey College Scholarships.

Number awarded   Varies each year; recently, 18 of these scholarships were awarded.

Deadline   February of each year.

[591]
ARTS AND SCIENCES AWARDS

Alexander Graham Bell Association for the Deaf and
  Hard of Hearing
Attn: Financial Aid Coordinator
3417 Volta Place, N.W.
Washington, DC 20007-2778
(202) 337-5220   Fax: (202) 337-8314
TDD: (202) 337-5221   E-mail: financialaid@agbell.org
Web: nc.agbell.org/page.aspx?pid=496

Summary   To provide financial aid to hearing impaired students who are participating in extracurricular activities in arts and sciences.

Eligibility   This program is open to residents of the United States or Canada who have been diagnosed prior to their fourth birthday as having a moderate to profound bilateral hearing loss and who use spoken language as their primary form of communication. They must be between 6 and 19 years of age and enrolled in an art or science program as an extracurricular activity during after-school time, summer, or weekends. Programs can be offered through museums, nature centers, art or music centers, zoological parks, space and science camps, dance and theater studios, martial arts studios, or any other program with a focus on the arts or sciences. Recreational summer camps, sports camps or sports, and travel and study abroad programs that do not have an explicit arts or science focus are not eligible. Membership in the Alexander Graham Bell Association is not required, but preference is given to members.

Financial data   The amount of the award varies, depending upon the cost of the program in which the recipient is enrolled.

Duration   1 year; may be renewed upon reapplication.

Number awarded   Varies each year.

Deadline   April of each year.

[592]
CALIFORNIA GRANGE FOUNDATION DEAF ACTIVITIES COMMITTEE SCHOLARSHIP

California Grange Foundation
Attn: Scholarship Committee
3830 U Street
Sacramento, CA 95817
(916) 454-5805   Toll Free: (866) 4-GRANGE
Fax: (916) 739-8189
E-mail: info@californiagrange.org
Web: www.californiagrange.org/scholarships.html

Summary   To provide financial assistance for college in any state to residents of California who are either deaf and interested in studying any field or hearing people interested in studying a field that will benefit deaf people.

Eligibility   This program is open to residents of California who are just entering, continuing, or returning to an accredited college, university, or vocational/technical school in any state. Applicants must be either 1) deaf persons and planning to major in any field; or 2) hearing persons and planning to major in American Sign Language, interpreting, teaching, or counseling the deaf. Along with their application, they must submit an essay introducing themselves and their goals, official transcripts, information on their past activities (including any leadership experiences and participation in other volunteer-related programs or projects), and a list of experience in sign language and helping the deaf. Community service and involvement are given special consideration in the selection process; financial need is not considered.

Financial data   A stipend is awarded (amount not specified).

Duration   1 year.

Number awarded   1 or more each year.

Deadline   March of each year.

[593]
CAROLINE KARK AWARD FOR DEAF STUDENTS

New York State Grange
100 Grange Place
Cortland, NY 13045
(607) 756-7553   Fax: (607) 756-7757
E-mail: nysgrange@nysgrange.org
Web: www.nysgrange.org/educationalassistance.html

Summary   To provide financial assistance to members of the Grange in New York who are deaf and attending college in any state.

Eligibility   This program is open to members of the New York State Grange who are currently enrolled at a college in any state. Applicants must be deaf.

Financial data   A stipend is awarded (amount not specified).

Duration   1 year; nonrenewable.

Number awarded   1 or more each year.

Deadline   April of each year.

[594]
FLORIDA CHAIRSCHOLARS PROGRAM

ChairScholars Foundation, Inc.
16101 Carencia Lane
Odessa, FL 33556-3278
(813) 926-0544   Toll Free: (888) 926-0544
Fax: (813) 920-7661
E-mail: chairscholars@tampabay.rr.com
Web: www.chairscholars.org/florida.html

Summary   To provide funding to students in Florida with specified disabilities who plan to attend college in the state.

Eligibility   This program is open to residents of Florida who are enrolled in grades 7-11 at a public school and have a serious physical disability. Qualifying disabilities include cerebral palsy, muscular dystrophy, spinal muscular atrophy, amputations, congenital missing or shortened limbs, multiple sclerosis, profound deafness, hearing impairments requiring FM modulator, blindness, various forms of cancer, any condition that permanently places the student in a wheelchair, or other illnesses, diseases, or conditions that severely impair mobility or motor skills. Applicants must have at least a "B" average and be able to demonstrate significant financial need (annual income

less than $20,137 for a family of 1, rising to $69,616 for a family of 8). They must be planning to attend a college, university, community college, or vocational school in the state. Along with their application, they must submit a 1-page essay outlining how they became physically challenged, how their situation has affected them or their family, their family situation, things they like to do, why they need this scholarship, and their goals and dreams for the future.

Financial data   The awards provide full payment of tuition at any public college, university, or community college, or vocational school in Florida.

Duration   Up to 4 years.

Additional data   This program began in 1996. Recipients are provided with a mentor until they graduate from high school. They must sign a "contract" pledging to remain drug and crime free.

Number awarded   Varies each year; recently, 24 of these scholarships were awarded. Since the program was established, it has awarded 502 scholarships.

Deadline   January of each year.

[595]
GEOFFREY FOUNDATION SCHOLARSHIPS

Geoffrey Foundation
Ocean Avenue
P.O. Box 1112
Kennebunkport, ME 04046
(207) 967-5798

Summary   To provide financial assistance to deaf students who attend school with hearing students and communicate using spoken language.

Eligibility   This program is open to U.S. citizens who are hearing impaired (severe to profound hearing loss greater than 80 dB) and are utilizing an auditory-verbal approach to communication. Applicants must be currently enrolled or planning to attend a preschool, elementary school, junior high or high school, or college for hearing students on a full-time basis in the forthcoming year. They must submit a current audiogram plus 3 letters of recommendation.

Financial data   The amount awarded varies, depending upon the needs of the recipient.

Duration   1 year or longer.

Additional data   The foundation is closely aligned with Auditory-Verbal International, Inc. and the Alexander Graham Bell Association for the Deaf. Funds are also available to support hearing research as well as programs, initiatives, or organizations of interest to the foundation. Applications may be requested only by mail.

Number awarded   Varies each year. The foundation awards grants in excess of $30,000 each year to children and college students.

Deadline   March of each year.

[596]
GRAEME CLARK SCHOLARSHIPS

Cochlear Americas
Attn: Scholarships
13059 East Peakview Avenue
Centennial, CO 80111
(303) 790-9010   Toll Free: (800) 523-5798
Fax: (303) 790-1157
E-mail: Recipients@Cochlear.com
Web: www.cochlearamericas.com/support/168.asp

Summary To provide financial assistance for college to students who have received a cochlear nucleus implant.

Eligibility This program is open to graduating high school seniors, current university students, and mature aged students who have been accepted into a university course. Applicants must have received a cochlear nucleus implant. They must have a GPA of 2.5 or higher. Along with their application, they must submit a 1,000-word personal statement on their academic aspirations and other interests, including why they chose their proposed area of study, their post-graduate aspirations, their definition of success, and why they wish to receive this scholarship. Selection is based on academic achievement and commitment to the ideals of leadership and humanity.

Financial data The stipend is $2,000 per year.

Duration 1 year; renewable up to 3 more years, provided the recipient maintains a GPA of 2.5 or higher.

Additional data This program was established in 2002.

Number awarded Varies each year; recently, 5 of these scholarships were awarded.

Deadline October of each year.

[597]
ITALIAN CATHOLIC FEDERATION GIFTS OF LOVE FOR SPECIAL PEOPLE

Italian Catholic Federation
8393 Capwell Drive, Suite 110
Oakland, CA 94621
(510) 633-9058   Toll Free: (888) ICF-1924
Fax: (510) 633-9758   E-mail: info@icf.org
Web: www.icf.org/charitable.html

Summary To provide funding to individuals who have specific disabilities and need additional training or instruction.

Eligibility This program is open to 1) individuals who have a disability and desire formal training or instruction in a particular vocation, academic, athletic, or artistic field; 2) qualified instructors on behalf of an individual with a disability who exhibits a particular skill to be developed and who desires formal instruction or training; or 3) adults with custodial responsibility for, and on behalf of, an individual with a disability who exhibits a particular skill to be developed and who desires formal instruction or training. The program defines individuals with a disability as those who have mental retardation, hearing impairments, speech and language impairments, visual impairments, emotional disturbances, orthopedic impairments, autism, traumatic brain injury, other health impairments, specific learning disabilities, or multiple disabilities who, because of their

needs, require special education or related services. Financial need is considered in the selection process.

Financial data A stipend is awarded (amount not specified).

Duration These are 1-time grants.

Number awarded Varies each year.

Deadline Deadline not specified.

[598]
J. PARIS MOSLEY SCHOLARSHIP

Cleveland Foundation
Attn: Scholarship Officer
1422 Euclid Avenue, Suite 1300
Cleveland, OH 44115-2001
(216) 861-3810   Fax: (216) 861-1729
E-mail: mbaker@clevefdn.org
Web: www.clevelandfoundation.org/Scholarships

Summary To provide financial assistance for college to high school seniors in any state 1) who are deaf or 2) whose primary caregivers are deaf.

Eligibility This program is open to high school seniors in any state who are deaf or hard of hearing or the children or grandchildren of deaf or hard of hearing parents or grandparents. Applicants must be planning to attend a college, university, vocational school, or other postsecondary program in any state. They must use some form of sign language, have a GPA of 2.5 or higher, and be able to demonstrate financial need. Preference is given to students of African, Latino, or Native American descent.

Financial data A stipend is awarded (amount not specified).

Duration 1 year.

Number awarded 1 or more each year.

Deadline March of each year.

[599]
LOUISE TUMARKIN ZAZOVE SCHOLARSHIPS

Louise Tumarkin Zazove Foundation
c/o Phillip Zazove
2903 Craig Road
Ann Arbor, MI 48103
E-mail: phillip@ltzfoundation.org
Web: www.ltzfoundation.org/scholarships.php

Summary To provide financial assistance for college (and possibly for high school or graduate school) to people with hearing loss.

Eligibility This program is open to U.S. citizens and permanent residents who have a significant bilateral hearing loss. Strong preference is given to undergraduate students, but support may be provided for graduate school or high school tuition in certain situations. Applicants must submit a transcript of high school and/or college grades, 3 recommendations, documentation of the severity of the hearing loss, information on any special circumstances by or about the family, and documented financial need.

Financial data A stipend is awarded (amount not specified). Funds are paid directly to schools.

Duration 1 year; may be renewed up to 3 additional years, provided the recipient continues to do well in school and demonstrate financial need.

Additional data This program was established in 2003.

Number awarded Varies each year; since the program was established, it has awarded 19 scholarships.

Deadline May of each year.

[600]
MARYLAND STATE GRANGE DEAF SCHOLARSHIP

Maryland State Grange
c/o Theresa Myrdon, Deaf Activities
14935 Athey Road
Burtonsville, MD 20866
(301) 421-0958   E-mail: tmyrdon@yahoo.com

Summary To provide financial assistance for college or graduate school to Maryland residents who are either deaf or preparing to work with hearing impaired people.

Eligibility This program is open to seniors graduating from high schools in Maryland and to graduates of those high schools who are attending or planning to attend college or graduate school in the state. Applicants must be 1) deaf or hearing impaired, or 2) preparing for a career working with deaf or hearing impaired people.

Financial data A stipend is awarded (amount not specified).

Duration 1 year; may be renewed if the recipient maintains a GPA of 3.0 or higher.

Number awarded 1 or more each year.

Deadline May of each year.

[601]
MINNIE PEARL SCHOLARSHIP PROGRAM

Hearing Bridges
Attn: Scholarship Program
415 Fourth Avenue South, Suite A
Nashville, TN 37201
(615) 248-8828   Toll Free: (866) 385-6524
Fax: (615) 248-4797   TDD: (615) 248-8828
E-mail: ap@hearingbridges.org
Web: hearingbridges.org/scholarships

Summary To provide financial assistance to hearing impaired high school seniors who want to attend college.

Eligibility This program is open to high school seniors who have severe to profound bilateral hearing loss and a GPA of 3.0 or higher. Applicants must be planning to enroll full time at a college, university, junior college, or technical school. Along with their application, they must submit brief essays on what a college education means to them, their goals after graduating from college, why they are a good candidate for this scholarship, and a difficult situation in their life and how they handled it. Selection is based on those essays, academic performance, extracurricular activities, an audiology report, and letters of recommendation. U.S. citizenship is required.

Financial data The stipend is $1,000 per year. Payment is made directly to the recipient's college, university, or school.

Duration 1 year; may be renewed up to 3 additional years, provided the recipient maintains a GPA of 3.0 or higher.

Additional data This program was established in 1986 when the sponsor was named EAR Foundation.

Number awarded 1 each year.

Deadline March of each year.

[602]
OPTIMIST INTERNATIONAL COMMUNICATION CONTEST FOR THE DEAF AND HARD OF HEARING

Optimist International
Attn: Programs Department
4494 Lindell Boulevard
St. Louis, MO 63108
(314) 371-6000   Toll Free: (800) 500-8130, ext. 235
Fax: (314) 371-6006   E-mail: programs@optimist.org
Web: optimist.org/e/member/scholarships2.cfm

Summary To recognize and reward, with college scholarships, outstanding presentations made by hearing impaired high school students.

Eligibility This program is open to young people up to and including grade 12 in the United States and Canada, to CEGEP in Québec, and to grade 13 in the Caribbean. Applicants must be identified by a qualified audiologist as deaf or hard of hearing with a hearing loss of 40 decibels or more. They are invited to make a presentation (using oral communication, sign language, or a combination of both) from 4 to 5 minutes on a topic that changes annually; a recent topic was "How my Optimism Helps me Overcome Obstacles." Competition is first conducted at the level of individual clubs, with winners advancing to zone and then district competitions. Selection is based on material organization (40 points), delivery and presentation (30 points), and overall effectiveness (30 points).

Financial data Each district winner receives a $2,500 college scholarship, payable to an educational institution of the recipient's choice, subject to the approval of Optimist International.

Duration The competition is held annually.

Additional data Entry information is available only from local Optimist Clubs.

Number awarded Nearly 300 Optimist International clubs participate in this program each year. Each participating district offers 1 scholarship; some districts may offer a second award with separate competitions for signing and oral competitors, or for male and female entrants.

Deadline Each club sets its own deadline. Districts must submit materials to the national office by June of each year.

[603]
SCHOLARSHIP TRUST FOR THE HEARING IMPAIRED

Travelers Protective Association of America
Attn: TPA Scholarship Trust for the Hearing Impaired
3755 Lindell Boulevard
St. Louis, MO 63108-3476
(314) 371-0533   Fax: (314) 371-0537
E-mail: support@tpahq.org
Web: www.tpahq.org/scholarshiptrust.html

Summary To provide assistance to deaf and hearing impaired persons interested in obtaining additional education, mechanical devices, specialized medical treatment, or other treatments.

Eligibility This assistance is available to U.S. residents who are deaf or hearing impaired. Applicants must be able to demonstrate that they will benefit from special programs, services, or other activities for the deaf, but that they are unable to provide the necessary funds.

Financial data The amount of the grant depends on the need of the recipient.

Duration 1 year; recipients may reapply.

Additional data This fund was established in 1975. Support has been provided to children as young as 2 months and to adults as old as 82 years. Funds have been used for mechanical devices, tuition at schools that specialize in educating the deaf (e.g., Gallaudet University, Rochester Institute of Technology, Central Institute for the Deaf), note takers and interpreters in classes in regular schools that do not provide those services to the deaf, speech and language therapy (especially for those who have had the cochlear implant), medical or other specialized treatments, and computer programs that assist the deaf and their families learn and apply skills presented in the classroom.

Number awarded Varies each year; since the trust was established, it has distributed more than $1.7 million to more than 4,100 recipients.

Deadline February of each year.

[604]
SCHOOL-AGE FINANCIAL AID PROGRAM

Alexander Graham Bell Association for the Deaf and
   Hard of Hearing
Attn: Financial Aid Coordinator
3417 Volta Place, N.W.
Washington, DC 20007-2778
(202) 337-5220   Fax: (202) 337-8314
TDD: (202) 337-5221   E-mail: financialaid@agbell.org
Web: nc.agbell.org/page.aspx?pid=491

Summary To provide financial aid to students at private schools who have a moderate to profound hearing loss.

Eligibility This program is open to students between 6 and 21 years of age who have been accepted or are enrolled full time at an independent, private, or parochial elementary, junior high, or high school for students with normal hearing (public school, home school, and college students are not eligible). Applicants must have been moderately to profoundly hearing impaired since prior to

their fourth birthday and must use spoken language as their primary form of communication. Their family must be able to demonstrate financial need. Membership in the Alexander Graham Bell Association is not required, but preference is given to members.

Financial data The amount of the award depends on the needs of the child; generally, awards range from $500 to $1,500 per year. Funds may be used for tuition, room and board, books, equipment, auditory and speech language support services, academic tutoring, transportation, and other school-related expenses.

Duration 1 year; may be renewed upon reapplication.

Number awarded Varies each year; recently, 135 students received $80,900 in support from this program.

Deadline May of each year.

[605]
SERTOMA SCHOLARSHIPS FOR HARD OF HEARING OR DEAF STUDENTS

Sertoma International
Attn: Director of Finance and Administration
1912 East Meyer Boulevard
Kansas City, MO 64132-1174
(816) 333-8300, ext. 214   Fax: (816) 333-4320
TDD: (816) 333-8300
E-mail: infosertoma@sertomahq.org
Web: www.sertoma.org/Scholarships

Summary To provide financial assistance for college to hearing impaired students.

Eligibility This program is open to students who have a minimum 40dB bilateral hearing loss and are interested in working full time on a bachelor's degree at a 4-year college or university in the United States. Students working on a graduate degree, community college degree, associate degree, or vocational program degree are ineligible. Applicants must have a GPA of 3.2 or higher. Along with their application, they must submit a statement of purpose on how this scholarship will help them achieve their goals. U.S. citizenship is required. Selection is based on academic achievement, honors and awards received, community volunteer activities, interscholastic activities, extracurricular activities, and 2 letters of recommendation.

Financial data The stipend is $1,000 per year.

Duration 1 year; may be renewed up to 4 times.

Additional data Sertoma, which stands for SERvice TO MAnkind, is a volunteer service organization with 25,000 members in 800 clubs across North America. Funding for this program is provided by Oticon, Inc. and the Sertoma Foundation.

Number awarded 20 each year.

Deadline April of each year.

[606]
TEXAS BLIND/DEAF STUDENT EXEMPTION PROGRAM

Texas Higher Education Coordinating Board
Attn: Grants and Special Programs
1200 East Anderson Lane
P.O. Box 12788
Austin, TX 78711-2788
(512) 427-6340   Toll Free: (800) 242-3062
Fax: (512) 427-6420
E-mail: grantinfo@thecb.state.tx.us
Web: www.collegeforalltexans.com

Summary   To provide a tuition exemption to blind and/or deaf residents of Texas.

Eligibility   This program is open to Texas residents who can present certification from the Department of Assistive and Rehabilitative Services of their deafness or blindness. Applicants must present to the registrar of a public college or university in Texas a copy of their high school transcript, a letter of recommendation, proof that they have met all admission requirements, and a statement of purpose that indicates the certificate, degree program, or professional enhancement that they intend to pursue.

Financial data   Eligible students are exempted from the payment of all dues, fees, and tuition charges at publicly-supported colleges and universities in Texas.

Duration   Up to 8 semesters.

Number awarded   Varies each year; recently, nearly 3,500 students received support through this program.

Deadline   Deadline not specified.

[607]
WISCONSIN HEARING AND VISUALLY HANDICAPPED STUDENT GRANT PROGRAM

Wisconsin Higher Educational Aids Board
131 West Wilson Street, Suite 902
P.O. Box 7885
Madison, WI 53707-7885
(608) 266-0888   Fax: (608) 267-2808
E-mail: cindy.cooley@wisconsin.gov
Web: heab.state.wi.us/programs.html

Summary   To provide funding for undergraduate study to Wisconsin residents who are legally deaf or blind.

Eligibility   This program is open to Wisconsin residents who can submit evidence of a severe or profound hearing or visual impairment certified by a medical examiner. Applicants must be enrolled at least half time at a branch of the University of Wisconsin, a technical college in the state, a Wisconsin independent college or university, a tribal college in the state, or an institution out of state that specializes in the training of deaf, hard of hearing, or visually handicapped students or that offers a program of study not offered by a Wisconsin institution. Financial need is considered in the selection process.

Financial data   Grants range from $250 to $1,800.

Duration   1 year; may be renewed up to 4 additional years.

Number awarded   Varies each year.

Deadline   Deadline not specified.

Fellowships

[608]
ALAN B., '32, AND FLORENCE B., '35, CRAMMATTE FELLOWSHIP

Gallaudet University Alumni Association
Attn: Graduate Fellowship Fund Committee
Peikoff Alumni House
Gallaudet University
800 Florida Avenue, N.E.
Washington, DC 20002-3695
(202) 651-5060   Fax: (202) 651-5062
TDD: (202) 651-5060
E-mail: alumni.relations@gallaudet.edu
Web: www.gallaudet.edu/gff_info.xml

Summary   To provide funding to deaf students who wish to work on a graduate degree in a field related to business at universities for people who hear normally.

Eligibility   This program is open to deaf and hard of hearing graduates of Gallaudet University or other accredited academic institutions who have been accepted for graduate study in a business-related field at colleges or universities for people who hear normally. Applicants must be working full time on a doctorate or other terminal degree. Need is considered in the selection process.

Financial data   The amount awarded varies, depending upon the recipient's needs and the availability of funds.

Duration   1 year; may be renewed.

Additional data   This fund is 1 of 12 designated funds included in the Graduate Fellowship Fund of the Gallaudet University Alumni Association.

Number awarded   Up to 1 each year.

Deadline   April of each year.

[609]
ALPHA SIGMA PI FRATERNITY FELLOWSHIP

Gallaudet University Alumni Association
Attn: Graduate Fellowship Fund Committee
Peikoff Alumni House
Gallaudet University
800 Florida Avenue, N.E.
Washington, DC 20002-3695
(202) 651-5060   Fax: (202) 651-5062
TDD: (202) 651-5060
E-mail: alumni.relations@gallaudet.edu
Web: www.gallaudet.edu/gff_info.xml

Summary   To provide financial assistance to deaf students who wish to work on a doctoral degree at universities for people who hear normally.

Eligibility   This program is open to deaf and hard of hearing graduates of Gallaudet University or other accredited colleges or universities who have been accepted for graduate study at academic institutions for people who hear normally. Applicants must be working full time on a doctorate or other terminal degree. Preference is given to alumni members of Alpha Sigma Pi Fraternity. Financial need is considered in the selection process.

Financial data The amount awarded varies, depending upon the recipients needs and the availability of funds.

Duration 1 year; may be renewed.

Additional data This program was established in 1999 as 1 of 12 designated funds within the Graduate Fellowship Fund of the Gallaudet University Alumni Association.

Number awarded Up to 1 each year.

Deadline April of each year.

[610]
ANNA AND HENRY PLAPINGER AWARD

Jewish Deaf Congress
Attn: President
6108 Gist Avenue
Baltimore, MD 21215
E-mail: phil@jewishdeafcongress.org
Web: www.jewishdeafcongress.org/jdchonors/index.html

Summary To recognize Jewish people who are deaf or hard of hearing.

Eligibility This award is available to Jewish deaf or hard of hearing individuals. Applicants must have demonstrated outstanding service to the Jewish deaf community for at least 5 years.

Financial data The amount of the award varies.

Duration The award is presented biennially.

Additional data This award was established in 1976.

Deadline Deadline not specified.

[611]
DORIS BALLANCE ORMAN, '25, FELLOWSHIP

Gallaudet University Alumni Association
Attn: Graduate Fellowship Fund Committee
Peikoff Alumni House
Gallaudet University
800 Florida Avenue, N.E.
Washington, DC 20002-3695
(202) 651-5060   Fax: (202) 651-5062
TDD: (202) 651-5060
E-mail: alumni.relations@gallaudet.edu
Web: www.gallaudet.edu/gff_info.xml

Summary To provide financial assistance to deaf women who wish to work on a graduate degree at universities for people who hear normally.

Eligibility This program is open to deaf or hard of hearing women graduates of Gallaudet University or other accredited academic institutions who have been accepted for graduate study at colleges or universities for people who hear normally. Applicants must be working full time on a doctorate or other terminal degree. They must have a particular interest in the arts, the humanities, or community leadership. Need is considered in the selection process.

Financial data The amount awarded varies, depending upon the recipient's needs and the availability of funds.

Duration 1 year; may be renewed.

Additional data This program is 1 of 12 designated funds within the Graduate Fellowship Fund of the Gallaudet University Alumni Association.

Number awarded Up to 1 each year.

Deadline April of each year.

[612]
GALLAUDET UNIVERSITY ALUMNI ASSOCIATION GRADUATE FELLOWSHIP FUND

Gallaudet University Alumni Association
Attn: Graduate Fellowship Fund Committee
Peikoff Alumni House
Gallaudet University
800 Florida Avenue, N.E.
Washington, DC 20002-3695
(202) 651-5060   Fax: (202) 651-5062
TDD: (202) 651-5060
E-mail: alumni.relations@gallaudet.edu
Web: www.gallaudet.edu/gff_info.xml

Summary To provide financial assistance to deaf students who wish to work on a graduate degree at universities for people who hear normally.

Eligibility This program is open to deaf and hard of hearing graduates of Gallaudet University or other accredited academic institutions who have been accepted for graduate study at colleges or universities for people who hear normally. Applicants must be working full time on a doctoral or other terminal degree. Financial need is considered in the selection process.

Financial data The amount awarded varies, depending upon the number of qualified candidates applying for assistance, the availability of funds, and the needs of individual applicants.

Duration 1 year; may be renewed.

Additional data This program includes the following named fellowships: the Boyce R. Williams, '32; Fellowship; the David Peikoff, '29 Fellowship; the James N. Orman, '23, Fellowship; the John A. Trundle, 1885, Fellowship; the Old Dominion Foundation Fellowship; the Waldo T., '49 and Jean Kelsch, '51, Cordano Fellowship; and the I. King Jordan, '70 Fellowship. Recipients must carry a full-time semester load.

Number awarded Varies each year.

Deadline April of each year.

[613]
GALLAUDET UNIVERSITY PRESIDENT'S FELLOWSHIP PROGRAM

Gallaudet University
Attn: Dean of the College of Liberal Arts, Sciences, and Technologies
HMB S242
800 Florida Avenue, N.E.
Washington, DC 20002
(202) 651-5224   Fax: (202) 448-6949
E-mail: Rebecca.Hogan@gallaudet.edu
Web: www.gallaudet.edu

Summary   To provide support to hearing impaired doctoral students interested in a teaching assistantship at Gallaudet University while they complete work on their degree.

Eligibility   This program is open to deaf and hard of hearing full-time graduate students working on a Ph.D. or other terminal degree at a university in the United States other than Gallaudet. Applicants must be able and willing to serve as a teaching assistant at Gallaudet while they complete work on their degree. They must already possess sign skills at an appropriate level and aspire to a teaching and research career. Fields of study vary each year; recently, they were education and mathematics and computer science.

Financial data   Grants provide up to $18,000 per year for tuition; an annual stipend (amount not specified) in return for teaching duties; academic privileges, such as library, WLRC, and e-mail access; and some travel support for professional conferences.

Duration   1 year; renewable up to 4 more years.

Additional data   This program was established in 2003. The program does not guarantee future employment at Gallaudet, but does require a 2-year commitment to teaching at the university if a faculty vacancy occurs. During their tenure at Gallaudet, fellows are expected to 1) serve as teaching assistants in appropriate departments and teach up to 2 courses per semester; 2) attend faculty development mentoring activities; 3) maintain good standing in their graduate program; and 4) make timely progress toward their degree.

Number awarded   Up to 5 each year.

Deadline   May of each year.

[614]
GEORGE H. NOFER SCHOLARSHIP

Alexander Graham Bell Association for the Deaf and
   Hard of Hearing
Attn: Financial Aid Coordinator
3417 Volta Place, N.W.
Washington, DC 20007-2778
(202) 337-5220   Fax: (202) 337-8314
TDD: (202) 337-5221   E-mail: financialaid@agbell.org
Web: nc.agbell.org/page.aspx?pid=492

Summary   To provide financial assistance to graduate students in public policy or law who have moderate to profound hearing loss.

Eligibility   This program is open to 1) graduate students working on a master's or doctoral degree in public policy; and 2) students accepted at an accredited law school. Applicants must have been diagnosed with a moderate to profound bilateral hearing loss prior to their fourth birthday and be committed to using spoken language as their primary mode of communication. They must be accepted or enrolled at a mainstream college or university as a full-time student and have an undergraduate GPA of 3.0 or higher. Along with their application, they must submit a 2-page essay discussing their career goals, including extra-curricular activity involvement, financial situation, their use of listening and spoken language, and the impact on them

of hearing loss. Need is considered in the selection process.

Financial data   The stipend is $5,000 per year.

Duration   1 year; may be renewed 2 additional years if the recipient maintains a GPA of 3.0 or higher.

Number awarded   Up to 3 each year.

Deadline   April of each year.

[615]
HENRY SYLE MEMORIAL FELLOWSHIP FOR SEMINARY STUDIES

Gallaudet University Alumni Association
Attn: Graduate Fellowship Fund Committee
Peikoff Alumni House
Gallaudet University
800 Florida Avenue, N.E.
Washington, DC 20002-3695
(202) 651-5060   Fax: (202) 651-5062
TDD: (202) 651-5060
E-mail: alumni.relations@gallaudet.edu
Web: www.gallaudet.edu/gff_info.xml

Summary   To provide financial assistance to deaf students who wish to pursue seminary studies at universities for people who hear normally.

Eligibility   This program is open to deaf and hard of hearing graduates of Gallaudet University or other accredited academic institutions who have been accepted for graduate seminary study at colleges or universities for people who hear normally. Applicants must be working full time on a doctoral or other terminal degree. Financial need is considered in the selection process.

Financial data   The amount awarded depends on the recipient's needs and the availability of funds.

Duration   1 year; may be renewed.

Additional data   This fund was established in 1990 as 1 of 12 designated funds within the Graduate Fellowship Fund of the Gallaudet University Alumni Association.

Number awarded   1 each year.

Deadline   April of each year.

[616]
HOLLY ELLIOTT AND LAUREL GLASS SCHOLARSHIP ENDOWMENT

United Methodist Higher Education Foundation
Attn: Scholarships Administrator
60 Music Square East, Suite 350
P.O. Box 340005
Nashville, TN 37203-0005
(615) 649-3990   Toll Free: (800) 811-8110
Fax: (615) 649-3980
E-mail: umhefscholarships@umhef.org
Web: www.umhef.org/receive.php

Summary   To provide financial assistance to students at United Methodist seminaries who are deaf or deaf-blind.

Eligibility   This program is open to students enrolled full time at United Methodist theological schools who are culturally deaf, orally deaf, deafened, late deafened, deaf-blind, or hard of hearing. Applicants must have a GPA of 3.0 or higher and be preparing for specialized ministries in the church, including (but not limited to) those wishing to become ordained. They must have been active, full members of a United Methodist Church for at least 1 year prior to applying. Financial need and U.S. citizenship or permanent resident status are required.

Financial data The stipend is at least $1,000 per year.

Duration 1 year; nonrenewable.

Additional data This program was established in 2004.

Number awarded 1 each year.

Deadline February of each year.

[617]
IADES FELLOWSHIP AWARD

International Alumnae of Delta Epsilon Sorority
c/o Virginia Borggaard
2453 Bear Den Road
Frederick, MD 21701-9321
Fax: (301) 663-3231   TDD: (301) 663-9235
E-mail: vborggaard@juno.com

Summary To provide financial assistance to deaf women who are working on a doctoral degree.

Eligibility This program is open to deaf women who have completed 12 or more units in a doctoral-level program and have a GPA of 3.0 or more. They need not be members of Delta Epsilon. Along with their application, they must submit official transcripts, a recent copy of their audiogram, and 2 letters of recommendation.

Financial data The stipend is $2,000.

Duration 1 year.

Number awarded 1 or more each year.

Deadline September of each year.

[618]
LOUISE TUMARKIN ZAZOVE SCHOLARSHIPS

Louise Tumarkin Zazove Foundation
c/o Phillip Zazove
2903 Craig Road
Ann Arbor, MI 48103
E-mail: phillip@ltzfoundation.org
Web: www.ltzfoundation.org/scholarships.php

Summary To provide financial assistance for college (and possibly for high school or graduate school) to people with hearing loss.

Eligibility This program is open to U.S. citizens and permanent residents who have a significant bilateral hearing loss. Strong preference is given to undergraduate students, but support may be provided for graduate school or high school tuition in certain situations. Applicants must submit a transcript of high school and/or college grades, 3 recommendations, documentation of the severity of the hearing loss, information on any special circumstances by or about the family, and documented financial need.

Financial data A stipend is awarded (amount not specified). Funds are paid directly to schools.

Duration 1 year; may be renewed up to 3 additional years, provided the recipient continues to do well in school and demonstrate financial need.

Additional data This program was established in 2003.

Number awarded Varies each year; since the program was established, it has awarded 19 scholarships.

Deadline May of each year.

[619]
MARYLAND STATE GRANGE DEAF SCHOLARSHIP

Maryland State Grange
c/o Theresa Myrdon, Deaf Activities
14935 Athey Road
Burtonsville, MD 20866
(301) 421-0958   E-mail: tmyrdon@yahoo.com

Summary To provide financial assistance for college or graduate school to Maryland residents who are either deaf or preparing to work with hearing impaired people.

Eligibility This program is open to seniors graduating from high schools in Maryland and to graduates of those high schools who are attending or planning to attend college or graduate school in the state. Applicants must be 1) deaf or hearing impaired, or 2) preparing for a career working with deaf or hearing impaired people.

Financial data A stipend is awarded (amount not specified).

Duration 1 year; may be renewed if the recipient maintains a GPA of 3.0 or higher.

Number awarded 1 or more each year.

Deadline May of each year.

[620]
REGINA OLSON HUGHES, '18, FELLOWSHIP

Gallaudet University Alumni Association
Attn: Graduate Fellowship Fund Committee
Peikoff Alumni House
Gallaudet University
800 Florida Avenue, N.E.
Washington, DC 20002-3695
(202) 651-5060   Fax: (202) 651-5062
TDD: (202) 651-5060
E-mail: alumni.relations@gallaudet.edu
Web: www.gallaudet.edu/gff_info.xml

Summary To provide financial assistance to deaf students who wish to work on a graduate degree in fine arts at universities for people who hear normally.

Eligibility This program is open to deaf and hard of hearing graduates of Gallaudet University or other accredited academic institutions who have been accepted for graduate study in fine arts at colleges or universities for people who hear normally. Applicants must be working full time on a doctoral or other terminal degree. Financial need is considered in the selection process.

Financial data The amount awarded depends on the recipient's needs and the availability of funds.

Duration 1 year; may be renewed.

Additional data This program, established in 1995, is 1 of 12 designated funds within the Graduate Fellowship Fund of the Gallaudet University Alumni Association.

Number awarded Up to 1 each year.

Deadline April of each year.

Grants-in-Aid

[621]
ALABAMA PERSONAL PROPERTY TAX EXEMPTION FOR THE DEAF

Alabama Department of Revenue
Attn: Property Tax Division
Gordon Persons Building
50 North Ripley Street, Room 4126
P.O. Box 327210
Montgomery, AL 36132-7210
(334) 242-1525
Web: www.ador.state.al.us

Summary   To exempt deaf residents of Alabama from taxation on a portion of their personal property.

Eligibility   Residents of Alabama are eligible for this personal property tax exemption if they are legally defined as "deaf mutes and insane persons."

Financial data   Up to $3,000 of personal property is exempt from taxation.

Duration   1 year; this exemption will be granted as long as the resident continues to meet the eligibility requirements.

Number awarded   Varies each year.

Deadline   Deadline not specified.

[622]
ALEXANDER GRAHAM BELL ASSOCIATION PARENT-INFANT FINANCIAL AID PROGRAM

Alexander Graham Bell Association for the Deaf and
   Hard of Hearing
Attn: Financial Aid Coordinator
3417 Volta Place, N.W.
Washington, DC 20007-2778
(202) 337-5220   Fax: (202) 337-8314
TDD: (202) 337-5221   E-mail: financialaid@agbell.org
Web: nc.agbell.org/page.aspx?pid=499

Summary   To provide financial aid to the parents of young children with moderate to profound hearing loss who need assistance to cover expenses associated with early intervention services.

Eligibility   Applicants must be parents or guardians of children less than 3 years of age who have been diagnosed as having a moderate to profound bilateral hearing loss or auditory neuropathy. Children with cochlear implants are eligible, but those with unilateral hearing loss are not. Spoken communication must be the child's primary mode of communication. The family must be able to demonstrate financial need. Residents of Canada, the United States, and its territories are eligible.

Financial data   The amount awarded depends on the needs of the child; most awards range from $300 to $2,000 per year.

Duration   1 year.

Number awarded   Varies each year.

Deadline   September of each year.

[623]
FORD MOBILITY MOTORING PROGRAM

Ford Motor Company
Attn: Mobility Program
500 Hulet Drive
P.O. Box 529
Bloomfield Hills, MI 48303
Toll Free: (800) 952-2248, ext. 111
Fax: (248) 333-0300
TDD: (800) 833-0312
E-mail: Mobilitymotoring@Fordprogramhq.com
Web: www.mobilitymotoringprogram.com

Summary   To provide a cash reimbursement for the cost of installing adaptive driving aids on new vehicles from Ford or Lincoln-Mercury.

Eligibility   Eligible for this rebate are people who purchase or lease new Ford, Lincoln, or Mercury vehicles that require adaptive driving aids or conversion equipment for users with disabilities.

Financial data   Up to $1,200 is reimbursed for adaptive equipment or up to $200 for alert hearing devices, lumbar support, or running boards.

Additional data   The program also provides 24-hour roadside assistance.

Number awarded   Varies each year.

Deadline   Applicants have 12 months from the date or purchase or lease to initiate the adaptive work and 1 year from that date to process their claim.

[624]
HAWAII INCOME TAX EXEMPTION FOR DISABLED RESIDENTS

Department of Taxation
Attn: Taxpayer Services Branch
425 Queen Street
P.O. Box 259
Honolulu, HI 96809-0259
(808) 587-4242   Toll Free: (800) 222-3229
Fax: (808) 587-1488   TDD: (808) 587-1418
Web: hawaii.gov/tax

Summary   To exempt a portion of the income of blind, deaf, and other disabled residents from state income tax in Hawaii.

Eligibility   Eligible for this exemption are 1) blind residents whose central visual acuity does not exceed 20/200 in the better eye with corrective lenses or whose visual acuity is greater than 20/200 but is accompanied by a limitation in the field of vision such that the widest diameter of the visual field subtends an angle no greater than 20 degrees; 2) deaf residents whose average loss in the speech frequencies in the better ear is 82 decibels A.S.A. or worse; or 3) totally disabled residents (physically or mentally) who are unable to engage in any substantial gainful business or occupation (a person whose gross income exceeds $30,000 per year is assumed to be engaged in a substantial gainful business or occupation).

Financial data   The maximum exemptions from state income tax are as follows: single disabled resident, $7,000; disabled husband and wife, $14,000; disabled husband or wife, with non-disabled spouse under 65, $8,040; disabled husband or wife, with non-disabled spouse 65 years of age or older, $9,080.

Duration The exemption continues as long as the recipient resides in Hawaii.

Additional data Residents who claim this special exemption are not eligible to claim additional exemptions for their children or other dependents.

Deadline Deadline not specified.

[625]
HIKE FUND GRANTS

The HIKE Fund, Inc.
c/o Shirley Terrill, Executive Secretary
10115 Cherryhill Place
Spring Hill, FL 34608-7116
(352) 688-2579   Fax: (352) 688-2579
E-mail: ceterrill1@aol.com
Web: www.thehikefund.org

Summary To provide funding to children with a hearing loss who need assistance to purchase a hearing aid or other device.

Eligibility This assistance is available to children under 20 years of age. Applicants must have been identified as 1) having a need for a hearing aid or other assistive listening device, and 2) having financial need. Selection is based on family income, size of household, other medical expenses for the applicant, and the cost of the hearing technology requested.

Financial data Grants depend on the need of the family and the price indicated in the prescription accompanying the application.

Duration These are 1-time grants.

Additional data The HIKE Fund, which stands for Hearing Impaired Kids Endowment, was established by Job's Daughters International in 1986. Girls who are members of that organization continue to support the program with fund-raising activities.

Number awarded Varies each year; recently 90 of these grants, totaling $226,185.44, were awarded.

Deadline Applications may be submitted at any time.

[626]
KANSAS STATE DEAF-BLIND FUND

Kansas State Department of Education
Special Education Services
Attn: Kansas State Deaf-Blind Fund
120 S.E. Tenth Avenue
Topeka, KS 66612-1182
(785) 296-2515   Toll Free: (800) 203-9462
Fax: (785) 296-6715   TDD: (785) 296-2515
E-mail: jhoughton@ksde.org
Web: www.ksde.org/Default.aspx?tabid=2322

Summary To provide supplementary financial assistance to deaf-blind or severely disabled students in Kansas.

Eligibility Applications may be submitted by school personnel for students in Kansas (up to the age of 21) who are deaf-blind and/or have severe multiple disabilities.

Approval for funding is granted on a first-come, first-served basis for the following areas: 1) assistive technology that enables a student with dual sensory impairments and with severe disabilities to participate more fully in an educational program (e.g., computers, adaptive equipment, eyeglasses, hearing aids, computer peripherals, augmentative communication devices, microswitches, software); 2) consultation; 3) evaluation for the cost of vision and/or hearing evaluations for students who are suspected of being deaf-blind, or a vision, hearing, or educational evaluation for recertification purposes; or 4) other costs associated with additional items or expenses that reflect best educational or effective practices, such as expenses involved in providing community activities. Applicants must provide documentation that other funding sources have been approached and that costs do not exceed the amount local education agencies are able to provide out of federal, state, or local funds. Priority candidates are students who have current deaf-blind certification, deaf-blind children from birth through 2 years of age, students who are exiting state hospital schools and returning to their home district, students who have a suspected vision loss and documented hearing loss and are in need of an evaluation, and students who have a suspected hearing loss and documented vision loss and are in need of an evaluation.

Financial data Eligible students are awarded up to $3,000 per year.

Duration 1 year; may be renewed.

Number awarded Varies each year; recently, 76 students received $108,160 in funding from this program. Grants provided $107,555 for assistive technology and $605 for consultants.

Deadline May of each year.

[627]
MICHIGAN INCOME TAX EXEMPTION FOR PEOPLE WITH DISABILITIES

Michigan Department of Treasury
Attn: Income Tax
Treasury Building
430 West Allegan Street
Lansing, MI 48922
(517) 373-3200   TDD: (800) 649-3777
E-mail: treasIndTax@michigan.gov
Web: www.michigan.gov/taxes

Summary To exempt a portion of the income of deaf, blind, and disabled residents of Michigan from state income taxation.

Eligibility Eligible for this exemption are residents of Michigan who 1) receive messages through a sense other than hearing, such as lip reading or sign language; 2) have vision in their better eye of 20/200 or less with corrective lenses or peripheral field of vision of 20 degrees or less; or 3) are hemiplegic, paraplegic, quadriplegic, or totally and permanently disabled.

Financial data Qualifying people with disabilities receive an exemption of $2,400 from their adjusted gross income for purposes of state taxation.

Duration The exemption continues as long as the recipient resides in Michigan.
Deadline Deadline not specified.

[628]
MOBILITY BY VOLVO

Volvo Cars of North America, LLC
Attn: Mobility by Volvo
1 Volvo Drive
Rockleigh, NJ 07647
Toll Free: (800) 803-5222   TDD: (800) 833-0312
E-mail: MobilitybyVolvo@Volvoprogramhq.com
Web: www.volvocars.us/mobility

Summary To provide a cash reimbursement for the cost of installing adaptive driving aids or alert hearing devices on new purchases of Volvo vehicles.
Eligibility This rebate is available to purchasers of new Volvo vehicles that require adaptive driving aids or alert hearing devices for users with disabilities. Applicants must obtain the equipment, have it installed, and submit a copy of their paid invoice and a copy of their medical prescription.
Financial data Up to $1,000 is provided for the cost of adding adaptive equipment or $200 for an alert hearing device.
Deadline Eligible vehicles must be upfitted with approved adaptive equipment or alert hearing devices, and requests must be submitted within 180 days of vehicle purchase.

[629]
NEW HAMPSHIRE DEAF PROPERTY TAX EXEMPTION

New Hampshire Department of Revenue
  Administration
109 Pleasant Street
Concord, NH 03301
(603) 271-2191   Fax: (603) 271-6121
TDD: (800) 735-2964
Web: revenue.nh.gov

Summary To provide deaf residents of New Hampshire with a partial exemption from real estate taxes.
Eligibility Residents of New Hampshire are covered by this program if they have lived in the state for at least 5 consecutive years, have suffered an average hearing loss of 71 Db in the better ear, own and occupy their primary residence in New Hampshire, and live in a municipality that has chosen through a referendum vote to grant an exemption to the legally deaf. Their income and assets may not exceed specified limits; the current income limit is $13,400 for single applicants or $20,400 for married applicants, and the current asset limit is $35,000, excluding the residence. Towns may set higher limits.
Financial data $15,000 of the value of the residential real estate is exempted from taxation for qualifying residents. Towns may exempt any amount they determine is appropriate to address significant increases in property values.

Duration 1 year; this exemption will be continued as long as the recipient meets the eligibility requirements.
Number awarded Varies each year; recently, 12 of these exemptions were granted, enabling deaf New Hampshire residents to save $12,760 in property taxes.
Deadline The original application for a permanent tax credit must be submitted by April.

[630]
NEW HAMPSHIRE PROPERTY TAX EXEMPTION FOR IMPROVEMENTS TO ASSIST THE DEAF

New Hampshire Department of Revenue
  Administration
109 Pleasant Street
Concord, NH 03301
(603) 271-2191   Fax: (603) 271-6121
TDD: (800) 735-2964
Web: revenue.nh.gov

Summary To exempt from real estate taxes improvements to assist deaf residents of New Hampshire.
Eligibility This program is open to residents of New Hampshire who own residential real estate where they reside and to which they have made improvements to assist a deaf person who also resides on such real estate.
Financial data The value of such improvements is deducted from the assessed value of the residential real estate.
Duration 1 year; this exemption will be continued as long as the recipient meets the eligibility requirements.
Number awarded Varies each year.
Deadline The original application for a permanent tax credit must be submitted by April.

[631]
PRESCHOOL FINANCIAL AID PROGRAM

Alexander Graham Bell Association for the Deaf and
  Hard of Hearing
Attn: Financial Aid Coordinator
3417 Volta Place, N.W.
Washington, DC 20007-2778
(202) 337-5220   Fax: (202) 337-8314
TDD: (202) 337-5221   E-mail: financialaid@agbell.org
Web: nc.agbell.org/page.aspx?pid=497

Summary To provide financial aid to the parents of preschool children with moderate to profound hearing loss who need assistance to cover expenses associated with early intervention services.
Eligibility Applicants must be parents or guardians of children between 4 and 6 years of age who have been diagnosed as having a moderate to profound bilateral hearing loss or auditory neuropathy. Children with cochlear implants are eligible, but those with unilateral hearing loss are not. Spoken communication must be the child's primary mode of communication. The family must be able to demonstrate financial need. Residents of Canada, the United States, and its territories are eligible.

Financial data The amount awarded depends on the needs of the child; most grants range from $275 to $1,100 per year.

Duration 1 year; may be renewed upon reapplication, but preference is given to new applicants who are just enrolling their child in preschool.

Number awarded Varies each year.

Deadline July of each year.

[632]
SCHOLARSHIP TRUST FOR THE HEARING IMPAIRED

Travelers Protective Association of America
Attn: TPA Scholarship Trust for the Hearing Impaired
3755 Lindell Boulevard
St. Louis, MO 63108-3476
(314) 371-0533   Fax: (314) 371-0537
E-mail: support@tpahq.org
Web: www.tpahq.org/scholarshiptrust.html

Summary To provide assistance to deaf and hearing impaired persons interested in obtaining additional education, mechanical devices, specialized medical treatment, or other treatments.

Eligibility This assistance is available to U.S. residents who are deaf or hearing impaired. Applicants must be able to demonstrate that they will benefit from special programs, services, or other activities for the deaf, but that they are unable to provide the necessary funds.

Financial data The amount of the grant depends on the need of the recipient.

Duration 1 year; recipients may reapply.

Additional data This fund was established in 1975. Support has been provided to children as young as 2 months and to adults as old as 82 years. Funds have been used for mechanical devices, tuition at schools that specialize in educating the deaf (e.g., Gallaudet University, Rochester Institute of Technology, Central Institute for the Deaf), note takers and interpreters in classes in regular schools that do not provide those services to the deaf, speech and language therapy (especially for those who have had the cochlear implant), medical or other specialized treatments, and computer programs that assist the deaf and their families learn and apply skills presented in the classroom.

Number awarded Varies each year; since the trust was established, it has distributed more than $1.7 million to more than 4,100 recipients.

Deadline February of each year.

[633]
SENTINELS OF FREEDOM SCHOLARSHIPS

Sentinels of Freedom
P.O. Box 1316
San Ramon, CA 94583
(925) 380-6342   Fax: (925) 867-1078
E-mail: info@sentinelsoffreedom.org
Web: www.sentinelsoffreedom.org

Summary To provide funding to veterans and current military personnel who became blind, deaf, or disabled as a result of injuries sustained in the line of duty on or after September 11, 2001.

Eligibility This program is open to members of the U.S. Air Force, Army, Coast Guard, Marines, or Navy who sustained injuries in the line of duty on or after September 11, 2001. Applicants must be rated as 60% or more disabled as a result of 1 or more of the following conditions: amputation, blindness, deafness, paraplegia, severe burns, limited traumatic brain injury (TBI), or limited post-traumatic stress disorder (PTSD); other severe injuries may be considered on a case-by-case basis. They must complete an interview process and demonstrate that they have the skills, experience, and attitude that lead to employment.

Financial data Assistance is available for the following needs: housing (adapted for physical needs if necessary), new furniture and other household supplies, career-placement assistance and training, new adaptive vehicles, educational opportunities in addition to the new GI Bill, or financial and personal mentorship.

Duration Assistance may be provided for up to 4 years.

Additional data The first assistance granted by this program was awarded in 2004.

Number awarded Varies each year. Since the program was established, it has supported 84 current and former service members.

Deadline Applications may be submitted at any time.

[634]
SUPPLEMENTAL SECURITY INCOME (SSI)

Social Security Administration
6401 Security Boulevard
Baltimore, MD 21235-0001
(410) 594-1234   Toll Free: (800) 772-1213
TDD: (800) 325-0778
Web: www.socialsecurity.gov/ssi/index.htm

Summary To provide monthly payments to disabled, blind, deaf, and elderly people who have limited income and resources.

Eligibility This assistance is available to U.S. citizens and certain categories of aliens who are 65 years of age or older, blind, or disabled. A person 18 years of age or older is considered disabled if a physical or mental impairment prevents him or her from doing any substantial gainful work and is expected to last for at least 12 months or to result in death. Children under the age of 18 are considered disabled if they have a physical or mental impairment that is comparable in severity to a disability that would prevent an adult from working and is expected to last at least 12 months or result in death. Children with certain conditions are automatically disabled and eligible for these benefits; the conditions include HIV infection, blindness, deafness, cerebral palsy, Down syndrome, muscular dystrophy, significant mental deficiency, diabetes (with amputation of 1 foot), amputation of 2 limbs, or amputation of leg at the hip. Regardless of age, a person whose vision is no better than 20/200 or who has a limited visual field of 20 degrees or less with the best corrective eyeglasses is considered blind; individuals with visual impairments not severe enough to meet the definition of blindness still may qualify as disabled persons. Applicants must have limited income and limited resources (less than $2,000 for an individual or $3,000 for a couple); items excluded from resources include the home used as a principal place of residence, personal and household goods, life insurance with face value of $1,500 or less, a car, burial plots for individuals and immediate family members, and burial funds up to $1,500.

Financial data The basic monthly payment is $698 for an eligible individual or $1,048 for an eligible individual with an eligible spouse. Many states add money to that basic payment. SSI recipients may also be eligible for food stamps and other nutrition programs.

Duration Assistance is provided as long as the recipient remains blind or disabled and in financial need.

Additional data Although SSI is administered through the Social Security Administration, it is not financed by Social Security taxes. Financing of SSI is provided through general funds of the U.S. Treasury. Recipients of SSI need not have been employed or paid Social Security taxes, but they may be eligible for both SSI and Social Security. Disabled and blind applicants for SSI are referred to their state vocational rehabilitation agency to determine their eligibility for a program of vocational rehabilitation. Disabled drug addicts or alcoholics are referred for appropriate treatment if it is available at an approved facility or institution.

Number awarded Recently, approximately 8,164,000 people (including 6,981,000 who were blind and disabled) were receiving SSI benefits, including 1,294,000 under 18 years of age, 4,806,000 who were 18 to 64 years of age, and 2,064,000 who were 65 or older.

Deadline Deadline not specified.

Physical/Orthopedic Disabilities

Scholarships •

Fellowships •

Grants-in-Aid •

Described here are 122 funding opportunities available to individuals with 1) a severe physical/orthopedic impairment caused by birth defects (e.g., absence of an extremity), diseases or disorders (e.g., multiple sclerosis), or other causes (e.g., accidents, amputations), or 2) a severe, chronic disability that was manifested before age 22 (for example, spina bifida and cerebral palsy). In all, 53 cover scholarships (funding to pursue study, research, or other activities on the undergraduate level in the United States); 17 describe fellowships (to support graduate or postgraduate study, research, or other activities in the United States); and 52 identify grants-in-aid (to pay for emergency situations, travel, income/property tax liabilities, the acquisition of assistive technology, or other personal needs). All of this is "free" money. Not one dollar will need to be repaid (provided, of course, that recipients meet all program requirements). If you are looking for a particular program and don't find it in this section, be sure to check the Program Title Index to see if it is covered elsewhere in the directory.

Scholarships

[635]
AMERIGLIDE ACHIEVER SCHOLARSHIP

AmeriGlide, Inc.
3901A Commerce Park Drive
Raleigh, NC 27610
Toll Free: (800) 790-1635   Fax: (800) 791-6524
E-mail: scholarship@ameriglide.com
Web: www.ameriglide.com/Scholarship

Summary   To provide financial assistance to college students who use a wheelchair.

Eligibility   This program is open to full-time students at 2- and 4-year colleges and universities who use a manual or electric wheelchair. Applicants must have completed at least 1 year of college and have a GPA of 3.0 or higher. They must be legal residents of the United States or have a valid student visa. Along with their application, they must submit a 500-word essay on topics that change annually; recently, students were invited to write on the area of their campus where accessibility could be improved.

Financial data   The stipend is $1,000.

Duration   1 year.

Additional data   This program was established in 2008.

Number awarded   2 each year.

Deadline   June of each year.

[636]
ANNE M. FASSETT SCHOLARSHIP

Southwest Florida Community Foundation
8771 College Parkway, Building 2, Suite 201
Fort Myers, FL 33919
(239) 274-5900   Fax: (239) 274-5930
Web: www.floridacommunity.com

Summary   To provide financial assistance to students who have a physical disability and use a wheelchair and are either high school seniors in designated Florida counties or attending college in the state.

Eligibility   This program is open to 1) seniors graduating from high schools in Charlotte, Collier, Glades, Hendry, or Lee counties in Florida; or 2) students enrolled or planning to enroll at a Florida state college, community college, or technical school. Applicants must have a physical disability and use a wheelchair. Financial need is considered in the selection process.

Financial data   The stipend varies each year.

Duration   1 year.

Additional data   This program was established in 2000.

Number awarded   Varies each year.

Deadline   February of each year.

[637]
ASSE DIVERSITY COMMITTEE SCHOLARSHIP

American Society of Safety Engineers
Attn: ASSE Foundation
1800 East Oakton Street
Des Plaines, IL 60018
(847) 768-3435   Fax: (847) 768-3434
E-mail: agabanski@asse.org
Web: www.asse.org

Summary   To provide funding to physically challenged and other diverse upper-division and graduate student members of the American Society of Safety Engineers (ASSE).

Eligibility   This program is open to ASSE student members who are working on an undergraduate or graduate degree in occupational safety, health, and environment or a closely-related field (e.g., industrial or environmental engineering, environmental science, industrial hygiene, occupational health nursing). Applicants must be full-time students who have completed at least 60 semester hours with a GPA of 3.0 or higher as undergraduates or at least 9 semester hours with a GPA of 3.5 or higher as graduate students. Along with their application, they must submit 2 essays of 300 words or less: 1) why they are seeking a degree in occupational safety and health or a closely-related field, a brief description of their current activities, and how those relate to their career goals and objectives; and 2) why they should be awarded this scholarship (including career goals and financial need). A goal of this program is to support individuals regardless of race, ethnicity, gender, religion, personal beliefs, age, sexual orientation, physical challenges, geographic location, university, or specific area of study. U.S. citizenship is not required.

Financial data   The stipend is $1,000 per year.

Duration   1 year; recipients may reapply.

Number awarded   1 each year.

Deadline   November of each year.

[638]
CANCER FOR COLLEGE SCHOLARSHIPS

Cancer for College
1345 Specialty Drive, Suite D
Vista, CA 92081
(760) 599-5096   E-mail: info@cancerforcollege.org
Web: www.cancerforcollege.org

Summary   To provide funding to college and graduate students who are cancer patients, survivors, or amputees.

Eligibility   This program is open to undergraduate and graduate students enrolled or planning to enroll at accredited colleges, universities, community colleges, and trade schools in the United States and Puerto Rico. Applicants must be a cancer patient, cancer survivor, and/or amputee. Along with a preliminary application, they must submit a brief statement on why they should receive further consideration for this scholarship and information on their financial situation. Preference is given to residents of California and students attending college in southern California.

Financial data Stipends are $4,000, $1,000, or $500.

Duration 1 year; some of the $4,000 scholarships (designated as Perpetual Scholarships) may be renewed up to 3 additional years.

Additional data This program was established in 1993. Perpetual Scholarship recipients must be willing to attend regional events associated with the program and be available for interviews and/or media coverage.

Number awarded Varies each year; recently, this program awarded 4 Perpetual Scholarships at $4,000 per year, 3 1-time scholarships at $4,000, 25 1-time scholarships at $1,000, and 6 1-time scholarships at $500.

Deadline Deadline not specified.

[639]
CHAIRSCHOLARS FOUNDATION NATIONAL SCHOLARSHIPS

ChairScholars Foundation, Inc.
16101 Carencia Lane
Odessa, FL 33556-3278
(813) 926-0544   Toll Free: (888) 926-0544
Fax: (813) 920-7661
E-mail: chairscholars@tampabay.rr.com
Web: www.chairscholars.org/national.html

Summary To provide financial assistance for college to physically challenged students.

Eligibility This program is open to high school seniors and college freshmen who have a significant physical challenge, although they are not required to be in a wheelchair. Applicants should be able to demonstrate financial need, have a GPA of 3.0 or higher, and show some form of community service or social contribution in the past. Along with their application, they must submit an essay of 300 to 500 words on how they became physically challenged, how their situation has affected them and their family, and their goals and aspirations for the future. Graduate students and all students over 21 years of age are not eligible.

Financial data Stipends range from $1,000 to $5,000 per year. The maximum total award is $20,000. Funds are to be used for tuition and school-related expenses.

Duration Up to 4 years for high school seniors; up to 3 years for college freshmen.

Additional data This program includes the Paul John "P.J." Zuker, Jr. Memorial Scholarship and the Pablo Aguilar, Jr. Memorial Scholarship.

Number awarded 15 to 20 each year.

Deadline February of each year.

[640]
CHILDREN'S BRITTLE BONE FOUNDATION AND OI FOUNDATION IMPACT GRANT PROGRAM

Children's Brittle Bone Foundation
Attn: Impact Grant Program
7701 95th Street
Pleasant Prairie, WI 53158
(773) 263-2223   Fax: (262) 947-0724
E-mail: info@cbbf.org
Web: www.cbbf.org/Impact_Grant.htm

Summary To provide funding for education or other purposes to people who have osteogenesis imperfecta (OI).

Eligibility This program is open to people who have OI and are seeking funding for equipment or services that will improve their quality of life. Examples of acceptable requests include education-related items such as tuition assistance at the preschool to postdoctoral level; prescribed exercise therapy equipment for physical or occupational therapy; orthotics, braces, and walkers; manual or electric wheelchairs or scooters; adaptive technology such as computers or hearing aids; dental intervention; vehicle modifications such as lifts or pedal extensions or vehicle purchases; travel reimbursement to receive specialized care; outdoor ramps that provide access to a home; or accessibility aides such as reachers, shower chairs, or kitchen carts.

Financial data Grants range from $500 to $20,000.

Duration Funds must be used within 12 months.

Additional data This program is provided jointly by the Children's Brittle Bone Foundation and the Osteogenesis Imperfecta (OI) Foundation.

Number awarded Varies; recently, 5 were awarded.

Deadline January of each year.

[641]
COLORADO-WYOMING CHAPTER MS SOCIETY SCHOLARSHIP PROGRAM

National Multiple Sclerosis Society-Colorado-Wyoming
   Chapter
900 South Broadway, Second Floor
Denver, CO 80209
(303) 698-7400   Toll Free: (800) 344-4867
Fax: (303) 698-7421
E-mail: COCreceptionist@nmss.org
Web: was.nationalmssociety.org

Summary To provide financial assistance to high school seniors and graduates from Colorado and Wyoming who have multiple sclerosis (MS) or have a parent with MS and are planning to attend college in any state.

Eligibility This program is open to graduating high school seniors, recent graduates, and GED recipients from Colorado and Wyoming who have MS or a parent who has MS. Applicants must be planning to enroll as an entering undergraduate student at a 2- or 4-year college, university, or vocational/technical school in the United States on at least a half-time basis. Along with their application, they must submit an essay on the impact MS has had on their lives. Selection is based on that essay, academic record, leadership and participation in school or community activities, work experience, goals and aspirations, an outside appraisal, special circumstances, and financial need. U.S. citizenship or permanent resident status is required.

Financial data The stipend is $1,000.

Duration 1 year.

Number awarded Varies each year; recently, 4 of these scholarships were awarded.

Deadline January of each year.

[642]
CONNECTICUT CHAPTER MS SOCIETY SCHOLARSHIP PROGRAM

National Multiple Sclerosis Society-Connecticut
Chapter
659 Tower Avenue, First Floor
Hartford, CT 06112-1269
(860) 913-2550   Toll Free: (800) 344-4867
Fax: (860) 714-2301
E-mail: programs@ctfightsMS.org
Web: was.nationalmssociety.org

Summary To provide financial assistance to high school seniors and graduates from Connecticut who have multiple sclerosis (MS) or have a parent with MS and are planning to attend college in any state.

Eligibility This program is open to graduating high school seniors, recent graduates, and GED recipients from Connecticut who have MS or a parent who has MS. Applicants must be planning to enroll as an entering undergraduate student at a 2- or 4-year college, university, or vocational/technical school in the United States on at least a half-time basis. Along with their application, they must submit an essay on the impact MS has had on their lives. Selection is based on that essay, academic record, leadership and participation in school or community activities, work experience, goals and aspirations, an outside appraisal, special circumstances, and financial need. U.S. citizenship or permanent resident status is required.

Financial data The stipend is $1,500.

Duration 1 year.

Additional data This program receives support from the Corn-Carter Family Scholarship Fund, the Jo-Ann Concilio Memorial Fund, and the Hayley's Hope and Michaela's Miracle MS Memorial Fund.

Number awarded Varies each year; recently, 10 of these scholarships were awarded.

Deadline January of each year.

[643]
CYNTHIA RUTH RUSSELL MEMORIAL GRANTS

Kansas Masonic Foundation, Inc.
2909 S.W. Maupin Lane
Topeka, KS 66614-5335
(785) 357-7646   Fax: (785) 357-7406
E-mail: kmf@kmfonline.org
Web: www.kmfonline.org/content/view/15/36

Summary To provide financial assistance to physically challenged Kansas residents attending a college or university in the state.

Eligibility This program is open to residents of Kansas who are physically challenged. Applicants must be attending or planning to attend an institution of higher education in the state as a full-time undergraduate or graduate student. Along with their application, they must submit a 300-word statement of their educational goals, a short autobiography that includes a discussion of their physical challenge, a list of extracurricular activities, their latest grade transcript, letters of reference, ACT and/or SAT scores, and documentation of financial need.

Financial data A stipend is awarded (amount not specified).

Duration 1 year; renewable, if the recipient remains enrolled full time and maintains a GPA of 2.5 or higher.

Number awarded 1 or more each year.

Deadline March of each year.

[644]
DELAWARE CHAPTER MS SOCIETY SCHOLARSHIP PROGRAM

National Multiple Sclerosis Society-Delaware Chapter
Two Mill Road, Suite 106
Wilmington, DE 19806
(302) 655-5610   Fax: (302) 655-0993
E-mail: kate.cowperthwait@nmss.org
Web: was.nationalmssociety.org

Summary To provide financial assistance to high school seniors and graduates from Delaware who have multiple sclerosis (MS) or have a parent with MS and are planning to attend college in any state.

Eligibility This program is open to graduating high school seniors, recent graduates, and GED recipients from Delaware who have MS or a parent who has MS. Applicants must be planning to enroll as a first-time student at a 2- or 4-year college, university, or vocational/technical school in the United States on at least a half-time basis. Along with their application, they must submit an essay on the impact MS has had on their lives. Selection is based on that essay, academic record, leadership and participation in school or community activities, work experience, goals and aspirations, an outside appraisal, special circumstances, and financial need. U.S. citizenship or permanent resident status is required.

Financial data A stipend is awarded (amount not specified).

Duration 1 year.

Number awarded Varies each year; recently, 9 of these scholarships were awarded.

Deadline January of each year.

[645]
EASTER SEALS SOUTH CAROLINA EDUCATIONAL SCHOLARSHIPS

Easter Seals South Carolina
Attn: Scholarship Program
3020 Farrow Road
P.O. Box 5715
Columbia, SC 29250
(803) 429-8474   Fax: (803) 356-6902
E-mail: TAdger@sc.easterseals.com
Web: sc.easterseals.com

Summary To provide financial assistance for college or graduate school to South Carolina students who have a mobility impairment.

Eligibility This program is open to South Carolina residents and students attending a college or university in the state who have a significant and medically certified mobility impairment. Applicants must be enrolled or planning to enroll in an undergraduate or graduate program. They must be able to demonstrate financial need. Preference is given to students carrying at least 9 credit hours and making satisfactory academic progress toward graduation.

Financial data The maximum stipend is $1,000.

Duration 1 year; may be renewed.

Additional data This program was established in 1985.

Number awarded 1 or more each year.

Deadline June of each year.

[646]
EASTERN AMPUTEE GOLF ASSOCIATION SCHOLARSHIP AWARD

Eastern Amputee Golf Association
Attn: Bob Buck, Executive Director
2015 Amherst Drive
Bethlehem, PA 18015-5606
Toll Free: (888) 868-0992   Fax: (610) 867-9295
E-mail: info@eaga.org
Web: www.eaga.org

Summary To provide financial assistance for college to members of the Eastern Amputee Golf Association (EAGA) and their families.

Eligibility This program is open to students who are residents of and/or currently enrolled or accepted for enrollment at a college or university in designated eastern states (Connecticut, Delaware, District of Columbia, Maine, Maryland, Massachusetts, New Hampshire, New Jersey, New York, Pennsylvania, Rhode Island, Vermont, Virginia, or West Virginia). Applicants must be amputee members of the association (those who have experienced the loss of 1 or more extremities at a major joint due to amputation or birth defect) or members of their families. Financial need is considered in the selection process.

Financial data The stipend is $1,000.

Duration 1 year; may be renewed if the recipient maintains a GPA of 2.0 or higher and continues to demonstrate financial need.

Additional data The EAGA was incorporated in 1987. It welcomes 2 types of members: amputee members and associate members (non-amputees who are interested in the organization and support its work but are not eligible for these scholarships). This program includes the following named scholarships: the Paul DesChamps Scholarship Award, the Tom Reed Scholarship, the Ray and Eileen Froncillo Scholarship, the Howard Taylor Scholarship, the Paul Leimkuehler Memorial Scholarship, the Thomas Armacost Memorial Scholarship, and the Sgt. Major William Wade Memorial Scholarship.

Number awarded Varies each year; recently, 16 of these scholarships were awarded.

Deadline June of each year.

[647]
FLORIDA CHAIRSCHOLARS PROGRAM

ChairScholars Foundation, Inc.
16101 Carencia Lane
Odessa, FL 33556-3278
(813) 926-0544   Toll Free: (888) 926-0544
Fax: (813) 920-7661
E-mail: chairscholars@tampabay.rr.com
Web: www.chairscholars.org/florida.html

Summary To provide funding to students in Florida with specified disabilities who plan to attend college in the state.

Eligibility This program is open to residents of Florida who are enrolled in grades 7-11 at a public school and have a serious physical disability. Qualifying disabilities include cerebral palsy, muscular dystrophy, spinal muscular atrophy, amputations, congenital missing or shortened limbs, multiple sclerosis, profound deafness, hearing impairments requiring FM modulator, blindness, various forms of cancer, any condition that permanently places the student in a wheelchair, or other illnesses, diseases, or conditions that severely impair mobility or motor skills. Applicants must have at least a "B" average and be able to demonstrate significant financial need (annual income less than $20,137 for a family of 1, rising to $69,616 for a family of 8). They must be planning to attend a college, university, community college, or vocational school in the state. Along with their application, they must submit a 1-page essay outlining how they became physically challenged, how their situation has affected them or their family, their family situation, things they like to do, why they need this scholarship, and their goals and dreams for the future.

Financial data The awards provide full payment of tuition at any public college, university, or community college, or vocational school in Florida.

Duration Up to 4 years.

Additional data This program began in 1996. Recipients are provided with a mentor until they graduate from high school. They must sign a "contract" pledging to remain drug and crime free.

Number awarded Varies each year; recently, 24 of these scholarships were awarded. Since the program was established, it has awarded 502 scholarships.

Deadline January of each year.

[648]
GREATER CAROLINAS CHAPTER MS SOCIETY SCHOLARSHIP PROGRAM

National Multiple Sclerosis Society-Greater Carolinas
  Chapter
9801-I Southern Pine Boulevard
Charlotte, NC 28273
(704) 525-2955   Fax: (704) 527-0406
E-mail: nct@nmss.org
Web: was.nationalmssociety.org

Summary To provide funding to high school seniors and graduates from South Carolina and parts of North Carolina who have multiple sclerosis (MS) or have a parent with MS and are planning to attend college in any state.

Eligibility This program is open to graduating high school seniors, recent graduates, and GED recipients from South Carolina and 82 counties of eastern and western North Carolina who have MS or a parent who has MS. Applicants must be planning to enroll as a first-time student at a 2- or 4-year college, university, or vocational/technical school in the United States on at least a half-time basis. Along with their application, they must submit an essay on the impact MS has had on their lives. Selection is based on that essay, academic record, leadership and participation in school or community activities, work experience, goals and aspirations, an outside appraisal, special circumstances, and financial need. U.S. citizenship or permanent resident status is required.

Financial data Stipends range up to $3,000.

Duration 1 year.

Additional data This program receives support from the Golden Corral Corporation.

Number awarded Varies each year; recently, 3 of these scholarships were awarded: 2 at $3,000 and 1 at $2,600.

Deadline January of each year.

[649]
GREATER NEW ENGLAND CHAPTER MS SOCIETY SCHOLARSHIP PROGRAM

National Multiple Sclerosis Society-Greater New
  England Chapter
101A First Avenue, Suite 6
Waltham, MA 02451-1115
(781) 890-4990   Fax: (781) 890-2089
E-mail: communications@mam.nmss.org
Web: was.nationalmssociety.org

Summary To provide financial assistance to high school seniors and graduates from designated New England states who have multiple sclerosis (MS) or have a parent with MS and are planning to attend college in any state.

Eligibility This program is open to graduating high school seniors, recent graduates, and GED recipients from Maine, Massachusetts, New Hampshire, or Vermont who have MS or a parent who has MS. Applicants must be planning to enroll as a first-time student at a 2- or 4-year college, university, or vocational/technical school in the United States on at least a half-time basis. Along with their application, they must submit an essay on the impact MS

has had on their lives. Selection is based on that essay, academic record, leadership and participation in school or community activities, work experience, goals and aspirations, an outside appraisal, special circumstances, and financial need. U.S. citizenship or permanent resident status is required.

Financial data The highest-ranked applicant receives a stipend of $3,000 per year. Other stipends range from $1,000 to $3,000.

Duration The award for the highest-ranked applicant is for 2 years. Other awards are 1 year and nonrenewable.

Additional data This program was established by the Massachusetts Chapter in 2003. In 2010, that chapter merged with the chapters in Maine, New Hampshire, and Vermont to form the Greater New England Chapter and the program became available to residents of those states.

Number awarded Varies each year; recently, 28 of these scholarships (total value of $55,000) were awarded.

Deadline January of each year.

[650]
GREATER NORTHWEST CHAPTER MS SOCIETY SCHOLARSHIP PROGRAM

National Multiple Sclerosis Society-Greater Northwest
  Chapter
192 Nickerson Street, Suite 100
Seattle, WA 98109
(206) 284-4254   Toll Free: (800) 344-4867
Fax: (206) 284-4972   E-mail: MSnorthwest@nmss.org
Web: was.nationalmssociety.org

Summary To provide financial assistance to high school seniors and graduates from Alaska, Montana, and Washington who have multiple sclerosis (MS) or have a parent with MS and are planning to attend college in any state as a first-time student.

Eligibility This program is open to graduating high school seniors, recent graduates, and GED recipients from Alaska, Montana, or Washington who have MS or a parent who has MS. Applicants must be planning to enroll as a first-time student at a 2- or 4-year college, university, or vocational/technical school in the United States on at least a half-time basis. Along with their application, they must submit an essay on the impact MS has had on their lives. Selection is based on that essay, academic record, leadership and participation in school or community activities, work experience, goals and aspirations, an outside appraisal, special circumstances, and financial need. U.S. citizenship or permanent resident status is required.

Financial data Stipends range from $1,500 to $3,000.

Duration 1 year.

Number awarded Varies each year; recently, 76 of these scholarships, worth $233,000, were awarded.

Deadline January of each year.

[651]
HIGHER EDUCATION ASSISTANCE PROGRAM SCHOLARSHIP

DREAM Institute
P.O. Box 52785
Tulsa, OK 74152-0785
(918) 660-3408   E-mail: dream@dreaminstitute.org
Web: www.dreaminstitute.org/Programs.htm

Summary To provide financial assistance to residents of Oklahoma who have a physical and/or learning disability and are interested in attending college in the state.

Eligibility This program is open to residents of Oklahoma who have been diagnosed with a physical and/or learning disability. Applicants must be enrolled or planning to enroll full time at a 2- or 4-year college or university in the state. They must be able to demonstrate financial need.

Financial data The stipend depends on the need of the recipient. Funds are available to help pay for tuition, fees, books, and dormitory fees.

Duration 1 year; may be renewed.

Additional data Scholars are invited to participate in an orientation workshop designed to equip them with the information they will require as a college student with a disability. They also qualify for special tutoring.

Number awarded Varies each year; recently, 3 new and 10 renewal scholarships were awarded.

Deadline April of each year.

[652]
ITALIAN CATHOLIC FEDERATION GIFTS OF LOVE FOR SPECIAL PEOPLE

Italian Catholic Federation
8393 Capwell Drive, Suite 110
Oakland, CA 94621
(510) 633-9058   Toll Free: (888) ICF-1924
Fax: (510) 633-9758   E-mail: info@icf.org
Web: www.icf.org/charitable.html

Summary To provide funding to individuals who have specific disabilities and need additional training or instruction.

Eligibility This program is open to 1) individuals who have a disability and desire formal training or instruction in a particular vocation, academic, athletic, or artistic field; 2) qualified instructors on behalf of an individual with a disability who exhibits a particular skill to be developed and who desires formal instruction or training; or 3) adults with custodial responsibility for, and on behalf of, an individual with a disability who exhibits a particular skill to be developed and who desires formal instruction or training. The program defines individuals with a disability as those who have mental retardation, hearing impairments, speech and language impairments, visual impairments, emotional disturbances, orthopedic impairments, autism, traumatic brain injury, other health impairments, specific learning disabilities, or multiple disabilities who, because of their needs, require special education or related services. Financial need is considered in the selection process.

Financial data A stipend is awarded (amount not specified).

Duration These are 1-time grants.

Number awarded Varies each year.

Deadline Deadline not specified.

[653]
JEAN DRISCOLL AWARD

Spina Bifida Association of Greater New England
Attn: Executive Director
219 East Main Street, Suite 100B
Milford, MA 01757
(508) 482-5300   Toll Free: (888) 479-1900
Fax: (508) 482-5301
E-mail: edugan@SBAGreaterNE.org
Web: www.sbagreaterne.org

Summary To provide funding for educational, developmental, or assistive programs to residents of New England who have spina bifida.

Eligibility This program is open to residents of New England who are 14 years of age or older and have spina bifida. Applicants must be seeking funding for educational, developmental, or assistive programs that will enable them to achieve their goals despite limitations imposed by spina bifida. Eligible degree programs include associate, technical, bachelor's, and graduate. Along with their application, they must submit a personal statement, at least 2 paragraphs in length, describing their goals in life and their determination to "dream big;" the statement should include future educational pursuits or examples of camps or training courses taken to assist them in achieving their dreams.

Financial data The stipend is $1,000.

Duration The award is granted annually.

Number awarded 1 each year.

Deadline May of each year.

[654]
JOHN E. MAYFIELD ABLE SCHOLARSHIP

Community Foundation of Middle Tennessee
Attn: Scholarship Committee
3833 Cleghorn Avenue, Suite 400
Nashville, TN 37215-2519
(615) 321-4939   Toll Free: (888) 540-5200
Fax: (615) 327-2746   E-mail: mail@cfmt.org
Web: www.cfmt.org/scholarships

Summary To provide financial assistance to high school seniors in Tennessee who have participated as a wheelchair athlete in programs of Athletes Building Life Experiences (ABLE) and plan to attend college in any state.

Eligibility This program is open to seniors graduating from high schools in Tennessee who plan to enroll full time at a college or university in any state. Applicants must have participated in wheelchair athletic activities of the ABLE program. Along with their application, they must submit an essay describing their educational plans and how those plans will help them reach their career goals. Financial need is considered in the selection process.

Financial data Stipends range from $500 to $2,500 per year. Funds are paid to the recipient's school and must be used for tuition, fees, books, supplies, room, board, or miscellaneous expenses.

Duration 1 year.

Number awarded 1 or more each year.

Deadline March of each year.

[655]
JOHN LEPPING MEMORIAL SCHOLARSHIP

Lep Foundation for Youth Education
Attn: Scholarship Selection Committee
9 Whispering Spring Drive
Millstone Township, NJ 08510
E-mail: lepfoundation@aol.com
Web: www.lepfoundation.org/application.htm

Summary To provide financial assistance to high school seniors in New Jersey, New York, or Pennsylvania who have a physical disability or psychological handicap and plan to attend college in any state.

Eligibility This program is open to seniors graduating from high schools in New Jersey, New York, or Pennsylvania and planning to enroll at a college, university, community college, or vocational school in any state. Applicants must have a disability, including (but not limited to) physical disabilities (e.g., spinal cord injury, loss of limb, birth defects, Lyme disease) or psychological handicaps (e.g., autism, cerebral palsy, post-traumatic stress). Along with their application, they must submit a brief statement of their career goals and ambitions for the future and a 500-word essay on why they feel they are the best candidate for this award. Financial need is considered in the selection process.

Financial data The stipend is $5,000. Funds are paid directly to the recipient's school.

Duration 1 year.

Number awarded At least 4 each year.

Deadline April of each year.

[656]
JUMPSTART MS SCHOLARSHIP

National Multiple Sclerosis Society-Upper Midwest
  Chapter
Attn: Jumpstart MS Scholarship Program
200 12th Avenue South
Minneapolis, MN 55415
(612) 335-7954   Toll Free: (800) 582-5296
Fax: (612) 335-7997
E-mail: bethany.hansen@nmss.org
Web: was.nationalmssociety.org

Summary To provide financial assistance to high school students from Iowa, Minnesota, and North and South Dakota who have multiple sclerosis (MS) or have a parent with MS and are planning to attend college in any state.

Eligibility This program is open to students currently enrolled as freshmen at high schools in Iowa, Minnesota, North Dakota, and South Dakota who have MS or a parent who has MS. Applicants must be planning to enroll at a 2- or 4-year college, university, or vocational/technical school

in the United States after they graduate from high school. Along with their application, they must submit an 850-word essay on the impact MS has had on their lives. Selection is based on the essay, academic record, leadership in school or community activities, goals and aspirations, and special circumstances (such as financial need).

Financial data The stipend is $1,500.

Duration 1 year.

Additional data This program is sponsored by Best Buy.

Number awarded 1 each year.

Deadline May of each year.

[657]
JUVENILE ARTHRITIS COLLEGE SCHOLARSHIPS

Arthritis Foundation-Northern and Southern New
  England Chapter
Attn: Scholarship Chair
35 Cold Spring Road, Suite 411
Rocky Hill, CT 06067
(860) 563-1177   Toll Free: (800) 541-8350
Fax: (860) 563-6018   E-mail: info.sne@arthritis.org
Web: www.arthritis.org

Summary To provide financial assistance for college to high school seniors from New England and northern New York who have arthritis or rheumatic disease.

Eligibility This program is open to 1) college-bound seniors graduating from high schools in Connecticut, Maine, New Hampshire, Rhode Island, Vermont, and northern New York (Clinton, Essex, and Franklin counties) and 2) residents of those areas currently attending college. Applicants must have been diagnosed with arthritis or rheumatic disease. Along with their application, they must submit a personal essay discussing who they are, their reasons for wanting to continue their education, their career objectives and goals, and how their juvenile arthritis has affected their education and goals. Selection is based on academics, impact of arthritis, and volunteer and community service; financial need is not considered.

Financial data The stipend is $1,000.

Duration 1 year.

Additional data Residents of Connecticut should contact the Arthritis Foundation office in Rocky Hill. Residents of Maine, New Hampshire, Vermont, and northern New York should contact the Arthritis Foundation. Residents of Rhode Island should contact the Arthritis Foundation.

Number awarded 3 each year.

Deadline April of each year.

[658]
L. MARIE HEARD EDUCATION SCHOLARSHIP PROGRAM

National Foundation for Ectodermal Dysplasias
Attn: Director of Family Support and Outreach
410 East Main Street
P.O. Box 114
Mascoutah, IL 62258-0114
(618) 566-2020   Fax: (618) 566-4718
E-mail: info@nfed.org
Web: nfed.org

Summary   To provide financial assistance for college to students who have ectodermal dysplasia.

Eligibility   This program is open to individuals who are affected by ectodermal dysplasia syndromes and are attending or planning to attend a college, university, trade school, or junior college. Applicants must submit a 500-word essay on their choice of assigned topics that change annually; recently, students were asked to write on either 1) how they have demonstrated leadership both in and out of school; or 2) what they consider the most important societal program and why. Selection is based on the essay, demonstrated academic ability, extracurricular activities, community involvement, volunteer activities for the sponsoring organization, employment, and financial need.

Financial data   Stipends are approximately $1,500.

Duration   1 year.

Additional data   This program, established in 1995, includes the following named scholarships: the Ethelyn Draser Boyd Scholarship, the Louis J. and June E. Kay Scholarship (both established in 2005) and the Clarence and Marion Bales Scholarship (established in 2008).

Number awarded   Varies each year; a total of $10,000 is available for this program annually.

Deadline   March of each year.

[659]
LAWRENCE MADEIROS SCHOLARSHIP

Lawrence Madeiros Scholarship Program
Attn: Scholarship Panel
P.O. Box 11
Mayfield, NY 12117
(518) 863-8998
Web: www.adirondackspintacular.com

Summary   To provide money for college to high school seniors who have a bleeding or other chronic disorder (muscular dystrophy, autism, diabetes, etc.).

Eligibility   This program is open to seniors graduating from high school who have been accepted at an accredited college or university. Applicants must be diagnosed with a bleeding or other chronic disorder. Along with their application, they must submit brief essays on 1) how living with or around a chronic disorder has impacted their life; 2) their goals and aspirations in life; and 3) their passion. Financial need may also be considered.

Financial data   The stipend is $1,000.

Duration   1 year.

Additional data   This program was established in 2001 by the Adirondack Spintacular, a charity event in which volunteers cycle, walk, or run to raise money. The last Spintacular was in 2011, but the scholarship program continues as a separate organization. Other chronic disorders have included muscular dystrophy, diabetes, cystic fibrosis, autism, and Asperger's Syndrome.

Number awarded   Varies each year.

Deadline   April of each year.

[660]
LOUISIANA CHAPTER MS SOCIETY SCHOLARSHIP PROGRAM

National Multiple Sclerosis Society-Louisiana Chapter
4613 Fairfield Street
Metairie, LA 70006
(504) 832-4013   Fax: (504) 831-7188
E-mail: louisianachapter@nmss.org
Web: was.nationalmssociety.org

Summary   To provide financial assistance to high school seniors and graduates from Louisiana who have multiple sclerosis (MS) or have a parent with MS and are planning to attend college in any state.

Eligibility   This program is open to graduating high school seniors, recent graduates, and GED recipients from Louisiana who have MS or a parent who has MS. Applicants must be planning to enroll as a first-time student at a 2- or 4-year college, university, or vocational/technical school in the United States on at least a half-time basis. Along with their application, they must submit an essay on the impact MS has had on their lives. Selection is based on that essay, academic record, leadership and participation in school or community activities, work experience, goals and aspirations, an outside appraisal, special circumstances, and financial need. U.S. citizenship or permanent resident status is required.

Financial data   The stipend is $2,000.

Duration   1 year; nonrenewable.

Number awarded   Varies each year; recently, 2 of these scholarships were awarded.

Deadline   January of each year.

[661]
LPA SCHOLARSHIPS

Little People of America, Inc.
Attn: Vice President of Programs
250 El Camino Real, Suite 201
Tustin, CA 92780
(714) 368-3689   Toll Free: (888) LPA-2001
Fax: (714) 368-3367   E-mail: info@lpaonline.org
Web: www.lpaonline.org/mc/page.do?sitePageID=49367

Summary   To provide financial assistance for college or graduate school to members of the Little People of America (LPA), to their families, and (in limited cases) to others.

Eligibility   This program is open to members of LPA (limited to people who, for medical reasons, are 4 feet 10 inches or under in height). Applicants must be high school seniors or students attending college, vocational school, or graduate school. Along with their application, they must submit a 500-word personal statement that explains their reasons for applying for a scholarship, their plans for the future, how they intend to be of service to LPA after graduation, and any other relevant information about themselves, their family, their background, and their educational achievements. Financial need is also considered in the selection process. If sufficient funds are available after all LPA members have been served, scholarships may also be given, first, to immediate family members of dwarfs who are also paid members of LPA, and, second, to people with dwarfism who are not members of LPA.

Financial data Stipends range from $250 to $1,000.

Duration 1 year; awards are limited to 2 for undergraduate study and 1 for graduate study.

Number awarded Varies; generally between 5 and 10 each year.

Deadline April of each year.

[662]
MID AMERICA CHAPTER MS SOCIETY SCHOLARSHIP PROGRAM

National Multiple Sclerosis Society-Mid America
  Chapter
Attn: Scholarship Program
7611 State Line Road, Suite 100
Kansas City, MO 64114
(913) 432-3926　　　　　　Fax: (816) 361-2369
E-mail: amy.goldstein@nmss.org
Web: was.nationalmssociety.org

Summary To provide financial assistance to high school seniors and graduates from the Midwest region who have multiple sclerosis (MS) or have a parent with MS and are planning to attend college in any state.

Eligibility This program is open to graduating high school seniors, recent graduates, and GED recipients from Kansas, western Missouri, Nebraska, or Pottawattamie County, Iowa who have MS or a parent who has MS. Applicants must be planning to enroll as a first-time student at a 2- or 4-year college, university, or vocational/technical school in the United States on at least a half-time basis. Along with their application, they must submit an essay on the impact MS has had on their lives. Selection is based on that essay, academic record, leadership and participation in school or community activities, work experience, goals and aspirations, an outside appraisal, special circumstances, and financial need. U.S. citizenship or permanent resident status is required.

Financial data The stipend is $1,000.

Duration 1 year.

Number awarded Varies; recently, 7 were awarded.

Deadline January of each year.

[663]
NAGA EDUCATIONAL SCHOLARSHIP GRANT

National Amputee Golf Association
Attn: Scholarship Grant Program
11 Walnut Hill Road
Amherst, NH 03031
(603) 672-6444　　　　　　Toll Free: (800) 633-NAGA
Fax: (603) 672-2987　　　　　E-mail: info@nagagolf.org
Web: www.nagagolf.org/scholarship1.shtml

Summary To provide money for college to members of the National Amputee Golf Association and their dependents.

Eligibility This program is open to amputee members in good standing in the association and their dependents. Applicants must submit information on their scholastic background (GPA in high school and college, courses of study); type of amputation and cause (if applicable), a cover letter describing their plans for the future; and documentation of financial need. They need not be competitive golfers. Selection is based on academic record, financial need, involvement in extracurricular or community activities, and area of study.

Financial data The stipend for a 4-year bachelor's degree program is $2,000 per year. The stipend for a 2-year technical or associate degree is $1,000 per year.

Duration Up to 4 years, provided the recipient maintains at least half-time enrollment and a GPA of 3.0 or higher and continues to demonstrate financial need.

Number awarded 1 or more each year.

Deadline August of each year.

[664]
NATIONAL MS SOCIETY SCHOLARSHIP PROGRAM

National Multiple Sclerosis Society
Attn: Scholarship Fund
900 South Broadway, Suite 200
Denver, CO 80209
(303) 698-6100, ext. 15259　　　　E-mail: nmss@act.org
Web: www.nationalmssociety.org

Summary To provide financial assistance for college to students who have Multiple Sclerosis (MS) or are the children of people with MS.

Eligibility This program is open to 1) high school seniors who have MS and will be attending an accredited postsecondary school for the first time; 2) high school seniors who are the children of parents with MS and will be attending an accredited postsecondary school for the first time; 3) high school (or GED) graduates of any age who have MS and will be attending an accredited postsecondary school for the first time; and 4) high school (or GED) graduates of any age who have a parent with MS and will be attending an accredited postgraduate school for the first time. Applicants must be U.S. citizens or permanent residents who plan to enroll for at least 6 credit hours per semester in an undergraduate course of study at an accredited 2- or 4-year college, university, or vocational/technical school in the United States or its territories to work on a degree, license, or certificate. Along with their application, they must submit a 1-page personal statement on the impact MS has had on their life. Selection is based on that statement, academic record, leadership and participation in school or community activities, work experience, goals and aspirations, an outside appraisal, special circumstances, and financial need.

Financial data Stipends range from $1,000 to $3,000.

Duration 1 year; may be renewed.

Additional data This program, which began in 2003, is managed by ACT Scholarship and Recognition Services.

Number awarded Varies each year; recently, 639 of these scholarships (439 new awards and 200 renewals), with a total value of $1,166,350, were awarded.

Deadline January of each year.

[665]
NEW JERSEY METRO CHAPTER MS SOCIETY SCHOLARSHIP PROGRAM

National Multiple Sclerosis Society-New Jersey Metro
  Chapter
Attn: Scholarship Program
246 Monmouth Road
Oakhurst, NJ 07755
(732) 660-1005   Fax: (732) 660-1338
E-mail: nancy.chazen@nmss.org
Web: was.nationalmssociety.org

Summary To provide financial assistance to high school seniors and graduates from New Jersey who have multiple sclerosis (MS) or have a parent with MS and are planning to attend college in any state.

Eligibility This program is open to graduating high school seniors, recent graduates, and GED recipients from New Jersey who have MS or a parent who has MS. Applicants must be planning to enroll as a first-time student at a 2- or 4-year college, university, or vocational/technical school in the United States on at least a half-time basis. Along with their application, they must submit an essay on the impact MS has had on their lives. Selection is based on that essay, academic record, leadership and participation in school or community activities, work experience, goals and aspirations, an outside appraisal, special circumstances, and financial need. U.S. citizenship or permanent resident status is required.

Financial data Stipends average more than $1,000.

Duration 1 year.

Additional data This program began in 1994.

Number awarded Varies each year; recently, 45 of these scholarships, worth $55,800, were awarded.

Deadline January of each year.

[666]
NORTH CAROLINA NATIONAL GUARD ASSOCIATION SPECIAL POPULATION SCHOLARSHIP

North Carolina National Guard Association
Attn: Educational Foundation, Inc.
7410 Chapel Hill Road
Raleigh, NC 27607-5047
(919) 851-3390   Toll Free: (800) 821-6159 (within NC)
Fax: (919) 859-4990
E-mail: peggyncngaef@bellsouth.net
Web: ncnga.org

Summary To provide funding to members and dependents of members of the North Carolina National Guard Association who have a learning or physical disability and are interested in attending college in any state.

Eligibility This program is open to active and associate members of the association as well as the spouses, children, grandchildren, and legal dependents of active, associate, or deceased members. Applicants must be learning disabled and/or physically disabled. They may be high school seniors, high school graduates, or students currently enrolled at a college or university in any state. Selection is based on financial need, academic achievement, citizenship, leadership, and other application information.

Financial data The stipend is $1,000.

Duration 1 year; may be renewed.

Number awarded 1 each year.

Deadline January of each year for high school graduates and college students; February for high school seniors.

[667]
OKLAHOMA CHAPTER MS SOCIETY SCHOLARSHIP PROGRAM

National Multiple Sclerosis Society-Oklahoma Chapter
4606 East 67th Street, Suite 103
Tulsa, OK 74136
(918) 488-0882   Fax: (918) 488-0913
E-mail: lisa.gray@oke.nmss.org
Web: was.nationalmssociety.org

Summary To provide financial assistance to high school seniors and graduates from Oklahoma who have multiple sclerosis (MS) or have a parent with MS and who are planning to attend college in any state.

Eligibility This program is open to graduating high school seniors, recent graduates, and GED recipients from Oklahoma who have MS or a parent who has MS. Applicants must be planning to enroll as a first-time student at a 2- or 4-year college, university, or vocational/technical school in the United States on at least a half-time basis. Along with their application, they must submit an essay on the impact MS has had on their lives. Selection is based on that essay, academic record, leadership and participation in school or community activities, work experience, goals and aspirations, an outside appraisal, special circumstances, and financial need. U.S. citizenship or permanent resident status is required.

Financial data Stipends range from $1,000 to $3,000.
Duration 1 year.
Additional data This program includes the Linda Chance Memorial Scholarship.
Number awarded Varies each year; recently, 11 of these scholarships were awarded.
Deadline January of each year.

[668]
OMAHA VOLUNTEERS FOR HANDICAPPED CHILDREN SCHOLARSHIPS

Omaha Volunteers for Handicapped Children
c/o Lois Carlson
2010 Country Club Avenue
Omaha, NE 68104
(402) 553-0378

Summary To provide financial assistance to Nebraska residents who have a physical disability or are preparing for a career related to people with orthopedic impairments or physical disabilities and are interested in attending college in any state.
Eligibility This program is open to residents of Nebraska who are U.S. citizens. First priority applicants must have an orthopedic impairment or physical disability and be 1) high school seniors with a GPA of 2.25 or higher and accepted into the school of their choice or 2) college students making satisfactory progress toward graduation. Second priority applicants must be enrolled in the college of their choice and preparing for a teaching or health-related career of service to people with orthopedic impairments or physical disabilities. All applicants must submit a 250-word essay on their future goals in relation to the orthopedically impaired and/or physically disabled and their need for the scholarship.
Financial data The stipend is $1,000 per year.
Duration 1 year; may be renewed.
Number awarded 5 to 10 each year.
Deadline July of each year.

[669]
OREGON CHAPTER MS SOCIETY SCHOLARSHIP PROGRAM

National Multiple Sclerosis Society-Oregon Chapter
104 S.W. Clay Street
Portland, OR 97201
(503) 223-9511   Toll Free: (800) 344-4867
Fax: (503) 223-2911 E-mail: Ann.Berryman@nmss.org
Web: was.nationalmssociety.org

Summary To provide financial assistance to high school seniors and graduates from Oregon who have multiple sclerosis (MS) or have a parent with MS and who are planning to attend college in any state.
Eligibility This program is open to graduating high school seniors, recent graduates, and GED recipients from Oregon who have MS or a parent who has MS. Applicants must be planning to enroll as a first-time student at a 2- or 4-year college, university, or vocational/technical school in the United States on at least a half-time basis. Along with their application, they must submit an essay on

the impact MS has had on their lives. Selection is based on that essay, academic record, leadership and participation in school or community activities, work experience, goals and aspirations, an outside appraisal, special circumstances, and financial need. U.S. citizenship or permanent resident status is required.
Financial data Stipends range from $1,000 to $3,000.
Duration 1 year.
Additional data This program began in 2006.
Number awarded Varies each year; recently, 7 of these scholarships were awarded. Since the program began, it has awarded 20 scholarships worth $38,200.
Deadline January of each year.

[670]
PACIFIC NORTHWEST SCHOLARSHIPS

Cancer for College
1345 Specialty Drive, Suite D
Vista, CA 92081
(760) 599-5096   E-mail: info@cancerforcollege.org
Web: www.cancerforcollege.org

Summary To provide financial assistance to undergraduate and graduate students from the Pacific Northwest who are cancer patients, survivors, or amputees.
Eligibility This program is open to undergraduate and graduate students who are originally from or current attending accredited colleges, universities, community colleges, and trade schools in Idaho, Montana, Oregon, or Washington. Applicants must be a cancer patient, cancer survivor, and/or amputee. Along with a preliminary application, they must submit a brief statement on why they should receive further consideration for this scholarship and information on their financial situation.
Financial data Stipends are $3,000, $2,000, $1,000, or $500.
Duration 1 year.
Number awarded Varies each year; recently, 14 of these scholarships were awarded: 3 at $3,000, 2 at $2,000, 6 at $1,000, and 3 at $500.
Deadline Deadline not specified.

[671]
PVA EDUCATIONAL SCHOLARSHIP PROGRAM

Paralyzed Veterans of America
Attn: Education and Training Foundation
801 18th Street, N.W.
Washington, DC 20006-3517
(202) 416-7651   Toll Free: (800) 424-8200, ext. 776
Fax: (202) 416-7641   TDD: (800) 795-HEAR
E-mail: christih@pva.org
Web: www.pva.org

Summary To provide money for college to members of the Paralyzed Veterans of America (PVA) and their families.
Eligibility This program is open to PVA members, spouses of members, and unmarried dependent children of members under 24 years of age. Applicants must be attending or planning to attend an accredited U.S. college or university. They must be U.S. citizens. Along with their

application, they must submit a personal statement explaining why they wish to further their education, short- and long-term academic goals, how this will meet their career objectives, and how it will affect the PVA membership. Selection is based on that statement, academic records, letters of recommendation, and extracurricular and community activities.

Financial data   Stipends are $1,000 for full-time students or $500 for part-time students.

Duration   1 year.

Additional data   This program was established in 1986.

Number awarded   Varies each year; recently 14 full-time and 3 part-time students received these scholarships. Since this program was established, it has awarded more than $300,000 in scholarships.

Deadline   May of each year.

[672]
ROBERT DOLE SCHOLARSHIP FUND FOR DISABLED STUDENTS

United Negro College Fund
Attn: Scholarships and Grants Department
8260 Willow Oaks Corporate Drive
P.O. Box 10444
Fairfax, VA 22031-8044
(703) 205-3466   Toll Free: (800) 331-2244
Fax: (703) 205-3574
Web: www.uncf.org

Summary   To provide funding to physically and mentally-challenged students at colleges and universities that are members of the United Negro College Fund (UNCF).

Eligibility   This program is open to students at UNCF-member institutions who have a physical or learning disability. Applicants must have a GPA of 2.5 or higher and be able to demonstrate financial need. Along with their application, they must submit a 500-word essay on the challenges of their disability.

Financial data   The stipend is $3,500.

Duration   1 year.

Number awarded   1 or more each year.

Deadline   February of each year.

[673]
SOUTHERN CALIFORNIA AND NEVADA CHAPTER MS SOCIETY SCHOLARSHIP PROGRAM

National Multiple Sclerosis Society-Southern California
  and Nevada Chapter
2400 South Sepulveda Boulevard, Suite 115
Los Angeles, CA 90064
(310) 479-4456   Fax: (310) 479-4436
Web: was.nationalmssociety.org

Summary   To provide financial assistance to high school seniors and graduates from southern California and Nevada who have multiple sclerosis (MS) or have a parent with MS and are planning to attend college in any state.

Eligibility   This program is open to graduating high school seniors, recent graduates, and GED recipients from southern California and Nevada who have MS or a parent who has MS. Applicants must be planning to enroll as an entering undergraduate student at a 2- or 4-year college, university, or vocational/technical school in the United States on at least a half-time basis. Along with their application, they must submit an essay on the impact MS has had on their lives. Selection is based on that essay, academic record, leadership and participation in school or community activities, work experience, goals and aspirations, an outside appraisal, special circumstances, and financial need. U.S. citizenship or permanent resident status is required.

Financial data   Stipends range from $1,000 to $3,000.

Duration   1 year.

Number awarded   Varies each year; recently, 26 of these scholarships were awarded.

Deadline   January of each year.

[674]
SPINA BIFIDA ASSOCIATION OF ALABAMA ADVANCED EDUCATION SCHOLARSHIP PROGRAM

Spina Bifida Association of Alabama
Attn: Scholarship Committee
P.O. Box 13254
Birmingham, AL 35202
(256) 617-1414   E-mail: info@sbaofal.org
Web: www.sbaofal.org/prog_services.html

Summary   To provide funding to Alabama residents who have spina bifida and are interested in working on an college or graduate degree at a school in any state.

Eligibility   This program is open to entering or continuing undergraduate and graduate students at colleges and universities in any state who have spina bifida. Applicants must reside in Alabama and have been residents of that state for at least 2 consecutive years. Along with their application, they must submit 1) an essay on their educational and career goals, aspects of their background and character relevant to their likelihood of academic success, and other factors they wish to have considered, all in relationship to spina bifida; 2) verification of disability, signed by a physician; and 3) transcripts of grades for high school and other educational levels.

Financial data   The stipend is $1,000 per year; funds are sent directly to the recipient's school.

Duration   1 year; may be renewed up to 3 additional years for undergraduates, up to 1 additional years for graduate students, or up to 2 additional years for students in postgraduate school, law school, or medical school. Renewal depends on the recipient's maintaining a GPA of 2.25 or higher each semester.

Number awarded   Up to 4 each year.

Deadline   April of each year.

[675]
SPINA BIFIDA ASSOCIATION OF CENTRAL INDIANA COLLEGE SCHOLARSHIP

Spina Bifida Association of Central Indiana
P.O. Box 19814
Indianapolis, IN 46219-0814
(317) 592-1630
Web: www.sbaci.org

Summary To provide financial assistance to residents of Indiana who have spina bifida and are interested in attending college in any state.

Eligibility This program is open to residents of Indiana who have spina bifida. Applicants must be enrolled or planning to enroll at a college, junior college, or approved trade, vocational, or business school in any state. They are not required to be members of the Spina Bifida Association of Central Indiana (SBACI), but they must join if granted a scholarship. Along with their application, they must submit a letter explaining their career plans and how education will contribute to their future plans. Financial need is not considered in the selection process.

Financial data The stipend is $500 per semester ($1,000 per year). Membership dues for SBACI are deducted from the disbursements.

Duration 1 semester; recipients may reapply.

Additional data The sponsoring organization has expanded its operations to serve all of Indiana.

Number awarded Up to 3 each year.

Deadline May of each year for fall semester; October of each year for spring semester.

[676]
SPINA BIFIDA ASSOCIATION OF CONNECTICUT SCHOLARSHIP FUND

Spina Bifida Association of Connecticut, Inc.
Attn: Scholarship Committee
P.O. Box 2545
Hartford, CT 06146-2545
(860) 832-8905   Toll Free: (800) 574-6274
Fax: (860) 832-6260   E-mail: sbac@sbac.org
Web: www.sbac.org/SBAC.org_Programs.htm

Summary To provide financial assistance to residents of Connecticut who have spina bifida and are interested in attending college in any state.

Eligibility This program is open to residents of Connecticut who have spina bifida and are attending or planning to attend a college, university, trade school, vocational institution, or business school in any state. Applicants must submit an essay (2 to 3 pages) on their educational goals; reasons for selecting those goals; outstanding accomplishments or contributions made through school, extracurricular, religious group, or Spina Bifida Association of Connecticut (SBAC) member activities; and community and volunteer work. Selection is based on academic record, other efforts shown in school, involvement in the community, leadership qualities, commitment to personal goals, and work history.

Financial data The stipend is $1,000. Funds are paid directly to the recipient's school.

Duration 1 year.

Number awarded 1 or more each year.

Deadline April of each year.

[677]
SPINA BIFIDA ASSOCIATION OF ILLINOIS SCHOLARSHIPS

Spina Bifida Association of Illinois
8765 West Higgins Road, Suite 403
Chicago, IL 60631
(773) 444-0305   Fax: (773) 444-0327
E-mail: sbail@sbail.org
Web: www.sbail.org/programs.html

Summary To provide financial assistance to residents of Illinois who have spina bifida and are interested in attending college or graduate school in any state.

Eligibility This program is open to residents of Illinois who have spina bifida. Applicants must be enrolled or planning to enroll at a 2- or 4-year college or university, technical or trade school, or business college in any state as an undergraduate or graduate student. Along with their application, they must submit essays of 250 to 500 words on 1) the accomplishments or contributions (school, extracurricular, church, community, or Spina Bifida Association of Illinois) they have made of which they are most proud; and 2) the reasons for selecting their vocational goals. Selection is based on those essays, GPA, test scores (ACT, SAT, GRE, GMAT), extracurricular activities, and financial need.

Financial data Stipends range up to $2,500.

Duration 1 year.

Additional data This program includes the Valiant Scholarship, awarded to an applicant who displays outstanding leadership, good will toward those less fortunate, and a dedication to making a difference. Recipients are expected to volunteer with the Spina Bifida Association of Illinois at least once during the following year.

Number awarded Varies each year; recently, 8 of these scholarships were awarded.

Deadline April of each year.

[678]
SPINA BIFIDA ASSOCIATION OF NORTH TEXAS SCHOLARSHIP

Spina Bifida Association of North Texas
Attn: Scholarship Chair
705 West Avenue B, Suite 409
Garland, TX 75040
(972) 238-8755   Fax: (214) 703-1981
E-mail: eparham@belo.com
Web: spinabifidant.org

Summary To provide financial assistance to residents of Texas who were born with spina bifida and are interested in attending college in any state.

Eligibility This program is open to residents of Texas who were born with spina bifida. Applicants must be enrolled in or accepted into a college, junior college, or approved trade school in any state. Along with their application, they must submit a personal statement describing their goals in life, future educational pursuits, and anything else they wish to selection committee to know about them. Selection is based on that statement, academic record, community service, work history, leadership, and need.

Financial data A stipend is awarded (amount not specified); funds are paid directly to the recipient to be used for payment of tuition, books, room and board, and specialized equipment needs.

Duration 1 year; may be renewed.

Number awarded Varies each year; recently, 3 of these scholarships were awarded.

Deadline April of each year.

[679]
SPINA BIFIDA ASSOCIATION OF WISCONSIN EDUCATIONAL SCHOLARSHIP IN MEMORY OF MARY ANN POTTS

Spina Bifida Association of Wisconsin
Attn: Scholarship Fund
830 North 109th Street, Suite 6
Wauwatosa, WI 53226
(414) 607-9061   Fax: (414) 607-9602
E-mail: sbawi@sbawi.org
Web: www.sbawi.org/learn-more.html

Summary To provide financial assistance to residents of Wisconsin who have spina bifida and are interested in attending college or graduate school in any state.

Eligibility This program is open to residents of Wisconsin of any age who are constituents of the Spina Bifida Association of Wisconsin (SBAWI). Applicants must be enrolled or planning to enroll at a college, graduate school, trade school, or specialized educational training program in any state. Along with their application, they must submit a personal statement explaining their goals and what they want to accomplish with the education or training they will receive. There is no age limitation. Selection is based on that statement, academic record, community service, work history, leadership, and financial need. Priority is given to applicants who are active in SBAWI.

Financial data A stipend is awarded (amount not specified); funds are paid directly to the recipient's institution to be used for payment of tuition, books, room and board, and specialized equipment needs.

Duration 1 year; recipients may reapply.

Additional data This program was established in 1996.

Number awarded 1 each year.

Deadline March of each year.

[680]
SPINA BIFIDA ASSOCIATION ONE-YEAR SCHOLARSHIP

Spina Bifida Association of America
Attn: Scholarship Committee
4590 MacArthur Boulevard, N.W., Suite 250
Washington, DC 20007-4226
(202) 944-3285, ext. 13
Toll Free: (800) 621-3141, ext. 13
Fax: (202) 944-3295   E-mail: cjhead@sbaa.org
Web: www.spinabifidaassociation.org

Summary To provide financial assistance to undergraduate and graduate students who have spina bifida.

Eligibility This program is open to persons of any age who were born with spina bifida and are enrolled in or accepted by a junior college, 4-year university, graduate school, or approved trade, vocational, or business school. Applicants must submit a 3-page personal statement explaining their educational goals; transcripts; standardized test scores (ACT, SAT, GRE, or equivalent; adult students may submit a recent transcript); verification of acceptance by a college; information related to financial need; letters of recommendation; and a physician's statement verifying disability.

Financial data The stipend is $2,000.

Duration 1 year.

Additional data This program was established in 1988.

Number awarded Up to 6 each year.

Deadline March of each year.

[681]
TUITION WAIVER FOR DISABLED CHILDREN OF KENTUCKY VETERANS

Kentucky Department of Veterans Affairs
Attn: Field Operations Branch
321 West Main Street, Suite 390
Louisville, KY 40202
(502) 595-4447   Toll Free: (800) 928-4012 (within KY)
Fax: (502) 595-4448   E-mail: Pamela.Cypert@ky.gov
Web: www.veterans.ky.gov/benefits/tuitionwaiver.htm

Summary To provide financial assistance for college to the children of Kentucky veterans who have spina bifida or another designated disability related to their parent's military service.

Eligibility This program is open to the children of veterans who have acquired a disability as a direct result of their parent's military service. The disability must have been designated by the U.S. Department of Veterans Affairs as compensable (currently defined as spina bifida). The veteran parent must 1) have served on active duty with the U.S. armed forces or in the National Guard or Reserve component on state active duty, active duty for training, or inactive duty training; and 2) be (or if deceased have been) a resident of Kentucky. Applicants must have been admitted to a state-supported university, college, or vocational training institute in Kentucky.

Financial data Eligible children are exempt from payment of tuition at state-supported institutions of higher education in Kentucky.

Duration There are no age or time limits on the waiver.

Number awarded Varies each year.

Deadline Deadline not specified.

[682]
UCB FAMILY RA SCHOLARSHIP PROGRAM

UCB, Inc.
c/o Summit Medical Communications
1421 East Broad Street, Suite 340
Fuquay-Varina, NC 27526
(919) 567-7590   Toll Free: (888) 854-4996
Fax: (919) 567-7591
E-mail: ucbrascholarship@summitmedcomm.com
Web: www.reachbeyondra.com

Summary   To provide financial assistance to undergraduate and graduate students who have rheumatoid arthritis (RA) and their families.

Eligibility   This program is open to students who are working on or planning to work on an associate, undergraduate, or graduate degree or are enrolled in a trade school educational program. Applicants must have been diagnosed with RA or be an immediate family member (parent, spouse, child, or sibling) of a person with RA. They may be of any age. Along with their application, they must submit an essay of 1 to 2 pages describing how they are living beyond the boundaries of RA to demonstrate academic ambition and personal achievement and how the scholarship would impact their life.

Financial data   Stipends range up to $5,000.

Duration   1 year; nonrenewable.

Additional data   This program began on a pilot basis in 2008.

Number awarded   30 each year.

Deadline   March of each year.

[683]
UNITED CEREBRAL PALSY OF METROBOSTON COLLEGE SCHOLARSHIP

United Cerebral Palsy of MetroBoston
Attn: Development and Marketing Department
71 Arsenal Street
Watertown, MA 02472
(617) 600-2450   Fax: (617) 926-3059
E-mail: ucpboston@ucpboston.org
Web: ucpboston.org

Summary   To provide financial assistance to residents of Massachusetts who have cerebral palsy and are interested in attending college or graduate school in any state.

Eligibility   This program is open to Massachusetts residents who are high school seniors, undergraduates, or graduate students and have a primary diagnosis of cerebral palsy. Applicants must be enrolled or planning to enroll full time at an accredited college or university in any state. Along with their application, they must submit a 250-word essay about their disability, based on such topics as how they have overcome the challenge of their disability, what having a disability means to them, someone who has been helpful in their success, or an achievement of which they are proud. They must also submit a letter from their doctor confirming that they have cerebral palsy, 2 letters of recommendation, transcripts, and an acceptance letter from the college or university of their choice.

Financial data   The stipend is $1,000.

Duration   1 year.

Number awarded   1 each year.

Deadline   April of each year.

[684]
UPPER MIDWEST CHAPTER MS SOCIETY SCHOLARSHIP PROGRAM

National Multiple Sclerosis Society-Upper Midwest Chapter
Attn: Scholarship Program
200 12th Avenue South
Minneapolis, MN 55415
(612) 335-7928   Toll Free: (800) 582-5296
Fax: (612) 335-7997
E-mail: shannon.wolkerstorfer@nmss.org
Web: was.nationalmssociety.org

Summary   To provide financial assistance to high school seniors and graduates from Iowa, Minnesota, and North and South Dakota who have multiple sclerosis (MS) or have a parent with MS and are planning to attend college in any state.

Eligibility   This program is open to graduating high school seniors, recent graduates, and GED recipients from Iowa, Minnesota, North Dakota, and South Dakota who have MS or a parent who has MS. Applicants must be planning to enroll as a first-time student at a 2- or 4-year college, university, or vocational/technical school in the United States on at least a half-time basis. Along with their application, they must submit an essay on the impact MS has had on their lives. Selection is based on that essay, academic record, leadership and participation in school or community activities, work experience, goals and aspirations, an outside appraisal, special circumstances, and financial need. U.S. citizenship or permanent resident status is required.

Financial data   Stipends average $2,000.

Duration   1 year.

Number awarded   Varies each year; recently, 54 of these scholarships, worth $98,500, were awarded.

Deadline   January of each year.

[685]
UTAH-SOUTHERN IDAHO CHAPTER MS SOCIETY SCHOLARSHIP PROGRAM

National Multiple Sclerosis Society-Utah-Southern Idaho Chapter
2400 South Sepulveda Boulevard, Suite 115
Los Angeles, CA 90064
(310) 479-4456   Fax: (310) 479-4436
Web: was.nationalmssociety.org

Summary   To provide financial assistance to high school seniors and graduates from southern Idaho and Utah who have multiple sclerosis (MS) or have a parent with MS and are planning to attend college in any state.

Eligibility   This program is open to graduating high school seniors, recent graduates, and GED recipients from southern Idaho and Utah who have MS or a parent who has MS. Applicants must be planning to enroll as an entering undergraduate student at a 2- or 4-year college, university, or vocational/technical school in the United States on at least a half-time basis. Along with their application, they must submit an essay on the impact MS has had on their lives. Selection is based on that essay, academic record, leadership and participation in school or community activities, work experience, goals and aspirations, an outside appraisal, special circumstances, and financial need. U.S. citizenship or permanent resident status is required.

Financial data　Stipends range from $1,000 to $5,000.
Duration　1 year.
Number awarded　Varies each year; recently, 11 of these scholarships were awarded: 1 at $5,000, 1 at $3,000, 2 at $2,500, 1 at $1,500, and 6 at $1,000.
Deadline　January of each year.

[686]
WINTERHOFF COLLEGIATE SCHOLARSHIP

Arthritis Foundation-Greater Southwest Chapter
1313 East Osborn Road, Suite 200
Phoenix, AZ 85014
(602) 264-7679　　　　　　Toll Free: (800) 477-7679
Fax: (602) 264-0563
Web: www.arthritis.org/arizona/aboutwinterhoff.php

Summary　To provide funding to students at public universities in Arizona who have a rheumatic disease.
Eligibility　This program is open to full-time undergraduate and graduate students at public 4-year universities in Arizona. Applicants must have some form of diagnosed rheumatic disease and provide a physician's certifying statement. They must be willing to be involved in Arthritis Foundation publicity and agree to meet with foundation officials in Phoenix.
Financial data　The stipend is $7,500 per year.
Duration　1 year; may be renewed up to 3 additional years, provided the recipient remains enrolled full time and maintains a GPA of 2.5 or higher.
Number awarded　1 or more each year.
Deadline　January of each year at Arizona State University; February of each year at The University of Arizona and Northern Arizona University.

[687]
WISCONSIN CHAPTER MS SOCIETY SCHOLARSHIP PROGRAM

National Multiple Sclerosis Society-Wisconsin Chapter
Attn: Scholarship Program
1120 James Drive, Suite A
Hartland, WI 53029
(262) 369-4420　Toll Free: (800) 242-3358 (within WI)
Fax: (262) 369-4410　　E-mail: info.wisMS@nmss.org
Web: was.nationalmssociety.org

Summary　To provide financial assistance to high school seniors and graduates from Wisconsin who have multiple sclerosis (MS) or have a parent with MS and are planning to attend college in any state.
Eligibility　This program is open to graduating high school seniors, recent graduates, and GED recipients from Wisconsin who have MS or a parent who has MS.

Applicants must be planning to enroll as a first-time student at a 2- or 4-year college, university, or vocational/technical school in the United States on at least a half-time basis. Along with their application, they must submit an essay on the impact MS has had on their lives. Selection is based on that essay, academic record, leadership and participation in school or community activities, work experience, goals and aspirations, an outside appraisal, special circumstances, and financial need. U.S. citizenship or permanent resident status is required.
Financial data　Stipends average $1,500.
Duration　1 year.
Number awarded　Varies each year; recently, 30 of these scholarships were awarded.
Deadline　January of each year.

Fellowships

[688]
ASSE DIVERSITY COMMITTEE SCHOLARSHIP

American Society of Safety Engineers
Attn: ASSE Foundation
1800 East Oakton Street
Des Plaines, IL 60018
(847) 768-3435　　　　　　Fax: (847) 768-3434
E-mail: agabanski@asse.org
Web: www.asse.org

Summary　To provide funding to physically challenged and other diverse upper-division and graduate student members of the American Society of Safety Engineers (ASSE).
Eligibility　This program is open to ASSE student members who are working on an undergraduate or graduate degree in occupational safety, health, and environment or a closely-related field (e.g., industrial or environmental engineering, environmental science, industrial hygiene, occupational health nursing). Applicants must be full-time students who have completed at least 60 semester hours with a GPA of 3.0 or higher as undergraduates or at least 9 semester hours with a GPA of 3.5 or higher as graduate students. Along with their application, they must submit 2 essays of 300 words or less: 1) why they are seeking a degree in occupational safety and health or a closely-related field, a brief description of their current activities, and how those relate to their career goals and objectives; and 2) why they should be awarded this scholarship (including career goals and financial need). A goal of this program is to support individuals regardless of race, ethnicity, gender, religion, personal beliefs, age, sexual orientation, physical challenges, geographic location, university, or specific area of study. U.S. citizenship is not required.
Financial data　The stipend is $1,000 per year.
Duration　1 year; recipients may reapply.

Number awarded 1 each year.
Deadline November of each year.

[689]
CANCER FOR COLLEGE SCHOLARSHIPS

Cancer for College
1345 Specialty Drive, Suite D
Vista, CA 92081
(760) 599-5096 E-mail: info@cancerforcollege.org
Web: www.cancerforcollege.org

Summary To provide funding to college and graduate students who are cancer patients, survivors, or amputees.

Eligibility This program is open to undergraduate and graduate students enrolled or planning to enroll at accredited colleges, universities, community colleges, and trade schools in the United States and Puerto Rico. Applicants must be a cancer patient, cancer survivor, and/or amputee. Along with a preliminary application, they must submit a brief statement on why they should receive further consideration for this scholarship and information on their financial situation. Preference is given to residents of California and students attending college in southern California.

Financial data Stipends are $4,000, $1,000, or $500.

Duration 1 year; some of the $4,000 scholarships (designated as Perpetual Scholarships) may be renewed up to 3 additional years.

Additional data This program was established in 1993. Perpetual Scholarship recipients must be willing to attend regional events associated with the program and be available for interviews and/or media coverage.

Number awarded Varies each year; recently, this program awarded 4 Perpetual Scholarships at $4,000 per year, 3 1-time scholarships at $4,000, 25 1-time scholarships at $1,000, and 6 1-time scholarships at $500.

Deadline Deadline not specified.

[690]
CHILDREN'S BRITTLE BONE FOUNDATION AND OI FOUNDATION IMPACT GRANT PROGRAM

Children's Brittle Bone Foundation
Attn: Impact Grant Program
7701 95th Street
Pleasant Prairie, WI 53158
(773) 263-2223 Fax: (262) 947-0724
E-mail: info@cbbf.org
Web: www.cbbf.org/Impact_Grant.htm

Summary To provide funding for education or other purposes to people who have osteogenesis imperfecta (OI).

Eligibility This program is open to people who have OI and are seeking funding for equipment or services that will improve their quality of life. Examples of acceptable requests include education-related items such as tuition assistance at the preschool to postdoctoral level; prescribed exercise therapy equipment for physical or occupational therapy; orthotics, braces, and walkers; manual or electric wheelchairs or scooters; adaptive technology such as computers or hearing aids; dental intervention; vehicle modifications such as lifts or pedal extensions or vehicle purchases; travel reimbursement to receive specialized care; outdoor ramps that provide access to a home; or accessibility aides such as reachers, shower chairs, or kitchen carts.

Financial data Grants range from $500 to $20,000.

Duration Funds must be used within 12 months.

Additional data This program is provided jointly by the Children's Brittle Bone Foundation and the Osteogenesis Imperfecta (OI) Foundation.

Number awarded Varies; recently, 5 were awarded.

Deadline January of each year.

[691]
CRAIG H. NEILSEN FOUNDATION AWARD

Vermont Studio Center
80 Pearl Street
P.O. Box 613
Johnson, VT 05656
(802) 635-2727 Fax: (802) 635-2730
E-mail: info@vermontstudiocenter.org
Web: www.vermontstudiocenter.org/fellowships

Summary To provide funding to artists and writers who have a spinal cord injury and are interested in a residency at the Vermont Studio Center in Johnson, Vermont.

Eligibility Eligible to apply for this support are painters, sculptors, printmakers, new and mixed-media artists, photographers, poets, and other writers of fiction and creative nonfiction who live with a spinal cord injury. Applicants must be interested in a residency at the center in Johnson, Vermont. Visual artists must submit up to 20 slides or visual images of their work, poets must submit up to 10 pages, and other writers must submit 10 to 15 pages. Selection is based on artistic merit.

Financial data The award pays $3,950, which covers all residency fees. Each award also includes a $500 stipend for travel expenses and, if necessary, a stipend for room, board, and travel for a personal care assistant.

Duration 4 weeks.

Additional data This award is sponsored by the Craig H. Neilsen Foundation. The application fee is $25.

Number awarded 4 each year.

Deadline February of each year.

[692]
CYNTHIA RUTH RUSSELL MEMORIAL GRANTS

Kansas Masonic Foundation, Inc.
2909 S.W. Maupin Lane
Topeka, KS 66614-5335
(785) 357-7646 Fax: (785) 357-7406
E-mail: kmf@kmfonline.org
Web: www.kmfonline.org/content/view/15/36

Summary To provide financial assistance to physically challenged Kansas residents attending a college or university in the state.

Eligibility This program is open to residents of Kansas who are physically challenged. Applicants must be attending or planning to attend an institution of higher education in the state as a full-time undergraduate or graduate student. Along with their application, they must submit a 300-word statement of their educational goals, a short autobiography that includes a discussion of their physical challenge, a list of extracurricular activities, their latest grade transcript, letters of reference, ACT and/or SAT scores, and documentation of financial need.

Financial data A stipend is awarded (amount not specified).

Duration 1 year; renewable, if the recipient remains enrolled full time and maintains a GPA of 2.5 or higher.

Number awarded 1 or more each year.

Deadline March of each year.

[693]
EASTER SEALS SOUTH CAROLINA EDUCATIONAL SCHOLARSHIPS

Easter Seals South Carolina
Attn: Scholarship Program
3020 Farrow Road
P.O. Box 5715
Columbia, SC 29250
(803) 429-8474   Fax: (803) 356-6902
E-mail: TAdger@sc.easterseals.com
Web: sc.easterseals.com

Summary To provide financial assistance for college or graduate school to South Carolina students who have a mobility impairment.

Eligibility This program is open to South Carolina residents and students attending a college or university in the state who have a significant and medically certified mobility impairment. Applicants must be enrolled or planning to enroll in an undergraduate or graduate program. They must be able to demonstrate financial need. Preference is given to students carrying at least 9 credit hours and making satisfactory academic progress toward graduation.

Financial data The maximum stipend is $1,000.

Duration 1 year; may be renewed.

Additional data This program was established in 1985.

Number awarded 1 or more each year.

Deadline June of each year.

[694]
JAY AND ROSE PHILLIPS AWARD

Courage Center
Attn: Vocational Services Department
3915 Golden Valley Road
Minneapolis, MN 55422
(763) 520-0263   Toll Free: (888) 8-INTAKE
Fax: (763) 520-0562   TDD: (763) 520-0245
E-mail: information@couragecenter.org
Web: www.couragecenter.org

Summary To recognize and reward residents of designated states who have a physical disability and have been employed successfully.

Eligibility This award is available to residents of Iowa, Minnesota, North Dakota, South Dakota, and Wisconsin who have a physical disability. Nominees must have been vocationally and financially independent for at least 3

years. Self-employed individuals are also eligible. In the selection process, attitude, leadership, character, and community involvement are considered.

Financial data The award is $2,000.

Duration The awards are presented annually.

Additional data This program was established in 1964. The sponsor also offers a $2,000 award for caregivers: the Jay and Rose Phillips Caregiver Award.

Number awarded Varies each year; recently, 3 of these awards were presented.

Deadline May of each year.

[695]
JEAN DRISCOLL AWARD

Spina Bifida Association of Greater New England
Attn: Executive Director
219 East Main Street, Suite 100B
Milford, MA 01757
(508) 482-5300   Toll Free: (888) 479-1900
Fax: (508) 482-5301
E-mail: edugan@SBAGreaterNE.org
Web: www.sbagreaterne.org

Summary To provide funding for educational, developmental, or assistive programs to residents of New England who have spina bifida.

Eligibility This program is open to residents of New England who are 14 years of age or older and have spina bifida. Applicants must be seeking funding for educational, developmental, or assistive programs that will enable them to achieve their goals despite limitations imposed by spina bifida. Eligible degree programs include associate, technical, bachelor's, and graduate. Along with their application, they must submit a personal statement, at least 2 paragraphs in length, describing their goals in life and their determination to "dream big;" the statement should include future educational pursuits or examples of camps or training courses taken to assist them in achieving their dreams.

Financial data The stipend is $1,000.

Duration The award is granted annually.

Number awarded 1 each year.

Deadline May of each year.

[696]
LPA SCHOLARSHIPS

Little People of America, Inc.
Attn: Vice President of Programs
250 El Camino Real, Suite 201
Tustin, CA 92780
(714) 368-3689   Toll Free: (888) LPA-2001
Fax: (714) 368-3367   E-mail: info@lpaonline.org
Web: www.lpaonline.org/mc/page.do?sitePageID=49367

Summary To provide financial assistance for college or graduate school to members of the Little People of America (LPA), to their families, and (in limited cases) to others.

Eligibility This program is open to members of LPA (limited to people who, for medical reasons, are 4 feet 10 inches or under in height). Applicants must be high school seniors or students attending college, vocational school, or graduate school. Along with their application, they must submit a 500-word personal statement that explains their reasons for applying for a scholarship, their plans for the future, how they intend to be of service to LPA after graduation, and any other relevant information about themselves, their family, their background, and their educational achievements. Financial need is also considered in the selection process. If sufficient funds are available after all LPA members have been served, scholarships may also be given, first, to immediate family members of dwarfs who are also paid members of LPA, and, second, to people with dwarfism who are not members of LPA.

Financial data   Stipends range from $250 to $1,000.

Duration   1 year; awards are limited to 2 for undergraduate study and 1 for graduate study.

Number awarded   Varies; generally between 5 and 10 each year.

Deadline   April of each year.

[697]
PACIFIC NORTHWEST SCHOLARSHIPS

Cancer for College
1345 Specialty Drive, Suite D
Vista, CA 92081
(760) 599-5096   E-mail: info@cancerforcollege.org
Web: www.cancerforcollege.org

Summary   To provide financial assistance to undergraduate and graduate students from the Pacific Northwest who are cancer patients, survivors, or amputees.

Eligibility   This program is open to undergraduate and graduate students who are originally from or current attending accredited colleges, universities, community colleges, and trade schools in Idaho, Montana, Oregon, or Washington. Applicants must be a cancer patient, cancer survivor, and/or amputee. Along with a preliminary application, they must submit a brief statement on why they should receive further consideration for this scholarship and information on their financial situation.

Financial data   Stipends are $3,000, $2,000, $1,000, or $500.

Duration   1 year.

Number awarded   Varies each year; recently, 14 of these scholarships were awarded: 3 at $3,000, 2 at $2,000, 6 at $1,000, and 3 at $500.

Deadline   Deadline not specified.

[698]
SPINA BIFIDA ASSOCIATION OF ALABAMA ADVANCED EDUCATION SCHOLARSHIP PROGRAM

Spina Bifida Association of Alabama
Attn: Scholarship Committee
P.O. Box 13254
Birmingham, AL 35202
(256) 617-1414   E-mail: info@sbaofal.org
Web: www.sbaofal.org/prog_services.html

Summary   To provide funding to Alabama residents who have spina bifida and are interested in working on an college or graduate degree at a school in any state.

Eligibility   This program is open to entering or continuing undergraduate and graduate students at colleges and universities in any state who have spina bifida. Applicants must reside in Alabama and have been residents of that state for at least 2 consecutive years. Along with their application, they must submit 1) an essay on their educational and career goals, aspects of their background and character relevant to their likelihood of academic success, and other factors they wish to have considered, all in relationship to spina bifida; 2) verification of disability, signed by a physician; and 3) transcripts of grades for high school and other educational levels.

Financial data   The stipend is $1,000 per year; funds are sent directly to the recipient's school.

Duration   1 year; may be renewed up to 3 additional years for undergraduates, up to 1 additional years for graduate students, or up to 2 additional years for students in postgraduate school, law school, or medical school. Renewal depends on the recipient's maintaining a GPA of 2.25 or higher each semester.

Number awarded   Up to 4 each year.

Deadline   April of each year.

[699]
SPINA BIFIDA ASSOCIATION OF ILLINOIS SCHOLARSHIPS

Spina Bifida Association of Illinois
8765 West Higgins Road, Suite 403
Chicago, IL 60631
(773) 444-0305   Fax: (773) 444-0327
E-mail: sbail@sbail.org
Web: www.sbail.org/programs.html

Summary   To provide financial assistance to residents of Illinois who have spina bifida and are interested in attending college or graduate school in any state.

Eligibility   This program is open to residents of Illinois who have spina bifida. Applicants must be enrolled or planning to enroll at a 2- or 4-year college or university, technical or trade school, or business college in any state as an undergraduate or graduate student. Along with their application, they must submit essays of 250 to 500 words on 1) the accomplishments or contributions (school, extracurricular, church, community, or Spina Bifida Association of Illinois) they have made of which they are most proud; and 2) the reasons for selecting their vocational goals. Selection is based on those essays, GPA, test scores (ACT, SAT, GRE, GMAT), extracurricular activities, and financial need.

Financial data   Stipends range up to $2,500.

Duration   1 year.

Additional data   This program includes the Valiant Scholarship, awarded to an applicant who displays outstanding leadership, good will toward those less fortunate, and a dedication to making a difference. Recipients are expected to volunteer with the Spina Bifida Association of Illinois at least once during the following year.

Number awarded   Varies each year; recently, 8 of these scholarships were awarded.

Deadline   April of each year.

[700]
SPINA BIFIDA ASSOCIATION OF WISCONSIN EDUCATIONAL SCHOLARSHIP IN MEMORY OF MARY ANN POTTS

Spina Bifida Association of Wisconsin
Attn: Scholarship Fund
830 North 109th Street, Suite 6
Wauwatosa, WI 53226
(414) 607-9061   Fax: (414) 607-9602
E-mail: sbawi@sbawi.org
Web: www.sbawi.org/learn-more.html

Summary To provide financial assistance to residents of Wisconsin who have spina bifida and are interested in attending college or graduate school in any state.

Eligibility This program is open to residents of Wisconsin of any age who are constituents of the Spina Bifida Association of Wisconsin (SBAWI). Applicants must be enrolled or planning to enroll at a college, graduate school, trade school, or specialized educational training program in any state. Along with their application, they must submit a personal statement explaining their goals and what they want to accomplish with the education or training they will receive. There is no age limitation. Selection is based on that statement, academic record, community service, work history, leadership, and financial need. Priority is given to applicants who are active in SBAWI.

Financial data A stipend is awarded (amount not specified); funds are paid directly to the recipient's institution to be used for payment of tuition, books, room and board, and specialized equipment needs.

Duration 1 year; recipients may reapply.

Additional data This program was established in 1996.

Number awarded 1 each year.

Deadline March of each year.

[701]
SPINA BIFIDA ASSOCIATION ONE-YEAR SCHOLARSHIP

Spina Bifida Association of America
Attn: Scholarship Committee
4590 MacArthur Boulevard, N.W., Suite 250
Washington, DC 20007-4226
(202) 944-3285, ext. 13
Toll Free: (800) 621-3141, ext. 13
Fax: (202) 944-3295   E-mail: cjhead@sbaa.org
Web: www.spinabifidaassociation.org

Summary To provide financial assistance to undergraduate and graduate students who have spina bifida.

Eligibility This program is open to persons of any age who were born with spina bifida and are enrolled in or accepted by a junior college, 4-year university, graduate school, or approved trade, vocational, or business school. Applicants must submit a 3-page personal statement explaining their educational goals; transcripts; standardized test scores (ACT, SAT, GRE, or equivalent; adult students may submit a recent transcript); verification of acceptance by a college; information related to financial need; letters of recommendation; and a physician's statement verifying disability.

Financial data The stipend is $2,000.

Duration 1 year.

Additional data This program was established in 1988.

Number awarded Up to 6 each year.

Deadline March of each year.

[702]
UCB FAMILY RA SCHOLARSHIP PROGRAM

UCB, Inc.
c/o Summit Medical Communications
1421 East Broad Street, Suite 340
Fuquay-Varina, NC 27526
(919) 567-7590   Toll Free: (888) 854-4996
Fax: (919) 567-7591
E-mail: ucbrascholarship@summitmedcomm.com
Web: www.reachbeyondra.com

Summary To provide financial assistance to undergraduate and graduate students who have rheumatoid arthritis (RA) and their families.

Eligibility This program is open to students who are working on or planning to work on an associate, undergraduate, or graduate degree or are enrolled in a trade school educational program. Applicants must have been diagnosed with RA or be an immediate family member (parent, spouse, child, or sibling) of a person with RA. They may be of any age. Along with their application, they must submit an essay of 1 to 2 pages describing how they are living beyond the boundaries of RA to demonstrate academic ambition and personal achievement and how the scholarship would impact their life.

Financial data Stipends range up to $5,000.

Duration 1 year; nonrenewable.

Additional data This program began on a pilot basis in 2008.

Number awarded 30 each year.

Deadline March of each year.

[703]
UNITED CEREBRAL PALSY OF METROBOSTON COLLEGE SCHOLARSHIP

United Cerebral Palsy of MetroBoston
Attn: Development and Marketing Department
71 Arsenal Street
Watertown, MA 02472
(617) 600-2450   Fax: (617) 926-3059
E-mail: ucpboston@ucpboston.org
Web: ucpboston.org

Summary To provide financial assistance to residents of Massachusetts who have cerebral palsy and are interested in attending college or graduate school in any state.

Eligibility This program is open to Massachusetts residents who are high school seniors, undergraduates, or graduate students and have a primary diagnosis of cerebral palsy. Applicants must be enrolled or planning to enroll full time at an accredited college or university in any state. Along with their application, they must submit a 250-word essay about their disability, based on such topics as how they have overcome the challenge of their disability, what having a disability means to them, someone who has been helpful in their success, or an achievement of which they are proud. They must also submit a letter from their doctor confirming that they have cerebral palsy, 2 letters of recommendation, transcripts, and an acceptance letter from the college or university of their choice.

Financial data The stipend is $1,000.

Duration 1 year.

Number awarded 1 each year.

Deadline April of each year.

[704]
WINTERHOFF COLLEGIATE SCHOLARSHIP

Arthritis Foundation-Greater Southwest Chapter
1313 East Osborn Road, Suite 200
Phoenix, AZ 85014
(602) 264-7679   Toll Free: (800) 477-7679
Fax: (602) 264-0563
Web: www.arthritis.org/arizona/aboutwinterhoff.php

Summary To provide funding to students at public universities in Arizona who have a rheumatic disease.

Eligibility This program is open to full-time undergraduate and graduate students at public 4-year universities in Arizona. Applicants must have some form of diagnosed rheumatic disease and provide a physician's certifying statement. They must be willing to be involved in Arthritis Foundation publicity and agree to meet with foundation officials in Phoenix.

Financial data The stipend is $7,500 per year.

Duration 1 year; may be renewed up to 3 additional years, provided the recipient remains enrolled full time and maintains a GPA of 2.5 or higher.

Number awarded 1 or more each year.

Deadline January of each year at Arizona State University; February of each year at The University of Arizona and Northern Arizona University.

Grants-in-Aid

[705]
ALPHA ONE HOME RETRO PROGRAM

Alpha One
127 Main Street
South Portland, ME 04106
(207) 767-2189   Toll Free: (800) 640-7200
Fax: (207) 799-8346   TDD: (207) 767-5387
E-mail: info@mpowerloans.org
Web: alphaonenow.com/info.php?id=55#grants

Summary To provide funding to homeowners in Maine who wish to make modifications for a resident who has a physical disability.

Eligibility This program is open to residents of Maine who own their residence and have a person with a disability (including children) living in their home. Applicants must have an income less than 80% of the median income

for their county. Their home must have indoor plumbing and (if a mobile home) have been built after June 15, 1976. They must be interested in making modifications to accommodate the disabled resident; examples include widening doorways; adding a roll in shower and fold down seat; building a ramp; remodeling a kitchen, bathroom, or bedroom; repairing a roof; or replacing windows. At least 75% of the funds must be used for accessibility rehabs that will improve the life of the disabled resident, with a focus on health and safety. The remaining 25% of the total expenses for access may be used for home repair.

Financial data Grants up to $15,000 are available.

Additional data This program is administered by Alpha One in collaboration with the Maine State Housing Authority.

Number awarded Varies each year.

Deadline Applications may be submitted at any time.

[706]
ALTERNATIVES IN MOTION GRANTS

Alternatives in Motion
201 Matilda, N.E.
Grand Rapids, MI 49503
(616) 493-2620   Toll Free: (877) 468-9335
Fax: (616) 493-2621
E-mail: info@alternativesinmotion.org
Web: www.alternativesinmotion.org

Summary To provide funding to people who need assistance to purchase a wheelchair.

Eligibility This program is open to people who can demonstrate a medical necessity for a wheelchair but do not have financial resources to purchase it. Interested parties must visit a local wheelchair vendor and determine their exact mobility needs in consultation with rehabilitation and seating specialists. They must submit that information (including estimates of the cost of the wheelchair), a letter of medical necessity from their physician, a letter of denial from an insurance company, and a copy of their most recent federal tax return.

Financial data Grants cover the full cost of wheelchairs as verified by the vendor and medical experts.

Duration These are 1-time grants.

Additional data This foundation was started in 1995.

Number awarded Varies each year; since the program began, it has made 1,014 grants to 673 individuals in 133 Michigan cities and 21 other states. The total value of cash and in-kind donations has been more than $4.1 million.

Deadline Applications may be submitted at any time.

[707]
ARKANSAS DISABLED VETERANS PROPERTY TAX EXEMPTION

Arkansas Assessment Coordination Department
1614 West Third Street
Little Rock, AR 72201-1815
(501) 324-9240   Fax: (501) 324-9242
E-mail: dasbury@acd.state.ar.us
Web: www.arkansas.gov/acd

Summary To exempt from taxation the property owned by blind or disabled veterans, surviving spouses, and minor dependent children in Arkansas.

Eligibility This program is open to disabled veterans in Arkansas who have been awarded special monthly compensation by the U.S. Department of Veterans Affairs and who have 1) the loss of or the loss of use of 1 or more limbs, 2) total blindness in 1 or both eyes, or 3) total and permanent disability. The benefit also extends to veterans' unremarried surviving spouses and their minor children.

Financial data Qualifying veterans (or their unremarried widows or dependent children) are exempt from payment of all state taxes on their homestead and personal property.

Duration This exemption continues as long as the qualifying veteran (or dependent) resides in Arkansas.

Number awarded Varies each year.

Deadline Applications may be submitted at any time.

[708]
AUTOMOBILE ALLOWANCE FOR DISABLED VETERANS

Department of Veterans Affairs
Attn: Veterans Benefits Administration
810 Vermont Avenue, N.W.
Washington, DC 20420
(202) 418-4343   Toll Free: (800) 827-1000
Web: www1.va.gov

Summary To provide funding to certain disabled veterans and current service personnel who require specially adapted automobiles.

Eligibility To be eligible for a grant for an automobile, a veteran or current service member must have a service-connected loss or permanent loss of use of 1 or both hands or feet or permanent impairment of vision of both eyes to a prescribed degree. For adaptive equipment eligibility only, veterans entitled to compensation for ankylosis of 1 or both knees, or 1 or both hips, also qualify.

Financial data The grant consists of a payment by the Department of Veterans Affairs (VA) of up to $18,900 toward the purchase of an automobile or other conveyance. The VA will also pay for the adaptive equipment, its repair, and the replacement or reinstallation required for the safe operation of the vehicle purchased with VA assistance or for a previously or subsequently acquired vehicle.

Duration This is a 1-time grant.

Number awarded Varies each year.

Deadline Applications may be submitted at any time.

[709]
BARR FOUNDATION AMPUTEE ASSISTANCE FUND

Barr Foundation
136 N.E. Olive Way
Boca Raton, FL 33432
(561) 391-7601   E-mail: t-barr@t-barr.com
Web: www.oandp.com/resources/organizations/barr

Summary To provide funding to amputees who require assistance for prosthetic care.

Eligibility This program is open to amputees who cannot afford limbs or other maintenance costs of prosthetic care. Applicants must be able to submit proof of denial of all other funding resources, although bilateral amputees are not eligible unless another source of funding from an individual or organization is also available. Requests for applications must be submitted by a board-certified or state-licensed prosthetist.

Financial data Grants provide reimbursement for materials and maintenance costs to prosthetists.

Duration These are 1-time grants.

Additional data This program was established in 1995.

Number awarded Varies each year. Since this program was established, it has provided assistance to more than 1,200 amputees.

Deadline Requests may be submitted at any time.

[710]
CALIFORNIA DISABLED VETERAN EXEMPTION FROM THE IN LIEU TAX FEE FOR A MANUFACTURED HOME OR MOBILEHOME

Department of Housing and Community Development
Attn: Registration and Titling
1800 Third Street
P.O. Box 2111
Sacramento, CA 95812-2111
(916) 323-9224   Toll Free: (800) 952-8356
Web: www.hcd.ca.gov

Summary To provide a special property tax exemption to blind or disabled California veterans and/or their spouses who own and occupy a mobile home.

Eligibility This program is open to disabled veterans and/or their spouses in California who have a manufactured home or mobile home as their principal place of residence. Veterans must be disabled as a result of injury or disease incurred in military service and have been a resident of California 1) at the time of entry into the service and be blind, or have lost the use of 1 or more limbs, or be totally disabled; 2) on November 7, 1972 and be blind in both eyes, or have lost the use of 2 or more limbs; or 3) on January 1, 1975 and be totally disabled. The spouses and unremarried surviving spouses of those disabled veterans are also eligible.

Financial data The exemption applies to the first $20,000 of the assessed market value of the manufactured home or mobile home. Veterans and/or spouses whose income falls below a specified level are entitled to an additional $10,000 exemption. The amount of the exemption is 100% if the home is owned by a veteran only, a veteran and spouse, or a spouse only; 50% if owned by a veteran and another person other than a spouse or by a spouse and another person other than the veteran; 67% if owned by a veteran, the spouse, and another person; 34% if owned by a veteran and 2 other people other than a spouse or by a spouse and 2 other people; 50% if owned by a veteran, the spouse, and 2 other people; or 25% if owned by a veteran and 3 other people or by a spouse and 3 other people.

Duration The exemption is available annually as long as the applicant meets all requirements.

Number awarded Varies each year.

Deadline Deadline not specified.

[711]
CHILDREN'S BRITTLE BONE FOUNDATION AND OI FOUNDATION IMPACT GRANT PROGRAM

Children's Brittle Bone Foundation
Attn: Impact Grant Program
7701 95th Street
Pleasant Prairie, WI 53158
(773) 263-2223   Fax: (262) 947-0724
E-mail: info@cbbf.org
Web: www.cbbf.org/Impact_Grant.htm

Summary To provide funding for education or other purposes to people who have osteogenesis imperfecta (OI).

Eligibility This program is open to people who have OI and are seeking funding for equipment or services that will improve their quality of life. Examples of acceptable requests include education-related items such as tuition assistance at the preschool to postdoctoral level; prescribed exercise therapy equipment for physical or occupational therapy; orthotics, braces, and walkers; manual or electric wheelchairs or scooters; adaptive technology such as computers or hearing aids; dental intervention; vehicle modifications such as lifts or pedal extensions or vehicle purchases; travel reimbursement to receive specialized care; outdoor ramps that provide access to a home; or accessibility aides such as reachers, shower chairs, or kitchen carts.

Financial data Grants range from $500 to $20,000.

Duration Funds must be used within 12 months.

Additional data This program is provided jointly by the Children's Brittle Bone Foundation and the Osteogenesis Imperfecta (OI) Foundation.

Number awarded Varies; recently, 5 were awarded.

Deadline January of each year.

[712]
CONNECTICUT REAL ESTATE TAX EXEMPTION FOR DISABLED VETERANS

Office of Policy and Management
Attn: Intergovernmental Policy Division
450 Capitol Avenue
Hartford, CT 06106-1308
(860) 418-6278   Toll Free: (800) 286-2214 (within CT)
Fax: (860) 418-6493   TDD: (860) 418-6456
E-mail: leeann.graham@ct.gov
Web: www.ct.gov

Summary To exempt disabled or blind Connecticut veterans and their surviving spouses from the payment of a portion of their local property taxes.

Eligibility There are 2 categories of Connecticut veterans who qualify for exemptions from their dwelling house and the lot on which it is located: 1) those with major service-connected disabilities (paraplegia or osteochondritis resulting in permanent loss of the use of both legs or per-

manent paralysis of both legs and lower parts of the body; hemiplegia with permanent paralysis of 1 leg and 1 arm or either side of the body resulting from injury to the spinal cord, skeletal structure, or brain, or from disease of the spinal cord not resulting from syphilis; total blindness; amputation of both arms, both legs, both hands or both feet, or the combination of a hand and a foot; sustained through enemy action or resulting from an accident occurring or disease contracted in such active service) and 2) those with less severe disabilities (loss of use of 1 arm or 1 leg because of service-connected injuries). Surviving unremarried spouses of eligible deceased veterans are entitled to the same exemption as would have been granted to the veteran, as long as they continue to be the legal owner/occupier of the exempted residence. An additional exemption is available to veterans and spouses whose total adjusted gross income is less than $32,300 if unmarried or $39,500 if married. If the veteran is rated as 100% disabled by the U.S. Department of Veterans Affairs (VA), the maximum income levels are $18,000 if unmarried or $21,000 if married.

Financial data Veterans in the first category receive an exemption from local property taxation of $10,000 of assessed valuation. Veterans in the second category receive exemptions of $5,000 of assessed valuation. For veterans whose income is less than the specified levels, additional exemptions of $20,000 for the first category or $10,000 for the second category are available from municipalities that choose to participate. For veterans whose income exceeds the specified levels, the additional exemption from participating municipalities is $5,000 for the first category or $2,500 for the second category. Connecticut municipalities may also elect to exempt from taxation specially adapted housing acquired or modified by a veteran under the provisions of Section 801 of Title 38 of the United States Code.

Duration 1 year; exemptions continue as long as the eligible resident (or surviving spouse) owns/occupies the primary residence and lives in Connecticut.

Number awarded Varies each year; recently, a total of 19,669 veterans received property tax exemptions through this and other programs in Connecticut.

Deadline Applications for the additional municipality exemption must be submitted to the assessor's office of the town or residence by September of every other year.

[713]
DELAWARE PENSION BENEFITS FOR PARAPLEGIC VETERANS

Delaware Commission of Veterans Affairs
Robbins Building
802 Silver Lake Boulevard, Suite 100
Dover, DE 19904
(302) 739-2792   Toll Free: (800) 344-9900 (within DE)
Fax: (302) 739-2794
E-mail: antonio.davila@state.de.us
Web: veteransaffairs.delaware.gov

Summary To provide a monthly pension to paraplegic veterans in Delaware.

Eligibility Eligible for this benefit are Delaware residents who are paraplegic as a result of service in the armed forces of the United States while it was officially at war or during a period when the United States was engaged in hostilities with another nation as a member of the United Nations. Applicants must be listed on the rolls of the U.S. Department of Veterans Affairs as totally disabled.

Financial data The pension is $3,000 per year.

Duration Recipients remain eligible for this pension as long as they reside in Delaware.

Deadline Deadline not specified.

[714]
FLORIDA PROPERTY TAX EXEMPTION FOR TOTALLY AND PERMANENTLY DISABLED PERSONS

Florida Department of Revenue
Attn: Taxpayer Services
5050 West Tennessee Street
Tallahassee, FL 32399-0100
(850) 617-8600   Toll Free: (800) 352-3671
E-mail: EMailDOR@dor.state.fl.us
Web: www.myflorida.com

Summary To exempt from property taxation real estate owned by blind or disabled people in Florida.

Eligibility This exemption is available to Florida residents who have real estate that they own and use as a homestead. Applications are accepted from 2 categories of residents: 1) those who are quadriplegic (regardless of income); or 2) those who are paraplegic or hemiplegic, have another total and permanent disability that requires use of a wheelchair for mobility, or are legally blind, and have an income below a specified limit that changes annually (recently, it was $25,544 per year).

Financial data All real estate used and owned as a homestead, less any portion used for commercial purposes, is exempt from taxation.

Duration The exemption applies as long as the taxpayer owns the property in Florida.

Additional data Initial applications should be made in person at the appropriate county property appraiser's office.

Number awarded Varies each year.

Deadline Applications must be submitted by February of the year for which the exemption is sought.

[715]
FORD MOBILITY MOTORING PROGRAM

Ford Motor Company
Attn: Mobility Program
500 Hulet Drive
P.O. Box 529
Bloomfield Hills, MI 48303
Toll Free: (800) 952-2248, ext. 111
Fax: (248) 333-0300
TDD: (800) 833-0312
E-mail: Mobilitymotoring@Fordprogramhq.com
Web: www.mobilitymotoringprogram.com

Summary To provide a cash reimbursement for the cost of installing adaptive driving aids on new vehicles from Ford or Lincoln-Mercury.

Eligibility Eligible for this rebate are people who purchase or lease new Ford, Lincoln, or Mercury vehicles that require adaptive driving aids or conversion equipment for users with disabilities.

Financial data Up to $1,200 is reimbursed for adaptive equipment or up to $200 for alert hearing devices, lumbar support, or running boards.

Additional data The program also provides 24-hour roadside assistance.

Number awarded Varies each year.

Deadline Applicants have 12 months from the date or purchase or lease to initiate the adaptive work and 1 year from that date to process their claim.

[716]
GEORGE BOCK CHARITABLE TRUST GRANTS

Little People of America, Inc.
Attn: Vice President of Programs
250 El Camino Real, Suite 201
Tustin, CA 92780
(714) 368-3689   Toll Free: (888) LPA-2001
Fax: (714) 368-3367   E-mail: info@lpaonline.org
Web: www.lpaonline.org

Summary To provide funding for medical expenses to members of the Little People of America (LPA).

Eligibility This program is open to members of LPA (limited to people who, for medical reasons, are 4 feet 10 inches or under in height). Applicants must be seeking funding for major dwarf-related medical expenses not covered by insurance. Support is not available for deductibles, co-insurance fees, routine medical expenses, well baby care, or accident-related costs. First priority is given to LPA members of the Garden State Chapter residing in New Jersey; funding is available to members from other states only after the needs of New Jersey members have been met.

Financial data Grant amounts depend on the need of the recipient.

Duration Grants may provide for payment of 1 medical bill or a portion thereof.

Number awarded Varies each year.

Deadline Applications may be submitted at any time.

[717]
GM MOBILITY PROGRAM

General Motors Corporation
Attn: GM Mobility Assistance Center
P.O. Box 5053
Troy, MI 48007
Toll Free: (800) 323-9935   TDD: (800) TDD-9935
Web: www.gmmobility.com

Summary To provide a cash reimbursement for the cost of installing adaptive driving aids on new purchases from General Motors.

Eligibility Eligible for this rebate are purchasers or lessees of new General Motors cars, trucks, or vans that require adaptive driving aids or conversion equipment for users with disabilities.

Financial data Up to $1,000 is reimbursed ($1,200 for Chevy Express and GMC Savana vans).

Additional data Applications for reimbursement are submitted through the dealer from whom the vehicle was originally purchased. Only retail purchases or leases of new General Motors vehicles qualify for this program. The reimbursement applies only to equipment installed by converters in the after market, not to factory installed equipment of any kind.

Deadline The conversion process must be completed within 12 months from the date of purchase or lease and the claim form must be submitted within 90 days after the completion of the conversion.

[718]
JACK NORTON FAMILY RESPITE CARE PROGRAM

ALS Association-MN/ND/SD Chapter
Attn: Patient Services Coordinator
333 North Washington Avenue, Suite 105
Minneapolis, MN 55401
(612) 672-0484   Toll Free: (888) 672-0484
Fax: (612) 672-9110   E-mail: anne@alsmn.org
Web: webmn.alsa.org

Summary To provide funding for respite care to residents of the upper Midwest who are a Person with Amyotrophic Lateral Sclerosis (PALS) or family member.

Eligibility This assistance is available to any PALS or family member living in Minnesota, North Dakota, eastern South Dakota, or Superior, Wisconsin. The family caregiver must be living with and caring for a PALS on a full-time basis.

Financial data The program provides funding to pay for a family caregiver to assist in caring for the PALS.

Duration Funding is provided for 18 hours a month.

Additional data The Minnesota Chapter of the ALS Association arranges with an appropriate licensed home care agency to provide the respite care.

Number awarded Varies each year.

Deadline Applications may be submitted at any time.

[719]
KARA CALDWELL-FREEMAN LEADERSHIP SCHOLARSHIP

California Dietetic Association
Attn: CDA Foundation
7740 Manchester Avenue, Suite 102
Playa del Rey, CA 90293-8499
(310) 822-0177   Fax: (310) 823-0264
E-mail: patsmith@dietitian.org
Web: www.dietitian.org/cdaf_scholarships.htm

Summary To provide financial assistance to members of the American Dietetic Association (ADA) from California who are interested in participating in a Supervised Practice Program in any state.

Eligibility This program is open to ADA members who graduated from or are attending a California college or

university. Applicants must have been accepted to an accredited Supervised Practice Program in any state to begin within 6 months. They must have a GPA of 3.0 or higher in undergraduate dietetic course work and a record of leadership by service as an officer in a department club. Along with their application, they must submit a letter of application that includes a discussion of their career goals. Selection is based on that letter (15%), academic ability (25%), work or volunteer experience (15%), letters of recommendation (15%), extracurricular activities (5%), and financial need (25%). Applications are especially encouraged from ethnic minorities, men, and people with physical disabilities.

Financial data The stipend is normally $1,000.

Duration 1 year.

Number awarded 1 each year.

Deadline February of each year.

[720]
KELLY BRUSH FOUNDATION INDIVIDUAL GRANT PROGRAM

Kelly Brush Foundation
7 Aspen Drive
South Burlington, VT 05403
(802) 846-5298   Fax: (802) 864-9990
E-mail: betsycabrera@kellybrushfoundation.org
Web: www.kellybrushfoundation.org

Summary To provide funding to people who are living with a spinal cord injury and are interested in obtaining adaptive sporting equipment.

Eligibility This program is open to paraplegics and quadriplegics who are paralyzed because of a spinal cord injury; people paralyzed because of other causes, such as multiple sclerosis or spina bifida, are not eligible. Applicants must be interested in obtaining funding to purchase adaptive sports or recreational equipment, such as a monoski or handcycle. Applications for adaptive equipment that does not fall into the sports and recreation category are not considered. Financial need is considered in the selection process.

Financial data The amounts of the grants vary; recently they averaged approximately $3,600.

Duration These are 1-time grants.

Additional data Recipients must supply the foundation with pictures of the equipment purchased with the grant funds and a description of how the grant enriched their quality of life.

Number awarded Varies each year; recently, 13 of these grants (worth more than $47,000) were awarded.

Deadline September of each year.

[721]
LIMBS FOR LIFE PROSTHESIS FUND

Limbs for Life Foundation
218 East Main Street
Oklahoma City, OK 73104
(405) 605-5462   Toll Free: (888) 235-5462
Fax: (405) 843-5123   E-mail: admin@limbsforlife.org
Web: www.limbsforlife.org/programs.htm

Summary To provide funding to amputees who lack financial resources to obtain adequate prosthetic care.

Eligibility This program is open to amputees who can demonstrate that their financial resources are inadequate to obtain prosthetic care. Applicants should write a letter (telephone calls and e-mails are not accepted) explaining their circumstances and need. They must be legal residents of the United States and never convicted of a felony.

Financial data Grants cover materials and fitting charges up to $2,000 for upper extremity or hip disarticulation, up to $1,500 for above knee, or up to $1,250 for below knee. An additional $500 is provided for repairs and adjustments for the first 6 months after the patient takes delivery of the prosthesis. For recent amputees receiving a temporary limb, an additional reimbursement of $500 for above knee or above elbow or $250 for below knee or below elbow is provided.

Duration Each patient may receive assistance once in a 36-month period.

Additional data The foundation started in 1995.

Number awarded Approximately 700 amputees receive assistance from the foundation each year.

Deadline Applications may be submitted at any time.

[722]
LITTLE PEOPLE OF AMERICA HEALTH ADVOCACY FUND GRANTS

Little People of America, Inc.
Attn: Vice President of Programs
250 El Camino Real, Suite 201
Tustin, CA 92780
(714) 368-3689   Toll Free: (888) LPA-2001
Fax: (714) 368-3367   E-mail: info@lpaonline.org
Web: www.lpaonline.org

Summary To provide funding for medical expenses to members of the Little People of America (LPA).

Eligibility This program is open to members of LPA (limited to people who, for medical reasons, are 4 feet 10 inches or under in height). Applicants must be seeking funding for major dwarf-related medical expenses, such as surgeries related to a specific dwarfism condition, placement or removal of shunts, decompression surgery, and orthopedic procedures. Support is not available for cosmetic purposes or extended leg-lengthening procedures.

Financial data Grants provide assistance for payment of remaining medical expenses after coinsurance, insurance deductibles, and other payments toward medical expenses have been applied.

Duration Grants may provide for payment of 1 medical bill or a portion thereof.

Number awarded Varies each year.

Deadline Applications may be submitted at any time.

[723]
MAINE TAX EXEMPTION FOR SPECIALLY ADAPTED HOUSING UNITS

Maine Revenue Services
Attn: Property Tax Division
P.O. Box 9106
Augusta, ME 04332-9106
(207) 287-2013   Fax: (207) 287-6396
E-mail: prop.tax@maine.gov
Web: www.maine.gov

Summary To exempt the specially adapted housing units of paraplegic veterans or their surviving spouses from taxation in Maine.

Eligibility Veterans who served in the U.S. armed forces during any federally-recognized war period, are legal residents of Maine, are paraplegic veterans within the meaning of U.S. statutes, and have received a grant from the U.S. government for specially adapted housing are eligible. The exemption also applies to property held in joint tenancy with the veteran's spouse and to the specially adapted housing of unremarried widow(er)s of eligible veterans.

Financial data Estates of paraplegic veterans are exempt up to $50,000 of just valuation for a specially adapted housing unit.

Duration The exemption is valid for the lifetime of the paraplegic veteran or unremarried widow(er).

Number awarded Varies each year.

Deadline When an eligible person first submits an application, the proof of entitlement must reach the assessors of the local municipality prior to the end of March. Once eligibility has been established, notification need not be repeated in subsequent years.

[724]
MASSACHUSETTS VETERANS ANNUITY PROGRAM

Department of Veterans' Services
Attn: Annuities
600 Washington Street, Seventh Floor
Boston, MA 02111
(617) 210-5480   Fax: (617) 210-5755
E-mail: mdvs@vet.state.ma.us
Web: www.mass.gov/veterans

Summary To provide an annuity to blind or disabled veterans from Massachusetts and to the parents and spouses of deceased military personnel.

Eligibility This program is open to 1) veterans who are blind, double amputee, paraplegic, or have a 100% service-connected disability; 2) the parents of military personnel who died of service-connected causes; and 3) the unremarried spouses of military personnel who died of service-connected causes. Veterans must have been residents of Massachusetts at the time of entry into military service who served during specified wartime periods and received other than a dishonorable discharge. All applicants must currently be residents of Massachusetts.

Financial data Recipients are entitled to an annuity of $2,000 per year.

Duration The annuity is paid as long as the recipient continues to reside in Massachusetts.

Deadline Deadline not specified.

[725]
MICHIGAN INCOME TAX EXEMPTION FOR PEOPLE WITH DISABILITIES

Michigan Department of Treasury
Attn: Income Tax
Treasury Building
430 West Allegan Street
Lansing, MI 48922
(517) 373-3200   TDD: (800) 649-3777
E-mail: treasIndTax@michigan.gov
Web: www.michigan.gov/taxes

Summary To exempt a portion of the income of deaf, blind, and disabled residents of Michigan from state income taxation.

Eligibility Eligible for this exemption are residents of Michigan who 1) receive messages through a sense other than hearing, such as lip reading or sign language; 2) have vision in their better eye of 20/200 or less with corrective lenses or peripheral field of vision of 20 degrees or less; or 3) are hemiplegic, paraplegic, quadriplegic, or totally and permanently disabled.

Financial data Qualifying people with disabilities receive an exemption of $2,400 from their adjusted gross income for purposes of state taxation.

Duration The exemption continues as long as the recipient resides in Michigan.

Deadline Deadline not specified.

[726]
MOBILITY BY VOLVO

Volvo Cars of North America, LLC
Attn: Mobility by Volvo
1 Volvo Drive
Rockleigh, NJ 07647
Toll Free: (800) 803-5222   TDD: (800) 833-0312
E-mail: MobilitybyVolvo@Volvoprogramhq.com
Web: www.volvocars.us/mobility

Summary To provide a cash reimbursement for the cost of installing adaptive driving aids or alert hearing devices on new purchases of Volvo vehicles.

Eligibility This rebate is available to purchasers of new Volvo vehicles that require adaptive driving aids or alert hearing devices for users with disabilities. Applicants must obtain the equipment, have it installed, and submit a copy of their paid invoice and a copy of their medical prescription.

Financial data Up to $1,000 is provided for the cost of adding adaptive equipment or $200 for an alert hearing device.

Deadline Eligible vehicles must be upfitted with approved adaptive equipment or alert hearing devices, and requests must be submitted within 180 days of vehicle purchase.

[727]
MULTIPLE SCLEROSIS HELPING HANDS FINANCIAL ASSISTANCE GRANTS

Multiple Sclerosis Helping Hands
Attn: Financial Assistance Scholarship Fund
9792 Edmonds Way, Suite 229
Edmonds, WA 98020
(425) 712-1804   Fax: (425) 776-1712
E-mail: info@mshelp.org
Web: www.mshelp.org

Summary To provide funding for special needs to residents of Washington who have multiple sclerosis.

Eligibility This program is open to Washington residents who have a medical diagnosis of multiple sclerosis. Applicants must be able to document financial need and a record of rejection by other agencies (e.g., Medicaid, DSHS, insurance companies). They must be in need of assistance to pay for housing (e.g., overdue rent or mortgage payments, utilities, phone bills), overdue medical expenses, food, expenses from a natural disaster, or durable medical equipment.

Financial data The maximum grant is $1,500 per year.

Duration Only 1 request per year is accepted.

Additional data This program began in 2006.

Number awarded Varies each year; since the program began, it has awarded more than $330,000 in grants.

Deadline Applications may be submitted at any time.

[728]
NATIONAL CRANIOFACIAL ASSOCIATION CLIENT TRAVEL GRANTS-IN-AID

FACES: The National Craniofacial Association
P.O. Box 11082
Chattanooga, TN 37401
(423) 266-1632   Toll Free: (800) 3-FACES-3
Fax: (423) 267-3124   E-mail: faces@faces-cranio.org
Web: www.faces-cranio.org

Summary To provide funding for travel expenses for persons with severe facial deformities who travel to comprehensive medical centers for reconstructive facial surgery.

Eligibility Persons with craniofacial deformities resulting from birth defects, injury, or disease are eligible to apply for these grants-in-aid if they need to travel to comprehensive medical centers to undergo reconstructive facial surgery and/or evaluation.

Financial data Funds are available for transportation, food, lodging, parking, and tolls related to the treatment. No medical costs are covered. Grants also provide for 1 accompanying person for each trip.

Additional data FACES: The National Craniofacial Association was founded in 1969 as the Debbie Fox Foundation. It changed its name because it no longer serves only Debbie.

Number awarded Varies each year.

Deadline Applications may be submitted at any time.

[729]
NEBRASKA HOMESTEAD EXEMPTION

Nebraska Department of Revenue
301 Centennial Mall South
P.O. Box 94818
Lincoln, NE 68509-4818
(402) 471-5729
Toll Free: (800) 742-7474 (within NE and IA)
Web: www.revenue.ne.gov/PAD/homestead.html

Summary   To exempt the property of Nebraska residents who are elderly, disabled, or veterans and their widow(er)s from a portion of taxation.

Eligibility   This exemption is available to 3 categories of Nebraska residents: the elderly, certain people with disabilities, and certain disabled veterans and their widow(er)s. Elderly people are those 65 years of age or older who own a homestead with a value less than $95,000 or 200% of their county's average assessed value of single family residential property, whichever is greater. Disabled people are those who 1) have a permanent physical disability and have lost all mobility such as to preclude locomotion without the regular use of a mechanical aid or prosthesis; 2) have undergone amputation of both arms above the elbow, or 3) have a permanent partial disability of both arms in excess of 75%. They must own a homestead with a value less than $110,000 or 225% of their county's average assessed value of single family residential property, whichever is greater. Veterans are those who served on active duty in the U.S. armed forces (or a government allied with the United States) during specified periods of war and received an honorable discharge. They must 1) be drawing compensation from the U.S. Department of Veterans Affairs (VA) because of a 100% service-connected disability; 2) be totally disabled by a nonservice-connected illness or accident; or 3) own a home that is substantially contributed to by VA. Also eligible are unremarried widow(er)s of veterans who died because of a service-connected disability, whose death while on active duty was service-connected, who died while on active duty during war time, or who drew compensation from VA because of a 100% service-connected disability The homestead maximum value is $110,000 or 225% of the county's average assessed value of single family residential property, whichever is greater. Elderly people must have a household income less than $31,801 if single or $37,401 if married. Disabled persons, veterans, and widow(er)s (except veterans and widow(er)s who own a home that is substantially contributed to by the VA) must have a household income less than $34,901 if single or $40,301 if married.

Financial data   Exemptions depend on the income of the applicant, ranging from 25% to 100% of the value of the homestead. For the elderly, the maximum exemption is the taxable value of the homestead up to $40,000 or 100% of the county's average assessed value of single family residential property, whichever is greater. For disabled people and veterans, the maximum exemption is the taxable value of the homestead up to $50,000 or 120% of the county's average assessed value of single family residential property, whichever is greater. For veterans and widow(er)s whose home was substantially contributed to by the VA, the homestead is 100% exempt regardless of the value of the homestead or the income of the owner.

Duration   The exemption is provided as long as the qualifying homestead owner resides in Nebraska.

Number awarded   Varies each year.

Deadline   Applications must be filed by June of each year.

[730]
NEW HAMPSHIRE PROPERTY TAX EXEMPTION FOR CERTAIN DISABLED VETERANS

New Hampshire Department of Revenue
  Administration
109 Pleasant Street
Concord, NH 03301
(603) 271-2191   Fax: (603) 271-6121
TDD: (800) 735-2964
Web: revenue.nh.gov

Summary   To exempt from taxation certain property owned by New Hampshire blind and other disabled veterans or their surviving spouses.

Eligibility   Eligible for this exemption are New Hampshire residents who are honorably discharged veterans with a total and permanent service-connected disability that involves double amputation of the upper or lower extremities or any combination thereof, paraplegia, or blindness of both eyes with visual acuity of 5/200 or less. Applicants or their surviving spouses must own a specially adapted homestead that has been acquired with the assistance of the U.S. Department of Veterans Affairs.

Financial data   Qualifying disabled veterans and surviving spouses are exempt from all taxation on their specially adapted homestead.

Duration   1 year; once the credit has been approved, it is automatically renewed as long as the qualifying person owns the same residence in New Hampshire.

Number awarded   Varies each year.

Deadline   The original application for a permanent tax credit must be submitted by April.

[731]
NEW HAMPSHIRE SERVICE-CONNECTED TOTAL AND PERMANENT DISABILITY TAX CREDIT

New Hampshire Department of Revenue
  Administration
109 Pleasant Street
Concord, NH 03301
(603) 271-2191   Fax: (603) 271-6121
TDD: (800) 735-2964
Web: revenue.nh.gov

Summary   To provide property tax credits in New Hampshire to disabled veterans or their surviving spouses.

Eligibility   Eligible for this tax credit are honorably discharged veterans residing in New Hampshire who 1) have a total and permanent service-connected disability, or 2) are a double amputee or paraplegic because of a service-connected disability. Unremarried surviving spouses of qualified veterans are also eligible.

Financial data Qualifying disabled veterans and surviving spouses receive an annual credit of $700 for property taxes on residential property. In addition, individual towns in New Hampshire may adopt a local option to increase the dollar amount credited to disabled veterans, to a maximum of $2,000.

Duration 1 year; once the credit has been approved, it is automatically renewed for as long as the qualifying person owns the same residence in New Hampshire.

Number awarded Varies each year.

Deadline The original application for a permanent tax credit must be submitted by April.

[732]
NEW YORK "ELIGIBLE FUNDS" PROPERTY TAX EXEMPTIONS FOR VETERANS

New York State Department of Taxation and Finance
Attn: Office of Real Property Tax Services
W.A. Harriman Campus
Building 8, Sixth Floor
Albany, NY 12227
(518) 486-4403   Fax: (518) 486-7754
Web: www.orps.state.ny.us

Summary To provide a partial exemption from property taxes to disabled and other veterans and their surviving spouses who are residents of New York.

Eligibility This program is open to veterans who have purchased properties in New York with such income as retirement pay, disability compensation, or death gratuities (referred to as "eligible funds"). Specially adapted homes of paraplegics, or the homes of their widowed spouses, are also covered.

Financial data This exemption reduces the property's assessed value to the extent that "eligible funds" were used in the purchase, generally to a maximum of $5,000. It is applicable to general municipal taxes but not to school taxes or special district levies.

Duration This exemption is available annually.

Number awarded Varies each year.

Deadline Applications must be filed with the local assessor by "taxable status date;" in most towns, that is the end of February.

[733]
NFED TREATMENT ASSISTANCE PROGRAM

National Foundation for Ectodermal Dysplasias
Attn: Director of Treatment Assistance Program
410 East Main Street
P.O. Box 114
Mascoutah, IL 62258-0114
(618) 566-2020   Fax: (618) 566-4718
E-mail: info@nfed.org
Web: nfed.org

Summary To provide funding for medical and dental care to people with ectodermal dysplasia (ED).

Eligibility This program is open to all people with an ED syndrome who need assistance for dental or medical care.

Typical care includes, but is not limited to, dentures, wigs, plastic surgery, dental implants, air conditioners, and personal cooling equipment. All care for which payment is sought must be related to ectodermal dysplasia. Selection is based on treatment needs, family income, extenuating circumstances, and the number of members of the family who are affected by an ED syndrome.

Financial data The amount of assistance depends on the need of the recipient and the availability of funds. Maximum grants are $2,500 for wigs, $600 for air conditioners, $4,000 for dentures, or $15,000 for complex dental care.

Duration Individuals receiving funding for dental care or wigs can reapply after 18 months have passed.

Additional data This program was established in 1987.

Number awarded Varies each year; recently, 38 of these grants, with a value of $247,000, were awarded.

Deadline March, June, September, or December of each year.

[734]
NORTH DAKOTA PROPERTY TAX CREDIT FOR DISABLED VETERANS

Office of State Tax Commissioner
State Capitol Building
600 East Boulevard Avenue, Department 127
Bismarck, ND 58505-0599
(701) 328-7088   Toll Free: (877) 328-7088
Fax: (701) 328-3700   TDD: (800) 366-6888
E-mail: taxinfo@state.nd.us
Web: www.nd.gov/tax/property

Summary To provide property tax credits to disabled North Dakota veterans and their surviving spouses.

Eligibility This property tax credit is available to honorably-discharged veterans who have more than a 50% service-connected disability as certified by the U.S. Department of Veterans Affairs. Applicants must own and occupy a homestead according to state law. Unremarried surviving spouses are also eligible. If a disabled veteran co-owns the property with someone other than a spouse, the credit is limited to the disabled veteran's interest in the fixtures, buildings, and improvements of the homestead.

Financial data The credit is applied against the first $120,000 of true and full valuation of the fixtures, buildings, and improvements of the homestead, to a maximum amount calculated by multiplying $120,000 by the percentage of the disabled veteran's disability compensation rating for service-connected disabilities.

Duration 1 year; renewable as long as qualified individuals continue to reside in North Dakota and live in their homes.

Number awarded Varies each year.

Deadline Applications may be submitted to the county auditor at any time.

[735]
NORTH DAKOTA PROPERTY TAX EXEMPTION FOR DISABLED PERSONS CONFINED TO A WHEELCHAIR

Office of State Tax Commissioner
State Capitol Building
600 East Boulevard Avenue, Department 127
Bismarck, ND 58505-0599
(701) 328-7088   Toll Free: (877) 328-7088
Fax: (701) 328-3700   TDD: (800) 366-6888
E-mail: taxinfo@state.nd.us
Web: www.nd.gov/tax/property

Summary To provide partial tax exemption in North Dakota to persons permanently confined to the use of a wheelchair and their spouses.

Eligibility Persons permanently confined to the use of a wheelchair are those who cannot walk with the assistance of crutches or any other device and will never be able to do so; this must be certified by a physician selected by a local governing board. The property must be owned and occupied as a homestead according to state law. The homestead may be owned by the spouse or jointly owned by the disabled person and spouse provided both reside on the homestead. Qualified residents and, if deceased, their unremarried surviving spouses are entitled to this exemption. Income and assets are not considered in determining eligibility for the exemption.

Financial data The maximum benefit may not exceed $3,600 taxable value, because a homestead is limited to $80,000 market value.

Duration The exemption continues as long as the homestead in North Dakota is owned by the disabled person and/or the spouse.

Additional data The exemption does not apply to special assessments levied upon the homestead.

Number awarded Varies each year.

Deadline Deadline not specified.

[736]
NORTH DAKOTA PROPERTY TAX EXEMPTION FOR VETERANS WHO LIVE IN SPECIALLY ADAPTED HOUSING

Office of State Tax Commissioner
State Capitol Building
600 East Boulevard Avenue, Department 127
Bismarck, ND 58505-0599
(701) 328-7088   Toll Free: (877) 328-7088
Fax: (701) 328-3700   TDD: (800) 366-6888
E-mail: taxinfo@state.nd.us
Web: www.nd.gov/tax/property

Summary To provide property tax exemptions to North Dakota veterans and their surviving spouses who have been awarded specially adapted housing.

Eligibility This exemption is available to paraplegic disabled veterans of the U.S. armed forces or any veteran who has been awarded specially adapted housing by the U.S. Department of Veterans Affairs. The paraplegic disability does not have to be service connected. The unremarried surviving spouses of such deceased veterans are

also eligible. Income and assets are not considered in determining eligibility for the exemption.

Financial data The maximum benefit may not exceed $5,400 taxable value, because the exemption is limited to the first $120,000 of true and full value of fixtures, buildings, and improvements.

Duration 1 year; renewable as long as qualified individuals reside in North Dakota and live in their homes.

Number awarded Varies each year.

Deadline Applications may be submitted to the county auditor at any time.

[737]
PARALYZED VETERANS OF AMERICA DISASTER RELIEF FUND

Paralyzed Veterans of America
Attn: Disaster Relief Fund
801 18th Street, N.W.
Washington, DC 20006-3517
Toll Free: (866) 734-0857   E-mail: info@pva.org
Web: www.pva.org

Summary To provide emergency assistance to members of Paralyzed Veterans of America (PVA) who have been victimized by natural disasters.

Eligibility This assistance is available to PVA members whose property has been severely damaged by natural disasters. Applicants may be seeking funding for transportation, temporary shelter, food, home repairs, or modifications that are needed for wheelchair accessibility, medical supplies, or prosthetic appliances.

Financial data Grants range up to $2,500; more than $100,000 is available for relief each year.

Additional data Membership in PVA is open to veterans with spinal cord injury or disease.

Number awarded 2 each year.

Deadline Applications may be submitted at any time.

[738]
PENNSYLVANIA DISABLED VETERANS REAL ESTATE TAX EXEMPTION

Office of the Deputy Adjutant General for Veterans
  Affairs
Building S-0-47, FTIG
Annville, PA 17003-5002
(717) 865-8907
Toll Free: (800) 54 PA VET (within PA)
Fax: (717) 861-8589   E-mail: RA-VA-Info@pa.gov
Web: www.dmva.state.pa.us

Summary To exempt blind and disabled Pennsylvania veterans and their unremarried surviving spouses from all state real estate taxes.

Eligibility Eligible to apply for this exemption are honorably-discharged veterans who are residents of Pennsylvania and who are blind, paraplegic, or 100% disabled from a service-connected disability sustained during wartime military service. The dwelling must be owned by the veteran solely or jointly with a spouse, and financial need for the exemption must be determined by the State Veterans' Commission. Veterans whose income is less than

$81,340 per year are presumed to have financial need; veterans with income greater than $81,340 must document need. Upon the death of the veteran, the tax exemption passes on to the veteran's unremarried surviving spouse.

Financial data This program exempts the principal residence (and the land on which it stands) from all real estate taxes.

Duration The exemption continues as long as the eligible veteran or unremarried widow resides in Pennsylvania.

Number awarded Varies each year.

Deadline Deadline not specified.

[739]
PENNSYLVANIA PARALYZED VETERANS PENSION

Office of the Deputy Adjutant General for Veterans
  Affairs
Building S-0-47, FTIG
Annville, PA 17003-5002
(717) 865-8911
Toll Free: (800) 54 PA VET (within PA)
Fax: (717) 861-8589   E-mail: RA-VA-Info@pa.gov
Web: www.dmva.state.pa.us

Summary To provide financial assistance to Pennsylvania veterans who became disabled while serving in the U.S. armed forces.

Eligibility Applicants must be current residents of Pennsylvania who suffered an injury or disease resulting in loss or loss of use of 2 or more extremities while serving in the U.S. armed forces during an established period of war or armed conflict or as a result of hostilities during combat-related activities in peacetime. They must be rated by the U.S. Department of Veterans Affairs as 100% permanent and service-connected disabled. At the time of entry into military service, applicants must have been residents of Pennsylvania.

Financial data The pension is $150 per month.

Duration The pension is awarded for the life of the veteran.

Number awarded Varies each year.

Deadline Applications may be submitted at any time.

[740]
QUARTERLY GRANT PROGRAM OF THE JIM "CATFISH" HUNTER CHAPTER

ALS Association-Jim "Catfish" Hunter Chapter
Attn: Care Services Administrative Coordinator
120-101 Penmarc Drive
Raleigh, NC 27603
(919) 755-9001   Toll Free: (877) 568-4347, ext. 225
Fax: (919) 755-0910
E-mail: claudia@catfishchapter.org
Web: www.catfishchapter.org/services/quarterly-grant

Summary To provide funding for specified expenses to patients with Amyotrophic Lateral Sclerosis (ALS) in North Carolina.

Eligibility This assistance is available to patients who have a definitive diagnosis of ALS and reside in North Car-

olina. Applicants must be seeking funding for expenses that are not traditionally covered by insurance, Medicare, Medicaid, or other assistance programs. Examples include, but are not limited to, home assistance (respite), travel costs, home and auto modifications, computer access, communication devices, environmental controls, generators, or home health care. Grants are awarded on a first-come, first-served basis and based on available funds; first-time applicants are given priority.

Financial data Each quarterly grant is $625 (maximum per year: $2,500).

Duration Patients may obtain 4 grants per fiscal year.

Additional data The North Carolina Chapter of the ALS Association was formed in 1987. In 2000, it expanded its services to include South Carolina and, in 2002, adopted the name of former professional baseball player Jim "Catfish" Hunter. In 2006, a separate South Carolina chapter was formed, so this chapter again limits its services to North Carolina. This program was established in 2007.

Number awarded Varies each year.

Deadline January, April, July, and October of each year.

[741]
SENTINELS OF FREEDOM SCHOLARSHIPS

Sentinels of Freedom
P.O. Box 1316
San Ramon, CA 94583
(925) 380-6342   Fax: (925) 867-1078
E-mail: info@sentinelsoffreedom.org
Web: www.sentinelsoffreedom.org

Summary To provide funding to veterans and current military personnel who became blind, deaf, or disabled as a result of injuries sustained in the line of duty on or after September 11, 2001.

Eligibility This program is open to members of the U.S. Air Force, Army, Coast Guard, Marines, or Navy who sustained injuries in the line of duty on or after September 11, 2001. Applicants must be rated as 60% or more disabled as a result of 1 or more of the following conditions: amputation, blindness, deafness, paraplegia, severe burns, limited traumatic brain injury (TBI), or limited post-traumatic stress disorder (PTSD); other severe injuries may be considered on a case-by-case basis. They must complete an interview process and demonstrate that they have the skills, experience, and attitude that lead to employment.

Financial data Assistance is available for the following needs: housing (adapted for physical needs if necessary), new furniture and other household supplies, career-placement assistance and training, new adaptive vehicles, educational opportunities in addition to the new GI Bill, or financial and personal mentorship.

Duration Assistance may be provided for up to 4 years.

Additional data The first assistance granted by this program was awarded in 2004.

Number awarded Varies each year. Since the program was established, it has supported 84 current and former service members.

Deadline Applications may be submitted at any time.

[742]
SOUTH CAROLINA DISABLED PERSON PROPERTY TAX EXEMPTION

South Carolina Department of Revenue
Attn: Property Division
301 Gervais Street
P.O. Box 125
Columbia, SC 29214
(803) 898-5480   Fax: (803) 898-5822
Web: www.sctax.org

Summary To exempt the home of disabled residents of South Carolina and their surviving spouses from property taxation.

Eligibility Eligible for this exemption are residents of South Carolina who are defined as paraplegic or hemiplegic and own a dwelling house that is their domicile. The exemption is allowed to the surviving spouse of the person as long as the spouse does not remarry, resides in the dwelling, and obtains the fee or a life estate in the dwelling. Paraplegic or hemiplegic includes a person with Parkinson's Disease, multiple sclerosis, or amyotrophic lateral sclerosis that has caused the same ambulatory difficulties as a person with paraperesis or hemiparesis. Surviving spouses of those persons are also eligible for this exemption as long as they remain unmarried.

Financial data The exemption applies to all taxes on 1 house and a lot (not to exceed 1 acre).

Duration The exemption extends as long as the person with a disability or the surviving spouse resides in the house.

Number awarded Varies each year.

Deadline Applications may be submitted at any time.

[743]
SOUTH DAKOTA PROPERTY TAX EXEMPTION FOR PARAPLEGIC VETERANS

South Dakota Department of Revenue and Regulation
Attn: Property Tax Division
445 East Capitol Avenue
Pierre, SD 57501-3185
(605) 773-3311   Toll Free: (800) TAX-9188
Fax: (605) 773-6729   E-mail: PropTaxIn@state.sd.us
Web: www.state.sd.us

Summary To exempt from property taxation the homes of paraplegic veterans in South Dakota and their widow(er)s.

Eligibility This benefit is available to residents of South Dakota who are 1) paraplegic veterans, 2) veterans with loss or loss of use of both lower extremities, or 3) unmarried widows or widowers of such veterans. Applicants must own and occupy a dwelling (including the house, garage, and up to 1 acre on which the building is located) that is specifically designed for wheelchair use within the structure. The veteran's injury does not have to be service connected.

Financial data Qualified dwellings are exempt from property taxation in South Dakota.

Duration The exemption applies as long as the dwelling is owned and occupied by the disabled veteran or widow(er).

Number awarded Varies each year.

Deadline Deadline not specified.

[744]
SOUTH DAKOTA PROPERTY TAX REDUCTION FOR PARAPLEGICS

South Dakota Department of Revenue and Regulation
Attn: Property Tax Division
445 East Capitol Avenue
Pierre, SD 57501-3185
(605) 773-3311   Toll Free: (800) TAX-9188
Fax: (605) 773-6729   E-mail: PropTaxIn@state.sd.us
Web: www.state.sd.us

Summary To provide a reduction in property taxes on the homes of people with disabilities in South Dakota and their widow(er)s.

Eligibility This benefit is available to residents of South Dakota who are 1) paraplegic individuals, 2) individuals with loss or loss of use of both lower extremities, or 3) unremarried widows or widowers of such individuals. Applicants must own and occupy a dwelling (including the house, garage, and up to 1 acre on which the building is located) that is specifically designed for wheelchair use within the structure. They must have a federal adjusted income of less than $8,000 if they live in a single-member household or less than $12,000 if they live in a multiple-member household.

Financial data The reduction depends on the federal adjusted gross income of the applicant. For single-member households, the reduction is 100% if the income is less than $5,000, 75% if the income is between $5,000 and $6,000, 50% if the income is between $6,000 and $7,000, or 25% if the income is between $7,000 and $8,000. For multiple-member household, the reduction is 100% if the income is less than $9,000, 75% if the income is between $9,000 and $10,000, 50% if the income is between $10,000 and $11,000, or 25% if the income is between $11,000 and $12,000.

Duration The reduction applies as long as the dwelling is owned and occupied by the disabled person or widow(er).

Number awarded Varies each year.

Deadline Deadline not specified.

[745]
SPECIAL HOUSING ADAPTATIONS GRANTS

Department of Veterans Affairs
Attn: Specially Adapted Housing
810 Vermont Avenue, N.W.
Washington, DC 20420
(202) 461-9546   Toll Free: (800) 827-1000
Web: www.benefits.va.gov/homeloans/sah_info.asp

Summary To provide grants to certain disabled or blind veterans or service members who wish to make adaptations to their home to meet their needs.

Eligibility These grants are available to veterans and service members who are entitled to compensation for permanent and total service-connected disability due to: 1) blindness in both eyes with 5/200 visual acuity or less; 2) the anatomical loss or loss of use of both hands; or 3) a severe burn injury. Applicants must be planning to 1) adapt a house which they plan to purchase and in which they intend to reside; 2) adapt a house which a member of their family plans to purchase and in which they intend to reside; 3) adapt a house which they already own and in which they intend to reside; 4) adapt a house which is already owned by a member of their family in which they intend to reside; or 5) purchase a house that has already been adapted with special features that are reasonably necessary because of their disability and in which they intend to reside.

Financial data Eligible veterans and service members are entitled to grants up to $12,756 to adapt a house.

Duration Eligible veterans and service members are entitled to up to 3 usages of these grants.

Number awarded Varies each year.

Deadline Applications are accepted at any time.

[746]
SPECIALLY ADAPTED HOUSING GRANTS

Department of Veterans Affairs
Attn: Specially Adapted Housing
810 Vermont Avenue, N.W.
Washington, DC 20420
(202) 461-9546   Toll Free: (800) 827-1000
Web: www.homeloans.va.gov/sah.htm

Summary To provide loans, grants, and loan guaranties to blind and disabled veterans and service members for a home specially adapted to their needs.

Eligibility These grants are available to veterans and service members who are entitled to compensation for permanent and total service-connected disability due to: 1) the loss or loss of use of both lower extremities, such as to preclude locomotion without the aid of braces, crutches, canes, or a wheelchair; or 2) blindness in both eyes, having only light perception, plus loss or loss of use of 1 lower extremity; 3) a loss or loss of use of 1 lower extremity together with residuals of organic disease or injury or the loss or loss of use of 1 upper extremity, such as to preclude locomotion without resort to braces, canes, crutches, or a wheelchair; 4) the loss or loss of use of both upper extremities, so as to preclude use of the arms at or above the elbows; or 5) a severe burn injury. Applicants must be planning to 1) construct a home on land to be acquired for that purpose; 2) build a home on land already owned if it is suitable for specially adapted housing; 3) remodel an existing home if it can be made suitable for specially adapted housing, or 4) apply funds against the unpaid principle mortgage balance of a specially adapted home that has already been acquired.

Financial data The U.S. Department of Veterans Affairs (VA) may approve a grant of not more than 50% of the cost of building, buying, or remodeling homes for eligible veterans, or paying indebtedness on such homes already acquired, up to a maximum grant of $63,780. Eligible veterans with available loan guarantee entitlements may also obtain a guaranteed loan from the VA to supplement the grant to acquire a specially adapted home. If private financing is not available, the VA may make a direct loan up to $33,000 to cover the difference between the total cost of the home and the grant.

Duration This is a 1-time grant, guaranteed loan, or direct loan.

Additional data Veterans who receive a specially adapted housing grant may be eligible for Veterans Mortgage Life Insurance.

Number awarded Varies each year.

Deadline Applications are accepted at any time.

[747]
SPINA BIFIDA PROGRAM FOR CHILDREN OF VETERANS

Department of Veterans Affairs
Attn: Veterans Benefits Administration
810 Vermont Avenue, N.W.
Washington, DC 20420
(202) 418-4343   Toll Free: (888) 820-1756
Web: www.va.gov/hac/forbeneficiaries/spina/spina.asp

Summary To provide support to children of certain veterans who have spina bifida.

Eligibility This program is open to spina bifida patients whose veteran parent performed active military, naval, or air service 1) in the Republic of Vietnam during the period from January 9, 1962 through May 7, 1975; or 2) in or near the Korean demilitarized zone during the period from September 1, 1967 through August 31, 1971. Children may be of any age or marital status, but they must have been conceived after the date on which the veteran first served in Vietnam or Korea. The monthly allowance is set at 3 levels, depending upon the degree of disability suffered by the child. The levels are based on neurological manifestations that define the severity of disability: impairment of the functioning of the extremities, impairment of bowel or bladder function, and impairment of intellectual functioning.

Financial data Support depends on the degree of disability. The monthly rate for children at the first level is $297, the second level $1,020, or at the third level $1,739.

Additional data Applications are available from the nearest VA medical center. Recipients are also entitled to vocational training and medical treatment.

Number awarded Varies each year; currently, approximately 1,100 children of veterans qualify for this program.

Deadline Applications are accepted at any time.

[748]
SUPPLEMENTAL SECURITY INCOME (SSI)

Social Security Administration
6401 Security Boulevard
Baltimore, MD 21235-0001
(410) 594-1234   Toll Free: (800) 772-1213
TDD: (800) 325-0778
Web: www.socialsecurity.gov/ssi/index.htm

Summary To provide monthly payments to disabled, blind, deaf, and elderly people who have limited income and resources.

Eligibility This assistance is available to U.S. citizens and certain categories of aliens who are 65 years of age or older, blind, or disabled. A person 18 years of age or older is considered disabled if a physical or mental impairment prevents him or her from doing any substantial gainful work and is expected to last for at least 12 months or to result in death. Children under the age of 18 are considered disabled if they have a physical or mental impairment that is comparable in severity to a disability that would prevent an adult from working and is expected to last at least 12 months or result in death. Children with certain conditions are automatically disabled and eligible for these benefits; the conditions include HIV infection, blindness, deafness, cerebral palsy, Down syndrome, muscular dystrophy, significant mental deficiency, diabetes (with amputation of 1 foot), amputation of 2 limbs, or amputation of leg at the hip. Regardless of age, a person whose vision is no better than 20/200 or who has a limited visual field of 20 degrees or less with the best corrective eyeglasses is considered blind; individuals with visual impairments not severe enough to meet the definition of blindness still may qualify as disabled persons. Applicants must have limited income and limited resources (less than $2,000 for an individual or $3,000 for a couple); items excluded from resources include the home used as a principal place of residence, personal and household goods, life insurance with face value of $1,500 or less, a car, burial plots for individuals and immediate family members, and burial funds up to $1,500.

Financial data The basic monthly payment is $698 for an eligible individual or $1,048 for an eligible individual with an eligible spouse. Many states add money to that basic payment. SSI recipients may also be eligible for food stamps and other nutrition programs.

Duration Assistance is provided as long as the recipient remains blind or disabled and in financial need.

Additional data Although SSI is administered through the Social Security Administration, it is not financed by Social Security taxes. Financing of SSI is provided through general funds of the U.S. Treasury. Recipients of SSI need not have been employed or paid Social Security taxes, but they may be eligible for both SSI and Social Security. Disabled and blind applicants for SSI are referred to their state vocational rehabilitation agency to determine their eligibility for a program of vocational rehabilitation. Disabled drug addicts or alcoholics are referred for appropriate treatment if it is available at an approved facility or institution.

Number awarded Recently, approximately 8,164,000 people (including 6,981,000 who were blind and disabled) were receiving SSI benefits, including 1,294,000 under 18 years of age, 4,806,000 who were 18 to 64 years of age, and 2,064,000 who were 65 or older.

Deadline Deadline not specified.

[749]
SUSAN BROWN TRANSPORTATION PROGRAM

ALS Association-DC/Maryland/Virginia Chapter
Attn: Director of Patient and Family Services
7507 Standish Place
Rockville, MD 20855
(301) 978-9855   Toll Free: (866) FITE-ALS
Fax: (301) 978-9854   E-mail: info@ALSinfo.org
Web: webdc.alsa.org

Summary To provide funding for transportation to Amyotrophic Lateral Sclerosis (ALS) patients in Maryland, Virginia, and Washington, D.C.

Eligibility This assistance is available to residents of Maryland, Virginia, and Washington, D.C. who have a confirmed diagnosis of ALS and their family caregivers. Applicants must be registered with the local chapter of the ALS Association and be seeking funding for wheelchair-van transportation or (if they are not wheelchair-bound) some other form of transportation. They may have no other form of transportation readily available. The program requires that they be able to exit their home or building without the assistance of the driver, either on foot or with a wheelchair ramp.

Financial data Grants provide up to $2,500 per year for medical appointments or up to $250 per year for non-medical transportation expenses.

Duration 1 year; may be renewed.

Number awarded Varies each year.

Deadline Applications may be submitted at any time.

[750]
TENNESSEE INCOME TAX EXEMPTION FOR QUADRIPLEGICS

Tennessee Department of Revenue
Andrew Jackson State Office Building
500 Deaderick Street
Nashville, TN 37242-1099
(615) 253-0600   Toll Free: (800) 342-1003 (within TN)
Fax: (615) 253-3580   E-mail: tn.revenue@state.tn.us
Web: www.tennessee.gov/revenue

Summary To exempt from state taxation the dividend and interest income of quadriplegic residents of Tennessee.

Eligibility This exemption is provided to residents of Tennessee who are certified by a medical doctor to be quadriplegic and who have taxable income that is from 1) dividends from stock, investment trusts, and mutual funds; and 2) interest from bonds, notes, and mortgages. The income must be derived from circumstances resulting in the individual's becoming a quadriplegic.

Financial data All income is exempt from taxation if the income is derived from circumstances resulting in the applicant's becoming a quadriplegic. However, when taxable interest/dividend income is received jointly by a quadriplegic and a spouse who is not a quadriplegic or who is quadriplegic but the taxable income was not derived from circumstances resulting in the spouse's becoming quadriplegic, only one half of the jointly received income is exempted from taxation. The spouse who is not quadriplegic or whose quadriplegic condition did not result in the income is entitled only to a $1,250 exemption.

Duration   The exemption continues as long as the recipient resides in Tennessee.

Deadline   Deadline not specified.

[751]
TENNESSEE PROPERTY TAX RELIEF FOR DISABLED VETERANS AND THEIR SPOUSES

Tennessee Comptroller of the Treasury
Attn: Property Tax Relief Program
James K. Polk State Office Building
505 Deaderick Street, Room 1700
Nashville, TN 37243-1402
(615) 747-8858   Fax: (615) 532-3866
E-mail: kim.darden@cot.tn.gov
Web: www.comptroller1.state.tn.us/pa/patxr.asp

Summary   To provide property tax relief to blind and disabled veterans and their spouses in Tennessee.

Eligibility   This exemption is offered to veterans or their surviving unremarried spouses who are residents of Tennessee and own and live in their home in the state. The veteran must have served in the U.S. armed forces and 1) have acquired, as a result of such service, a disability from paraplegia, permanent paralysis of both legs and lower part of the body resulting from traumatic injury, disease to the spinal cord or brain, legal blindness, or loss or loss of use of both legs or arms from any service-connected cause; 2) have been rated by the U.S. Department of Veterans Affairs (VA) as 100% permanently disabled as a result of service as a prisoner of war for at least 5 months; or 3) have been rated by the VA as 100% permanently and totally disabled from any other service-connected cause. Unremarried spouses of deceased veterans are also eligible if 1) the veteran was receiving tax relief as a disabled veteran before death; 2) death resulted from a service-connected, combat-related cause, or killed in action; or 3) death resulted from being deployed, away from any home base of training, and in support of combat operations.

Financial data   The amount of the relief depends on the property assessment and the tax rate in the city or county where the beneficiary lives. The maximum market value on which tax relief is calculated is $175,000.

Duration   1 year; may be renewed as long as the eligible veteran or surviving unremarried spouse owns and occupies the primary residence.

Number awarded   Varies each year.

Deadline   Deadline not specified.

[752]
TEXAS PROPERTY TAX EXEMPTION FOR DISABLED VETERANS AND THEIR FAMILIES

Texas Veterans Commission
P.O. Box 12277
Austin, TX 78711-2277
(512) 463-5538
Toll Free: (800) 252-VETS (within TX)
Fax: (512) 475-2395   E-mail: info@tvc.state.tx.us
Web: texas-veterans.com/claims/property-tax-exemption

Summary   To extend property tax exemptions on the appraised value of their property to blind, disabled, and other Texas veterans and their surviving family members.

Eligibility   Eligible veterans must be Texas residents rated at least 10% service-connected disabled. Surviving spouses and children of eligible veterans are also covered by this program.

Financial data   For veterans in Texas whose disability is rated as 10% through 29%, the first $5,000 of the appraised property value is exempt from taxation; veterans rated as 30% through 49% disabled are exempt from the first $7,500 of appraised value; those with a 50% through 69% disability are exempt from the first $10,000 of appraised value; the exemption applies to the first $12,000 of appraised value for veterans with disabilities rated as 70% to 99%; veterans rated as 100% disabled are exempt from 100% of the appraised value of their property. A veteran whose disability is 10% or more and who is 65 years or older is entitled to exemption of the first $12,000 of appraised property value. A veteran whose disability consists of the loss of use of 1 or more limbs, total blindness in 1 or both eyes, or paraplegia is exempt from the first $12,000 of the appraised value. The unremarried surviving spouse of a deceased veteran who died on active duty and who, at the time of death had a compensable disability and was entitled to an exemption, is entitled to the same exemption. The surviving spouse of a person who died on active duty is entitled to exemption of the first $5,000 of appraised value of the spouse's property; they are also eligible for the 100% exemption. A surviving child of a person who dies on active duty is entitled to exemption of the first $5,000 of appraised value of the child's property, as long as the child is unmarried and under 21 years of age.

Duration   1 year; may be renewed as long as the eligible veteran (or unremarried surviving spouse or child) owns and occupies the primary residence in Texas.

Additional data   This program is administered at the local level by the various taxing authorities.

Number awarded   Varies each year.

Deadline   April of each year.

[753]
TOYOTA MOBILITY PROGRAM

Toyota Motor Sales, U.S.A., Inc.
Attn: Mobility Assistance Center
19001 South Western Avenue
Mail Drop WC10
Torrance, CA 90509-2714
Toll Free: (800) 331-4331   TDD: (800) 443-4999
Web: www.toyotamobility.com/financial_assistance.html

Summary   To provide a cash reimbursement for the cost of installing adaptive driving aids on new purchases of Toyota vehicles.

Eligibility   This rebate is available to purchasers or lessors of new Toyota vehicles that require an aftermarket alteration or equipment installation to provide a disabled user convenient access and/or the ability to drive the vehicle. Examples include adaptations that involve vehicle entry and exit, driver position, steering system, or brake and accelerator system.

Financial data Up to $1,000 is provided for the cost of adding adaptive equipment.

Deadline The adaptive equipment must be purchased and installed within 12 months of vehicle purchase or lease. A reimbursement application must be submitted within 90 days of complete installation of adaptive equipment.

[754]
TRAVIS ROY FOUNDATION GRANTS

Travis Roy Foundation
c/o Hemenway & Barnes LLP
60 State Street, 8th Floor
Boston, MA 02109
(617) 619-8257   Fax: (617) 227-0781
E-mail: info@travisroyfoundation.org
Web: www.travisroyfoundation.org

Summary To provide funding to paraplegics and quadriplegics to pay for equipment or modifications to improve their daily life.

Eligibility This program is open to paraplegics and quadriplegics who reside in the United States. Applicants must be paralyzed due to a spinal cord injury; individuals with paralysis due to other causes, such as multiple sclerosis or spina bifida, are not eligible. Grant funds must be sought for equipment or modifications, including upgrade and maintenance of wheelchairs, assistance in van purchases, vehicle modifications (e.g., hand controls or lifts), home modifications (e.g., ramp and elevator installation), exercise equipment, or other adaptive equipment. Financial need must be demonstrated.

Financial data Grants range up to $7,500. Funds are distributed directly to suppliers of the desired equipment or modification.

Duration These are 1-time grants.

Additional data This foundation was established in 1997.

Number awarded Varies each year.

Deadline Applications may be submitted at any time.

[755]
UPPER MIDWEST CHAPTER MS SOCIETY ADAPTIVE EQUIPMENT/HOME AND VEHICLE MODIFICATION GRANTS

National Multiple Sclerosis Society-Upper Midwest
  Chapter
Attn: Independent Living Grants
200 12th Avenue South
Minneapolis, MN 55415
(612) 335-7967   Toll Free: (800) 582-5296
Fax: (612) 335-7997   TDD: (800) 582-5296
E-mail: sahlgren@mssociety.org
Web: was.nationalmssociety.org

Summary To provide funding to residents of upper Midwestern states who have multiple sclerosis (MS) and are interested in purchasing adaptive equipment or modifying their home or vehicle.

Eligibility This program is open to residents of Iowa, Minnesota, North Dakota, and South Dakota who have MS and are registered with the Upper Midwest Chapter of the National Multiple Sclerosis Society. Applicants must be interested in acquiring adaptive equipment or modifying their home or vehicle to help them live independently. They must have a doctor's prescription for the item or modification. Examples of eligible items include wheelchairs, walking aids, bath safety, scooters, patient lifts, leg braces, hospital beds, seating systems, ramps, lift chairs, stair glides, cooling vests, air conditioners, service dogs, exercise equipment, and urological and incontinent supplies.

Financial data The maximum reimbursement per person per fiscal year is $1,500.

Duration 1 year; recipients may reapply.

Number awarded Varies each year.

Deadline Applications may be submitted at any time.

[756]
VOLKSWAGEN OF AMERICA MOBILITY ACCESS PROGRAM

Volkswagen Group of America
Attn: VW Incentives Help Desk
3800 West Hamlin Road HCW 2A01
Auburn Hills, MI 48326
(678) 995-5005   Fax: (248) 754-6513
Web: vwmobility.com/vwmobilityrebate.html

Summary To provide a cash reimbursement for the cost of installing adaptive driving aids on new purchases of Volkswagen vehicles.

Eligibility This rebate is available to people with disabilities who purchase or lease new Volkswagen vehicles and require adaptive driving aids (e.g., lift equipment, carriers, hand controls, pedal extensions). Applicants must obtain the equipment, have it installed, and submit a copy of their paid invoice.

Financial data Reimbursements up to $1,000 are available.

Duration Applications must be submitted during the calendar year of the lease or purchase.

Number awarded Varies each year.

Deadline Applications may be submitted at any time during the calendar year.

Other Disabilities/ Disorders

Scholarships ●

Fellowships ●

Grants-in-Aid ●

Described here are 264 funding opportunities available to individuals who have a communication disorder (such as stuttering or voice impairment), have a learning disability (including such conditions as brain injury and dyslexia), are emotionally disturbed, or have other chronic or acute health problems, such as cancer or hemophilia. Of these, 183 cover scholarships (funding to pursue study, research, or other activities on the undergraduate level in the United States); 41 describe fellowships (to support graduate or postgraduate study, research, or other activities in the United States); and 40 identify grants-in-aid (to pay for emergency situations, travel, income/ property tax liabilities, the acquisition of assistive technology, or other personal needs). All of this is "free" money. Not one dollar will need to be repaid (provided, of course, that recipients meet all program requirements). If you are looking for a particular program and don't find it in this section, be sure to check the Program Title Index to see if it is covered elsewhere in the directory.

Scholarships

[757]
ADVOCACY SCHOLARSHIP OF THE JUVENILE DIABETES RESEARCH FOUNDATION

Diabetes Scholars Foundation
2118 Plum Grove Road, Suite 356
Rolling Meadows, IL 60008
(312) 215-9861   Fax: (847) 991-8739
E-mail: collegescholarships@diabetesscholars.org
Web: www.diabetesscholars.org/college.html

Summary   To provide financial assistance to high school seniors who have diabetes and plan to major in political science in college.

Eligibility   This program is open to graduating high school seniors who have Type 1 diabetes and plan to attend an accredited 4-year university, college, or technical/trade school in any state. Applicants must be planning to major in political science. They must be able to demonstrate active involvement in the diabetes community, high academic performance, participation in community and/or extracurricular activities, and successful management of the challenges of living with diabetes. Financial need is not considered in the selection process. U.S. citizenship or permanent resident status is required.

Financial data   The stipend is $1,000.

Duration   1 year.

Additional data   This program is sponsored by the Juvenile Diabetes Research Foundation (JDRF).

Number awarded   1 each year.

Deadline   May of each year.

[758]
ALLEGRA FORD SCHOLARSHIP

National Center for Learning Disabilities
Attn: Scholarship
381 Park Avenue South, Suite 1401
New York, NY 10016-8806
(212) 545-7510   Toll Free: (888) 575-7373
Fax: (212) 545-9665   E-mail: afscholarship@ncld.org
Web: www.ncld.org

Summary   To provide financial assistance to high school seniors who have a learning disability and plan to attend a community college or vocational training program.

Eligibility   This program is open to high school seniors who have a documented learning disability and plan to attend a 2-year community college, vocational/technical training program, or specialized program for students with learning disabilities. Applicants must be able to demonstrate financial need. They must 1) articulate their learning disability and recognize the need for self-advocacy; 2) be committed to postsecondary academic study or career training and have begun to set realistic career goals; 3) participate in school and community activities; and 4) have demonstrated perseverance and commitment to achieving

personal goals despite the challenges of learning disabilities. U.S. citizenship is required.

Financial data   The stipend is $2,500.

Duration   1 year; nonrenewable.

Additional data   This program was established in 2002 as the Anne Ford Scholarship. In 2009 it was expanded with support from Allegra Ford (Anne's daughter) and named the Anne Ford and Allegra Ford Scholarships. Effective in 2012, the program was separated into 2 separate scholarships.

Number awarded   1 each year.

Deadline   December of each year.

[759]
ANDRE SOBEL AWARD

André Sobel River of Life Foundation
Attn: Awards
8581 Santa Monica Boulevard, Suite 80
P.O. Box 361640
Los Angeles, CA 90036
(310) 276-7111   Fax: (310) 276-0244
E-mail: info@andreriveroflife.org
Web: andreriveroflife.org/participate/award

Summary   To recognize and reward young survivors of life-threatening illnesses who submit outstanding essays on their illness.

Eligibility   This competition is open to survivors of life-threatening illnesses between 12 and 21 years of age. Applicants are allowed to define themselves as a survivor; no medical definition or certain amount of time is required. They must submit an essay, up to 1,500 words in length, on a topic that changes annually but relates to their illness.

Financial data   First prize is $5,000. Other cash prizes are awarded to second- and third-place winners.

Duration   The competition is held annually.

Additional data   This program began in 2000.

Number awarded   3 cash prizes are awarded each year.

Deadline   March of each year.

[760]
ANGEL ON MY SHOULDER SCHOLARSHIPS

Angel on My Shoulder
P.O. Box 747
St. Germain, WI 54558
Toll Free: (800) 860-3431
E-mail: info@angelonmyshoulder.org
Web: www.angelonmyshoulder.org

Summary   To provide funding to high school seniors in Wisconsin who plan to attend college in any state and are cancer survivors or relatives affected by cancer.

Eligibility   This program is open to seniors who are graduating from high schools in Wisconsin and planning to attend a 4-year college, technical school, or specialty school in any state. Applicants must be survivors of cancer or have an immediate family member (father, mother, sibling) affected by cancer. Along with their application, they must submit a 250-word essay on why they wish to further their formal education, including their goals and values and how the cancer experience or affiliation with the sponsoring organization has affected their life. Financial need is considered in the selection process.

Financial data The stipend is $1,000.

Duration 1 year.

Additional data This program was established in 2008.

Number awarded Varies each year; recently, 25 of these scholarships were awarded.

Deadline February of each year.

[761]
ANNE AND MATT HARBISON SCHOLARSHIP

P. Buckley Moss Society
74 Poplar Grove Lane
Mathews, VA 23109
(540) 932-1728   Toll Free: (800) 430-1320
E-mail: society@mosssociety.org
Web: www.mosssociety.org/page.php?id=30

Summary To provide money for college to high school seniors with language-related learning disabilities.

Eligibility Eligible to be nominated for this scholarship are high school seniors with language-related learning disabilities. Nominations must be submitted by a member of the P. Buckley Moss Society. The nomination packet must include verification of a language-related learning disability from a counselor or case manager, a high school transcript, 2 recommendations, and 4 essays by the nominees (on themselves; their learning disability and its effect on their lives; their extracurricular, community, work, and church accomplishments; and their plans for next year).

Financial data The stipend is $1,500. Funds are paid to the recipient's college or university.

Duration 1 year; renewable up to 3 additional years.

Additional data This scholarship began in 1998.

Number awarded 1 each year.

Deadline March of each year.

[762]
ANNE FORD SCHOLARSHIP

National Center for Learning Disabilities
Attn: Scholarship
381 Park Avenue South, Suite 1401
New York, NY 10016-8806
(212) 545-7510   Toll Free: (888) 575-7373
Fax: (212) 545-9665   E-mail: afscholarship@ncld.org
Web: www.ncld.org

Summary To provide financial assistance to high school seniors who have a learning disability and plan to attend a 4-year college or university.

Eligibility This program is open to high school seniors who have a documented learning disability and plan to work full time on a bachelor's degree at a 4-year college or university. Applicants must have a GPA of 3.0 or higher and be able to demonstrate financial need. They must 1) articulate their learning disability and recognize the importance of self-advocacy; 2) be committed to completing a 4-year college degree and have begun to set realistic career goals; 3) participate in school and community activities; 4) have demonstrated academic achievements consistent

with college and career goals; 5) plan to contribute to society in ways that increase opportunities for other individuals with learning disabilities; and 6) excel as a role model and spokesperson for others who struggle with learning disabilities. U.S. citizenship is required.

Financial data The stipend is $2,500 per year.

Duration 4 years.

Additional data This program was established in 2002 as the Anne Ford Scholarship. In 2009 it was expanded with support from Allegra Ford (Anne's daughter) and named the Anne Ford and Allegra Ford Scholarships. Effective in 2012, the program was separated into 2 separate scholarships.

Number awarded 1 each year.

Deadline December of each year.

[763]
BERRI MITCHELL SCHOLARSHIP FUND

Asthma and Allergy Foundation of America-Greater
  Kansas City Chapter
400 East Red Bridge Road, Suite 214
Kansas City, MO 64131
(816) 333-6608   Toll Free: (888) 542-8252
Fax: (816) 333-6684   E-mail: info@aafakc.org
Web: www.aafakc.org

Summary To provide money for college to high school seniors in Kansas and western Missouri who have asthma.

Eligibility This program is open to seniors at high schools in Kansas and western Missouri. Applicants must have a history of asthma, have succeeded academically, and have shown an interest in their school and community. Along with their application, they must submit a 2-page essay describing how their asthma has affected their life and how they have dealt with it in school and other aspects of their life; the essay should include their goals in life.

Financial data The stipend is $2,000.

Duration 1 year.

Number awarded Varies each year; recently, 6 of these scholarships were awarded.

Deadline February of each year.

[764]
BETH CAREW MEMORIAL SCHOLARSHIPS

Colburn-Keenan Foundation, Inc.
31 Moody Road
P.O. Box 811
Enfield, CT 06083-0811
Toll Free: (800) 966-2431   Fax: (888) 345-0259
E-mail: admin@colkeen.org
Web: www.colkeen.org/?page_id=123

Summary To provide financial assistance for college to students who have a bleeding disorder.

Eligibility This program is open to high school seniors and college freshmen, sophomores, and juniors who have hemophilia, von Willebrand Disease, or another related inherited bleeding disorder. Applicants must be attending or planning to attend an accredited 2- or 4-year college or university in the United States as a full-time student. Along with their application, they must submit essays on their academic goals, what they would like to be able to do after they receive their undergraduate degree, why they would be a good choice for this scholarship, their participation in volunteer activities in the bleeding disorder community, their greatest challenge as a person living with a bleeding disorder, and examples of choices they have made that demonstrate good and poor judgment on their part.

Financial data The stipend is $4,000 per year.

Duration 1 year; recipients may reapply.

Additional data This program was established by AHF, Inc. in 2002 to honor Beth Carew, who died in 1994 as 1 of the very few women to have hemophilia A. Following the deaths of Donald Colburn and Kathy Ann Keenan, founders of AHF, the Colburn-Keenan Foundation was established; in 2007, it assumed responsibility for administering this program.

Number awarded 10 each year.

Deadline April of each year.

[765]
BEYOND THE CURE SCHOLARSHIPS

National Children's Cancer Society
Attn: Scholarships
One South Memorial Drive, Suite 800
St. Louis, MO 63102
(314) 241-1600   Toll Free: (800) 532-6459
Fax: (314) 241-1996   E-mail: pgabris@thenccs.org
Web: www.thenccs.org/page.aspx?pid=700

Summary To provide financial assistance for college to childhood cancer survivors.

Eligibility This program is open to childhood cancer survivors currently younger than 25 years of age who were diagnosed with cancer or a high grade or anaplastic brain tumor before the age of 18. Applicants must be enrolled or planning to enroll full time at an accredited college, university, or vocational/technical school. They must have a GPA of 2.5 or higher. Along with their application, they must submit a 2-page essay on how being diagnosed with cancer at a young age has impacted their life and future goals. Selection is based on that essay, GPA, medical history, commitment to community service, and financial need. U.S. citizenship is required.

Financial data Stipends range up to $5,000. Funds are disbursed directly to the recipient's institution.

Duration 1 year; renewable up to 3 more years, provided the recipient remains enrolled full time, maintains an overall GPA of 2.5 or higher, and completes 15 hours of volunteer work with the sponsoring organization.

Additional data This program was established in 2008.

Number awarded 35 to 40 each year; a total of $125,000 is available for this program annually.

Deadline March of each year.

[766]
BILL MCADAM SCHOLARSHIP FUND

Hemophilia Foundation of Michigan
c/o Cathy McAdam
22226 Doxtator
Dearborn, MI 48128
(313) 563-1412   E-mail: mcmcadam@comcast.net

Summary To provide money for college to students with a bleeding disorder or members of their families.

Eligibility This program is open to 1) students with a hereditary bleeding disorder (hemophilia, von Willebrand, etc.) or 2) members of their families (spouse, partner, child, sibling). Applicants must be U.S. citizens and enrolled or planning to enroll at an accredited 2- or 4-year college, trade or technical school, or other certification program. Along with their application, they must submit 2 letters of recommendation and 3 essays: 1) what they would like the scholarship committee to know about their dream career and the passion that moves them toward furthering their education; 2) how they would describe a favorite painting or photograph to someone who is blind; and 3) how they will make a difference in the fight against stigma, fear, and discrimination for people facing chronic illness or disability. Financial need is not considered in the selection process.

Financial data The stipend is $2,000. Funds are paid directly to the recipient's institution.

Duration 1 year; nonrenewable.

Number awarded 1 each year.

Deadline May of each year.

[767]
BIORX/HEMOPHILIA OF NORTH CAROLINA EDUCATIONAL SCHOLARSHIPS

Hemophilia of North Carolina
Attn: Scholarship Committee
260 Town Hall Drive, Suite A
Morrisville, NC 27560-5544
(919) 319-0014   Toll Free: (800) 990-5557
Fax: (919) 319-0016   E-mail: info@hemophilia-nc.org
Web: www. hemophilia-nc.org/scholarships.html

Summary To provide financial assistance for college to people with hemophilia, their caregivers, and their families.

Eligibility This program is open to caregivers of children affected with bleeding disorders, people who have been diagnosed with hemophilia, and siblings and parents of people diagnosed with hemophilia. Residents of all states are eligible. Applicants must be enrolled or planning to enroll at an accredited college, university, or certified training program. Along with their application, they must submit an essay of 1 to 2 pages describing their occupational goals and objectives in life and how their or their family's experiences with bleeding disorders have affected their choices. Preference is given to applicants who are studying or planning to study a health care-related field. Selection is primarily based on merit, although financial need may be considered as well.

Financial data The stipend is $2,000.

Duration 1 year.

Additional data This program, established in 2004, is sponsored by BioRx.

Number awarded 4 each year, of which at least 1 of which is reserved for an applicant studying in a health-related field.

Deadline April of each year.

[768]
BLEEDING AND CLOTTING DISORDERS INSTITUTE SCHOLARSHIP FUND

Community Foundation of Central Illinois
331 Fulton Street, Suite 310
Peoria, IL 61602
(309) 674-8730   Fax: (309) 674-8754
E-mail: kristan@communityfoundationci.org
Web: www.communityfoundationci.org

Summary To provide funding to students who have a bleeding or clotting disorder, live in the service area of the Bleeding and Clotting Disorders Institute (BCDI) in Illinois, and are interested in attending college in any state.

Eligibility This program is open to residents of the BCDI service area (all of Illinois outside of Chicago) who are diagnosed with a congenital or acquired chronic bleeding disorder or a congenital clotting disorder. Applicants must be enrolled or planning to enroll full time at an accredited vocational/trade school, junior college, or 4-year college or university in any state. They must have a GPA of 2.5 or higher. Along with their application, they must submit a 250-word essay on how receiving this scholarship will help them to meet their career goals. Selection is based on the essay and demonstrated desire to succeed.

Financial data The stipend is $1,000. Funds are disbursed directly to the recipient's school to be used to cover the cost of tuition, books, and required fees.

Duration 1 year.

Additional data This program is supported by the BCDI.

Number awarded 1 or more each year.

Deadline March of each year.

[769]
BMW HOPE ENDOWMENT SCHOLARSHIP

Epsilon Sigma Alpha International
Attn: ESA Foundation
363 West Drake Road
Fort Collins, CO 80526
(970) 223-2824   Fax: (970) 223-4456
E-mail: esainfo@epsilonsigmaalpha.org
Web: www.epsilonsigmaalpha.org

Summary To provide financial assistance for college to students who have epilepsy.

Eligibility This program is open to students who have epilepsy. Applicants must be 1) graduating high school seniors with a GPA of 3.0 or higher or with minimum scores of 22 on the ACT or 1030 on the combined critical reading and mathematics SAT; 2) enrolled in college with a GPA of 3.0 or higher; 3) enrolled at a technical school or

returning to school after an absence for retraining of job skills or obtaining a degree; or 4) engaged in online study through an accredited college, university, or vocational school. They may be attending or planning to attend an accredited school anywhere in the United States and major in any field. Selection is based on character (10%), leadership (10%), service (35%), financial need (35%), and scholastic ability (10%).

Financial data The stipend is $1,000.

Duration 1 year; may be renewed.

Additional data Epsilon Sigma Alpha (ESA) is a women's service organization, but scholarships are available to both men and women. This scholarship was first awarded in 2009. Completed applications must be submitted to the ESA state counselor who then verifies the information before forwarding them to the scholarship director. A $5 processing fee is required.

Number awarded 1 each year.

Deadline January of each year.

[770]
BOB HERSH MEMORIAL SCHOLARSHIP

Mary M. Gooley Hemophilia Center
Attn: Scholarship Selection Committee
1415 Portland Avenue, Suite 500
Rochester, NY 14621
(585) 922-5700   Fax: (585) 922-5775
E-mail: Kristina.Ritchie@rochestergeneral.org
Web: www.hemocenter.org

Summary To provide funding to people with a bleeding disorder and their families who plan to attend college to prepare for a career in a teaching or helping profession.

Eligibility This program is open to people who are affected directly or indirectly by hemophilia, von Willebrand Disease, hereditary bleeding disorder, or hemochromatosis. Applicants must be enrolled or planning to enroll at an accredited 2- or 4-year college or university, vocational/technical school, or certified training program. They must be preparing for a career in a teaching or helping profession. Along with their application, they must submit 1) a 1,000-word essay on their goals and aspirations, their biggest challenge and how they met it, and anything else they want the selection committee to know about them; and 2) a 250-word essay on any unusual family or personal circumstances that have affected their achievement in school, work, or participation in school and community activities, including how their bleeding disorder or that of their family member has affected their life. Selection is based on the essays, academic performance, participation in school and community activities, work or volunteer experience, personal or family circumstances, recommendations, and financial need.

Financial data The stipend is $1,000.

Duration 1 year.

Additional data This program was established in 2009.

Number awarded 1 each year.

Deadline March of each year.

[771]
BONNIE STRANGIO EDUCATION SCHOLARSHIP

Boomer Esiason Foundation
c/o Jerry Cahill
483 Tenth Avenue, Suite 300
New York, NY 10018
(646) 292-7930 Fax: (646) 292-7945
E-mail: jcahill@esiason.org
Web: esiason.org/thriving-with-cf/scholarships.php

Summary To provide financial assistance to undergraduate and graduate students who have cystic fibrosis (CF) and a demonstrated commitment to the prevention and cure of the disease.

Eligibility This program is open to CF patients who are working on an undergraduate or graduate degree. Applicants must be able to demonstrate exemplary service and commitment to the prevention and cure of CF. Along with their application, they must submit a letter from their doctor confirming the diagnosis of CF and a list of daily medications, information on financial need, a detailed breakdown of tuition costs from their academic institution, transcripts, and a 2-page essay on 1) their post-graduation goals; and 2) the importance of compliance with CF therapies and what they practice on a daily basis to stay healthy. Selection is based on academic ability, character, leadership potential, service to the community, and financial need. Finalists are interviewed by telephone.

Financial data The stipend ranges from $500 to $1,000. Funds are paid directly to the academic institution to assist in covering the cost of tuition and fees.

Duration 1 year; nonrenewable.

Additional data This program was established in 2005.

Number awarded 1 each year.

Deadline June of each year.

[772]
BOOMER ESIASON FOUNDATION GENERAL ACADEMIC SCHOLARSHIPS

Boomer Esiason Foundation
c/o Jerry Cahill
483 Tenth Avenue, Suite 300
New York, NY 10018
(646) 292-7930 Fax: (646) 292-7945
E-mail: jcahill@esiason.org
Web: esiason.org/thriving-with-cf/scholarships.php

Summary To provide financial assistance to undergraduate and graduate students who have cystic fibrosis (CF).

Eligibility This program is open to CF patients who are working on an undergraduate or graduate degree. Applicants must submit a letter from their doctor confirming the diagnosis of CF and a list of daily medications, information on financial need, a detailed breakdown of tuition costs from their academic institution, transcripts, and a 2-page essay on 1) their post-graduation goals; and 2) the importance of compliance with CF therapies and what they practice on a daily basis to stay healthy. Selection is based on academic ability, character, leadership potential, service to the community, and financial need. Finalists are interviewed by telephone.

Financial data Stipends range from $500 to $2,500. Funds are paid directly to the academic institution to assist in covering the cost of tuition and fees.

Duration 1 year; nonrenewable.

Additional data Recipients must be willing to participate in the sponsor's CF Ambassador Program by speaking once a year at a designated CF event to help educate the general public about CF.

Number awarded 10 to 15 each year.

Deadline March, June, September, or December of each year.

[773]
BRADLEY D. GENDRON MEMORIAL SCHOLARSHIP

Diabetes Scholars Foundation
2118 Plum Grove Road, Suite 356
Rolling Meadows, IL 60008
(312) 215-9861 Fax: (847) 991-8739
E-mail: collegescholarships@diabetesscholars.org
Web: www.diabetesscholars.org/college.html

Summary To provide financial assistance to high school seniors from Colorado who have diabetes and plan to attend college in any state.

Eligibility This program is open to seniors graduating from high schools in Colorado who have Type 1 diabetes and plan to attend an accredited 4-year university, college, or technical/trade school in any state. Applicants must be able to demonstrate active involvement in the diabetes community, high academic performance, participation in community and/or extracurricular activities, and successful management of the challenges of living with diabetes. Financial need is not considered in the selection process. U.S. citizenship or permanent resident status is required.

Financial data The stipend is $5,000.

Duration 1 year.

Number awarded 1 each year.

Deadline May of each year.

[774]
BRADLEY KRUEGER SCHOLARSHIP

Hemophilia Foundation of Illinois
Attn: Executive Director
210 South DesPlaines
Chicago, IL 60661-5500
(312) 427-1495 E-mail: brobinson@hfi-il.org
Web: www.hemophiliaillinois.org/scholarships.htm

Summary To provide financial assistance for attendance at a college in any state to residents of Illinois who have a bleeding disorder and their families.

Eligibility This program is open to residents of Illinois who have a bleeding disorder and their parents, siblings, and children; people who are carriers of the disease are also eligible. Applicants must be attending or planning to attend a postsecondary institution, including a trade school, in any state. Along with their application, they must submit essays on their goals for furthering their education, the steps they have taken to meet those goals, how this scholarship will help them achieve those goals, what it means to them to live with hemophilia, and what they consider their responsibility to the bleeding disorders community. Financial need is not considered.

Financial data Stipends range up to $5,000. Funds are paid directly to the educational institution to be used for payment of tuition, room and board, books, and supplies (including computer equipment).

Duration 1 year.

Number awarded 1 or more each year.

Deadline June of each year.

[775]
BRIAN MORDEN MEMORIAL SCHOLARSHIP

Brian Morden Foundation
2809 Columbia Drive
Altoona, PA 16602
E-mail: fdj@brianmordenfoundation.org
Web: www.brianmordenfoundation.org/scholarship.htm

Summary To provide financial assistance to students, including cancer survivors, who are interested in studying computer science, medicine, or music in college.

Eligibility This program is open to U.S. citizens who, by summer of the year they apply, will have graduated from high school. Applicants must be majoring or planning to major in computer-related fields, medicine, or music. They are not required to be cancer survivors, but cancer survivors are asked to share information on their treatment and to explain how their cancer experience has affected their life. All applicants are asked to submit 5 other brief statements on assigned topics. Selection is based on those statements, GPA, extracurricular activities, awards and honors, and their plan of study.

Financial data The stipend is $1,000.

Duration 1 year.

Additional data This program honors Brian Morden, who died of cancer in 2003 when he was 19 years of age.

Number awarded 1 or more each year.

Deadline March of each year.

[776]
BRYON RIESCH SCHOLARSHIPS

Bryon Riesch Paralysis Foundation
P.O. Box 1388
Waukesha, WI 53187-1388
(262) 547-2083   E-mail: briesch@brpf.org
Web: www.brpf.org/Grants/ApplicationScholarships.html

Summary To provide financial assistance to undergraduate and graduate students who have a neurological disability or the children of people with such a disability.

Eligibility This program is open to students entering or enrolled at a 2- or 4-year college or university as an undergraduate or graduate student. Applicants must have a neurological disability or be the child of a person with such a disability. They must have a GPA of 2.5 or higher in high school or college. Along with their application, they must submit a 200-word essay on why they deserve the schol-

arship, a statement of their 5- and 10-year goals, and a list of work experience. Financial need is not considered.

Financial data Stipends range from $1,000 to $2,000.

Duration 1 year; may be renewed.

Number awarded Varies each semester; recently, 5 scholarships (all at $1,000) were awarded for the fall semester and 3 (including 1 at $2,000 and 2 at $1,000) were awarded for the spring semester.

Deadline May of each year for fall semester; December of each year for spring semester.

[777]
CALIFORNIA YOUNG CANCER SURVIVOR SCHOLARSHIP PROGRAM

American Cancer Society-California Division
1710 Webster Street
Oakland, CA 94612
(510) 832-7012   Toll Free: (800) 877-1710, ext. 221
Fax: (510) 763-8826
E-mail: anna.edgcomb@cancer.org
Web: www.cancer.org

Summary To provide money for college to residents of California who have been diagnosed as having cancer.

Eligibility This program is open to residents of California who were diagnosed with cancer before the age of 18. Applicants must be currently younger than 25 years of age and attending or planning to attend an accredited 2- or 4-year institution of higher education in California. Along with their application, they must submit 3 essays (250 words each) on their goals, life experiences, and community service. Selection is based on financial need; medical hardship; determination, motivation, and educational goals; GPA (2.5 or higher); and community service.

Financial data Stipends range up to $7,500 per year, depending on the need of the recipient. Funds are paid directly to the recipient's institution.

Duration 1 year; renewable up to 3 more years.

Additional data Recipients are expected to serve a minimum of 50 volunteer hours with the American Cancer Society.

Number awarded Varies each year; recently, 45 of these scholarships were awarded.

Deadline April of each year.

[778]
CALVIN DAWSON MEMORIAL SCHOLARSHIP

Hemophilia Foundation of Greater Florida
1350 Orange Avenue, Suite 227
Winter Park, FL 32789
Toll Free: (800) 293-6527   Fax: (407) 629-9600
E-mail: info@hemophiliaflorida.org
Web: www.hemophiliaflorida.org

Summary To provide financial assistance to residents of Florida who have a bleeding disorder and are interested in attending college in any state.

Eligibility This program is open to residents of Florida who have hemophilia or other related hereditary bleeding disorder. Applicants may be graduating high school seniors or students already enrolled at a college, technical or trade school, or other certification program in any state. Along with their application, they must submit a brief essay on their occupational objectives and goals in life. Selection is based on that essay, merit, community service, and financial need.

Financial data Stipends range up to $1,000. Funds are paid directly to the recipient's college.

Duration 1 year.

Number awarded Varies each year; recently, 4 of these scholarships were awarded.

Deadline April of each year.

[779]
CANCER FOR COLLEGE SCHOLARSHIPS

Cancer for College
1345 Specialty Drive, Suite D
Vista, CA 92081
(760) 599-5096   E-mail: info@cancerforcollege.org
Web: www.cancerforcollege.org

Summary To provide funding to college and graduate students who are cancer patients, survivors, or amputees.

Eligibility This program is open to undergraduate and graduate students enrolled or planning to enroll at accredited colleges, universities, community colleges, and trade schools in the United States and Puerto Rico. Applicants must be a cancer patient, cancer survivor, and/or amputee. Along with a preliminary application, they must submit a brief statement on why they should receive further consideration for this scholarship and information on their financial situation. Preference is given to residents of California and students attending college in southern California.

Financial data Stipends are $4,000, $1,000, or $500.

Duration 1 year; some of the $4,000 scholarships (designated as Perpetual Scholarships) may be renewed up to 3 additional years.

Additional data This program was established in 1993. Perpetual Scholarship recipients must be willing to attend regional events associated with the program and be available for interviews and/or media coverage.

Number awarded Varies each year; recently, this program awarded 4 Perpetual Scholarships at $4,000 per year, 3 1-time scholarships at $4,000, 25 1-time scholarships at $1,000, and 6 1-time scholarships at $500.

Deadline Deadline not specified.

[780]
CANCER SURVIVORS' SCHOLARSHIP

Cancer Survivors' Fund
P.O. Box 792
Missouri City, TX 77459
(281) 437-7142   Fax: (281) 437-9568
E-mail: csf@cancersurvivorsfund.org
Web: www.cancersurvivorsfund.org

Summary To provide financial assistance for college to students who have had cancer.

Eligibility This program is open to students who are enrolled in or accepted for enrollment in an accredited undergraduate school. Applicants must be a cancer survi-

vor or currently diagnosed with cancer; they do not have to be receiving treatment to qualify. They must submit an essay, from 500 to 1,200 words in length, on how their experience with cancer has impacted their life values and career goals. Selection is based on the applicant's personal hardship and financial need.

Financial data A stipend is awarded (amount not specified).

Duration 1 year.

Additional data Recipients must agree to do volunteer work to use their cancer experience to help other young cancer patients and survivors cope with a life-threatening or life-altering event.

Number awarded Varies each year; recently, 41 of these scholarships were awarded.

Deadline March of each year for fall semester; October of each year for spring semester.

[781]
CANDICE'S SICKLE CELL ANEMIA SCHOLARSHIP

Candice's Sickle Cell Fund, Inc.
c/o Candice Young
P.O. Box 672237
Bronx, NY 10467-0237
(646) 436-0477   E-mail: cscfinc@gmail.com
Web: candicessicklecellfund.org

Summary To provide financial assistance to students who have sickle cell disease and are interested in attending college in any state.

Eligibility This program is open to students who are enrolled or planning to enroll at a college or university in any state. Applicants must have been diagnosed with sickle cell disease. Along with their application, they must submit a 250-word essay on how sickle cell disease has affected their life; their educational goals and how they expect to achieve those; and the person who has been instrumental in helping them to persevere.

Financial data The stipend is $1,500.

Duration 1 year.

Additional data This program began in 2001.

Number awarded 3 each year.

Deadline May of each year.

[782]
CFCAREFORWARD SCHOLARSHIPS

Abbott Laboratories
c/o Ruder Finn
Attn: CFCareForward Scholarship Program
301 East 57th Street
New York, NY 10022
Web: www.cfcareforwardscholarship.com

Summary To provide financial assistance for college or graduate school to students with cystic fibrosis (CF).

Eligibility This program is open to high school seniors, vocational school students, college students, and graduate students with CF. U.S. citizenship is required. Applicants must submit 1) a creative presentation (e.g., written work, a piece of art, a craft, collage, photograph) on what sets them apart from their peers, what inspires them to live life to the fullest, or anything else that they think makes them unique; 2) a photograph; and 3) a 250-word essay on the topic, "My dream for the future is..." Selection is based on academic excellence, creativity, community involvement, and ability to serve as a role model to others with CF. Information on all winners is posted on the sponsor's web site to allow the public to select a Thriving Undergraduate Student and a Thriving Graduate Student.

Financial data The stipend is $2,500. The Thriving Students receive an additional award (recently, $16,500 for a total award of $19,000 to honor the program's 19th year).

Duration 1 year.

Additional data This program started in 1992 and was previously sponsored by Solvay Pharmaceuticals, Inc. with the name SolvayCARES Scholarships. Winners also receive a 1-year supply of nutritional drinks and vitamins. The essay, creative presentations, and photograph of all recipients who agree to be considered are posted online so patients, families, friends, physicians, the CF community, and the general public can vote to select the Thriving Students.

Number awarded 40 each year, of whom 1 is designated the Thriving Undergraduate Student and 1 the Thriving Graduate Student.

Deadline May of each year.

[783]
COLORADO CHAPTER NHF ACADEMIC SCHOLARSHIP PROGRAM

National Hemophilia Foundation-Colorado Chapter
Attn: Academic Scholarship Program
1536 Wynkoop Street, Box 26
Denver, CO 80202
(720) 336-0156   E-mail: info@cohemo.org
Web: www.cohemo.org

Summary To provide financial assistance to residents of Colorado who have a bleeding disorder or are relatives of a person with a bleeding disorder and are interested in attending college in any state.

Eligibility This program is open to residents of Colorado who are 1) persons with hemophilia or a related inherited bleeding disorder; 2) parents of a minor child with a bleeding disorder; 3) siblings of a person with a bleeding disorder; and 4) immediate family members of persons who died because of complications of a bleeding disorder. Applicants must be enrolled or planning to enroll at a college, university, or trade school in any state. Along with their application, they must submit a 300-word essay on the impact this scholarship would have on their education. Selection is based on the essay, academic merit, letters of recommendation, impact of the bleeding disorder on educational activities, employment status, and financial need.

Financial data The stipend is $1,000. Funds must be used for tuition, room, board, and related educational expenses.

Duration 1 year; nonrenewable.

Number awarded 2 each year.

Deadline March of each year.

[784]
COMPREHENSIVE BLEEDING DISORDERS CENTER SCHOLARSHIP FUND

Community Foundation of Central Illinois
331 Fulton Street, Suite 310
Peoria, IL 61602
(309) 674-8730   Fax: (309) 674-8754
E-mail: kristan@communityfoundationci.org
Web: www.communityfoundationci.org

Summary To provide financial assistance to students who have a bleeding disorder, live in the service area of the Comprehensive Bleeding Disorders Center (CBDC) in Illinois, and are interested in attending college in any state.

Eligibility This program is open to residents of the CBDC service area (all of Illinois outside of Chicago) who are diagnosed with a congenital or acquired chronic bleeding disorder or a congenital clotting disorder and have attended any hemophilia treatment center's comprehensive clinic during the past year. Applicants must be enrolled or planning to enroll full or part time at an accredited vocational/trade school, junior college, or 4-year college or university in any state. They must have a GPA of 2.0 or higher. Selection is based on their motivation to accomplish their educational and career goals, potential for scholarship, citizenship, and leadership; financial need is considered only if other factors are equal.

Financial data The stipend is $2,000. Funds are disbursed directly to the recipient's school to be used to cover the cost of tuition, books, and required fees.

Duration 1 year.

Additional data This program is supported by the CBDC, 4727 North Sheridan Road, Peoria, IL 61614, (309) 688-1345, ext. 118, E-mail: tjoseph@compbleed.com.

Number awarded 1 or more each year.

Deadline March of each year.

[785]
COOLEY'S ANEMIA FOUNDATION PATIENT INCENTIVE AWARDS

Cooley's Anemia Foundation, Inc.
Attn: National Executive Director
330 Seventh Avenue, Suite 900
New York, NY 10001
(212) 279-8090   Toll Free: (800) 522-7222
Fax: (212) 279-5999 E-mail: info@cooleysanemia.org
Web: www.thalassemia.org

Summary To provide financial assistance to undergraduate and graduate students who have Cooley's anemia (thalassemia).

Eligibility This program is open to U.S. residents who have thalassemia intermediate or major. Applicants must be attending or planning to attend a vocational, undergraduate, or graduate school.

Financial data Stipends depend on the academic level of the recipient, ranging from $250 for students in certificate programs to $2,000 for graduate students.
Duration 1 year.
Number awarded Varies each year; recently, 25 of these scholarships (worth $29,500) were awarded.
Deadline December of each year.

[786]
CRISTIN ANN BAMBINO MEMORIAL SCHOLARSHIP

New York Schools Insurance Reciprocal
Attn: Executive Director
333 Earle Ovington Boulevard, Suite 1030
Uniondale, NY 11553-3624
(516) 393-2329   Toll Free: (800) 476-9747
E-mail: jgoncalves@nysir.org
Web: nysir.org/nysir-student-asbo-scholarships

Summary To provide financial assistance to special education seniors graduating from high schools that subscribe to the New York Schools Insurance Reciprocal (NYSIR) who plan to attend college in any state.
Eligibility This program is open to seniors graduating from NYSIR-subscriber high schools who have been enrolled in special education and have worked through special challenges to complete high school. Applicants must be planning to attend a college or university in any state. Along with their application, they must submit a 650-word essay on their accomplishments, how they overcame their challenges, how they can serve as a role model for other young people with special challenges, and what they plan to study in college. Financial need is not considered in the selection process.
Financial data The grand award winner receives $5,000. Regional winners receive $4,000 or $3,000.
Duration 1 year.
Number awarded 9 each year: the grand award winner and 8 regional winners, of whom 1 receives $4,000 and 7 receive $3,000.
Deadline March of each year.

[787]
CULPEPPER EXUM SCHOLARSHIP FOR PEOPLE WITH KIDNEY DISEASE

National Kidney Foundation Serving Kansas and
   Western Missouri
Attn: Scholarship Program
6405 Metcalf Avenue, Suite 204
Overland Park, KS 66202-4086
(913) 262-1551   Toll Free: (800) 596-7943
Fax: (913) 722-4841   E-mail: nkfkswmo@kidney.org
Web: www.kidney.org/site/index.cfm?ch=305

Summary To provide funding to residents of Kansas and western Missouri who are dialysis or transplant patients and interested in attending college in any state.
Eligibility This program is open to residents of Kansas and western Missouri who are attending or planning to attend a college or university in any state. Applicants must be dialysis or transplant patients. Along with their applica-

tion, they must submit brief essays on their educational plans and goals and why the sponsor should choose them for this scholarship. Financial need is considered.
Financial data The stipend is $1,000. Funds are paid directly to the recipient's institution.
Duration 1 year.
Number awarded 2 each year: 1 to a resident of Kansas and 1 to a resident of western Missouri.
Deadline May of each year.

[788]
CYSTIC FIBROSIS SCHOLARSHIPS

Cystic Fibrosis Scholarship Foundation
1555 Sherman Avenue, Suite 116
Evanston, IL 60201
(847) 328-0127   Fax: (847) 328-0127
E-mail: mkbcfsf@aol.com
Web: www.cfscholarship.org

Summary To provide financial assistance to undergraduate students who have cystic fibrosis (CF).
Eligibility This program is open to students enrolled or planning to enroll in college (either a 2- or 4-year program) or vocational school. Applicants must have CF. Along with their application, they must submit an essay on a topic that changes annually; recently, students were asked to select a personal or historical situation they would like to observe as a "fly on the wall," what they would hope to learn, and how it would benefit them. Selection is based on academic achievement, leadership, and financial need.
Financial data Most stipends are $1,000 per year, although some designated awards (funded by single-year donations) may range up to $2,500. Funds are sent directly to the student's institution to be used for tuition, books, room, and board.
Duration 1 year; some awards may be renewed up to 3 additional years.
Additional data These scholarships were first awarded for 2002. Recent 1-time awards included the Kevin Tidwell Memorial Scholarship of $2,500 per year for 4 years, the Glen Parsons Memorial Scholarship of $2,500 per year for 4 years, and the Tim and Ritch Dangel Memorial Scholarship of $2,000 per year for 4 years.
Number awarded Varies each year; recently, 45 of these scholarships were awarded.
Deadline March of each year.

[789]
DAKOTA PEQUENO MEMORIAL SCHOLARSHIP

Epilepsy Foundation of Michigan
Attn: Development Director
20300 Civic Center Drive, Suite 250
Southfield, MI 48076-4154
(248) 351-7979   Toll Free: (800) 377-6226
Fax: (248) 351-2101
E-mail: bromines@epilepsymichigan.org
Web: www.epilepsymichigan.org/page?php?id=223

Summary To provide financial assistance to high school seniors and graduates in Michigan who have epilepsy and are planning to attend college in any state.
Eligibility This program is open to high school seniors and graduates between 17 and 25 years of age in Michigan who have a diagnosis of epilepsy or a seizure disorder. Applicants must be planning to enroll at a postsecondary academic or vocational program in any state. Along with their application, they must submit a brief essay about their experience dealing with epilepsy. Selection is based on that essay, how the applicant has faced challenges due to epilepsy, career goals, recommendations, and community involvement; financial need is not considered.
Financial data The stipend is $1,000.
Duration 1 year.
Additional data This program began in 2009.
Number awarded 1 each year.
Deadline March of each year.

[790]
DANA WALTERS SCHOLARSHIPS

Dana Walters Scholarship Foundation
P.O. Box 723243
Atlanta, GA 31139
(770) 436-0190   E-mail: sonickaren@aol.com
Web: www.dwscholarship.com

Summary To provide money for college in any state to residents of Georgia who have cystic fibrosis (CF) or are members of their immediate families.
Eligibility This program is open to residents of Georgia who have CF or are a member of a family (including parents) of a person who has CF. Applicants must be graduating high school seniors or already have a high school diploma. They must have a combined SAT score of at least 900 or an ACT score of at least 21 and either a GPA of 2.7 or higher or a rank in the top 30% of their class. Financial need is not considered in the selection process.
Financial data The stipend is $1,000. Funds are paid directly to the recipient's college.
Duration 1 year; may be renewed.
Number awarded 1 or more each year.
Deadline March of each year.

[791]
DAVE MADEIROS CONTINUED EDUCATION SCHOLARSHIPS

Factor Foundation of America
Attn: Scholarship Committee
P.O. Box 812542
Boca Raton, FL 33481-2542
(561) 504-6531
E-mail: kmadeiros@factorfoundation.org
Web: www.factorfoundation.org/programs.htm

Summary To provide financial assistance for college to people with a bleeding disorder and their families.
Eligibility This program is open to people with a bleeding disorder and their siblings, parents, and children. Applicants must be attending or planning to attend an accredited 2- or 4-year college or university or technical school. They must be recommended by a local hemophilia chapter, physician, and/or hemophilia treatment center. Along with their application, they must submit a 500-word letter describing their goals and aspirations and how the bleeding disorders community has played a part in their life. Financial need is also considered in the selection process.
Financial data The stipend is $2,000 per year.
Duration 1 year; may be renewed if the recipient remains in good academic standing.
Additional data This program began in 2006.
Number awarded Varies each year; recently, 12 of these scholarships were awarded.
Deadline June of each year.

[792]
DEANNA LYNN POTTS SCHOLARSHIP

Cystinosis Foundation
Attn: Scholarship Committee
58 Miramonte Drive
Moraga, CA 94556
Toll Free: (888) 631-1588
Web: www.cystinosisfoundation.org/Potts_Award.html

Summary To provide financial assistance for college to students who have cystinosis.
Eligibility This program is open to high school seniors and graduates who have had to postpone entry into college but who have now been accepted at an accredited college, university, or vocational school. Applicants must have cystinosis. Along with their application, they must submit a 500-word essay about a person who played a vital role in their life. Selection is based on that essay (40 points), transcripts (20 points), and letters of recommendation (20 points).
Financial data The stipend is $1,000. Funds are paid directly to the educational institution to be applied to tuition, room, and board.
Duration 1 year.
Number awarded 1 each year.
Deadline March of each year.

[793]
DIABETES, INCORPORATED COLLEGE SCHOLARSHIP

Diabetes, Incorporated
Attn: Executive Director
P.O. Box 9368
Rapid City, SD 57709-9368
(605) 341-1273   Fax: (605) 342-5887
E-mail: diabetesinc@qwestoffice.net
Web: www.disabetesincorporated.org/Scholarship.html

Summary To provide financial assistance to high school seniors and current college students who have or have a family member who has diabetes and is a member of Diabetes, Incorporated.
Eligibility This program is open to graduating high school seniors and students who are continuing their education beyond high school. Applicants must have diabetes

or have a family member who has diabetes. In either case, they must have relative who is a current member of Diabetes, Incorporated. Along with their application, they must submit a 100-word essay on how their life has been affected by diabetes. Selection is based on that essay, GPA and SAT/ACT score, honors and awards, and community contribution. Preference is given to previous participants in the sponsor's Kamp for Kids.

Financial data The scholarship stipend is $1,000 per year; honorable mentions, if awarded, are $150. Funds are paid directly to the educational institution.

Duration 1 year; recipients may reapply.

Additional data This program includes the following named awards: the Kris Sanders Scholarship, the Micah Jerde Scholarship, and the Daniel Silvernail Scholarship.

Number awarded Varies each year; recently, 5 scholarships and 1 honorable mention were awarded.

Deadline April of each year.

[794]
DIABETES SCHOLARS FOUNDATION SCHOLARSHIPS

Diabetes Scholars Foundation
2118 Plum Grove Road, Suite 356
Rolling Meadows, IL 60008
(312) 215-9861　　　　　　Fax: (847) 991-8739
E-mail: collegescholarships@diabetesscholars.org
Web: www.diabetesscholars.org/college.html

Summary To provide financial assistance for college to high school seniors who have diabetes.

Eligibility This program is open to graduating high school seniors who have Type 1 diabetes and plan to attend an accredited 4-year university, college, or technical/trade school in any state. Applicants must be able to demonstrate active involvement in the diabetes community, high academic performance, participation in community and/or extracurricular activities, and successful management of the challenges of living with diabetes. Financial need is not considered in the selection process. U.S. citizenship or permanent resident status is required.

Financial data Stipends are $5,000.

Duration 1 year.

Additional data This program began in 2008.

Number awarded At least 5 each year.

Deadline May of each year.

[795]
DICK GRIFFITHS MEMORIAL SCHOLARSHIP

California Association for Postsecondary Education
　and Disability
Attn: Executive Assistant
71423 Biskra Road
Rancho Mirage, CA 92270
(760) 346-8206　　　　　　Fax: (760) 340-5275
TDD: (760) 341-4084　　E-mail: caped2000@aol.com
Web: www.caped.net/scholarships.html

Summary To provide financial assistance to undergraduate and graduate students in California who have a learning disability, especially involving mathematics.

Eligibility This program is open to students at public and private colleges and universities in California who have a learning disability and are especially challenged in mathematics. Undergraduates must have completed at least 6 semester credits and have a GPA of 2.5 or higher. Graduate students must have completed at least 3 semester units and have a GPA of 3.0 or higher. Along with their application, they must submit a 1-page personal letter that demonstrates their writing skills, progress towards meeting their educational and vocational goals, management of their disability, and involvement in community activities. They must also submit a letter of recommendation from a faculty member, verification of disability, official transcripts, proof of current enrollment, an essay on strategies they use to overcome their mathematics challenges, and documentation of financial need.

Financial data The stipend is $1,000.

Duration 1 year.

Number awarded 1 each year.

Deadline September of each year.

[796]
DONNA T. DARRIEN MEMORIAL SCHOLARSHIP

Donna T. Darrien Memorial Foundation for Sickle Cell,
　Inc.
P.O. Box 3331
Newark, NJ 07103
(973) 282-1997　　　E-mail: dtdsicklecell@hotmail.com
Web: www.dtdsicklecell.org/scholarship-information

Summary To provide financial assistance to residents of New Jersey who have sickle cell disease and are interested in attending college in any state.

Eligibility This program is open to residents of New Jersey who are able to document a diagnosis of sickle cell disease. Applicants must be enrolled or planning to enroll at an accredited college, university, or vocational/technical school in any state and have a GPA of 2.0 or higher. Along with their application, they must submit a 1,000-word essay on how they face their challenges, their educational plans, and their career objectives. Financial need is not considered in the selection process.

Financial data A stipend is awarded (amount not specified).

Duration 1 year; recipients may reapply.

Additional data This program was established in 2001.

Number awarded 1 or more each year.

Deadline April of each year.

[797]
DOTTIE LOURIE MEMORIAL SCHOLARSHIP

National Kidney Foundation Serving New England
Attn: Academic Awards Committee
85 Astor Avenue, Suite 2
Norwood, MA 02062-5040
(781) 278-0222　　　　　　Toll Free: (800) 542-4001
Fax: (781) 278-0333　　E-mail: nkfmarinhvt@kidney.org
Web: www.kidney.org/site/index.cfm?ch=105

Summary To provide funding to residents of New England who have kidney disease, are related to a person with kidney disease, or have received a kidney transplant and are interested in attending college in any state.
Eligibility This program is open to residents of Massachusetts, Rhode Island, New Hampshire, and Vermont who are enrolled or planning to enroll at a college or university in any state. Applicants must be a patient with Chronic Kidney Disease (CKD), have an immediate family member (parent, sibling) with CKD, or have had a life-saving organ transplant. Along with their application, they must submit a 2-page essay on how kidney disease or organ transplantation has impacted their life. Selection is based on academic achievement and financial need.
Financial data The stipend is $1,000. Funds are paid directly to the student.
Duration 1 year.
Number awarded 1 each year.
Deadline March of each year.

[798]
DOUG HITESHEW MEMORIAL SCHOLARSHIPS FOR STUDENTS

Hemophilia Foundation of Maryland
Attn: Executive Director
13 Class Court, Suite 200
Parkville, MD 21234
(410) 661-2307   Toll Free: (800) 964-3131
Fax: (410) 661-2308   E-mail: miller8043@comcast.net
Web: www.hfmonline.org

Summary To provide financial assistance to students who have hemophilia or von Willebrand Disease and are residents of Maryland or attending college in the state.
Eligibility This program is open to students who have hemophilia or von Willebrand Disease and are entering or attending a community college, junior college, 4-year college, university, or vocational school. Applicants must be Maryland residents or a student who has attended a Maryland school for at least 1 year. Along with their application, they must submit 1-page essays on 1) their career goals, and 2) their previous participation with the Hemophilia Foundation of Maryland or another chapter and how they plan to contribute to the chapter in the future. Selection is based on those essays, academic goals, transcripts of current academic work, volunteer work, and letters of recommendation.
Financial data The stipend is $2,000.
Duration 1 year.
Additional data This program was established in 2010.
Number awarded 3 each year.
Deadline April of each year.

[799]
DUGDALE/VAN EYS SCHOLARSHIP AWARD

Tennessee Hemophilia and Bleeding Disorders
   Foundation
Attn: Scholarship Committee
1819 Ward Drive, Suite 102
Murfreesboro, TN 37129
(615) 900-1486   Toll Free: (888) 703-3269
Fax: (615) 900-1487   E-mail: mail@thbdf.org
Web: www.thbdf.org

Summary To provide money for college to students with hemophilia or their family members in Tennessee.
Eligibility This program is open to college-bound high school seniors, college students, and technical school students who have a bleeding disorder and are receiving treatment in Tennessee. Their children, spouses, and guardians are also eligible. Applicants must have a GPA of 2.5 or higher and be enrolled or planning to enroll full time. They must submit a 500-word essay on their life goals, a resume, 3 letters of recommendation, proof of enrollment, and documentation of community service of at least 10 hours per semester. Financial need is considered in the selection process.
Financial data Stipends range from $500 to $2,000.
Duration 1 year; recipients may reapply.
Number awarded 6 each year: 1 at $2,000, 1 at $1,500, 1 at $1,000, and 3 at $500.
Deadline April of each year.

[800]
EDUCATION ADVANTAGE COMMUNITY COLLEGE OR TECHNICAL SCHOLARSHIP

Baxter Healthcare Corporation
c/o Scholarship America
Scholarship Management Services
P.O. Box 297
One Scholarship Way
St. Peter, MN 56082
Toll Free: (877) 544-3018
E-mail: baxter@scholarshipamerica.org
Web: www.myeducationadvantage.com/scholarship

Summary To provide financial assistance to people who have hemophilia A and are interested in working on an associate degree or technical certificate.
Eligibility This program is open to people who have hemophilia A or hemophilia with inhibitors and are enrolled or planning to enroll part or full time at a community college, junior college, trade or vocational school, or other eligible program. Applicants must submit a personal statement that focuses on their unique experiences that make them stand out from other students (e.g., their experiences of living with hemophilia, how it impacts their education or career goals, noteworthy volunteer activities within the hemophilia community). Both merit and need-based scholarships are available. U.S. citizenship or permanent residency is required.
Financial data The stipend ranges up to $2,500 per year for need-based scholarships or $1,000 per year for merit-based scholarships.

Duration 1 year; may be renewed 1 additional year, provided the recipient remains enrolled full time, maintains a GPA of 2.0 or higher, provides evidence of participation in annual comprehensive clinic and routine dental care, performs 20 hours of community service, and submits a 250-word essay on their academic progress, their career goals, and the value of funding assistance.

Number awarded Varies each year; recently, 10 of these scholarships were awarded.

Deadline April of each year.

[801]
EDUCATION ADVANTAGE UNIVERSITY SCHOLARSHIP

Baxter Healthcare Corporation
c/o Scholarship America
Scholarship Management Services
One Scholarship Way
P.O. Box 297
St. Peter, MN 56082
Toll Free: (877) 544-3018
E-mail: baxter@scholarshipamerica.org
Web: www.myeducationadvantage.com

Summary To provide financial assistance to people who have hemophilia A and are interested in working on a bachelor's degree.

Eligibility This program is open to people who have hemophilia A or hemophilia with inhibitors and are enrolled or planning to enroll full time at a 4-year college or university. Applicants must submit a personal statement that focuses on their unique experiences that make them stand out from other students (e.g., their experiences of living with hemophilia, how it impacts their education or career goals, noteworthy volunteer activities within the hemophilia community). They must have a GPA of 2.0 or higher. Both merit-based and need-based scholarships are available. U.S. citizenship or permanent resident status is required.

Financial data The stipend ranges up to $15,000 per year for need-based scholarships or $1,000 per year for merit-based scholarships.

Duration 1 year; may be renewed up to 3 additional years, provided the recipient remains enrolled full time, maintains a GPA of 2.0 or higher, provides evidence of participation in annual comprehensive clinic and routine dental care, performs 20 hours of community service, and submits a 250-word essay on their academic progress, their career goals and developments, and the value of funding assistance.

Number awarded Varies each year; recently, 30 of these scholarships were awarded.

Deadline April of each year.

[802]
EDUCATION IS POWER SCHOLARSHIPS

MedProRx, Inc.
Attn: Scholarship Coordinator
140 Northway Court
Raleigh, NC 27615-4916
Toll Free: (866) KATHY-MD
E-mail: educationispower@medprorx.com
Web: www.medprorx.com/scholarship.html

Summary To provide financial assistance for college to people with a bleeding disorder.

Eligibility This program is open to residents of the United States who are living with hemophilia or von Willebrand Disease. Applicants must be entering or attending a community college, junior college, 4-year college, university, or vocational school. They must be able to demonstrate a record of community involvement and/or volunteer work. Along with their application, they must submit a 250-word essay on their dreams and aspirations, what they are most passionate about, how living with a bleeding disorder has affected their life, and what they would change if they had the power to change something in the world.

Financial data Stipends range from $500 to $2,500.

Duration 1 year.

Additional data This program began in 2006.

Number awarded At least 20 each year.

Deadline April of each year.

[803]
ELAM BAER AND JANIS CLAY EDUCATIONAL SCHOLARSHIP

Epilepsy Foundation of Minnesota
Attn: Scholarships
1600 University Avenue West, Suite 300
St. Paul, MN 55104
(651) 287-2312   Toll Free: (800) 779-0777, ext. 2312
Fax: (651) 287-2325   E-mail: skolari@efmn.org
Web: www.epilepsyfoundationmn.org/scholarships.aspx

Summary To provide financial assistance to residents of Minnesota and eastern North Dakota who have epilepsy and are interested in attending college in any state.

Eligibility This program is open to graduating high school seniors and high school graduates who live in Minnesota or eastern North Dakota. Applicants must have a diagnosis of epilepsy or other seizure disorder. They must have been accepted at a postsecondary academic or vocational program. Along with their application, they must submit a 250-word essay on something of direct personal importance to them as a person with epilepsy. Selection is based on how the applicant has faced challenges due to epilepsy, career goals, achievements, community activity, and recommendations; financial need is not considered.

Financial data The stipend is $1,000.

Duration 1 year.

Additional data These scholarships were first awarded in 2006.

Number awarded 10 each year.

Deadline March of each year.

[804]
ELIZABETH LULU SCHOLARSHIP

Elizabeth Lulu Scholarship Foundation
c/o Beth and Allen Lulu
1760 West 25th Street
Los Angeles, CA 90018
(323) 734-5858
E-mail: elizabethluluscholarship@gmail.com
Web: www.lizzielulu.org/index.php

Summary To provide financial assistance for college to high school seniors who have cystic fibrosis.

Eligibility This program is open to graduating high school seniors who have cystic fibrosis and plans to attend a college or university. Applicants must submit academic information (GPA, SAT and/or ACT scores), a list of extracurricular activities, a letter from their doctor or social worker confirming their cystic fibrosis, information on financial need, a 1-page essay on their future goals and aspirations, and a 1-paragraph statement on what they have accomplished in spite of cystic fibrosis.

Financial data The stipend is $1,000.

Duration 1 year.

Additional data This foundation was established in 2006 following the death of Elizabeth Lulu from cystic fibrosis at 13 years of age.

Number awarded 1 or more each year; since the foundation was established, it has awarded 4 scholarships.

Deadline April of each year.

[805]
ELIZABETH NASH FOUNDATION
SCHOLARSHIP PROGRAM

Elizabeth Nash Foundation
P.O. Box 1260
Los Gatos, CA 95031-1260
E-mail: scholarships@elizabethnashfoundation.org
Web: www.elizabethnashfoundation.org

Summary To provide financial assistance for college or graduate school to individuals with cystic fibrosis (CF).

Eligibility This program is open to undergraduate and graduate students who have CF. Applicants must be able to demonstrate clear academic goals and a commitment to participate in activities outside the classroom. U.S. citizenship is required. Selection is based on academic record, character, demonstrated leadership, service to CF-related causes and the broader community, and financial need.

Financial data Stipends range from $1,000 to $2,500. Funds are paid directly to the academic institution to be applied to tuition and fees.

Duration 1 year; recipients may reapply.

Additional data This program began in 2005. Recipients must speak at a local event or write an article for publication by the foundation.

Number awarded Varies each year; recently, 17 of these scholarships were awarded. Since the program was established, it has awarded 78 scholarships.

Deadline April of each year.

[806]
EPILEPSY FOUNDATION OF NEW JERSEY
SCHOLARSHIP PROGRAM

Epilepsy Foundation of New Jersey
Attn: Scholarship Program
2516 Highway 35
Manasquan, NJ 08736
Toll Free: (800) 336-5843   Fax: (732) 528-4744
TDD: (800) 852-7899   E-mail: aracioppi@efnj.com
Web: www.efnj.com/content/info/scholarship.html

Summary To provide financial assistance to high school seniors in New Jersey who have epilepsy and are planning to attend college in any state.

Eligibility This program is open to seniors graduating from high schools in New Jersey who have epilepsy. Applicants must be planning to attend a college or university in any state. Along with their application, they must submit a brief personal statement explaining their academic and career goals. Selection is based on academic achievement, participation in activities, and financial need.

Financial data The stipend is $1,000 per year. Funds are paid directly to the recipient.

Duration 1 year.

Number awarded 4 each year.

Deadline May of each year.

[807]
ERIC C. MARDER SCHOLARSHIP PROGRAM

Immune Deficiency Foundation
Attn: Scholarship Programs
40 West Chesapeake Avenue, Suite 308
Towson, MD 21204-4803
(410) 321-6647   Toll Free: (800) 296-4433
Fax: (410) 321-9165   E-mail: idf@primaryimmune.org
Web: primaryimmune.org

Summary To provide financial assistance to undergraduates with a primary immune deficiency disease.

Eligibility This program is open to undergraduates entering or attending college or technical training school who have a primary immune deficiency disease. Applicants must submit an autobiographical essay, 2 letters of recommendation, a family financial statement, and a letter of verification from their immunologist. Financial need is the main factor considered in selecting the recipients and the size of the award.

Financial data Stipends range from $750 to $2,000, depending on the recipient's financial need.

Duration 1 year; may be renewed.

Additional data This program was established in 1986.

Number awarded Varies each year.

Deadline March of each year.

[808]
ERIC DELSON MEMORIAL SCHOLARSHIP

CVS Caremark
c/o Scholarship America
Scholarship Management Services
One Scholarship Way
P.O. Box 297
St. Peter, MN 56082
(507) 931-1682
Web: cvscaremarkspecialtyrx.com

Summary To provide financial assistance for high school, college, or graduate school to students with a bleeding disorder.

Eligibility This program is open to students diagnosed with a bleeding disorder who are 1) high school seniors, high school graduates or equivalent (GED), college students, or graduate students currently enrolled or planning to enroll full time at an accredited 2- or 4-year college, university, or vocational/technical school; or 2) students entering grades 7-12 at a private secondary school in the United States. Selection is based on academic record, demonstrated leadership and participation in school and community activities, work experience, a statement of educational and career goals, unusual personal or family circumstances, and an outside appraisal.

Financial data The stipend is $2,500 for college students or $1,500 for high school students. Funds are paid in 2 equal installments directly to the recipient.

Duration 1 year; may be renewed for up to 3 additional years, provided the recipient maintains a GPA of 2.5 or higher for the freshman year and 3.0 or higher for subsequent years.

Number awarded 4 each year: 3 for college students and 1 for a high school student.

Deadline June of each year.

[809]
ERIC DOSTIE MEMORIAL COLLEGE SCHOLARSHIP

NuFACTOR Specialty Pharmacy
Attn: Scholarship Administrator
41093 Country Center Drive, Suite B
Temecula, CA 92591
(951) 296-2516   Toll Free: (800) 323-6832, ext. 1300
Fax: (877) 432-6258   E-mail: info@kelleycom.com
Web: www.nufactor.com

Summary To provide financial assistance for college to students with hemophilia or members of their families.

Eligibility This program is open to 1) students with hemophilia or a related bleeding disorder; or 2) members of their families. Applicants must be U.S. citizens and enrolled or planning to enroll full time at an accredited 2- or 4-year college or university. They must have a GPA of 2.5 or higher. Along with their application, they must submit an essay on how their education will be used to serve humankind and to encourage self-improvement and enrichment. Selection is based on academic achievement, community service, and financial need.

Financial data The stipend is $1,000.

Duration 1 year.

Number awarded 10 each year.

Deadline February of each year.

[810]
EXERCISE FOR LIFE ATHLETIC SCHOLARSHIPS

Boomer Esiason Foundation
c/o Jerry Cahill
483 Tenth Avenue, Suite 300
New York, NY 10018
(646) 292-7930   Fax: (646) 292-7945
E-mail: jcahill@esiason.org
Web: esiason.org/thriving-with-cf/scholarships.php

Summary To provide financial assistance for college to high school seniors who have been involved in athletics and who have cystic fibrosis (CF).

Eligibility This program is open to CF patients who are college-bound high school seniors. Applicants must have been involved in athletics. They should be jogging on a regular basis and training for a 1.5 mile run. Along with their application, they must submit a letter from their doctor confirming the diagnosis of CF and a list of daily medications, information on financial need, a detailed breakdown of tuition costs from their academic institution, a completed running log, transcripts, and a 2-page essay on 1) their post-graduation goals; and 2) the importance of compliance with CF therapies and what they practice on a daily basis to stay healthy. Selection is based on academic ability, athletic ability, character, leadership potential, service to the community, financial need, and daily compliance to CF therapy. Male and female students compete separately.

Financial data The stipend is $10,000. Funds are paid directly to the academic institution to assist in covering the cost of tuition and fees.

Duration 1 year; nonrenewable.

Number awarded 1 to a male and 1 to a female.

Deadline June of each year.

[811]
FLICKER OF HOPE SCHOLARSHIPS

Flicker of Hope Foundation
Attn: Scholarship Committee
8624 Janet Lane
Vienna, VA 22180
(703) 698-1626   Fax: (703) 698-6225
E-mail: info@flickerofhope.org
Web: www.flickerofhope.org/whatwedo.htm

Summary To provide money for college to burn survivors.

Eligibility This program is open to high school seniors and graduates who are burn survivors and enrolled or planning to enroll in college. Applicants must submit a 500-word essay describing the circumstances of how they were burned, how that injury has affected their life, and the benefits to be derived from their planned course of study. Selection is based on severity of burn injury, academic performance, community service, and financial need.

Financial data A stipend is awarded (amount not specified). Funds are paid directly to the recipient's school.
Duration 1 year.
Number awarded Varies each year; recently, 14 of these scholarships were awarded.
Deadline May of each year.

[812]
FLORIDA CHAIRSCHOLARS PROGRAM

ChairScholars Foundation, Inc.
16101 Carencia Lane
Odessa, FL 33556-3278
(813) 926-0544   Toll Free: (888) 926-0544
Fax: (813) 920-7661
E-mail: chairscholars@tampabay.rr.com
Web: www.chairscholars.org/florida.html

Summary To provide funding to students in Florida with specified disabilities who plan to attend college in the state.

Eligibility This program is open to residents of Florida who are enrolled in grades 7-11 at a public school and have a serious physical disability. Qualifying disabilities include cerebral palsy, muscular dystrophy, spinal muscular atrophy, amputations, congenital missing or shortened limbs, multiple sclerosis, profound deafness, hearing impairments requiring FM modulator, blindness, various forms of cancer, any condition that permanently places the student in a wheelchair, or other illnesses, diseases, or conditions that severely impair mobility or motor skills. Applicants must have at least a "B" average and be able to demonstrate significant financial need (annual income less than $20,137 for a family of 1, rising to $69,616 for a family of 8). They must be planning to attend a college, university, community college, or vocational school in the state. Along with their application, they must submit a 1-page essay outlining how they became physically challenged, how their situation has affected them or their family, their family situation, things they like to do, why they need this scholarship, and their goals and dreams for the future.

Financial data The awards provide full payment of tuition at any public college, university, or community college, or vocational school in Florida.
Duration Up to 4 years.
Additional data This program began in 1996. Recipients are provided with a mentor until they graduate from high school. They must sign a "contract" pledging to remain drug and crime free.
Number awarded Varies each year; recently, 24 of these scholarships were awarded. Since the program was established, it has awarded 502 scholarships.
Deadline January of each year.

[813]
FRANK SELENY SCHOLARSHIPS

Hawaii Children's Cancer Foundation
1814 Liliha Street
Honolulu, HI 96817
(808) 528-5161 Toll Free: (866) 443-HCCF (within HI)
Fax: (808) 521-4689   E-mail: info@hccf.org
Web: www.hccf.org/family-support

Summary To provide financial assistance to residents of Hawaii who have had cancer and are interested in attending college in any state.

Eligibility This program is open to residents of Hawaii who were diagnosed with cancer before 18 years of age. Applicants must have been accepted into a college or vocational training program in any state.
Financial data The stipend is $1,000.
Duration 1 year.
Additional data This foundation started in 1991.
Number awarded 2 each year.
Deadline Deadline not specified.

[814]
GEORGE AND LINDA PRICE SCHOLARSHIP

Hemophilia Association of the Capital Area
10560 Main Street, Suite 419
Fairfax, VA 22030-7182
(703) 352-7641   Fax: (540) 427-6589
E-mail: admin@hacacares.org
Web: www.hacacares.org

Summary To provide financial assistance to individuals with bleeding disorders and their families who are members of the Hemophilia Association of the Capital Area (HACA) and interested in attending college or graduate school in any state.

Eligibility This program is open to residents of northern Virginia, Montgomery and Prince George's County in Maryland, and Washington, D.C. who have a bleeding disorder and their siblings and parents. Applicants must be members of HACA. They must be 1) high school seniors or graduates who have not yet attended college; 2) full-time freshmen, sophomores, or juniors at a college, university, or vocational/technical school in any state; or 3) college seniors planning to attend graduate school and students already enrolled at a graduate school in any state. Along with their application, they must submit a 500-word essay on what they have done to contribute to the bleeding disorders community and how they plan to contribute to that community in the future. Financial need is not considered.

Financial data The stipend is $2,500.
Duration 1 year; recipients may reapply.
Number awarded 2 each year.
Deadline April of each year.

[815]
GERTRUDE DAWSON SCHOLARSHIP

Northwest Sickle Cell Collaborative
c/o Odessa Brown Children's Clinic
2101 East Yesler Way
Seattle, WA 98122
(206) 987-7200   E-mail: info@odessabrown.org
Web: www.nwsicklecell.org/for-kids/scholarships.php

Summary To provide funding to Washington residents who have sickle cell disease and are attending college in the state.

Eligibility This program is open to residents of Washington who are currently enrolled at a college, university, or technical/trade school in the state. Applicants must have sickle cell disease. They must have a GPA of 2.5 or higher and be able to demonstrate financial need.

Financial data A stipend is awarded (amount not specified). Funds are disbursed through the financial aid office at the recipient's school.

Duration 1 year.

Number awarded 1 or more each year.

Deadline June of each year.

[816]
GREAT LAKES HEMOPHILIA FOUNDATION EDUCATION SCHOLARSHIPS

Great Lakes Hemophilia Foundation
Attn: Program Services Committee
638 North 18th Street, Suite 108
Milwaukee, WI 53233
(414) 257-0200   Toll Free: (888) 797-GLHF
Fax: (414) 257-1225   E-mail: info@glhf.org
Web: www.glhf.org/scholar.htm

Summary To provide financial assistance to Wisconsin residents who have a bleeding disorder (and their families) and are interested in attending college in any state.

Eligibility This program is open to members of the bleeding disorder community in Wisconsin. Applicants must be attending or planning to attend college, vocational school, technical school, or a certification program in any state. Along with their application, they must submit an essay of 500 to 750 words on their educational and career goals, what they have done to work toward achieving those goals, how the education or training program in which they are enrolled will help them meet their goals, what they consider the most significant challenges associated with living with a bleeding disorder, the opportunities or benefits have those challenges provided them, and how they plan on contributing back to the bleeding disorders community. First priority is given to people affected by bleeding disorders, then to parents of young children with bleeding disorders, and then to spouses of individuals with bleeding disorders. If sufficient funds are available, consideration may be given to siblings and other family members of individuals with a bleeding disorder. Financial need is considered in the selection process.

Financial data Stipends range up to $3,000.

Duration 1 year.

Number awarded Varies each year; recently, 3 of these scholarships were awarded.

Deadline April of each year.

[817]
GREAT WEST DIVISION CHILDHOOD CANCER SURVIVOR COLLEGE SCHOLARSHIP PROGRAM

American Cancer Society-Great West Division
Attn: Randi Cress
920 North Washington, Suite 200
Spokane, WA 99201
(509) 455-3440   Toll Free: (866) 500-3272
Fax: (509) 455-3990
Web: www.cancer.org

Summary To provide financial assistance for college to high school seniors in selected western states who have been diagnosed as having cancer.

Eligibility This program is open to U.S. citizens younger than 25 years of age who are residents of Alaska, Arizona, Colorado, Idaho, Montana, North Dakota, New Mexico, Nevada, Oregon, Utah, Washington, or Wyoming. Applicants must have had a diagnosis of cancer before the age of 21 and have been accepted as a continuing or entering full-time student at an accredited community college, university, college, or vocational/technical school in any state. They must have a GPA of 2.5 or higher. Along with their application, they must submit a 500-word essay on how this scholarship will help further their academic career, including their educational, occupational, and personal goals. Selection is based on that essay (15%), financial need (50%), community service and involvement with the American Cancer Society (20%), letters of recommendation (9%), and GPA (6%).

Financial data The stipend is $2,500 per year.

Duration 1 year; may be renewed up to 3 additional years, provided the recipient remains enrolled full time with a GPA of 2.5 or higher and volunteers with the American Cancer Society for at least 25 hours per calendar year.

Number awarded Varies each year.

Deadline February of each year.

[818]
GUTHRIE-KOCH PKU SCHOLARSHIP

National PKU News
6869 Woodlawn Avenue, N.E., Suite 116
Seattle, WA 98115-5469
(206) 525-8140   Fax: (206) 525-5023
E-mail: schuett@pkunews.org
Web: www.pkunews.org/guthrie/guthrie.htm

Summary To provide financial assistance for college to students with phenylketonuria (PKU).

Eligibility This program is open to college-age people from any country who have PKU and are on the required diet. Applicants must be accepted as an undergraduate at an accredited college or technical school before the scholarship is awarded, but they may apply before acceptance is confirmed. Along with their application, they must submit a statement that includes why they are applying for the scholarship, educational objectives and career plans, school and community activities, honors and awards, work history, current diet and how they cope with it on a daily basis, overall experience with PKU, attitudes toward the PKU diet now and in the past, and the influence PKU has had on their life. Selection is based on that statement, academic record, educational and career goals, extracurricular activities, volunteer work, and letters of recommendation. Financial need is considered but is not required; students can be awarded a scholarship without having significant financial need.

Financial data Stipends vary but recently have been $2,000.

Duration 1 year.

Additional data This program began in 1998 as the Robert Guthrie PKU Scholarship to honor Dr. Robert Guthrie, who had died in 1995. After the death of Dr. Richard Koch in 2011, the name was changed to recognize his contributions to research on PKU.

Number awarded Varies each year; recently, 6 of these scholarships were awarded.

Deadline October of each year.

[819]
HARVEY SIMON MEMORIAL SCHOLARSHIP

The Simon Cancer Foundation
P.O. Box 25093
Tamarac, FL 33320
(954) 288-8455   E-mail: thescf@gmail.com
Web: www.thescf.org/Scholarships.html

Summary To provide financial assistance to cancer patients and survivors who are currently attending college.

Eligibility This program is open to cancer patients and survivors who are currently enrolled at a 4-year college or university. Applicants must have a GPA of 3.0 or higher and a record of strong leadership and community service.

Financial data The stipend is $1,000.

Duration 1 year; nonrenewable.

Number awarded Varies each year; recently, 5 of these scholarships were awarded.

Deadline January of each year.

[820]
HEMOPHILIA FEDERATION OF AMERICA EDUCATIONAL SCHOLARSHIPS

Hemophilia Federation of America
Attn: Scholarship Committee
210 Seventh Street, S.E., Suite 200B
Washington, DC 20003
(202) 675-6984   Toll Free: (800) 230-9797
Fax: (202) 675-6983   E-mail: info@hemophiliafed.org
Web: hemophiliafed.org

Summary To provide financial assistance for college to students who have a blood clotting disorder.

Eligibility This program is open to high school seniors and current college students who have a blood clotting disorder. Applicants must be attending or planning to attend an accredited 2- or 4-year college, university, or

trade school in the United States. Along with their application, they must submit a 1-page essay on their goals and aspirations and how the blood clotting community has played a part in their lives. Financial need is also required.

Financial data The stipend is $1,500 per year.

Duration 1 year; may be renewed.

Number awarded 6 each year.

Deadline April of each year.

[821]
HEMOPHILIA FOUNDATION OF MICHIGAN ACADEMIC SCHOLARSHIPS

Hemophilia Foundation of Michigan
Attn: Client Services Coordinator
1921 West Michigan Avenue
Ypsilanti, MI 48197
(734) 544-0015   Toll Free: (800) 482-3041
Fax: (734) 544-0095   E-mail: colleen@hfmich.org
Web: www.hfmich.org/?module=Page&sID=scholarships

Summary To provide financial assistance to Michigan residents with hemophilia and their families who are interested in attending college in any state.

Eligibility This program is open to high school seniors, high school graduates, and currently-enrolled college students who are Michigan residents and have hemophilia or another bleeding disorder. Family members of people with bleeding disorders and family members of people who have died from the complications of a bleeding disorder are also eligible. Applicants must submit a 300-word statement on their educational and career goals, the role that the bleeding disorder has played in influencing those goals, and how receiving the scholarship will help them to meet those goals. Selection is based on that statement, academic merit, employment status, reference letters, financial need, and the impact of bleeding disorder on educational activities.

Financial data The stipend is $2,500.

Duration 1 year; recipients may reapply.

Number awarded 2 each year.

Deadline March of each year.

[822]
HEMOPHILIA FOUNDATION OF MINNESOTA/ DAKOTAS SCHOLARSHIPS

Hemophilia Foundation of Minnesota/Dakotas
Attn: Scholarship Program
750 South Plaza Drive, Suite 207
Mendota Heights, MN 55120
(651) 406-8655   Toll Free: (800) 994-HFMD
Fax: (651) 406-8656
E-mail: hemophiliafound@visi.com
Web: www.hfmd.org/Scholarships/Scholarships.html

Summary To provide funding to residents of Minnesota, North Dakota, and South Dakota who have a bleeding disorder and are interested in attending college in any state.

Eligibility This program is open to residents of Minnesota, North Dakota, and South Dakota who have an inherited bleeding disorder and/or are patients at a hemophilia treatment center in those states. Applicants must be participating in programs and services of the Hemophilia Foundation of Minnesota/Dakotas. They must be attending or planning to attend a college or university in any state. Financial need is considered in the selection process.

Financial data The stipend is $1,000. Funds are paid to the academic institution.

Duration 1 year.

Number awarded 10 each year.

Deadline May of each year.

[823] HEMOPHILIA HEALTH SERVICES MEMORIAL SCHOLARSHIPS

Accredo's Hemophilia Health Services
Attn: Scholarship Committee
201 Great Circle Road
Nashville, TN 37228
(615) 850-5210   Toll Free: (800) 800-6606
Fax: (615) 261-6730
E-mail: lisa.dabrowiak@accredo.com
Web: www.hemophiliahealth.com/Scholarships.html

Summary To provide money for college or graduate school to people who have hemophilia or other bleeding disorders.

Eligibility This program is open to individuals with hemophilia (factor VIII or IX), von Willebrand Disease (type 1, 2, 2A, 2B, 2M, 2N, or 3), factor I (fibrinogen), factor II (prothrombin), factor V (proaccelerin), factor VII (proconvertin), factor X, factor XI, factor XIII, or Glanzmann's thrombasthenia. Applicants must be 1) high school seniors; 2) college freshmen, sophomores, or juniors; or 3) college seniors planning to attend graduate school or students already enrolled in graduate school. Applicants must be enrolled or planning to enroll full time at an accredited nonprofit college, university, or vocational/technical school in the United States or Puerto Rico. Along with their application, they must submit an essay, up to 250 words, on the following topic: "What has been your own personal challenge in living with a bleeding disorder?" U.S. citizenship is required. Selection is based on the essay, academic record, community involvement, and financial need.

Financial data The stipend is at least $1,500. Funds are issued payable to the recipient's school.

Duration 1 year; recipients may reapply.

Additional data This program, which started in 1995, includes programs named after former employees of the sponsoring organization. Past scholarships have been named the Cindy Beck Scholarship, the Becky Cohn Scholarship, the Osborne DeWitt Scholarship, the Tim Haas Scholarship, the Ricky Hobson Scholarship, the Michael Moses Scholarship, the Jim Stineback Scholarship, and the Scott Tarbell Scholarship. It is administered by International Scholarship and Tuition Services, Inc.

Number awarded Several each year.

Deadline April of each year.

[824] HEMOPHILIA OF IOWA SCHOLARSHIPS

Hemophilia of Iowa, Inc.
c/o Shane Kelley, Scholarship Committee Chair
22930 20th Street
Fairbank, IA 50629
Toll Free: (319) 239-3948
E-mail: ssckelley@yahoo.com
Web: www.hemophiliaofiowa.com

Summary To provide financial assistance to members of Hemophilia of Iowa who are interested in attending college in any state.

Eligibility This program is open to members of the sponsoring organization who either have hemophilia (or a related bleeding disorder) or are the immediate family member (caregiver, sibling, child) of someone who has hemophilia or a related bleeding disorder. Applicants may be graduating high school seniors or students currently enrolled at an accredited college, university, or trade school in any state. Along with their application, they must submit brief statements on 1) their short- and long-range career plans; 2) their personal background related to the bleeding disorder community and any specific contributions they have made to the Hemophilia of Iowa community; and 3) their key reasons for selecting the profession they are pursuing. Selection is based on personal qualities and community service. Applicants who have supported the mission of Hemophilia of Iowa are considered for supplemental funding: the John Heisner Scholarship and the Dude Cremer Scholarship.

Financial data The stipend is $1,500 for students with a bleeding disorder or $1,000 for family members. Applicants selected for the supplemental funding provided by the named scholarships receive an additional $1,000.

Duration 1 semester; recipients may reapply.

Number awarded Varies each year; recently, 20 of these scholarships were awarded.

Deadline March of each year.

[825] HIGH PLAINS CANCER SURVIVOR SCHOLARSHIPS

American Cancer Society-High Plains Division
2433 Ridgepoint Drive, Suite B
Austin, TX 78754
(512) 919-1910   Toll Free: (877) 227-1618
Fax: (512) 919-1846 E-mail: Phyllis.Caron@cancer.org
Web: www.cancer.org

Summary To provide money for college or graduate school to cancer patients and survivors in Guam, Hawaii, Kansas, Missouri, Nebraska, Oklahoma, and Texas.

Eligibility This program is open to residents of Guam, Hawaii, Kansas, Missouri, Nebraska, Oklahoma, and Texas who have had a cancer diagnosis before age 21. Applicants must be accepted at or attending an accredited university, graduate school, community college, or vocational/technical school in any state. They must be 25 years of age or younger at the time of applying and have a GPA of 2.0 or higher. Along with their application, they must submit 2 recommendations (including 1 from a physician verifying diagnosis), an acceptance letter from an academic institution, documentation of financial need, academic transcripts, and a 2-page essay describing their life experiences, future goals, community involvement, and cancer-related involvement.

Financial data   The stipend is $1,000 per year. Funds are paid directly to the academic institution.

Duration   1 year; may be renewed.

Number awarded   Varies each year; recently, 100 of these scholarships were awarded.

Deadline   March of each year.

[826]
HIGHER EDUCATION ASSISTANCE PROGRAM SCHOLARSHIP

DREAM Institute
P.O. Box 52785
Tulsa, OK 74152-0785
(918) 660-3408   E-mail: dream@dreaminstitute.org
Web: www.dreaminstitute.org/Programs.htm

Summary   To provide financial assistance to residents of Oklahoma who have a physical and/or learning disability and are interested in attending college in the state.

Eligibility   This program is open to residents of Oklahoma who have been diagnosed with a physical and/or learning disability. Applicants must be enrolled or planning to enroll full time at a 2- or 4-year college or university in the state. They must be able to demonstrate financial need.

Financial data   The stipend depends on the need of the recipient. Funds are available to help pay for tuition, fees, books, and dormitory fees.

Duration   1 year; may be renewed.

Additional data   Scholars are invited to participate in an orientation workshop designed to equip them with the information they will require as a college student with a disability. They also qualify for special tutoring.

Number awarded   Varies each year; recently, 3 new and 10 renewal scholarships were awarded.

Deadline   April of each year.

[827]
HUEY AND ANGELINA WILSON NONTRADITIONAL SCHOLARSHIPS

Louisiana Hemophilia Foundation
Attn: Scholarship Committee
3636 South Sherwood Forest Boulevard, Suite 390
Baton Rouge, LA 70816
(225) 291-1675   Toll Free: (800) 749-1680
Fax: (225) 291-1679   E-mail: contact@lahemo.org
Web: lahemo.org/news.html

Summary   To provide financial assistance for college to Louisiana residents who are nontraditional students and a hemophilia patient or the parent of a patient.

Eligibility   This program is open to residents of Louisiana who are a hemophilia patient or the parent of a patient. Applicants must be enrolled or planning to enroll at a Louisiana college or university as a nontraditional stu-

dent. Along with their application, they must submit a 250-word essay on why they should receive this scholarship.

Financial data   The stipend is $1,000 per semester.

Duration   1 semester. Recipients may reapply if they remain enrolled full time, have a GPA of 2.75 or higher, and provide 8 hours of community service to the sponsoring organization.

Number awarded   Varies each semester; the foundation first awards scholarships to traditional students; if funds remain, it may award scholarships to qualified nontraditional students.

Deadline   June of each year for fall semester; December of each year for spring semester.

[828]
HUEY AND ANGELINA WILSON TRADITIONAL SCHOLARSHIPS

Louisiana Hemophilia Foundation
Attn: Scholarship Committee
3636 South Sherwood Forest Boulevard, Suite 390
Baton Rouge, LA 70816
(225) 291-1675   Toll Free: (800) 749-1680
Fax: (225) 291-1679   E-mail: contact@lahemo.org
Web: lahemo.org/news.html

Summary   To provide money for college to Louisiana residents who have hemophilia or another bleeding disorder.

Eligibility   This program is open to residents of Louisiana who have hemophilia or another bleeding disorder. Applicants must be enrolled or planning to enroll at a 4-year Louisiana college or university as a full-time undergraduate student. They must have completed a high school curriculum to qualify for the TOPS program. Along with their application, they must submit a 250-word essay on why they should receive this scholarship.

Financial data   The stipend is $1,000 per semester.

Duration   1 semester. Recipients may reapply if they remain enrolled full time, have a GPA of 2.5 or higher, and provide 8 hours of community service to the sponsoring organization.

Number awarded   Up to 15 each semester.

Deadline   June of each year for fall semester; December of each year for spring semester.

[829]
INA BRUDNICK SCHOLARSHIP AWARD

Great Comebacks Award Program
c/o ConvaTec Customer Interaction Center
100 Headquarters Park Drive
Skillman, NJ 08558
Toll Free: (800) 422-8811
E-mail: info@greatcomebacks.com
Web: www.greatcomebacks.com

Summary   To provide financial assistance to college students with an inflammatory bowel disease (IBD) or other related physical conditions.

Eligibility   This program is open to people between 17 and 24 years of age who have undergone an ostomy and/or have an IBD (Crohn's disease or ulcerative colitis).

Applicants must be able to demonstrate financial need. Along with their application, they must submit brief essays on how their comeback from their disease was achieved and the positive effects that have resulted, how their life was changed or affected by their medical condition and having an ostomy, the role that others played in their comeback, any current activities or interests that they are now able to enjoy and any specific dreams or goals they have accomplished or want to accomplish in the near future, and the advice from their story that others might find beneficial.

Financial data The stipend is $1,000.

Duration 1 year.

Additional data This scholarship is provided by ConvaTec, a Bristol-Myers Squibb Company, and the Crohn's and Colitis Foundation of America.

Number awarded 4 each year: 1 from each region of the country.

Deadline July of each year.

[830]
INTERNATIONAL TRANSPLANT NURSES SOCIETY GEORGIA CHAPTER SCHOLARSHIP

Georgia Transplant Foundation
Attn: Scholarship Program
500 Sugar Mill Road, Suite 170A
Atlanta, GA 30350
(770) 457-3796   Fax: (770) 457-7916
Web: gatransplant.org

Summary To provide financial assistance to residents of Georgia who are either transplant recipients or their siblings or dependents and interested in attending college in any state to work on a degree in health care.

Eligibility This program is open to residents of Georgia who are entering or continuing at an accredited institution of higher learning in any state to work on a degree in health care. Applicants must be an organ transplant recipient, a dependent of a recipient, a parent of a recipient, a living donor, or the sibling of a recipient (both the sibling and the recipient must be under 22 years of age). Along with their application, they must submit a 2-page personal statement on their career objectives, how this scholarship will help them attain their goals, and any other pertinent information. Selection is based on that statement, transcripts, high school exit examination scores, ACT/SAT scores, 3 letters of reference, and financial need.

Financial data The stipend is $1,000.

Duration 1 year; nonrenewable.

Additional data This program is sponsored by the Georgia Chapter of the International Transplant Nurses Society.

Number awarded 1 each year.

Deadline May of each year.

[831]
IOPO FOUNDATION SCHOLARSHIPS

Indiana Organ Procurement Organization, Inc.
Attn: IOPO Foundation Inc.
3760 Guion Road
P.O. Box 6069, Department 172
Indianapolis, IN 46202-6069
Toll Free: (888) ASK-IOPO   Fax: (317) 685-1687
E-mail: info@iopo.org
Web: www.iopo.org

Summary To provide financial assistance for college attendance in any state to Indiana residents who are organ, tissue, or eye transplant donors, recipients, candidates, or their families.

Eligibility This program is open to Indiana residents who are organ, tissue, or eye transplant donors, recipients, candidates, or relatives (including spouses, parents, children, grandchildren, siblings, aunts, uncles, nieces, nephews, and cousins). Applicants must be high school seniors or students already attending a college or technical school in any state on a full- or part-time basis. They must have a GPA of 2.0 or higher; high school seniors must be in the top 50% of their class. Along with their application, they must submit a 1,500-word essay describing their career goals, experience with organ or tissue donation and/or transplantation, and personal goals. Financial need is considered in the selection process.

Financial data Stipends are $3,000 or $1,500.

Duration 1 year; nonrenewable.

Number awarded Varies each year; recently, 4 of these scholarships were awarded: 1 at $3,000 and 3 at $1,500.

Deadline February of each year.

[832]
ISABELLE CHRISTENSON MEMORIAL SCHOLARSHIP

Izzie's Gifts of Hope Foundation
c/o C.O.R.E.
204 Sigma Drive
RIDC Park
Pittsburgh, PA 15238
E-mail: izziesgifts@gmail.com
Web: www.izziesgifts.org/scholarships.php

Summary To provide money for college to organ transplant candidates, donors, recipients, and their families.

Eligibility This program is open to organ transplant candidates, recipients, donor family members, and immediate family members of a transplant candidate or recipient. Applicants must be attending or planning to attend a college, university, or trade/technical school. Along with their application, they must submit 1) a 500-word statement on their educational goals; and 2) a 500-word statement of how donation/transplantation has influenced their life.

Financial data A stipend is awarded (amount not specified).

Duration 1 year; nonrenewable.

Additional data This program awarded its first scholarship in 2010.
Number awarded 1 or 2 each year.
Deadline March of each year.

[833]
ITALIAN CATHOLIC FEDERATION GIFTS OF LOVE FOR SPECIAL PEOPLE

Italian Catholic Federation
8393 Capwell Drive, Suite 110
Oakland, CA 94621
(510) 633-9058   Toll Free: (888) ICF-1924
Fax: (510) 633-9758   E-mail: info@icf.org
Web: www.icf.org/charitable.html

Summary To provide funding to individuals who have specific disabilities and need additional training or instruction.

Eligibility This program is open to 1) individuals who have a disability and desire formal training or instruction in a particular vocation, academic, athletic, or artistic field; 2) qualified instructors on behalf of an individual with a disability who exhibits a particular skill to be developed and who desires formal instruction or training; or 3) adults with custodial responsibility for, and on behalf of, an individual with a disability who exhibits a particular skill to be developed and who desires formal instruction or training. The program defines individuals with a disability as those who have mental retardation, hearing impairments, speech and language impairments, visual impairments, emotional disturbances, orthopedic impairments, autism, traumatic brain injury, other health impairments, specific learning disabilities, or multiple disabilities who, because of their needs, require special education or related services. Financial need is considered in the selection process.

Financial data A stipend is awarded (amount not specified).
Duration These are 1-time grants.
Number awarded Varies each year.
Deadline Deadline not specified.

[834]
JAMES AND COLIN LEE WOZUMI SCHOLARSHIP

Pride Foundation
Attn: Scholarship Program Director
1122 East Pike Street
PMB 1001
Seattle, WA 98122-3934
(206) 323-3318   Toll Free: (800) 735-7287
Fax: (206) 323-1017
E-mail: scholarships@pridefoundation.org
Web: www.pridefoundation.org

Summary To provide money for college to residents of the Northwest who are HIV positive and/or focusing on the treatment and/or eradication of the HIV virus.

Eligibility This program is open to residents of Alaska, Idaho, Montana, Oregon, or Washington who attending or planning to attend a college, university, or vocational school in any state. Applicants must be goal-oriented, HIV positive, and/or focusing on the treatment and/or eradication of the HIV virus. Preference is given to students who are self-identified as lesbian, gay, bisexual, or transgender (LGBT), members of LGBT families, or allies who have been strongly supportive of the LGBT community. They must have demonstrated commitment to social justice and LGBT concerns, leadership in their communities, the ability to be academically and personally successful, and some financial need.

Financial data The average stipend is approximately $3,300. Funds are paid directly to the recipient's school.
Duration 1 year; recipients may reapply.
Additional data The Pride Foundation was established in 1987 to strengthen the LGBT community.
Number awarded 1 each year. Since it began offering scholarships in 1993, the foundation has awarded nearly $2.5 million to more than 1,000 recipients.
Deadline January of each year.

[835]
JAY FRANKE SCHOLARSHIPS

Diabetes Scholars Foundation
2118 Plum Grove Road, Suite 356
Rolling Meadows, IL 60008
(312) 215-9861   Fax: (847) 991-8739
E-mail: collegescholarships@diabetesscholars.org
Web: www.diabetesscholars.org/college.html

Summary To provide funding to high school seniors who have diabetes and plan to major in the arts in college.

Eligibility This program is open to graduating high school seniors who have Type 1 diabetes and plan to attend an accredited 4-year university, college, or technical/trade school in any state. Applicants must be planning to major in the arts (e.g., music, theater, dance). They must be able to demonstrate active involvement in the diabetes community, high academic performance, participation in community and/or extracurricular activities, and successful management of the challenges of living with diabetes. Financial need is not considered in the selection process. U.S. citizenship or permanent resident status is required.

Financial data Stipends are $5,000 or $3,500.
Duration 1 year.
Number awarded 1 at $5,000 and 1 at $3,500.
Deadline May of each year.

[836]
JEFF APODACA CELEBRATION OF LIFE SCHOLARSHIP

Jeff Apodaca Celebration of Life Foundation
c/o UNM Children's Hospital Development Office
Two Woodward Center, Suite 100
700 Lomas Boulevard, N.E.
Albuquerque, NM 87102
(505) 277-5685   Fax: (505) 277-5687
E-mail: placencia@salud.unm.edu
Web: www.jeffapodaca.com/scholorship.html

Summary To provide financial assistance to residents of New Mexico who have survived cancer and are interested in attending college in the state.

Eligibility This program is open to New Mexico residents who are attending or planning to attend a 4-year college or university in the state. Applicants must have survived cancer.

Financial data The stipend is $5,000.

Duration 1 year.

Additional data This program began in 2001.

Number awarded Varies each year; recently, 3 of these scholarships were awarded.

Deadline September of each year.

[837]
JESSICA BETH SCHWARTZ MEMORIAL SCHOLARSHIP

Gift of Life Donor Program
Attn: Volunteer Liaison
401 North Third Street
Philadelphia, PA 19123-4101
Toll Free: (800) DONORS-1
Web: www.donors1.org/patients/resources/jessiesday

Summary To provide funding to transplant recipients who live in the service area of the Gift of Life Donor Program and are interested in attending college in any state.

Eligibility This program is open to transplant recipients who live in the eastern half of Pennsylvania, southern New Jersey, or Delaware. Applicants must be younger than 25 years of age and either graduating high school seniors or students currently enrolled at a 2- or 4-year college, university, or trade/technical school in any state. Along with their application, they must submit 1) a 200-word essay describing an educational initiative to promote organ and tissue donation and transplantation awareness in high school or college students; 2) a 500-word personal statement describing their transplant story and extracurricular and/or volunteer activities; 3) letters of reference; and 4) a current transcript. Financial need is not required.

Financial data The stipend is $2,500.

Duration 1 year.

Number awarded 1 or more each year.

Deadline February of each year.

[838]
JOHN BULLER SCHOLARSHIP

Greater Houston Community Foundation
Attn: Scholarship Coordinator
5120 Woodway Drive, Suite 6000
Houston, TX 77056
(713) 333-2205   Fax: (713) 333-2220
E-mail: lgardner@ghcf.org
Web: www.ghcf.org

Summary To provide financial assistance to residents of Texas who have cystic fibrosis and are interested in attending college or graduate school in the state.

Eligibility This program is open to Texas residents who have cystic fibrosis. Applicants must be enrolled or planning to enroll as an undergraduate or graduate student at an accredited 2- or 4-year college or university in Texas. Along with their application, they must submit transcripts and information on their extracurricular activities, work experience, community service, and other activities. Financial need is considered in the selection process. U.S. citizenship is required.

Financial data The stipend is $1,000 per year.

Duration 1 year; renewable up to 3 more years.

Additional data This program was established in 1997.

Number awarded 1 or more each year.

Deadline March of each year.

[839]
JOHN LEPPING MEMORIAL SCHOLARSHIP

Lep Foundation for Youth Education
Attn: Scholarship Selection Committee
9 Whispering Spring Drive
Millstone Township, NJ 08510
E-mail: lepfoundation@aol.com
Web: www.lepfoundation.org/application.htm

Summary To provide financial assistance to high school seniors in New Jersey, New York, or Pennsylvania who have a physical disability or psychological handicap and plan to attend college in any state.

Eligibility This program is open to seniors graduating from high schools in New Jersey, New York, or Pennsylvania and planning to enroll at a college, university, community college, or vocational school in any state. Applicants must have a disability, including (but not limited to) physical disabilities (e.g., spinal cord injury, loss of limb, birth defects, Lyme disease) or psychological handicaps (e.g., autism, cerebral palsy, post-traumatic stress). Along with their application, they must submit a brief statement of their career goals and ambitions for the future and a 500-word essay on why they feel they are the best candidate for this award. Financial need is considered in the selection process.

Financial data The stipend is $5,000. Funds are paid directly to the recipient's school.

Duration 1 year.

Number awarded At least 4 each year.

Deadline April of each year.

[840]
JOHN YOUTSEY MEMORIAL SCHOLARSHIP FUND

Hemophilia of Georgia
8800 Roswell Road, Suite 170
Atlanta, GA 30350-1844
(770) 518-8272   Fax: (770) 518-3310
E-mail: mail@hog.org
Web: www.hog.org/programs/page/scholarship

Summary To provide financial assistance to residents of Georgia who have a bleeding disorder or have lost a parent because of the disorder and are interested in attending college in any state.

Eligibility This program is open to residents of Georgia who 1) have hemophilia, von Willebrand Disease, or other inherited bleeding disorder; or 2) are children whose parent died as a result of complications from a bleeding disorder. Applicants or their deceased parents must be or have been clients of Hemophilia of Georgia. They may be graduating high school seniors or students currently enrolled at an accredited college, university, vocational/technical school, or professional degree program in any state. Selection is based on academic record, financial need, and personal goals.

Financial data A stipend is awarded (amount not specified).

Duration 1 year.

Additional data Recipients must provide at least 12 hours of volunteer service with Hemophilia of Georgia.

Number awarded Varies each year. Since this program was established, it has awarded more than 275 scholarship with a value greater than $800,000.

Deadline April of each year.

[841]
JOSH SMITH MEMORIAL SCHOLARSHIP

Diabetes Scholars Foundation
2118 Plum Grove Road, Suite 356
Rolling Meadows, IL 60008
(312) 215-9861   Fax: (847) 991-8739
E-mail: collegescholarships@diabetesscholars.org
Web: www.diabetesscholars.org/college.html

Summary To provide financial assistance to high school seniors from Ohio who have diabetes and plan to attend college in any state.

Eligibility This program is open to seniors graduating from high schools in Ohio who have Type 1 diabetes and plan to attend an accredited 4-year university, college, or technical/trade school in any state. Applicants must be able to demonstrate active involvement in the diabetes community, high academic performance, participation in community and/or extracurricular activities, and successful management of the challenges of living with diabetes. Financial need is not considered in the selection process. U.S. citizenship or permanent resident status is required.

Financial data The stipend is $1,000.

Duration 1 year.

Number awarded 1 each year.

Deadline May of each year.

[842]
JOSHUA GOMES MEMORIAL SCHOLARSHIP

Joshua Gomes Memorial Scholarship Fund
2700 South Emerson Street
Englewood, CO 80113-1737
(303) 761-3055   E-mail: Info@joshuagomes.org
Web: www.joshuagomes.org

Summary To provide financial assistance for college or graduate school to students who have AIDS or are HIV positive.

Eligibility This program is open to full-time undergraduate and graduate students accepted or enrolled at a college or university in the United States. Applicants must have AIDS or be HIV positive. Along with their application, they must submit a 500-word essay that explains their

hopes, plans, and goals for the future; how their schooling will help lay a path to fulfilling those; what motivates them to pursue higher education; what subjects they plan to study; and what led them to that path of study. Selection is based on merit and financial need.

Financial data The stipend is $1,000.

Duration 1 year; recipients may reapply.

Additional data This program was established in 2005.

Number awarded 1 or more each year.

Deadline July of each year.

[843]
JOSHUA O'NEILL AND ZESHAN TABANI ENRICHMENT FUND

National Down Syndrome Society
666 Broadway, Eighth Floor
New York, NY 10012-2317
(212) 460-9330   Toll Free: (800) 221-4602
Fax: (212) 979-2873   E-mail: info@ndss.org
Web: www.ndss.org

Summary To provide financial assistance to students who have Down Syndrome and wish to obtain postsecondary or other additional education.

Eligibility This program is open to young adults who are 18 years of age or older and have Down Syndrome. Applicants must be interested in participating in an postsecondary education program or enrichment courses to gain employment and other important life skills contributing to their independence. Along with their application, they must submit a 1-page essay on why they want to pursue postsecondary education, a list of activities or groups in which they participate or to which they belong, their personal or professional goals, the classes they want to take, and their reasons for taking those classes.

Financial data Stipends range up to $2,000 per year. Funds must be used to pay for tuition or other educational expenses at a college, educational institution, learning center, or employment training program.

Duration 1 year; students who receive an award may wait 1 year and then reapply.

Additional data This program began in 2005.

Number awarded Varies each year; recently, 6 of these scholarships were awarded.

Deadline July of each year.

[844]
KERMIT B. NASH ACADEMIC SCHOLARSHIP

Sickle Cell Disease Association of America
Attn: Scholarship Committee
231 East Baltimore Street, Suite 800
Baltimore, MD 21202
(410) 528-1555   Toll Free: (800) 421-8453
Fax: (410) 528-1495
E-mail: scdaa@sicklecelldisease.org
Web: www.sicklecelldisease.org

Summary To provide financial assistance for college to graduating high school seniors who have sickle cell disease and are members of the Sickle Cell Disease Association of America (SCDAA).

Eligibility This program is open to graduating high school seniors who are SCDAA members and have sickle cell disease (not just the trait). Applicants must have a GPA of 3.0 or higher and be U.S. citizens or permanent residents planning to attend an accredited 4-year college or university as a full-time student. They must submit a personal essay, up to 1,000 words, on an aspect of the impact of the disease on their lives or on society. Selection is based on GPA, general academic achievement and promise, SAT scores, leadership and community service, severity of academic challenges and obstacles posed by sickle cell disease, and the quality of their essay.

Financial data The stipend is $5,000 per year.

Duration Up to 4 years, provided the recipient maintains a GPA of 2.5 or higher.

Additional data The Sickle Cell Disease Association of America (SCDAA) was formerly the National Association for Sickle Cell Disease. It established this program in 1999.

Number awarded 1 each year.

Deadline May of each year.

[845]
KEVIN CHILD SCHOLARSHIP

National Hemophilia Foundation
Attn: Information Resource Center
116 West 32nd Street, 11th Floor
New York, NY 10001-3212
(212) 328-3750   Toll Free: (800) 42-HANDI, ext. 3750
Fax: (212) 328-3777   E-mail: handi@hemophilia.org
Web: www.hemophilia.org

Summary To provide financial assistance for college to students with hemophilia.

Eligibility This program is open to high school seniors entering their first year of undergraduate study as well as those currently enrolled in college. Applicants must have hemophilia A or B. Along with their application, they must submit a 1-page essay on their occupational objectives and goals in life and how the educational program they have planned will meet those objectives. Selection is based on that essay, academic performance, and participation in school and community activities.

Financial data The stipend is $1,000.

Duration 1 year.

Additional data The program was established in 1989.

Number awarded 1 each year.

Deadline May of each year.

[846]
KYLE LEE FOUNDATION SCHOLARSHIP

Kyle Lee Foundation, Inc.
3843 South Bristol Street, Number 293
Santa Ana, CA 92704
(714) 433-3204   E-mail: foundation@kylelee28.com
Web: www.kylelee28.com

Summary To provide money for college to cancer survivors.

Eligibility This program is open to high school seniors and current college students who have had cancer, especially Ewing's sarcoma. Applicants must submit a letter from their doctor confirming their cancer diagnosis, copies of academic transcripts, 2 letters of recommendation, and a 700-word essay outlining their goals in college and how their fight with cancer has affected their life and goals.

Financial data Stipends are $1,000 or $500.

Duration 1 year.

Additional data This program was founded following the death of Kyle Lee in 2003.

Number awarded Varies each year; recently, 5 of these scholarships were awarded.

Deadline May of each year.

[847]
LARRY DEAN DAVIS SCHOLARSHIP FUND

Brain Tumor Foundation for Children, Inc.
Attn: Scholarship Committee
6065 Roswell Road, N.E., Suite 505
Atlanta, GA 30328-4015
(404) 252-4107   Fax: (404) 252-4108
E-mail: info@braintumorkids.org
Web: www.braintumorkids.org/scholarships.html

Summary To provide financial assistance to residents of Georgia who have had a brain or spinal cord tumor and are interested in attending college in any state.

Eligibility This program is open to Georgia residents who are survivors of a pediatric brain or spinal cord tumor. Applicants must be entering or continuing in an advanced educational setting (college, university, vocational school, or other setting) in any state. They must be able to demonstrate financial need. Along with their application, they must submit 1) an essay about their brain or spinal cord tumor experience, including surgery and/or treatment; and 2) a brief biographical sketch about themselves and their future aspirations.

Financial data The stipend is $2,500.

Duration 1 year; nonrenewable.

Number awarded Up to 2 each year.

Deadline April of each year.

[848]
LARRY SMOCK SCHOLARSHIP

National Kidney Foundation of Indiana, Inc.
Attn: Program Coordinator
911 East 86th Street, Suite 100
Indianapolis, IN 46204-1848
(317) 722-5640   Toll Free: (800) 382-9971
Fax: (317) 722-5650   E-mail: nkfi@kidneyindiana.org
Web: www.kidney.org/site/303/patientAid.cfm?ch=303

Summary To provide financial assistance to kidney patients in Indiana who are interested in pursuing higher education in an academic or monitored occupational setting in any state.

Eligibility This program is open to Indiana residents who have at least a high school diploma or its equivalent and who have received a kidney transplant or are on dialysis. Applicants must be interested in attending college, trade school, or vocational school in any state to work on an academic or occupational degree. Finalists are interviewed. Financial need is considered.

Financial data A stipend is awarded (amount not specified). Funds are paid directly to the recipient's school.

Duration 1 year; may be renewed.

Additional data This fund was established in 1992.

Number awarded Several each year.

Deadline February of each year.

[849]
LAWRENCE MADEIROS SCHOLARSHIP

Lawrence Madeiros Scholarship Program
Attn: Scholarship Panel
P.O. Box 11
Mayfield, NY 12117
(518) 863-8998
Web: www.adirondackspintacular.com

Summary To provide money for college to high school seniors who have a bleeding or other chronic disorder (muscular dystrophy, autism, diabetes, etc.).

Eligibility This program is open to seniors graduating from high school who have been accepted at an accredited college or university. Applicants must be diagnosed with a bleeding or other chronic disorder. Along with their application, they must submit brief essays on 1) how living with or around a chronic disorder has impacted their life; 2) their goals and aspirations in life; and 3) their passion. Financial need may also be considered.

Financial data The stipend is $1,000.

Duration 1 year.

Additional data This program was established in 2001 by the Adirondack Spintacular, a charity event in which volunteers cycle, walk, or run to raise money. The last Spintacular was in 2011, but the scholarship program continues as a separate organization. Other chronic disorders have included muscular dystrophy, diabetes, cystic fibrosis, autism, and Asperger's Syndrome.

Number awarded Varies each year.

Deadline April of each year.

[850]
LEAD FOUNDATION COMMUNITY SCHOLARSHIP

Learning & Education About Disabilities
Attn: LEAD Foundation
c/o Pikes Peak Community Foundation
730 North Nevada Avenue
Colorado Springs, CO 80903
(719) 389-1251   Fax: (719) 389-1252
E-mail: LEADourkids@yahoo.com
Web: www.leadcolorado.org/scholarships.aspx

Summary To provide financial assistance to residents of Colorado who have a learning disability and are interested in attending college in any state.

Eligibility This program is open to Colorado residents who have a documented, specific learning disability or AD/HD (e.g., dyslexia, perceptual, or communicative disabilities). Applicants must be working on or planning to work on a postsecondary degree at a college or university in

any state. They must have a GPA of 2.8 or higher. Preference is given to applicants who understand the importance of advocacy and self-knowledge in overcoming the challenges of having a learning disability.

Financial data The stipend is $1,000.

Duration 1 year.

Number awarded 1 each year.

Deadline February of each year.

[851]
LEARNING DISABILITIES ASSOCIATION OF IOWA SCHOLARSHIPS

Learning Disabilities Association of Iowa
Attn: Scholarship Chair
5665 Greendale Road, Suite D
Johnston, IA 50131
(515) 280-8558   Toll Free: (888) 690-LDAI
E-mail: cjpaup@wccta.net
Web: www.lda-ia.org

Summary To provide financial assistance to high school seniors in Iowa who have a learning disability and are interested in attending college in any state.

Eligibility This program is open to students with learning disabilities who are graduating from high schools in Iowa. Applicants must be planning to enroll in a 2- or 4-year college or in vocational training at a school in any state. Along with their application, they must submit an essay about themselves, including their extracurricular and community achievements, most significant accomplishments, volunteer and paid jobs, methods of financing their education, college and career goals, and any accommodations they feel will help them succeed in meeting those goals.

Financial data The stipend is $1,000.

Duration 1 year.

Number awarded 3 each year.

Deadline March of each year.

[852]
LESLIE DELK, SR. ACADEMIC SCHOLARSHIP

Taylor Delk Sickle Cell Foundation
418 Chapel Cove
Brownsville, TN 38012
(731) 694-8727   E-mail: tiffanydelk@tdscf.org
Web: tdscf.org/program.html

Summary To provide financial assistance for college to high school seniors who have sickle cell disease.

Eligibility This program is open to seniors graduating from high school in any state and planning to enroll at a 4-year college or university. Applicants must be U.S. citizens or permanent residents who have sickle cell disease. Finalists are interviewed by telephone. Selection is based primarily on academic achievement.

Financial data The stipend is $1,000.

Duration 1 year.

Number awarded 1 each year.

Deadline Deadline not specified.

[853]
LILLY REINTEGRATION SCHOLARSHIPS

The Center for Reintegration, Inc.
Attn: Lilly Secretariat
310 Busse Highway
PMB 327
Park Ridge, IL 60068-3251
Toll Free: (800) 809-8202
E-mail: lillyscholarships@reintegration.com
Web: www.reintegration.com

Summary To provide financial assistance to undergraduate and graduate students diagnosed with schizophrenia.

Eligibility This program is open to U.S. citizens diagnosed with bipolar disorder, schizophrenia, schizophreniform disorder, or schizoaffective disorder. Applicants must be receiving medical treatment for the disease and be actively involved in rehabilitative or reintegrative efforts. They must be interested in pursuing postsecondary education, including trade or vocational school programs, high school equivalency programs, associate degrees, bachelor's degrees, and graduate programs. Along with their application, they must submit an essay on their career goal and their rationale for choosing that goal, how this course of study will help them achieve their career goal, obstacles they have faced in life and how they have overcome them, steps they have taken to prepare for pursuit of this education, rationale for the specific school chosen, and their plans to continue treatment while pursuing an education. Selection is based on the quality of the essay, academic success, 3 references, thoughtfulness and appropriateness of academic and vocational/career goals, rehabilitation involvement, success in dealing with the disease, recent volunteer and/or vocational experience, and completion of application requirements.

Financial data The amount awarded varies, depending upon the specific needs of the recipient. Funds may be used to pay for tuition and related expenses, such as textbooks and laboratory fees.

Duration 1 year; may be renewed.

Additional data This program, established in 1998, is funded by Eli Lilly and Company.

Number awarded Varies each year; generally, 70 to 120 of these scholarships (including renewals) are awarded annually.

Deadline January of each year.

[854]
LISA HIGGINS-HUSSMAN FOUNDATION SCHOLARSHIP

Ulman Cancer Fund for Young Adults
Attn: Scholarship Committee
10440 Little Patuxent Parkway, Suite G1
Columbia, MD 21044
(410) 964-0202   Toll Free: (888) 393-FUND
Fax: (410) 964-0402
E-mail: scholarship@ulmanfund.org
Web: www.ulmanfund.org/scholarship.aspx

Summary To provide financial assistance for college or graduate school to students from Washington, D.C., Maryland, or Virginia who have been diagnosed with cancer or have or have lost a family member with cancer.

Eligibility This program is open to students who 1) have been diagnosed with cancer; 2) have a parent, sibling, or guardian living with cancer; or 3) have lost a parent, sibling, or guardian to cancer. Applicants must be residents of Washington, D.C., Maryland, or Virginia or attending college there. They must be 35 years of age or younger and attending, or planning to attend, a 2- or 4-year college, university, or vocational program to work on an undergraduate or graduate degree. The first diagnosis of cancer (whether of the applicant, a parent, a sibling, or a guardian) must have occurred after the applicant was 15 years of age. Along with their application, they must submit an essay of at least 1,000 words on how the cancer experience has impacted their outlook on life and the legacy that they desire to leave behind. Selection is based on demonstrated dedication to community service, commitment to educational and professional goals, use of their cancer experience to impact the lives of other young adults affected by cancer, medical hardship, and financial need.

Financial data The stipend is $2,500. Funds are paid directly to the educational institution.

Duration 1 year.

Additional data Recipients must agree to complete 40 hours of community service.

Number awarded 1 each year.

Deadline March of each year.

[855]
LIVING BREATH FOUNDATION SCHOLARSHIPS

Living Breath Foundation
2031 Marsala Circle
Monterey, CA 93940
(831) 392-5285
E-mail: LivingBreathFoundation@gmail.com
Web: thelivingbreathfoundation.com/aid.html

Summary To provide financial assistance to individuals who have cystic fibrosis and are interested in attending college or graduate school.

Eligibility This program is open to U.S. citizens who have cystic fibrosis and are graduating high school seniors or undergraduate or graduate students continuing their education at a 2- or 4-year college, university, or trade school in any state. Applicants must submit an essay on how continuing their education will benefit their future. Selection is based on academic record, leadership, community service, and financial need.

Financial data The stipend ranges from $500 to $2,000. Funds are disbursed directly to the student to assist in payment of tuition, books, or the expenses of going to school while having cystic fibrosis (e.g., private rooms, food, rooms with running water, bathrooms, parking).

Duration 1 year.

Additional data This foundation was established in 2008.

Number awarded 1 or more each year.

Deadline February of each year.

[856]
LOUISIANA HEMOPHILIA FOUNDATION SCHOLARSHIPS

Louisiana Hemophilia Foundation
Attn: Scholarship Committee
3636 South Sherwood Forest Boulevard, Suite 390
Baton Rouge, LA 70816
(225) 291-1675　　　　Toll Free: (800) 749-1680
Fax: (225) 291-1679　　　E-mail: contact@lahemo.org
Web: lahemo.org/news.html

Summary To provide money for college to Louisiana residents who have hemophilia or other bleeding disorder.

Eligibility This program is open to residents of Louisiana who have hemophilia or other bleeding disorder. Applicants must be enrolled or planning to enroll at a 2- or 4-year Louisiana college, university, or trade school. Along with their application, they must submit a 250-word essay on why they should receive this scholarship.

Financial data The stipend is $500 per semester ($1,000 per year).

Duration 1 semester. Recipients may reapply if they remain enrolled full time, have a GPA of 2.5 or higher, and provide 8 hours of community service to the sponsoring organization.

Number awarded Up to 4 each semester.

Deadline June of each year for fall semester; December of each year for spring semester.

[857]
LYMAN FISHER SCHOLARSHIPS

Virginia Hemophilia Foundation
P.O. Box 188
Midlothian, VA 23113-0188
Toll Free: (800) 266-8438　　　Fax: (800) 266-8438
E-mail: vahemophiliaed@verizon.net
Web: www.vahemophilia.org

Summary To provide funding to people from Virginia who have participated in the Virginia Hemophilia Foundation (VHF) and are interested in attending college.

Eligibility This program is open members of the bleeding disorder community and their families who are attending or planning to attend college. Applicants must have a record of prior participation with VHF and be a resident of Virginia or planning to attend college in Virginia. Along with their application, they must submit a brief biographical sketch of themselves that includes their interests, hobbies, vocational and educational goals, volunteer and community involvement, and work or internship experience; a description of their previous participation with VHF and how they plan to contribute to the organization and support other persons with inherited bleeding disorders; a detailed statement of financial need; a 1-page essay on their career goals; another 1-page essay on a topic of their choice; and 3 letters of recommendation.

Financial data The stipend is $2,000.

Duration 1 year.

Number awarded 2 each year.

Deadline May of each year.

[858]
MALLORY SMITH MEMORIAL SCHOLARSHIP

Georgia Transplant Foundation
Attn: Scholarship Program
500 Sugar Mill Road, Suite 170A
Atlanta, GA 30350
(770) 457-3796　　　　　　Fax: (770) 457-7916
Web: gatransplant.org

Summary To provide financial assistance to residents of Georgia who are transplant recipients or dependents of recipients and interested in attending college in any state.

Eligibility This program is open to residents of Georgia who are entering or continuing at an accredited institution of higher learning in any state. Applicants must be an organ transplant recipient or the dependent of a recipient. Along with their application, they must submit a 2-page personal statement on their career objectives, how this scholarship will help them attain their goals, and any other pertinent information. Selection is based on that statement, transcripts, high school exit examination scores, ACT/SAT scores, 3 letters of reference, and financial need.

Financial data The stipend is $1,000 per year.

Duration 1 year; may be renewed up to 3 additional years.

Number awarded 1 each year.

Deadline May of each year.

[859]
MARCENA LOZANO DONATE LIFE SCHOLARSHIP FUND

Marcena Lozano Donate Life Scholarship Fund Committee
15 Winston Road
Buffalo, NY 14216
(716) 836-7045
E-mail: admin@marcenasmiracles.com
Web: marcenasmiracles.com/the-elephant-run.html

Summary To provide funding to organ transplant recipients who are interested in attending college in any state.

Eligibility This program is open to organ transplant recipients who are graduating high school seniors or students currently enrolled at an accredited college, university, or trade/technical certificate program in any state. Preference is given to residents of western New York. Applicants must submit a statement of their educational objectives and future life goals. Selection is based primarily on financial need.

Financial data Stipends range from $1,000 to $3,000 per year, depending on the availability of funds. Payment is made directly to the recipient's institution.

Duration 1 year; may be renewed.

Number awarded 1 or more each year.

Deadline July of each year for fall admission; November of each year for spring admission.

[860]
MARCO CAMASTRA SCHOLARSHIP AWARD

Learning Disabilities Association of North Carolina
1854A Hendersonville Road, Suite 239
Asheville, NC 28803
E-mail: support@ldanc.org
Web: www.ldanc.org/services

Summary To provide financial assistance to high school seniors in North Carolina who have a learning disability and are interested in attending college in any state.

Eligibility This program is open to seniors graduating from high schools in North Carolina who have been diagnosed as having a learning disability or attention disorder. Applicants must be planning to attend a college, university, community college, or technical school in any state. They must be able to demonstrate that they have participated in school activities (e.g., sports, music, art, drama), persisted in academics, participated in community or church activities, and shown sensitivity to the needs or feelings of others. Along with their application, they must submit a short essay about their learning disability and how they feel they have adapted in order to succeed in school and/or life in general. Financial need is not considered.

Financial data The stipend is $1,000.

Duration 1 year.

Number awarded 1 each year.

Deadline March of each year.

[861]
MARION HUBER LEARNING THROUGH LISTENING AWARDS

Learning Ally
Attn: Training and Support Center
20 Roszel Road
Princeton, NJ 08540
(609) 243-7087   Toll Free: (800) 221-4792
Fax: (609) 987-8116
E-mail: mGreenwald@LearningAlly.org
Web: www.learningally.org/awards

Summary To provide financial assistance to outstanding high school students with learning disabilities who plan to continue their education.

Eligibility This program is open to seniors graduating from public or private high schools in the United States or its territories who have a specific learning disability (visual impairment or physical disability alone does not satisfy this requirement). Applicants must be planning to continue their education at a 2- or 4-year college or vocational school. They must have been registered members of Learning Ally for at least 1 year and have earned a GPA of 3.0 or higher in grades 9-12. Selection is based on academic excellence, leadership, and service to others.

Financial data Stipends are $6,000 or $2,000.

Duration 1 year.

Additional data This program began in 1991. Learning Ally was formerly named Recording for the Blind and Dyslexic.

Number awarded 3 at $6,000 and 3 at $2,000.

Deadline March of each year.

[862]
MARY M. GOOLEY HEMOPHILIA SCHOLARSHIP

Mary M. Gooley Hemophilia Center
Attn: Scholarship Selection Committee
1415 Portland Avenue, Suite 500
Rochester, NY 14621
(585) 922-5700   Fax: (585) 922-5775
E-mail: Kristina.Ritchie@rochestergeneral.org
Web: www.hemocenter.org

Summary To provide funding to people with a bleeding disorder and their families who plan to attend college.

Eligibility This program is open to people who are affected directly or indirectly by hemophilia, von Willebrand Disease, hereditary bleeding disorder, or hemochromatosis. Applicants must be enrolled or planning to enroll at an accredited 2- or 4-year college or university, vocational/technical school, or certified training program. Along with their application, they must submit 1) a 1,000-word essay on their goals and aspirations, their biggest challenge and how they met it, and anything else they want the selection committee to know about them; and 2) a 250-word essay on any unusual family or personal circumstances have affected their achievement in school, work, or participation in school and community activities, including how the bleeding disorder has affected their life. Selection is based on the essays, academic performance, participation in school and community activities, work or volunteer experience, personal or family circumstances, recommendations, and financial need.

Financial data The maximum stipend is $2,000.

Duration 1 year.

Additional data This program was established in 1996.

Number awarded 1 or 2 each year.

Deadline March of each year.

[863]
MEDICAL/RESEARCH SCHOLARSHIP OF THE JUVENILE DIABETES RESEARCH FOUNDATION

Diabetes Scholars Foundation
2118 Plum Grove Road, Suite 356
Rolling Meadows, IL 60008
(312) 215-9861   Fax: (847) 991-8739
E-mail: collegescholarships@diabetesscholars.org
Web: www.diabetesscholars.org/college.html

Summary To provide financial assistance to high school seniors who have diabetes and plan to major in a health care field in college.

Eligibility This program is open to graduating high school seniors who have Type 1 diabetes and plan to attend an accredited 4-year university, college, or technical/trade school in any state. Applicants must be planning to major in a health care field. They must be able to demonstrate active involvement in the diabetes community, high academic performance, participation in community and/or extracurricular activities, and successful management of the challenges of living with diabetes. Financial need is not considered in the selection process. U.S. citizenship or permanent resident status is required.

Financial data   The stipend is $1,000.

Duration   1 year.

Additional data   This program is sponsored by the Juvenile Diabetes Research Foundation (JDRF).

Number awarded   1 each year.

Deadline   May of each year.

[864]
MEG JEFFREY MEMORIAL SCHOLARSHIP

Georgia Transplant Foundation
Attn: Scholarship Program
500 Sugar Mill Road, Suite 170A
Atlanta, GA 30350
(770) 457-3796   Fax: (770) 457-7916
Web: gatransplant.org

Summary   To provide financial assistance to residents of Georgia who are transplant recipients and interested in attending college in any state.

Eligibility   This program is open to residents of Georgia who are entering or continuing at an accredited institution of higher learning in any state. Applicants must be an organ transplant recipient. Along with their application, they must submit a 2-page personal statement on their career objectives, how this scholarship will help them attain their goals, and any other pertinent information. Selection is based on that statement, transcripts, high school exit examination scores, ACT/SAT scores, 3 letters of reference, and financial need.

Financial data   The stipend is $1,000 per year.

Duration   1 year; renewable up to 3 more years.

Number awarded   1 each year.

Deadline   May of each year.

[865]
MICHAEL A. COREA MEMORIAL SCHOLARSHIP

Transplant Recipients International Organization-
  Greater Cleveland Chapter
Attn: Scholarship Committee
P.O. Box 93163
Cleveland, OH 44101-5163
(440) 473-8979   E-mail: triocleveland@hotmail.com
Web: www.triocleveland.org/Scholarship_Program.html

Summary   To provide financial assistance to residents of Ohio who are transplant candidates, recipients, or donors and interested in attending college in any state.

Eligibility   This program is open to Ohio residents who are incoming college freshmen, continuing college students, or adults returning to college and attending or planning to attend a college, university, or trade/technical institution in any state. Applicants must be organ or tissue transplant candidates, recipients, or living donors. They

must have a cumulative GPA of 2.5 or higher and be able to demonstrate financial need. Along with their application, they must submit a 300-word statement of educational goals and objectives, a statement (250 to 300 words in length) describing how transplantation influences their life, and 3 letters of recommendation.

Financial data   The stipend is $1,000. Funds are disbursed directly to the recipient's institution.

Duration   1 year; nonrenewable.

Additional data   This program was established in 2009.

Number awarded   At least 1 each year.

Deadline   September of each year.

[866]
MICHAEL A. HUNTER MEMORIAL SCHOLARSHIP

Orange County Community Foundation
Attn: Scholarship Associate
4041 MacArthur Boulevard, Suite 510
Newport Beach, CA 92660
(949) 553-4202, ext. 46   Fax: (949) 553-4211
E-mail: alee@oc-cf.org
Web: www.oc-cf.org/Page.aspx?pid=869

Summary   To provide financial assistance for college to leukemia and lymphoma patients and the children of nonsurviving leukemia and lymphoma patients.

Eligibility   This program is open to graduating high school seniors, community college students, and 4-year university students nationwide. Applicants must be leukemia or lymphoma patients and/or the children of non-surviving leukemia or lymphoma patients who are enrolled or planning to enroll full time. They must have a GPA of 3.0 or higher and be able to document financial need.

Financial data   Stipends range from $1,000 to $2,500.

Duration   1 year.

Number awarded   2 each year.

Deadline   March of each year.

[867]
MICHAEL BENDIX SUTTON SCHOLARSHIPS

Michael Bendix Sutton Foundation
c/o Marion B. Sutton
300 Martine Avenue
White Plains, NY 10601-3459

Summary   To provide financial assistance to people with hemophilia who are pre-law students.

Eligibility   This program is open to pre-law students who have hemophilia.

Financial data   The stipend is $2,000.

Duration   1 year.

Number awarded   2 each year.

Deadline   March of each year.

[868]
MID-SOUTH DIVISION COLLEGE SCHOLARSHIPS

American Cancer Society-Mid-South Division
Attn: College Scholarship Committee
10528 Kentshire Court
Baton Rouge, LA 70810
(225) 767-4556
E-mail: MidsouthScholarship@cancer.org
Web: www.cancer.org

Summary To provide funding to residents of designated southern states who have been diagnosed as having cancer and are interested in attending college in any state.

Eligibility This program is open to residents of Alabama, Arkansas, Kentucky, Louisiana, Mississippi, Tennessee, and the Indiana counties of Clark and Floyd. Applicants must be younger than 25 years of age, have had a cancer diagnosis before age 19, have a GPA of 2.5 or higher, and have been accepted at an accredited 2- or 4-year college or university in any state. Selection is based on academic achievement, leadership, community service, and financial need.

Financial data The stipend is $1,000.

Duration 1 year.

Additional data This program began in 2001.

Number awarded Varies each year; recently, 223 of these scholarships were awarded.

Deadline January of each year.

[869]
MIDWEST DIVISION YOUTH SCHOLARSHIP PROGRAM

American Cancer Society-Midwest Division
Attn: Youth Scholarship Program
8317 Elderberry Road
Madison, WI 53717
(608) 662-7581   Toll Free: (877) 423-9123, ext. 7581
Fax: (262) 523-5533
E-mail: tiffany.carlson@cancer.org
Web: www.cancer.org

Summary To provide financial assistance for college to residents of selected midwestern states who have been diagnosed as having cancer.

Eligibility This program is open to residents (for at least 1 year) of Iowa, Minnesota, South Dakota, or Wisconsin who were diagnosed with cancer before the age of 21 and are currently younger than 25 years of age. Applicants must have maintained a GPA above the average level and be attending or planning to attend an accredited 2- or 4-year college, university or vocational/technical school in any state. Along with their application, they must submit an essay on 1 of the following topics: 1) how cancer has impacted their life and what they want to accomplish over the next 10 to 15 years; 2) how they have demonstrated leadership ability both in and out of school; and 3) an experience from their own life and how it has influenced their development. Selection is based on their commitment to academic or vocational goals, leadership, community service, and financial need.

Financial data The stipend is $1,000. Funds are paid directly to the recipient's institution.

Duration 1 year.

Number awarded Varies each year; recently, 40 of these scholarships were awarded.

Deadline March of each year.

[870]
MIKE HYLTON AND RON NIEDERMAN SCHOLARSHIPS

Factor Support Network Pharmacy
Attn: Scholarship Committee
900 Avenida Acaso, Suite A
Camarillo, CA 93012-8749
(805) 388-9336   Toll Free: (877) 376-4968
Fax: (805) 482-6324
E-mail: Scholarships@FactorSupport.com
Web: www.factorsupport.com/scholarships.htm

Summary To provide financial assistance for college to men with hemophilia and their immediate families.

Eligibility This program is open to men with bleeding disorders and their immediate family members. Applicants must be entering or attending a college, university, juniors college, or vocational school. They must submit 3 short essays: 1) their career goals; 2) how hemophilia or von Willebrand Disease has affected their life; and 3) their efforts to be involved in the bleeding disorder community and what they can do to education their peers and others outside their family about bleeding disorders. Selection is based on academic goals, volunteer work, school activities, achievements, and financial need.

Financial data The stipend is $1,000. Funds are paid directly to the recipient.

Duration 1 year.

Additional data This program was established in 1999.

Number awarded 10 each year.

Deadline April of each year.

[871]
MILLIE GONZALEZ MEMORIAL SCHOLARSHIPS

Factor Support Network Pharmacy
Attn: Scholarship Committee
900 Avenida Acaso, Suite A
Camarillo, CA 93012-8749
(805) 388-9336   Toll Free: (877) 376-4968
Fax: (805) 482-6324
E-mail: Scholarships@FactorSupport.com
Web: www.factorsupport.com/scholarships.htm

Summary To provide financial assistance to women with a bleeding disorder.

Eligibility This program is open to women with hemophilia or von Willebrand Disease who are entering or attending a college, university, juniors college, or vocational school. Applicants must submit 3 short essays: 1) their career goals; 2) how hemophilia or von Willebrand Disease has affected their life; and 3) their efforts to be involved in the bleeding disorder community and what they can do to education their peers and others outside their family about bleeding disorders. Selection is based on academic goals, volunteer work, school activities, other pertinent experience and achievements, and financial need.

Financial data   The stipend is $1,000. Funds are paid directly to the recipient.

Duration   1 year.

Number awarded   5 each year.

Deadline   April of each year.

[872]
MOULTON-FARNSWORTH SCHOLARSHIPS

American Deficit Disorder Association
P.O. Box 7557
Wilmington, DE 19803-9997
(800) 939-1019   Fax: (800) 939-1019
E-mail: info@add.org
Web: www.add.org/?page=MoultonFarnsworth

Summary   To provide money for college to students who have attention deficit/hyperactivity disorder (AD/HD).

Eligibility   This program is open to students who have been diagnosed with AD/HD by a licensed physician or mental health professional. Applicants must be enrolled or planning to enroll at an approved college or university. Along with their application, they must submit a 500-word essay on why they would like to be considered for this scholarship, the ways in which AD/HD has been a challenge for them in the educational setting, and the strategies they have used to meet the challenge.

Financial data   The stipend is $1,000 per year. Funds are paid directly to the recipient's college.

Duration   1 year; recipients may reapply.

Number awarded   2 each year.

Deadline   March of each year.

[873]
NATIONAL COLLEGIATE CANCER
FOUNDATION SCHOLARSHIP

National Collegiate Cancer Foundation
Attn: Scholarship Committee
4858 Battery Lane, Suite 216
Bethesda, MD 20814
(240) 515-6262   E-mail: info@collegiatecancer.org
Web: www.collegiatecancer.org/scholarships.html

Summary   To provide financial assistance for college or graduate school to cancer survivors.

Eligibility   This program is open to students between 18 and 35 who are cancer survivors or currently undergoing treatment for cancer. Applicants must be enrolled or planning to enroll at a college or university to work on a certificate or an associate, bachelor's, master's, or doctoral degree. Along with their application, they must submit a 1,000-word essay on their experiences with cancer and college. Selection is based on the essay, recommendations, displaying a "Will Win" attitude, overall story of cancer survivorship, commitment to education, and financial need.

Financial data   The stipend is $1,000.

Duration   1 year.

Number awarded   1 or more each year.

Deadline   May of each year.

[874]
NATIONAL CORNERSTONE HEALTHCARE
SERVICES SCHOLARSHIPS

National Cornerstone Healthcare Services Inc.
24747 Redlands Boulevard, Suite B
Loma Linda, CA 92354
Toll Free: (877) 616-6247   Fax: (877) 777-5717
E-mail: inquiry@nc-hs.com
Web: www.nc-hs.com

Summary   To provide money for college to people who have a bleeding disorder and members of their family.

Eligibility   This program is open to graduating high school seniors who are planning to attend an accredited technical school, college, or university. Applicants must have been diagnosed with a bleeding disorder or be the parent, spouse, partner, child, or sibling of a person with such a disorder. They must have a GPA of 2.5 or higher during their entire senior year of high school. Along with their application, they must submit a brief essay on their dreams, goals, and objectives for attending postsecondary education. Selection is based on that statement, academic merit, employment status, reference letters, impact of the bleeding disorders community, and financial need.

Financial data   Stipends range from $500 to $1,000.

Duration   1 year.

Number awarded   1 or more each year.

Deadline   March of each year.

[875]
NATIONAL KIDNEY FOUNDATION OF UTAH
AND IDAHO EDUCATIONAL SCHOLARSHIP
PROGRAM

National Kidney Foundation of Utah and Idaho
3707 North Canyon Road, Suite 1D
Provo, UT 84604-4585
(801) 226-5111   Toll Free: (800) 869-5277
Fax: (801) 226-8278   E-mail: nkfu@kidneyut.org
Web: www.kidneyut.org/ps-educational-scholarship.php

Summary   To provide financial assistance for college to kidney patients in Utah and Idaho.

Eligibility   This program is open to residents of Utah and Idaho who are kidney transplant recipients or dialysis patients. Applicants must be attending or planning to attend a college or university in Utah, Wyoming, or Idaho.

Financial data   A stipend is awarded (amount not specified).

Duration   1 year.

Number awarded   Varies each year; recently, 23 of these scholarships were awarded.

Deadline   Deadline not specified.

[876]
NATIONAL KIDNEY FOUNDATION SERVING CONNECTICUT AND WESTERN MASSACHUSETTS SCHOLARSHIPS

National Kidney Foundation Serving Connecticut and
Western Massachusetts
2139 Silas Deane Highway, Suite 208
Rocky Hill, CT 06067-2337
(860) 257-3770 Toll Free: (800) 441-1280, ext. 24
Fax: (860) 257-3429
E-mail: Donna.Sciacca@kidney.org
Web: www.kidneyct.org

Summary To provide financial assistance to residents of Connecticut and western Massachusetts who are dialysis patients, kidney recipients or donors, or dependents of patients and interested in attending college in any state.

Eligibility This program is open to residents of Connecticut (except Fairfield County) and western Massachusetts who are dialysis patients, transplant recipients, dependents of a dialysis or transplant patient, or living kidney donors. Applicants must be attending or planning to attend a 2- or 4-year college, university, or trade/technical school in any state. Along with their application, they must submit a 2-page essay on their choice of 5 topics that relate to their personal goals and experiences. Selection is based on the essay, academic merit, extracurricular activities or community service, and financial need. For applicants who have been out of school for many years, work or life experience may also be considered. U.S. citizenship is required.

Financial data The stipend is $1,000.

Duration 1 year.

Number awarded 3 each year.

Deadline May of each year.

[877]
NATIONAL KIDNEY FOUNDATION SERVING MAINE SCHOLARSHIPS

National Kidney Foundation Serving Maine
470 Forest Avenue, Suite 202
Portland, ME 04101-2009
(207) 772-7270 Toll Free: (800) 639-7220
Fax: (207) 772-4202 E-mail: nkfme@kidney.org
Web: www.kidneyme.org

Summary To provide financial assistance to residents of Maine who are kidney patients or their families and interested in attending college in any state.

Eligibility This program is open to residents of Maine who are kidney patients (dialysis patients, kidney transplant recipients, or newly diagnosed patients who are in early intervention programs) or immediate family members of patients. Applicants must be attending or planning to attend an accredited college or university in any state. Along with their application, they must submit documentation of financial need and brief essays on their educational goals and how kidney disease has impacted their life. Financial need is considered in the selection process.

Financial data A stipend is awarded (amount not specified).

Duration 1 year.

Number awarded Varies each year; recently, 7 of these scholarships were awarded.

Deadline July of each year.

[878]
NEBRASKA CHAPTER NHF SCHOLARSHIPS

National Hemophilia Foundation-Nebraska Chapter
Attn: Scholarship Selection Committee
215 Centennial Mall South, Suite 512
Lincoln, NE 68508
(402) 742-5663 Fax: (402) 742-5677
E-mail: office@nebraskanhf.org
Web: www.nebraskanhf.org

Summary To provide financial assistance for attendance at a college in any state to high school seniors in Nebraska who have a bleeding disorder, are relatives of a person with a bleeding disorder, or are a carrier of a defective gene related to a bleeding disorder.

Eligibility This program is open to seniors graduating from high schools in Nebraska who plan to attend a college or university in any state. Applicants must have a bleeding disorder, be an immediately family member of a person with a bleeding disorder, or be the carrier of a defective gene related to a bleeding disorder. Along with their application, they must submit a brief statement on how a bleeding disorder influences their family life and a 250-word essay on their purpose and motivation for pursuing a postsecondary educational degree. Selection is based on that statement and essay, academic promise in their major field, and financial need. Preference is given to members of the Nebraska Chapter of the National Hemophilia Foundation (NHF).

Financial data The stipend ranges from $500 to $1,000 per academic term ($1,000 to $2,000 per year).

Duration 1 year.

Number awarded 1 or more each year.

Deadline June of each year.

[879]
NEW JERSEY CENTER FOR TOURETTE SYNDROME SCHOLARSHIP

New Jersey Center for Tourette Syndrome, Inc.
50 Division Street, Suite 205
Somerville, NJ 08876
(908) 575-7350 Fax: (908) 575-8699
E-mail: info@njcts.org
Web: www.njcts.org/scholarships.php

Summary To provide financial assistance to high school seniors in New Jersey who have Tourette Syndrome and plan to attend college in any state.

Eligibility This program is open to seniors graduating from high schools in New Jersey who plan to attend a college or trade school in any state. Applicants must have been diagnosed with Tourette Syndrome. Along with their application, they must submit either 1) an essay of 1 to 2 pages describing how Tourette Syndrome has played a part in their life; or 2) a CD, cassette, DVD, or video of about 5 minutes in length displaying their talent in music, art, sports, or other field. Selection is based on those submissions, academic record, and recommendations. Financial need is not considered.

Financial data A stipend is awarded (amount not specified).

Duration 1 year.

Number awarded 1 each year.

Deadline April of each year.

[880]
NEW JERSEY CHRONIC FATIGUE SYNDROME ASSOCIATION COLLEGE SCHOLARSHIP

New Jersey Chronic Fatigue Syndrome Association, Inc.
P.O. Box 477
Florham Park, NJ 07932
(609) 219-0662   Toll Free: (888) 835-3677
Fax: (973) 765-0653
Web: njcfsa.org/scholarships

Summary To provide funding to high school seniors in New Jersey who have Chronic Fatigue Syndrome (CFS) are planning to attend college in any state.

Eligibility This program is open to seniors graduating from high schools in New Jersey and planning to attend a college, university, or technical school in any state. Applicants must have been diagnosed with CFS. They must have a GPA of 2.0 or higher. Recent high school graduates who had to delay continuing their education because of CFS are also eligible. Along with their application, they must submit a 350-word essay on what they see as their goal for higher education or career direction and how having CFS has influenced their choice. Selection is based on that essay, merit, and financial need.

Financial data The stipend is $1,000.

Duration 1 year.

Number awarded 1 each year.

Deadline April of each year.

[881]
NORTH CAROLINA NATIONAL GUARD ASSOCIATION SPECIAL POPULATION SCHOLARSHIP

North Carolina National Guard Association
Attn: Educational Foundation, Inc.
7410 Chapel Hill Road
Raleigh, NC 27607-5047
(919) 851-3390   Toll Free: (800) 821-6159 (within NC)
Fax: (919) 859-4990
E-mail: peggyncngaef@bellsouth.net
Web: ncnga.org

Summary To provide funding to members and dependents of members of the North Carolina National Guard Association who have a learning or physical disability and are interested in attending college in any state.

Eligibility This program is open to active and associate members of the association as well as the spouses, children, grandchildren, and legal dependents of active, associate, or deceased members. Applicants must be learning disabled and/or physically disabled. They may be high

school seniors, high school graduates, or students currently enrolled at a college or university in any state. Selection is based on financial need, academic achievement, citizenship, leadership, and other application information.

Financial data The stipend is $1,000.

Duration 1 year; may be renewed.

Number awarded 1 each year.

Deadline January of each year for high school graduates and college students; February for high school seniors.

[882]
NOVO NORDISK DONNELLY AWARDS

World Team Tennis, Inc.
Attn: Billie Jean King WTT Charities
1776 Broadway, Suite 600
New York, NY 10019
(212) 586-3444, ext. 20   Fax: (212) 586-6277
E-mail: dstone@wtt.com
Web: www.wtt.com/page.aspx?article_id=1429

Summary To recognize and reward young tennis players who have diabetes.

Eligibility This program is open to scholar/athletes between 12 and 21 years of age who play tennis competitively either on a school team or as a ranked tournament player and have type I diabetes. Applicants must submit a 500-word essay on the significance of diabetes in their lives. Selection is based on values, commitment, sportsmanship, community involvement, and financial need.

Financial data Awards are $5,000 for winners or $2,500 for regional finalists; funds may be used for education, tennis development, and/or medical care.

Duration The awards are presented annually.

Additional data This program was established in 1998 by the Billie Jean King Foundation in cooperation with the American Diabetes Association. It includes 2 scholarships named after sisters, Diane Donnelly Stone and Tracey Donnelly Maltby, who have had diabetes since childhood and have played tennis competitively. Novo Nordisk sponsors the program.

Number awarded 8 each year: 2 winners and 6 regional finalists.

Deadline April of each year.

[883]
NOVOTNI COLLEGE SCHOLARSHIP FUND

American Deficit Disorder Association
P.O. Box 7557
Wilmington, DE 19803-9997
(800) 939-1019   Fax: (800) 939-1019
E-mail: info@add.org
Web: www.add.org/?page=NovotniScholarship

Summary To provide financial assistance for college to students who have attention deficit/hyperactivity disorder (AD/HD).

Eligibility This program is open to students who have been diagnosed with AD/HD by a licensed physician or mental health professional. Applicants must be enrolled or planning to enroll at an approved college or university as an undergraduate student. Along with their application, they must submit a 500-word essay on why they would like to be considered for this scholarship, the ways in which AD/HD has been a challenge for them in the educational setting, and the strategies they have used to meet the challenge.

Financial data Stipends are $5,000, $3,000, or $1,000 per year. Funds are paid directly to the recipient's college.

Duration 1 year; recipients may reapply.

Number awarded 1 or more each year.

Deadline March of each year.

[884]
ORION FUND GRANTS

The Orion Fund
P.O. Box 11518
Piedmont, CA 94611
(510) 482-2226   E-mail: theorionfund@gmail.com
Web: theorionfund.org/OrionGrants.htm

Summary To provide financial assistance to California college and graduate students who have a serious illness or injury.

Eligibility This program is open to undergraduate and graduate students at colleges and universities in California who are younger than 30 years of age and have a serious medical condition that affects their ability to stay in school. Applicants must submit a personal statement describing the purpose of the grant and providing justification for the request, a letter of support from a campus administrator or a medical provider, unofficial transcripts, and information on financial resources.

Financial data Stipends range from $300 to $3,000. Funds may be used for unpaid medical bills, medical technology, and educational and living expenses.

Duration 1 year.

Additional data This program was established in 2004.

Number awarded 1 or more each year.

Deadline Applications normally must be submitted by April of each year. In special circumstances, they may be accepted at any time.

[885]
OUTREACH SCHOLARSHIP OF THE JUVENILE DIABETES RESEARCH FOUNDATION

Diabetes Scholars Foundation
2118 Plum Grove Road, Suite 356
Rolling Meadows, IL 60008
(312) 215-9861   Fax: (847) 991-8739
E-mail: collegescholarships@diabetesscholars.org
Web: www.diabetesscholars.org/college.html

Summary To provide financial assistance to high school seniors who have diabetes and plan to major in a field related to mental health in college.

Eligibility This program is open to graduating high school seniors who have Type 1 diabetes and plan to attend an accredited 4-year university, college, or technical/trade school in any state. Applicants must be planning to major in psychology, social work, or other field related to

mental health. They must be able to demonstrate active involvement in the diabetes community, high academic performance, participation in community and/or extracurricular activities, and successful management of the challenges of living with diabetes. Financial need is not considered in the selection process. U.S. citizenship or permanent resident status is required.

Financial data The stipend is $1,000.

Duration 1 year.

Additional data This program is sponsored by the Juvenile Diabetes Research Foundation (JDRF).

Number awarded 1 each year.

Deadline May of each year.

[886]
P. BUCKLEY MOSS ENDOWED SCHOLARSHIP

P. Buckley Moss Society
74 Poplar Grove Lane
Mathews, VA 23109
(540) 932-1728   Toll Free: (800) 430-1320
E-mail: society@mosssociety.org
Web: www.mosssociety.org/page.php?id=69

Summary To provide financial assistance to high school seniors with language-related learning disabilities who plan to study visual arts in college.

Eligibility Eligible to be nominated for this scholarship are high school seniors with language-related learning disabilities and visual arts talent. Nominations must be submitted by a member of the P. Buckley Moss Society. Nominees must be planning to attend a 4-year college or university or a 2-year community college and prepare for a career in a visual art field. The nomination packets must include evidence of financial need, verification of a language-related learning disability from a counselor or case manager, a high school transcript, 2 letters of recommendation, and 3 essays by the nominees: 1) themselves; 2) their learning disability, how it has challenged them, specific strategies they have used to cope, and its effect on their lives; and 3) where they intend to go to school and why, how they plan to use their artistic talent, and what they see themselves doing with their art in 10 years.

Financial data The stipend is $1,500. Funds are paid to the recipient's college or university.

Duration 1 year; may be renewed for up to 3 additional years.

Additional data This scholarship was first awarded in 2007.

Number awarded 1 each year.

Deadline March of each year.

[887]
PACIFIC NORTHWEST SCHOLARSHIPS

Cancer for College
1345 Specialty Drive, Suite D
Vista, CA 92081
(760) 599-5096   E-mail: info@cancerforcollege.org
Web: www.cancerforcollege.org

Summary To provide financial assistance to undergraduate and graduate students from the Pacific Northwest who are cancer patients, survivors, or amputees.

Eligibility This program is open to undergraduate and graduate students who are originally from or current attending accredited colleges, universities, community colleges, and trade schools in Idaho, Montana, Oregon, or Washington. Applicants must be a cancer patient, cancer survivor, and/or amputee. Along with a preliminary application, they must submit a brief statement on why they should receive further consideration for this scholarship and information on their financial situation.

Financial data Stipends are $3,000, $2,000, $1,000, or $500.

Duration 1 year.

Number awarded Varies each year; recently, 14 of these scholarships were awarded: 3 at $3,000, 2 at $2,000, 6 at $1,000, and 3 at $500.

Deadline Deadline not specified.

[888]
PATIENT ADVOCATE FOUNDATION SCHOLARSHIPS FOR SURVIVORS

Patient Advocate Foundation
Attn: Scholarship Coordinator
421 Butler Farm Road
Hampton, VA 23669
Toll Free: (800) 532-5274   Fax: (757) 873-8999
E-mail: help@patientadvocate.org
Web: www.patientadvocate.org/events.php?p=69

Summary To provide financial assistance for college or graduate school to students seeking to initiate or complete a course of study that has been interrupted or delayed by a diagnosis of cancer or other life threatening disease.

Eligibility This program is open to students under 25 years of age who are working full time on a 2-year, 4-year, or advanced degree. The college or graduate education of applicants must have been interrupted or delayed by a diagnosis of cancer or other chronic or life threatening disease within the past 5 years. They must be willing to commit to completing 20 hours of community service for the year if they are awarded a scholarship. Along with their application, they must submit a 1,000-word essay on how their diagnosis has impacted their life and future goals. Financial need is also considered in the selection process.

Financial data The stipend is $3,000. Funds are paid directly to the college or university to help cover tuition and other fee costs. The cost of books is not included.

Duration 1 year; may be renewed up to 3 additional years, provided the recipient remains enrolled full time, maintains a GPA of 3.0 or higher, and performs 20 hours of community service.

Number awarded Varies each year; recently, 12 of these scholarships were awarded.

Deadline March of each year.

[889]
PEDIATRIC BRAIN TUMOR FOUNDATION SCHOLARSHIP PROGRAM

Pediatric Brain Tumor Foundation of the United States
Attn: Family Support Program Manager
302 Ridgefield Court
Asheville, NC 28806
(828) 665-6891, ext. 306   Toll Free: (800) 253-6530
Fax: (828) 665-6894   E-mail: info@pbtfus.org
Web: www.pbtfus.org/survivors/education/scholarships

Summary To provide financial assistance for college to survivors of a brain or spinal cord tumor.

Eligibility This program is open to high school seniors and current college students who have been diagnosed with a childhood brain or spinal cord tumor. Applicants must be enrolled or planning to enroll at a technical school, vocational school, junior college, or 4-year college or university. They must submit an essay, proof of tumor diagnosis, GPA, intent to register for college, high school transcripts, and recommendations.

Financial data The stipend is $2,500 per year.

Duration 2 years.

Additional data This program receives funding from the Tim and Tom Gullikson Family Support Fund and the *Cycle World* Joseph C. Parkhurst Education Fund.

Number awarded Approximately 100 each year.

Deadline February of each year.

[890]
PEGGY SHERRELL MEMORIAL SCHOLARSHIP

Epilepsy Foundation of Kentuckiana
Attn: Director of Education
Kosair Charities Centre
982 Eastern Parkway
Louisville, KY 40217-1566
(502) 637-4440   Toll Free: (866) 275-1078
Fax: (502) 637-4442
Web: old.epilepsyfoundation.org

Summary To provide financial assistance to nontraditional students in Kentucky and southern Indiana who have epilepsy and are interested in attending college in any state.

Eligibility This program is open to residents of Kentucky (except Boone, Campbell, Grant, and Kenton counties) or southern Indiana (Clark, Floyd, and Harrison counties) who have epilepsy or another seizure disorder and are under a physician's care. Applicants be adult learners entering college for the first time or nontraditional students returning to college to complete their degree or certification. Along with their application, they must 500-word essays on 1) something of direct personal importance to them as a person with epilepsy; and 2) their plans for their future educational and professional endeavors. Financial need is also considered in the selection process.

Financial data The stipend is $1,000.

Duration 1 year.

Additional data This program was established in 2011.

Number awarded 1 each year.

Deadline May of each year.

[891]
PERLITA LIWANAG MEMORIAL SCHOLARSHIP

Ulman Cancer Fund for Young Adults
Attn: Scholarship Committee
10440 Little Patuxent Parkway, Suite G1
Columbia, MD 21044
(410) 964-0202   Toll Free: (888) 393-FUND
Fax: (410) 964-0402
E-mail: scholarship@ulmanfund.org
Web: www.ulmanfund.org/scholarship.aspx

Summary   To provide financial assistance for college or graduate school to students from Washington, D.C., Maryland, or Virginia who have been diagnosed with cancer or have or have lost a family member with cancer.

Eligibility   This program is open to students who 1) have been diagnosed with cancer; 2) have a parent, sibling, or guardian living with cancer; or 3) have lost a parent, sibling, or guardian to cancer. Applicants must be residents of Washington, D.C., Maryland, or Virginia or attending college there. They must be 35 years of age or younger and attending, or planning to attend, a 2- or 4-year college, university, or vocational program to work on an undergraduate or graduate degree. The first diagnosis of cancer (whether of the applicant, a parent, a sibling, or a guardian) must have occurred after the applicant was 15 years of age. Along with their application, they must submit an essay of at least 1,000 words on how the cancer experience has impacted their outlook on life and the legacy that they desire to leave behind. Selection is based on demonstrated dedication to community service, commitment to educational and professional goals, use of their cancer experience to impact the lives of other young adults affected by cancer, medical hardship, and financial need.

Financial data   The stipend is $2,500. Funds are paid directly to the educational institution.

Duration   1 year.

Additional data   These scholarships were first awarded in 2011. Recipients must agree to complete 40 hours of community service.

Number awarded   1 each year.

Deadline   March of each year.

[892]
PETER AND BRUCE BIDSTRUP SCHOLARSHIP FUND

National Kidney Foundation of Arizona
Attn: Patient Services Director
4203 East Indian School Road, Suite 140
Phoenix, AZ 85018
(602) 840-1644   Fax: (602) 840-2360
E-mail: glennas@azkidney.org
Web: www.azkidney.org/Patients/Scholarship.aspx

Summary   To provide financial assistance for college to kidney patients in Arizona.

Eligibility   This program is open to students in Arizona who are undergoing dialysis treatment or have received kidney transplants. Applicants must be attending or planning to attend a college, community college, or technical school in Arizona. Financial need is considered in the selection process.

Financial data   This scholarship pays the tuition fees at schools in Arizona.

Additional data   This scholarship fund was established in 1985 to honor Peter and Bruce Bidstrup, who did not survive kidney disease. Its selection committee is chaired by their mother, Carol Bidstrup. Recipients must attend school in Arizona.

Number awarded   Varies each year.

Deadline   Deadline not specified.

[893]
PROFESSOR ULLA HEDNER SCHOLARSHIPS

Novo Nordisk Inc.
Attn: Customer Care
100 College Road West
Princeton, NJ 08540
(609) 987-5800   Toll Free: (877) NOVO-777
Fax: (800) 826-6993
Web: www.changingpossibilities-us.com

Summary   To provide financial assistance to high school seniors and current college students who have a bleeding disorder.

Eligibility   This program is open to high school seniors and students under 23 years of age currently enrolled in college or vocational school. Applicants must have hemophilia with an inhibitor or factor VII deficiency. Along with their application, they must submit a 500-word essay on how changes in the health care landscape will affect their life with a bleeding disorder.

Financial data   Stipends range from $2,000 to $7,000 per year.

Duration   1 year; recipients may reapply.

Additional data   This program is offered as part of SevenSECURE, P.O. Box 18648, Louisville, KY 40261.

Number awarded   Varies each year.

Deadline   May of each year.

[894]
RALPH G. NORMAN SCHOLARSHIPS

Learning Disabilities Association of Arkansas
P.O. Box 23514
Little Rock, AR 72221
(501) 666-8777   E-mail: info@ldarkansas.org
Web: www.ldarkansas.org/norman.cfm

Summary   To provide financial assistance for college to residents of Arkansas who have a learning disability.

Eligibility   This program is open to Arkansas residents who have a learning disability but are ineligible for Social Security Disability (SSD) or Supplemental Security Income (SSI). Applicants must be graduating high school seniors, current college students, or GED recipients. Along with their application, they must submit documentation of their disability, transcripts of all high school and/or college courses, 2 letters of recommendation, and a 1,000-word essay about how their disability has impacted their life and about their future educational and career goals.

Financial data   The stipend is $2,000.

Duration   1 year.

Number awarded   1 or more each year.

Deadline   March of each year.

[895]
RIMINGTON TROPHY SCHOLARSHIP

Boomer Esiason Foundation
c/o Jerry Cahill
483 Tenth Avenue, Suite 300
New York, NY 10018
(646) 292-7930   Fax: (646) 292-7945
E-mail: jcahill@esiason.org
Web: esiason.org/thriving-with-cf/scholarships.php

Summary   To provide financial assistance to undergraduate and graduate students who have cystic fibrosis (CF).

Eligibility   This program is open to CF patients who are working on an undergraduate or graduate degree. Applicants must submit a letter from their doctor confirming the diagnosis of CF and a list of daily medications, information on financial need, a detailed breakdown of tuition costs from their academic institution, transcripts, and a 2-page essay on 1) their post-graduation goals; and 2) the importance of compliance with CF therapies and what they practice to stay healthy. Selection is based on academic ability, character, leadership potential, community service, financial need, and daily compliance to CF therapy.

Financial data   The stipend ranges from $100 to $2,000. Funds are paid directly to the academic institution to assist in covering the cost of tuition and fees.

Duration   1 year; nonrenewable.

Additional data   This program was established in 2012 in association with the Rimington Trophy, a college football award named in honor of Dave Rimington, a former player for the University of Nebraska and the president of the Boomer Esiason Foundation.

Number awarded   1 each year.

Deadline   June of each year.

[896]
RISE SCHOLARSHIPS

Rise Scholarship Foundation, Inc.
Attn: Awards Selection Committee
P.O. Box 422417
Atlanta, GA 30342
Web: www.risescholarshipfoundation.org/rise-award

Summary   To provide financial assistance for college to high school seniors who have a learning disability.

Eligibility   This program is open to graduating high school seniors who have a documented learning disability (a diagnosis of ADHD or ADD alone does not qualify). Applicants must be planning to enroll in at least 2 or more core classes each semester at an accredited college or university. They must have a GPA of 2.5 or higher. Along with their application, they must submit a high school transcript, documentation of a learning disability (e.g., an I.E.P. and/or 504 plan), letters of recommendation, and an essay on the advice they would give a child newly diagnosed as a student with a learning difference. Financial need is not considered. U.S. citizenship is required.

Financial data   A stipend is awarded (amount not specified).

Duration   1 year.

Additional data   The Rise Scholarship Foundation (which stands for Rewarding Individual Success in Education) was established in 2010.

Number awarded   Varies each year; recently, 3 of these scholarships were awarded.

Deadline   February of each year.

[897]
RISING STAR SCHOLARSHIP OF THE JUVENILE DIABETES RESEARCH FOUNDATION

Diabetes Scholars Foundation
2118 Plum Grove Road, Suite 356
Rolling Meadows, IL 60008
(312) 215-9861   Fax: (847) 991-8739
E-mail: collegescholarships@diabetesscholars.org
Web: www.diabetesscholars.org/college.html

Summary   To provide financial assistance for college to high school seniors who have diabetes.

Eligibility   This program is open to graduating high school seniors who have Type 1 diabetes and plan to attend an accredited 4-year university, college, or technical/trade school in any state. Applicants must be able to demonstrate active involvement in the diabetes community, high academic performance, participation in community and/or extracurricular activities, and successful management of the challenges of living with diabetes. Financial need is not considered in the selection process. U.S. citizenship or permanent resident status is required.

Financial data   The stipend is $1,000.

Duration   1 year.

Additional data   This program is sponsored by the Juvenile Diabetes Research Foundation (JDRF).

Number awarded   1 each year.

Deadline   May of each year.

[898]
ROBERT DOLE SCHOLARSHIP FUND FOR DISABLED STUDENTS

United Negro College Fund
Attn: Scholarships and Grants Department
8260 Willow Oaks Corporate Drive
P.O. Box 10444
Fairfax, VA 22031-8044
(703) 205-3466   Toll Free: (800) 331-2244
Fax: (703) 205-3574
Web: www.uncf.org

Summary   To provide funding to physically and mentally-challenged students at colleges and universities that are members of the United Negro College Fund (UNCF).

Eligibility   This program is open to students at UNCF-member institutions who have a physical or learning disability. Applicants must have a GPA of 2.5 or higher and be able to demonstrate financial need. Along with their application, they must submit a 500-word essay on the challenges of their disability.

Financial data The stipend is $3,500.

Duration 1 year.

Number awarded 1 or more each year.

Deadline February of each year.

[899]
R.O.C.K. COLLEGE SCHOLARSHIP PROGRAM

American Cancer Society-Florida Division
3709 West Jetton Avenue
Tampa, FL 33629-5146
(813) 349-4239
Toll Free: (800) 444-1410, ext. 4239 (within FL)
Fax: (813) 254-5857   E-mail: susan.lee@cancer.org
Web: www.cancer.org

Summary To provide financial assistance to students in Florida who have been diagnosed with cancer and are interested in attending college in any state.

Eligibility This program is open to Florida residents who have been diagnosed with cancer before the age of 21, are under 21 at the time of application, are high school seniors or graduates, and have been accepted to an accredited 2- or 4-year college, university, or vocational/technical school in Florida. Applicants must submit a completed application form, 3 letters of recommendation (including 1 from a physician), their financial aid form, an official transcript, their SAT and/or ACT test scores, and a 500-word essay on their journey as a cancer survivor, goals, ambitions, and how this scholarship will help them achieve academic success. Selection is based on financial need, academic record, leadership ability, and community service.

Financial data Stipends provide up to $2,700 per year for tuition plus $300 per year for textbooks.

Duration 1 year; may be renewed to a maximum of 130 semester hours over 5 years, whichever comes first.

Additional data These scholarships were first awarded in 1992 as part of the Florida division's Reaching Out to Cancer Kids (R.O.C.K.) program. Recipients are expected to complete at least 10 hours of American Cancer Society community service annually.

Number awarded Varies each year; recently, 154 of these scholarships were awarded.

Deadline April of each year.

[900]
ROSEMARY QUIGLEY MEMORIAL SCHOLARSHIP

Boomer Esiason Foundation
c/o Jerry Cahill
483 Tenth Avenue, Suite 300
New York, NY 10018
(646) 292-7930   Fax: (646) 292-7945
E-mail: jcahill@esiason.org
Web: esiason.org/thriving-with-cf/scholarships.php

Summary To provide financial assistance to undergraduate and graduate students who have cystic fibrosis (CF) and a demonstrated commitment to living life to the fullest.

Eligibility This program is open to CF patients who are working on an undergraduate or graduate degree. Applicants must be able to demonstrate a clear sense of life goals and a commitment to living life to the fullest, despite having CF. Along with their application, they must submit a letter from their doctor confirming the diagnosis of CF and a list of daily medications, information on financial need, a detailed breakdown of tuition costs from their academic institution, transcripts, and a 2-page essay on 1) their post-graduation goals; and 2) the importance of compliance with CF therapies and what they practice on a daily basis to stay healthy. Selection is based on academic ability, character, leadership potential, service to the community, and financial need. Finalists are interviewed by telephone.

Financial data The stipend ranges from $500 to $2,000. Funds are paid directly to the academic institution to assist in covering the cost of tuition and fees.

Duration 1 year; nonrenewable.

Number awarded 1 each year.

Deadline June of each year.

[901]
RYAN MULLALY SECOND CHANCE SCHOLARSHIPS

Ryan Mullaly Second Chance Fund
26 Meadow Lane
Pennington, NJ 08534
(609) 737-1800   E-mail: The2dChanceFund@aol.com
Web: www.ryans2dchancefund.org

Summary To provide financial assistance for college to high school seniors who are fighting lymphoma.

Eligibility This program is open to U.S. citizens and permanent residents who were diagnosed with lymphoma or a recurrence of lymphoma between age 13 and graduation from high school. Applicants must have a treatment history that includes chemotherapy and/or radiation and must be able to demonstrate that their high school years were substantially impacted by treatment and/or side effects of treatment. They must be high school seniors planning to 1) work on an associate or bachelor's degree at an accredited 2- or 4-year college or university; or 2) enroll in an accredited postsecondary vocational or trade program that will culminate in certification. Priority is given to students still undergoing treatment and those with permanent effects from treatment.

Financial data The stipend is $1,000.

Duration 1 year; nonrenewable.

Additional data This program was established in 2003.

Number awarded Up to 15 each year.

Deadline July of each year.

[902]
SACKS FOR CF SCHOLARSHIPS

Boomer Esiason Foundation
c/o Jerry Cahill
483 Tenth Avenue, Suite 300
New York, NY 10018
(646) 292-7930   Fax: (646) 292-7945
E-mail: jcahill@esiason.org
Web: esiason.org/thriving-with-cf/scholarships.php

Summary   To provide financial assistance to undergraduate and graduate students who have cystic fibrosis (CF).

Eligibility   This program is open to CF patients who are working on an undergraduate or graduate degree. Applicants must submit a letter from their doctor confirming the diagnosis of CF and a list of daily medications, information on financial need, a detailed breakdown of tuition costs from their academic institution, transcripts, and a 2-page essay on 1) their post-graduation goals; and 2) the importance of compliance with CF therapies and what they practice to stay healthy. Selection is based on academic ability, character, leadership potential, community service, financial need, and adherence to daily CF therapy.

Financial data   The stipend ranges from $3,000 to $10,000. Funds are paid directly to the academic institution to assist in covering the cost of tuition and fees.

Duration   1 year; nonrenewable.

Additional data   This program is funded by a corporate sponsor which donates $1,000 each time a quarterback is sacked on NFL Monday Night Football games.

Number awarded   30 each year.

Deadline   January of each year.

[903]
SALVATORE E. QUINCI SCHOLARSHIPS

Salvatore E. Quinci Foundation
178 Florence Street
Melrose, MA 02176-3710
(781) 760-7138
Web: www.seqfoundation.org

Summary   To provide financial assistance for college to people who have a bleeding disorder.

Eligibility   This program is open to people who have been diagnosed with hemophilia or another bleeding disorder. Applicants must be attending or accepted at an accredited college, university, or vocational/technical school. Along with their application, they must submit a 1-page statement that discusses their future educational and career goals and how they plan to use the scholarship money. Selection is based on that statement, the quality of the application, grades, and financial need.

Financial data   The stipend is $2,000. Funds must be used for tuition, fees, books, or other education-related expenses.

Duration   1 year.

Additional data   Scholarships must be used within 12 months of the award date.

Number awarded   2 each year.

Deadline   April of each year.

[904]
SARAH ELIZABETH STUBBLEFIELD
FOUNDATION SCHOLARSHIP

Sarah Elizabeth Stubblefield Foundation
c/o Matthew Flanigan
Black, Hedin, Ballard, McDonald, P.C.
108 South Ninth Street
P.O. Box 4007
Mt. Vernon, IL 62864
(618) 242-3310   Fax: (618) 242-3735

Summary   To provide financial assistance to high school seniors in Illinois who have epilepsy and plan to attend college in any state.

Eligibility   This program is open to seniors graduating from high schools in Illinois who have epilepsy and are under a physician's care for the disease. Applicants must be planning to enroll at a college or vocational/technical school in any state. Along with their application, they must submit 250-word essays on 1) something of direct personal importance to them as a person living with epilepsy; and 2) their plans for their future educational and personal endeavors. Financial need is also considered in the selection process.

Financial data   The stipend is $2,000 per year.

Duration   1 year; recipients may reapply.

Additional data   This program was established in 2011.

Number awarded   1 each year.

Deadline   April of each year.

[905]
SCHOLARSHIP OF THE ARTS

Boomer Esiason Foundation
c/o Jerry Cahill
483 Tenth Avenue, Suite 300
New York, NY 10018
(646) 292-7930   Fax: (646) 292-7945
E-mail: jcahill@esiason.org
Web: esiason.org/thriving-with-cf/scholarships.php

Summary   To provide financial assistance to undergraduate and graduate students who have cystic fibrosis (CF) and are working on a degree in the arts.

Eligibility   This program is open to CF patients who are working on an undergraduate or graduate degree in the arts. Applicants must submit a sample of their work (video, painting, sketching, sculpture), a letter from their doctor confirming the diagnosis of CF and a list of daily medications, information on financial need, a detailed breakdown of tuition costs from their academic institution, transcripts, and a 2-page essay on 1) their post-graduation goals; and 2) the importance of compliance with CF therapies and what they practice on a daily basis to stay healthy. Selection is based on academic ability, character, leadership potential, service to the community, and financial need.

Financial data   Stipends range from $500 to $1,000. Funds are paid directly to the academic institution to assist in covering the cost of tuition and fees.

Duration   1 year; nonrenewable.

Number awarded   1 each year.

Deadline   May of each year.

[906]
SCHWALLIE FAMILY SCHOLARSHIPS

Organization for Autism Research
Attn: Scholarship
2000 North 14th Street, Suite 710
Arlington, VA 22201
(703) 243-9710
Web: www.researchautism.org

Summary To provide financial assistance for college to individuals with autism or Asperger's Syndrome.

Eligibility This program is open to individuals with an established autism or Asperger's Syndrome diagnosis who are attending or planning to attend an accredited 2- or 4-year college, university, or vocational/technical institute. Applicants must be enrolled at least part time and be working toward certification or accreditation in a particular field. Along with their application, they must submit a 1,000-word autobiographical essay that includes their reasons for applying for this scholarship. Selection is based on originality of content, previous challenges overcome, future aspirations, and financial need.

Financial data The stipend is $3,000.

Duration 1 year; nonrenewable.

Additional data This program was established in 2007.

Number awarded Varies each year; recently, 22 of these scholarships were awarded. Since the program began, it has awarded $178,500 in scholarships to 55 students.

Deadline April of each year.

[907]
SCOTT DELGADILLO SCHOLARSHIP

Friends of Scott Foundation
Attn: Scholarship Fund
6977 Navajo Road, Number 168
San Diego, CA 92119
(619) 223-7268   Fax: (619) 223-7002
E-mail: aztec.graphics@yahoo.com
Web: www.friendsofscott.org/scholarship.aspx

Summary To provide financial assistance for college or graduate school to childhood cancer survivors.

Eligibility This program is open to survivors of childhood cancer and to patients currently receiving treatment. Applicants must be attending or planning to attend a technical school, vocational school, junior college, or 4-year college or university as an undergraduate or graduate student. Along with their application, they must submit a 500-word essay on how their experience with cancer has impacted their life. Selection is based on financial need and personal hardship.

Financial data The stipend is $1,000.

Duration 1 year.

Number awarded Varies each year; recently, 4 of these scholarships were awarded.

Deadline April of each year.

[908]
SEAN SILVER MEMORIAL SCHOLARSHIP

Ulman Cancer Fund for Young Adults
Attn: Scholarship Committee
10440 Little Patuxent Parkway, Suite G1
Columbia, MD 21044
(410) 964-0202   Toll Free: (888) 393-FUND
Fax: (410) 964-0402
E-mail: scholarship@ulmanfund.org
Web: www.ulmanfund.org/scholarship.aspx

Summary To provide financial assistance for college or graduate school to young adults who have cancer.

Eligibility This program is open to students who are younger than 30 years of age and currently undergoing active treatment for cancer. Applicants must be attending or planning to attend a 4-year college or university to work on an undergraduate or graduate degree. They must be U.S. citizens or permanent residents. Along with their application, they must submit an essay of at least 1,000 words on what they have discovered about themselves while attending school as a young adult receiving treatment for or living with cancer. Selection is based on demonstrated dedication to community service, commitment to educational and professional goals, use of their cancer experience to impact the lives of other young adults affected by cancer, medical hardship, and financial need.

Financial data The stipend is $2,500. Funds are paid directly to the educational institution.

Duration 1 year.

Additional data This scholarship was first awarded in 2008. Recipients must agree to complete 40 hours of community service.

Number awarded 1 each year.

Deadline March of each year.

[909]
SEVENSECURE ADULT EDUCATION GRANTS

Novo Nordisk Inc.
Attn: Customer Care
100 College Road West
Princeton, NJ 08540
(609) 987-5800   Toll Free: (877) NOVO-777
Fax: (800) 826-6993
Web: www.changingpossibilities-us.com

Summary To provide financial assistance for college to adults who have a bleeding disorder.

Eligibility This program is open to adults over 23 years of age currently enrolled in college or vocational school. Applicants must have hemophilia with an inhibitor or factor VII deficiency. They must be working on a certificate or associate or bachelor's degree to get more training to help improve their career or transition to a new field.

Financial data Stipends range up to $2,500 per year. Funds are paid directly to the university or institution.

Duration 1 year.

Number awarded Varies each year.

Deadline Applications may be submitted at any time.

[910]
SHANNON O'DANIEL MEMORIAL SCHOLARSHIP

Epilepsy Foundation of Kentuckiana
Attn: Director of Education
Kosair Charities Centre
982 Eastern Parkway
Louisville, KY 40217-1566
(502) 637-4440   Toll Free: (866) 275-1078
Fax: (502) 637-4442
Web: old.epilepsyfoundation.org

Summary   To provide financial assistance to high school seniors in Kentucky and southern Indiana who have epilepsy and are interested in attending college in any state.

Eligibility   This program is open to seniors graduating from high schools in Kentucky (except Boone, Campbell, Grant, and Kenton counties) or southern Indiana (Clark, Floyd, and Harrison counties) who have epilepsy or another seizure disorder and are under a physician's care. Applicants be planning to attend a college or university in any state. Along with their application, they must 250-word essays on 1) something of direct personal importance to them as a person with epilepsy; and 2) their plans for their future educational and professional endeavors. Financial need is also considered in the selection process.

Financial data   The stipend is $1,000.

Duration   1 year.

Additional data   This program was established in 2001.

Number awarded   1 each year.

Deadline   May of each year.

[911]
SHIRE ADHD SCHOLARSHIP PROGRAM

Shire US Inc.
Attn: ADHD Scholarship Program
860 High Street
P.O. Box 562
Chestertown, MD 21620
(484) 595-8248   Toll Free: (855) 474-4732
E-mail: mcabrey@shire.com
Web: www.shireadhdscholarship.com

Summary   To provide money for college to students who have attention deficit/hyperactivity disorder (ADHD).

Eligibility   This program is open to legal residents of the United States who have been diagnosed with ADHD and are enrolled or accepted in an undergraduate program at an accredited 2- or 4-year college, university, or trade/technical/vocational school. Applicants must be under the care of a licensed health professional, although they are not required to be taking medication or to have a specific future or ongoing plan of management for treatment of their ADHD. Along with their application, they must submit a 500-word essay on how ADHD has impacted their life, the challenges they have faced, and how they managed them or what you are doing to manage them. Selection is based on that essay (50%), letters of recommendation (20%), a 100-word statement on how having an ADHD coach will help them transition to higher education (15%),

and a list of community, volunteer, and extracurricular activities (15%).

Financial data   The stipend is $2,000. Funds are paid directly to the recipient's institution.

Duration   1 year; nonrenewable.

Additional data   This program, established in 2011, also provides scholarship recipients with a year of ADHD coaching services from the Edge Foundation.

Number awarded   50 each year.

Deadline   March of each year.

[912]
SICKLE CELL THALASSEMIA PATIENTS NETWORK UNDERGRADUATE SCHOLARSHIPS

Sickle Cell Thalassemia Patients Network
Attn: Scholarships
1139 St. Johns Place
Brooklyn, NY 11213
(347) 533-8485   Fax: (718) 789-5767
E-mail: scholarships@sctpn.org
Web: sctpn.net/scholarship.php

Summary   To provide financial assistance to high school seniors and current college students who are living with an inherited blood disorder and are interested in attending college in any state.

Eligibility   This program is open to high school seniors and college students who have been diagnosed with sickle cell disease or thalassemia (Cooley's anemia). Applicants must be attending or planning to attend an accredited 2- or 4-year college or university in any state. Along with their application, they must submit statements on their extracurricular activities, their educational and career goals, and how they plan to use this scholarship.

Financial data   A stipend is awarded (amount not specified).

Duration   1 year; recipients may reapply.

Number awarded   1 or more each year.

Deadline   May of each year.

[913]
SMART KIDS WITH LEARNING DISABILITIES YOUTH ACHIEVEMENT AWARD

Smart Kids with Learning Disabilities, Inc.
38 Kings Highway North
Westport, CT 06880
(203) 226-6831   Fax: (203) 226-4861
E-mail: info@smartkidswithld.org
Web: www.smartkidswithld.org/award

Summary   To recognize and reward high school students with learning disabilities who demonstrate outstanding achievement.

Eligibility   This award is available to students who are 19 years of age or younger and have a learning disability and/or AD/HD. Nominees must have demonstrated initiative, talent, determination, and accomplishment in any field, including art, music, science, mathematics, athletics, or community service. They may be nominated by a parent, teacher, mentor, coach, or themselves.

Financial data The award is $1,000.
Duration The award is presented annually.
Additional data This award was first presented in 2004.
Number awarded 1 each year.
Deadline February of each year.

[914]
SNOWDROP FOUNDATION SCHOLARSHIPS

Snowdrop Foundation
Attn: Kevin Kline, President
2310 Upland Park Drive
Sugar Land, TX 77479
(713) 232-9052
E-mail: kevin@snowdropfoundation.org
Web: www.snowdropfoundation.org

Summary To provide money for college or graduate school to students who have been diagnosed with cancer.
Eligibility This program is open to students entering or attending college or graduate school. Applicants must have been diagnosed with cancer. Along with their application, they must submit a 250-word description of themselves; a 250-word description of their family situation; information on financial need; a letter from their attending physician verifying their medical history and current medical situation; and an essay of 500 to 1,000 words on how their experience with cancer has impacted their life values and career goals.
Financial data A stipend is awarded (amount not specified).
Duration 1 year.
Number awarded Varies each year.
Deadline April of each year.

[915]
SOOZIE COURTER SHARING A BRIGHTER TOMORROW HEMOPHILIA SCHOLARSHIP

Pfizer Inc.
Attn: Hemophilia Scholarship Program (QD Healthcare Group)
One Dock Street, Suite 520
Stamford, CT 06902
Toll Free: (888) 999-2349
Web: www.hemophiliavillage.com

Summary To provide financial assistance for college or graduate school in any field to persons with hemophilia.
Eligibility This program is open to persons with hemophilia (A or B) who are high school seniors, have a GED, or are currently attending an accredited college, university, junior college, vocational school, or graduate school. Along with their application, they must submit a 2-page essay on 1 of the following topics: 1) how hemophilia has affected their school life and how they have overcome those challenges; 2) the advice they would give to a child with hemophilia who is beginning school; or 3) the time in history they would travel back to if they could and why. Financial need is not considered in the selection process.
Financial data The stipends are $2,500 for undergraduate students or $4,000 for graduate students.

Duration 1 year.
Additional data This program was established in 1998 and given its current name in 2000.
Number awarded 17 each year: 12 to undergraduates and 5 to graduate students.
Deadline July of each year.

[916]
SPIBELT ATHLETIC SCHOLARSHIP

Diabetes Scholars Foundation
2118 Plum Grove Road, Suite 356
Rolling Meadows, IL 60008
(312) 215-9861   Fax: (847) 991-8739
E-mail: collegescholarships@diabetesscholars.org
Web: www.diabetesscholars.org/college.html

Summary To provide financial assistance for college to high school seniors who have diabetes and have participated in athletics.
Eligibility This program is open to graduating high school seniors who have Type 1 diabetes and plan to attend an accredited 4-year university, college, or technical/trade school in any state. Applicants must have participated in athletics. They must be able to demonstrate active involvement in the diabetes community, high academic performance, participation in community and/or extracurricular activities, and successful management of the challenges of living with diabetes. Financial need is not considered in the selection process. U.S. citizenship or permanent resident status is required.
Financial data The stipend is $1,000.
Duration 1 year.
Additional data This program is sponsored by Overton Enterprises, LLC, manufacturer of the Spibelt small personal item belt.
Number awarded 1 each year.
Deadline May of each year.

[917]
STEPHEN T. MARCHELLO SCHOLARSHIPS

Stephen T. Marchello Scholarship Foundation
1170 East Long Place
Centennial, CO 80122
(303) 886-5018   E-mail: fmarchello@earthlink.net
Web: www.stmfoundation.org

Summary To provide financial assistance to students from Colorado and Montana who have survived childhood cancer and are interested in attending college in any state.
Eligibility This program is open to high school seniors who either live in or were treated for cancer in Colorado or Montana. Applicants must be working on or planning to work on an undergraduate degree at a school in any state. They must submit essays on 2 topics: 1) their academic and professional goals, why they have chosen to pursue those goals, and how this scholarship will help them obtain their goals; and 2) an event in world history that has made a significant positive contribution and their reasons why they feel this was important. In addition to those 2 essays, selection is based on high school GPA; SAT or ACT scores; information provided by the doctor, clinic, or

hospital where they were treated; and 2 letters of reference.

Financial data Stipends range up to $2,000 per year.

Duration 1 year; may be renewed.

Additional data This foundation was established by the family of Stephen T. Marchello, who died of cancer in 1999. It awarded its first scholarship in 2000.

Number awarded 1 at $2,000, 1 at $1,500, and 1 at $1,000.

Deadline March of each year.

[918]
STEVEN M. PEREZ FOUNDATION SCHOLARSHIPS

Steven M. Perez Foundation
P.O. Box 955
Melville, NY 11747
(631) 367-9016   Fax: (631) 367-3848
E-mail: info@smpfoundation.org
Web: www.smpfoundation.org

Summary To provide financial assistance for college to high school seniors who have survived leukemia or lost a family member to cancer or a related disease.

Eligibility This program is open to graduating high school seniors who have survived leukemia or who have lost a parent or sibling to cancer or a related disease. Applicants must be planning to attend a college in any state. Along with their application, they must submit medical certification, a recommendation from a counselor, and an essay describing their connection to leukemia.

Financial data Stipend amounts vary; recently, they averaged approximately $1,450.

Duration 1 year.

Number awarded Varies each year; recently, 17 of these scholarships were awarded.

Deadline April of each year.

[919]
SUSAN BUNCH MEMORIAL SCHOLARSHIP

California Association for Postsecondary Education
  and Disability
Attn: Executive Assistant
71423 Biskra Road
Rancho Mirage, CA 92270
(760) 346-8206   Fax: (760) 340-5275
TDD: (760) 341-4084   E-mail: caped2000@aol.com
Web: www.caped.net/scholarships.html

Summary To provide funding to college and graduate students in California who have a learning disability.

Eligibility This program is open to students at public and private colleges and universities in California who have a learning disability. Undergraduates must have completed at least 6 semester credits and have a GPA of 2.5 or higher. Graduate students must have completed at least 3 semester units and have a GPA of 3.0 or higher. Along with their application, they must submit a 1-page personal letter that demonstrates their writing skills, progress towards meeting their educational and vocational goals, management of their disability, and involvement in

community activities. They must also submit a letter of recommendation from a faculty member, verification of disability, official transcripts, proof of current enrollment, and documentation of financial need.

Financial data The stipend is $1,000.

Duration 1 year.

Number awarded 1 each year.

Deadline September of each year.

[920]
SUSAN G. KOMEN BREAST CANCER FOUNDATION COLLEGE SCHOLARSHIP AWARDS

Susan G. Komen Breast Cancer Foundation
Attn: Scholarship Program Office
5005 LBJ Freeway, Suite 250
Dallas, TX 75244
(972) 855-1616   Toll Free: (877) GO-KOMEN
Fax: (972) 855-1605
E-mail: collegescholarships@komen.org
Web: ww5.komen.org

Summary To provide financial assistance for college to high school seniors and college students who lost a parent to breast cancer or are breast cancer survivors.

Eligibility This program is open to high school seniors and college freshmen, sophomores, and juniors who have lost a parent to breast cancer or are a breast cancer survivor diagnosed at 25 years of age or younger. Applicants must be under 25 years of age, be U.S. citizens or permanent residents, have a high school and/or college GPA of 2.8 or higher, and be enrolled or planning to enroll full time at a state-supported college or university in the state where they permanently reside. Along with their application, they must submit 2 essays of 500 words each on 1) how breast cancer has changed them, and 2) how their education will help them achieve their career objectives and personal goals. Selection is based on the essay, academic achievements or records, community involvement, letters of reference, and financial need.

Financial data Stipends up to $10,000 per year are available. Funds may be used for tuition, books, fees, and on-campus room and board.

Duration 4 years, provided the recipient remains enrolled full time and makes reasonable progress toward completion of a baccalaureate degree.

Number awarded 5 each year.

Deadline January of each year.

[921]
SUSAN STEIN SCHOLARSHIP

American College of Nurse-Midwives
Attn: ACNM Foundation, Inc.
8403 Colesville Road, Suite 1550
Silver Spring, MD 20910-6374
(240) 485-1850   Fax: (240) 485-1818
E-mail: fdn@acnm.org
Web: www.midwife.org

Summary To provide financial assistance for midwifery education to student members of the American College of

Nurse-Midwives (ACNM) who have had a personal experience with breast cancer.

Eligibility This program is open to ACNM members who are currently enrolled in an accredited basic midwife education program and have successfully completed 1 academic or clinical semester/quarter or clinical module. Applicants must have had or currently have a personal experience with breast cancer, either their own or a family member's. Along with their application, they must submit a 150-word essay on their midwifery career plans; a 100-word essay on their intended future participation in ACNM activities; and a 300-word essay on the effect of breast cancer in themselves or a close family member on their choice of midwifery. Selection is based primarily on the quality of the application, although leadership, financial need, academics, and personal goals may also be considered.

Financial data The stipend is $3,000.

Duration 1 year.

Additional data This program was established in 2010.

Number awarded 1 each year.

Deadline March of each year.

[922]
SUSANNA DELAURENTIS MEMORIAL SCHOLARSHIPS

Susanna DeLaurentis Charitable Foundation
P.O. Box 11208
Elkins Park, PA 19027
(215) 635-9405   Fax: (215) 635-9406
E-mail: info@thesusannafoundation.org
Web: thesusannafoundation.org/scholarships

Summary To provide financial assistance for college to high school seniors who have serious medical difficulties.

Eligibility This program is open to graduating high school seniors who contend with a chronic disease or other serious challenge to physical or mental health. Applicants must be planning to enroll at a college or university. Along with their application, they must submit a brief statement describing their health condition, how they have managed to excel in spite of the condition, and their plans for advanced education after high school. They should also submit information about their academic standing (GPA, ACT and/or SAT scores, class rank) and their participation in extracurricular or community activities. Financial need is not considered in the selection process.

Financial data The stipend is $1,000.

Duration 1 year.

Additional data This foundation was established in 1999 to honor Susanna DeLaurentis, who died from neuroblastoma, a form of cancer of the nervous system, when she was 10 years of age. Her surviving sister is currently living with cystic fibrosis.

Number awarded Varies each year; recently, 12 of these scholarships were awarded.

Deadline April of each year.

[923]
THOMARA LATIMER CANCER FOUNDATION SCHOLARSHIPS

Thomara Latimer Cancer Foundation
Attn: Scholarship Committee
Franklin Plaza Center
29193 Northeastern Highway, Suite 528
Southfield, MI 48034-1006
(248) 557-2346   Fax: (248) 557-8063
E-mail: scholarships@thomlatimercares.org
Web: www.thomlatimercares.org

Summary To provide financial assistance to African American residents of Michigan (especially those who have had cancer) who are interested in studying a medically-related field at a college in any state.

Eligibility This program is open to African American residents of Michigan between 17 and 30 years of age. Applicants must be 1) a high school senior accepted at an accredited college or university in any state in a medically-related program (e.g., medical technician, physician assistant); or 2) a student admitted to a medically-related professional program (e.g., nursing, medicine, physical or occupational therapy) at a college or university in any state. They must have a GPA of 3.0 or higher. Along with their application, they must submit a brief essay on why they should be awarded this scholarship. Financial need is not considered in the selection process. Special consideration is given to students who are cancer survivors.

Financial data The stipend is $1,000.

Duration 1 year; may be renewed 1 additional year.

Number awarded 10 each year.

Deadline December of each year.

[924]
THOMAS F. SMITH SCHOLARSHIP

Georgia Transplant Foundation
Attn: Scholarship Program
500 Sugar Mill Road, Suite 170A
Atlanta, GA 30350
(770) 457-3796   Fax: (770) 457-7916
Web: gatransplant.org

Summary To provide financial assistance to residents of Georgia who are transplant recipients and interested in attending college in any state.

Eligibility This program is open to residents of Georgia who are entering or continuing at an accredited institution of higher learning in any state. Applicants must be an organ transplant recipient. Along with their application, they must submit a 2-page personal statement on their career objectives, how this scholarship will help them attain their goals, and any other pertinent information. Selection is based on that statement, transcripts, high school exit examination scores, ACT/SAT scores, 3 letters of reference, and financial need.

Financial data The stipend is $1,000 per year.

Duration 1 year; renewable up to 3 more years.

Number awarded 1 each year.

Deadline May of each year.

[925]
THOMAS J. SEEFRED TRUST SCHOLARSHIPS

Thomas J. Seefred Trust
23 Lisbon Street, Suite K
Canfield, OH 44406
(330) 533-9900   E-mail: info@seefredtrust.org
Web: www.seefredtrust.org

Summary   To provide financial assistance to residents of Ohio who have juvenile diabetes and are currently enrolled at a college or university in any state.

Eligibility   This program is open to students between 18 and 25 years of age who have been diagnosed with juvenile diabetes and are working full time on a bachelor's degree at an accredited college or university in any state. Applicants must be residents of Ohio; preference is given to residents of Columbiana, Mahoning, and Trumbull counties. Along with their application, they must submit a 500-word personal essay describing the impact juvenile diabetes has had on them and why they feel they should receive this scholarship. Selection is based on that essay, academic promise, recommendations, and financial need.

Financial data   The stipend is $3,000.

Duration   1 year.

Additional data   This program was established in 2005.

Number awarded   1 or more each year.

Deadline   March of each year.

[926]
TOGETHER FORWARD SCHOLARSHIP PROGRAM

Coram Hemophilia Services
555 17th Street, Suite 1500
Denver, CO 80202
Toll Free: (888) 699-7440   Fax: (888) 699-7441
Web: www.coramhemophilia.com/scholarship

Summary   To provide financial assistance for college to individuals who have a bleeding disorder.

Eligibility   This program is open to graduating high school seniors and current undergraduates who have hemophilia or related genetic blood clotting disorder. Applicants must be enrolled or planning to enroll full time at a 4-year college or university. Along with their application, they must submit an essay, current transcripts, class rank and class size, ACT or SAT composite scores, and documentation of volunteerism or community service. Financial need is not considered. U.S. citizenship is required.

Financial data   The stipend is $2,500 per year.

Duration   1 year; renewable up to 3 more years.

Additional data   This program, established in 2011, is administered by International Scholarship and Tuition Services, Inc.

Number awarded   4 each year.

Deadline   March of each year.

[927]
TONY AND JAN VIESSMAN MEMORIAL SCHOLARSHIPS

Epilepsy Foundation of Missouri and Kansas
c/o Julie Viessman MacCash
10698 Lakemont Drive
Rolla, MO 65401
Web: epilepsyfoundation.ning.com

Summary   To provide funding to residents of any state who have epilepsy or are caring for someone who does and want to attend college or graduate school.

Eligibility   This program is open to residents of any state who are under a physician's care for epilepsy or are the caretaker for a person living with epilepsy. Applicants may be 1) high school seniors planning to attend a technical school, community college, or 4-year college or university; 2) freshmen, sophomores, or juniors at 1 of those institutions; 3) college seniors planning to enroll in graduate school; or 4) adults interested in working on a college degree. Along with their application, they must submit a 500-word essay on 1 of the following topics: 1) what the youth of today should focus on to improve the lives of others; 2) why they think it is important for high school graduates to further their education; or 3) the current event, from their community or around the glove, that they find most interesting and why. They must also submit a 500-word essay on how they have overcome, or are working to overcome, the challenges that epilepsy presents.

Financial data   The stipend is $1,000.

Duration   1 year.

Number awarded   4 each year.

Deadline   March of each year.

[928]
TRANSPLANT RECIPIENTS INTERNATIONAL ORGANIZATION SCHOLARSHIPS

Transplant Recipients International Organization, Inc.
Attn: Scholarship Committee
2100 M Street, N.W., Suite 170-353
Washington, DC 20037-1233
(202) 293-0980   Toll Free: (800) TRIO-386
E-mail: info@trioweb.org
Web: www.trioweb.org

Summary   To provide financial assistance for college to members of the Transplant Recipients International Organization (TRIO) and their families.

Eligibility   This program is open to TRIO members and their immediate family who are solid organ or bone marrow candidates, recipients, donors, or their immediate family members. Applicants must be attending or planning to attend an accredited college, university, or trade/technical certificate program. They must have a cumulative GPA of 2.5 or higher and be able to demonstrate financial need. Along with their application, they must submit a 500-word essay on their personal history and educational and career ambitions and a statement on how transplantation has affected their life.

Financial data   The stipend is $1,000.

Duration   1 year; nonrenewable.

Number awarded Several each year. Since the program began 16 years ago, it has awarded 108 scholarships.

Deadline June of each year.

[929]
TRANSPLANT SCHOLARS AWARDS

Astellas Pharma US, Inc.
Attn: Transplant Scholars Award
Three Parkway North
Deerfield, IL 60015-2548
Toll Free: (800) 888-7704
Web: astellastransplant.com/events_scholar.php

Summary To recognize and reward, with scholarships for college or graduate school, transplant recipients and donors who submit outstanding essays on their transplant experience.

Eligibility This competition is open to liver, kidney, or heart transplant recipients who are taking Prograf and to organ donors who have donated a portion of their liver or a kidney. Applicants must be beginning higher education, returning to school after their surgery, or working on an advanced degree. They must submit a 500-word essay that describes their transplant or donation experience, how the experience has changed their life, and how they would use the scholarship award to further their education and give back to the transplant community. Selection is based on the compelling nature of the story, the educational goals of the applicant and how those were affected by transplantation, and the applicant's intention to impact the transplant community positively.

Financial data The award is a $5,000 scholarship to be used for educational expenses.

Duration The awards are presented annually.

Number awarded Varies each year; recently, 12 of these scholarships were awarded.

Deadline June of each year.

[930]
UCB CROHN'S SCHOLARSHIP PROGRAM

UCB, Inc.
c/o Summit Medical Communications
1421 East Broad Street, Suite 340
Fuquay-Varina, NC 27526
Toll Free: (866) 757-4440
E-mail: ucbcrohnsscholarship@summitmedcomm.com
Web: www.crohnsandme.com/crohns-scholarship

Summary To provide financial assistance to undergraduate and graduate students who have Crohn's disease.

Eligibility This program is open to students who are working on or planning to work on an associate, undergraduate, or graduate degree or are enrolled in a trade school educational program. Applicants must have been diagnosed with Crohn's disease by a physician. They may be of any age. Along with their application, they must submit an essay of 1 to 2 pages describing how they are living beyond the boundaries of Crohn's disease to demonstrate academic ambition and personal achievement and how the scholarship would impact their life.

Financial data Stipends range up to $5,000.

Duration 1 year; nonrenewable.

Additional data This program began in 2006.

Number awarded 30 each year.

Deadline February of each year.

[931]
UCB FAMILY EPILEPSY SCHOLARSHIP PROGRAM

UCB, Inc.
Family Scholarship Program
c/o Hudson Medical Communications
200 White Plains Road, Second Floor
Tarrytown, NY 10591
Toll Free: (866) 825-1920
E-mail: UCBScholarship@hudsongloballlc.com
Web: www.ucbepilepsyscholarship.com

Summary To provide financial assistance for college or graduate school to epilepsy patients and their family members and caregivers.

Eligibility This program is open to epilepsy patients and their family members and caregivers. Applicants must be working on or planning to work on an undergraduate or graduate degree at an institution of higher education in the United States. They must be able to demonstrate academic achievement, a record of participation in activities outside of school, and service as a role model. Along with their application, they must submit a 1-page essay explaining why they should be selected for the scholarship, how epilepsy has impacted their life either as a patient or as a family member or caregiver, and how they will benefit from the scholarship. U.S. citizenship or permanent resident status is required.

Financial data The stipend is $5,000.

Duration 1 year; nonrenewable.

Additional data This program, previously known as the Keppra Family Epilepsy Scholarship Program, was established in 2004.

Number awarded 30 each year.

Deadline April of each year.

[932]
UTAH HEMOPHILIA FOUNDATION SCHOLARSHIPS

Utah Hemophilia Foundation
772 East 3300 South, Suite 210
Salt Lake City, UT 84106
(801) 484-0325   Toll Free: (877) INFO-VWD
Fax: (801) 746-2488
E-mail: western@hemophiliautah.org
Web: www.hemophiliautah.org

Summary To provide financial assistance for attendance at a college in any state to residents of Utah who have a bleeding disorder and their families.

Eligibility This program is open to people in Utah with bleeding disorders and to their spouses, children, and parents. Applicants must be members of the bleeding disorders community served by the Utah Hemophilia Foundation and/or the Intermountain Hemophilia and Thrombosis

Center in Salt Lake City. They must be attending or planning to attend a college, university, trade school, or technical program in any state. Along with their application, they must submit essays on 1) where they see themselves in 10 years and how their education will impact their future dealings with a bleeding disorder; and 2) a quality they possess that allows them to advance the interests of Utah's bleeding disorders community.

Financial data Stipends range from $100 to $1,500.

Duration 1 year.

Additional data This program includes the Robert Price Memorial Scholarship.

Number awarded Varies each year.

Deadline May of each year.

[933]
VARUN BHASKARAN WAS SCHOLARSHIP PROGRAM

Immune Deficiency Foundation
Attn: Scholarship Programs
40 West Chesapeake Avenue, Suite 308
Towson, MD 21204-4803
(410) 321-6647   Toll Free: (800) 296-4433
Fax: (410) 321-9165   E-mail: idf@primaryimmune.org
Web: primaryimmune.org

Summary To provide financial assistance to undergraduate and graduate students who are living with Wiskott-Aldrich Syndrome (WAS).

Eligibility This program is open to students entering or attending college or graduate school who are living with WAS. Applicants must submit an autobiographical essay, 2 letters of recommendation, a family financial statement, and a letter of verification from their immunologist. Financial need is the main factor considered in selecting the recipients and the size of the award.

Financial data Stipends range from $750 to $2,000, depending on the recipient's financial need.

Duration 1 year; may be renewed.

Additional data This program was established in 2011.

Number awarded Varies each year.

Deadline March of each year.

[934]
VERA YIP MEMORIAL SCHOLARSHIP

Ulman Cancer Fund for Young Adults
Attn: Scholarship Committee
10440 Little Patuxent Parkway, Suite G1
Columbia, MD 21044
(410) 964-0202   Toll Free: (888) 393-FUND
Fax: (410) 964-0402
E-mail: scholarship@ulmanfund.org
Web: www.ulmanfund.org/scholarship.aspx

Summary To provide money for college or graduate school to students who have cancer or have lost a parent with cancer.

Eligibility This program is open to students who have or have lost a parent or guardian to cancer. Applicants must be 35 years of age or younger and attending, or planning to attend, a 2- or 4-year college, university, or

vocational program to work on an undergraduate or graduate degree. The parent or guardian must have been first diagnosed with cancer after the applicant was 15 years of age. Along with their application, they must submit an essay of at least 1,000 words on how their parent's cancer experience has impacted their outlook on life and the legacy that they desire to leave behind. This award is presented to the applicant who best demonstrates the qualities of Vera Yip of courage, determination, motivation, and dedication.

Financial data The stipend is $2,500. Funds are paid directly to the educational institution.

Duration 1 year; nonrenewable.

Additional data Recipients must agree to complete 40 hours of community service.

Number awarded 1 each year.

Deadline March of each year.

[935]
VICTORY FOR WOMEN ACADEMIC SCHOLARSHIP FOR WOMEN WITH BLEEDING DISORDERS

National Hemophilia Foundation
Attn: Manager of Education
P.O. Box 971483
Ypsilanti, MI 48197
(734) 890-2504   E-mail: pflax@hemophilia.org
Web: www.hemophilia.org

Summary To provide financial assistance for college or graduate school to women who have a bleeding disorder.

Eligibility This program is open to women who are entering or already enrolled in an undergraduate or graduate program at a university, college, or accredited vocational school. Applicants must have von Willebrand Disease, hemophilia or other clotting factor deficiency, or carrier status. Along with their application, they must submit a 250-word essay that describes how their education and future career plans will benefit others in the bleeding disorders community. Selection is based on that essay, achievements, and community service to the bleeding disorders community.

Financial data The stipend is $2,500.

Duration 1 year.

Additional data The program, known also as V4W, was established in 2005 as the Project Red Flag Academic Scholarship for Women with Bleeding Disorders.

Number awarded 2 each year.

Deadline May of each year.

[936]
VINCENT STEFANO SCHOLARSHIP AWARD

Kidney & Urology Foundation of America
Attn: Program Director
2 West 47th Street, Suite 401
New York, NY 10036
(212) 629-9770   Toll Free: (800) 633-6628
Fax: (212) 629-5652   E-mail: info@kidneyurology.org
Web: www.kidneyurology.org

Summary To provide financial assistance for college to patients who have been diagnosed with kidney disease.
Eligibility This program is open to young adults between 17 and 25 years of age who are attending or planning to attend college. Applicants must have been diagnosed with kidney disease. Along with their application, they must submit an essay of 1 to 2 pages on how kidney disease has impacted their life; their educational background, extracurricular activities, hobbies, and personal interests; their educational goals and how this scholarship will help them to achieve those goals; their contributions to the renal or transplant community; any extenuating circumstances involving them or their family; and why they should receive this scholarship. Selection is based on achievements, educational commitment, and financial need. Priority is given to applicants from the sponsoring organization's participating partner centers.
Financial data The stipend is $2,000 per year. Funds are paid directly to the recipient's institution.
Duration 1 year; renewable up to 3 more years.
Additional data This program was established in 2011.
Number awarded 1 or more each year.
Deadline May of each year.

[937]
WILLIAM L. RITCHIE LEARNING THROUGH LISTENING AWARD

Learning Ally
Attn: Training and Support Center
20 Roszel Road
Princeton, NJ 08540
(609) 243-7087   Toll Free: (800) 221-4792
Fax: (609) 987-8116
E-mail: mGreenwald@LearningAlly.org
Web: www.learningally.org/awards

Summary To recognize and reward high school students who live in the Washington, D.C. metropolitan area and have a learning disability or visual impairment.
Eligibility This award is available to students currently enrolled in a public, private, or parochial high school (or home school) in Washington, D.C.; the Virginia counties of Arlington, Fairfax, Fauquier, Loudoun, or Prince William; the Virginia cities of Alexandria or Fairfax; or the Maryland counties of Anne Arundel, Frederick, Howard, Montgomery, or Prince Georges. Applicants must 1) have a learning disability or visual impairment; and 2) have been registered members of Learning Ally for at least 1 year. The award is presented to the student who, "through persistence and determination, has overcome obstacles to accomplish his or her goals."
Financial data The award is $1,000.
Duration The award is presented annually.
Additional data Learning Ally was formerly named Recording for the Blind and Dyslexic.
Number awarded 1 each year.
Deadline March of each year.

[938]
YOUNG HEROES SCHOLARSHIPS

Wipe Out Kids' Cancer
Attn: Young Heroes Scholarships
1349 Empire Central, Suite 240
Dallas, TX 75247
(214) 987-4662   Fax: (214) 987-4668
E-mail: ecostolo@wokc.org
Web: www.wokc.org

Summary To provide financial assistance for college to pediatric cancer survivors.
Eligibility This program is open to pediatric cancer survivors who are enrolled or planning to enroll at a college or university. Applicants must submit a 500-word essay on how their personal journey with cancer has prepared them for college. Selection is based on the content, originality, and overall impression of the essay (80%), and school and community recommendations (20%).
Financial data The stipend is $1,000. Winners also receive a laptop and printer.
Duration 1 year.
Additional data This program was established in 2006 by Michael Young, a baseball player for the Texas Rangers, and his wife, Christina Barbosa-Young. Support is provided by the Texas Rangers Foundation.
Number awarded 10 each year.
Deadline February of each year.

[939]
YOUTH OPPORTUNITY SCHOLARSHIPS

Delaware Community Foundation
Attn: Executive Vice President
100 West Tenth Street, Suite 115
P.O. Box 1636
Wilmington, DE 19899
(302) 571-8004   Fax: (302) 571-1553
E-mail: rgentsch@delcf.org
Web: www.delcf.org/scholarships_guidelines.html

Summary To provide financial assistance to Delaware residents who have experienced a chronic illness and are interested in attending college in any state.
Eligibility This program is open to students and former students of Delaware schools who have experienced a chronic illness, lasting 6 months or longer, that has impaired their ability to pursue their education. Applicants must be interested in pursuing academic or vocational education at an institution in any state. Priority is given to students of the First State School and any of its branches. Preference may be given to students with the greatest financial need.
Financial data The program provides tuition assistance at academic or vocational qualified institutions of higher education in Delaware or other states.
Duration 1 year; recipients may reapply.
Number awarded 1 or more each year.
Deadline March of each year.

Fellowships

[940]
BONNIE STRANGIO EDUCATION SCHOLARSHIP

Boomer Esiason Foundation
c/o Jerry Cahill
483 Tenth Avenue, Suite 300
New York, NY 10018
(646) 292-7930   Fax: (646) 292-7945
E-mail: jcahill@esiason.org
Web: esiason.org/thriving-with-cf/scholarships.php

Summary To provide financial assistance to undergraduate and graduate students who have cystic fibrosis (CF) and a demonstrated commitment to the prevention and cure of the disease.

Eligibility This program is open to CF patients who are working on an undergraduate or graduate degree. Applicants must be able to demonstrate exemplary service and commitment to the prevention and cure of CF. Along with their application, they must submit a letter from their doctor confirming the diagnosis of CF and a list of daily medications, information on financial need, a detailed breakdown of tuition costs from their academic institution, transcripts, and a 2-page essay on 1) their post-graduation goals; and 2) the importance of compliance with CF therapies and what they practice on a daily basis to stay healthy. Selection is based on academic ability, character, leadership potential, service to the community, and financial need. Finalists are interviewed by telephone.

Financial data The stipend ranges from $500 to $1,000. Funds are paid directly to the academic institution to assist in covering the cost of tuition and fees.

Duration 1 year; nonrenewable.

Additional data This program was established in 2005.

Number awarded 1 each year.

Deadline June of each year.

[941]
BOOMER ESIASON FOUNDATION GENERAL ACADEMIC SCHOLARSHIPS

Boomer Esiason Foundation
c/o Jerry Cahill
483 Tenth Avenue, Suite 300
New York, NY 10018
(646) 292-7930   Fax: (646) 292-7945
E-mail: jcahill@esiason.org
Web: esiason.org/thriving-with-cf/scholarships.php

Summary To provide financial assistance to undergraduate and graduate students who have cystic fibrosis (CF).

Eligibility This program is open to CF patients who are working on an undergraduate or graduate degree. Applicants must submit a letter from their doctor confirming the diagnosis of CF and a list of daily medications, information on financial need, a detailed breakdown of tuition costs from their academic institution, transcripts, and a 2-page

essay on 1) their post-graduation goals; and 2) the importance of compliance with CF therapies and what they practice on a daily basis to stay healthy. Selection is based on academic ability, character, leadership potential, service to the community, and financial need. Finalists are interviewed by telephone.

Financial data Stipends range from $500 to $2,500. Funds are paid directly to the academic institution to assist in covering the cost of tuition and fees.

Duration 1 year; nonrenewable.

Additional data Recipients must be willing to participate in the sponsor's CF Ambassador Program by speaking once a year at a designated CF event to help educate the general public about CF.

Number awarded 10 to 15 each year.

Deadline March, June, September, or December of each year.

[942]
BRYON RIESCH SCHOLARSHIPS

Bryon Riesch Paralysis Foundation
P.O. Box 1388
Waukesha, WI 53187-1388
(262) 547-2083   E-mail: briesch@brpf.org
Web: www.brpf.org/Grants/ApplicationScholarships.html

Summary To provide financial assistance to undergraduate and graduate students who have a neurological disability or the children of people with such a disability.

Eligibility This program is open to students entering or enrolled at a 2- or 4-year college or university as an undergraduate or graduate student. Applicants must have a neurological disability or be the child of a person with such a disability. They must have a GPA of 2.5 or higher in high school or college. Along with their application, they must submit a 200-word essay on why they deserve the scholarship, a statement of their 5- and 10-year goals, and a list of work experience. Financial need is not considered.

Financial data Stipends range from $1,000 to $2,000.

Duration 1 year; may be renewed.

Number awarded Varies each semester; recently, 5 scholarships (all at $1,000) were awarded for the fall semester and 3 (including 1 at $2,000 and 2 at $1,000) were awarded for the spring semester.

Deadline May of each year for fall semester; December of each year for spring semester.

[943]
CANCER FOR COLLEGE SCHOLARSHIPS

Cancer for College
1345 Specialty Drive, Suite D
Vista, CA 92081
(760) 599-5096   E-mail: info@cancerforcollege.org
Web: www.cancerforcollege.org

Summary To provide funding to college and graduate students who are cancer patients, survivors, or amputees.

Eligibility This program is open to undergraduate and graduate students enrolled or planning to enroll at accredited colleges, universities, community colleges, and trade schools in the United States and Puerto Rico. Applicants must be a cancer patient, cancer survivor, and/or ampu-tee. Along with a preliminary application, they must submit a brief statement on why they should receive further con-sideration for this scholarship and information on their financial situation. Preference is given to residents of Cali-fornia and students attending college in southern Califor-nia.

Financial data Stipends are $4,000, $1,000, or $500.

Duration 1 year; some of the $4,000 scholarships (des-ignated as Perpetual Scholarships) may be renewed up to 3 additional years.

Additional data This program was established in 1993. Perpetual Scholarship recipients must be willing to attend regional events associated with the program and be avail-able for interviews and/or media coverage.

Number awarded Varies each year; recently, this pro-gram awarded 4 Perpetual Scholarships at $4,000 per year, 3 1-time scholarships at $4,000, 25 1-time scholar-ships at $1,000, and 6 1-time scholarships at $500.

Deadline Deadline not specified.

[944]
CFCAREFORWARD SCHOLARSHIPS

Abbott Laboratories
c/o Ruder Finn
Attn: CFCareForward Scholarship Program
301 East 57th Street
New York, NY 10022
Web: www.cfcareforwardscholarship.com

Summary To provide financial assistance for college or graduate school to students with cystic fibrosis (CF).

Eligibility This program is open to high school seniors, vocational school students, college students, and gradu-ate students with CF. U.S. citizenship is required. Appli-cants must submit 1) a creative presentation (e.g., written work, a piece of art, a craft, collage, photograph) on what sets them apart from their peers, what inspires them to live life to the fullest, or anything else that they think makes them unique; 2) a photograph; and 3) a 250-word essay on the topic, "My dream for the future is..." Selection is based on academic excellence, creativity, community involvement, and ability to serve as a role model to others with CF. Information on all winners is posted on the spon-sor's web site to allow the public to select a Thriving Undergraduate Student and a Thriving Graduate Student.

Financial data The stipend is $2,500. The Thriving Students receive an additional award (recently, $16,500 for a total award of $19,000 to honor the program's 19th year).

Duration 1 year.

Additional data This program started in 1992 and was previously sponsored by Solvay Pharmaceuticals, Inc. with the name SolvayCARES Scholarships. Winners also receive a 1-year supply of nutritional drinks and vitamins. The essay, creative presentations, and photograph of all recipients who agree to be considered are posted online so patients, families, friends, physicians, the CF commu-nity, and the general public can vote to select the Thriving Students.

Number awarded 40 each year, of whom 1 is desig-nated the Thriving Undergraduate Student and 1 the Thriving Graduate Student.

Deadline May of each year.

[945]
COOLEY'S ANEMIA FOUNDATION PATIENT INCENTIVE AWARDS

Cooley's Anemia Foundation, Inc.
Attn: National Executive Director
330 Seventh Avenue, Suite 900
New York, NY 10001
(212) 279-8090   Toll Free: (800) 522-7222
Fax: (212) 279-5999 E-mail: info@cooleysanemia.org
Web: www.thalassemia.org

Summary To provide financial assistance to undergrad-uate and graduate students who have Cooley's anemia (thalassemia).

Eligibility This program is open to U.S. residents who have thalassemia intermediate or major. Applicants must be attending or planning to attend a vocational, under-graduate, or graduate school.

Financial data Stipends depend on the academic level of the recipient, ranging from $250 for students in certifi-cate programs to $2,000 for graduate students.

Duration 1 year.

Number awarded Varies each year; recently, 25 of these scholarships (worth $29,500) were awarded.

Deadline December of each year.

[946]
DICK GRIFFITHS MEMORIAL SCHOLARSHIP

California Association for Postsecondary Education
   and Disability
Attn: Executive Assistant
71423 Biskra Road
Rancho Mirage, CA 92270
(760) 346-8206   Fax: (760) 340-5275
TDD: (760) 341-4084   E-mail: caped2000@aol.com
Web: www.caped.net/scholarships.html

Summary To provide financial assistance to undergrad-uate and graduate students in California who have a learning disability, especially involving mathematics.

Eligibility This program is open to students at public and private colleges and universities in California who have a learning disability and are especially challenged in mathematics. Undergraduates must have completed at least 6 semester credits and have a GPA of 2.5 or higher. Graduate students must have completed at least 3 semes-ter units and have a GPA of 3.0 or higher. Along with their application, they must submit a 1-page personal letter that demonstrates their writing skills, progress towards meet-ing their educational and vocational goals, management of their disability, and involvement in community activities. They must also submit a letter of recommendation from a faculty member, verification of disability, official tran-scripts, proof of current enrollment, an essay on strategies they use to overcome their mathematics challenges, and documentation of financial need.

Financial data   The stipend is $1,000.
Duration   1 year.
Number awarded   1 each year.
Deadline   September of each year.

[947]
ELIZABETH NASH FOUNDATION SCHOLARSHIP PROGRAM

Elizabeth Nash Foundation
P.O. Box 1260
Los Gatos, CA 95031-1260
E-mail: scholarships@elizabethnashfoundation.org
Web: www.elizabethnashfoundation.org

Summary   To provide financial assistance for college or graduate school to individuals with cystic fibrosis (CF).

Eligibility   This program is open to undergraduate and graduate students who have CF. Applicants must be able to demonstrate clear academic goals and a commitment to participate in activities outside the classroom. U.S. citizenship is required. Selection is based on academic record, character, demonstrated leadership, service to CF-related causes and the broader community, and financial need.

Financial data   Stipends range from $1,000 to $2,500. Funds are paid directly to the academic institution to be applied to tuition and fees.

Duration   1 year; recipients may reapply.

Additional data   This program began in 2005. Recipients must speak at a local event or write an article for publication by the foundation.

Number awarded   Varies each year; recently, 17 of these scholarships were awarded. Since the program was established, it has awarded 78 scholarships.

Deadline   April of each year.

[948]
ERIC DELSON MEMORIAL SCHOLARSHIP

CVS Caremark
c/o Scholarship America
Scholarship Management Services
One Scholarship Way
P.O. Box 297
St. Peter, MN 56082
(507) 931-1682
Web: cvscaremarkspecialtyrx.com

Summary   To provide financial assistance for high school, college, or graduate school to students with a bleeding disorder.

Eligibility   This program is open to students diagnosed with a bleeding disorder who are 1) high school seniors, high school graduates or equivalent (GED), college students, or graduate students currently enrolled or planning to enroll full time at an accredited 2- or 4-year college, university, or vocational/technical school; or 2) students entering grades 7-12 at a private secondary school in the United States. Selection is based on academic record, demonstrated leadership and participation in school and community activities, work experience, a statement of

educational and career goals, unusual personal or family circumstances, and an outside appraisal.

Financial data   The stipend is $2,500 for college students or $1,500 for high school students. Funds are paid in 2 equal installments directly to the recipient.

Duration   1 year; may be renewed for up to 3 additional years, provided the recipient maintains a GPA of 2.5 or higher for the freshman year and 3.0 or higher for subsequent years.

Number awarded   4 each year: 3 for college students and 1 for a high school student.

Deadline   June of each year.

[949]
GEORGE AND LINDA PRICE SCHOLARSHIP

Hemophilia Association of the Capital Area
10560 Main Street, Suite 419
Fairfax, VA 22030-7182
(703) 352-7641   Fax: (540) 427-6589
E-mail: admin@hacacares.org
Web: www.hacacares.org

Summary   To provide financial assistance to individuals with bleeding disorders and their families who are members of the Hemophilia Association of the Capital Area (HACA) and interested in attending college or graduate school in any state.

Eligibility   This program is open to residents of northern Virginia, Montgomery and Prince George's County in Maryland, and Washington, D.C. who have a bleeding disorder and their siblings and parents. Applicants must be members of HACA. They must be 1) high school seniors or graduates who have not yet attended college; 2) full-time freshmen, sophomores, or juniors at a college, university, or vocational/technical school in any state; or 3) college seniors planning to attend graduate school and students already enrolled at a graduate school in any state. Along with their application, they must submit a 500-word essay on what they have done to contribute to the bleeding disorders community and how they plan to contribute to that community in the future. Financial need is not considered.

Financial data   The stipend is $2,500.

Duration   1 year; recipients may reapply.

Number awarded   2 each year.

Deadline   April of each year.

[950]
HEMOPHILIA FEDERATION OF AMERICA ARTISTIC ENCOURAGEMENT GRANTS

Hemophilia Federation of America
Attn: Scholarship Committee
210 Seventh Street, S.E., Suite 200B
Washington, DC 20003
(202) 675-6984   Toll Free: (800) 230-9797
Fax: (202) 675-6983   E-mail: info@hemophiliafed.org
Web: hemophiliafed.org

Summary   To provide funding to artists who have a blood clotting disorder and are interested in a creative endeavor.

Eligibility This program is open to artists who have a blood clotting disorder. Applicants must be interested in engaging in a creative endeavor, such as mounting an exhibit of their work (e.g., photography, painting, watercolor, animation), publishing a story or book, writing a play, or having a recital. Along with their application, they must submit 1) an explanation of the proposed project including a timeframe for the completion of the project, what they expect to get out of it, and how it will help them in their future artistic pursuits; 2) letters of reference; 3) a portfolio or sample of their work; and 4) documentation of financial need.

Financial data The grant is $1,500.

Duration 1 year.

Number awarded 2 each year.

Deadline April of each year.

[951]
HEMOPHILIA HEALTH SERVICES MEMORIAL SCHOLARSHIPS

Accredo's Hemophilia Health Services
Attn: Scholarship Committee
201 Great Circle Road
Nashville, TN 37228
(615) 850-5210　　　　　Toll Free: (800) 800-6606
Fax: (615) 261-6730
E-mail: lisa.dabrowiak@accredo.com
Web: www.hemophiliahealth.com/Scholarships.html

Summary To provide money for college or graduate school to people who have hemophilia or other bleeding disorders.

Eligibility This program is open to individuals with hemophilia (factor VIII or IX), von Willebrand Disease (type 1, 2, 2A, 2B, 2M, 2N, or 3), factor I (fibrinogen), factor II (prothrombin), factor V (proaccelerin), factor VII (proconvertin), factor X, factor XI, factor XIII, or Glanzmann's thrombasthenia. Applicants must be 1) high school seniors; 2) college freshmen, sophomores, or juniors; or 3) college seniors planning to attend graduate school or students already enrolled in graduate school. Applicants must be enrolled or planning to enroll full time at an accredited nonprofit college, university, or vocational/technical school in the United States or Puerto Rico. Along with their application, they must submit an essay, up to 250 words, on the following topic: "What has been your own personal challenge in living with a bleeding disorder?" U.S. citizenship is required. Selection is based on the essay, academic record, community involvement, and financial need.

Financial data The stipend is at least $1,500. Funds are issued payable to the recipient's school.

Duration 1 year; recipients may reapply.

Additional data This program, which started in 1995, includes programs named after former employees of the sponsoring organization. Past scholarships have been named the Cindy Beck Scholarship, the Becky Cohn Scholarship, the Osborne DeWitt Scholarship, the Tim Haas Scholarship, the Ricky Hobson Scholarship, the Michael Moses Scholarship, the Jim Stineback Scholar-

ship, and the Scott Tarbell Scholarship. It is administered by International Scholarship and Tuition Services, Inc.

Number awarded Several each year.

Deadline April of each year.

[952]
HIGH PLAINS CANCER SURVIVOR SCHOLARSHIPS

American Cancer Society-High Plains Division
2433 Ridgepoint Drive, Suite B
Austin, TX 78754
(512) 919-1910　　　　　Toll Free: (877) 227-1618
Fax: (512) 919-1846 E-mail: Phyllis.Caron@cancer.org
Web: www.cancer.org

Summary To provide money for college or graduate school to cancer patients and survivors in Guam, Hawaii, Kansas, Missouri, Nebraska, Oklahoma, and Texas.

Eligibility This program is open to residents of Guam, Hawaii, Kansas, Missouri, Nebraska, Oklahoma, and Texas who have had a cancer diagnosis before age 21. Applicants must be accepted at or attending an accredited university, graduate school, community college, or vocational/technical school in any state. They must be 25 years of age or younger at the time of applying and have a GPA of 2.0 or higher. Along with their application, they must submit 2 recommendations (including 1 from a physician verifying diagnosis), an acceptance letter from an academic institution, documentation of financial need, academic transcripts, and a 2-page essay describing their life experiences, future goals, community involvement, and cancer-related involvement.

Financial data The stipend is $1,000 per year. Funds are paid directly to the academic institution.

Duration 1 year; may be renewed.

Number awarded Varies each year; recently, 100 of these scholarships were awarded.

Deadline March of each year.

[953]
JOHN BULLER SCHOLARSHIP

Greater Houston Community Foundation
Attn: Scholarship Coordinator
5120 Woodway Drive, Suite 6000
Houston, TX 77056
(713) 333-2205　　　　　Fax: (713) 333-2220
E-mail: lgardner@ghcf.org
Web: www.ghcf.org

Summary To provide financial assistance to residents of Texas who have cystic fibrosis and are interested in attending college or graduate school in the state.

Eligibility This program is open to Texas residents who have cystic fibrosis. Applicants must be enrolled or planning to enroll as an undergraduate or graduate student at an accredited 2- or 4-year college or university in Texas. Along with their application, they must submit transcripts and information on their extracurricular activities, work experience, community service, and other activities. Financial need is considered in the selection process. U.S. citizenship is required.

Financial data The stipend is $1,000 per year.
Duration 1 year; renewable up to 3 more years.
Additional data This program was established in 1997.
Number awarded 1 or more each year.
Deadline March of each year.

[954]
LILLY REINTEGRATION SCHOLARSHIPS

The Center for Reintegration, Inc.
Attn: Lilly Secretariat
310 Busse Highway
PMB 327
Park Ridge, IL 60068-3251
Toll Free: (800) 809-8202
E-mail: lillyscholarships@reintegration.com
Web: www.reintegration.com

Summary To provide financial assistance to undergraduate and graduate students diagnosed with schizophrenia.

Eligibility This program is open to U.S. citizens diagnosed with bipolar disorder, schizophrenia, schizophreniform disorder, or schizoaffective disorder. Applicants must be receiving medical treatment for the disease and be actively involved in rehabilitative or reintegrative efforts. They must be interested in pursuing postsecondary education, including trade or vocational school programs, high school equivalency programs, associate degrees, bachelor's degrees, and graduate programs. Along with their application, they must submit an essay on their career goal and their rationale for choosing that goal, how this course of study will help them achieve their career goal, obstacles they have faced in life and how they have overcome them, steps they have taken to prepare for pursuit of this education, rationale for the specific school chosen, and their plans to continue treatment while pursuing an education. Selection is based on the quality of the essay, academic success, 3 references, thoughtfulness and appropriateness of academic and vocational/career goals, rehabilitation involvement, success in dealing with the disease, recent volunteer and/or vocational experience, and completion of application requirements.

Financial data The amount awarded varies, depending upon the specific needs of the recipient. Funds may be used to pay for tuition and related expenses, such as textbooks and laboratory fees.
Duration 1 year; may be renewed.
Additional data This program, established in 1998, is funded by Eli Lilly and Company.
Number awarded Varies each year; generally, 70 to 120 of these scholarships (including renewals) are awarded annually.
Deadline January of each year.

[955]
LISA HIGGINS-HUSSMAN FOUNDATION SCHOLARSHIP

Ulman Cancer Fund for Young Adults
Attn: Scholarship Committee
10440 Little Patuxent Parkway, Suite G1
Columbia, MD 21044
(410) 964-0202   Toll Free: (888) 393-FUND
Fax: (410) 964-0402
E-mail: scholarship@ulmanfund.org
Web: www.ulmanfund.org/scholarship.aspx

Summary To provide financial assistance for college or graduate school to students from Washington, D.C., Maryland, or Virginia who have been diagnosed with cancer or have or have lost a family member with cancer.

Eligibility This program is open to students who 1) have been diagnosed with cancer; 2) have a parent, sibling, or guardian living with cancer; or 3) have lost a parent, sibling, or guardian to cancer. Applicants must be residents of Washington, D.C., Maryland, or Virginia or attending college there. They must be 35 years of age or younger and attending, or planning to attend, a 2- or 4-year college, university, or vocational program to work on an undergraduate or graduate degree. The first diagnosis of cancer (whether of the applicant, a parent, a sibling, or a guardian) must have occurred after the applicant was 15 years of age. Along with their application, they must submit an essay of at least 1,000 words on how the cancer experience has impacted their outlook on life and the legacy that they desire to leave behind. Selection is based on demonstrated dedication to community service, commitment to educational and professional goals, use of their cancer experience to impact the lives of other young adults affected by cancer, medical hardship, and financial need.

Financial data The stipend is $2,500. Funds are paid directly to the educational institution.
Duration 1 year.
Additional data Recipients must agree to complete 40 hours of community service.
Number awarded 1 each year.
Deadline March of each year.

[956]
LIVING BREATH FOUNDATION SCHOLARSHIPS

Living Breath Foundation
2031 Marsala Circle
Monterey, CA 93940
(831) 392-5285
E-mail: LivingBreathFoundation@gmail.com
Web: thelivingbreathfoundation.com/aid.html

Summary To provide financial assistance to individuals who have cystic fibrosis and are interested in attending college or graduate school.

Eligibility This program is open to U.S. citizens who have cystic fibrosis and are graduating high school seniors or undergraduate or graduate students continuing their education at a 2- or 4-year college, university, or trade school in any state. Applicants must submit an essay on how continuing their education will benefit their future. Selection is based on academic record, leadership, community service, and financial need.

Financial data The stipend ranges from $500 to $2,000. Funds are disbursed directly to the student to assist in payment of tuition, books, or the expenses of going to school while having cystic fibrosis (e.g., private rooms, food, rooms with running water, bathrooms, parking).

Duration 1 year.

Additional data This foundation was established in 2008.

Number awarded 1 or more each year.

Deadline February of each year.

[957]
NATIONAL COLLEGIATE CANCER FOUNDATION SCHOLARSHIP

National Collegiate Cancer Foundation
Attn: Scholarship Committee
4858 Battery Lane, Suite 216
Bethesda, MD 20814
(240) 515-6262   E-mail: info@collegiatecancer.org
Web: www.collegiatecancer.org/scholarships.html

Summary To provide financial assistance for college or graduate school to cancer survivors.

Eligibility This program is open to students between 18 and 35 who are cancer survivors or currently undergoing treatment for cancer. Applicants must be enrolled or planning to enroll at a college or university to work on a certificate or an associate, bachelor's, master's, or doctoral degree. Along with their application, they must submit a 1,000-word essay on their experiences with cancer and college. Selection is based on the essay, recommendations, displaying a "Will Win" attitude, overall story of cancer survivorship, commitment to education, and financial need.

Financial data The stipend is $1,000.

Duration 1 year.

Number awarded 1 or more each year.

Deadline May of each year.

[958]
OUTSTANDING INDIVIDUAL WITH AUTISM OF THE YEAR AWARD

Autism Society of America
Attn: Awards and Scholarships
4340 East-West Highway, Suite 350
Bethesda, MD 20814-4579
(301) 657-0881   Toll Free: (800) 3-AUTISM
Fax: (301) 657-0869   E-mail: info@autism-society.org
Web: www.autism-society.org

Summary To recognize and reward people with autism who have excelled in an area of human activity.

Eligibility This award is presented for a demonstration of exceptional dedication or effort on the part of an individual with autism who has excelled in 1 or more areas of life experiences or contributions. Achievement may include,

but is not limited to, academics, the arts, athletics, community service, employment, extracurricular activities, transitions, or independent living skills.

Financial data The awardee receives complimentary registration to the annual conference, a special commemorative plaque, and a cash award of $1,000.

Duration The award is presented annually.

Number awarded 1 each year.

Deadline March of each year.

[959]
PACIFIC NORTHWEST SCHOLARSHIPS

Cancer for College
1345 Specialty Drive, Suite D
Vista, CA 92081
(760) 599-5096   E-mail: info@cancerforcollege.org
Web: www.cancerforcollege.org

Summary To provide financial assistance to undergraduate and graduate students from the Pacific Northwest who are cancer patients, survivors, or amputees.

Eligibility This program is open to undergraduate and graduate students who are originally from or current attending accredited colleges, universities, community colleges, and trade schools in Idaho, Montana, Oregon, or Washington. Applicants must be a cancer patient, cancer survivor, and/or amputee. Along with a preliminary application, they must submit a brief statement on why they should receive further consideration for this scholarship and information on their financial situation.

Financial data Stipends are $3,000, $2,000, $1,000, or $500.

Duration 1 year.

Number awarded Varies each year; recently, 14 of these scholarships were awarded: 3 at $3,000, 2 at $2,000, 6 at $1,000, and 3 at $500.

Deadline Deadline not specified.

[960]
PATIENT ADVOCATE FOUNDATION SCHOLARSHIPS FOR SURVIVORS

Patient Advocate Foundation
Attn: Scholarship Coordinator
421 Butler Farm Road
Hampton, VA 23669
Toll Free: (800) 532-5274   Fax: (757) 873-8999
E-mail: help@patientadvocate.org
Web: www.patientadvocate.org/events.php?p=69

Summary To provide financial assistance for college or graduate school to students seeking to initiate or complete a course of study that has been interrupted or delayed by a diagnosis of cancer or other life threatening disease.

Eligibility This program is open to students under 25 years of age who are working full time on a 2-year, 4-year, or advanced degree. The college or graduate education of applicants must have been interrupted or delayed by a diagnosis of cancer or other chronic or life threatening disease within the past 5 years. They must be willing to commit to completing 20 hours of community service for the year if they are awarded a scholarship. Along with their application, they must submit a 1,000-word essay on how their diagnosis has impacted their life and future goals. Financial need is also considered in the selection process.

Financial data The stipend is $3,000. Funds are paid directly to the college or university to help cover tuition and other fee costs. The cost of books is not included.

Duration 1 year; may be renewed up to 3 additional years, provided the recipient remains enrolled full time, maintains a GPA of 3.0 or higher, and performs 20 hours of community service.

Number awarded Varies each year; recently, 12 of these scholarships were awarded.

Deadline March of each year.

[961] PERLITA LIWANAG MEMORIAL SCHOLARSHIP

Ulman Cancer Fund for Young Adults
Attn: Scholarship Committee
10440 Little Patuxent Parkway, Suite G1
Columbia, MD 21044
(410) 964-0202   Toll Free: (888) 393-FUND
Fax: (410) 964-0402
E-mail: scholarship@ulmanfund.org
Web: www.ulmanfund.org/scholarship.aspx

Summary To provide financial assistance for college or graduate school to students from Washington, D.C., Maryland, or Virginia who have been diagnosed with cancer or have or have lost a family member with cancer.

Eligibility This program is open to students who 1) have been diagnosed with cancer; 2) have a parent, sibling, or guardian living with cancer; or 3) have lost a parent, sibling, or guardian to cancer. Applicants must be residents of Washington, D.C., Maryland, or Virginia or attending college there. They must be 35 years of age or younger and attending, or planning to attend, a 2- or 4-year college, university, or vocational program to work on an undergraduate or graduate degree. The first diagnosis of cancer (whether of the applicant, a parent, a sibling, or a guardian) must have occurred after the applicant was 15 years of age. Along with their application, they must submit an essay of at least 1,000 words on how the cancer experience has impacted their outlook on life and the legacy that they desire to leave behind. Selection is based on demonstrated dedication to community service, commitment to educational and professional goals, use of their cancer experience to impact the lives of other young adults affected by cancer, medical hardship, and financial need.

Financial data The stipend is $2,500. Funds are paid directly to the educational institution.

Duration 1 year.

Additional data These scholarships were first awarded in 2011. Recipients must agree to complete 40 hours of community service.

Number awarded 1 each year.

Deadline March of each year.

[962] RIMINGTON TROPHY SCHOLARSHIP

Boomer Esiason Foundation
c/o Jerry Cahill
483 Tenth Avenue, Suite 300
New York, NY 10018
(646) 292-7930   Fax: (646) 292-7945
E-mail: jcahill@esiason.org
Web: esiason.org/thriving-with-cf/scholarships.php

Summary To provide financial assistance to undergraduate and graduate students who have cystic fibrosis (CF).

Eligibility This program is open to CF patients who are working on an undergraduate or graduate degree. Applicants must submit a letter from their doctor confirming the diagnosis of CF and a list of daily medications, information on financial need, a detailed breakdown of tuition costs from their academic institution, transcripts, and a 2-page essay on 1) their post-graduation goals; and 2) the importance of compliance with CF therapies and what they practice to stay healthy. Selection is based on academic ability, character, leadership potential, community service, financial need, and daily compliance to CF therapy.

Financial data The stipend ranges from $100 to $2,000. Funds are paid directly to the academic institution to assist in covering the cost of tuition and fees.

Duration 1 year; nonrenewable.

Additional data This program was established in 2012 in association with the Rimington Trophy, a college football award named in honor of Dave Rimington, a former player for the University of Nebraska and the president of the Boomer Esiason Foundation.

Number awarded 1 each year.

Deadline June of each year.

[963] ROSEMARY QUIGLEY MEMORIAL SCHOLARSHIP

Boomer Esiason Foundation
c/o Jerry Cahill
483 Tenth Avenue, Suite 300
New York, NY 10018
(646) 292-7930   Fax: (646) 292-7945
E-mail: jcahill@esiason.org
Web: esiason.org/thriving-with-cf/scholarships.php

Summary To provide financial assistance to undergraduate and graduate students who have cystic fibrosis (CF) and a demonstrated commitment to living life to the fullest.

Eligibility This program is open to CF patients who are working on an undergraduate or graduate degree. Applicants must be able to demonstrate a clear sense of life goals and a commitment to living life to the fullest, despite having CF. Along with their application, they must submit a letter from their doctor confirming the diagnosis of CF and a list of daily medications, information on financial need, a detailed breakdown of tuition costs from their academic institution, transcripts, and a 2-page essay on 1) their post-graduation goals; and 2) the importance of compliance with CF therapies and what they practice on a daily basis to stay healthy. Selection is based on academic ability, character, leadership potential, service to the community, and financial need. Finalists are interviewed by telephone.

Financial data The stipend ranges from $500 to $2,000. Funds are paid directly to the academic institution to assist in covering the cost of tuition and fees.

Duration 1 year; nonrenewable.

Number awarded 1 each year.

Deadline June of each year.

[964]
SACKS FOR CF SCHOLARSHIPS

Boomer Esiason Foundation
c/o Jerry Cahill
483 Tenth Avenue, Suite 300
New York, NY 10018
(646) 292-7930   Fax: (646) 292-7945
E-mail: jcahill@esiason.org
Web: esiason.org/thriving-with-cf/scholarships.php

Summary To provide financial assistance to undergraduate and graduate students who have cystic fibrosis (CF).

Eligibility This program is open to CF patients who are working on an undergraduate or graduate degree. Applicants must submit a letter from their doctor confirming the diagnosis of CF and a list of daily medications, information on financial need, a detailed breakdown of tuition costs from their academic institution, transcripts, and a 2-page essay on 1) their post-graduation goals; and 2) the importance of compliance with CF therapies and what they practice to stay healthy. Selection is based on academic ability, character, leadership potential, community service, financial need, and adherence to daily CF therapy.

Financial data The stipend ranges from $3,000 to $10,000. Funds are paid directly to the academic institution to assist in covering the cost of tuition and fees.

Duration 1 year; nonrenewable.

Additional data This program is funded by a corporate sponsor which donates $1,000 each time a quarterback is sacked on NFL Monday Night Football games.

Number awarded 30 each year.

Deadline January of each year.

[965]
SAMFUND GRANTS AND SCHOLARSHIPS

The SAMFund for Young Adult Survivors of Cancer
89 South Street, Suite LL02
Boston, MA 02211
(617) 938-3484   Toll Free: (866) 439-9365
Fax: (484) 842-2643   E-mail: grants@thesamfund.org
Web: www.thesamfund.org/pages/grants.html

Summary To provide funding to young adult cancer survivors who need assistance for the transition to post-treatment life.

Eligibility This program is open to cancer survivors between 17 and 35 years of age who are finished with active treatment and are moving forward with their lives. Applicants must demonstrate a need for funding for such purposes as graduate (but not undergraduate) tuition and expenses, car and health insurance premiums, rent, utili-

ties, family-building expenses, gym memberships, transportation costs, or current and residual medical bills. U.S. citizenship or permanent resident status is required.

Financial data Grant amounts vary; recently, they averaged approximately $2,500.

Duration These are 1-time grants.

Additional data This program, which stands for Surviving and Moving Forward, was established in 2003.

Number awarded Varies each year; since the program was established, it has awarded grants with a total value of more than $600,000.

Deadline Deadline not specified.

[966]
SCHOLARSHIP OF THE ARTS

Boomer Esiason Foundation
c/o Jerry Cahill
483 Tenth Avenue, Suite 300
New York, NY 10018
(646) 292-7930   Fax: (646) 292-7945
E-mail: jcahill@esiason.org
Web: esiason.org/thriving-with-cf/scholarships.php

Summary To provide financial assistance to undergraduate and graduate students who have cystic fibrosis (CF) and are working on a degree in the arts.

Eligibility This program is open to CF patients who are working on an undergraduate or graduate degree in the arts. Applicants must submit a sample of their work (video, painting, sketching, sculpture), a letter from their doctor confirming the diagnosis of CF and a list of daily medications, information on financial need, a detailed breakdown of tuition costs from their academic institution, transcripts, and a 2-page essay on 1) their post-graduation goals; and 2) the importance of compliance with CF therapies and what they practice on a daily basis to stay healthy. Selection is based on academic ability, character, leadership potential, service to the community, and financial need.

Financial data Stipends range from $500 to $1,000. Funds are paid directly to the academic institution to assist in covering the cost of tuition and fees.

Duration 1 year; nonrenewable.

Number awarded 1 each year.

Deadline May of each year.

[967]
SCOTT DELGADILLO SCHOLARSHIP

Friends of Scott Foundation
Attn: Scholarship Fund
6977 Navajo Road, Number 168
San Diego, CA 92119
(619) 223-7268   Fax: (619) 223-7002
E-mail: aztec.graphics@yahoo.com
Web: www.friendsofscott.org/scholarship.aspx

Summary To provide financial assistance for college or graduate school to childhood cancer survivors.

Eligibility This program is open to survivors of childhood cancer and to patients currently receiving treatment. Applicants must be attending or planning to attend a technical school, vocational school, junior college, or 4-year college or university as an undergraduate or graduate student. Along with their application, they must submit a 500-word essay on how their experience with cancer has impacted their life. Selection is based on financial need and personal hardship.

Financial data The stipend is $1,000.

Duration 1 year.

Number awarded Varies each year; recently, 4 of these scholarships were awarded.

Deadline April of each year.

[968]
SEAN SILVER MEMORIAL SCHOLARSHIP

Ulman Cancer Fund for Young Adults
Attn: Scholarship Committee
10440 Little Patuxent Parkway, Suite G1
Columbia, MD 21044
(410) 964-0202   Toll Free: (888) 393-FUND
Fax: (410) 964-0402
E-mail: scholarship@ulmanfund.org
Web: www.ulmanfund.org/scholarship.aspx

Summary To provide financial assistance for college or graduate school to young adults who have cancer.

Eligibility This program is open to students who are younger than 30 years of age and currently undergoing active treatment for cancer. Applicants must be attending or planning to attend a 4-year college or university to work on an undergraduate or graduate degree. They must be U.S. citizens or permanent residents. Along with their application, they must submit an essay of at least 1,000 words on what they have discovered about themselves while attending school as a young adult receiving treatment for or living with cancer. Selection is based on demonstrated dedication to community service, commitment to educational and professional goals, use of their cancer experience to impact the lives of other young adults affected by cancer, medical hardship, and financial need.

Financial data The stipend is $2,500. Funds are paid directly to the educational institution.

Duration 1 year.

Additional data This scholarship was first awarded in 2008. Recipients must agree to complete 40 hours of community service.

Number awarded 1 each year.

Deadline March of each year.

[969]
SNOWDROP FOUNDATION SCHOLARSHIPS

Snowdrop Foundation
Attn: Kevin Kline, President
2310 Upland Park Drive
Sugar Land, TX 77479
(713) 232-9052
E-mail: kevin@snowdropfoundation.org
Web: www.snowdropfoundation.org

Summary To provide money for college or graduate school to students who have been diagnosed with cancer.

Eligibility This program is open to students entering or attending college or graduate school. Applicants must

have been diagnosed with cancer. Along with their application, they must submit a 250-word description of themselves; a 250-word description of their family situation; information on financial need; a letter from their attending physician verifying their medical history and current medical situation; and an essay of 500 to 1,000 words on how their experience with cancer has impacted their life values and career goals.

Financial data A stipend is awarded (amount not specified).

Duration 1 year.

Number awarded Varies each year.

Deadline April of each year.

[970]
SOOZIE COURTER SHARING A BRIGHTER TOMORROW HEMOPHILIA SCHOLARSHIP

Pfizer Inc.
Attn: Hemophilia Scholarship Program (QD Healthcare Group)
One Dock Street, Suite 520
Stamford, CT 06902
Toll Free: (888) 999-2349
Web: www.hemophiliavillage.com

Summary To provide financial assistance for college or graduate school in any field to persons with hemophilia.

Eligibility This program is open to persons with hemophilia (A or B) who are high school seniors, have a GED, or are currently attending an accredited college, university, junior college, vocational school, or graduate school. Along with their application, they must submit a 2-page essay on 1 of the following topics: 1) how hemophilia has affected their school life and how they have overcome those challenges; 2) the advice they would give to a child with hemophilia who is beginning school; or 3) the time in history they would travel back to if they could and why. Financial need is not considered in the selection process.

Financial data The stipends are $2,500 for undergraduate students or $4,000 for graduate students.

Duration 1 year.

Additional data This program was established in 1998 and given its current name in 2000.

Number awarded 17 each year: 12 to undergraduates and 5 to graduate students.

Deadline July of each year.

[971]
SUSAN BUNCH MEMORIAL SCHOLARSHIP

California Association for Postsecondary Education and Disability
Attn: Executive Assistant
71423 Biskra Road
Rancho Mirage, CA 92270
(760) 346-8206   Fax: (760) 340-5275
TDD: (760) 341-4084   E-mail: caped2000@aol.com
Web: www.caped.net/scholarships.html

Summary To provide funding to college and graduate students in California who have a learning disability.

Eligibility This program is open to students at public and private colleges and universities in California who have a learning disability. Undergraduates must have completed at least 6 semester credits and have a GPA of 2.5 or higher. Graduate students must have completed at least 3 semester units and have a GPA of 3.0 or higher. Along with their application, they must submit a 1-page personal letter that demonstrates their writing skills, progress towards meeting their educational and vocational goals, management of their disability, and involvement in community activities. They must also submit a letter of recommendation from a faculty member, verification of disability, official transcripts, proof of current enrollment, and documentation of financial need.

Financial data The stipend is $1,000.

Duration 1 year.

Number awarded 1 each year.

Deadline September of each year.

[972]
SUSAN STEIN SCHOLARSHIP

American College of Nurse-Midwives
Attn: ACNM Foundation, Inc.
8403 Colesville Road, Suite 1550
Silver Spring, MD 20910-6374
(240) 485-1850   Fax: (240) 485-1818
E-mail: fdn@acnm.org
Web: www.midwife.org

Summary To provide financial assistance for midwifery education to student members of the American College of Nurse-Midwives (ACNM) who have had a personal experience with breast cancer.

Eligibility This program is open to ACNM members who are currently enrolled in an accredited basic midwife education program and have successfully completed 1 academic or clinical semester/quarter or clinical module. Applicants must have had or currently have a personal experience with breast cancer, either their own or a family member's. Along with their application, they must submit a 150-word essay on their midwifery career plans; a 100-word essay on their intended future participation in ACNM activities; and a 300-word essay on the effect of breast cancer in themselves or a close family member on their choice of midwifery. Selection is based primarily on the quality of the application, although leadership, financial need, academics, and personal goals may also be considered.

Financial data The stipend is $3,000.

Duration 1 year.

Additional data This program was established in 2010.

Number awarded 1 each year.

Deadline March of each year.

[973]
THOMARA LATIMER CANCER FOUNDATION SCHOLARSHIPS

Thomara Latimer Cancer Foundation
Attn: Scholarship Committee
Franklin Plaza Center
29193 Northeastern Highway, Suite 528
Southfield, MI 48034-1006
(248) 557-2346   Fax: (248) 557-8063
E-mail: scholarships@thomlatimercares.org
Web: www.thomlatimercares.org

Summary To provide financial assistance to African American residents of Michigan (especially those who have had cancer) who are interested in studying a medically-related field at a college in any state.

Eligibility This program is open to African American residents of Michigan between 17 and 30 years of age. Applicants must be 1) a high school senior accepted at an accredited college or university in any state in a medically-related program (e.g., medical technician, physician assistant); or 2) a student admitted to a medically-related professional program (e.g., nursing, medicine, physical or occupational therapy) at a college or university in any state. They must have a GPA of 3.0 or higher. Along with their application, they must submit a brief essay on why they should be awarded this scholarship. Financial need is not considered in the selection process. Special consideration is given to students who are cancer survivors.

Financial data The stipend is $1,000.

Duration 1 year; may be renewed 1 additional year.

Number awarded 10 each year.

Deadline December of each year.

[974]
TONY AND JAN VIESSMAN MEMORIAL SCHOLARSHIPS

Epilepsy Foundation of Missouri and Kansas
c/o Julie Viessman MacCash
10698 Lakemont Drive
Rolla, MO 65401
Web: epilepsyfoundation.ning.com

Summary To provide funding to residents of any state who have epilepsy or are caring for someone who does and want to attend college or graduate school.

Eligibility This program is open to residents of any state who are under a physician's care for epilepsy or are the caretaker for a person living with epilepsy. Applicants may be 1) high school seniors planning to attend a technical school, community college, or 4-year college or university; 2) freshmen, sophomores, or juniors at 1 of those institutions; 3) college seniors planning to enroll in graduate school; or 4) adults interested in working on a college degree. Along with their application, they must submit a 500-word essay on 1 of the following topics: 1) what the youth of today should focus on to improve the lives of others; 2) why they think it is important for high school graduates to further their education; or 3) the current event, from their community or around the glove, that they find most interesting and why. They must also submit a 500-word essay on how they have overcome, or are working to overcome, the challenges that epilepsy presents.

Financial data The stipend is $1,000.

Duration 1 year.

Number awarded 4 each year.

Deadline March of each year.

[975]
TRANSPLANT SCHOLARS AWARDS

Astellas Pharma US, Inc.
Attn: Transplant Scholars Award
Three Parkway North
Deerfield, IL 60015-2548
Toll Free: (800) 888-7704
Web: astellastransplant.com/events_scholar.php

Summary To recognize and reward, with scholarships for college or graduate school, transplant recipients and donors who submit outstanding essays on their transplant experience.

Eligibility This competition is open to liver, kidney, or heart transplant recipients who are taking Prograf and to organ donors who have donated a portion of their liver or a kidney. Applicants must be beginning higher education, returning to school after their surgery, or working on an advanced degree. They must submit a 500-word essay that describes their transplant or donation experience, how the experience has changed their life, and how they would use the scholarship award to further their education and give back to the transplant community. Selection is based on the compelling nature of the story, the educational goals of the applicant and how those were affected by transplantation, and the applicant's intention to impact the transplant community positively.

Financial data The award is a $5,000 scholarship to be used for educational expenses.

Duration The awards are presented annually.

Number awarded Varies each year; recently, 12 of these scholarships were awarded.

Deadline June of each year.

[976]
UCB CROHN'S SCHOLARSHIP PROGRAM

UCB, Inc.
c/o Summit Medical Communications
1421 East Broad Street, Suite 340
Fuquay-Varina, NC 27526
Toll Free: (866) 757-4440
E-mail: ucbcrohnsscholarship@summitmedcomm.com
Web: www.crohnsandme.com/crohns-scholarship

Summary To provide financial assistance to undergraduate and graduate students who have Crohn's disease.

Eligibility This program is open to students who are working on or planning to work on an associate, undergraduate, or graduate degree or are enrolled in a trade school educational program. Applicants must have been diagnosed with Crohn's disease by a physician. They may be of any age. Along with their application, they must submit an essay of 1 to 2 pages describing how they are living beyond the boundaries of Crohn's disease to demonstrate

academic ambition and personal achievement and how the scholarship would impact their life.

Financial data Stipends range up to $5,000.

Duration 1 year; nonrenewable.

Additional data This program began in 2006.

Number awarded 30 each year.

Deadline February of each year.

[977]
UCB FAMILY EPILEPSY SCHOLARSHIP PROGRAM

UCB, Inc.
Family Scholarship Program
c/o Hudson Medical Communications
200 White Plains Road, Second Floor
Tarrytown, NY 10591
Toll Free: (866) 825-1920
E-mail: UCBScholarship@hudsongloballlc.com
Web: www.ucbepilepsyscholarship.com

Summary To provide financial assistance for college or graduate school to epilepsy patients and their family members and caregivers.

Eligibility This program is open to epilepsy patients and their family members and caregivers. Applicants must be working on or planning to work on an undergraduate or graduate degree at an institution of higher education in the United States. They must be able to demonstrate academic achievement, a record of participation in activities outside of school, and service as a role model. Along with their application, they must submit a 1-page essay explaining why they should be selected for the scholarship, how epilepsy has impacted their life either as a patient or as a family member or caregiver, and how they will benefit from the scholarship. U.S. citizenship or permanent resident status is required.

Financial data The stipend is $5,000.

Duration 1 year; nonrenewable.

Additional data This program, previously known as the Keppra Family Epilepsy Scholarship Program, was established in 2004.

Number awarded 30 each year.

Deadline April of each year.

[978]
VERA YIP MEMORIAL SCHOLARSHIP

Ulman Cancer Fund for Young Adults
Attn: Scholarship Committee
10440 Little Patuxent Parkway, Suite G1
Columbia, MD 21044
(410) 964-0202   Toll Free: (888) 393-FUND
Fax: (410) 964-0402
E-mail: scholarship@ulmanfund.org
Web: www.ulmanfund.org/scholarship.aspx

Summary To provide money for college or graduate school to students who have cancer or have lost a parent with cancer.

Eligibility This program is open to students who have or have lost a parent or guardian to cancer. Applicants must be 35 years of age or younger and attending, or planning to attend, a 2- or 4-year college, university, or vocational program to work on an undergraduate or graduate degree. The parent or guardian must have been first diagnosed with cancer after the applicant was 15 years of age. Along with their application, they must submit an essay of at least 1,000 words on how their parent's cancer experience has impacted their outlook on life and the legacy that they desire to leave behind. This award is presented to the applicant who best demonstrates the qualities of Vera Yip of courage, determination, motivation, and dedication.

Financial data The stipend is $2,500. Funds are paid directly to the educational institution.

Duration 1 year; nonrenewable.

Additional data Recipients must agree to complete 40 hours of community service.

Number awarded 1 each year.

Deadline March of each year.

[979]
VICTORY FOR WOMEN ACADEMIC SCHOLARSHIP FOR WOMEN WITH BLEEDING DISORDERS

National Hemophilia Foundation
Attn: Manager of Education
P.O. Box 971483
Ypsilanti, MI 48197
(734) 890-2504   E-mail: pflax@hemophilia.org
Web: www.hemophilia.org

Summary To provide financial assistance for college or graduate school to women who have a bleeding disorder.

Eligibility This program is open to women who are entering or already enrolled in an undergraduate or graduate program at a university, college, or accredited vocational school. Applicants must have von Willebrand Disease, hemophilia or other clotting factor deficiency, or carrier status. Along with their application, they must submit a 250-word essay that describes how their education and future career plans will benefit others in the bleeding disorders community. Selection is based on that essay, achievements, and community service to the bleeding disorders community.

Financial data The stipend is $2,500.

Duration 1 year.

Additional data The program, known also as V4W, was established in 2005 as the Project Red Flag Academic Scholarship for Women with Bleeding Disorders.

Number awarded 2 each year.

Deadline May of each year.

[980]
WORDS+/ISAAC OUTSTANDING CONSUMER LECTURE AWARD

United States Society for Augmentative and Alternative Communication
Attn: Office Manager
34 Market Street
Hatfield, PA 19440
Toll Free: (215) 631-1877   Fax: (267) 645-4021
E-mail: info@ussaac.org
Web: www.ussaac.org/awards.htm

Summary To recognize and reward people who use augmentative/alternative communication (AAC).

Eligibility This award is available to people who are either severely speech impaired or unable to speak and use AAC. Applicants must be interested in attending the biennial conference of the International Society for Augmentative and Alternative Communication (ISAAC) and presenting a speech, using any voice output communication system. Their presentation may highlight their talents (e.g., storytelling, creative writing, humor), perspectives (on current events, relationships, etc.), or individual endeavors (e.g., scholarly, entrepreneurial, recreational). Proposed speeches that focus on AAC, how they obtained their system, how it has affected their life, or other AAC topics are not acceptable. Applicants must submit an essay of 500 to 1,000 words explaining the proposed topic of presentation, method of delivery, presentation style, and a detailed outline of the specific content of the lecture. They must be an ISAAC member or applying for membership. Residents of all countries are eligible, but the speech must be in English.

Financial data The award is $5,000.

Duration The award is presented biennially, at the ISAAC convention where the speech is given.

Additional data The United States Society for Augmentative and Alternative Communication (USSAAC) is the national chapter of ISAAC. This award is sponsored by ISAAC and Words+, Inc., a commercial manufacturer of augmentative communication devices.

Number awarded 1 every even-numbered year.

Deadline October of each odd-numbered year.

Grants-in-Aid

[981]
AGMA EMERGENCY RELIEF FUND

American Guild of Musical Artists
Attn: National Executive Secretary
1430 Broadway, 14th Floor
New York, NY 10018
(212) 265-3687   Toll Free: (800) 543-2462
Fax: (212) 262-9088 E-mail: agma@MusicalArtists.org
Web: www.musicalartists.org/AGMAReliefFund.html

Summary To provide emergency assistance to members of the American Guild of Musical Artists (AGMA) who are dealing with accidents, illness, or other traumatic events.

Eligibility This assistance is available to members of the guild who are classical performing artists of opera, concert, and dance, and the stage managers, directors, and choreographers of opera and dance. Applicants may include young performers faced with unexpected injury or illness, artists living with AIDS, or mature performers in need of medical assistance.

Financial data The amount of the assistance varies.

Number awarded Varies each year.

Deadline Applications may be submitted at any time.

[982]
AMERICAN KIDNEY FUND HEALTH INSURANCE PREMIUM PROGRAM

American Kidney Fund
Attn: Patient Services Department
6110 Executive Boulevard, Suite 1010
Rockville, MD 20852
(301) 881-3052   Toll Free: (800) 638-8299
Fax: (301) 881-0898
E-mail: patientservice@kidneyfund.org
Web: www.kidneyfund.org/patient-grants/hipp

Summary To assist kidney dialysis patients with payment of their health insurance premiums.

Eligibility This assistance is available to kidney dialysis patients who are referred by their renal social worker and/or nephrologists because they cannot afford health insurance coverage. Applicants must need assistance to pay Part B Medicare, Medigap, commercial, and COBRA premiums. Transplant recipients are not eligible.

Financial data Grants depend on the recipient's needs.

Number awarded Varies each year; recently, the fund served more than 70,000 low-income dialysis patients.

Deadline Applications may be submitted at any time.

[983]
AMERICAN KIDNEY FUND SAFETY NET GRANTS

American Kidney Fund
Attn: Patient Services Department
6110 Executive Boulevard, Suite 1010
Rockville, MD 20852
(301) 881-3052   Toll Free: (800) 638-8299
Fax: (301) 881-0898
E-mail: patientservice@kidneyfund.org
Web: www.kidneyfund.org

Summary To provide assistance to needy dialysis and kidney transplant patients.

Eligibility This assistance is available to dialysis or kidney transplant patients whose need is not covered by insurance or other programs and who can demonstrate financial need. Funding is available for 1) treatment-specific expenses, such as transportation costs to reach dialysis, over-the-counter medicines, medication co-payments, kidney donor expenses, and other necessities

such as dentures; 2) disaster relief assistance, which provides funds to assist patients replace medications, food, and household items and pay for other necessities lost because of natural disasters; 3) cost of dialysis while traveling, which provides reimbursement to dialysis patients for travel costs not covered by Medicare or other sources that are necessitated by death or serious illness in the family or for the purpose of kidney workup; and 4) support for qualified renal patients to receive medications, nutritional products, and durable medical supplies at discount prices.

Financial data Grants depend on the need of the recipient. Payment for the cost of dialysis while traveling is limited to 20% of treatment.

Number awarded Varies each year; recently, the fund served more than 25,000 low-income kidney patients.

Deadline Applications may be submitted at any time.

[984]
AVONCARES PROGRAM FOR MEDICALLY UNDERSERVED WOMEN

Cancer Care, Inc.
Attn: Director, Social Services
275 Seventh Avenue, 22nd Floor
New York, NY 10001
(212) 712-8085   Toll Free: (800) 813-HOPE
Fax: (212) 712-8495   E-mail: info@cancercare.org
Web: www.cancercare.org/financial/information

Summary To provide financial assistance to women who have breast cancer.

Eligibility This assistance is available to women with breast cancer. Applicants must demonstrate limited income and resources for diagnostic services and/or treatment for cancer. They must be under- or uninsured and underserved.

Financial data Limited financial assistance is provided for transportation, child care, and escort services. Funding is also available to pay for diagnostic (post-screening) services. Grants do not cover basic living expenses, such as rent, mortgages, utility payments, or food.

Duration This is a 1-time award.

Additional data Funding for this program is provided by a grant from the Avon Foundation.

Number awarded Varies each year.

Deadline Applications may be submitted at any time.

[985]
CALIFORNIA EASTERN STAR CANCER ASSISTANCE

Order of the Eastern Star-Grand Chapter of California
Attn: Cancer Assistance Committee
16960 Bastanchury Road, Suite E
Yorba Linda, CA 92886-1711
(714) 986-2380   Fax: (714) 986-2385
Web: www.oescal.org/CESF/applications.htm

Summary To provide funding to members of the Order of the Eastern Star in California and their dependents who have cancer.

Eligibility This assistance is available to members of Eastern Star in California and their immediate families (including spouses, children, parents, and grandparents) who reside in their household or are dependent upon them for support. Applicants must be cancer patients who can demonstrate need of financial assistance.

Financial data For Eastern Star members and minor children, grants range up to $15,000, although an additional $1,000 may be awarded in terminal cases or emergency situations. For other dependents, grants range up to $7,500.

Duration These are 1-time grants.

Additional data Funding for this program is provided by the J. Clifford Lee Memorial Cancer Fund and the Marguerite Rennie Memorial Fund.

Number awarded Varies each year.

Deadline Applications may be submitted at any time.

[986]
CAMERON SIEMERS LIFE GRANTS

Cameron Siemers Foundation for Hope
P.O. Box 1074
Los Alamitos, CA 90720
Toll Free: (877) 509-9516   Fax: (714) 386-5313
E-mail: cameronsiemers@gmail.com
Web: www.cameronsiemers.org/life-grants.html

Summary To provide funding to young adults with life-threatening illnesses who wish to conduct a project that will make a difference in their life and the lives of others.

Eligibility This program is open to people between 18 and 28 years of age who have been diagnosed with a life-threatening illness. Applicants must need funding to conduct a project that will fulfill their dream or goal. The only requirement is that it will make a difference in their life and the lives of others.

Financial data Grants are $5,000.

Duration These are 1-time grants.

Number awarded 1 or more each year.

Deadline Applications may be submitted at any time.

[987]
CANCER CARE FINANCIAL ASSISTANCE

Cancer Care, Inc.
Attn: Director, Social Services
275 Seventh Avenue, 22nd Floor
New York, NY 10001
(212) 712-8085   Toll Free: (800) 813-HOPE
Fax: (212) 711-8495   E-mail: info@cancercare.org
Web: www.cancercare.org/financial

Summary To provide financial assistance to people who have cancer and need financial assistance to cover treatment-related costs.

Eligibility This program is open to anyone who is suffering from cancer. Applicants must provide the sponsoring organization's social workers and/or case managers with information about their source of income, monthly income and expenses, and (in some cases) invoices for the cost of services. Patients who are Medicaid-eligible, in the process of applying for Medicaid homemaker/home attendant service, or Medicaid pending are eligible automatically.

Financial data Funds are available to cover the costs of home care, child care for cancer patients and their families, pain medication, and transportation to chemotherapy or radiation treatments. Grants do not cover living expenses, such as rent, mortgages, utility payments, or food.

Additional data Financial assistance is reassessed every 3 months, to determine if there are any changes in the patient or family's needs.

Number awarded Varies each year.

Deadline Applications may be submitted at any time.

[988]
CANCER SURVIVORS' FUND PROSTHETIC LIMB ASSISTANCE PROGRAM

Cancer Survivors' Fund
P.O. Box 792
Missouri City, TX 77459
(281) 437-7142   Fax: (281) 437-9568
E-mail: csf@cancersurvivorsfund.org
Web: www.cancersurvivorsfund.org

Summary To provide funding to children and young adults who need prostheses related to cancer.

Eligibility This assistance is available to children and young adults who are facing the cost of prostheses and artificial limbs. Applicants must be a cancer survivor or currently diagnosed with cancer whose need for the prosthetic limb(s) is cancer-related. Along with their application, they must submit an essay, from 500 to 1,200 words in length, on how their experience with cancer has impacted their life values and career goals.

Financial data Grants provide assistance toward the cost of prostheses and artificial limbs.

Additional data Recipients must agree to do volunteer work to use their cancer experience to help other young cancer patients and survivors cope with a life-threatening or life-altering event.

Number awarded Varies each year.

Deadline Deadline not specified.

[989]
CARE PROGRAM

National Gaucher Foundation, Inc.
Attn: Program Director, National Gaucher Care Foundation
267 Kentlands Boulevard, Box 1084
Gaithersburg, MD 20878
Toll Free: (866) 346-8176   Fax: (301) 963-4489
E-mail: blichtenstein@comcast.net
Web: www.gaucherdisease.org/psp.php

Summary To assist Gaucher patients who need help with paying their insurance premiums.

Eligibility This assistance is available to patients who have been diagnosed with Gaucher Disease and are able to demonstrate extraordinary financial hardship. Applicants must be seeking funding to help pay insurance premiums (primary, secondary, or both).

Financial data This program provides funds to subsidize, or purchase in full, a health insurance policy that includes coverage for enzyme replacement therapy.

Duration The time period varies, depending on each individual case. Patients who receive grants are required to reapply on an annual basis or at the end of the designated grant period.

Number awarded Varies each year.

Deadline Applications may be submitted at any time and are considered on a quarterly basis.

[990]
CARE+PLUS PROGRAM

National Gaucher Foundation, Inc.
Attn: Program Director, National Gaucher Care
  Foundation
267 Kentlands Boulevard, Box 1084
Gaithersburg, MD 20878
Toll Free: (866) 346-8176   Fax: (301) 963-4489
E-mail: blichtenstein@comcast.net
Web: www.gaucherdisease.org/psp.php

Summary To provide assistance to Gaucher patients who face extreme financial hardship and need funding for a variety of Gaucher-related expenses.

Eligibility This assistance is available to patients who have been diagnosed with Gaucher Disease and are able to demonstrate extraordinary financial hardship. Applicants must need funding for Gaucher-related expenses such as diagnostic tests and other ancillary medical expenses for Gaucher Disease not covered by insurance; infusion charges for enzyme replacement therapy not covered by insurance; membership fees for organizations that provide access to insurance for Gaucher patients; travel expenses to and from office/hospital for enzyme replacement therapy or a Gaucher medical evaluation; day care expenses for Gaucher patient's family members while the patient receives enzyme replacement therapy or a Gaucher medical evaluation; and over-the-counter medications that are prescribed for Gaucher patients.

Financial data Grants provide partial payment of eligible expenses.

Duration The time period varies, depending on each individual case. Patients who receive grants are required to reapply on an annual basis or at the end of the designated grant period.

Number awarded Varies each year.

Deadline Applications may be submitted at any time and are considered on a quarterly basis.

[991]
CHILDREN'S LEUKEMIA RESEARCH ASSOCIATION PATIENT AID GRANTS

Children's Leukemia Research Association, Inc.
Attn: Patient Aid Department
585 Stewart Avenue, Suite 18
Garden City, NY 11530
(516) 222-1944   Fax: (516) 222-0457
E-mail: info@childrensleukemia.org
Web: www.childrensleukemia.org/patientaid.html

Summary To provide financial assistance to leukemia patients and their families.

Eligibility This assistance is available to leukemia patients and their families. Applicants must be seeking support for laboratory fees associated with leukemia, x-ray therapy treatment or chemotherapy treatment of leukemia, or leukemia drugs. They must submit a letter of diagnosis from the attending physician.

Financial data Grant support ranges up to $3,000 per year.

Additional data The sponsoring organization is also known as the National Leukemia Research Association, Inc.

Number awarded Varies each year.

Deadline Applications may be submitted at any time.

[992]
COAL MINERS BLACK LUNG BENEFITS

Department of Labor
Employment Standards Administration
Office of Workers' Compensation Programs
Attn: Division of Coal Mine Workers' Compensation
200 Constitution Avenue, N.W., Room C3520
Washington, DC 20210
(202) 693-0046   Toll Free: (800) 638-7072
TDD: (800) 326-2577
Web: www.dol.gov/dol/topic/workcomp/index.htm

Summary To provide monthly benefits to coal miners who are disabled because of pneumoconiosis (black lung disease) and to their surviving dependents.

Eligibility Present and former coal miners (including certain transportation and construction workers who were exposed to coal mine dust) and their surviving dependents, including surviving spouses, orphaned children, and totally dependent parents, brothers, and sisters, may file claims if they are totally disabled.

Financial data Benefit amounts vary; recently; the basic monthly benefit was $625 for a single totally disabled miner or surviving spouse, $938 per month for a claimant with 1 dependent, $1,094 per month for a claimant with 2 dependents, or $1,251 per month for a claimant with 3 or more dependents. Benefit payments are reduced by the amounts received for pneumoconiosis under state workers' compensation awards and by excess earnings.

Duration Benefits are paid as long as the miner is unable to work in the mines or until the miner dies.

Number awarded Varies; recently, 7,699 miners, 21,913 surviving spouses, 1,214 other eligible persons, 5,726 dependents of miners, 723 dependents of surviving spouses, and 122 dependents of other eligible persons received benefits from this program.

Deadline Deadline not specified.

[993]
DAVE MADEIROS CREATIVE ARTS SCHOLARSHIP

Factor Foundation of America
Attn: Scholarship Committee
P.O. Box 812542
Boca Raton, FL 33481-2542
(561) 504-6531
E-mail: kmadeiros@factorfoundation.org
Web: www.factorfoundation.org/programs.htm

Summary To provide financial assistance for artistic or sports activities to young people with a bleeding disorder and their siblings.

Eligibility This program is open to children between 5 and 17 years of age who have a bleeding disorder or are the sibling of such a person. Applicants must be interested in taking musical lessons, joining a sports team, taking drawing lessons, taking a drama class, taking a private sports class, etc. They must be recommended by a local hemophilia chapter, physician, and/or hemophilia treatment center. Parents must submit an application that includes a 500-word essay on their desire for their child to take part in a creative art and how that experience will benefit him or her, 2 letters of reference, and documentation of financial need.

Financial data The stipend is $1,000.

Duration 1 year; recipients may reapply.

Additional data This program began in 2006.

Number awarded At least 1 each year.

Deadline June of each year.

[994]
DONATE LIFE SOUTH CAROLINA PATIENT ASSISTANCE PROGRAM

Donate Life South Carolina
Attn: Office Program Manager
22 Centre East
4200 East North Street
Greenville, SC 29615
(864) 609-5270   Toll Free: (877) 277-4866
Fax: (864) 609-5387
Web: www.donatelifesc.org

Summary To provide emergency funding to residents of South Carolina who have received an organ transplant.

Eligibility This assistance is available to transplant recipients in South Carolina. Applicants must be able to demonstrate a need for emergency support for rent or mortgage payments, utility bills, groceries, or direct costs associated with the transplant (e.g., prescriptions, travel costs, hotel stays). They must have an income less than $30,000 per year for a family of 4.

Financial data The amount of the assistance depends on several variables, including (but not limited to) type of organ transplant, the extent to which Medicaid or Medicare becomes available, types of medications involved, or types of extraneous expenses involved.

Duration Grants are provided as needed.

Additional data This sponsoring organization was formerly known as Gift of Life.

Number awarded Varies each year; recently, the program managed 73 active cases and provided $63,518 in emergency financial assistance.

Deadline Applications may be submitted at any time.

[995]
EPILEPSY THERAPY PROJECT PATIENT ASSISTANCE FUND

Epilepsy Therapy Project
Attn: Patient Assistance Fund
P.O. Box 742
Middleburg, VA 20118
(540) 687-8077   Fax: (540) 687-8066
E-mail: info@epilepsytdp.org
Web: www.epilepsy.com

Summary To provide funding to people with epilepsy who have agreed to participate in a clinical trial of an epilepsy therapy and need help to cover costs of participation.

Eligibility This program is open to individuals who have been accepted for enrollment in an IRB-approved clinical trial of an epilepsy therapy and have signed an informed consent form for that trial. Applicants must be able to document that they need assistance to help cover out-of-pocket costs associated with participation in the clinical trial, including travel expenses to the study site, co-payments, deductibles, and co-insurance required by their health plan. In general, they must have income below 300% of the federal poverty level. Funds are awarded on a first-come, first-served basis.

Financial data The maximum award is $5,000 per 2-year period. Funds are provided only as reimbursement for the patient's own out-of-pocket expenses that are not covered by health insurance, Medicare, Medicaid, other federal or state assistance program, or the study sponsor.

Number awarded Varies each year.

Deadline Applications may be submitted at any time.

[996]
FUND FOR WRITERS AND EDITORS WITH HIV/AIDS

PEN American Center
Attn: Coordinator, Writers Emergency Fund
588 Broadway, Suite 303
New York, NY 10012
(212) 334-1660, ext. 126   Fax: (212) 334-2181
E-mail: jasmine@pen.org
Web: www.pen.org/page.php/prmID/251

Summary To provide financial assistance to published writers, produced playwrights, and editors with Acquired Immune Deficiency Syndrome (AIDS) or HIV.

Eligibility Professional authors and editors with HIV or AIDS are eligible to apply if they are in need of emergency financial assistance. They must be U.S. residents and have had their works published or produced (applicants will be asked to submit samples of their work). Applicants need not be members of PEN, however. Funding is not provided to pay for research activities, to enable the completion of writing projects, or to cover publication or education expenses.

Financial data Grants up to $2,000 are available.

Duration These are 1-time grants.

Number awarded Varies each year.

Deadline June of each year.

[997]
HACA FAMILY ASSISTANCE PROGRAM

Hemophilia Association of the Capital Area
10560 Main Street, Suite 419
Fairfax, VA 22030-7182
(703) 352-7641   Fax: (540) 427-6589
E-mail: admin@hacacares.org
Web: www.hacacares.org

Summary To provide emergency financial aid to individuals with bleeding disorders and their families in the Washington, D.C. area.

Eligibility This program is open to 1) residents of northern Virginia, Montgomery and Prince George's County in Maryland, and Washington, D.C.; and 2) people who receive treatment for bleeding disorders at Children's National Medical Center or Georgetown University Hospital in Washington, D.C. Also eligible are parents and caregivers of people living in their home who have a bleeding disorder relevant to the mission of the Hemophilia Association of the Capital Area (HACA). Applicants must be able to demonstrate need for assistance for 1) uncovered medical bills associated with the diagnosis and treatment of a bleeding disorder and any complications from that; or 2) basic living expense emergencies.

Financial data The amount of the assistance depends on the need of the grantee.

Duration Assistance is provided only once per calendar year.

Number awarded Varies each year.

Deadline Applications may be submitted at any time.

[998]
HAWAII INCOME TAX EXCLUSION FOR PATIENTS WITH HANSEN'S DISEASE

Department of Taxation
Attn: Taxpayer Services Branch
425 Queen Street
P.O. Box 259
Honolulu, HI 96809-0259
(808) 587-4242   Toll Free: (800) 222-3229
Fax: (808) 587-1488   TDD: (808) 587-1418
Web: hawaii.gov/tax

Summary To exempt payments to patients with Hansen's Disease from state income taxation in Hawaii.

Eligibility Compensation paid by the state of Hawaii or the United States to a patient affected with Hansen's Disease (also known as leprosy) is subject to this exclusion.

Financial data All compensation is excluded from income for purposes of state taxation.

Duration The exclusion continues as long as the recipient resides in Hawaii.

Deadline Deadline not specified.

[999]
HEALTHWELL FOUNDATION GRANTS

HealthWell Foundation
P.O. Box 4133
Gaithersburg, MD 20878-4133
Toll Free: (800) 675-8416   Fax: (800) 282-7692
E-mail: info@healthwellfoundation.org
Web: www.healthwellfoundation.org

Summary To help pay the insurance premiums and copayments for people with designated illnesses.

Eligibility This assistance is available to people who need help in paying their insurance premiums or copayments (but not both) so they can obtain medications needed for designated diseases. They must have a household income below 300% to 400% of the federal poverty level (depending on the disease) and be receiving treatment for a specific disease or condition with medication dispensed in the United States. The diseases or conditions for which assistance is available are acute porphyrias, ANCA-associate vasculitis and Wegeners, asthma (moderate to severe), AutoImmune (e.g., ankylosing spondylitis, psoriasis, psoriatic arthritis, rheumatoid arthritis), carcinoid tumors and related symptoms, chemotherapy induced anemia, chronic gout, Crohn's Disease, cytomegalovirus, Dupuytren's Disease, head and neck cancer, immunosuppressive treatment for solid organ transplants, metastatic melanoma, systemic lupus erythematosus, and Wilms' Tumor. The diagnosis must be verified by a physician. Individuals covered by private insurance, employer-sponsored plans, Medicare, or Medicaid may be eligible.

Financial data Grants provide full or partial assistance.

Duration Up to 12 months; enrollment may be renewed.

Number awarded Varies each year. Grants are awarded on a first-come, first-served basis for each disease as long as funds are available. Recently, more 44,000 patients received more than $144 million.

Deadline Applications may be submitted at any time.

[1000]
HEMOPHILIA FOUNDATION OF ILLINOIS FINANCIAL ASSISTANCE PROGRAM

Hemophilia Foundation of Illinois
Attn: Executive Director
210 South DesPlaines
Chicago, IL 60661-5500
(312) 427-1495   E-mail: brobinson@hfi-il.org
Web: www.hemophiliaillinois.org/services.htm

Summary To provide financial assistance for personal and other needs to residents of Illinois who have a bleeding disorder and their families.

Eligibility This program is open to residents of Illinois who have a bleeding disorder and their families. Applicants must have exhausted all other resources and still need funds to pay for housing or rent, utilities, funeral expenses, or other needs such as those caused by fire or flood. Along with their application, they must submit copies of supporting documents, such as rent bills, mortgage statements, actual utility bills, and proof of medical premium payments or funeral director bills.

Financial data   The amount of the assistance depends on the need of the applicant and the availability of funds. This program is intended to provide funding of last resort.

Duration   Each family may be awarded 1 grant within a 12-month period. They may apply for a renewal grant, but after a family has been granted assistance for a third year in a row, they are ineligible for funding the following year in all categories except funeral expense.

Number awarded   Varies each year.

Deadline   Applications may be submitted at any time.

[1001]
HEMOPHILIA FOUNDATION OF MICHIGAN EMERGENCY FINANCIAL ASSISTANCE PROGRAM

Hemophilia Foundation of Michigan
Attn: Client Services Coordinator
1921 West Michigan Avenue
Ypsilanti, MI 48197
(734) 544-0015   Toll Free: (800) 482-3041
Fax: (734) 544-0095   E-mail: colleen@hfmich.org
Web: www.hfmich.org/?module=Page&sID=financial-aid

Summary   To provide financial assistance for emergency needs to Michigan residents with hemophilia.

Eligibility   This program is open to residents of Michigan who have a bleeding disorder and have a temporary financial emergency. The need may be for food, utilities, rent, or car repair for individuals whose bleeding disorder impacts their income. Selection is based on severity of the need and the ability of applicants to change their financial standing. Requests may come directly from applicants or their hemophilia treatment center.

Financial data   Grants depend on the availability of funds and the need of the recipient.

Duration   Recipients may obtain these funds only once in each 12-month period.

Number awarded   Varies each year.

Deadline   Applications may be submitted at any time.

[1002]
IDAHO INCOME TAX EXEMPTION FOR MAINTAINING A HOME FOR THE DEVELOPMENTALLY DISABLED

Idaho State Tax Commission
Attn: Public Information Office
800 Park Boulevard, Plaza IV
P.O. Box 36
Boise, ID 83722-0410
(208) 334-7660   Toll Free: (800) 972-7660
TDD: (800) 377-3529
Web: tax.idaho.gov/i-1039.cfm

Summary   To exempt from state taxation a portion of the income of residents of Idaho who maintain a home for a family member, including themselves and their spouses, who is developmentally disabled.

Eligibility   Individuals in Idaho who maintain a household that includes a developmentally disabled person (of any age) are eligible for this program if they provide at least half of the support of the developmentally disabled family member. The taxpayer and spouse may be included as a member of the family. Developmental disability is defined as a chronic disability that 1) is attributable to an impairment such as mental retardation, cerebral palsy, epilepsy, autism, or related condition; 2) results in substantial functional limitation in 3 or more of the following areas of life activity: self-care, receptive and expressive language, learning, mobility, self-direction, capacity for independent living, or economic self-sufficiency; and 3) reflects the need for a combination and sequence of special, interdisciplinary or generic care, treatment, or other services that are of lifelong or extended duration and individually planned and coordinated.

Financial data   The amount of the deduction is $1,000 for each developmentally disabled family member, up to a maximum of $3,000.

Duration   Application for the deduction must be submitted each year.

Additional data   This deduction also applies to taxpayers maintaining a home for a family member who is 65 years of age or older. Taxpayers who do not claim the $1,000 deduction may be able to claim a tax credit of $100 for each member of the family who is developmentally disabled or elderly, to a maximum of 3 members.

Number awarded   Varies each year.

Deadline   April of each year.

[1003]
LEUKEMIA & LYMPHOMA SOCIETY CO-PAY ASSISTANCE PROGRAM

Leukemia & Lymphoma Society of America
Attn: Co-Pay Assistance Program
P.O. Box 12268
Newport News, VA 23612
Toll Free: (877) 557-2672   Fax: (877) 267-2932
E-mail: copay@lls.org
Web: www.lls.org

Summary   To provide funding to patients with leukemia and related diseases who need assistance with their pharmacy co-payments and insurance premiums.

Eligibility   This program is open to residents of the United States and Puerto Rico who have been diagnosed with Hodgkin lymphoma, non-Hodgkin lymphoma, chronic myelogenous leukemia, chronic lymphocytic leukemia, myelodysplastic syndromes (MDS), myeloma, or Waldenstrom macroglobulinemia. Applicants must have household income at or within 500% above the U.S. federal poverty guidelines (currently ranging from $55,850 for a family of 1 up to $194,450 for a family of 8). They must need assistance for cancer treatment-related co-pays, private health insurance premiums, private insurance co-pay obligations, Medicare Part B, Medicare Plan D, Medicare supplementary health insurance, or Medicare Advantage premium or co-pay obligations.

Financial data For patients with chronic myelogenous leukemia, the maximum grant is $500. For patients with Hodgkin lymphoma, non-Hodgkin lymphoma, chronic lymphocytic leukemia, or myelodysplastic syndromes (MDS), the maximum grant is $5,000. For patients with myeloma or Waldenstrom macroglobulinemia, the maximum grant is $10,000.

Number awarded Varies each year.

Deadline Applications may be submitted at any time.

[1004]
LIVING BREATH FOUNDATION FINANCIAL AID GRANTS

Living Breath Foundation
2031 Marsala Circle
Monterey, CA 93940
(831) 392-5285
E-mail: LivingBreathFoundation@gmail.com
Web: thelivingbreathfoundation.com/aid.html

Summary To provide funding to individuals who have cystic fibrosis and their families for assistance with expenses related to the disease.

Eligibility This program is open to U.S. residents who have cystic fibrosis and members of their families. Applicants must document a need for assistance in payment of bills from hospitals, doctors, or pharmacies; rent or utility bills; hotel expenses incurred while a child or spouse is in the hospital; or unreimbursed medical equipment. They must submit a 1- to 2-paragraph statement explaining why they need financial assistance at this time and how the foundation can provide that.

Financial data Grants depend on the recipient's needs.

Duration These are 1-time grants.

Additional data This foundation started in 2008.

Number awarded Varies each year.

Deadline Applications may be submitted at any time.

[1005]
MARY KAY ASH CHARITABLE FOUNDATION GRANTS

Cancer Care, Inc.
Attn: Director, Social Services
275 Seventh Avenue, 22nd Floor
New York, NY 10001
(212) 712-8080   Toll Free: (800) 813-HOPE
Fax: (212) 712-8495   E-mail: info@cancercare.org
Web: www.cancercare.org/financial/information

Summary To provide financial assistance to women who have cancer.

Eligibility This assistance is available to women who have any type of cancer (except breast cancer). Applicants must provide the sponsoring organization's social workers and/or case managers with information about their source of income, monthly income and expenses, and (in some cases) invoices for the cost of services.

Financial data Limited financial assistance is provided for transportation, home care, pain medication, and child

care services. Grants do not cover basic living expenses, such as rent, mortgages, utility payments, or food.

Duration This is a 1-time award.

Additional data This program is sponsored by the Mary Kay Ash Charitable Foundation.

Number awarded Varies each year.

Deadline Applications may be submitted at any time.

[1006]
NATIONAL KIDNEY FOUNDATION OF COLORADO, MONTANA AND WYOMING PATIENT EMERGENCY ASSISTANCE GRANTS

National Kidney Foundation of Colorado, Montana and
  Wyoming, Inc.
Attn: Division Development Director
650 South Cherry Street, Suite 435
Denver, CO 80246-1896
(720) 748-9991   Toll Free: (800) 596-7943
Fax: (720) 748-1273   E-mail: nkfcmw@kidney.org
Web: www.kidney.org/site/patients/index.cfm?ch=505

Summary To provide funding to patients with kidney or urinary tract diseases who live in Colorado, Montana, and Wyoming.

Eligibility These programs are open patients with kidney or urinary tract diseases who reside in Colorado, Montana, or Wyoming. In general, they should be referred by a social worker because they are in need of funds to supplement the cost of medications, treatment supplies, dental needs, and transportation expenses.

Financial data The amount awarded varies, depending upon the needs of the recipient.

Duration Funds are provided as needed.

Number awarded Varies each year.

Deadline Applications may be submitted at any time.

[1007]
NATIONAL KIDNEY FOUNDATION OF INDIANA EMERGENCY FINANCIAL AID

National Kidney Foundation of Indiana, Inc.
Attn: Program Coordinator
911 East 86th Street, Suite 100
Indianapolis, IN 46204-1848
(317) 722-5640   Toll Free: (800) 382-9971
Fax: (317) 722-5650   E-mail: nkfi@kidneyindiana.org
Web: www.kidney.org/site/303/patientAid.cfm?ch=303

Summary To provide emergency financial assistance to individuals in Indiana who have kidney or urinary tract diseases.

Eligibility This assistance is available to patients in Indiana who have kidney or urinary tract diseases or are a kidney transplant recipient. Applicants must need assistance for groceries, utilities, telephone bills, rent, and medical supplies and equipment not covered by a health plan. They must be referred by a social worker at a dialysis unit or transplant center.

Financial data The amount awarded varies, depending upon the needs of the recipient.

Duration In general, these are 1-time funds.

Additional data This fund does not pay medical bills.

Number awarded Varies each year.

Deadline Applications may be submitted at any time.

[1008]
NATIONAL KIDNEY FOUNDATION OF UTAH AND IDAHO PATIENT EMERGENCY GRANTS

National Kidney Foundation of Utah and Idaho
3707 North Canyon Road, Suite 1D
Provo, UT 84604-4585
(801) 226-5111   Toll Free: (800) 869-5277
Fax: (801) 226-8278   E-mail: nkfu@kidneyut.org
Web: www.kidneyut.org/ps-grants.php

Summary To provide emergency financial assistance to kidney patients in Utah and Idaho.

Eligibility This program is open to residents of Utah and Idaho who are kidney transplant recipients or dialysis patients. Applicants must need assistance to help pay for food, rent, utilities, transportation, vehicle maintenance, medical insurance, medications, or doctors' bills.

Financial data Grants depend on the recipient's need.

Duration These are 1-time grants.

Number awarded Varies each year.

Deadline Applications may be submitted at any time.

[1009]
NATIONAL KIDNEY FOUNDATION SERVING OHIO EMERGENCY FINANCIAL ASSISTANCE

National Kidney Foundation Serving Ohio and
   Kentucky
Attn: Ohio Division Office
2800 Corporate Exchange Drive, Suite 260
Columbus, OH 43231-8617
(614) 882-6184   Toll Free: (800) 242-2133
Fax: (614) 882-6564   E-mail: nkfoh@kidney.org
Web: www.kidney.org/site/patients/index.cfm?ch=310

Summary To provide emergency financial assistance to kidney patients in Ohio.

Eligibility This assistance is available to residents of Ohio who have Chronic Kidney Disease (CKD) and are facing emergency situations. Applications must be submitted by a renal social worker.

Financial data Limited funds are available.

Number awarded Varies each year.

Deadline Applications may be submitted at any time.

[1010]
NCCS FINANCIAL ASSISTANCE

National Children's Cancer Society
Attn: Patient and Family Services
One South Memorial Drive, Suite 800
St. Louis, MO 63102
(314) 241-1600   Toll Free: (800) 532-6459
Fax: (314) 735-2014
E-mail: SSchuetz@children-cancer.org
Web: www.thenccs.org/assist

Summary To provide funding for expenses related to cancer or brain tumors to children with cancer (or their families).

Eligibility This assistance is available to children (under 18 years of age) who have a pediatric cancer or a high grade or anaplastic brain tumor. Applicants must be facing medical and non-medical expenses related to treatment, including meals during treatment, health insurance premiums, medical expenses not covered by insurance, lodging during treatment, and transportation during treatment. Families with liquid assets in excess of $5,000 may be asked to partially or completely "spend down" those assets prior to receiving this assistance. Children must be U.S. citizens or permanent residents who have maintained been in the United States for at least 12 consecutive months.

Financial data Assistance depends on the recipient's need.

Duration Assistance may be provided for up to 2 months; if continuing support is still required, a request for renewal may be submitted by a hospital professional.

Number awarded Varies each year.

Deadline Applications may be submitted at any time.

[1011]
PATIENT ACCESS NETWORK FINANCIAL ASSISTANCE

Patient Access Network Foundation
P.O. Box 221858
Charlotte, NC 28222-1858
Toll Free: (866) 316-PANF   Fax: (866) 316-7261
E-mail: contact@panfoundation.org
Web: www.panfoundation.org

Summary To provide co-payment assistance to people who have inadequate medical insurance and have specific diseases.

Eligibility This assistance is available to U.S. residents who meet specified financial, insurance, and medical criteria. Applicants must be undergoing treatment for 1 of the following diseases or conditions: acromegaly, anaplastic large cell lymphoma, advanced basal cell carcinoma, ankylosing spondylitis, bone metastases, chemotherapy induced neutropenia, chronic lymphocytic leukemia (CLL), colorectal cancer, cutaneous T-cell lymphoma (CTCL), cystic fibrosis, cytomegalovirus (CMV) prevention and treatment, diabetic foot ulcers, Gaucher's Disease, growth hormone deficiency, hepatitis B or C, Hodgkin's lymphoma, kidney transplant immunosuppressant, idiopathic thrombocytopenic purpura, metastatic breast cancer, multiple myeloma, multiple sclerosis, myelodysplastic syndrome, myeloproliferative neoplasms (MF, PV, ET), pancreatic cancer, plaque psoriasis, postmenopausal osteoporosis, prostate cancer, psoriatic arthritis, renal cell carcinoma, respiratory syncytial virus (RSV), retinal vein occlusion (RVO), rheumatoid arthritis, secondary hyperparathyroidism (SHPT), solid organ transplant immunosuppressant therapy, uveitis, well-differentiated thyroid cancer, or wet age-related macular degeneration (AMD). They must be insured and their insurance must cover the medication for which they seek assistance. The medication must fight the disease directly. The fund for each disease specifies that patient's income must fall below a specified amount, either 400% or 500% of the federal poverty level. Physicians must verify all information provided on the application.

Financial data Each disease fund specifies a maximum award level of co-payment assistance for that disease; those range from $500 to $10,000 per year.

Duration 1 year.

Additional data This program was established in 2004.

Number awarded Varies each year. Since this program was established, it has awarded nearly $165 million in co-payment assistance to more than 120,000 patients.

Deadline Applications may be submitted at any time.

[1012]
PATIENT ADVOCATE FOUNDATION CO-PAY RELIEF PROGRAM

Patient Advocate Foundation
Attn: Co-Pay Relief
421 Butler Farm Road
Hampton, VA 23669
(757) 952-0118   Toll Free: (866) 512-3861
Fax: (757) 952-0119 E-mail: info@patientadvocate.org
Web: www.copays.org

Summary To provide funding to people who are taking medication for specified diseases and need assistance to make the co-payments required by their insurance plans.

Eligibility This program is open to patients diagnosed with the following diseases or conditions: breast cancer, chemotherapy induced neutropenia, colon cancer, cutaneous T-cell lymphoma (CTCL), hepatitis C, hormone suppression therapy, kidney cancer, lung cancer, multiple myeloma, myelodysplastic syndrome, non-muscle invasive bladder cancer, osteoporosis, pain, prostate cancer, rheumatoid arthritis, or sarcoma. Applicants must be able to demonstrate financial need. Medicare Part D beneficiaries are also eligible.

Financial data Assistance with prescription drug co-payments is provided.

Duration These are 1-time grants.

Number awarded Varies each year.

Deadline Applications may be submitted at any time.

[1013]
PATIENT AID PROGRAM

Bone Marrow Foundation
30 East End Avenue, Suite 1F
New York, NY 10028
(212) 838-3029   Toll Free: (800) 365-1336
Fax: (212) 223-0081
E-mail: TheBMF@bonemarrow.org
Web: www.bonemarrow.org/resources/patient_aid.html

Summary To provide financial assistance to bone marrow transplant patients and their families.

Eligibility This program is open to both children and adult bone marrow transplant patients. Patients must be affiliated with a certified transplant center that is associated with the Bone Marrow Foundation (for a list, write to the foundation). They must have a social worker and physician at the transplant center verify information about diagnosis, treatment, and financial status.

Financial data Each patient is eligible for up to $1,000. Funds are to be used to cover the costs of support services (e.g., donor searches, compatibility testing, donor harvesting, medications, home and day care, medical and psychosocial supplies, transportation, accommodations, sperm banking, cord blood banking, legal fees, insurance premiums and co-pays, caregiver expenses related to transplant, and housing and living expenses). This funding cannot be used to pay outstanding medical bills or any other pre-existing bills associated with the transplant.

Duration This is generally a 1-time award, although occasionally recipients can reapply.

Additional data This program was started in 1992. Currently, it operates in 70 certified transplant centers across the country.

Number awarded Varies each year.

Deadline Applications may be submitted at any time.

[1014]
PATIENT SERVICES INCORPORATED ASSISTANCE

Patient Services Incorporated
P.O. Box 5930
Midlothian, VA 23112
Toll Free: (800) 366-7741   Fax: (804) 744-5407
Web: www.patientservicesinc.org

Summary To provide funding to people with chronic medical illnesses who need help in paying their health insurance premiums or pharmacy co-payments.

Eligibility This assistance is available to people with chronic medical illnesses who are experiencing financial difficulty in paying their health insurance premiums or pharmacy co-payments. Currently, applicants must be affected by 1 of the following illnesses: acromegaly, alpha1 antitrypsin deficiency, bleeding disorders, bone metastases, breast cancer MRI screening, chronic inflammatory demyelinating polyneuropathy (CIDP), chronic myelogenous leukemia (CML), complement mediated diseases (CMD), cutaneous T-cell lymphoma (CTCL), cystic fibrosis (with pseudomonas), Fabry Disease, gastrointestinal stromal tumors (GIST), hereditary angioedema (HAE), inhibitors, malignant ascites, metastatic melanoma, metastatic renal cellcarcinoma, mucopolyacchari-dosis 1 MPS 1, pseudobulbar affect (PBA), Pompe Disease, primary immune deficiency (PIDD), or severe congenital protein C deficiency.

Financial data The amount of assistance depends on the need of the recipient and the availability of funds. Recently, support averaged approximately $6,538 per patient per year.

Duration Assistance may be granted for 1 year.

Number awarded Varies each year.

Deadline Applications may be submitted at any time.

[1015]
SAMFUND GRANTS AND SCHOLARSHIPS

The SAMFund for Young Adult Survivors of Cancer
89 South Street, Suite LL02
Boston, MA 02211
(617) 938-3484   Toll Free: (866) 439-9365
Fax: (484) 842-2643   E-mail: grants@thesamfund.org
Web: www.thesamfund.org/pages/grants.html

Summary   To provide funding to young adult cancer survivors who need assistance for the transition to post-treatment life.

Eligibility   This program is open to cancer survivors between 17 and 35 years of age who are finished with active treatment and are moving forward with their lives. Applicants must demonstrate a need for funding for such purposes as graduate (but not undergraduate) tuition and expenses, car and health insurance premiums, rent, utilities, family-building expenses, gym memberships, transportation costs, or current and residual medical bills. U.S. citizenship or permanent resident status is required.

Financial data   Grant amounts vary; recently, they averaged approximately $2,500.

Duration   These are 1-time grants.

Additional data   This program, which stands for Surviving and Moving Forward, was established in 2003.

Number awarded   Varies each year; since the program was established, it has awarded grants with a total value of more than $600,000.

Deadline   Deadline not specified.

[1016]
SENTINELS OF FREEDOM SCHOLARSHIPS

Sentinels of Freedom
P.O. Box 1316
San Ramon, CA 94583
(925) 380-6342   Fax: (925) 867-1078
E-mail: info@sentinelsoffreedom.org
Web: www.sentinelsoffreedom.org

Summary   To provide funding to veterans and current military personnel who became blind, deaf, or disabled as a result of injuries sustained in the line of duty on or after September 11, 2001.

Eligibility   This program is open to members of the U.S. Air Force, Army, Coast Guard, Marines, or Navy who sustained injuries in the line of duty on or after September 11, 2001. Applicants must be rated as 60% or more disabled as a result of 1 or more of the following conditions: amputation, blindness, deafness, paraplegia, severe burns, limited traumatic brain injury (TBI), or limited post-traumatic stress disorder (PTSD); other severe injuries may be considered on a case-by-case basis. They must complete an interview process and demonstrate that they have the skills, experience, and attitude that lead to employment.

Financial data   Assistance is available for the following needs: housing (adapted for physical needs if necessary), new furniture and other household supplies, career-placement assistance and training, new adaptive vehicles, educational opportunities in addition to the new GI Bill, or financial and personal mentorship.

Duration   Assistance may be provided for up to 4 years.

Additional data   The first assistance granted by this program was awarded in 2004.

Number awarded   Varies each year. Since the program was established, it has supported 84 current and former service members.

Deadline   Applications may be submitted at any time.

[1017]
SOUTH CAROLINA NATIONAL KIDNEY FOUNDATION EMERGENCY FINANCIAL ASSISTANCE

National Kidney Foundation Serving the Carolinas-
South Carolina Region
Attn: Patient Services
508 Hampton Street, Suite 200
Columbia, SC 29201-2765
(803) 799-3870   Toll Free: (800) 488-2277
Fax: (803) 799-3871   E-mail: sderrick@kidneysc.org
Web: www.kidney.org/site/patients/index.cfm?ch=209

Summary   To provide emergency financial assistance to kidney patients in South Carolina.

Eligibility   This assistance is available to South Carolina residents who are kidney patients. Applicants must be facing a crisis situation in which they need assistance with such expenses as medications, utilities, and rent. They must apply through their clinic's social worker.

Financial data   The amount of the assistance depends on the need of the patient.

Duration   These are 1-time grants.

Number awarded   Varies each year.

Deadline   Applications may be submitted at any time.

[1018]
SUPPLEMENTAL SECURITY INCOME (SSI)

Social Security Administration
6401 Security Boulevard
Baltimore, MD 21235-0001
(410) 594-1234   Toll Free: (800) 772-1213
TDD: (800) 325-0778
Web: www.socialsecurity.gov/ssi/index.htm

Summary   To provide monthly payments to disabled, blind, deaf, and elderly people who have limited income and resources.

Eligibility   This assistance is available to U.S. citizens and certain categories of aliens who are 65 years of age or older, blind, or disabled. A person 18 years of age or older is considered disabled if a physical or mental impairment prevents him or her from doing any substantial gainful work and is expected to last for at least 12 months or to result in death. Children under the age of 18 are considered disabled if they have a physical or mental impairment that is comparable in severity to a disability that would prevent an adult from working and is expected to last at least 12 months or result in death. Children with certain conditions are automatically disabled and eligible for these benefits; the conditions include HIV infection, blindness, deafness, cerebral palsy, Down syndrome, muscular dystrophy, significant mental deficiency, diabetes (with amputation of 1 foot), amputation of 2 limbs, or amputation of leg at the hip. Regardless of age, a person whose vision is no better than 20/200 or who has a limited visual field of 20 degrees or less with the best corrective eyeglasses is considered blind; individuals with visual impairments not severe enough to meet the definition of blindness still may qualify as disabled persons. Applicants must have limited income and limited resources (less than $2,000 for an individual or $3,000 for a couple); items excluded from resources include the home used as a principal place of residence, personal and household goods, life insurance with face value of $1,500 or less, a car, burial plots for individuals and immediate family members, and burial funds up to $1,500.

Financial data   The basic monthly payment is $698 for an eligible individual or $1,048 for an eligible individual with an eligible spouse. Many states add money to that basic payment. SSI recipients may also be eligible for food stamps and other nutrition programs.

Duration   Assistance is provided as long as the recipient remains blind or disabled and in financial need.

Additional data   Although SSI is administered through the Social Security Administration, it is not financed by Social Security taxes. Financing of SSI is provided through general funds of the U.S. Treasury. Recipients of SSI need not have been employed or paid Social Security taxes, but they may be eligible for both SSI and Social Security. Disabled and blind applicants for SSI are referred to their state vocational rehabilitation agency to determine their eligibility for a program of vocational rehabilitation. Disabled drug addicts or alcoholics are referred for appropriate treatment if it is available at an approved facility or institution.

Number awarded   Recently, approximately 8,164,000 people (including 6,981,000 who were blind and disabled) were receiving SSI benefits, including 1,294,000 under 18 years of age, 4,806,000 who were 18 to 64 years of age, and 2,064,000 who were 65 or older.

Deadline   Deadline not specified.

[1019]
THOMARA LATIMER CANCER FOUNDATION GRANTS

Thomara Latimer Cancer Foundation
Attn: Cancer Funding Committee
Franklin Plaza Center
29193 Northeastern Highway, Suite 528
Southfield, MI 48034-1006
(248) 557-2346   Fax: (248) 557-8063
E-mail: funding@thomlatimercares.org
Web: www.thomlatimercares.org

Summary   To provide funding to cancer patients and family members who are unable to meet expenses.

Eligibility   This program is open to cancer patients and family members who, after a thorough investigation of other resources, are unable to meet expenses that are causing a financial burden. Applicants must be seeking funding for homecare assistance (including child care); medication or treatment not covered by insurance (includ-

ing alternative care, family lodging for out-of-town treatment); transportation to and from treatment, physician, support facilities; special needs funds for wigs or head coverings for diagnosis or treatment related to hair loss; or assistance with final arrangements.

Financial data   Grant amounts depend on the availability of funds.

Duration   These are 1-time grants.

Number awarded   Varies each year.

Deadline   Applications may be submitted at any time.

[1020]
VIRGINIA AIDS DRUG ASSISTANCE PROGRAM

Patient Services Incorporated
Attn: State Department
P.O. Box 5930
Midlothian, VA 23112
Toll Free: (866) 392-1309   Fax: (877) 251-0415
Web: www.patientservicesinc.org

Summary   To provide funding to residents of Virginia who have AIDS and need help in paying for their medication.

Eligibility   This assistance is available to residents of Virginia who have AIDS. Applicants must not have insurance coverage or third party benefits to pay for medications. Their family income must be below 400% of the federal poverty level. If they are unemployed, they must be able to document that status and explain how they are financially supported.

Financial data   The amount of assistance depends on the need of the recipient and the availability of funds.

Additional data   This program, known as Virginia ADAP, is sponsored by the Virginia Department of Health.

Number awarded   Varies each year.

Deadline   Applications may be submitted at any time.

Families of the Disabled

Scholarships ●

Fellowships ●

Grants-in-Aid ●

Described here are 363 funding opportunities open to the children, stepchildren, adopted children, grandchildren, parents, siblings, or other dependents or family members of persons with disabilities. Of these, 204 cover scholarships (funding to pursue study, research, or other activities on the undergraduate level in the United States); 35 describe fellowships (to support graduate or postgraduate study, research, or other activities in the United States); and 124 identify grants-in-aid (to pay for emergency situations, travel, income/property tax liabilities, the acquisition of assistive technology, or other personal needs). All of this is "free" money. Not one dollar will need to be repaid (provided, of course, that recipients meet all program requirements). If you are looking for a particular program and don't find it in this section, be sure to check the Program Title Index to see if it is covered elsewhere in the directory.

Scholarships

[1021]
ALABAMA G.I. DEPENDENTS' SCHOLARSHIP PROGRAM

Alabama Department of Veterans Affairs
770 Washington Avenue, Suite 470
Montgomery, AL 36102-1509
(334) 242-5077   Fax: (334) 242-5102
E-mail: willie.moore@va.state.al.us
Web: www.va.state.al.us/scholarship.htm

Summary To provide educational benefits for college or graduate school to the dependents of disabled, deceased, and other Alabama veterans.

Eligibility This program is open to children, spouses, and unremarried widow(er)s of veterans who are currently rated as 20% or more service-connected disabled or were so rated at time of death, were a former prisoner of war, have been declared missing in action, died as the result of a service-connected disability, or died while on active military duty in the line of duty. The veteran must have been a permanent civilian resident of Alabama for at least 1 year prior to entering active military service and served honorably for at least 90 days during war time (or less, in case of death or service-connected disability). Veterans who were not Alabama residents at the time of entering active military service may also qualify if they have a 100% disability and were permanent residents of Alabama for at least 5 years prior to filing the application for this program or prior to death, if deceased. Children and stepchildren must be under the age of 26, but spouses and widow(er)s may be of any age. Spouses cease to be eligible if they become divorced from the qualifying veteran. Widow(er)s cease to be eligible if they remarry.

Financial data Eligible dependents may attend any state-supported Alabama institution of higher learning or enroll in a prescribed course of study at any Alabama state-supported trade school without payment of any tuition, book fees, or laboratory charges.

Duration This is an entitlement program for 5 years of full-time undergraduate or graduate study or part-time equivalent for all qualifying children and for spouses and unremarried widow(er)s who veteran spouse is or was rated 100% disabled or meets other qualifying requirements. Spouses and unremarried widow(er)s whose veteran spouse is or was rated between 20% and 90% disabled may attend only 3 standard academic years.

Additional data Benefits for children, spouses, and unremarried widow(er)s are available in addition to federal government benefits. Assistance is not provided for non-credit courses, placement testing, GED preparation, continuing educational courses, pre-technical courses, or state board examinations.

Number awarded Varies each year.

Deadline Applications may be submitted at any time.

[1022]
ALABAMA SCHOLARSHIPS FOR DEPENDENTS OF BLIND PARENTS

Alabama Department of Rehabilitation Services
Attn: Debra Culver
602 South Lawrence Street
Montgomery, AL 36104
(256) 293-7500   Toll Free: (800) 441-7607
Fax: (256) 293-7383   TDD: (800) 499-1816
E-mail: dculver@rehab.state.al.us
Web: www.rehab.state.al.us

Summary To provide financial assistance for college to students whose blind parents are residents of Alabama.

Eligibility Eligible to apply are seniors or recent graduates of Alabama high schools whose family head of household is blind and whose annual family income is limited (less than $9,000 for a family with 1 child, $12,000 with 2 children, $15,000 with 3 children, or $18,000 with 4 or more children). Applicants must 1) have been permanent residents of Alabama for at least 5 years, 2) apply within 2 years after graduation from high school, and 3) be under 23 years of age.

Financial data Eligible students receive free tuition, waiver of fees, and necessary textbooks at any Alabama state-supported postsecondary institution.

Duration Up to 36 months at an institution of higher education, or for the period required to complete a course of study at a trade school.

Additional data Recipients must complete their course of study within 5 years (unless interrupted by military service), but at least prior to the age of 30.

Number awarded Varies each year.

Deadline Deadline not specified.

[1023]
ALL IN FOR SKIN SCHOLARSHIP

Greater Kansas City Community Foundation
Attn: Scholarship Coordinator
1055 Broadway, Suite 130
Kansas City, MO 64105-1595
(816) 842-0944   Fax: (816) 842-8079
E-mail: scholarships@gkccf.org
Web: www.gkccf.org/scholarships

Summary To provide financial assistance to residents of Kansas and Missouri who have lost a parent due to melanoma cancer and are interested in attending college in any state.

Eligibility This program is open to graduating high school seniors and current undergraduate students who are residents of Kansas or Missouri. Applicants must have lost a parent due to melanoma cancer. They must be able to demonstrate academic ability and leadership qualities. Financial need is not considered in the selection process.

Financial data The stipend ranges up to $5,000.

Duration 1 year.

Number awarded 1 or more each year.

Deadline March of each year.

[1024]
ALPA SCHOLARSHIP PROGRAM

Air Line Pilots Association
Attn: Maggie Erzen
1625 Massachusetts Avenue, N.W.
Washington, DC 20036
(703) 689-2270   E-mail: Maggie.Erzen@alpa.org
Web: www.alpa.org

Summary   To provide financial assistance for college to the children of disabled or deceased members of the Air Line Pilots Association.

Eligibility   This program is open to children of medically retired, long-term disabled, or deceased members of the Air Line Pilots Association. Although the program envisions selection of students enrolling as college freshman, eligible individuals who are already enrolled in college may also apply. Selection is based on a number of factors, including academic record and financial need.

Financial data   The stipend is $3,000 per year.

Duration   1 year; may be renewed up to 3 additional years, if the student maintains a GPA of 3.0 or higher.

Number awarded   Each year, the association grants 1 new 4-year award and continues 3 previously-made awards.

Deadline   March of each year.

[1025]
AMERICAN PATRIOT FREEDOM SCHOLARSHIP AWARD

Homefront America
27375 Paseo La Serna
San Juan Capistrano, CA 92675
(949) 248-9468   E-mail: info@homefrontamerica.org
Web: www.homefrontamerica.org

Summary   To provide funding to children of active, Reserve, disabled, deceased, or retired military personnel.

Eligibility   This program is open to students between 18 and 21 years of age who are children of 1) full-time active duty or Reserve service members; 2) service members disabled as a direct result of injuries sustained during a military operation; 3) deceased service members killed in action during a military operation; or 4) service members who are retired with an honorable discharge. Applicants must be enrolled or planning to enroll at an accredited college, university, or vocational/technical institute to work on an undergraduate degree. Selection is based primarily on a 500-word essay on significant contributions of America's greatest generation to our country.

Financial data   The stipend is $1,000.

Duration   1 year.

Number awarded   5 each year.

Deadline   Applications may be submitted at any time, but they must be received in time for the announcement of recipients at the end of May of each year.

[1026]
ANGEL ON MY SHOULDER SCHOLARSHIPS

Angel on My Shoulder
P.O. Box 747
St. Germain, WI 54558
Toll Free: (800) 860-3431
E-mail: info@angelonmyshoulder.org
Web: www.angelonmyshoulder.org

Summary   To provide funding to high school seniors in Wisconsin who plan to attend college in any state and are cancer survivors or relatives affected by cancer.

Eligibility   This program is open to seniors who are graduating from high schools in Wisconsin and planning to attend a 4-year college, technical school, or specialty school in any state. Applicants must be survivors of cancer or have an immediate family member (father, mother, sibling) affected by cancer. Along with their application, they must submit a 250-word essay on why they wish to further their formal education, including their goals and values and how the cancer experience or affiliation with the sponsoring organization has affected their life. Financial need is considered in the selection process.

Financial data   The stipend is $1,000.

Duration   1 year.

Additional data   This program was established in 2008.

Number awarded   Varies each year; recently, 25 of these scholarships were awarded.

Deadline   February of each year.

[1027]
ARKANSAS LAW ENFORCEMENT OFFICERS' DEPENDENTS' SCHOLARSHIPS

Arkansas Department of Higher Education
Attn: Financial Aid Division
114 East Capitol Avenue
Little Rock, AR 72201-3818
(501) 371-2050   Toll Free: (800) 54-STUDY
Fax: (501) 371-2001   E-mail: finaid@adhe.edu
Web: www.adhe.edu

Summary   To provide financial assistance for undergraduate education to the dependents of deceased or disabled Arkansas law enforcement officers, fire fighters, or other designated public employees.

Eligibility   This program is open to the spouses and/or children (natural, adopted, or step) of Arkansas residents who were killed or permanently disabled in the line of duty as law enforcement officers, municipal and/or college or university police officers, sheriffs and deputy sheriffs, constables, state correction employees, game wardens, state park employees who are commissioned law enforcement officers or emergency response employees, full-time or volunteer fire fighters, state forestry employees engaged in fighting forest fires, certain Arkansas Highway and Transportation Department employees, emergency medical technicians, or Department of Community Punishment employees. Children must be less than 23 years of age. Spouses may not have remarried. All applicants must have been Arkansas residents for at least 6 months.

Financial data The scholarship covers tuition, on-campus room charges, and fees (but not books, school supplies, food, materials, or dues for extracurricular activities) at any state-supported college or university in Arkansas.

Duration Up to 8 semesters, as long as the student is working on a baccalaureate or associate degree and maintains a GPA of 2.0 or higher.

Number awarded Varies each year.

Deadline May of each year for late summer and fall terms; October of each year for spring and early summer terms.

[1028]
ARKANSAS MILITARY DEPENDENTS' SCHOLARSHIP PROGRAM

Arkansas Department of Higher Education
Attn: Financial Aid Division
114 East Capitol Avenue
Little Rock, AR 72201-3818
(501) 371-2050   Toll Free: (800) 54-STUDY
Fax: (501) 371-2001   E-mail: finaid@adhe.edu
Web: www.adhe.edu

Summary To provide financial assistance for educational purposes to dependents of certain categories of Arkansas veterans.

Eligibility This program is open to the natural children, adopted children, stepchildren, and spouses of Arkansas residents who have been declared to be a prisoner of war, killed in action, missing in action, killed on ordnance delivery, or 100% totally and permanently disabled during, or as a result of, active military service. Applicants and their parent or spouse must be residents of Arkansas. They must be working on, or planning to work on, a bachelor's degree or certificate of completion at a public college, university, or technical school in Arkansas.

Financial data The program pays for tuition, general registration fees, special course fees, activity fees, room and board (if provided in campus facilities), and other charges associated with earning a degree or certificate.

Duration 1 year; undergraduates may obtain renewal as long as they make satisfactory progress toward a baccalaureate degree; graduate students may obtain renewal as long as they maintain a minimum GPA of 2.0 and make satisfactory progress toward a degree.

Additional data This program was established in 1973 as the Arkansas Missing in Action/Killed in Action Dependents Scholarship Program to provide assistance to the dependents of veterans killed in action, missing in action, or declared a prisoner of war. In 2005, it was amended to include dependents of disabled veterans and given its current name. Applications must be submitted to the financial aid director at an Arkansas state-supported institution of higher education.

Number awarded Varies each year; recently, 4 of these scholarships were awarded.

Deadline May of each year for late summer and fall terms; October of each year for spring and early summer terms.

[1029]
BERNICE MCNAMARA MEMORIAL SCHOLARSHIP

Ulman Cancer Fund for Young Adults
Attn: Scholarship Committee
10440 Little Patuxent Parkway, Suite G1
Columbia, MD 21044
(410) 964-0202   Toll Free: (888) 393-FUND
Fax: (410) 964-0402
E-mail: scholarship@ulmanfund.org
Web: www.ulmanfund.org/scholarship.aspx

Summary To provide money for college or graduate school to students who have or have lost a parent with cancer.

Eligibility This program is open to students who have or have lost a parent or guardian to cancer. Applicants must be 35 years of age or younger and attending, or planning to attend, a 2- or 4-year college, university, or vocational program to work on an undergraduate or graduate degree. The parent or guardian must have been first diagnosed with cancer after the applicant was 15 years of age. Along with their application, they must submit an essay of at least 1,000 words on how their parent's cancer experience has impacted their outlook on life and the legacy that they desire to leave behind. Selection is based on demonstrated dedication to community service, commitment to educational and professional goals, use of their cancer experience to impact the lives of other young adults affected by cancer, medical hardship, and financial need.

Financial data The stipend is $2,500. Funds are paid directly to the educational institution.

Duration 1 year; nonrenewable.

Additional data Recipients must agree to complete 40 hours of community service.

Number awarded 1 each year.

Deadline March of each year.

[1030]
BILL MCADAM SCHOLARSHIP FUND

Hemophilia Foundation of Michigan
c/o Cathy McAdam
22226 Doxtator
Dearborn, MI 48128
(313) 563-1412   E-mail: mcmcadam@comcast.net

Summary To provide money for college to students with a bleeding disorder or members of their families.

Eligibility This program is open to 1) students with a hereditary bleeding disorder (hemophilia, von Willebrand, etc.) or 2) members of their families (spouse, partner, child, sibling). Applicants must be U.S. citizens and enrolled or planning to enroll at an accredited 2- or 4-year college, trade or technical school, or other certification program. Along with their application, they must submit 2 letters of recommendation and 3 essays: 1) what they would like the scholarship committee to know about their dream career and the passion that moves them toward furthering their education; 2) how they would describe a favorite painting or photograph to someone who is blind;

and 3) how they will make a difference in the fight against stigma, fear, and discrimination for people facing chronic illness or disability. Financial need is not considered in the selection process.

Financial data The stipend is $2,000. Funds are paid directly to the recipient's institution.

Duration 1 year; nonrenewable.

Number awarded 1 each year.

Deadline May of each year.

[1031]
BIORX/HEMOPHILIA OF NORTH CAROLINA EDUCATIONAL SCHOLARSHIPS

Hemophilia of North Carolina
Attn: Scholarship Committee
260 Town Hall Drive, Suite A
Morrisville, NC 27560-5544
(919) 319-0014   Toll Free: (800) 990-5557
Fax: (919) 319-0016   E-mail: info@hemophilia-nc.org
Web: www. hemophilia-nc.org/scholarships.html

Summary To provide financial assistance for college to people with hemophilia, their caregivers, and their families.

Eligibility This program is open to caregivers of children affected with bleeding disorders, people who have been diagnosed with hemophilia, and siblings and parents of people diagnosed with hemophilia. Residents of all states are eligible. Applicants must be enrolled or planning to enroll at an accredited college, university, or certified training program. Along with their application, they must submit an essay of 1 to 2 pages describing their occupational goals and objectives in life and how their or their family's experiences with bleeding disorders have affected their choices. Preference is given to applicants who are studying or planning to study a health care-related field. Selection is primarily based on merit, although financial need may be considered as well.

Financial data The stipend is $2,000.

Duration 1 year.

Additional data This program, established in 2004, is sponsored by BioRx.

Number awarded 4 each year, of which at least 1 of which is reserved for an applicant studying in a health-related field.

Deadline April of each year.

[1032]
BLACKHORSE SCHOLARSHIP

Blackhorse Association
P.O. Box 223
Hemphill, TX 75948-0223
E-mail: info@blackhorse.org
Web: www.blackhorse.org/scholarships.cfm

Summary To provide financial assistance for college to children of disabled and other members of the Blackhorse Association who are currently serving or have served with the 11th Armored Cavalry Regiment (ACR).

Eligibility This program is open to the natural and adopted children of current or former 11th ACR solders who are also members of the association. Applicants must be attending or planning to attend college. In the selection process, first priority is given to children who lost a parent in service of the regiment; second priority is given to children of those incapacitated by wounds or injury while serving the regiment; third priority is given based on financial need of the applicant and family.

Financial data The stipend is $3,000 per year.

Duration 1 year; renewable up to 3 more years.

Additional data The Blackhorse Association was founded in 1970 by veterans of the 11th ACR who had served in Vietnam.

Number awarded Varies each year; recently, 14 of these scholarships were awarded. Since this program began, it has awarded more than $500,000 in scholarships.

Deadline March of each year.

[1033]
BOB HERSH MEMORIAL SCHOLARSHIP

Mary M. Gooley Hemophilia Center
Attn: Scholarship Selection Committee
1415 Portland Avenue, Suite 500
Rochester, NY 14621
(585) 922-5700   Fax: (585) 922-5775
E-mail: Kristina.Ritchie@rochestergeneral.org
Web: www.hemocenter.org

Summary To provide funding to people with a bleeding disorder and their families who plan to attend college to prepare for a career in a teaching or helping profession.

Eligibility This program is open to people who are affected directly or indirectly by hemophilia, von Willebrand Disease, hereditary bleeding disorder, or hemochromatosis. Applicants must be enrolled or planning to enroll at an accredited 2- or 4-year college or university, vocational/technical school, or certified training program. They must be preparing for a career in a teaching or helping profession. Along with their application, they must submit 1) a 1,000-word essay on their goals and aspirations, their biggest challenge and how they met it, and anything else they want the selection committee to know about them; and 2) a 250-word essay on any unusual family or personal circumstances that have affected their achievement in school, work, or participation in school and community activities, including how their bleeding disorder or that of their family member has affected their life. Selection is based on the essays, academic performance, participation in school and community activities, work or volunteer experience, personal or family circumstances, recommendations, and financial need.

Financial data The stipend is $1,000.

Duration 1 year.

Additional data This program was established in 2009.

Number awarded 1 each year.

Deadline March of each year.

[1034]
BRADLEY KRUEGER SCHOLARSHIP

Hemophilia Foundation of Illinois
Attn: Executive Director
210 South DesPlaines
Chicago, IL 60661-5500
(312) 427-1495   E-mail: brobinson@hfi-il.org
Web: www.hemophiliaillinois.org/scholarships.htm

Summary To provide financial assistance for attendance at a college in any state to residents of Illinois who have a bleeding disorder and their families.

Eligibility This program is open to residents of Illinois who have a bleeding disorder and their parents, siblings, and children; people who are carriers of the disease are also eligible. Applicants must be attending or planning to attend a postsecondary institution, including a trade school, in any state. Along with their application, they must submit essays on their goals for furthering their education, the steps they have taken to meet those goals, how this scholarship will help them achieve those goals, what it means to them to live with hemophilia, and what they consider their responsibility to the bleeding disorders community. Financial need is not considered.

Financial data Stipends range up to $5,000. Funds are paid directly to the educational institution to be used for payment of tuition, room and board, books, and supplies (including computer equipment).

Duration 1 year.

Number awarded 1 or more each year.

Deadline June of each year.

[1035]
BRYON RIESCH SCHOLARSHIPS

Bryon Riesch Paralysis Foundation
P.O. Box 1388
Waukesha, WI 53187-1388
(262) 547-2083   E-mail: briesch@brpf.org
Web: www.brpf.org/Grants/ApplicationScholarships.html

Summary To provide financial assistance to undergraduate and graduate students who have a neurological disability or the children of people with such a disability.

Eligibility This program is open to students entering or enrolled at a 2- or 4-year college or university as an undergraduate or graduate student. Applicants must have a neurological disability or be the child of a person with such a disability. They must have a GPA of 2.5 or higher in high school or college. Along with their application, they must submit a 200-word essay on why they deserve the scholarship, a statement of their 5- and 10-year goals, and a list of work experience. Financial need is not considered.

Financial data Stipends range from $1,000 to $2,000.

Duration 1 year; may be renewed.

Number awarded Varies each semester; recently, 5 scholarships (all at $1,000) were awarded for the fall semester and 3 (including 1 at $2,000 and 2 at $1,000) were awarded for the spring semester.

Deadline May of each year for fall semester; December of each year for spring semester.

[1036]
CALIFORNIA FEE WAIVER PROGRAM FOR CHILDREN OF VETERANS

California Department of Veterans Affairs
Attn: Division of Veterans Services
1227 O Street, Room 105
P.O. Box 942895
Sacramento, CA 94295
(916) 653-2573   Toll Free: (877) 741-8532
Fax: (916) 653-2563   TDD: (800) 324-5966
Web: www.cdva.ca.gov/VetServices/Education.aspx

Summary To provide financial assistance for college to the children of disabled or deceased veterans in California.

Eligibility Eligible for this program are the children of veterans who 1) died of a service-connected disability; 2) had a service-connected disability at the time of death; or 3) currently have a service-connected disability of any level of severity. Applicants must plan to attend a community college in California, branch of the California State University system, or campus of the University of California. Their income, including the value of support received from parents, cannot exceed $11,369. The veteran is not required to have a connection to California for this program. Dependents in college who are eligible to receive federal education benefits from the U.S. Department of Veterans Affairs are not eligible for these fee waivers.

Financial data This program provides for waiver of registration fees to students attending any publicly-supported college or university in California.

Duration 1 year; may be renewed.

Number awarded Varies each year.

Deadline Deadline not specified.

[1037]
CALIFORNIA FEE WAIVER PROGRAM FOR DEPENDENTS OF DECEASED OR DISABLED NATIONAL GUARD MEMBERS

California Department of Veterans Affairs
Attn: Division of Veterans Services
1227 O Street, Room 105
P.O. Box 942895
Sacramento, CA 94295
(916) 653-2573   Toll Free: (877) 741-8532
Fax: (916) 653-2563   TDD: (800) 324-5966
Web: www.cdva.ca.gov/VetServices/Education.aspx

Summary To provide financial assistance for college to dependents of disabled and deceased members of the California National Guard.

Eligibility Eligible for this program are dependents, unremarried surviving spouses, and current registered domestic partners (RDPs) of members of the California National Guard who, in the line of duty and in the active service of the state, were killed, died of a disability, or became permanently disabled. Applicants must be attending or planning to attend a community college, branch of the California State University system, or campus of the University of California.

Financial data Full-time college students receive a waiver of tuition and registration fees at any publicly-supported college or university in California.

Duration 1 year; may be renewed.

Number awarded Varies each year.

Deadline Deadline not specified.

[1038]
CALIFORNIA FEE WAIVER PROGRAM FOR DEPENDENTS OF TOTALLY DISABLED VETERANS

California Department of Veterans Affairs
Attn: Division of Veterans Services
1227 O Street, Room 105
P.O. Box 942895
Sacramento, CA 94295
(916) 653-2573   Toll Free: (877) 741-8532
Fax: (916) 653-2563   TDD: (800) 324-5966
Web: www.cdva.ca.gov/VetServices/Education.aspx

Summary To provide financial assistance for college to dependents of disabled and other California veterans.

Eligibility Eligible for this program are spouses, children, and unremarried spouses or registered domestic partners (RDPs) of veterans who are currently totally service-connected disabled (or are being compensated for a service-connected disability at a rate of 100%) or who died of a service-connected cause or disability. The veteran parent must have served during a qualifying war period and must have been discharged or released from military service under honorable conditions. Children must be younger than 27 years of age (extended to 30 if the child is a veteran); there are no age restrictions for spouses, surviving spouses, or RDPs. This program does not have an income limit. Dependents in college are not eligible if they are qualified to receive educational benefits from the U.S. Department of Veterans Affairs. Applicants must be attending or planning to attend a community college, branch of the California State University system, or campus of the University of California.

Financial data Full-time college students receive a waiver of tuition and registration fees at any publicly-supported college or university in California.

Duration Children of eligible veterans may receive postsecondary benefits until the needed training is completed or until the dependent reaches 27 years of age (extended to 30 if the dependent serves in the armed forces). Spouses and surviving spouses are limited to a maximum of 48 months' full-time training or the equivalent in part-time training.

Number awarded Varies each year.

Deadline Deadline not specified.

[1039]
CALIFORNIA LAW ENFORCEMENT PERSONNEL DEPENDENTS GRANT PROGRAM

California Student Aid Commission
Attn: Specialized Programs Operations Branch
10811 International Drive, Suite 100
P.O. Box 419029
Rancho Cordova, CA 95741-9029
(916) 526-8276   Toll Free: (888) CA-GRANT
Fax: (916) 464-7977   E-mail: specialized@csac.ca.gov
Web: www.csac.ca.gov/doc.asp?id=109

Summary To provide financial assistance for college to the dependents of California law enforcement officers who have been totally disabled or killed in the line of duty.

Eligibility This program is open to the natural children, adopted children, and spouses of a California peace officer (Highway Patrol, marshal, sheriff, police officer), employee of the Department of Corrections or Youth Authority, or fire fighter. The parent or spouse must have died or become totally disabled as the result of an accident or injury caused by external violence or physical force incurred in the performance of duty. Applicants must be enrolled in at least 6 units at an accredited California postsecondary institution and able to demonstrate need.

Financial data Stipends range from $100 to $11,259 per year, depending on the need of the recipient.

Duration 1 academic year; may be renewed for up to 5 additional years at 4-year colleges and universities or up to 3 additional years at community colleges.

Additional data If the student receives other scholarships or grants, the award may be adjusted or withdrawn, depending upon financial need. Acceptance of work-study, loans, or employment will generally not affect the amount of money offered through this program.

Number awarded Varies each year; recently, 11 students received $82,000 in assistance from this program.

Deadline Applications may be submitted at any time.

[1040]
CFA INSTITUTE 11 SEPTEMBER MEMORIAL SCHOLARSHIP

CFA Institute
Attn: Research Foundation
560 Ray C. Hunt Drive
P.O. Box 2082
Charlottesville, VA 22902-2082
(434) 951-5499   Toll Free: (800) 237-8132
Fax: (434) 951-5240   E-mail: rf@cfainstitute.org
Web: www.cfainstitute.org

Summary To provide financial assistance to individuals and their families who were disabled or killed in the September 11, 2001 terrorist attacks and wish to major in business-related fields in college.

Eligibility This program is open to residents of any state or country who either 1) were permanently disabled in the attacks of September 11, 2001; or 2) are the spouses, domestic partners, or children of anyone killed or permanently disabled in the attacks. Applicants must be working full or part time on an undergraduate degree in finance, economics, accounting, or business ethics. Selection is based on demonstrated leadership and good citizenship, academic record, and financial need.

Financial data Stipends range up to $25,000 per year, depending on the need of the recipient.

Duration 1 year; renewable up to 4 additional years.

Additional data The CFA (Chartered Financial Analyst) Institute was formerly the Association for Investment Management and Research (AIMR). It lost at least 56 of its members and CFA candidates in the terrorist attacks of 11 September. This program is managed by Scholarship Management Services, a division of Scholarship America.

Number awarded Varies each year; recently, 12 of these scholarships were awarded.

Deadline May of each year.

[1041]
CHIEF MASTER SERGEANTS OF THE AIR FORCE SCHOLARSHIPS

Air Force Sergeants Association
Attn: Scholarship Coordinator
5211 Auth Road
Suitland, MD 20746
(301) 899-3500   Toll Free: (800) 638-0594
Fax: (301) 899-8136 E-mail: balsobrooks@hqafsa.org
Web: www.hqafsa.org

Summary To provide financial assistance for college to the dependent children of enlisted Air Force personnel, particularly those facing special challenges.

Eligibility This program is open to the unmarried children (including stepchildren and legally adopted children) of enlisted active-duty, retired, or veteran members of the U.S. Air Force, Air National Guard, or Air Force Reserves. Applicants must be attending or planning to attend an accredited academic institution. They must have an unweighted GPA of 3.5 or higher. Along with their application, they must submit 1) a paragraph on their life objectives and what they plan to do with the education they receive; and 2) an essay on the most urgent problem facing society today. High school seniors must also submit a transcript of all high school grades and a record of their SAT or ACT scores. Selection is based on academic record, character, leadership skills, writing ability, versatility, and potential for success. Financial need is not a consideration. A unique aspect of these scholarships is that applicants may supply additional information regarding circumstances that entitle them to special consideration; examples of such circumstances include student disabilities, financial hardships, parent disabled and unable to work, parent missing in action/killed in action/prisoner of war, or other unusual extenuating circumstances.

Financial data Stipends range from $1,000 to $3,000; funds may be used for tuition, room and board, fees, books, supplies, and transportation.

Duration 1 year; may be renewed if the recipient maintains full-time enrollment.

Additional data The Air Force Sergeants Association administers this program on behalf of the Airmen Memorial Foundation. It was established in 1987 and named in honor of CMSAF Richard D. Kisling, the late third Chief Master Sergeant of the Air Force. In 1997, following the deaths of CMSAF's (Retired) Andrews and Harlow, it was given its current name. The highest-ranked applicant receives the Paul W. Airey Memorial Scholarship.

Number awarded 1 at $3,000, 1 at $2,500, 1 at $2,000, 1 at $1,500 and 7 at $1,000. Since this program began, it has awarded more than $250,000.

Deadline March of each year.

[1042]
CHILDREN OF FALLEN SOLDIERS RELIEF FUND COLLEGE GRANTS

Children of Fallen Soldiers Relief Fund
P.O. Box 3968
Gaithersburg, MD 20885-3968
(301) 685-3421   Toll Free: (866) 96-CFSRF
Fax: (301) 630-0592   E-mail: grants@cfsrf.org
Web: www.cfsrf.org

Summary To provide financial assistance for college to children and spouses of military personnel killed or severely disabled during service in Iraq or Afghanistan.

Eligibility This program is open to spouses and children of military personnel killed or severely disabled as a result of service in Operation Iraqi Freedom or Operation Enduring Freedom. Applicants must be enrolled or planning to enroll at a college or university. They must have a GPA of 2.75 or higher and be able to demonstrate financial need.

Financial data Grants have ranged from $1,000 to $28,000, depending on the need of the recipient.

Duration These are 1-time grants.

Number awarded Varies each year; since the organization was founded, it has awarded 14 of these grants.

Deadline Applications may be submitted at any time.

[1043]
CHILDREN OF INJURED WORKERS SCHOLARSHIPS

Children of Injured Workers, Inc.
4983 Brittonfield Parkway
East Syracuse, NY 13057
(315) 449-4306   Fax: (315) 449-4358
E-mail: info@kidschanceny.org
Web: www.kidschanceny.org

Summary To provide financial assistance to residents of New York whose parent was seriously injured or killed in a workplace accident and who are interested in attending college in any state.

Eligibility This program is open to New York residents attending or planning to attend a college or technical school in any state. Applicants must be the child of a worker who suffered injury or death in an accident that is either established or accepted under the Workers' Compensation Law of the state of New York. The injury or death must have had a demonstrable impact on the financial ability of the child to attend college.

Financial data   A stipend is awarded (amount not specified).

Duration   1 year; recipients may reapply.

Number awarded   Varies each year.

Deadline   Deadline not specified.

[1044]
CODA INTERNATIONAL MILLIE BROTHER SCHOLARSHIPS

Children of Deaf Adults Inc.
c/o Jennie E. Pyers, Scholarship Committee
Wellesley College
106 Central Street, SCI480
Wellesley, MA 02842
(781) 283-3736   Fax: (781) 283-3730
E-mail: coda.scholarship@gmail.com
Web: coda-international.org/blog/scholarship

Summary   To provide financial assistance for college to the children of deaf parents.

Eligibility   This program is open to the hearing children of deaf parents who are high school seniors or graduates attending or planning to attend college. Applicants must submit a 2-page essay on 1) how their experience as the child of deaf parents has shaped their life and goals; and 2) their future career aspirations. Essays are judged on organization, content, and creativity. In addition to the essay, selection is based on a high school and/or college transcript and 2 letters of recommendation.

Financial data   The stipend is $3,000.

Duration   1 year; recipients may reapply.

Number awarded   2 each year.

Deadline   March of each year.

[1045]
COLORADO CHAPTER NHF ACADEMIC SCHOLARSHIP PROGRAM

National Hemophilia Foundation-Colorado Chapter
Attn: Academic Scholarship Program
1536 Wynkoop Street, Box 26
Denver, CO 80202
(720) 336-0156   E-mail: info@cohemo.org
Web: www.cohemo.org

Summary   To provide financial assistance to residents of Colorado who have a bleeding disorder or are relatives of a person with a bleeding disorder and are interested in attending college in any state.

Eligibility   This program is open to residents of Colorado who are 1) persons with hemophilia or a related inherited bleeding disorder; 2) parents of a minor child with a bleeding disorder; 3) siblings of a person with a bleeding disorder; and 4) immediate family members of persons who died because of complications of a bleeding disorder. Applicants must be enrolled or planning to enroll at a college, university, or trade school in any state. Along with their application, they must submit a 300-word essay on the impact this scholarship would have on their education. Selection is based on the essay, academic merit, letters of recommendation, impact of the bleeding disorder

on educational activities, employment status, and financial need.

Financial data   The stipend is $1,000. Funds must be used for tuition, room, board, and related educational expenses.

Duration   1 year; nonrenewable.

Number awarded   2 each year.

Deadline   March of each year.

[1046]
COLORADO DEPENDENTS TUITION ASSISTANCE PROGRAM

Colorado Commission on Higher Education
1560 Broadway, Suite 1600
Denver, CO 80202
(303) 866-2723   Fax: (303) 866-4266
E-mail: cche@state.co.us
Web: highered.colorado.gov

Summary   To provide money for college to the dependents of disabled or deceased Colorado National Guardsmen, law enforcement officers, and fire fighters.

Eligibility   Eligible are dependents of Colorado law enforcement officers, fire fighters, and National Guardsmen disabled or killed in the line of duty, as well as dependents of prisoners of war or service personnel listed as missing in action. Students must be Colorado residents under 22 years of age enrolled at 1) a state-supported 2- or 4-year Colorado college or university; 2) a private college, university, or vocational school in Colorado approved by the commission; or 3) an out-of-state 4-year college. Need is considered in the selection process.

Financial data   Eligible students receive free tuition at Colorado public institutions of higher education. If the recipient wishes to attend a private college, university, or proprietary school, the award is limited to the amount of tuition at a comparable state-supported institution. Students who have applied to live in a dormitory, but have not been accepted because there is not enough space, may be provided supplemental assistance. Students who choose to live off-campus are not eligible for room reimbursement or a meal plan. Students who attend a nonresidential Colorado institution and do not live at home are eligible for a grant of $1,000 per semester to assist with living expenses. Students who attend an out-of-state institution are eligible for the amount of tuition equivalent to that at a comparable Colorado public institution, but they are not eligible for room and board.

Duration   Up to 6 years or until completion of a bachelor's degree, provided the recipient maintains a GPA of 2.5 or higher.

Additional data   Recipients must attend accredited postsecondary institutions in Colorado.

Number awarded   Varies each year; recently, nearly $365,000 was allocated to this program.

Deadline   Deadline not specified.

[1047]
COLORADO-WYOMING CHAPTER MS SOCIETY SCHOLARSHIP PROGRAM

National Multiple Sclerosis Society-Colorado-Wyoming
  Chapter
900 South Broadway, Second Floor
Denver, CO 80209
(303) 698-7400   Toll Free: (800) 344-4867
Fax: (303) 698-7421
E-mail: COCreceptionist@nmss.org
Web: was.nationalmssociety.org

Summary To provide financial assistance to high school seniors and graduates from Colorado and Wyoming who have multiple sclerosis (MS) or have a parent with MS and are planning to attend college in any state.

Eligibility This program is open to graduating high school seniors, recent graduates, and GED recipients from Colorado and Wyoming who have MS or a parent who has MS. Applicants must be planning to enroll as an entering undergraduate student at a 2- or 4-year college, university, or vocational/technical school in the United States on at least a half-time basis. Along with their application, they must submit an essay on the impact MS has had on their lives. Selection is based on that essay, academic record, leadership and participation in school or community activities, work experience, goals and aspirations, an outside appraisal, special circumstances, and financial need. U.S. citizenship or permanent resident status is required.

Financial data The stipend is $1,000.

Duration 1 year.

Number awarded Varies each year; recently, 4 of these scholarships were awarded.

Deadline January of each year.

[1048]
CONNECTICUT CHAPTER MS SOCIETY SCHOLARSHIP PROGRAM

National Multiple Sclerosis Society-Connecticut
  Chapter
659 Tower Avenue, First Floor
Hartford, CT 06112-1269
(860) 913-2550   Toll Free: (800) 344-4867
Fax: (860) 714-2301
E-mail: programs@ctfightsMS.org
Web: was.nationalmssociety.org

Summary To provide financial assistance to high school seniors and graduates from Connecticut who have multiple sclerosis (MS) or have a parent with MS and are planning to attend college in any state.

Eligibility This program is open to graduating high school seniors, recent graduates, and GED recipients from Connecticut who have MS or a parent who has MS. Applicants must be planning to enroll as an entering undergraduate student at a 2- or 4-year college, university, or vocational/technical school in the United States on at least a half-time basis. Along with their application, they must submit an essay on the impact MS has had on their lives. Selection is based on that essay, academic record,

leadership and participation in school or community activities, work experience, goals and aspirations, an outside appraisal, special circumstances, and financial need. U.S. citizenship or permanent resident status is required.

Financial data The stipend is $1,500.

Duration 1 year.

Additional data This program receives support from the Corn-Carter Family Scholarship Fund, the Jo-Ann Concilio Memorial Fund, and the Hayley's Hope and Michaela's Miracle MS Memorial Fund.

Number awarded Varies each year; recently, 10 of these scholarships were awarded.

Deadline January of each year.

[1049]
DANA WALTERS SCHOLARSHIPS

Dana Walters Scholarship Foundation
P.O. Box 723243
Atlanta, GA 31139
(770) 436-0190   E-mail: sonickaren@aol.com
Web: www.dwscholarship.com

Summary To provide money for college in any state to residents of Georgia who have cystic fibrosis (CF) or are members of their immediate families.

Eligibility This program is open to residents of Georgia who have CF or are a member of a family (including parents) of a person who has CF. Applicants must be graduating high school seniors or already have a high school diploma. They must have a combined SAT score of at least 900 or an ACT score of at least 21 and either a GPA of 2.7 or higher or a rank in the top 30% of their class. Financial need is not considered in the selection process.

Financial data The stipend is $1,000. Funds are paid directly to the recipient's college.

Duration 1 year; may be renewed.

Number awarded 1 or more each year.

Deadline March of each year.

[1050]
DAVE MADEIROS CONTINUED EDUCATION SCHOLARSHIPS

Factor Foundation of America
Attn: Scholarship Committee
P.O. Box 812542
Boca Raton, FL 33481-2542
(561) 504-6531
E-mail: kmadeiros@factorfoundation.org
Web: www.factorfoundation.org/programs.htm

Summary To provide financial assistance for college to people with a bleeding disorder and their families.

Eligibility This program is open to people with a bleeding disorder and their siblings, parents, and children. Applicants must be attending or planning to attend an accredited 2- or 4-year college or university or technical school. They must be recommended by a local hemophilia chapter, physician, and/or hemophilia treatment center. Along with their application, they must submit a 500-word letter describing their goals and aspirations and how the bleeding disorders community has played a part in their life. Financial need is also considered in the selection process.

Financial data   The stipend is $2,000 per year.

Duration   1 year; may be renewed if the recipient remains in good academic standing.

Additional data   This program began in 2006.

Number awarded   Varies each year; recently, 12 of these scholarships were awarded.

Deadline   June of each year.

[1051]
DAVID NELSON JR. MEMORIAL FUND SCHOLARSHIP

Gift of Life Donor Program
Attn: David Nelson Jr. Memorial Fund
401 North Third Street
Philadelphia, PA 19123-4101
Toll Free: (800) DONORS-1
Web: www.donors1.org

Summary   To provide financial assistance to the children of organ and tissue donors who live in the service area of the Gift of Life Donor Program and are interested in attending high school in the region or college in any state.

Eligibility   This program is open to the children of organ and tissue donors who live in the eastern half of Pennsylvania, southern New Jersey, or Delaware. Applicants must be younger than 25 years of age and either currently enrolled at 1) a private or parochial high school in the region, or 2) a 2- or 4-year college, university, or trade/technical school in any state. Along with their application, they must submit a brief statement summarizing their academic ambitions and extracurricular and/or volunteer activities and a 500-word essay describing how donation has touched their life. Financial need is not considered in the selection process.

Financial data   The stipend is $1,000.

Duration   1 year.

Number awarded   1 or more each year.

Deadline   March of each year.

[1052]
DELAWARE CHAPTER MS SOCIETY SCHOLARSHIP PROGRAM

National Multiple Sclerosis Society-Delaware Chapter
Two Mill Road, Suite 106
Wilmington, DE 19806
(302) 655-5610   Fax: (302) 655-0993
E-mail: kate.cowperthwait@nmss.org
Web: was.nationalmssociety.org

Summary   To provide financial assistance to high school seniors and graduates from Delaware who have multiple sclerosis (MS) or have a parent with MS and are planning to attend college in any state.

Eligibility   This program is open to graduating high school seniors, recent graduates, and GED recipients from Delaware who have MS or a parent who has MS. Applicants must be planning to enroll as a first-time student at a 2- or 4-year college, university, or vocational/

technical school in the United States on at least a half-time basis. Along with their application, they must submit an essay on the impact MS has had on their lives. Selection is based on that essay, academic record, leadership and participation in school or community activities, work experience, goals and aspirations, an outside appraisal, special circumstances, and financial need. U.S. citizenship or permanent resident status is required.

Financial data   A stipend is awarded (amount not specified).

Duration   1 year.

Number awarded   Varies each year; recently, 9 of these scholarships were awarded.

Deadline   January of each year.

[1053]
DIABETES, INCORPORATED COLLEGE SCHOLARSHIP

Diabetes, Incorporated
Attn: Executive Director
P.O. Box 9368
Rapid City, SD 57709-9368
(605) 341-1273   Fax: (605) 342-5887
E-mail: diabetesinc@qwestoffice.net
Web: www.disabetesincorporated.org/Scholarship.html

Summary   To provide financial assistance to high school seniors and current college students who have or have a family member who has diabetes and is a member of Diabetes, Incorporated.

Eligibility   This program is open to graduating high school seniors and students who are continuing their education beyond high school. Applicants must have diabetes or have a family member who has diabetes. In either case, they must have relative who is a current member of Diabetes, Incorporated. Along with their application, they must submit a 100-word essay on how their life has been affected by diabetes. Selection is based on that essay, GPA and SAT/ACT score, honors and awards, and community contribution. Preference is given to previous participants in the sponsor's Kamp for Kids.

Financial data   The scholarship stipend is $1,000 per year; honorable mentions, if awarded, are $150. Funds are paid directly to the educational institution.

Duration   1 year; recipients may reapply.

Additional data   This program includes the following named awards: the Kris Sanders Scholarship, the Micah Jerde Scholarship, and the Daniel Silvernail Scholarship.

Number awarded   Varies each year; recently, 5 scholarships and 1 honorable mention were awarded.

Deadline   April of each year.

[1054]
DISABLED AMERICAN VETERANS AUXILIARY NATIONAL EDUCATION SCHOLARSHIP FUND

Disabled American Veterans Auxiliary
Attn: National Education Scholarship Fund
3725 Alexandria Pike
Cold Spring, KY 41076
(859) 441-7300   Toll Free: (877) 426-2838, ext. 4020
Fax: (859) 442-2095   E-mail: dava@davmail.org
Web: auxiliary.dav.org/membership/Programs.aspx

Summary   To provide financial assistance to members of the Disabled American Veterans (DAV) Auxiliary who are interested in attending college or graduate school.

Eligibility   This program is open to paid life members of the auxiliary who are attending or planning to attend a college, university, or vocational school as a full- or part-time student. Applicants must be at least seniors in high school, but there is no maximum age limit. Selection is based on academic achievement; participation in DAV activities; participation in other activities for veterans in their school, community, or elsewhere; volunteer work; membership in clubs or organizations; honors and awards; academic goals; and financial need.

Financial data   Stipends are $1,500 per year for full-time students or $750 per year for part-time students.

Duration   1 year; renewable up to 4 more years, provided the recipient maintains a GPA of 2.5 or higher.

Additional data   Membership in the DAV Auxiliary is available to extended family members of veterans eligible for membership in Disabled American Veterans (i.e., any man or woman who served in the armed forces during a period of war or under conditions simulating war and was wounded, disabled to any degree, or left with long-term illness as a result of military service and was discharged or retired from military service under honorable conditions). This program was established in September 2010 as a replacement for the educational loan program that the DAV Auxiliary operated from 1931 until August 2010.

Number awarded   Varies each year.

Deadline   March of each year.

[1055]
DISABLED WORKERS COMMITTEE SCHOLARSHIP

Disabled Workers Committee
Attn: Joanna Y. Lazarus, Scholarship Committee Chair
Suisman Shapiro Attorneys At Law
2 Union Plaza, Suite 200
P.O. Box 1591
New London, CT 06320
(860) 442-4416   Fax: (860) 442-0495

Summary   To provide financial assistance to children of people with disabilities in Connecticut who are interested in attending college in any state.

Eligibility   This program is open to seniors graduating from high schools in Connecticut whose parent is totally and permanently disabled as the result of an injury. The injury must arise out of the workplace. Applicants must be

interested in attending a college in any state. Selection is based on academic achievement and financial need.

Financial data   The stipend is $5,000.

Duration   1 year.

Number awarded   2 each year.

Deadline   April of each year.

[1056]
DKF VETERANS ASSISTANCE FOUNDATION SCHOLARSHIPS

DKF Veterans Assistance Foundation
P.O. Box 7166
San Carlos, CA 94070
(650) 595-3896   E-mail: admin@dkfveterans.com
Web: www.dkfveterans.com

Summary   To provide financial assistance for college in any state to California residents who are veterans of Operation Enduring Freedom (OEF) in Afghanistan or Operation Iraqi Freedom (OIF) or the dependents of deceased or disabled veterans of those actions.

Eligibility   This program is open to 1) veterans of the U.S. armed forces (including the Coast Guard) who served in support of OEF or OIF within the central command area of responsibility; and 2) dependents of those veterans who were killed in action or incurred disabilities rated as 75% or more. Applicants must be residents of California enrolled or planning to enroll full time at a college, university, community college, or trade institution in any state. Along with their application, they must submit a cover letter introducing themselves and their educational goals.

Financial data   The stipend is $5,000 per year for students at universities and state colleges or $1,500 per year for students at community colleges and trade institutions.

Duration   1 year; may be renewed up to 3 additional years, provided the recipient maintains a GPA of 3.0 or higher.

Additional data   This foundation was established in 2005.

Number awarded   A limited number of these scholarships are awarded each year.

Deadline   Deadline not specified.

[1057]
DOTTIE LOURIE MEMORIAL SCHOLARSHIP

National Kidney Foundation Serving New England
Attn: Academic Awards Committee
85 Astor Avenue, Suite 2
Norwood, MA 02062-5040
(781) 278-0222   Toll Free: (800) 542-4001
Fax: (781) 278-0333   E-mail: nkfmarinhvt@kidney.org
Web: www.kidney.org/site/index.cfm?ch=105

Summary   To provide funding to residents of New England who have kidney disease, are related to a person with kidney disease, or have received a kidney transplant and are interested in attending college in any state.

Eligibility   This program is open to residents of Massachusetts, Rhode Island, New Hampshire, and Vermont who are enrolled or planning to enroll at a college or university in any state. Applicants must be a patient with Chronic Kidney Disease (CKD), have an immediate family member (parent, sibling) with CKD, or have had a life-saving organ transplant. Along with their application, they must submit a 2-page essay on how kidney disease or organ transplantation has impacted their life. Selection is based on academic achievement and financial need.

Financial data The stipend is $1,000. Funds are paid directly to the student.

Duration 1 year.

Number awarded 1 each year.

Deadline March of each year.

[1058]
DOUG HITESHEW MEMORIAL SCHOLARSHIPS FOR SIBLINGS

Hemophilia Foundation of Maryland
Attn: Executive Director
13 Class Court, Suite 200
Parkville, MD 21234
(410) 661-2307   Toll Free: (800) 964-3131
Fax: (410) 661-2308 E-mail: miller8043@comcast.net
Web: www.hfmonline.org

Summary To provide financial assistance to residents of Maryland who are siblings of persons with hemophilia or von Willebrand Disease and are interested in attending college in any state.

Eligibility This program is open to residents of Maryland who have a sibling with hemophilia or von Willebrand Disease. Applicants must be entering or attending a community college, junior college, 4-year college, university, or vocational school in any state. Along with their application, they must submit 1-page essays on 1) their career goals, and 2) their previous participation with the Hemophilia Foundation of Maryland or another chapter and how they plan to contribute to the chapter in the future. Selection is based on the essays, goals, transcripts, volunteer work, and recommendations.

Financial data The stipend is $1,000.

Duration 1 year.

Additional data This program was established in 2010.

Number awarded 3 each year.

Deadline April of each year.

[1059]
DUGDALE/VAN EYS SCHOLARSHIP AWARD

Tennessee Hemophilia and Bleeding Disorders
  Foundation
Attn: Scholarship Committee
1819 Ward Drive, Suite 102
Murfreesboro, TN 37129
(615) 900-1486   Toll Free: (888) 703-3269
Fax: (615) 900-1487   E-mail: mail@thbdf.org
Web: www.thbdf.org

Summary To provide money for college to students with hemophilia or their family members in Tennessee.

Eligibility This program is open to college-bound high school seniors, college students, and technical school students who have a bleeding disorder and are receiving

treatment in Tennessee. Their children, spouses, and guardians are also eligible. Applicants must have a GPA of 2.5 or higher and be enrolled or planning to enroll full time. They must submit a 500-word essay on their life goals, a resume, 3 letters of recommendation, proof of enrollment, and documentation of community service of at least 10 hours per semester. Financial need is considered in the selection process.

Financial data Stipends range from $500 to $2,000.

Duration 1 year; recipients may reapply.

Number awarded 6 each year: 1 at $2,000, 1 at $1,500, 1 at $1,000, and 3 at $500.

Deadline April of each year.

[1060]
DUNKERLEY FAMILY SCHOLARSHIP

Georgia Transplant Foundation
Attn: Scholarship Program
500 Sugar Mill Road, Suite 170A
Atlanta, GA 30350
(770) 457-3796   Fax: (770) 457-7916
Web: gatransplant.org

Summary To provide financial assistance to residents of Georgia who are dependents of transplant recipients and interested in attending college in any state.

Eligibility This program is open to residents of Georgia who are entering or continuing at an accredited college, university, or vocational/technical school in any state. Applicants must be the dependent of an organ transplant recipient. Along with their application, they must submit a 2-page statement on their career objectives, how this scholarship will help them attain their goals, and other pertinent information. Selection is based on that statement, transcripts, high school exit examination scores, ACT/SAT scores, 3 letters of reference, and financial need.

Financial data The stipend is $1,000 per year.

Duration 1 year; renewable up to 3 more years.

Number awarded 1 each year.

Deadline May of each year.

[1061]
EASTERN AMPUTEE GOLF ASSOCIATION SCHOLARSHIP AWARD

Eastern Amputee Golf Association
Attn: Bob Buck, Executive Director
2015 Amherst Drive
Bethlehem, PA 18015-5606
Toll Free: (888) 868-0992   Fax: (610) 867-9295
E-mail: info@eaga.org
Web: www.eaga.org

Summary To provide financial assistance for college to members of the Eastern Amputee Golf Association (EAGA) and their families.

Eligibility This program is open to students who are residents of and/or currently enrolled or accepted for enrollment at a college or university in designated eastern states (Connecticut, Delaware, District of Columbia, Maine, Maryland, Massachusetts, New Hampshire, New Jersey, New York, Pennsylvania, Rhode Island, Vermont,

Virginia, or West Virginia). Applicants must be amputee members of the association (those who have experienced the loss of 1 or more extremities at a major joint due to amputation or birth defect) or members of their families. Financial need is considered in the selection process.

Financial data   The stipend is $1,000.

Duration   1 year; may be renewed if the recipient maintains a GPA of 2.0 or higher and continues to demonstrate financial need.

Additional data   The EAGA was incorporated in 1987. It welcomes 2 types of members: amputee members and associate members (non-amputees who are interested in the organization and support its work but are not eligible for these scholarships). This program includes the following named scholarships: the Paul DesChamps Scholarship Award, the Tom Reed Scholarship, the Ray and Eileen Froncillo Scholarship, the Howard Taylor Scholarship, the Paul Leimkuehler Memorial Scholarship, the Thomas Armacost Memorial Scholarship, and the Sgt. Major William Wade Memorial Scholarship.

Number awarded   Varies each year; recently, 16 of these scholarships were awarded.

Deadline   June of each year.

[1062]
EDWARD T. CONROY MEMORIAL SCHOLARSHIP PROGRAM

Maryland Higher Education Commission
Attn: Office of Student Financial Assistance
6 North Liberty Street, Ground Suite
Baltimore, MD 21201
(410) 767-3300   Toll Free: (800) 974-0203
Fax: (410) 332-0250   TDD: (800) 735-2258
E-mail: osfamail@mhec.state.md.us
Web: www.mhec.state.md.us

Summary   To provide financial assistance for college or graduate school in Maryland to children and spouses of victims of the September 11, 2001 terrorist attacks and specified categories of veterans, public safety employees, and their children or spouses.

Eligibility   This program is open to entering and continuing undergraduate and graduate students in the following categories: 1) children and surviving spouses of victims of the September 11, 2001 terrorist attacks who died in the World Trade Center in New York City, in the Pentagon in Virginia, or on United Airlines Flight 93 in Pennsylvania; 2) veterans who have, as a direct result of military service, a disability of 25% or greater and have exhausted or are no longer eligible for federal veterans' educational benefits; 3) children of armed forces members whose death or 100% disability was directly caused by military service; 4) POW/MIA veterans of the Vietnam Conflict and their children; 5) state or local public safety officers or volunteers who became 100% disabled in the line of duty; and 6) children and unremarried surviving spouses of state or local public safety employees or volunteers who died or became 100% disabled in the line of duty. The parent, spouse, veteran, POW, or public safety officer or volunteer must have been a resident of Maryland at the time

of death or when declared disabled. Financial need is not considered.

Financial data   The amount awarded is equal to tuition and fees at a Maryland postsecondary institution, up to $19,000, for children and spouses of the September 11 terrorist attacks or $9,000 for all other recipients.

Duration   Up to 5 years of full-time study or 8 years of part-time study.

Additional data   Recipients must enroll at a 2- or 4-year Maryland college or university as a full-time or part-time degree-seeking undergraduate or graduate student or attend a private career school.

Number awarded   Varies each year.

Deadline   July of each year.

[1063]
EMERGENCY EDUCATIONAL FUND GRANTS

Elks National Foundation
Attn: Scholarship Department
2750 North Lake View Avenue
Chicago, IL 60614-2256
(773) 755-4732   Fax: (773) 755-4729
E-mail: scholarship@elks.org
Web: www.elks.org/enf/scholars/eefgrants.cfm

Summary   To provide emergency financial assistance to college students who are children of deceased or disabled members of B.P.O. Elks.

Eligibility   This program is open to children of Elks who have died or are totally disabled. Applicants must be unmarried, under 23 years of age, able to demonstrate financial need, and attending a college or university in the United States as a full-time undergraduate student. The student's parent must have been a member in good standing for at least 1 year at the time of death or, if disabled, have been a member in good standing for at least 1 year before he or she became incapacitated and must continue to be an Elk in good standing when the application for assistance is submitted. Applications must give the B.P.O. Elks Lodge affiliation of the Elk parent.

Financial data   The amount of the assistance depends on the need of the applicant but normally ranges up to $4,000 per year.

Duration   1 year; may be renewed up to 3 additional years.

Number awarded   Varies each year.

Deadline   December of each year for new applications; October of each year for renewal applications.

[1064]
ERIC DOSTIE MEMORIAL COLLEGE SCHOLARSHIP

NuFACTOR Specialty Pharmacy
Attn: Scholarship Administrator
41093 Country Center Drive, Suite B
Temecula, CA 92591
(951) 296-2516   Toll Free: (800) 323-6832, ext. 1300
Fax: (877) 432-6258   E-mail: info@kelleycom.com
Web: www.nufactor.com

Summary To provide financial assistance for college to students with hemophilia or members of their families.

Eligibility This program is open to 1) students with hemophilia or a related bleeding disorder; or 2) members of their families. Applicants must be U.S. citizens and enrolled or planning to enroll full time at an accredited 2- or 4-year college or university. They must have a GPA of 2.5 or higher. Along with their application, they must submit an essay on how their education will be used to serve humankind and to encourage self-improvement and enrichment. Selection is based on academic achievement, community service, and financial need.

Financial data The stipend is $1,000.

Duration 1 year.

Number awarded 10 each year.

Deadline February of each year.

[1065]
EXEMPTION FOR DEPENDENTS OF TEXAS VETERANS

Texas Higher Education Coordinating Board
Attn: Grants and Special Programs
1200 East Anderson Lane
P.O. Box 12788
Austin, TX 78711-2788
(512) 427-6340   Toll Free: (800) 242-3062
Fax: (512) 427-6420
E-mail: grantinfo@thecb.state.tx.us
Web: www.collegeforalltexans.com

Summary To exempt children and spouses of disabled or deceased U.S. veterans from payment of tuition at public universities in Texas.

Eligibility This program is open to residents of Texas whose parent or spouse was a resident of the state at the time of entry into the U.S. armed forces, the Texas National Guard, or the Texas Air National Guard. The veteran parent or spouse must have died as a result of service-related injuries or illness, be missing in action, or have become totally disabled as a result of service-related injury or illness. Applicants must have no remaining federal education benefits. They must be attending or planning to attend a public college or university in the state. Children of veterans must be 25 years of age or younger.

Financial data Eligible students are exempt from payment of tuition, dues, fees, and charges at state-supported colleges and universities in Texas.

Duration 1 year; may be renewed.

Additional data This program was established under provisions of the Hazlewood Act; it is also referred to as Hazlewood Exemption for Dependents of Texas Veterans.

Number awarded Varies each year; recently, 9 of these awards were granted.

Deadline Deadline not specified.

[1066]
FAMILIES OF FREEDOM SCHOLARSHIP FUND

Scholarship America
Attn: Scholarship Management Services
One Scholarship Way
P.O. Box 297
St. Peter, MN 56082
(507) 931-1682   Toll Free: (877) 862-0136
Fax: (507) 931-9168
E-mail: info@familiesoffreedom.org
Web: www.familiesoffreedom.org

Summary To provide college scholarships to financially-needy individuals and the families of individuals who were victims of the terrorist attacks on September 11, 2001.

Eligibility This program is open to the individuals who were disabled as a result of the terrorist attacks on September 11, 2001 and to the relatives of those individuals who were killed or permanently disabled during the attacks. Primarily, the fund will benefit dependents (including spouses and children) of the following groups: airplane crew and passengers; World Trade Center workers and visitors; Pentagon workers and visitors; and rescue workers, including fire fighters, emergency medical personnel, and law enforcement personnel. Applicants must be enrolled or planning to enroll in an accredited U.S. 2- or 4-year college, university, or vocational/technical school. They must demonstrate financial need.

Financial data Stipends range from $1,000 to $28,000 per year, depending upon the need of the recipient. Recently, awards averaged $17,100 per academic year. Funds are distributed annually, in 2 equal installments. Checks are made payable jointly to the student and the student's school.

Duration 1 year; may be renewed.

Additional data This program was established on September 17, 2001. The fundraising goal of $100 million was reached on September 4, 2002. The fund will operate until December 31, 2030.

Number awarded This is an entitlement program; all eligible students will receive funding. Recently 1,876 students had received more than $74 million in scholarship funds, including 641 students who received more than $11 million in the most recent single year.

Deadline Applications may be submitted at any time.

[1067]
FIRST CAVALRY DIVISION ASSOCIATION SCHOLARSHIPS

First Cavalry Division Association
Attn: Foundation
302 North Main Street
Copperas Cove, TX 76522-1703
(254) 547-6537   Fax: (254) 547-8853
E-mail: firstcav@1cda.org
Web: www.1cda.org/Foundation_Overview.htm

Summary To provide financial assistance for undergraduate education to soldiers currently or formerly assigned to the First Cavalry Division and their families.

Eligibility This program is open to children of soldiers who died or have been declared totally and permanently disabled from injuries incurred while serving with the First Cavalry Division during any armed conflict; children of soldiers who died while serving in the First Cavalry Division during peacetime; and active-duty soldiers currently assigned or attached to the First Cavalry Division and their spouses and children.

Financial data The stipend is $1,200 per year. The checks are made out jointly to the student and the school and may be used for whatever the student needs, including tuition, books, and clothing.

Duration 1 year; may be renewed up to 3 additional years.

Additional data Requests for applications must be accompanied by a self-addressed stamped envelope.

Number awarded Varies each year; since the program was established, it has awarded more than $783,800 to 468 children of disabled and deceased Cavalry members and more than $212,900 to 300 current members of the Division and their families.

Deadline June of each year.

[1068]
FIRST MARINE DIVISION ASSOCIATION SCHOLARSHIPS

First Marine Division Association
403 North Freeman Street
Oceanside, CA 92054
(760) 967-8561   Toll Free: (877) 967-8561
Fax: (760) 967-8567   E-mail: oldbreed@sbcglobal.net
Web: www.1stmarinedivisionassociation.org

Summary To provide financial assistance for college to dependents of deceased or disabled veterans of the First Marine Division.

Eligibility This program is open to dependents of veterans who served in the First Marine Division or in a unit attached to that Division, are honorably discharged, and now are either totally and permanently disabled or deceased from any cause. Applicants must be attending or planning to attend an accredited college, university, or trade school as a full-time undergraduate student. Graduate students and students still in high school or prep school are not eligible.

Financial data The stipend is $1,750 per year.

Duration 1 year; renewable up to 3 more years.

Additional data Recipients who marry before completing the course or drop out for non-academic reasons must submit a new application before benefits can be resumed.

Number awarded Varies each year; recently, 28 of these scholarships were awarded.

Deadline Deadline not specified.

[1069]
FLEETWOOD MEMORIAL FOUNDATION GRANTS

Fleetwood Memorial Foundation
501 South Fielder Road
Arlington, TX 76013
(817) 825-6699   Fax: (817) 542-0839
E-mail: fleetwood@fleetwoodmemorial.org
Web: www.fleetwoodmemorial.org/form.php

Summary To provide no-strings-attached grants to injured law enforcement or fire protection personnel in Texas or to the families of deceased or disabled personnel.

Eligibility Open to certified Texas law enforcement or fire protection personnel who have been injured in the performance of their duties or to the families of personnel who were killed or permanently disabled in the performance of their duties. For the purposes of this program, "line of duty" does not automatically mean "on duty;" for example, no injuries considered Section V or strains during normal exercise, automobile accidents while going to lunch, etc. are viewed as "line of duty" by this program.

Financial data These grants, of varying amounts, are designed to provide immediate financial relief to meet unexpected expenses until insurance or more permanent sources of funds can be arranged. Grants may be used to re-educate qualified personnel if they are unable to return to their normal duties after an accident. Educational funds are also available to the dependent children of deceased or disabled peace and fire personnel as long as they attend a public junior or senior college in Texas. Those funds are intended to provide support for housing and other needs not covered by funding from the Texas Higher Education Coordinating Board.

Duration These are 1-time grants.

Number awarded Since its inception in 1974, the foundation has provided more than 500 grants to qualified recipients, totaling nearly $2 million.

Deadline Applications may be submitted at any time.

[1070]
FLORIDA SCHOLARSHIPS FOR CHILDREN AND SPOUSES OF DECEASED OR DISABLED VETERANS

Florida Department of Education
Attn: Office of Student Financial Assistance
325 West Gaines Street
Tallahassee, FL 32399-0400
(850) 410-5160   Toll Free: (888) 827-2004
Fax: (850) 487-1809   E-mail: osfa@fldoe.org
Web: www.floridastudentfinancialaid.org

Summary To provide financial assistance for college to the children and spouses of Florida veterans who are disabled, deceased, or officially classified as prisoners of war (POW) or missing in action (MIA).

Eligibility This program is open to residents of Florida who are U.S. citizens or eligible noncitizens and the dependent children or spouses of veterans or service members who 1) died as a result of service-connected injuries, diseases, or disabilities sustained while on active duty during a period of war; 2) have a service-connected 100% total and permanent disability; or 3) were classified as POW or MIA by the U.S. armed forces or as civilian personnel captured while serving with the consent or authorization of the U.S. government during wartime service. The veteran or service member must have been a U.S. citizen or eligible noncitizen and a resident of Florida for at least 1 year before death, disability, or POW/MIA status. Children must be between 16 and 22 years old. Spouses of deceased veterans or service members must be unremarried and apply within 5 years of their spouse's death. Spouses of disabled veterans must have been married for at least 1 year.

Financial data Awards provide payment of tuition and registration fees at public institutions in Florida or an equivalent sum at private institutions.

Duration 1 quarter or semester; may be renewed for up to 110% of the required credit hours of an initial associate, baccalaureate, diploma, or certificate program, provided the student maintains a GPA of 2.0 or higher.

Number awarded Varies each year; recently, 233 new and 553 renewal scholarships were awarded.

Deadline March of each year.

[1071]
FOLDS OF HONOR SCHOLARSHIPS

Folds of Honor Foundation
Attn: Scholarships
5800 North Patriot Drive
Owasso, OK 74055
(918) 591-2406   Fax: (918) 494-9826
E-mail: scholarships@foldsofhonor.org
Web: www.foldsofhonor.com/scholarships

Summary To provide financial assistance for college to the spouses and children of service members killed or disabled as a result of service in the Global War on Terror.

Eligibility This program is open to the spouses and children of 1) an active-duty or Reserve component soldier, sailor, airman, Marine, or Coast Guardsman killed or disabled in the Global War on Terror; 2) an active-duty or Reserve component soldier, sailor, airman, Marine, or Coast Guardsman who is currently classified as a POW or MIA; 3) a veteran who died from any cause while such service-connected disability was in existence; 4) a service member missing in action or captured in the line of duty by a hostile force; 5) a service member forcibly detained or interned in the line of duty by a foreign government or power; or 6) a service member who received a Purple Heart medal. Applicants must submit a 1-page personal essay that includes a short biography, a description of the service members disability or death, and a statement of what the scholarship would mean to them and how it will help them achieve their career goals. Immediate-use scholarships are available to spouses or dependents currently attending or accepted into a 2- or 4-year college or university or a vocational, technical, or other certification program. Future-use scholarships are available to young children of service members and held for them until they are ready to attend college.

Financial data Stipends range up to $2,500 per semester ($5,000 per year), depending on the recipient's needs. Funds are dispersed directly to the recipient's institution.

Duration 1 year.

Additional data This program began in 2008.

Number awarded Varies each year; since the program was established, it has awarded 2,539 immediate-use scholarships and 99 future-use scholarships.

Deadline May or November of each year for immediate-use scholarships; May of for future-use scholarships.

[1072]
FREEDOM ALLIANCE SCHOLARSHIPS

Freedom Alliance
Attn: Scholarship Fund
22570 Markey Court, Suite 240
Dulles, VA 20166-6915
(703) 444-7940   Toll Free: (800) 475-6620
Fax: (703) 444-9893
Web: www.freedomalliance.org

Summary To provide financial assistance for college to the children of deceased and disabled military personnel.

Eligibility This program is open to high school seniors, high school graduates, and college students under 26 years of age who are dependent children of military personnel (soldier, sailor, airman, Marine, or Guardsman). The military parent must 1) have been killed or permanently disabled as a result of an operational mission or training accident, or 2) be currently classified as a POW or MIA. For disabled parents, the disability must be permanent, service-connected, and rated at 100% by the U.S. Department of Veterans Affairs. Applicants must submit an essay on what their parent's service means to them.

Financial data Stipends range up to $6,000 per year.

Duration 1 year; may be renewed up to 3 additional years, provided the recipient remains enrolled full time with a GPA of 2.0 or higher.

Number awarded Varies each year; recently, 225 of these scholarships were awarded.

Deadline July of each year.

[1073]
FRIENDS OF 440 SCHOLARSHIPS

Friends of 440 Scholarship Fund, Inc.
One Datran Center
9100 South Dadeland Boulevard, Suite 1010
Miami, FL 33156-7800
(305) 423-8710   Fax: (305) 670-0716
E-mail: info@440scholarship.org
Web: www.440scholarship.org

Summary To provide financial assistance to Florida residents whose parent was killed or permanently disabled in an employment-related accident and who are interested in attending college in any state.

Eligibility This program is open to students who are dependents or descendants of workers injured or killed at work and who are eligible to receive benefits under the Florida Workers' Compensation Law. Dependents and descendants of people who are primarily engaged in the administration of the Florida Workers' Compensation Law are also eligible. Applicants must be attending or planning to attend a college or university in any state. High school seniors must have a GPA of 2.7 or higher; students currently enrolled in college must have 3.0 or higher. Selection is based on merit, financial need, and connection to the worker's compensation field.

Financial data Stipends range up to $6,000 per year. Funds may be used to cover the cost of tuition, room, board, and books.

Duration 1 year; may be renewed, provided the recipient maintains a GPA of 3.0 or higher.

Additional data This program, established in 1991, takes its name from the Florida Workers' Compensation Law, which is chapter 440 of Florida Statutes.

Number awarded Varies each year; recently, 44 of these scholarships, worth $77,100, were awarded. Since the program was established, it has awarded more than $1.2 million to more than 600 students.

Deadline February of each year.

[1074]
GENERAL HENRY H. ARNOLD EDUCATION GRANT PROGRAM

Air Force Aid Society
Attn: Education Assistance Department
241 18th Street South, Suite 202
Arlington, VA 22202-3409
(703) 607-3072, ext. 51   Toll Free: (800) 769-8951
Fax: (703) 607-3022
Web: www.afas.org/Education/ArnoldEdGrant.cfm

Summary To provide financial assistance for college to dependents of active-duty, retired, disabled, or deceased Air Force personnel.

Eligibility This program is open to 1) dependent children of Air Force personnel who are active duty, Reservists on extended active duty, retired due to length of active-duty service or disability, or deceased while on active duty or in retired status; 2) spouses of active-duty Air Force members and Reservists on extended active duty; and 3) surviving spouses of Air Force members who died while on active duty or in retired status. Applicants must be enrolled or planning to enroll as full-time undergraduate students at an accredited college, university, or vocational/trade school. Spouses must be attending school within the 48 contiguous states. Selection is based on family income and education costs.

Financial data The stipend is $2,000.

Duration 1 year; may be renewed if the recipient maintains a GPA of 2.0 or higher.

Additional data Since this program began in 1988-89, it has awarded more than 94,000 grants.

Number awarded Varies each year.

Deadline March of each year.

[1075]
GEORGE AND LINDA PRICE SCHOLARSHIP

Hemophilia Association of the Capital Area
10560 Main Street, Suite 419
Fairfax, VA 22030-7182
(703) 352-7641   Fax: (540) 427-6589
E-mail: admin@hacacares.org
Web: www.hacacares.org

Summary To provide financial assistance to individuals with bleeding disorders and their families who are members of the Hemophilia Association of the Capital Area (HACA) and interested in attending college or graduate school in any state.

Eligibility This program is open to residents of northern Virginia, Montgomery and Prince George's County in Maryland, and Washington, D.C. who have a bleeding disorder and their siblings and parents. Applicants must be members of HACA. They must be 1) high school seniors or graduates who have not yet attended college; 2) full-time freshmen, sophomores, or juniors at a college, university, or vocational/technical school in any state; or 3) college seniors planning to attend graduate school and students already enrolled at a graduate school in any state. Along with their application, they must submit a 500-word essay on what they have done to contribute to the bleeding disorders community and how they plan to contribute to that community in the future. Financial need is not considered.

Financial data The stipend is $2,500.

Duration 1 year; recipients may reapply.

Number awarded 2 each year.

Deadline April of each year.

[1076]
GEORGE BARTOL MEMORIAL SCHOLARSHIPS

George Bartol Memorial Scholarship Fund
c/o Kari Bartol Romano
4616 Edgewater Drive
Orlando, FL 32804
(407) 718-7601   E-mail: livebait3@gmail.com
Web: www.mindsmatterusa.org/Scholarship.html

Summary To provide financial assistance for college to children of brain tumor patients.

Eligibility This program is open to students who are enrolled full time at an accredited 2- or 4-year college or university and have a GPA of 2.5 or higher. Applicants must have a parent battling a primary brain tumor or a parent who has passed away as a result of a primary brain tumor. They must be between 18 and 23 years of age. Along with their application, they must submit 5 essays on the following topics: 1) their parent who has lost their battle to a primary brain tumor or who is currently battling a primary brain tumor; 2) their academic and professional goals; 3) the person who has motivated and inspired them the most in their life; 4) their current financial status and how their parent's medical condition has increased their financial need for this scholarship; and 5) how their parent's medical condition has changed their outlook on life.

Selection is based on the essays, grades, letters of recommendation, and financial need. Children of Vietnam veterans who have not been awarded VA Chapter 35 benefits are strongly encouraged to apply.

Financial data The stipend is $1,000 per semester ($3,000 per year, including summer semester). Students at schools on the quarter system may receive $750 per quarter ($3,000 per year, including summer quarter). Funds are paid directly to the financial aid office at the school the recipient is attending.

Duration 1 semester or quarter; may be renewed if the recipient maintains a GPA of 2.5 or higher.

Additional data This program was established in 2004.

Number awarded Varies each year; recently, 3 of these scholarships were awarded.

Deadline September of each year.

[1077]
GEORGIA COUNCIL OF THE BLIND SCHOLARSHIPS

Georgia Council of the Blind
850 Gaines School Road
Athens, GA 30605
(706) 208-7132   Toll Free: (888) 519-3988
E-mail: gcbfyi@yahoo.com
Web: www.georgiacounciloftheblind.org

Summary To provide funding to students in Georgia who plan to attend college or graduate school in any state and are either legally blind or have legally blind parents.

Eligibility This program is open to residents of Georgia who are either 1) legally blind students, or 2) sighted students financially dependent on legally blind parents. Applicants must be enrolled or accepted for enrollment at a vocational/technical school, a 2- or 4-year college, or a master's or doctoral program in any state. All fields of study are eligible. Selection is based on academic transcripts, 2 letters of recommendation, a 1-page typed statement of the applicant's educational goals, an audio cassette recording of the applicant reading the goals statement, extracurricular activities, and financial need.

Financial data Stipends range up to $1,000 per year.

Duration 1 year; recipients may reapply.

Additional data This program began in 1988.

Number awarded 1 or more each year.

Deadline June of each year.

[1078]
GEORGIA PUBLIC SAFETY MEMORIAL GRANT

Georgia Student Finance Commission
Attn: Scholarships and Grants Division
2082 East Exchange Place, Suite 200
Tucker, GA 30084-5305
(770) 724-9000   Toll Free: (800) 505-GSFC
Fax: (770) 724-9089   E-mail: gacollege411@gsfc.org
Web: www.gacollege411.org

Summary To provide financial assistance for college to the children of Georgia public safety officers who have been permanently disabled or killed in the line of duty.

Eligibility This program is open to dependent children of Georgia law enforcement officers, fire fighters, EMT, correction officers, or prison guards who have been permanently disabled or killed in the line of duty. Applicants must be enrolled or accepted as full-time undergraduate students in a Georgia public or private college, university, or technical institution and be in compliance with the Georgia Drug-Free Postsecondary Education Act. U.S. citizenship or status as a national or permanent resident is required. Financial need is not considered in the selection process.

Financial data The award covers the cost of attendance at a public postsecondary school in Georgia, minus any other aid received, to a maximum of $18,000 per year.

Duration 1 year; may be renewed (if satisfactory progress is maintained) for up to 3 additional years.

Additional data This program, which began in 1994, is funded by the Georgia Lottery for Education.

Number awarded Varies each year; recently, 18 of these grants were awarded.

Deadline July of each year.

[1079]
GEORGIA TRANSPLANT FOUNDATION SIBLING SCHOLARSHIP

Georgia Transplant Foundation
Attn: Scholarship Program
500 Sugar Mill Road, Suite 170A
Atlanta, GA 30350
(770) 457-3796   Fax: (770) 457-7916
Web: gatransplant.org

Summary To provide financial assistance to residents of Georgia who are siblings of transplant recipients and interested in attending college in any state.

Eligibility This program is open to residents of Georgia who are entering or continuing at an accredited institution of higher learning in any state. Applicants must be the sibling of an organ transplant recipient (both the sibling and the recipient must be under 22 years of age). Along with their application, they must submit a 2-page personal statement on their career objectives, how this scholarship will help them attain their goals, and any other pertinent information. Selection is based on that statement, transcripts, high school exit examination scores, ACT/SAT scores, 3 letters of reference, and financial need.

Financial data The stipend is $1,000 per year.

Duration 1 year; renewable up to 3 more years.

Number awarded 1 each year.

Deadline May of each year.

[1080]
GREAT LAKES HEMOPHILIA FOUNDATION EDUCATION SCHOLARSHIPS

Great Lakes Hemophilia Foundation
Attn: Program Services Committee
638 North 18th Street, Suite 108
Milwaukee, WI 53233
(414) 257-0200   Toll Free: (888) 797-GLHF
Fax: (414) 257-1225   E-mail: info@glhf.org
Web: www.glhf.org/scholar.htm

Summary To provide financial assistance to Wisconsin residents who have a bleeding disorder (and their families) and are interested in attending college in any state.

Eligibility This program is open to members of the bleeding disorder community in Wisconsin. Applicants must be attending or planning to attend college, vocational school, technical school, or a certification program in any state. Along with their application, they must submit an essay of 500 to 750 words on their educational and career goals, what they have done to work toward achieving those goals, how the education or training program in which they are enrolled will help them meet their goals, what they consider the most significant challenges associated with living with a bleeding disorder, the opportunities or benefits have those challenges provided them, and how they plan on contributing back to the bleeding disorders community. First priority is given to people affected by bleeding disorders, then to parents of young children with bleeding disorders, and then to spouses of individuals with bleeding disorders. If sufficient funds are available, consideration may be given to siblings and other family members of individuals with a bleeding disorder. Financial need is considered in the selection process.

Financial data Stipends range up to $3,000.

Duration 1 year.

Number awarded Varies each year; recently, 3 of these scholarships were awarded.

Deadline April of each year.

[1081]
GREATER CAROLINAS CHAPTER MS SOCIETY SCHOLARSHIP PROGRAM

National Multiple Sclerosis Society-Greater Carolinas
  Chapter
9801-I Southern Pine Boulevard
Charlotte, NC 28273
(704) 525-2955   Fax: (704) 527-0406
E-mail: nct@nmss.org
Web: was.nationalmssociety.org

Summary To provide funding to high school seniors and graduates from South Carolina and parts of North Carolina who have multiple sclerosis (MS) or have a parent with MS and are planning to attend college in any state.

Eligibility This program is open to graduating high school seniors, recent graduates, and GED recipients from South Carolina and 82 counties of eastern and western North Carolina who have MS or a parent who has MS. Applicants must be planning to enroll as a first-time student at a 2- or 4-year college, university, or vocational/

technical school in the United States on at least a half-time basis. Along with their application, they must submit an essay on the impact MS has had on their lives. Selection is based on that essay, academic record, leadership and participation in school or community activities, work experience, goals and aspirations, an outside appraisal, special circumstances, and financial need. U.S. citizenship or permanent resident status is required.

Financial data Stipends range up to $3,000.

Duration 1 year.

Additional data This program receives support from the Golden Corral Corporation.

Number awarded Varies each year; recently, 3 of these scholarships were awarded: 2 at $3,000 and 1 at $2,600.

Deadline January of each year.

[1082]
GREATER NEW ENGLAND CHAPTER MS SOCIETY SCHOLARSHIP PROGRAM

National Multiple Sclerosis Society-Greater New
  England Chapter
101A First Avenue, Suite 6
Waltham, MA 02451-1115
(781) 890-4990   Fax: (781) 890-2089
E-mail: communications@mam.nmss.org
Web: was.nationalmssociety.org

Summary To provide financial assistance to high school seniors and graduates from designated New England states who have multiple sclerosis (MS) or have a parent with MS and are planning to attend college in any state.

Eligibility This program is open to graduating high school seniors, recent graduates, and GED recipients from Maine, Massachusetts, New Hampshire, or Vermont who have MS or a parent who has MS. Applicants must be planning to enroll as a first-time student at a 2- or 4-year college, university, or vocational/technical school in the United States on at least a half-time basis. Along with their application, they must submit an essay on the impact MS has had on their lives. Selection is based on that essay, academic record, leadership and participation in school or community activities, work experience, goals and aspirations, an outside appraisal, special circumstances, and financial need. U.S. citizenship or permanent resident status is required.

Financial data The highest-ranked applicant receives a stipend of $3,000 per year. Other stipends range from $1,000 to $3,000.

Duration The award for the highest-ranked applicant is for 2 years. Other awards are 1 year and nonrenewable.

Additional data This program was established by the Massachusetts Chapter in 2003. In 2010, that chapter merged with the chapters in Maine, New Hampshire, and Vermont to form the Greater New England Chapter and the program became available to residents of those states.

Number awarded Varies each year; recently, 28 of these scholarships (total value of $55,000) were awarded.

Deadline January of each year.

[1083]
GREATER NORTHWEST CHAPTER MS SOCIETY SCHOLARSHIP PROGRAM

National Multiple Sclerosis Society-Greater Northwest
   Chapter
192 Nickerson Street, Suite 100
Seattle, WA 98109
(206) 284-4254   Toll Free: (800) 344-4867
Fax: (206) 284-4972   E-mail: MSnorthwest@nmss.org
Web: was.nationalmssociety.org

Summary   To provide financial assistance to high school seniors and graduates from Alaska, Montana, and Washington who have multiple sclerosis (MS) or have a parent with MS and are planning to attend college in any state as a first-time student.

Eligibility   This program is open to graduating high school seniors, recent graduates, and GED recipients from Alaska, Montana, or Washington who have MS or a parent who has MS. Applicants must be planning to enroll as a first-time student at a 2- or 4-year college, university, or vocational/technical school in the United States on at least a half-time basis. Along with their application, they must submit an essay on the impact MS has had on their lives. Selection is based on that essay, academic record, leadership and participation in school or community activities, work experience, goals and aspirations, an outside appraisal, special circumstances, and financial need. U.S. citizenship or permanent resident status is required.

Financial data   Stipends range from $1,500 to $3,000.
Duration   1 year.
Number awarded   Varies each year; recently, 76 of these scholarships, worth $233,000, were awarded.
Deadline   January of each year.

[1084]
HARVEY PICKER HORIZON SCHOLARSHIPS

Maine Employers' Mutual Insurance Company
Attn: MEMIC Education Fund
261 Commercial Street
P.O. Box 11409
Portland, ME 04104
(207) 791-3300   Toll Free: (800) 660-1306
Fax: (207) 791-3336   E-mail: mbourque@memic.com
Web: www.memic.com

Summary   To provide financial assistance to Maine residents whose parent or spouse was killed or permanently disabled in a work-related accident and who are interested in attending college or graduate school in any state.

Eligibility   This program is open to Maine residents who are the child or spouse of a worker killed or permanently disabled as the result of a work-related injury. The worker must have been insured through the sponsor at the time of the workplace injury. Applicants must be attending or planning to attend an accredited college or university in any state as an undergraduate or graduate student. They must submit a personal statement describing the impact of the workplace injury on their life. Selection is based on financial need, academic performance, community involvement, other life experiences, and future promise.

Financial data   Stipends range up to $5,000, depending on the need of the recipient. Funds are paid directly to the recipient's institution.
Duration   1 year; may be renewed.
Additional data   The Maine Employers' Mutual Insurance Company (MEMIC) began in 1993 as the result of reforms in Maine's workers' compensation laws. It is currently the largest workers' compensation insurance company in the state. It established this scholarship in 2001.
Number awarded   1 or more each year.
Deadline   April of each year.

[1085]
HEMOPHILIA FOUNDATION OF MICHIGAN ACADEMIC SCHOLARSHIPS

Hemophilia Foundation of Michigan
Attn: Client Services Coordinator
1921 West Michigan Avenue
Ypsilanti, MI 48197
(734) 544-0015   Toll Free: (800) 482-3041
Fax: (734) 544-0095   E-mail: colleen@hfmich.org
Web: www.hfmich.org/?module=Page&sID=scholarships

Summary   To provide financial assistance to Michigan residents with hemophilia and their families who are interested in attending college in any state.

Eligibility   This program is open to high school seniors, high school graduates, and currently-enrolled college students who are Michigan residents and have hemophilia or another bleeding disorder. Family members of people with bleeding disorders and family members of people who have died from the complications of a bleeding disorder are also eligible. Applicants must submit a 300-word statement on their educational and career goals, the role that the bleeding disorder has played in influencing those goals, and how receiving the scholarship will help them to meet those goals. Selection is based on that statement, academic merit, employment status, reference letters, financial need, and the impact of bleeding disorder on educational activities.

Financial data   The stipend is $2,500.
Duration   1 year; recipients may reapply.
Number awarded   2 each year.
Deadline   March of each year.

[1086]
HEMOPHILIA OF IOWA SCHOLARSHIPS

Hemophilia of Iowa, Inc.
c/o Shane Kelley, Scholarship Committee Chair
22930 20th Street
Fairbank, IA 50629
Toll Free: (319) 239-3948
E-mail: ssckelley@yahoo.com
Web: www.hemophiliaofiowa.com

Summary   To provide financial assistance to members of Hemophilia of Iowa who are interested in attending college in any state.

Eligibility   This program is open to members of the sponsoring organization who either have hemophilia (or a related bleeding disorder) or are the immediate family member (caregiver, sibling, child) of someone who has hemophilia or a related bleeding disorder. Applicants may be graduating high school seniors or students currently enrolled at an accredited college, university, or trade school in any state. Along with their application, they must submit brief statements on 1) their short- and long-range career plans; 2) their personal background related to the bleeding disorder community and any specific contributions they have made to the Hemophilia of Iowa community; and 3) their key reasons for selecting the profession they are pursuing. Selection is based on personal qualities and community service. Applicants who have supported the mission of Hemophilia of Iowa are considered for supplemental funding: the John Heisner Scholarship and the Dude Cremer Scholarship.

Financial data The stipend is $1,500 for students with a bleeding disorder or $1,000 for family members. Applicants selected for the supplemental funding provided by the named scholarships receive an additional $1,000.

Duration 1 semester; recipients may reapply.

Number awarded Varies each year; recently, 20 of these scholarships were awarded.

Deadline March of each year.

[1087]
HERO SCHOLARSHIP PROGRAM

Georgia Student Finance Commission
Attn: Scholarships and Grants Division
2082 East Exchange Place, Suite 200
Tucker, GA 30084-5305
(770) 724-9000   Toll Free: (800) 505-GSFC
Fax: (770) 724-9089   E-mail: gacollege411@gsfc.org
Web: www.gacollege411.org

Summary To provide financial assistance for college to members of the National Guard or Reserves in Georgia and their children and spouses.

Eligibility This program is open to Georgia residents who are active members of the Georgia National Guard or U.S. Military Reserves, were deployed outside the United States for active-duty service on or after February 1, 2003 to a location designated as a combat zone, and served in that combat zone for at least 181 consecutive days. Also eligible are 1) the children, younger than 25 years of age, of Guard and Reserve members who completed at least 1 term of service (of 181 days each) overseas on or after February 1, 2003; 2) the children, younger than 25 years of age, of Guard and Reserve members who were killed or totally disabled during service overseas on or after February 1, 2003, regardless of their length of service; and 3) the spouses of Guard and Reserve members who were killed in a combat zone, died as a result of injuries, or became 100% disabled as a result of injuries received in a combat zone during service overseas on or after February 1, 2003, regardless of their length of service. Applicants must be interested in attending a unit of the University System of Georgia, a unit of the Georgia Department of Technical and Adult Education, or an eligible private college or university in Georgia.

Financial data The stipend for full-time study is $2,000 per academic year, not to exceed $8,000 during an entire program of study. The stipend for part-time study is pro-rated appropriately.

Duration 1 year; may be renewed (if satisfactory progress is maintained) for up to 3 additional years.

Additional data The HERO program, which stands for Helping Educate Reservists and their Offspring, was established in 2005.

Number awarded Varies each year.

Deadline June of each year.

[1088]
HEROES LEGACY SCHOLARSHIPS

Fisher House Foundation
111 Rockville Pike, Suite 420
Rockville, MD 20850
Toll Free: (888) 294-8560
E-mail: bgawne@fisherhouse.org
Web: www.militaryscholar.org/legacy/index.html

Summary To provide money for college to the children of deceased and disabled veterans and military personnel.

Eligibility This program is open to the unmarried sons and daughters of U.S. military service members (including active duty, retirees, Guard/Reserves, and survivors) who are high school seniors or full-time freshmen at an accredited college, university, or community college and younger than 23 years of age. Applicants must have at least 1 parent who, while serving on active duty after September 11, 2001, either died or became disabled, defined as qualified for receipt of Traumatic Service members Group Life Insurance (TSGLI) or rated as 100% permanently and totally disabled by the U.S. Department of Veterans Affairs. They must have a GPA of 2.5 or higher. Along with their application, they must submit a 500-word essay on a topic that changes annually; recently, students were asked to identify the 4 persons whose faces they would place on a 21st century Mount Rushmore type of monument and why. Selection is based on merit.

Financial data A stipend is awarded (amount not specified).

Duration 1 year.

Additional data This program was established in 2010 with proceeds from the sale of the book *Of Thee I Sing: A Letter to My Daughters* by President Barack Obama.

Number awarded Varies each year, depending on the availability of funds.

Deadline March of each year.

[1089]
HOPE FOR THE WARRIORS SPOUSE/ CAREGIVER SCHOLARSHIPS

Hope for the Warriors
Attn: Spouse/Caregiver Scholarships Director
1011 South MacDill Avenue, Suite 812
Tampa, FL 33629
Toll Free: (877) 246-7349
E-mail: scholarship@hopeforthewarriors.org
Web: www.hopeforthewarriors.org/spouse.html

Summary To provide money for college or graduate school to the spouses and caregivers of wounded or deceased military personnel or veterans.

Eligibility This program is open to spouses and caregivers of current and former service members who were wounded or killed in the line of duty since September 11, 2001. Applicants must be enrolled or planning to enroll full or part time at an accredited college, university, or trade school to work on a bachelor's degree, master's degree, or vocational certification. They must have a high school GPA of 2.6 or higher or a GED score of 650 or higher. Along with their application, they must submit a 500-word essay on how their life has been impacted by the Global War on Terror and how that impact played a role in their pursuit of higher education. Selection is based on that essay, academic achievement, goals, and recommendations.

Financial data The stipend is $5,000 or $1,250.

Duration 1 year; renewable up to 3 more years.

Additional data This program includes the following named scholarships: the Shannon Maxwell Award, the Bonnie Amos Award, the Karin Dickerson Award, the Robin Kelleher-New Beginnings Award, and the Sidney Popkin Memorial Scholarship.

Number awarded 4 at $5,000 and 1 at $1,250.

Deadline March of each year.

[1090]
HUEY AND ANGELINA WILSON NONTRADITIONAL SCHOLARSHIPS

Louisiana Hemophilia Foundation
Attn: Scholarship Committee
3636 South Sherwood Forest Boulevard, Suite 390
Baton Rouge, LA 70816
(225) 291-1675   Toll Free: (800) 749-1680
Fax: (225) 291-1679   E-mail: contact@lahemo.org
Web: lahemo.org/news.html

Summary To provide financial assistance for college to Louisiana residents who are nontraditional students and a hemophilia patient or the parent of a patient.

Eligibility This program is open to residents of Louisiana who are a hemophilia patient or the parent of a patient. Applicants must be enrolled or planning to enroll at a Louisiana college or university as a nontraditional student. Along with their application, they must submit a 250-word essay on why they should receive this scholarship.

Financial data The stipend is $1,000 per semester.

Duration 1 semester. Recipients may reapply if they remain enrolled full time, have a GPA of 2.75 or higher,

and provide 8 hours of community service to the sponsoring organization.

Number awarded Varies each semester; the foundation first awards scholarships to traditional students; if funds remain, it may award scholarships to qualified nontraditional students.

Deadline June of each year for fall semester; December of each year for spring semester.

[1091]
IDAHO PUBLIC SAFETY OFFICER DEPENDENT SCHOLARSHIP

Idaho State Board of Education
Len B. Jordan Office Building
650 West State Street, Room 307
P.O. Box 83720
Boise, ID 83720-0037
(208) 332-1574   Fax: (208) 334-2632
E-mail: scholarshiphelp@osbe.idaho.gov
Web: www.boardofed.idaho.gov

Summary To provide money for college to dependents of disabled or deceased Idaho public safety officers.

Eligibility Eligible for these scholarships are dependents of full-time Idaho public safety officers employed in the state who were killed or disabled in the line of duty.

Financial data Each scholarship provides a full waiver of tuition and fees at public institutions of higher education or public vocational schools within Idaho, an allowance of $500 per semester for books, on-campus housing, and a campus meal plan.

Duration Benefits are provided up to 36 months.

Number awarded Varies each year; recently, 4 of these scholarships were awarded.

Deadline Deadline not specified.

[1092]
ILLINOIS CHILDREN OF VETERANS SCHOLARSHIPS

Illinois Department of Veterans' Affairs
833 South Spring Street
P.O. Box 19432
Springfield, IL 62794-9432
(217) 782-6641   Toll Free: (800) 437-9824 (within IL)
Fax: (217) 524-0344   TDD: (217) 524-4645
E-mail: webmail@dva.state.il.us
Web: www2.illinois.gov

Summary To provide financial assistance for college to the children of Illinois veterans (with preference given to the children of disabled or deceased veterans).

Eligibility Each county in the state is entitled to award an honorary scholarship to the child of a veteran of World War I, World War II, the Korean Conflict, the Vietnam Conflict, or any time after August 2, 1990. Preference is given to children of disabled or deceased veterans.

Financial data Recipients are given free tuition at any branch of the University of Illinois.

Duration Up to 4 years.

Number awarded Each county in Illinois is entitled to award 1 scholarship. The Board of Trustees of the univer-

sity may, from time to time, add to the number of honorary scholarships (when such additions will not create an unnecessary financial burden on the university).
Deadline Deadline not specified.

[1093]
ILLINOIS GRANT PROGRAM FOR DEPENDENTS OF CORRECTIONAL OFFICERS

Illinois Student Assistance Commission
Attn: Scholarship and Grant Services
1755 Lake Cook Road
Deerfield, IL 60015-5209
(847) 948-8550   Toll Free: (800) 899-ISAC
Fax: (847) 831-8549   TDD: (800) 526-0844
E-mail: isac.studentservices@isac.illinois.gov
Web: www.collegeillinois.org

Summary To provide financial assistance to the children or spouses of disabled or deceased Illinois correctional workers who plan to attend college in the state.

Eligibility This program is open to the spouses and children of Illinois correctional officers who were at least 90% disabled or killed in the line of duty. Applicants must be enrolled at least half-time basis at an approved Illinois public or private 2- or 4-year college or university. They need not be Illinois residents at the time of application. U.S. citizenship or eligible noncitizen status is required.

Financial data The grants provide full payment of tuition and mandatory fees at approved public colleges in Illinois or an equivalent amount at private colleges.

Duration Up to 8 academic semesters or 12 academic quarters of study.

Number awarded Varies each year.

Deadline September of each year for the academic year; February of each year for spring semester or winter or spring quarter; June of each year for summer term.

[1094]
ILLINOIS GRANT PROGRAM FOR DEPENDENTS OF POLICE OR FIRE OFFICERS

Illinois Student Assistance Commission
Attn: Scholarship and Grant Services
1755 Lake Cook Road
Deerfield, IL 60015-5209
(847) 948-8550   Toll Free: (800) 899-ISAC
Fax: (847) 831-8549   TDD: (800) 526-0844
E-mail: isac.studentservices@isac.illinois.gov
Web: www.collegeillinois.org

Summary To provide funding to the children or spouses of disabled or deceased Illinois police or fire officers who plan to attend college or graduate school in the state.

Eligibility This program is open to the spouses and children of Illinois police and fire officers who were at least 90% disabled or killed in the line of duty. Applicants must be enrolled at least a half-time in either undergraduate or graduate study at an approved Illinois public or private 2- or 4-year college, university, or hospital school. They need not be Illinois residents. U.S. citizenship or eligible noncitizen status is required.

Financial data The grants provide full payment of tuition and mandatory fees at approved public colleges in Illinois or an equivalent amount at private colleges.

Duration Up to 8 academic semesters or 12 academic quarters of study.

Number awarded Varies each year.

Deadline September of each year for the academic year; February of each year for spring semester or winter or spring quarter; June of each year for summer term.

[1095]
ILLINOIS MIA/POW SCHOLARSHIP

Illinois Department of Veterans' Affairs
833 South Spring Street
P.O. Box 19432
Springfield, IL 62794-9432
(217) 782-6641   Toll Free: (800) 437-9824 (within IL)
Fax: (217) 524-0344   TDD: (217) 524-4645
E-mail: webmail@dva.state.il.us
Web: www2.illinois.gov

Summary To provide financial assistance for 1) the undergraduate education of Illinois dependents of disabled or deceased veterans or those listed as prisoners of war or missing in action, and 2) the rehabilitation or education of disabled dependents of those veterans.

Eligibility This program is open to the spouses, natural children, legally adopted children, or stepchildren of a veteran or service member who 1) has been declared by the U.S. Department of Defense or the U.S. Department of Veterans Affairs to be permanently disabled from service-connected causes with 100% disability, deceased as the result of a service-connected disability, a prisoner of war, or missing in action, and 2) at the time of entering service was an Illinois resident or was an Illinois resident within 6 months of entering such service. Special support is available for dependents who are disabled.

Financial data An eligible dependent is entitled to full payment of tuition and certain fees at any Illinois state-supported college, university, or community college. In lieu of that benefit, an eligible dependent who has a physical, mental, or developmental disability is entitled to receive a grant to be used to cover the cost of treating the disability at 1 or more appropriate therapeutic, rehabilitative, or educational facilities. The total benefit cannot exceed the cost of 4 years of full-time enrollment, including summer terms, at the University of Illinois.

Duration This scholarship may be used for a period equivalent to 4 calendar years, including summer terms. Dependents have 12 years from the initial term of study to complete the equivalent of 4 calendar years. Disabled dependents who elect to use the grant for rehabilitative purposes may do so as long as the total benefit does not exceed the cost equivalent of 4 calendar years of full-time enrollment at the University of Illinois.

Additional data An eligible child must begin using the scholarship prior to his or her 26th birthday. An eligible spouse must begin using the scholarship prior to 10 years from the effective date of eligibility (e.g., prior to August 12, 1989 or 10 years from date of disability or death).

Number awarded Varies each year.
Deadline Deadline not specified.

[1096]
INDIANA BREAST CANCER LEGACY SCHOLARSHIP FUND

Central Indiana Community Foundation
Attn: Scholarship Program
615 North Alabama Street, Suite 119
Indianapolis, IN 46204-1498
(317) 631-6542, ext. 279   Fax: (317) 684-0943
E-mail: scholarships@cicf.org
Web: www.cicf.org/page26452.cfm

Summary To provide money for college to high school seniors in Indiana who are children of breast cancer patients.

Eligibility This program is open to seniors graduating from high schools in Indiana who plan to attend a college or university. Applicants must have lost a parent to breast cancer or have a parent who has survived breast cancer. Along with their application, they must submit a 1-page essay describing their experience with breast cancer and/ or the impact on their family. Financial need is considered.

Financial data The stipend is at least $1,000.

Duration 1 year.

Additional data This program was established in 2004.

Number awarded Varies each year; recently, 2 of these scholarships were awarded.

Deadline March of each year.

[1097]
INDIANA CHILD OF VETERAN AND PUBLIC SAFETY OFFICER SUPPLEMENTAL GRANT PROGRAM

State Student Assistance Commission of Indiana
Attn: Grants and Scholarships
W462 Indiana Government Center South
402 West Washington Street
Indianapolis, IN 46204
(317) 232-2355   Toll Free: (888) 528-4719 (within IN)
Fax: (317) 232-3260   E-mail: grants@ssaci.in.gov
Web: www.in.gov/ssaci/2338.htm

Summary To provide financial assistance to residents of Indiana who are the children or spouses of specified categories of deceased or disabled veterans or public safety officers and interested in attending college or graduate school in the state.

Eligibility This program is open to 1) children of deceased or disabled Indiana veterans, children of Purple Heart recipients, and children of Vietnam War veterans who were listed as POW or MIA; 2) children and spouses of members of the Indiana National Guard who suffered a service-connected death while serving on state active duty; 3) Indiana veterans who received a Purple Heart; 4) current and former students at the Indiana Soldiers' and Sailors' Children's Home (Morton Memorial High School); and 5) children and spouses of Indiana police officers, fire fighters, or emergency medical technicians killed in the line of duty or Indiana state police troopers permanently

and totally disabled in the line of duty. The veterans and National Guard portions of this program are open to Indiana residents who are the natural or adopted children or spouses of veterans who served in the active-duty U.S. armed forces during a period of war time.

Financial data Qualified applicants receive a 100% remission of tuition and all mandatory fees for undergraduate or graduate work at state-supported postsecondary schools and universities in Indiana. Support is not provided for such fees as room and board.

Duration Up to 124 semester hours of study.

Additional data The veterans portion of this program is administered by the Indiana Department of Veterans' Affairs. The National Guard portion of this program is administered by Joint Forces Headquarters.

Number awarded Varies each year.

Deadline Applications must be submitted at least 30 days before the start of the college term.

[1098]
INTERNATIONAL TRANSPLANT NURSES SOCIETY GEORGIA CHAPTER SCHOLARSHIP

Georgia Transplant Foundation
Attn: Scholarship Program
500 Sugar Mill Road, Suite 170A
Atlanta, GA 30350
(770) 457-3796   Fax: (770) 457-7916
Web: gatransplant.org

Summary To provide financial assistance to residents of Georgia who are either transplant recipients or their siblings or dependents and interested in attending college in any state to work on a degree in health care.

Eligibility This program is open to residents of Georgia who are entering or continuing at an accredited institution of higher learning in any state to work on a degree in health care. Applicants must be an organ transplant recipient, a dependent of a recipient, a parent of a recipient, a living donor, or the sibling of a recipient (both the sibling and the recipient must be under 22 years of age). Along with their application, they must submit a 2-page personal statement on their career objectives, how this scholarship will help them attain their goals, and any other pertinent information. Selection is based on that statement, transcripts, high school exit examination scores, ACT/SAT scores, 3 letters of reference, and financial need.

Financial data The stipend is $1,000.

Duration 1 year; nonrenewable.

Additional data This program is sponsored by the Georgia Chapter of the International Transplant Nurses Society.

Number awarded 1 each year.

Deadline May of each year.

[1099]
IOPO FOUNDATION SCHOLARSHIPS

Indiana Organ Procurement Organization, Inc.
Attn: IOPO Foundation Inc.
3760 Guion Road
P.O. Box 6069, Department 172
Indianapolis, IN 46202-6069
Toll Free: (888) ASK-IOPO   Fax: (317) 685-1687
E-mail: info@iopo.org
Web: www.iopo.org

Summary To provide financial assistance for college attendance in any state to Indiana residents who are organ, tissue, or eye transplant donors, recipients, candidates, or their families.

Eligibility This program is open to Indiana residents who are organ, tissue, or eye transplant donors, recipients, candidates, or relatives (including spouses, parents, children, grandchildren, siblings, aunts, uncles, nieces, nephews, and cousins). Applicants must be high school seniors or students already attending a college or technical school in any state on a full- or part-time basis. They must have a GPA of 2.0 or higher; high school seniors must be in the top 50% of their class. Along with their application, they must submit a 1,500-word essay describing their career goals, experience with organ or tissue donation and/or transplantation, and personal goals. Financial need is considered in the selection process.

Financial data Stipends are $3,000 or $1,500.

Duration 1 year; nonrenewable.

Number awarded Varies each year; recently, 4 of these scholarships were awarded: 1 at $3,000 and 3 at $1,500.

Deadline February of each year.

[1100]
ISABELLE CHRISTENSON MEMORIAL SCHOLARSHIP

Izzie's Gifts of Hope Foundation
c/o C.O.R.E.
204 Sigma Drive
RIDC Park
Pittsburgh, PA 15238
E-mail: izziesgifts@gmail.com
Web: www.izziesgifts.org/scholarships.php

Summary To provide money for college to organ transplant candidates, donors, recipients, and their families.

Eligibility This program is open to organ transplant candidates, recipients, donor family members, and immediate family members of a transplant candidate or recipient. Applicants must be attending or planning to attend a college, university, or trade/technical school. Along with their application, they must submit 1) a 500-word statement on their educational goals; and 2) a 500-word statement of how donation/transplantation has influenced their life.

Financial data A stipend is awarded (amount not specified).

Duration 1 year; nonrenewable.

Additional data This program awarded its first scholarship in 2010.

Number awarded 1 or 2 each year.

Deadline March of each year.

[1101]
J. PARIS MOSLEY SCHOLARSHIP

Cleveland Foundation
Attn: Scholarship Officer
1422 Euclid Avenue, Suite 1300
Cleveland, OH 44115-2001
(216) 861-3810   Fax: (216) 861-1729
E-mail: mbaker@clevefdn.org
Web: www.clevelandfoundation.org/Scholarships

Summary To provide financial assistance for college to high school seniors in any state 1) who are deaf or 2) whose primary caregivers are deaf.

Eligibility This program is open to high school seniors in any state who are deaf or hard of hearing or the children or grandchildren of deaf or hard of hearing parents or grandparents. Applicants must be planning to attend a college, university, vocational school, or other postsecondary program in any state. They must use some form of sign language, have a GPA of 2.5 or higher, and be able to demonstrate financial need. Preference is given to students of African, Latino, or Native American descent.

Financial data A stipend is awarded (amount not specified).

Duration 1 year.

Number awarded 1 or more each year.

Deadline March of each year.

[1102]
JAMES DOYLE CASE MEMORIAL SCHOLARSHIPS

Mississippi Council of the Blind
c/o Kenneth Maddox
217 Taylor Street
Jackson, MS 39216
Web: www.acb.org/mcb

Summary To provide financial assistance to legally blind residents of Mississippi and their children who plan to attend college or graduate school in any state.

Eligibility This program is open to residents of Mississippi who are legally blind or the children of at least 1 legally blind parent. Applicants must be enrolled or accepted for enrollment in an undergraduate or graduate program in any state and carrying or planning to carry at least 12 academic hours. Along with their application, they must submit a 2-page autobiographical sketch, transcripts, standardized test scores (ACT or SAT for undergraduates; GRE, MCAT, LSAT, etc. for graduate students), 2 letters of recommendation, proof of acceptance from a postsecondary school, and verification of blindness of the qualifying person (applicant or parent).

Financial data The stipend is $1,500 per year.

Duration 4 years.

Number awarded 2 each year.

Deadline February of each year.

[1103]
JEANNE E. BRAY MEMORIAL SCHOLARSHIP

National Rifle Association of America
Attn: Law Enforcement Activities Division
11250 Waples Mill Road
Fairfax, VA 22030-7400
(703) 267-1131   E-mail: selkin@nrahq.org
Web: www.nrahq.org/law/lebenefits.asp

Summary   To provide financial assistance for college to children of disabled and other law enforcement officers who are members of the National Rifle Association (NRA).

Eligibility   This program is open to NRA members who are the dependent children of 1) currently serving full-time commissioned peace officers who are also NRA members; 2) deceased full-time commissioned peace officers who lost their lives in the performance of assigned peace officer duties and were current members of NRA at the time of their death; 3) retired full-time commissioned peace officers who are also NRA members; and 4) full-time commissioned peace officers, disabled and retired as a result of a line of duty incident, who are also current NRA members. Applicants must be U.S. citizens who have a GPA of 3.0 or higher and scores of at least 950 on the SAT I or 25 on the ACT. Along with their application, they must submit an essay of 500 to 700 words in support of the rights secured by the second amendment to the constitution.

Financial data   The stipend is $2,000 per year.

Duration   Up to 4 years, provided the recipient maintains a GPA of 2.0 or higher.

Number awarded   1 or more each year.

Deadline   November of each year.

[1104]
JIM NOLAND FOUNDATION SCHOLARSHIP

Three Rivers Community Foundation
Attn: Executive Director
1333 Columbia Park Trail, Suite 310
Richland, WA 99352
(509) 735-5559   E-mail: carrie@3rcf.org
Web: 3rcf.org/press_releases.php

Summary   To provide financial assistance to high school seniors in Washington who have lost a parent to cancer or are dealing with cancer in the immediate family and plan to attend college in any state.

Eligibility   This program is open to seniors graduating from high schools in Washington who plan to enroll full time at a 2-year community college or 4-year public university in any state. Applicants must have lost a parent to cancer or be dealing with cancer in the immediate family. They must have a GPA of 3.0 or higher and be able to demonstrate financial need. Along with their application, they must submit a 250-word essay about themselves, their educational achievements, their future career goals, and how they plan to accomplish their goals; the essay must discuss how losing a parent to cancer or having an immediate family member with cancer has affected their life.

Financial data   The stipend is $1,000 per year.

Duration   1 year; may be renewed, provided the recipient maintains a GPA of 3.0 or higher.

Number awarded   1 each year.

Deadline   June of each year.

[1105]
JOHN YOUTSEY MEMORIAL SCHOLARSHIP FUND

Hemophilia of Georgia
8800 Roswell Road, Suite 170
Atlanta, GA 30350-1844
(770) 518-8272   Fax: (770) 518-3310
E-mail: mail@hog.org
Web: www.hog.org/programs/page/scholarship

Summary   To provide financial assistance to residents of Georgia who have a bleeding disorder or have lost a parent because of the disorder and are interested in attending college in any state.

Eligibility   This program is open to residents of Georgia who 1) have hemophilia, von Willebrand Disease, or other inherited bleeding disorder; or 2) are children whose parent died as a result of complications from a bleeding disorder. Applicants or their deceased parents must be or have been clients of Hemophilia of Georgia. They may be graduating high school seniors or students currently enrolled at an accredited college, university, vocational/technical school, or professional degree program in any state. Selection is based on academic record, financial need, and personal goals.

Financial data   A stipend is awarded (amount not specified).

Duration   1 year.

Additional data   Recipients must provide at least 12 hours of volunteer service with Hemophilia of Georgia.

Number awarded   Varies each year. Since this program was established, it has awarded more than 275 scholarship with a value greater than $800,000.

Deadline   April of each year.

[1106]
JON C. LADDA MEMORIAL FOUNDATION SCHOLARSHIP

Jon C. Ladda Memorial Foundation
P.O. Box 55
Unionville, CT 06085
E-mail: info@jonladda.org
Web: www.jonladda.org/scholarship.htm

Summary   To provide financial assistance for college to children of deceased and disabled U.S. Naval Academy graduates and members of the Navy submarine service.

Eligibility   This program is open to children of U.S. Naval Academy graduates and members of the U.S. Navy submarine service. The parent must have died on active duty or been medically retired with a 100% disability. Applicants must be enrolled or accepted at a 4-year college or university, including any of the service academies. Along with their application, they must submit an essay on a topic that changes annually. Selection is based on academic achievement, financial need, and merit.

Financial data A stipend is awarded (amount not specified). Funds are sent to the recipient's institution.
Duration 1 year; may be renewed.
Number awarded 1 or more each year.
Deadline March of each year.

[1107]
JOSEPH W. MAYO ALS SCHOLARSHIP

Maine Community Foundation
Attn: Program Director
245 Main Street
Ellsworth, ME 04605
(207) 667-9735   Toll Free: (877) 700-6800
Fax: (207) 667-0447   E-mail: info@mainecf.org
Web: www.mainecf.org/statewidescholars.aspx

Summary To provide financial assistance to college students from Maine who have a relative with Amyotrophic Lateral Sclerosis (ALS).
Eligibility This program is open to students enrolled at a 2- or 4-year college or university who graduated from a Maine high school or GED program. Applicants must be the child, stepchild, grandchild, spouse, domestic partner, or primary caregiver of an ALS patient. Along with their application, they must submit essays on their educational plans and involvement with school or community service activities, including any associated with ALS programs.
Financial data Stipends range from $500 to $3,000.
Duration 1 year.
Additional data This program was established in 2001.
Number awarded Varies each year; recently, 6 of these scholarships were awarded.
Deadline April of each year.

[1108]
JUMPSTART MS SCHOLARSHIP

National Multiple Sclerosis Society-Upper Midwest
    Chapter
Attn: Jumpstart MS Scholarship Program
200 12th Avenue South
Minneapolis, MN 55415
(612) 335-7954   Toll Free: (800) 582-5296
Fax: (612) 335-7997
E-mail: bethany.hansen@nmss.org
Web: was.nationalmssociety.org

Summary To provide financial assistance to high school students from Iowa, Minnesota, and North and South Dakota who have multiple sclerosis (MS) or have a parent with MS and are planning to attend college in any state.
Eligibility This program is open to students currently enrolled as freshmen at high schools in Iowa, Minnesota, North Dakota, and South Dakota who have MS or a parent who has MS. Applicants must be planning to enroll at a 2- or 4-year college, university, or vocational/technical school in the United States after they graduate from high school. Along with their application, they must submit an 850-word essay on the impact MS has had on their lives. Selection is based on the essay, academic record, leadership in school or community activities, goals and aspirations, and special circumstances (such as financial need).

Financial data The stipend is $1,500.
Duration 1 year.
Additional data This program is sponsored by Best Buy.
Number awarded 1 each year.
Deadline May of each year.

[1109]
KATHERN F. GRUBER SCHOLARSHIPS

Blinded Veterans Association
477 H Street, N.W.
Washington, DC 20001-2694
(202) 371-8880   Toll Free: (800) 669-7079
Fax: (202) 371-8258   E-mail: bva@bva.org
Web: www.bva.org/services.html

Summary To provide funding for undergraduate or graduate study to spouses and children of blinded veterans.
Eligibility This program is open to dependent children and spouses of blinded veterans of the U.S. armed forces. The veteran must be legally blind; the blindness may be either service connected or nonservice connected. Applicants must have been accepted or be currently enrolled as a full-time student in an undergraduate or graduate program at an accredited institution of higher learning. Along with their application, they must submit a 300-word essay on their career goals and aspirations. Financial need is not considered in the selection process.
Financial data The stipend is $2,000; funds are intended to cover the student's expenses, including tuition, academic fees, books, dormitory fees, and cafeteria fees. Funds are paid directly to the recipient's school.
Duration 1 year; recipients may reapply for up to 3 additional years.
Number awarded 6 each year.
Deadline April of each year.

[1110]
KENTUCKY DECEASED OR DISABLED LAW ENFORCEMENT OFFICER AND FIRE FIGHTER DEPENDENT TUITION WAIVER

Kentucky Fire Commission
Attn: Executive Director
300 North Main Street
Versailles, KY 40383
(859) 256-3478   Toll Free: (800) 782-6823
Fax: (859) 256-3125   E-mail: ronnie.day@kctcs.net
Web: kyfirecommission.kcts.edu

Summary To provide financial assistance for college to the children and spouses of Kentucky police officers or fire fighters deceased or disabled in the line of duty.
Eligibility This program is open to spouses, widow(er)s, and children of Kentucky residents who became a law enforcement officer, fire fighter, or volunteer fire fighter and who 1) were killed while in active service or training for active service; 2) died as a result of a service-connected disability; or 3) became permanently and totally disabled as a result of active service or training for

active service. Children must be between 17 and 23 years of age; spouses and widow(er)s may be of any age.

Financial data Recipients are entitled to a waiver of tuition at state-supported universities, community colleges, and technical training institutions in Kentucky.

Duration 1 year; may be renewed up to a maximum total of 36 months.

Number awarded Varies each year; all qualified applicants are entitled to this aid.

Deadline Deadline not specified.

[1111]
KENTUCKY VETERANS TUITION WAIVER PROGRAM

Kentucky Department of Veterans Affairs
Attn: Field Operations Branch
321 West Main Street, Suite 390
Louisville, KY 40202
(502) 595-4447   Toll Free: (800) 928-4012 (within KY)
Fax: (502) 595-4448   E-mail: Pamela.Cypert@ky.gov
Web: www.veterans.ky.gov/benefits/tuitionwaiver.htm

Summary To provide financial assistance for college to the children, spouses, or unremarried widow(er)s of disabled or deceased Kentucky veterans.

Eligibility This program is open to the children, stepchildren, spouses, and unremarried widow(er)s of veterans who are residents of Kentucky (or were residents at the time of their death). The qualifying veteran must meet 1 of the following conditions: 1) died on active duty (regardless of wartime service); 2) died as a result of a service-connected disability (regardless of wartime service); 3) has a 100% service-connected disability; 4) is totally disabled (non-service connected) with wartime service; or 5) is deceased and served during war time. The military service may have been as a member of the U.S. armed forces, the Kentucky National Guard, or a Reserve component; service in the Guard or Reserves must have been on state active duty, active duty for training, inactive duty training, or active duty with the U.S. armed forces. Children of veterans must be under 26 years of age; no age limit applies to spouses or unremarried widow(er)s. All applicants must be attending or planning to attend a 2-year, 4-year, or vocational technical school operated and funded by the Kentucky Department of Education.

Financial data Eligible dependents and survivors are exempt from tuition and matriculation fees at any state-supported institution of higher education in Kentucky.

Duration Tuition is waived until the recipient completes 45 months of training, receives a college degree, or (in the case of children of veterans) reaches 26 years of age, whichever comes first. Spouses and unremarried widow(er)s are not subject to the age limitation.

Number awarded Varies each year.

Deadline Deadline not specified.

[1112]
KERIN KELLER MEMORIAL SCHOLARSHIP

College Planning Network
Attn: Vicki Breithaupt
43 Bentley Place
Port Townsend, WA 98368
(206) 323-0624   E-mail: seacpn@collegeplan.org
Web: www.collegeplan.org

Summary To provide funding to residents of Washington who are related to a cancer patient and planning to study business or communications at a college in the state.

Eligibility This program is open to residents of Washington who are attending or planning to attend an accredited 2- or 4-year college or university in the state. Applicants must major in business or communications; a focus in marketing, advertising, and public relations is strongly encouraged. They must be related to a victim of cancer. Along with their application, they must submit 2 letters of recommendation, a list of significant activities and honors, an official transcript from the high school or college they are currently attending, and a 1-page essay explaining their relationship to a victim of cancer and how this award will help them attain their educational goals. Financial need is considered in the selection process, but it is not the determining factor.

Financial data The stipend is $1,000.

Duration 1 year; nonrenewable.

Additional data This program is sponsored by Ad Club Seattle, formerly the Seattle Advertising Federation.

Number awarded 1 each year.

Deadline March of each year.

[1113]
KIDS' CHANCE OF ARIZONA SCHOLARSHIPS

Kids' Chance of Arizona
P.O. Box 36753
Phoenix, AZ 85067-6753
(602) 253-4360   Toll Free: (877) 253-4360
Web: www.azkidschance.org

Summary To provide financial assistance to Arizona residents whose parent was killed or permanently disabled in an employment-related accident and who are interested in attending college in any state.

Eligibility This program is open to Arizona residents between 16 and 25 years of age whose parent was killed or disabled in an employment-related accident. Applicants must be attending or planning to attend a college, university, or trade school in any state. They must submit high school transcripts, letters of recommendation, verification of school attendance, and a 1-page letter explaining their educational goals and need for financial assistance.

Financial data Stipends are approximately $2,000.

Duration 1 year; may be renewed.

Additional data This program was established in 1997.

Number awarded Varies each year; since the program was established, it has awarded 137 scholarships worth $260,987.57.

Deadline Deadline not specified.

[1114]
KIDS' CHANCE OF ARKANSAS SCHOLARSHIPS

Kids' Chance of Arkansas, Inc.
Attn: Scholarship Board
P.O. Box 250249
Little Rock, AR 72225-0249
Toll Free: (866) 880-8444
E-mail: KidsChance@awcc.state.ar.us
Web: www.awcc.state.ar.us/kids_chance/kchance2.html

Summary To provide financial assistance to Arkansas residents whose parent was killed or permanently disabled in an employment-related accident and who are interested in attending college in any state.

Eligibility This program is open to children of workers who have been killed or become permanently and totally disabled from a compensable Arkansas Workers' Compensation injury or accident. Applicants must be between 16 and 22 years of age; be able to demonstrate academic achievement and aptitude; and be attending or planning to attend an accredited vocational/technical school, college, or university in any state. The injury or death of their parent must have resulted in a decrease in family earnings that creates an obstacle to the continuation of their education. Along with their application, they must submit a 2-page essay that describes 1) the circumstances of the work-related injury or death of their parent or guardian; 2) their academic and career aspirations; and 3) the biggest challenge in attending college and plans to overcome it.

Financial data Stipends are approximately $2,000.

Duration 1 year.

Additional data This program was established in 2002.

Number awarded Varies each year; recently, 26 of these scholarships, with a value of $48,500, were awarded. Since the program was established, it has awarded 205 scholarships with a total value of $368,000.

Deadline May of each year.

[1115]
KIDS' CHANCE OF GEORGIA SCHOLARSHIPS

Kids' Chance of Georgia, Inc.
2024 Powers Ferry Road, Suite 225
Atlanta, GA 30339
(770) 933-7767   E-mail: info@kidschancega.org
Web: www.kidschancega.org

Summary To provide financial assistance to Georgia residents whose parent was killed or permanently disabled in an employment-related accident and who are interested in attending college in any state.

Eligibility This program is open to Georgia residents between 16 and 25 years of age whose parent's work-related death or injury resulted in a substantial decline in family income. Applicants must be enrolled or planning to enroll full time at a college, university, or technical school in any state.

Financial data The stipend depends on the financial need of the recipient, ranging from $1,500 to $4,500. Funds may be used for tuition, books, housing, meals, transportation, and/or as a supplement to the income of the family to compensate for money the student would earn by dropping out of school.

Duration 1 year; may be renewed up to 4 additional years, provided the recipient maintains satisfactory academic progress and a GPA of 2.0 or higher.

Additional data This program was established by the Workers' Compensation Section of the Georgia Bar in 1988. It has served as a model for comparable programs that currently operate in 29 other states.

Number awarded Varies each year; recently, 32 were awarded: 1 at $4,500, 2 at $4,000, 2 at $3,600, 1 at $3,500, 24 at $3,000, and 2 at $1,500.

Deadline Deadline not specified.

[1116]
KIDS' CHANCE OF INDIANA SCHOLARSHIP PROGRAM

Kids' Chance of Indiana, Inc.
Attn: President
721 East Broadway
Fortville, IN 46040
(317) 485-0043, ext. 123   Fax: (317) 485-4299
E-mail: ngath@fdgtlaborlaw.com
Web: www.kidschancein.org/scholarship.html

Summary To provide financial assistance to Indiana residents whose parent was killed or permanently disabled in a work-related accident and who are interested in attending college or graduate school in any state.

Eligibility This program is open to Indiana residents between 16 and 25 years of age who are the children of workers fatally or catastrophically injured as a result of a work-related accident or occupational disease. The death or injury must be compensable by the Workers' Compensation Board of the state of Indiana and must have resulted in a substantial decline in the family's income that is likely to impede the student's pursuit of his or her educational objectives. Applicants must be attending or planning to attend a trade/vocational school, industrial/commercial training institution, junior/community college, 4-year college or university, or graduate school in any state. Financial need is considered in the selection process.

Financial data Stipends range up to $3,000 per year. Funds may be used for tuition and fees, books, room and board, and utilities.

Duration 1 year; may be renewed.

Number awarded Varies each year.

Deadline Deadline not specified.

[1117]
KIDS' CHANCE OF KENTUCKY SCHOLARSHIPS

Kids' Chance of Kentucky
Attn: Scholarship Committee
P.O. Box 910234
Lexington, KY 40591
(859) 219-0194   E-mail: gdavis5@windstream.net
Web: www.kidschanceky.org

Summary To provide financial assistance to Kentucky residents whose parent was killed or seriously injured in an employment-related accident and who are interested in attending college in any state.

Eligibility This program is open to residents of Kentucky between 16 and 25 years of age. Applicants must be the natural child, adopted child, stepchild, or full dependent of a worker killed or permanently injured in a compensable work-related accident during the course of employment with a Kentucky employer and entitled to receive benefits under the Kentucky Workers' Compensation Act. They must be attending or planning to attend college in any state. The parent's death or injury must have resulted in a substantial decline in the family income. Selection is based primarily on financial need, although academics, aptitude, and service are also considered.

Financial data The stipend depends on the need of the recipient. Funds may be used to cover tuition, books, housing, and meals.

Duration 1 year; recipients may reapply.

Additional data This program was established in 2003.

Number awarded Varies each year.

Deadline April of each year for fall semester; October of each year for spring semester.

[1118]
KIDS' CHANCE OF LOUISIANA SCHOLARSHIPS

Kids' Chance of Louisiana
c/o The Louisiana Bar Foundation
909 Poydras Street, Suite 1550
New Orleans, LA 70112
(504) 561-1046   Fax: (504) 566-1926
E-mail: kidschance@raisingthebar.org
Web: www.raisingthebar.org

Summary To provide financial assistance to Louisiana residents whose parent was killed or permanently disabled in an employment-related accident and who are interested in attending college in the state.

Eligibility This program is open to Louisiana residents between 16 and 25 years of age who are the dependent of a worker killed or permanently and totally disabled in an accident that is compensable under a state or federal Workers' Compensation Act or law. Applicants must be working on or planning to work on a certificate, license, or associate or bachelor's degree from an accredited Louisiana university, community college, vocational/technical institute, or state-approved proprietary school. Financial need is considered in the selection process.

Financial data Stipends range from $500 to $3,000. Funds, paid directly to the school where the child is enrolled, may be used for tuition, books, fees, room, and general living expenses.

Duration 1 year; recipients may reapply as long as they maintain a "C" average or higher.

Additional data This program was established in 2004.

Number awarded Varies each year; recently, 23 of these scholarships were awarded. Since the program began, it has awarded 156 scholarships worth $277,600.

Deadline February of each year.

[1119]
KIDS' CHANCE OF MARYLAND SCHOLARSHIPS

Kids' Chance of Maryland, Inc.
P.O. Box 20262
Baltimore, MD 21284-0262
(410) 832-4702   Fax: (410) 832-4726
E-mail: info@kidschance-md.org
Web: www.kidschance-md.org

Summary To provide financial assistance to Maryland residents whose parent was killed or permanently disabled in an employment-related accident and who are interested in attending college in any state.

Eligibility This program is open to Maryland residents between 16 and 25 years of age who have a parent permanently or catastrophically injured or killed in an employment-related accident compensable under the Maryland Workers' Compensation Act. The parent's death or injury must have resulted in a substantial decline in the family income. Applicants must be attending or planning to attend college or technical school in any state. Financial need is considered in the selection process.

Financial data Stipends depend on the need of the students. Recently, they ranged from $3,500 to $8,000. Funds are intended to cover tuition and books but may also include housing and meals.

Duration 1 semester; recipients may reapply.

Number awarded Varies each year; recently, 14 of these scholarships were awarded.

Deadline Deadline not specified.

[1120]
KIDS' CHANCE OF MISSISSIPPI SCHOLARSHIP FUND

Mississippi Bar Foundation
Attn: Administrative Law and Workers' Compensation
  Section
643 North State Street
P.O. Box 2168
Jackson, MS 39225-2168
(601) 948-5234   Fax: (601) 355-8635
E-mail: acook@msbar.org
Web: www.msbar.org/kidchance.php

Summary To provide financial assistance to Mississippi residents whose parent was killed or disabled on the job and who are interested in attending college in any state.

Eligibility This program is open to Mississippi residents between 17 and 23 years of age who have had a parent killed or permanently and totally disabled in an accident that is compensable under the Mississippi Workers' Compensation Act. Applicants must demonstrate substantial financial need.

Financial data A stipend is awarded (amount not specified).

Duration 1 year; may be renewed.

Number awarded Varies each year.

Deadline April of each year.

[1121]
KIDS' CHANCE OF MISSOURI SCHOLARSHIPS

Kids' Chance Inc. of Missouri
Attn: Scholarship Committee
P.O. Box 410384
St. Louis, MO 63141
(314) 997-3390   Toll Free: (800) 484-5733, ext. 5437
Fax: (314) 432-5894   E-mail: susgroup@gmail.com
Web: www.mokidschance.org

Summary To provide financial assistance to Missouri residents whose parent was killed or permanently disabled in a work-related accident and who are interested in attending college in any state.

Eligibility This program is open to Missouri residents whose parent sustained a serious injury or fatality in a Missouri work-related accident covered by workers' compensation. Applicants must be attending or planning to attend an accredited U.S. vocational school or college. They must be able to demonstrate financial need.

Financial data Stipends depend on the need of the recipient. Funds may be used to cover tuition, books, supplies, housing, meals, and other expenses not covered by other grants and/or scholarships.

Duration 1 year; recipients may reapply.

Additional data This program was established in 1996.

Number awarded Varies each year.

Deadline April of each year for academic year scholarships; October for spring semester scholarships.

[1122]
KIDS' CHANCE OF NORTH CAROLINA SCHOLARSHIPS

Kids' Chance of North Carolina, Inc.
P.O. Box 13756
Greensboro, NC 27415
(336) 404-5069   E-mail: kidschancenc@gmail.com
Web: www.kidschancenc.org/scholarship.php

Summary To provide financial assistance to North Carolina residents whose parent was seriously injured or killed in a workplace accident and who are interested in attending college in any state.

Eligibility This program is open to residents of North Carolina between 16 and 25 years of age who are attending or planning to attend college or vocational school in any state. Applicants must be children of employees who have been seriously injured or killed as a result of a workplace accident that is covered under the North Carolina Workers' Compensation Act. They must be able to demonstrate financial hardship caused by the death or serious injury of their parent.

Financial data Stipends range up to $5,000 per year. Funds may be used for tuition, books, meals, housing, and transportation, and/or they may be used to supplement the income of the family to compensate for money the student would earn by dropping out of school.

Duration 1 year; may be renewed if the recipient maintains an acceptable academic level.

Additional data This program was established in 2004.

Number awarded Varies each year; recently, 8 of these scholarships were awarded.

Deadline Deadline not specified.

[1123]
KIDS' CHANCE OF OHIO SCHOLARSHIPS

Kids' Chance of Ohio
Attn: Executive Director
52 East Gay Street
P.O. Box 1008
Columbus, OH 43216-1008
(614) 464-6410   E-mail: raminor@vssp.com
Web: www.kidschanceohio.org/scholarshipprogram.html

Summary To provide financial assistance for undergraduate or graduate study in any state to children of Ohio employees who were killed or disabled as a result of a work-related injury or occupational disease.

Eligibility This program is open to the children between 16 and 25 years of age of employees who have been declared to be permanently and totally disabled or who were fatally injured as a result of a work-related injury or occupational disease. The death, injury, or illness must have occurred as a result of work activities performed for an Ohio employer covered by the Ohio workers' compensation law, although neither the student nor the parent is required to be an Ohio resident. The injury or death must have resulted in a decline in the family's income. Applicants must be attending or planning to attend a college, university, community college, trade/vocational school, industrial/commercial training institute, or graduate school in any state.

Financial data The stipend depends on the need of the recipient, to a maximum of $5,000 per year. Funds may be used for payment of tuition, fees, books, room, and board.

Duration 1 year; recipients may reapply.

Number awarded Varies each year.

Deadline Applications must be submitted at least 1 month prior to the beginning of the semester or quarter.

[1124]
KIDS' CHANCE OF PENNSYLVANIA SCHOLARSHIPS

Kids' Chance of Pennsylvania
P.O. Box 543
Pottstown, PA 19464
(610) 970-9143   Fax: (610) 970-7520
E-mail: info@kidschanceofpa.org
Web: www.kidschanceofpa.org/scholarship.html

Summary To provide financial assistance to Pennsylvania residents whose parent was killed or permanently disabled in a work-related accident and who are interested in attending college in any state.

Eligibility This program is open to Pennsylvania residents between 16 and 25 years of age who have been accepted by an accredited postsecondary educational institution anywhere in the United States. At least 1 parent must have been killed or seriously injured as a result of a work-related accident covered under the Pennsylvania

Workers' Compensation Act. Financial need is considered in the selection process.

Financial data Stipends range from $500 to $5,000; recently, they averaged $2,337.

Duration 1 year; may be renewed.

Additional data This program began in 1997. Matching funding for students with remaining unmet financial need is provided by the Pennsylvania Higher Education Assistance Agency (PHEAA) with American Education Services. Students who demonstrate exceptional academic progress and significant financial need receive funding from the ACE INA Foundation.

Number awarded Varies each year; recently, 46 of these scholarships, worth $107,500, were awarded.

Deadline April of each year.

[1125]
KIDS' CHANCE OF SOUTH CAROLINA SCHOLARSHIPS

Kids' Chance of South Carolina
P.O. Box 2957
Georgetown, SC 29442-2957
(843) 546-5837   E-mail: info@kidschancesc.org
Web: www.kidschancesc.org/scholarship-information

Summary To provide financial assistance to South Carolina residents whose parent was killed or permanently disabled in a work-related accident and who are interested in attending college or graduate school in any state.

Eligibility This program is open to South Carolina residents between 16 and 25 years of age who are the children of workers fatally or catastrophically injured as a result of a work-related accident or occupational disease. Applicants must be attending or planning to attend a trade school, vocational school, community or junior college, 4-year college or university, or graduate school in any state. They must have a GPA of 2.0 or higher. The work-related injury or occupational disease from which their parent suffers or died must be compensable by the Workers' Compensation Board of the state of South Carolina and must have resulted in a substantial decline in the family's income that is likely to interfere with the student's pursuit of his or her educational objectives.

Financial data Stipends range up to $3,000 per semester ($6,000 per year). Funds may be used for tuition and fees, books, room and board, and utilities.

Duration 1 semester; may be renewed up to 7 additional semesters, provided the recipient maintains a GPA of 2.5 or higher.

Number awarded Varies each year; recently, 11 of these scholarships were awarded.

Deadline Applications must be submitted 1 month before the beginning of the semester, or July for the fall semester and December for the spring semester.

[1126]
KIDS' CHANCE OF TENNESSEE SCHOLARSHIP PROGRAM

Kids' Chance of Tennessee
c/o Kathy Kirby-Smithson
809 North Hampton Cove
Franklin, TN 37064
(615) 336-1956
Web: www.tnselfinsurers.org/news

Summary To provide financial assistance to Tennessee residents whose parent was killed or permanently disabled in a work-related accident and who are interested in attending college in any state.

Eligibility This program is open to Tennessee residents between 16 and 22 years of age who are the children of workers who died or suffered a serious or catastrophic injury or a permanent disability as a result of an employment-related accident. The parent or deceased parent's family must be entitled to receive benefits under the Tennessee Workers' Compensation Act. The parent's death or injury must have resulted in a substantial decline in the family's income that is likely to impede the student's pursuit of his or her educational objectives. Applicants must be attending or planning to attend a college, university, or vocational/technical school in any state.

Financial data A stipend is awarded (amount not specified).

Duration 1 year.

Additional data This program operates in partnership with the Tennessee Self-Insurers' Association.

Number awarded 1 or more each year.

Deadline Deadline not specified.

[1127]
KIDS' CHANCE OF VIRGINIA SCHOLARSHIPS

Kids' Chance of Virginia
12701 Marblestone Drive, Suite 250
Woodbridge, VA 22192
(703)586-6300   E-mail: kidschanceva@gmail.com
Web: www.kidschanceva.org

Summary To provide financial assistance to Virginia residents whose parent was killed or disabled in a work-related accident and who are interested in attending college in any state.

Eligibility This program is open to residents of Virginia between 16 and 25 years of age who are attending or planning to attend a college, university, or vocational/technical institute in any state. Applicants be the child of a parent whose death or disability resulted from a work-related injury that was covered by workers' compensation. That injury must have caused a significant decline in family income and circumstances.

Financial data A stipend is awarded (amount not specified).

Duration 1 year.

Additional data This program was established in 2011.

Number awarded 1 or more each year.

Deadline Deadline not specified.

[1128]
KIDS' CHANCE OF WASHINGTON SCHOLARSHIPS

Kids' Chance of Washington
P.O. Box 185
Olympia, WA 98507-0185
Toll Free: (800) 572-5762   Fax: (360) 943-2333
E-mail: debbie@wscff.org
Web: www.kidschancewa.com

Summary To provide financial assistance to residents of Washington whose parent or spouse was killed or seriously disabled in a workplace accident and who are interested in attending college in any state.

Eligibility This program is open to Washington residents attending or planning to attend an accredited community college, university, college, or technical/vocational school in any state. Applicants must be the child or spouse of a Washington worker permanently or catastrophically injured or deceased while on the job. Selection is based primarily on financial need.

Financial data A stipend is awarded (amount not specified). Funds are paid to the student's school for tuition, books, fees, room, and general living expenses.

Duration 1 year; may be renewed.

Additional data This program was established in 2001.

Number awarded Varies each year.

Deadline Deadline not specified.

[1129]
KIDS' CHANCE OF WEST VIRGINIA SCHOLARSHIPS

Greater Kanawha Valley Foundation
Attn: Scholarship Program Officer
1600 Huntington Square
900 Lee Street East, 16th Floor
Charleston, WV 25301
(304) 346-3620   Toll Free: (800) 467-5909
Fax: (304) 346-3640   E-mail: shoover@tgkvf.org
Web: www.tgkvf.org/page.aspx?pid=409

Summary To provide financial assistance for college to students whose parent was injured or killed in a West Virginia work-related accident.

Eligibility This program is open to children between 16 and 25 years of age whose parent 1) was fatally injured in a West Virginia work-related accident, or 2) is currently receiving permanent total disability benefits from the West Virginia Workers' Compensation Division. Applicants may reside in any state and be pursuing any field of study at an accredited trade or vocational school, college, or university. They must have at least a 2.5 GPA and demonstrate good moral character. Preference is given to applicants who demonstrate financial need, academic excellence, leadership, and contributions to school and community.

Financial data The stipend is $1,500 per year.

Duration 1 year; may be renewed.

Additional data This program is sponsored by Kids' Chance of West Virginia, Inc.

Number awarded Varies each year; recently, 6 of these scholarships were awarded.

Deadline January of each year.

[1130]
KIDS' CHANCE SCHOLARSHIP FUND

Alabama Law Foundation
415 Dexter Avenue
P.O. Box 4129
Montgomery, AL 36101
(334) 269-1515   Fax: (334) 261-6310
E-mail: tdaniel@alfinc.org
Web: www.alfinc.org/kidschance.cfm

Summary To provide financial assistance to Alabama residents whose parent was killed or disabled on the job and who are interested in attending college in any state.

Eligibility This program is open to high school seniors and college students (including students at technical colleges) in Alabama whose parent was killed or permanently and totally disabled in an on-the-job accident. Applicants must be attending or planning to attend a college or technical school in any state. Financial need is considered in the selection process.

Financial data Stipends range from $500 to $3,000 but do not exceed the cost of tuition and books at the most expensive public university in Alabama.

Additional data This program was established in 1992 by the Workers' Compensation Section of the Alabama State Bar and is currently administered by the Alabama Law Foundation.

Number awarded Varies each year; since the program was established, it has awarded more than 100 scholarships worth more than $375,000.

Deadline April of each year.

[1131]
KNIGHTS OF COLUMBUS/FRANCIS P. MATTHEWS AND JOHN E. SWIFT EDUCATIONAL TRUST SCHOLARSHIPS

Knights of Columbus
Attn: Department of Scholarships
P.O. Box 1670
New Haven, CT 06507-0901
(203) 752-4332   Fax: (203) 772-2696
E-mail: info@kofc.org
Web: www.kofc.org/en/scholarships/matthews_swift.html

Summary To provide financial assistance at Catholic colleges or universities in any country to children of disabled or deceased veterans, law enforcement officers, or firemen who are/were also Knights of Columbus members.

Eligibility This program is open to children of members of the sponsoring organization who are high school seniors in any country planning to attend a 4-year Catholic college or university in their country. The parent must be a member of Knights of Columbus who 1) was serving in the military forces of their country and was killed by hostile action or wounded by hostile action, resulting within 2 years in permanent and total disability; 2) was a full-time law enforcement officer who became disabled or died as a result of criminal violence; or 3) was a fire fighter who became disabled or deceased in the line of duty.

Financial data The amounts of the awards vary but are designed to cover tuition, to a maximum of $25,000 per year, at the Catholic college or university of the recipient's choice in the country of their residence. Funds are not available for room, board, books, fees, transportation, dues, computers, or supplies.

Duration 1 year; renewable up to 3 more years.

Additional data This program was established in 1944 to provide scholarships to the children of Knights who became totally and permanently disabled through service during World War II. It has been modified on many occasions, most recently in 2007 to its current requirements.

Number awarded Varies each year.

Deadline February of each year.

[1132]
LANFORD FAMILY HIGHWAY WORKER MEMORIAL SCHOLARSHIP PROGRAM

American Road and Transportation Builders
  Association
Attn: Transportation Development Foundation
1219 28th Street, N.W.
Washington, DC 20007-3389
(202) 289-4434, ext. 411   Fax: (202) 289-4435
E-mail: hbolton@artba.org
Web: www.artba.org

Summary To provide financial assistance for college to children of highway workers killed or disabled on the job.

Eligibility This program is open to the sons, daughters, and legally adopted children of highway workers who have died or become permanently disabled in roadway construction zone accidents. Applicants must be attending or planning to attend an accredited 4-year college or university, 2-year college, or vocational/technical school. Their parent must have been employed by a transportation construction firm or a transportation public agency at the time of death or disabling injury. Selection is based on academic performance (GPA of 2.5 or higher), a 200-word statement from the applicant on reasons for wanting to continue education, recommendations, and need.

Financial data The stipend is $2,000. Funds are paid directly to the recipient's institution to be used for tuition, books, or required fees, but not for room and board.

Duration 1 year.

Additional data This program began in 1999.

Number awarded Varies each year; recently, 7 of these scholarships were awarded.

Deadline March of each year.

[1133]
LISA HIGGINS-HUSSMAN FOUNDATION SCHOLARSHIP

Ulman Cancer Fund for Young Adults
Attn: Scholarship Committee
10440 Little Patuxent Parkway, Suite G1
Columbia, MD 21044
(410) 964-0202   Toll Free: (888) 393-FUND
Fax: (410) 964-0402
E-mail: scholarship@ulmanfund.org
Web: www.ulmanfund.org/scholarship.aspx

Summary To provide financial assistance for college or graduate school to students from Washington, D.C., Maryland, or Virginia who have been diagnosed with cancer or have or have lost a family member with cancer.

Eligibility This program is open to students who 1) have been diagnosed with cancer; 2) have a parent, sibling, or guardian living with cancer; or 3) have lost a parent, sibling, or guardian to cancer. Applicants must be residents of Washington, D.C., Maryland, or Virginia or attending college there. They must be 35 years of age or younger and attending, or planning to attend, a 2- or 4-year college, university, or vocational program to work on an undergraduate or graduate degree. The first diagnosis of cancer (whether of the applicant, a parent, a sibling, or a guardian) must have occurred after the applicant was 15 years of age. Along with their application, they must submit an essay of at least 1,000 words on how the cancer experience has impacted their outlook on life and the legacy that they desire to leave behind. Selection is based on demonstrated dedication to community service, commitment to educational and professional goals, use of their cancer experience to impact the lives of other young adults affected by cancer, medical hardship, and financial need.

Financial data The stipend is $2,500. Funds are paid directly to the educational institution.

Duration 1 year.

Additional data Recipients must agree to complete 40 hours of community service.

Number awarded 1 each year.

Deadline March of each year.

[1134]
LOUISIANA CHAPTER MS SOCIETY SCHOLARSHIP PROGRAM

National Multiple Sclerosis Society-Louisiana Chapter
4613 Fairfield Street
Metairie, LA 70006
(504) 832-4013   Fax: (504) 831-7188
E-mail: louisianachapter@nmss.org
Web: was.nationalmssociety.org

Summary To provide financial assistance to high school seniors and graduates from Louisiana who have multiple sclerosis (MS) or have a parent with MS and are planning to attend college in any state.

Eligibility This program is open to graduating high school seniors, recent graduates, and GED recipients from Louisiana who have MS or a parent who has MS.

Applicants must be planning to enroll as a first-time student at a 2- or 4-year college, university, or vocational/technical school in the United States on at least a half-time basis. Along with their application, they must submit an essay on the impact MS has had on their lives. Selection is based on that essay, academic record, leadership and participation in school or community activities, work experience, goals and aspirations, an outside appraisal, special circumstances, and financial need. U.S. citizenship or permanent resident status is required.

Financial data The stipend is $2,000.

Duration 1 year; nonrenewable.

Number awarded Varies each year; recently, 2 of these scholarships were awarded.

Deadline January of each year.

[1135]
LOUISIANA EDUCATIONAL BENEFITS FOR CHILDREN, SPOUSES, AND SURVIVING SPOUSES OF VETERANS

Louisiana Department of Veterans Affairs
Attn: Education Program
1885 Wooddale Boulevard, Room 1013
P.O. Box 94095, Capitol Station
Baton Rouge, LA 70804-9095
(225) 219-5000   Toll Free: (877) GEAUXVA
Fax: (225) 219-5590   E-mail: veteran@la.gov
Web: vetaffairs.la.gov/education

Summary To provide funding to children, spouses, and surviving spouses of certain disabled or deceased Louisiana veterans who plan to attend college in the state.

Eligibility This program is open to children (between 16 and 25 years of age), spouses, or surviving spouses of veterans who served during specified periods of war time and 1) were killed in action or died in active service; 2) died of a service-connected disability; 3) are missing in action (MIA) or a prisoner of war (POW); 4) sustained a disability rated as 90% or more by the U.S. Department of Veterans Affairs; or 5) have been determined to be unemployable as a result of a service-connected disability. Deceased, MIA, and POW veterans must have resided in Louisiana for at least 12 months prior to entry into service. Living disabled veterans must have resided in Louisiana for at least 24 months prior to the child's or spouse's admission into the program.

Financial data Eligible persons accepted as full-time students at Louisiana state-supported colleges, universities, trade schools, or vocational/technical schools are admitted free and are exempt from payment of tuition, laboratory, athletic, medical, and other special fees. Free registration does not cover books, supplies, room and board, or fees assessed by the student body on themselves (such as yearbooks and weekly papers).

Duration Support is provided for a maximum of 4 school years, to be completed in not more than 5 years from date of original entry.

Additional data Attendance must be on a full-time basis. Surviving spouses must remain unremarried and

must take advantage of the benefit within 10 years after eligibility is established.

Number awarded Varies each year.

Deadline Applications must be received no later than 3 months prior to the beginning of a semester.

[1136]
LPA SCHOLARSHIPS

Little People of America, Inc.
Attn: Vice President of Programs
250 El Camino Real, Suite 201
Tustin, CA 92780
(714) 368-3689   Toll Free: (888) LPA-2001
Fax: (714) 368-3367   E-mail: info@lpaonline.org
Web: www.lpaonline.org/mc/page.do?sitePageID=49367

Summary To provide financial assistance for college or graduate school to members of the Little People of America (LPA), to their families, and (in limited cases) to others.

Eligibility This program is open to members of LPA (limited to people who, for medical reasons, are 4 feet 10 inches or under in height). Applicants must be high school seniors or students attending college, vocational school, or graduate school. Along with their application, they must submit a 500-word personal statement that explains their reasons for applying for a scholarship, their plans for the future, how they intend to be of service to LPA after graduation, and any other relevant information about themselves, their family, their background, and their educational achievements. Financial need is also considered in the selection process. If sufficient funds are available after all LPA members have been served, scholarships may also be given, first, to immediate family members of dwarfs who are also paid members of LPA, and, second, to people with dwarfism who are not members of LPA.

Financial data Stipends range from $250 to $1,000.

Duration 1 year; awards are limited to 2 for undergraduate study and 1 for graduate study.

Number awarded Varies; generally between 5 and 10 each year.

Deadline April of each year.

[1137]
LYMAN FISHER SCHOLARSHIPS

Virginia Hemophilia Foundation
P.O. Box 188
Midlothian, VA 23113-0188
Toll Free: (800) 266-8438   Fax: (800) 266-8438
E-mail: vahemophiliaed@verizon.net
Web: www.vahemophilia.org

Summary To provide funding to people from Virginia who have participated in the Virginia Hemophilia Foundation (VHF) and are interested in attending college.

Eligibility This program is open members of the bleeding disorder community and their families who are attending or planning to attend college. Applicants must have a record of prior participation with VHF and be a resident of Virginia or planning to attend college in Virginia. Along with their application, they must submit a brief biographical sketch of themselves that includes their interests, hobbies, vocational and educational goals, volunteer and community involvement, and work or internship experience; a description of their previous participation with VHF and how they plan to contribute to the organization and support other persons with inherited bleeding disorders; a detailed statement of financial need; a 1-page essay on their career goals; another 1-page essay on a topic of their choice; and 3 letters of recommendation.

Financial data The stipend is $2,000.

Duration 1 year.

Number awarded 2 each year.

Deadline May of each year.

[1138]
MAINE VETERANS DEPENDENTS EDUCATIONAL BENEFITS

Bureau of Veterans' Services
117 State House Station
Augusta, ME 04333-0117
(207) 430-6035   Toll Free: (800) 345-0116 (within ME)
Fax: (207) 626-4471   E-mail: mainebvs@maine.gov
Web: www.maine.gov

Summary To provide financial assistance for undergraduate or graduate education to dependents of disabled and other Maine veterans.

Eligibility Applicants for these benefits must be children (high school seniors or graduates under 22 years of age), non-divorced spouses, or unremarried widow(er)s of veterans who meet 1 or more of the following requirements: 1) living and determined to have a total permanent disability resulting from a service-connected cause; 2) killed in action; 3) died from a service-connected disability; 4) died while totally and permanently disabled due to a service-connected disability but whose death was not related to the service-connected disability; or 5) a member of the armed forces on active duty who has been listed for more than 90 days as missing in action, captured, forcibly detained, or interned in the line of duty by a foreign government or power. The veteran parent must have been a resident of Maine at the time of entry into service or a resident of Maine for 5 years preceding application for these benefits. Children may be working on an associate or bachelor's degree. Spouses, widows, and widowers may work on an associate, bachelor's, or master's degree.

Financial data Recipients are given free tuition at institutions of higher education supported by the state.

Duration Children may receive up to 8 semesters of support; they have 6 years from the date of first entrance to complete those 8 semesters. Continuation in the program is based on their earning a GPA of 2.0 or higher each semester. Spouses are entitled to receive up to 120 credit hours of educational benefits and have 10 years from the date of first entrance to complete their program.

Additional data College preparatory schooling and correspondence courses are not supported.

Number awarded Varies each year.

Deadline Deadline not specified.

[1139]
MALLORY SMITH MEMORIAL SCHOLARSHIP

Georgia Transplant Foundation
Attn: Scholarship Program
500 Sugar Mill Road, Suite 170A
Atlanta, GA 30350
(770) 457-3796   Fax: (770) 457-7916
Web: gatransplant.org

Summary To provide financial assistance to residents of Georgia who are transplant recipients or dependents of recipients and interested in attending college in any state.

Eligibility This program is open to residents of Georgia who are entering or continuing at an accredited institution of higher learning in any state. Applicants must be an organ transplant recipient or the dependent of a recipient. Along with their application, they must submit a 2-page personal statement on their career objectives, how this scholarship will help them attain their goals, and any other pertinent information. Selection is based on that statement, transcripts, high school exit examination scores, ACT/SAT scores, 3 letters of reference, and financial need.

Financial data The stipend is $1,000 per year.

Duration 1 year; may be renewed up to 3 additional years.

Number awarded 1 each year.

Deadline May of each year.

[1140]
MARILYN YETSO MEMORIAL SCHOLARSHIP

Ulman Cancer Fund for Young Adults
Attn: Scholarship Committee
10440 Little Patuxent Parkway, Suite G1
Columbia, MD 21044
(410) 964-0202   Toll Free: (888) 393-FUND
Fax: (410) 964-0402
E-mail: scholarship@ulmanfund.org
Web: www.ulmanfund.org/scholarship.aspx

Summary To provide funding for college or graduate school to students who have or have lost a parent to cancer.

Eligibility This program is open to students who have or have lost a parent or guardian to cancer. Applicants must be 35 years of age or younger and attending, or planning to attend, a 2- or 4-year college, university, or vocational program to work on an undergraduate or graduate degree. The parent or guardian must have been first diagnosed with cancer after the applicant was 15 years of age. Along with their application, they must submit an essay of at least 1,000 words on how their parent's cancer experience has impacted their outlook on life and the legacy that they desire to leave behind. Selection is based on demonstrated dedication to community service, commitment to educational and professional goals, use of their cancer experience to impact the lives of other young adults affected by cancer, medical hardship, and financial need.

Financial data The stipend is $2,500. Funds are paid directly to the educational institution.

Duration 1 year.

Additional data These scholarships were first awarded in 2002. Recipients must agree to complete 40 hours of community service.

Number awarded 1 each year.

Deadline March of each year.

[1141]
MARY M. GOOLEY HEMOPHILIA SCHOLARSHIP

Mary M. Gooley Hemophilia Center
Attn: Scholarship Selection Committee
1415 Portland Avenue, Suite 500
Rochester, NY 14621
(585) 922-5700   Fax: (585) 922-5775
E-mail: Kristina.Ritchie@rochestergeneral.org
Web: www.hemocenter.org

Summary To provide funding to people with a bleeding disorder and their families who plan to attend college.

Eligibility This program is open to people who are affected directly or indirectly by hemophilia, von Willebrand Disease, hereditary bleeding disorder, or hemochromatosis. Applicants must be enrolled or planning to enroll at an accredited 2- or 4-year college or university, vocational/technical school, or certified training program. Along with their application, they must submit 1) a 1,000-word essay on their goals and aspirations, their biggest challenge and how they met it, and anything else they want the selection committee to know about them; and 2) a 250-word essay on any unusual family or personal circumstances have affected their achievement in school, work, or participation in school and community activities, including how the bleeding disorder has affected their life. Selection is based on the essays, academic performance, participation in school and community activities, work or volunteer experience, personal or family circumstances, recommendations, and financial need.

Financial data The maximum stipend is $2,000.

Duration 1 year.

Additional data This program was established in 1996.

Number awarded 1 or 2 each year.

Deadline March of each year.

[1142]
MARYELLEN LOCHER FOUNDATION SCHOLARSHIP

MaryEllen Locher Foundation
Attn: Cindy Pare
P.O. Box 4032
Chattanooga, TN 37405
(423) 490-4555   E-mail: cindy@melfoundation.org
Web: www.melfoundation.org/scholarships.html

Summary To provide money for college to students who have a parent who died from or survived breast cancer.

Eligibility This program is open to students who have been accepted as a full-time enrollee at an accredited 2- or 4-year college or university. Applicants must have lost a parent to breast cancer or complication resulting from breast cancer, or have a parent who has survived breast cancer. They must have a GPA of 2.0 or higher and be a legal resident of the United States. Along with their application, they must submit 2 essays on assigned topics related to the impact of breast cancer on their family. Selection is based on their essays, grades, and need.

Financial data Stipends are $3,000 or $1,500.

Duration 1 year; may be renewed up to 3 additional years.

Additional data This program began in 2002 as the Children of Breast Cancer Foundation Scholarship.

Number awarded Varies each year; recently, 30 of these scholarships were awarded.

Deadline January of each year.

[1143]
MERFELD FAMILY FOUNDATION SCHOLARSHIPS

Ventura County Community Foundation
Attn: Scholarships
1317 Del Norte Road, Suite 150
Camarillo, CA 93010-8364
(805) 988-0196, ext. 119   Fax: (805) 988-3379
E-mail: vweber@vccf.org
Web: www.vccf.org/funds/scholarship_fund/list.shtml

Summary To provide financial assistance to college students who parents have been diagnosed with amyotrophic lateral sclerosis (ALS).

Eligibility This program is open to students currently enrolled in college who have a parent diagnosed with ALS. Applicants may be residents of any state, but preference is given to those from Iowa and southern California.

Financial data The stipend is $2,500.

Duration 1 year.

Additional data These scholarships were first awarded in 2012.

Number awarded 4 to 6 each year.

Deadline January of each year.

[1144]
MICHAEL A. HUNTER MEMORIAL SCHOLARSHIP

Orange County Community Foundation
Attn: Scholarship Associate
4041 MacArthur Boulevard, Suite 510
Newport Beach, CA 92660
(949) 553-4202, ext. 46   Fax: (949) 553-4211
E-mail: alee@oc-cf.org
Web: www.oc-cf.org/Page.aspx?pid=869

Summary To provide financial assistance for college to leukemia and lymphoma patients and the children of non-surviving leukemia and lymphoma patients.

Eligibility This program is open to graduating high school seniors, community college students, and 4-year university students nationwide. Applicants must be leukemia or lymphoma patients and/or the children of non-surviving leukemia or lymphoma patients who are enrolled or planning to enroll full time. They must have a GPA of 3.0 or higher and be able to document financial need.

Financial data   Stipends range from $1,000 to $2,500.
Duration   1 year.
Number awarded   2 each year.
Deadline   March of each year.

[1145]
MICHIGAN CHILDREN OF VETERANS TUITION GRANTS

Michigan Department of Treasury
Michigan Higher Education Assistance Authority
Attn: Office of Scholarships and Grants
P.O. Box 30462
Lansing, MI 48909-7962
(517) 373-0457   Toll Free: (888) 4-GRANTS
Fax: (517) 241-5835   E-mail: osg@michigan.gov
Web: www.michigan.gov/mistudentaid

Summary   To provide financial assistance for college to the children of Michigan veterans who are totally disabled or deceased as a result of service-connected causes.
Eligibility   This program is open to natural and adopted children of veterans who have been totally and permanently disabled as a result of a service-connected illness or injury prior to death and have now died, have died or become totally and permanently disabled as a result of a service-connected illness or injury, have been killed in action or died from another cause while serving in a war or war condition, or are listed as missing in action in a foreign country. The veteran must have been a legal resident of Michigan immediately before entering military service and did not reside outside of Michigan for more than 2 years, or must have established legal residency in Michigan after entering military service. Applicants must be between 16 and 26 years of age and must have lived in Michigan at least 12 months prior to the date of application. They must be enrolled or planning to enroll at least half time at a community college, public university, or independent degree-granting college or university in Michigan. U.S. citizenship or permanent resident status is required.
Financial data   Recipients are exempt from payment of the first $2,800 per year of tuition or any other fee that takes the place of tuition.
Duration   1 year; may be renewed for up to 3 additional years if the recipient maintains full-time enrollment and a GPA of 2.25 or higher.
Additional data   This program was formerly known as the Michigan Veterans Trust Fund Tuition Grants, administered by the Michigan Veterans Trust Fund within the Department of Military and Veterans Affairs. It was transferred to the Office of Scholarships and Grants in 2006.
Number awarded   Varies each year; recently, 400 of these grants were awarded.
Deadline   Deadline not specified.

[1146]
MID AMERICA CHAPTER MS SOCIETY SCHOLARSHIP PROGRAM

National Multiple Sclerosis Society-Mid America Chapter
Attn: Scholarship Program
7611 State Line Road, Suite 100
Kansas City, MO 64114
(913) 432-3926   Fax: (816) 361-2369
E-mail: amy.goldstein@nmss.org
Web: was.nationalmssociety.org

Summary   To provide financial assistance to high school seniors and graduates from the Midwest region who have multiple sclerosis (MS) or have a parent with MS and are planning to attend college in any state.
Eligibility   This program is open to graduating high school seniors, recent graduates, and GED recipients from Kansas, western Missouri, Nebraska, or Pottawattamie County, Iowa who have MS or a parent who has MS. Applicants must be planning to enroll as a first-time student at a 2- or 4-year college, university, or vocational/technical school in the United States on at least a half-time basis. Along with their application, they must submit an essay on the impact MS has had on their lives. Selection is based on that essay, academic record, leadership and participation in school or community activities, work experience, goals and aspirations, an outside appraisal, special circumstances, and financial need. U.S. citizenship or permanent resident status is required.
Financial data   The stipend is $1,000.
Duration   1 year.
Number awarded   Varies; recently, 7 were awarded.
Deadline   January of each year.

[1147]
MIKE HYLTON AND RON NIEDERMAN SCHOLARSHIPS

Factor Support Network Pharmacy
Attn: Scholarship Committee
900 Avenida Acaso, Suite A
Camarillo, CA 93012-8749
(805) 388-9336   Toll Free: (877) 376-4968
Fax: (805) 482-6324
E-mail: Scholarships@FactorSupport.com
Web: www.factorsupport.com/scholarships.htm

Summary   To provide financial assistance for college to men with hemophilia and their immediate families.
Eligibility   This program is open to men with bleeding disorders and their immediate family members. Applicants must be entering or attending a college, university, juniors college, or vocational school. They must submit 3 short essays: 1) their career goals; 2) how hemophilia or von Willebrand Disease has affected their life; and 3) their efforts to be involved in the bleeding disorder community and what they can do to education their peers and others outside their family about bleeding disorders. Selection is based on academic goals, volunteer work, school activities, achievements, and financial need.

Financial data The stipend is $1,000. Funds are paid directly to the recipient.

Duration 1 year.

Additional data This program was established in 1999.

Number awarded 10 each year.

Deadline April of each year.

[1148]
MINNESOTA G.I. BILL PROGRAM

Minnesota Office of Higher Education
Attn: Manager of State Financial Aid Programs
1450 Energy Park Drive, Suite 350
St. Paul, MN 55108-5227
(651) 642-0567   Toll Free: (800) 657-3866
Fax: (651) 642-0675   TDD: (800) 627-3529
E-mail: info@ohe.state.mn.us
Web: www.ohe.state.mn.us/mPg.cfm?pageID=891

Summary To provide financial assistance for college or graduate school in the state to residents of Minnesota who served in the military after September 11, 2001 and the families of deceased or disabled military personnel.

Eligibility This program is open to residents of Minnesota enrolled at colleges and universities in the state as undergraduate or graduate students. Applicants must be 1) a veteran who is serving or has served honorably in a branch of the U.S. armed forces at any time on or after September 11, 2001; 2) a non-veteran who has served honorably for a total of 5 years or more cumulatively as a member of the Minnesota National Guard or other active or Reserve component of the U.S. armed forces, and any part of that service occurred on or after September 11, 2001; or 3) a surviving child or spouse of a person who has served in the military at any time on or after September 11, 2001 and who has died or has a total and permanent disability as a result of that military service. Financial need is also considered in the selection process.

Financial data The stipend is $1,000 per semester for full-time study or $500 per semester for part-time study. The maximum award is $3,000 per fiscal year or $10,000 per lifetime.

Duration 1 year; may be renewed, provided the recipient continues to make satisfactory academic progress.

Additional data This program was established by the Minnesota Legislature in 2007.

Number awarded Varies each year.

Deadline Deadline not specified.

[1149]
MISSISSIPPI LAW ENFORCEMENT OFFICERS AND FIREMEN SCHOLARSHIP PROGRAM

Mississippi Office of Student Financial Aid
3825 Ridgewood Road
Jackson, MS 39211-6453
(601) 432-6997   Toll Free: (800) 327-2980 (within MS)
Fax: (601) 432-6527   E-mail: sfa@mississippi.edu
Web: www.mississippi.edu

Summary To provide financial assistance to the spouses and children of disabled or deceased Mississippi

law enforcement officers and fire fighters who are interested in attending college in the state.

Eligibility This program is open to children and spouses of law enforcement officers, full-time fire fighters, and volunteer fire fighters who became permanently and totally disabled or who died in the line of duty and were Mississippi residents at the time of death or injury. Applicants must be high school seniors or graduates interested in attending a state-supported postsecondary institution in Mississippi on a full-time basis. Children may be natural, adopted, or stepchildren up to 23 years of age; spouses may be of any age.

Financial data Students in this program receive full payment of tuition fees, the average cost of campus housing, required fees, and applicable course fees at state-supported colleges and universities in Mississippi. Funds may not be used to pay for books, food, school supplies, materials, dues, or fees for extracurricular activities.

Duration Up to 8 semesters.

Number awarded Varies each year; recently, 21 of these awards, worth more than $178,000, were granted.

Deadline September of each year.

[1150]
MISSOURI PUBLIC SERVICE OFFICER OR EMPLOYEE'S CHILD SURVIVOR GRANT PROGRAM

Missouri Department of Higher Education
Attn: Student Financial Assistance
205 Jefferson Street
P.O. Box 1469
Jefferson City, MO 65102-1469
(573) 526-7958   Toll Free: (800) 473-6757
Fax: (573) 751-6635   E-mail: info@dhe.mo.gov
Web: www.dhe.mo.gov

Summary To provide financial assistance to disabled public safety officers in Missouri and the spouses and children of disabled or deceased officers who are interested in attending college in the state.

Eligibility This program is open to residents of Missouri who are 1) public safety officers who were permanently and totally disabled in the line of duty; 2) spouses of public safety officers who were killed or permanently and totally disabled in the line of duty; or 3) children of Missouri public safety officers or Department of Transportation employees who were killed or permanently and totally disabled while engaged in the construction or maintenance of highways, roads, and bridges. Applicants must be Missouri residents enrolled or accepted for enrollment as a full-time undergraduate student at a participating Missouri college or university; children must be younger than 24 years of age. Students working on a degree or certificate in theology or divinity are not eligible. U.S. citizenship or permanent resident status is required.

Financial data The maximum annual grant is the lesser of 1) the actual tuition charged at the school where the recipient is enrolled, or 2) the amount of tuition charged to a Missouri undergraduate resident enrolled full time in the same class level and in the same academic major as an applicant at the University of Missouri at Columbia.

Duration 1 year; may be renewed.

Additional data Public safety officers include fire fighters, police officers, capitol police officers, parole officers, probation officers, state correctional employees, water safety officers, conservation officers, park rangers, and highway patrolmen.

Number awarded Varies each year; recently, 11 students received $47,045 in support from this program.

Deadline There is no application deadline, but early submission of the completed application is encouraged.

[1151]
MISSOURI WARTIME VETERAN'S SURVIVOR GRANT PROGRAM

Missouri Department of Higher Education
Attn: Student Financial Assistance
205 Jefferson Street
P.O. Box 1469
Jefferson City, MO 65102-1469
(573) 526-7958   Toll Free: (800) 473-6757
Fax: (573) 751-6635   E-mail: info@dhe.mo.gov
Web: www.dhe.mo.gov

Summary To provide financial assistance to survivors of deceased or disabled Missouri post-September 11, 2001 veterans who plan to attend college in the state.

Eligibility This program is open to spouses and children of veterans whose deaths or injuries were a result of combat action or were attributed to an illness that was contracted while serving in combat action, or who became 80% disabled as a result of injuries or accidents sustained in combat action since September 11, 2001. The veteran must have been a Missouri resident when first entering military service or at the time of death or injury. The spouse or child must be a U.S. citizen or permanent resident or otherwise lawfully present in the United States; children of veterans must be younger than 25 years of age. All applicants must be enrolled or accepted for enrollment at least half time at participating public college or university in Missouri.

Financial data The maximum annual grant is the lesser of 1) the actual tuition charged at the school where the recipient is enrolled, or 2) the amount of tuition charged to a Missouri resident enrolled in the same number of hours at the University of Missouri at Columbia. Additional allowances provide up to $2,000 per semester for room and board and the lesser of the actual cost for books or $500.

Duration 1 year. May be renewed, provided the recipient maintains a GPA of 2.5 or higher and makes satisfactory academic progress; children of veterans are eligible until they turn 25 years of age or receive their first bachelor's degree, whichever occurs first.

Number awarded Up to 25 each year.

Deadline There is no application deadline, but early submission of the completed application is encouraged.

[1152]
MONTANA POLICE PROTECTIVE ASSOCIATION SCHOLARSHIPS

Montana Police Protective Association
Attn: MPPA Foundation, Inc.
P.O. Box 7
Butte, MT 59703
(406) 490-1947   Toll Free: (800) 565-8557
E-mail: jdwilli@bresnan.net
Web: www.mppaonline.org/foundation/scholarship.php

Summary To provide financial assistance to children of disabled and other members of the Montana Police Protective Association (MPPA) who are interested in attending college in any state.

Eligibility This program is open to children of Montana police officers who are MPPA members, whether active, retired, or medical disability retired. Applicants must be enrolled or planning to enroll full time at a college, university, junior college, or vocational/technical school in any state. They must have a GPA of 2.5 or higher.

Financial data The maximum lifetime award for each recipient is $5,000 over 5 years.

Duration 1 year; may be renewed up to 4 additional years, provided the recipient maintains a GPA of 2.85 or higher.

Number awarded 1 or more each year.

Deadline June of each year.

[1153]
MOUSE HOLE SCHOLARSHIPS

Blind Mice, Inc.
16810 Pinemoor Way
Houston, TX 77058
(713) 893-7277   E-mail: blindmicemart@att.net
Web: www.blindmicemegamall.com

Summary To provide financial assistance for college to blind students and the children of blind parents.

Eligibility This program is open to visually impaired students and to sighted students who have visually impaired parents. Applicants must be high school seniors or graduates who have never been enrolled in college. Along with their application, they must submit an essay, between 4 and 15 pages in length, on a topic that changes annually; recently, students were asked to speculate on what their life will be like in 10 years. Essays are judged on originality, creativity, grammar, spelling, and the judge's overall impression of the applicant.

Financial data Stipends are $2,000 for the winner and $1,000 for the first runner-up.

Duration 1 year.

Additional data These scholarships were first awarded in 2003. The winner receives the Antonia M. Derks Memorial Scholarship and the first runner-up receives the Kelsey Campbell Memorial Scholarship.

Number awarded 2 each year.

Deadline May of each year.

[1154]
NAGA EDUCATIONAL SCHOLARSHIP GRANT

National Amputee Golf Association
Attn: Scholarship Grant Program
11 Walnut Hill Road
Amherst, NH 03031
(603) 672-6444   Toll Free: (800) 633-NAGA
Fax: (603) 672-2987   E-mail: info@nagagolf.org
Web: www.nagagolf.org/scholarship1.shtml

Summary   To provide money for college to members of the National Amputee Golf Association and their dependents.

Eligibility   This program is open to amputee members in good standing in the association and their dependents. Applicants must submit information on their scholastic background (GPA in high school and college, courses of study); type of amputation and cause (if applicable), a cover letter describing their plans for the future; and documentation of financial need. They need not be competitive golfers. Selection is based on academic record, financial need, involvement in extracurricular or community activities, and area of study.

Financial data   The stipend for a 4-year bachelor's degree program is $2,000 per year. The stipend for a 2-year technical or associate degree is $1,000 per year.

Duration   Up to 4 years, provided the recipient maintains at least half-time enrollment and a GPA of 3.0 or higher and continues to demonstrate financial need.

Number awarded   1 or more each year.

Deadline   August of each year.

[1155]
NANCY JAYNES MEMORIAL SCHOLARSHIP AWARD

Indiana Breast Cancer Awareness Trust, Inc.
P.O. Box 8212
Evansville, IN 47716
Toll Free: (866) 724-2228   Fax: (812) 868-8773
E-mail: ibcat@insightbb.com
Web: bcplates.mediamite.com

Summary   To provide financial assistance to high school seniors in Indiana whose parent has or had cancer and who are planning to attend college in the state.

Eligibility   This program is open to seniors graduating from high schools in Indiana who are planning to attend a college, university, or technical school in the state. Applicants must have lost a parent to breast cancer or have a parent who is battling breast cancer. They must have a GPA of 2.8 or higher.

Financial data   The stipend is $1,000.

Duration   1 year.

Number awarded   Varies each year; recently, 2 of these scholarships were awarded.

Deadline   February of each year.

[1156]
NATIONAL CORNERSTONE HEALTHCARE SERVICES SCHOLARSHIPS

National Cornerstone Healthcare Services Inc.
24747 Redlands Boulevard, Suite B
Loma Linda, CA 92354
Toll Free: (877) 616-6247   Fax: (877) 777-5717
E-mail: inquiry@nc-hs.com
Web: www.nc-hs.com

Summary   To provide money for college to people who have a bleeding disorder and members of their family.

Eligibility   This program is open to graduating high school seniors who are planning to attend an accredited technical school, college, or university. Applicants must have been diagnosed with a bleeding disorder or be the parent, spouse, partner, child, or sibling of a person with such a disorder. They must have a GPA of 2.5 or higher during their entire senior year of high school. Along with their application, they must submit a brief essay on their dreams, goals, and objectives for attending postsecondary education. Selection is based on that statement, academic merit, employment status, reference letters, impact of the bleeding disorders community, and financial need.

Financial data   Stipends range from $500 to $1,000.

Duration   1 year.

Number awarded   1 or more each year.

Deadline   March of each year.

[1157]
NATIONAL GUARD ASSOCIATION OF INDIANA EDUCATIONAL GRANTS

National Guard Association of Indiana
Attn: Educational Grant Committee
2002 South Holt Road, Building 9
Indianapolis, IN 46241-4839
(317) 247-3196   Toll Free: (800) 219-2173
Fax: (317) 247-3575   E-mail: membership@ngai.net
Web: www.ngai.net/membership

Summary   To provide financial assistance to members of the National Guard Association of Indiana (NGAI) and their dependents who plan to attend college in any state.

Eligibility   This program is open to NGAI members who are currently serving in the Indiana National Guard and their dependents. Children and widow(er)s of former Guard members killed or permanently disabled while on duty with the Indiana National Guard are also eligible. Applicants must be attending or planning to attend a college or university in any state. Along with their application, they must submit 2 letters of recommendation, a copy of high school or college transcripts, SAT or ACT scores (if taken), a letter of acceptance from a college or university (if not currently attending college), and a 2-page essay on the educational program they intend to pursue and the goals they wish to attain. Selection is based on academic achievement, commitment and desire to achieve, extracurricular activities, accomplishments, goals, and financial need.

Financial data   The stipend is $1,000.

Duration   1 year; recipients may reapply.

Number awarded 10 each year: 5 to military members and 5 to dependents.
Deadline March of each year.

[1158]
NATIONAL KIDNEY FOUNDATION SERVING CONNECTICUT AND WESTERN MASSACHUSETTS SCHOLARSHIPS

National Kidney Foundation Serving Connecticut and
Western Massachusetts
2139 Silas Deane Highway, Suite 208
Rocky Hill, CT 06067-2337
(860) 257-3770   Toll Free: (800) 441-1280, ext. 24
Fax: (860) 257-3429
E-mail: Donna.Sciacca@kidney.org
Web: www.kidneyct.org

Summary To provide financial assistance to residents of Connecticut and western Massachusetts who are dialysis patients, kidney recipients or donors, or dependents of patients and interested in attending college in any state.
Eligibility This program is open to residents of Connecticut (except Fairfield County) and western Massachusetts who are dialysis patients, transplant recipients, dependents of a dialysis or transplant patient, or living kidney donors. Applicants must be attending or planning to attend a 2- or 4-year college, university, or trade/technical school in any state. Along with their application, they must submit a 2-page essay on their choice of 5 topics that relate to their personal goals and experiences. Selection is based on the essay, academic merit, extracurricular activities or community service, and financial need. For applicants who have been out of school for many years, work or life experience may also be considered. U.S. citizenship is required.
Financial data The stipend is $1,000.
Duration 1 year.
Number awarded 3 each year.
Deadline May of each year.

[1159]
NATIONAL KIDNEY FOUNDATION SERVING MAINE SCHOLARSHIPS

National Kidney Foundation Serving Maine
470 Forest Avenue, Suite 202
Portland, ME 04101-2009
(207) 772-7270   Toll Free: (800) 639-7220
Fax: (207) 772-4202   E-mail: nkfme@kidney.org
Web: www.kidneyme.org

Summary To provide financial assistance to residents of Maine who are kidney patients or their families and interested in attending college in any state.
Eligibility This program is open to residents of Maine who are kidney patients (dialysis patients, kidney transplant recipients, or newly diagnosed patients who are in early intervention programs) or immediate family members of patients. Applicants must be attending or planning to attend an accredited college or university in any state. Along with their application, they must submit documentation of financial need and brief essays on their educational

goals and how kidney disease has impacted their life. Financial need is considered in the selection process.
Financial data A stipend is awarded (amount not specified).
Duration 1 year.
Number awarded Varies each year; recently, 7 of these scholarships were awarded.
Deadline July of each year.

[1160]
NATIONAL MS SOCIETY SCHOLARSHIP PROGRAM

National Multiple Sclerosis Society
Attn: Scholarship Fund
900 South Broadway, Suite 200
Denver, CO 80209
(303) 698-6100, ext. 15259   E-mail: nmss@act.org
Web: www.nationalmssociety.org

Summary To provide financial assistance for college to students who have Multiple Sclerosis (MS) or are the children of people with MS.
Eligibility This program is open to 1) high school seniors who have MS and will be attending an accredited postsecondary school for the first time; 2) high school seniors who are the children of parents with MS and will be attending an accredited postsecondary school for the first time; 3) high school (or GED) graduates of any age who have MS and will be attending an accredited postsecondary school for the first time; and 4) high school (or GED) graduates of any age who have a parent with MS and will be attending an accredited postgraduate school for the first time. Applicants must be U.S. citizens or permanent residents who plan to enroll for at least 6 credit hours per semester in an undergraduate course of study at an accredited 2- or 4-year college, university, or vocational/technical school in the United States or its territories to work on a degree, license, or certificate. Along with their application, they must submit a 1-page personal statement on the impact MS has had on their life. Selection is based on that statement, academic record, leadership and participation in school or community activities, work experience, goals and aspirations, an outside appraisal, special circumstances, and financial need.
Financial data Stipends range from $1,000 to $3,000.
Duration 1 year; may be renewed.
Additional data This program, which began in 2003, is managed by ACT Scholarship and Recognition Services.
Number awarded Varies each year; recently, 639 of these scholarships (439 new awards and 200 renewals), with a total value of $1,166,350, were awarded.
Deadline January of each year.

[1161]
NCFOP FOUNDATION SCHOLARSHIPS

North Carolina Fraternal Order of Police
Attn: NCFOB Foundation, Inc.
1500 Walnut Street
Cary, NC 27511-5927
(919) 461-4939   Toll Free: (877) 628-8063
E-mail: ncfop@nc.rr.com
Web: www.ncfop.com/ht/d/sp/i/204/pid/204

Summary   To provide money for college to families of disabled or deceased law enforcement officers in North Carolina.

Eligibility   This program is open to North Carolina residents who are enrolled in an appropriate postsecondary institution, including colleges and vocational schools. Applicants must be the child or spouse of a North Carolina law enforcement officer killed or disabled in the line of duty.

Financial data   A stipend is awarded (amount not specified).

Duration   1 year.

Number awarded   Varies each year; recently, 3 of these scholarships were awarded.

Deadline   Deadline not specified.

[1162]
NCTA SCHOLARSHIPS

North Carolina Troopers Association
3505 Vernon Woods Drive
Summerfield, NC 27358
Toll Free: (800) 446-7334   Fax: (336) 644-6205
E-mail: info@nctroopers.org
Web: www.nctroopers.org

Summary   To provide financial assistance for college to children of members of the North Carolina Troopers Association (NCTA) and of disabled and deceased North Carolina Highway Patrol troopers.

Eligibility   This program is open to dependent children between 16 and 23 years of age of active or deceased members of the NCTA. Applicants must be attending or planning to attend a university, college, community college, technical college, or trade school in North Carolina as a full-time student. Along with their application, they must submit an essay on how the scholarship will benefit them. Special applications are accepted from the children of disabled or deceased troopers of the North Carolina State Highway Patrol.

Financial data   Stipends are $1,000 for students at 4-year colleges and universities or $500 for students at community, technical, and trade colleges.

Duration   1 year; renewable as long as the recipient remains enrolled full time with a GPA of "C" or higher.

Additional data   This program includes the Colonel Bob Barefoot Scholarship for a student at a 4-year college or university and the Captain Ivan Stroud Scholarship for a student at a community college.

Number awarded   10 each year: 5 at $1,000 to students at 4-year institutions and 5 at $500 to students at 2-year institutions.

Deadline   March of each year.

[1163]
NEBRASKA CHAPTER NHF SCHOLARSHIPS

National Hemophilia Foundation-Nebraska Chapter
Attn: Scholarship Selection Committee
215 Centennial Mall South, Suite 512
Lincoln, NE 68508
(402) 742-5663   Fax: (402) 742-5677
E-mail: office@nebraskanhf.org
Web: www.nebraskanhf.org

Summary   To provide financial assistance for attendance at a college in any state to high school seniors in Nebraska who have a bleeding disorder, are relatives of a person with a bleeding disorder, or are a carrier of a defective gene related to a bleeding disorder.

Eligibility   This program is open to seniors graduating from high schools in Nebraska who plan to attend a college or university in any state. Applicants must have a bleeding disorder, be an immediately family member of a person with a bleeding disorder, or be the carrier of a defective gene related to a bleeding disorder. Along with their application, they must submit a brief statement on how a bleeding disorder influences their family life and a 250-word essay on their purpose and motivation for pursuing a postsecondary educational degree. Selection is based on that statement and essay, academic promise in their major field, and financial need. Preference is given to members of the Nebraska Chapter of the National Hemophilia Foundation (NHF).

Financial data   The stipend ranges from $500 to $1,000 per academic term ($1,000 to $2,000 per year).

Duration   1 year.

Number awarded   1 or more each year.

Deadline   June of each year.

[1164]
NEBRASKA WAIVER OF TUITION FOR VETERANS' DEPENDENTS

Department of Veterans' Affairs
State Office Building
301 Centennial Mall South, Sixth Floor
P.O. Box 95083
Lincoln, NE 68509-5083
(402) 471-2458   Fax: (402) 471-2491
E-mail: john.hilgert@nebraska.gov
Web: www.vets.state.ne.us/benefits.html

Summary   To provide financial assistance for college to dependents of deceased and disabled veterans and military personnel in Nebraska.

Eligibility   Eligible are spouses, widow(er)s, and children who are residents of Nebraska and whose parent, stepparent, or spouse was a member of the U.S. armed forces and 1) died of a service-connected disability; 2) died subsequent to discharge as a result of injury or illness sustained while in service; 3) is permanently and totally disabled as a result of military service; or 4) is classified as missing in action or as a prisoner of war during armed hostilities. Applicants must be attending or planning to attend a branch of the University of Nebraska, a state college, or a community college in Nebraska.

Financial data Tuition is waived at public institutions in Nebraska.

Duration The waiver is valid for 1 degree, diploma, or certificate from a community college and 1 baccalaureate degree.

Additional data Applications may be submitted through 1 of the recognized veterans' organizations or any county service officer.

Number awarded Varies each year; recently, 311 of these grants were awarded.

Deadline Deadline not specified.

[1165]
NEW JERSEY BANKERS EDUCATION FOUNDATION SCHOLARSHIPS

New Jersey Bankers Association
Attn: New Jersey Bankers Education Foundation, Inc.
411 North Avenue East
Cranford, NJ 07016-2436
(908) 272-8500, ext. 614   Fax: (908) 272-6626
E-mail: j.meredith@njbankers.com
Web: www.njbankers.com

Summary To provide financial assistance to dependents of deceased and disabled military personnel who have a connection to New Jersey and are interested in attending college in any state.

Eligibility This program is open to the spouses, children, stepchildren, and grandchildren of members of the armed services who died or became disabled while on active duty; it is not required that the military person died in combat. Applicants must have a high school or equivalency diploma and be attending college in any state. Adult dependents who wish to obtain a high school equivalency diploma are also eligible. Either the dependent or the service member must have a connection to New Jersey; the applicant's permanent address must be in New Jersey or the service member's last permanent address or military base must have been in the state. Financial need is considered in the selection process.

Financial data A stipend is awarded (amount not specified).

Duration 1 year; may be renewed if the recipient maintains a "C" average.

Additional data This program was established in 2005.

Number awarded 1 or more each year.

Deadline June of each year.

[1166]
NEW JERSEY METRO CHAPTER MS SOCIETY SCHOLARSHIP PROGRAM

National Multiple Sclerosis Society-New Jersey Metro Chapter
Attn: Scholarship Program
246 Monmouth Road
Oakhurst, NJ 07755
(732) 660-1005   Fax: (732) 660-1338
E-mail: nancy.chazen@nmss.org
Web: was.nationalmssociety.org

Summary To provide financial assistance to high school seniors and graduates from New Jersey who have multiple sclerosis (MS) or have a parent with MS and are planning to attend college in any state.

Eligibility This program is open to graduating high school seniors, recent graduates, and GED recipients from New Jersey who have MS or a parent who has MS. Applicants must be planning to enroll as a first-time student at a 2- or 4-year college, university, or vocational/technical school in the United States on at least a half-time basis. Along with their application, they must submit an essay on the impact MS has had on their lives. Selection is based on that essay, academic record, leadership and participation in school or community activities, work experience, goals and aspirations, an outside appraisal, special circumstances, and financial need. U.S. citizenship or permanent resident status is required.

Financial data Stipends average more than $1,000.

Duration 1 year.

Additional data This program began in 1994.

Number awarded Varies each year; recently, 45 of these scholarships, worth $55,800, were awarded.

Deadline January of each year.

[1167]
NEW YORK STATE MILITARY SERVICE RECOGNITION SCHOLARSHIPS

New York State Higher Education Services Corporation
Attn: Student Information
99 Washington Avenue
Albany, NY 12255
(518) 473-1574   Toll Free: (888) NYS-HESC
Fax: (518) 473-3749   TDD: (800) 445-5234
E-mail: webmail@hesc.com
Web: www.hesc.com

Summary To provide financial assistance to disabled veterans and the family members of deceased or disabled veterans who are residents of New York and interested in attending college in the state.

Eligibility This program is open to New York residents who served in the armed forces of the United States or state organized militia at any time on or after August 2, 1990 and became severely and permanently disabled as a result of injury or illness suffered or incurred in a combat theater or combat zone or during military training operations in preparation for duty in a combat theater or combat zone of operations. Also eligible are the children, spouses, or financial dependents of members of the armed forces of the United States or state organized militia who at any time after August 2, 1990 1) died, became severely and permanently disabled as a result of injury or illness suffered or incurred, or are classified as missing in action in a combat theater or combat zone of operations; 2) died as a result of injuries incurred in those designated areas; or 3) died or became severely and permanently disabled as a result of injury or illness suffered or incurred during military training operations in preparation for duty in a combat theater or combat zone of operations. Applicants must be attending or accepted at an approved program of study as full-time undergraduates at a public college or university or private institution in New York.

Financial data At public colleges and universities, this program provides payment of actual tuition and mandatory educational fees; actual room and board charged to students living on campus or an allowance for room and board for commuter students; and allowances for books, supplies, and transportation. At private institutions, the award is equal to the amount charged at the State University of New York (SUNY) for 4-year tuition and average mandatory fees (or the student's actual tuition and fees, whichever is less) plus allowances for room, board, books, supplies, and transportation.

Duration This program is available for 4 years of full-time undergraduate study (or 5 years in an approved 5-year bachelor's degree program).

Number awarded Varies each year.

Deadline April of each year.

[1168]
NORTH CAROLINA BAR ASSOCIATION SCHOLARSHIPS

North Carolina Bar Association
Attn: Young Lawyers Division Scholarship Committee
8000 Weston Parkway
P.O. Box 3688
Cary, NC 27519-3688
(919) 677-0561   Toll Free: (800) 662-7407
Fax: (919) 677-0761   E-mail: jterrell@ncbar.org
Web: younglawyers.ncbar.org

Summary To provide financial assistance for college or graduate school to the children of disabled or deceased law enforcement officers in North Carolina.

Eligibility This program is open to the natural or adopted children of North Carolina law enforcement officers who were permanently disabled or killed in the line of duty. Applicants must be younger than 27 years of age and enrolled or planning to enroll full time at an accredited institution of higher learning (including community colleges, trade schools, colleges, universities, and graduate programs) in North Carolina. Selection is based on academic performance and financial need.

Financial data The stipend is $2,000 per year.

Duration Up to 4 years.

Number awarded Varies each year; recently, 17 of these scholarships were awarded.

Deadline March of each year.

[1169]
NORTH CAROLINA LIONS EDUCATION GRANT PROGRAM

North Carolina Lions, Inc.
7050 Camp Dogwood Drive
P.O. Box 39
Sherrills Ford, NC 28673
(828) 478-2135   Toll Free: (800) 662-7401
Fax: (828) 478-4419   E-mail: nclions@nclionsinc.org
Web: nclionsinc.org/?page_id=105

Summary To provide money for college to sighted children of blind or visually impaired parents in North Carolina.

Eligibility This program is open to residents of North Carolina who are sighted children of blind or visually impaired parents. Applicants must be working on or planning to work on an undergraduate degree or certificate. Family income may not exceed $40,000 for families with 1 dependent child, increasing by $10,000 for each additional dependent child. Selection is based on the financial need of the family and the academic record and character of the applicant.

Financial data The stipend is $1,500. Funds are paid to the recipient's college, community college, or trade/technical school.

Duration 1 year; may be renewed up to 4 additional years, provided the recipient maintains full-time enrollment and a GPA of 2.0 or higher.

Additional data This program was formerly known as the William L. Woolard Educational Grant Program.

Number awarded 1 or more each year.

Deadline March of each year.

[1170]
NORTH CAROLINA NATIONAL GUARD ASSOCIATION SPECIAL POPULATION SCHOLARSHIP

North Carolina National Guard Association
Attn: Educational Foundation, Inc.
7410 Chapel Hill Road
Raleigh, NC 27607-5047
(919) 851-3390   Toll Free: (800) 821-6159 (within NC)
Fax: (919) 859-4990
E-mail: peggyncngaef@bellsouth.net
Web: ncnga.org

Summary To provide funding to members and dependents of members of the North Carolina National Guard Association who have a learning or physical disability and are interested in attending college in any state.

Eligibility This program is open to active and associate members of the association as well as the spouses, children, grandchildren, and legal dependents of active, associate, or deceased members. Applicants must be learning disabled and/or physically disabled. They may be high school seniors, high school graduates, or students currently enrolled at a college or university in any state. Selection is based on financial need, academic achievement, citizenship, leadership, and other application information.

Financial data The stipend is $1,000.
Duration 1 year; may be renewed.
Number awarded 1 each year.
Deadline January of each year for high school graduates and college students; February for high school seniors.

[1171]
NORTH CAROLINA SCHOLARSHIPS FOR CHILDREN OF WAR VETERANS

Division of Veterans Affairs
Albemarle Building
325 North Salisbury Street, Suite 1065
1315 Mail Service Center
Raleigh, NC 27699-1315
(919) 733-3851   Fax: (919) 733-2834
E-mail: ncdva.aso@ncmail.net
Web: www.ncveterans.com/benefitlist.aspx

Summary To provide financial assistance to the children of disabled and other classes of North Carolina veterans who plan to attend college in the state.
Eligibility Eligible applicants come from 5 categories: Class I-A: the veteran parent died in wartime service or as a result of a service-connected condition incurred in wartime service; Class I-B: the veteran parent is rated by the U.S. Department of Veterans Affairs (VA) as 100% disabled as a result of wartime service and currently or at the time of death was drawing compensation for such disability; Class II: the veteran parent is rated by the VA as much as 20% but less than 100% disabled due to wartime service, or was awarded a Purple Heart medal for wounds received, and currently or at the time of death drawing compensation for such disability; Class III: the veteran parent is currently or was at the time of death receiving a VA pension for total and permanent disability, or the veteran parent is deceased but does not qualify under any other provisions, or the veteran parent served in a combat zone or waters adjacent to a combat zone and received a campaign badge or medal but does not qualify under any other provisions; Class IV: the veteran parent was a prisoner of war or missing in action. For all classes, applicants must 1) be under 25 years of age and have a veteran parent who was a North Carolina resident at the time of entrance into the armed forces; or 2) be the natural child, or adopted child prior to age 15, who was born in North Carolina, has been a state resident continuously since birth, and is the child of a veteran whose disabilities occurred during a war period.
Financial data Students in Classes I-A, II, III, and IV receive $4,500 per academic year if they attend a private college or junior college; if attending a public postsecondary institution, they receive free tuition, a room allowance, a board allowance, and exemption from certain mandatory fees. Students in Class I-B receive $1,500 per academic year if they attend a private college or junior college; if attending a public postsecondary institution, they receive free tuition and exemption from certain mandatory fees.
Duration 4 academic years.

Number awarded An unlimited number of awards are made under Classes I-A, I-B, and IV. Classes II and III are limited to 100 awards each year in each class.
Deadline Applications for Classes I-A, I-B, and IV may be submitted at any time; applications for Classes II and III must be submitted by February of each year.

[1172]
NORTH CAROLINA SHERIFFS' ASSOCIATION UNDERGRADUATE CRIMINAL JUSTICE SCHOLARSHIPS

North Carolina State Education Assistance Authority
Attn: Grants, Training, and Outreach Department
10 T.W. Alexander Drive
P.O. Box 13663
Research Triangle Park, NC 27709-3663
(919) 549-8614   Toll Free: (800) 700-1775
Fax: (919) 248-4687   E-mail: information@ncseaa.edu
Web: www.ncseaa.edu/Ncsheriffs.htm

Summary To provide financial assistance to residents of North Carolina, especially children of deceased or disabled law enforcement officers, who are majoring in criminal justice at a college in the state.
Eligibility Eligible for this program are North Carolina residents enrolled full time in a criminal justice program at any of the 10 state institutions offering that major: Appalachian State University, East Carolina University, Elizabeth City State University, Fayetteville State University, North Carolina Central University, North Carolina State University, the University of North Carolina at Charlotte, the University of North Carolina at Pembroke, the University of North Carolina at Wilmington, and Western Carolina University. First priority in selection is given to children of law enforcement officers killed in the line of duty; second priority is given to children of sheriffs or deputy sheriffs who are deceased, retired (regular or disability), or currently active in law enforcement in North Carolina; third priority is given to other resident criminal justice students meeting their institution's academic and financial need criteria.
Financial data The stipend is $2,000 per year.
Duration 1 year; nonrenewable.
Additional data Funding for this program is provided by the North Carolina Sheriffs' Association. Recipients are selected by the financial aid office at the university they plan to attend or are currently attending; after selection, students obtain a letter of endorsement from the sheriff of the county in North Carolina where they reside.
Number awarded Up to 10 each year: 1 at each of the participating universities.
Deadline Deadline not specified.

[1173]
NORTH DAKOTA EDUCATIONAL ASSISTANCE FOR DEPENDENTS OF VETERANS

Department of Veterans Affairs
4201 38th Street S.W., Suite 104
P.O. Box 9003
Fargo, ND 58106-9003
(701) 239-7165   Toll Free: (866) 634-8387
Fax: (701) 239-7166
Web: www.nd.gov/veterans/benefits/waiver.html

Summary To provide financial assistance for college to the spouses, widow(er)s, and children of disabled and other North Dakota veterans and military personnel.

Eligibility This program is open to the spouses, widow(er)s, and dependent children of veterans who were killed in action, died from wounds or other service-connected causes, were totally disabled as a result of service-connected causes, died from service-connected disabilities, were a prisoners of war, or were declared missing in action. Veteran parents must have been born in and lived in North Dakota until entrance into the armed forces (or must have resided in the state for at least 6 months prior to entrance into military service) and must have served during war time.

Financial data Eligible dependents receive free tuition and are exempt from fees at any state-supported institution of higher education, technical school, or vocational school in North Dakota.

Duration Up to 45 months or 10 academic semesters.

Number awarded Varies each year.

Deadline Deadline not specified.

[1174]
NYS WORLD TRADE CENTER MEMORIAL SCHOLARSHIPS

New York State Higher Education Services Corporation
Attn: Student Information
99 Washington Avenue
Albany, NY 12255
(518) 473-1574   Toll Free: (888) NYS-HESC
Fax: (518) 473-3749   TDD: (800) 445-5234
E-mail: webmail@hesc.com
Web: www.hesc.com

Summary To provide financial assistance to undergraduates in New York who are survivors or victims of the terrorist attacks on September 11, 2001 or their relatives.

Eligibility This program is open to 1) the children, spouses, and financial dependents of deceased or severely and permanently disabled victims of the September 11, 2001 terrorist attacks or the subsequent rescue and recovery operations; and 2) survivors of the terrorist attacks who are severely and permanently disabled as a result of injuries sustained in the attacks or the subsequent rescue and recovery operations. Applicants must be attending or accepted at an approved program of study as full-time undergraduates at a public college or university or private institution in New York.

Financial data At public colleges and universities, this program provides payment of actual tuition and manda-

tory educational fees; actual room and board charged to students living on campus or an allowance for room and board for commuter students; and allowances for books, supplies, and transportation. At private institutions, the award is equal to the amount charged at the State University of New York (SUNY) for 4-year tuition and average mandatory fees (or the student's actual tuition and fees, whichever is less) plus allowances for room, board, books, supplies, and transportation.

Duration This program is available for 4 years of full-time undergraduate study (or 5 years in an approved 5-year bachelor's degree program).

Number awarded Varies each year.

Deadline April of each year.

[1175]
OHIO LEGION AUXILIARY DEPARTMENT PRESIDENT'S SCHOLARSHIP

American Legion Auxiliary
Department of Ohio
1100 Brandywine Boulevard, Suite D
P.O. Box 2760
Zanesville, OH 43702-2760
(740) 452-8245   Fax: (740) 452-2620
E-mail: ala_katie@rrohio.com
Web: www.alaohio.org/Scholarships

Summary To provide financial assistance to disabled and other veterans and their descendants in Ohio who are interested in attending college in any state.

Eligibility This program is open to honorably-discharged veterans and the children, grandchildren, and great-grandchildren of living, deceased, or disabled honorably-discharged veterans who served during designated periods of war time. Applicants must be residents of Ohio, seniors at an accredited high school, planning to enter a college in any state, and sponsored by an American Legion Auxiliary Unit. Along with their application, they must submit an original article (up to 500 words) written by the applicant on a topic that changes annually. Recently, students were asked to write on "Education and the American Dream." Selection is based on character, Americanism, leadership, scholarship, and financial need.

Financial data Stipends are $1,500 or $1,000. Funds are paid to the recipient's school.

Duration 1 year.

Number awarded 2 each year: 1 at $1,500 and 1 at $1,000.

Deadline February of each year.

[1176]
OHIO WAR ORPHANS SCHOLARSHIP

Ohio Board of Regents
Attn: State Grants and Scholarships
30 East Broad Street, 36th Floor
Columbus, OH 43215-3414
(614) 752-9528   Toll Free: (888) 833-1133
Fax: (614) 466-5866
E-mail: jabdullah-simmons@regents.state.oh.us
Web: students.ohio.highered.org

Summary To provide financial assistance to the children of deceased or disabled Ohio veterans who plan to attend college in the state.
Eligibility This program is open to residents of Ohio who are under 25 years of age and interested in enrolling full time at an eligible college or university in the state. Applicants must be the child of a veteran who 1) was a member of the U.S. armed forces, including the organized Reserves and Ohio National Guard, for a period of 90 days or more (or discharged because of a disability incurred after less than 90 days of service); 2) served during specified periods of war time; 3) entered service as a resident of Ohio; and 4) as a result of that service, either was killed or became at least 60% service-connected disabled. Also eligible are children of veterans who have a permanent and total non-service connected disability and are receiving disability benefits from the U.S. Department of Veterans Affairs. If the veteran parent served only in the organized Reserves or Ohio National Guard, the parent must have been killed or became permanently and totally disabled while at a scheduled training assembly, field training period (of any duration or length), or active duty for training, pursuant to bona fide orders issued by a competent authority. Need is considered in the selection process.
Financial data At Ohio public colleges and universities, the program provides payment of 80% of tuition and fees. At Ohio private colleges and universities, the stipend is $4,797 per year (or 80% of the average amount paid to students attending public institutions).
Duration 1 year; renewable up to 4 more years, provided the recipient maintains a GPA of 2.0 or higher.
Additional data Eligible institutions are Ohio state-assisted colleges and universities and Ohio institutions approved by the Board of Regents. This program was established in 1957.
Number awarded Varies, depending upon the funds available. If sufficient funds are available, all eligible applicants are given a scholarship. Recently, 861 students received benefits from this program.
Deadline June of each year.

[1177]
OKLAHOMA CHAPTER MS SOCIETY SCHOLARSHIP PROGRAM

National Multiple Sclerosis Society-Oklahoma Chapter
4606 East 67th Street, Suite 103
Tulsa, OK 74136
(918) 488-0882   Fax: (918) 488-0913
E-mail: lisa.gray@oke.nmss.org
Web: was.nationalmssociety.org

Summary To provide financial assistance to high school seniors and graduates from Oklahoma who have multiple sclerosis (MS) or have a parent with MS and who are planning to attend college in any state.
Eligibility This program is open to graduating high school seniors, recent graduates, and GED recipients from Oklahoma who have MS or a parent who has MS. Applicants must be planning to enroll as a first-time student at a 2- or 4-year college, university, or vocational/

technical school in the United States on at least a half-time basis. Along with their application, they must submit an essay on the impact MS has had on their lives. Selection is based on that essay, academic record, leadership and participation in school or community activities, work experience, goals and aspirations, an outside appraisal, special circumstances, and financial need. U.S. citizenship or permanent resident status is required.
Financial data Stipends range from $1,000 to $3,000.
Duration 1 year.
Additional data This program includes the Linda Chance Memorial Scholarship.
Number awarded Varies each year; recently, 11 of these scholarships were awarded.
Deadline January of each year.

[1178]
OREGON CHAPTER MS SOCIETY SCHOLARSHIP PROGRAM

National Multiple Sclerosis Society-Oregon Chapter
104 S.W. Clay Street
Portland, OR 97201
(503) 223-9511   Toll Free: (800) 344-4867
Fax: (503) 223-2911 E-mail: Ann.Berryman@nmss.org
Web: was.nationalmssociety.org

Summary To provide financial assistance to high school seniors and graduates from Oregon who have multiple sclerosis (MS) or have a parent with MS and who are planning to attend college in any state.
Eligibility This program is open to graduating high school seniors, recent graduates, and GED recipients from Oregon who have MS or a parent who has MS. Applicants must be planning to enroll as a first-time student at a 2- or 4-year college, university, or vocational/technical school in the United States on at least a half-time basis. Along with their application, they must submit an essay on the impact MS has had on their lives. Selection is based on that essay, academic record, leadership and participation in school or community activities, work experience, goals and aspirations, an outside appraisal, special circumstances, and financial need. U.S. citizenship or permanent resident status is required.
Financial data Stipends range from $1,000 to $3,000.
Duration 1 year.
Additional data This program began in 2006.
Number awarded Varies each year; recently, 7 of these scholarships were awarded. Since the program began, it has awarded 20 scholarships worth $38,200.
Deadline January of each year.

[1179]
OREGON DECEASED OR DISABLED PUBLIC SAFETY OFFICER GRANT PROGRAM

Oregon Student Access Commission
Attn: Public Programs
1500 Valley River Drive, Suite 100
Eugene, OR 97401-2130
(541) 687-7443   Toll Free: (800) 452-8807, ext. 7443
Fax: (541) 687-7414   TDD: (800) 735-2900
E-mail: awardinfo@osac.state.or.us
Web: www.oregonstudentaid.gov/ddpso-grant.aspx

Summary To provide financial assistance for college or graduate school in the state to the children of disabled or deceased Oregon public safety officers.

Eligibility This program is open to the natural, adopted, or stepchildren of Oregon public safety officers (fire fighters, state fire marshals, chief deputy fire marshals, deputy state fire marshals, police chiefs, police officers, sheriffs, deputy sheriffs, county adult parole and probation officers, correction officers, and investigators of the Criminal Justice Division of the Department of Justice) who, in the line of duty, were killed or disabled. Applicants must be enrolled or planning to enroll as a full-time undergraduate student at a public or private college or university in Oregon. Children of deceased officers are also eligible for graduate study. Financial need must be demonstrated.

Financial data At a public 2- or 4-year college, the amount of the award is equal to the cost of tuition and fees. At a private college, the award is equal to the cost of tuition and fees at the University of Oregon.

Duration 1 year; may be renewed for up to 3 additional years of undergraduate study, if the student maintains satisfactory academic progress and demonstrates continued financial need. Children of deceased public safety officers may receive support for 12 quarters of graduate study.

Number awarded Varies each year.

Deadline Deadline not specified.

[1180]
OREGON LEGION AUXILIARY DEPARTMENT NURSES SCHOLARSHIP

American Legion Auxiliary
Department of Oregon
30450 S.W. Parkway Avenue
P.O. Box 1730
Wilsonville, OR 97070-1730
(503) 682-3162   Fax: (503) 685-5008
E-mail: contact@alaoregon.org
Web: www.alaoregon.org

Summary To provide financial assistance to the wives, widows, and children of disabled and other Oregon veterans who are interested in studying nursing at a school in any state.

Eligibility This program is open to Oregon residents who are the wives or children of veterans with disabilities or the widows of deceased veterans. Applicants must have been accepted by an accredited hospital or university school of nursing in any state. Selection is based on

ability, aptitude, character, determination, seriousness of purpose, and financial need.

Financial data The stipend is $1,500.

Duration 1 year; may be renewed.

Number awarded 1 each year.

Deadline May of each year.

[1181]
OREGON LEGION AUXILIARY DEPARTMENT SCHOLARSHIPS

American Legion Auxiliary
Department of Oregon
30450 S.W. Parkway Avenue
P.O. Box 1730
Wilsonville, OR 97070-1730
(503) 682-3162   Fax: (503) 685-5008
E-mail: contact@alaoregon.org
Web: www.alaoregon.org

Summary To provide financial assistance to the dependents of disabled and other Oregon veterans who are interested in attending college in any state.

Eligibility This program is open to Oregon residents who are children or wives of disabled veterans or widows of veterans. Applicants must be interested in obtaining education beyond the high school level at a college, university, business school, vocational school, or any other accredited postsecondary school in the state of Oregon. Selection is based on ability, aptitude, character, seriousness of purpose, and financial need.

Financial data The stipend is $1,000.

Duration 1 year; nonrenewable.

Number awarded 3 each year; 1 of these is to be used for vocational or business school.

Deadline March of each year.

[1182]
OREGON OCCUPATIONAL SAFETY AND HEALTH DIVISION WORKERS MEMORIAL SCHOLARSHIPS

Oregon Student Access Commission
Attn: Grants and Scholarships Division
1500 Valley River Drive, Suite 100
Eugene, OR 97401-2146
(541) 687-7395   Toll Free: (800) 452-8807, ext. 7395
Fax: (541) 687-7414   TDD: (800) 735-2900
E-mail: awardinfo@osac.state.or.us
Web: www.oregonstudentaid.gov/scholarships.aspx

Summary To provide funding to children and spouses of disabled or deceased workers in Oregon who are interested in attending college or graduate school.

Eligibility This program is open to residents of Oregon who are U.S. citizens or permanent residents. Applicants must be high school seniors or graduates who 1) are dependents or spouses of an Oregon worker who has suffered permanent total disability on the job; or 2) are receiving, or have received, fatality benefits as dependents or spouses of a worker fatally injured in Oregon. They may be attending a college or graduate school in any state. Along with their application, they must submit an essay of up to 500 words on how the injury or death of their parent or spouse has affected or influenced their decision to further their education. Financial need is not required, but it is considered in the selection process.

Financial data Stipends range up to $1,000.

Duration 1 year.

Additional data This program, started in 1991, is sponsored by the Oregon Occupational Safety and Health Division of the Department of Consumer Services.

Number awarded Varies each year; recently, 7 of these scholarships were awarded.

Deadline February of each year.

[1183]
OUR BROTHER'S KEEPER FOUNDATION SCHOLARSHIPS

Our Brother's Keeper Foundation
3127 Oriole Drive
Gulf Breeze, FL 32563
(850) 733-3968   E-mail: garywhidby@att.net
Web: helpingrrfamilies.org

Summary To provide financial assistance for college to spouses and children of railroad workers injured on the job.

Eligibility This program is open to students entering or enrolled at an accredited college, university, or technical/trade school. Applicants must be the spouse or child of a worker seriously injured in a career-ending railroad accident who was a member of the Brotherhood of Locomotive Engineers and Trainmen (BLET) at the time of the injury. Along with their application, they must submit information on the career fields that interest them the most, why they are interested in that career field, their SAT/ACT scores, their most recent work-related activities, their most recent volunteer activities, their favorite hobbies, and other scholarships they have been awarded along with an estimate of the annual cost of attending their chosen institution. Primary consideration is given to families of workers who have not yet settled their legal claims or those whose claim settlements have left the family with insufficient resources to fund educational opportunities.

Financial data The stipend is $1,000.

Duration 1 year.

Additional data This program was established in 2008.

Number awarded 1 in each of the 4 BLET regions.

Deadline Applications must be submitted 30 days prior to the start of the meeting of the BLET region to which the injured worker belongs; that means deadlines are normally May of each year for the Southeastern Meeting Association (SMA), June of each year for the Eastern Union Meeting Association (EUMA), July of each year for the International Western Convention (IWC), or August of each year for the Southwestern Convention Meeting (SWCM).

[1184]
PARENT CONTINUING EDUCATION SCHOLARSHIPS

Hemophilia Federation of America
Attn: Scholarship Committee
210 Seventh Street, S.E., Suite 200B
Washington, DC 20003
(202) 675-6984   Toll Free: (800) 230-9797
Fax: (202) 675-6983   E-mail: info@hemophiliafed.org
Web: hemophiliafed.org

Summary To provide financial assistance for college to parents of children with a blood clotting disorder.

Eligibility This program is open to parents of children who have a blood clotting disorder. Applicants must be attending or planning to attend an accredited 2- or 4-year college, university, or trade school in any state. Along with their application, they must submit a 1-page essay on their goals and aspirations and how the blood clotting community has played a part in their lives. Financial need is considered in the selection process.

Financial data The stipend is $1,500 per year.

Duration 1 year; may be renewed.

Number awarded 1 each year.

Deadline April of each year.

[1185]
PENNSYLVANIA EDUCATIONAL GRATUITY FOR VETERANS' DEPENDENTS

Office of the Deputy Adjutant General for Veterans
  Affairs
Building S-0-47, FTIG
Annville, PA 17003-5002
(717) 865-8910
Toll Free: (800) 54 PA VET (within PA)
Fax: (717) 861-8589   E-mail: RA-VA-Info@pa.gov
Web: www.dmva.state.pa.us

Summary To provide money for college to the children of disabled or deceased Pennsylvania veterans.

Eligibility This program is open to children (between 16 and 23 years of age) of honorably-discharged veterans who are rated totally and permanently disabled as a result of wartime service or who have died of such a disability. Applicants must have lived in Pennsylvania for at least 5 years immediately preceding the date of application, be able to demonstrate financial need, and have been accepted or be currently enrolled in a Pennsylvania state-aided secondary or postsecondary institution.

Financial data The stipend is $500 per semester ($1,000 per year). The money is paid to the recipient's school and to be used for tuition, board, room, books, supplies, and/or matriculation fees.

Duration The allowance is paid for up to 4 years or the duration of their course of study, whichever is less.

Number awarded Varies each year.

Deadline Deadline not specified.

[1186]
PENNSYLVANIA NATIONAL GUARD SCHOLARSHIP FUND

Pennsylvania National Guard Associations
Attn: Pennsylvania National Guard Scholarship Fund
Biddle Hall (Building 9-109)
Fort Indiantown Gap
Annville, PA 17003-5002
(717) 865-9631   Toll Free: (800) 997-8885
Fax: (717) 861-5560   E-mail: oswalddean@aol.com
Web: www.pngas.net

Summary To provide financial assistance to Pennsylvania National Guard members and the children of disabled or deceased members who are interested in attending college in any state.

Eligibility This program is open to active members of the Pennsylvania Army or Air National Guard. Children of members of the Guard who died or were permanently disabled while on Guard duty are also eligible. Applicants must be entering their first year of higher education as a full-time student or presently attending a college or vocational school in any state as a full-time student. Along with their application, they must submit an essay that outlines their military and civilian plans for the future. Selection is based on that essay, academic achievement, leadership abilities, and contributions to citizenship.

Financial data Stipends range from $500 to $2,000.

Duration 1 year.

Additional data The sponsoring organization includes the National Guard Association of Pennsylvania (NGAP) and the Pennsylvania National Guard Enlisted Association (PNGEA). This program, which began in 1977, includes the following named scholarships: the BG Richard E. Thorn Memorial Scholarship, the Murtha Memorial Scholarship, the BG Hugh S. Niles Memorial Scholarship, the PNGEA USAA Scholarship (sponsored by the USAA Insurance Corporation), and the 28th Infantry Division Scholarship.

Number awarded Varies each year; recently, 13 of these scholarships were awarded: 2 at $2,000, 1 at $1,500, 1 at $1,000, and 9 at $500.

Deadline June of each year.

[1187]
PERLITA LIWANAG MEMORIAL SCHOLARSHIP

Ulman Cancer Fund for Young Adults
Attn: Scholarship Committee
10440 Little Patuxent Parkway, Suite G1
Columbia, MD 21044
(410) 964-0202   Toll Free: (888) 393-FUND
Fax: (410) 964-0402
E-mail: scholarship@ulmanfund.org
Web: www.ulmanfund.org/scholarship.aspx

Summary To provide financial assistance for college or graduate school to students from Washington, D.C., Maryland, or Virginia who have been diagnosed with cancer or have or have lost a family member with cancer.

Eligibility This program is open to students who 1) have been diagnosed with cancer; 2) have a parent, sibling, or guardian living with cancer; or 3) have lost a parent, sibling, or guardian to cancer. Applicants must be residents of Washington, D.C., Maryland, or Virginia or attending college there. They must be 35 years of age or younger and attending, or planning to attend, a 2- or 4-year college, university, or vocational program to work on an undergraduate or graduate degree. The first diagnosis of cancer (whether of the applicant, a parent, a sibling, or a guardian) must have occurred after the applicant was 15 years of age. Along with their application, they must submit an essay of at least 1,000 words on how the cancer experience has impacted their outlook on life and the legacy that they desire to leave behind. Selection is based on demonstrated dedication to community service, commitment to educational and professional goals, use of their cancer experience to impact the lives of other young adults affected by cancer, medical hardship, and financial need.

Financial data The stipend is $2,500. Funds are paid directly to the educational institution.

Duration 1 year.

Additional data These scholarships were first awarded in 2011. Recipients must agree to complete 40 hours of community service.

Number awarded 1 each year.

Deadline March of each year.

[1188]
PINKROSE BREAST CANCER SCHOLARSHIP

PinkRose Foundation, Inc.
P.O. Box 4025
Dedham, MA 02027
E-mail: info@pinkrose.org
Web: www.pinkrose.org/scholarship.htm

Summary To provide money for college to high school graduates who have lost a parent to breast cancer.

Eligibility This program is open to legal residents of the United States who are younger than 25 years of age and have lost a parent or legal guardian to breast cancer. Applicants must have a high school diploma or equivalent and be planning to enroll in a postsecondary education or certificate training program. Along with their application, they must submit a 2-page statement that includes 1) autobiographical information describing the significant impact of breast cancer on their life and how it altered their academic motivation and interests, professional and volunteer experience, and career objectives; and 2) their interest in this scholarship, especially how obtaining a postsecondary degree or certificate will benefit their future by helping to fulfill their goals and dreams. Financial need is not considered in the selection process.

Financial data The stipend is $1,000.

Duration 1 year.

Number awarded Varies each year.

Deadline August of each year.

[1189]
PINNACOL FOUNDATION SCHOLARSHIP PROGRAM

Pinnacol Foundation
Attn: Elizabeth Starkey
7501 East Lowry Boulevard
Denver, CO 80230
(303) 361-4775   Toll Free: (800) 873-7248, ext. 4775
Fax: (303) 361-5775
E-mail: pinnacol.foundation@pinnacol.com
Web: www.pinnacol.com/foundation

Summary   To provide financial assistance to Colorado residents whose parent was killed or permanently disabled in a work-related accident and who are interested in attending college in any state.

Eligibility   This program is open to the natural, adopted, step, or fully dependent children of workers killed or permanently injured in a compensable work-related accident during the course and scope of employment with a Colorado-based employer and entitled to receive benefits under the Colorado Workers' Compensation Act. Applicants must be between 16 and 25 years of age and attending or planning to attend a college or technical school in any state. Selection is based on academic achievement and aptitude, extracurricular activities, community service, and financial need.

Financial data   The amount of the stipend depends on the need of the recipient; recently, the average award was approximately $4,200.

Duration   1 year; may be renewed.

Additional data   Pinnacol Assurance, a workers' compensation insurance carrier, established this program in 2001. Students are eligible regardless of the insurance carrier for their parent's accident.

Number awarded   Varies each year; recently, 136 of these scholarships, with a value of $579,000, were awarded.

Deadline   March of each year.

[1190]
PVA EDUCATIONAL SCHOLARSHIP PROGRAM

Paralyzed Veterans of America
Attn: Education and Training Foundation
801 18th Street, N.W.
Washington, DC 20006-3517
(202) 416-7651   Toll Free: (800) 424-8200, ext. 776
Fax: (202) 416-7641   TDD: (800) 795-HEAR
E-mail: christih@pva.org
Web: www.pva.org

Summary   To provide money for college to members of the Paralyzed Veterans of America (PVA) and their families.

Eligibility   This program is open to PVA members, spouses of members, and unmarried dependent children of members under 24 years of age. Applicants must be attending or planning to attend an accredited U.S. college or university. They must be U.S. citizens. Along with their application, they must submit a personal statement explaining why they wish to further their education, short-term and long-term academic goals, how this will meet their career objectives, and how it will affect the PVA membership. Selection is based on that statement, academic records, letters of recommendation, and extracurricular and community activities.

Financial data   Stipends are $1,000 for full-time students or $500 for part-time students.

Duration   1 year.

Additional data   This program was established in 1986.

Number awarded   Varies each year; recently 14 full-time and 3 part-time students received these scholarships. Since this program was established, it has awarded more than $300,000 in scholarships.

Deadline   May of each year.

[1191]
REDUCED TUITION FOR CHILDREN AND SPOUSES OF SOUTH DAKOTA NATIONAL GUARDSMEN DISABLED OR DECEASED IN THE LINE OF DUTY

South Dakota Board of Regents
Attn: Scholarship Committee
306 East Capitol Avenue, Suite 200
Pierre, SD 57501-2545
(605) 773-3455   Fax: (605) 773-2422
E-mail: info@sdbor.edu
Web: www.sdbor.edu

Summary   To provide reduced tuition at public universities in South Dakota to the children and spouses of disabled and deceased members of the National Guard.

Eligibility   This program is open to the spouses and children (24 years of age or younger) of members of the South Dakota Army or Air National Guard who died or sustained a total and permanent disability while on state active duty, federal active duty, or any authorized duty training. Applicants must be proposing to work on an undergraduate degree at a public college in South Dakota.

Financial data   Qualifying applicants are granted a 100% tuition waiver at state-supported postsecondary institutions in South Dakota. The waiver applies only to tuition, not fees.

Duration   8 semesters or 12 quarters of either full- or part-time study.

Number awarded   Varies each year.

Deadline   Deadline not specified.

[1192]
RENEE FELDMAN SCHOLARSHIPS

Blinded Veterans Association Auxiliary
c/o Hazel C. Compton, Scholarship Chair
P.O. Box 267
Richlands, VA 24641
(276) 963-3745
Web: www.bvaaux.org

Summary   To provide financial assistance for college to spouses and children of blinded veterans.

Eligibility   This program is open to children and spouses of blinded veterans who are enrolled or planning to enroll full time at a college, university, community college, or vocational school. The veteran is not required to be a member of the Blinded Veterans Association. Applicants must submit a 300-word essay on their career goals and aspirations. Selection is based on that essay, academic achievement, and letters of reference.

Financial data Stipends are $2,000 or $1,000 per year. Funds are paid directly to the recipient's school to be applied to tuition, books, and general fees.

Duration 1 year; renewable up to 3 more years.

Number awarded 2 at $2,000 and 1 at $1,000.

Deadline April of each year.

[1193]
ROADWAY WORKER MEMORIAL SCHOLARSHIPS

American Traffic Safety Services Foundation
Attn: Foundation Director
15 Riverside Parkway, Suite 100
Fredericksburg, VA 22406-1022
(540) 368-1701   Toll Free: (800) 272-8772
Fax: (540) 368-1717   E-mail: foundation@atssa.com
Web: www.atssa.com

Summary To provide money for college to children of roadway workers killed or disabled in work zones.

Eligibility This program is open to students enrolled or planning to enroll at a 4-year college or university, 2-year accredited college, or vocational/technical school or training institution. Applicants must be children of roadway workers killed or permanently disabled in work zones, including mobile operations and the installation of roadway safety features. They must submit a statement, up to 200 words, explaining their reasons for wanting to continue their education and listing any volunteer activities or accomplishments. Selection is based on that statement, academic performance, 2 recommendations, and need.

Financial data The stipend is $2,000. The Chuck Bailey Scholarship provides an additional $1,000 to recipients who demonstrate a strong commitment to volunteerism.

Duration 1 year.

Additional data This program was established in 2001.

Number awarded Varies each year; recently, 5 of these scholarships were awarded.

Deadline February of each year.

[1194]
ROBYN KIMBERLY MEREDITH MULTIPLE SCLEROSIS MEMORIAL SCHOLARSHIP

National Multiple Sclerosis Society-Blue Ridge Chapter
One Morton Drive, Suite 106
Charlottesville, VA 22903
(434) 971-8010   Toll Free: (800) 344-4867
Fax: (434) 979-4475   E-mail: vab@nmss.org
Web: was.nationalmssociety.org

Summary To provide funding to high school seniors and current college students from the area served by the Blue Ridge Chapter of the National Multiple Sclerosis Society whose parent has multiple sclerosis (MS) and who are attending or planning to attend college in any state.

Eligibility This program is open to graduating high school seniors and current college students from 51 counties in western Virginia, eastern Kentucky, and the state or West Virginia who have a parent who has MS. Applicants must be planning to enroll as a first-time student at a 2- or 4-year college or university in the United States. Along with their application, they must submit a 2-page essay on their experiences growing up in a household in which a parent has MS, their goals for the future, what they plan as their major field of study, and any career plans they may have.

Financial data A stipend is awarded (amount not specified).

Duration 1 year.

Number awarded Varies each year.

Deadline Applications may be submitted at any time.

[1195]
SAD SACKS NURSING SCHOLARSHIP

AMVETS-Department of Illinois
2200 South Sixth Street
Springfield, IL 62703
(217) 528-4713   Toll Free: (800) 638-VETS (within IL)
Fax: (217) 528-9896
Web: www.ilamvets.org/prog_scholarships.cfm

Summary To provide financial assistance for nursing education to Illinois residents, especially descendants of disabled or deceased veterans.

Eligibility This program is open to seniors at high schools in Illinois who have been accepted to an approved nursing program and students already enrolled in an approved school of nursing in Illinois. Priority is given to dependents of deceased or disabled veterans. Selection is based on academic record, character, interest and activity record, and financial need. Preference is given to students in the following order: third-year students, second-year students, and first-year students.

Financial data A stipend is awarded (amount not specified).

Duration 1 year.

Number awarded Varies each year; recently, 2 of these scholarships were awarded.

Deadline February of each year.

[1196]
SEPTEMBER 11 MEMORIAL SCHOLARSHIPS

United Methodist Higher Education Foundation
Attn: Scholarships Administrator
60 Music Square East, Suite 350
P.O. Box 340005
Nashville, TN 37203-0005
(615) 649-3990   Toll Free: (800) 811-8110
Fax: (615) 649-3980
E-mail: umhefscholarships@umhef.org
Web: www.umhef.org

Summary To provide financial assistance to Methodists and undergraduate and graduate students at Methodist institutions whose parent or guardian was disabled or killed in the terrorist attacks on September 11, 2001.

Eligibility This program is open to 1) students attending a United Methodist-related college or university in the United States, and 2) United Methodist students attending a higher education institution in the United States. All applicants must have lost a parent or guardian or had a parent or guardian disabled as a result of the September 11, 2001 terrorist attacks. They must be enrolled as full-time undergraduate or graduate students and be able to demonstrate financial need. U.S. citizenship or permanent resident status is required.

Financial data The stipend depends on the number of applicants.

Duration 1 year; may be renewed as long as the recipients maintain satisfactory academic progress as defined by their institution.

Number awarded Varies each year; a total of $30,000 is available for this program.

Deadline Applications may be submitted at any time.

[1197]
SFM FOUNDATION SCHOLARSHIP

SFM Foundation
P.O. Box 582992
Minneapolis, MN 55458-2992
(952) 838-4323   Fax: (952) 838-2055
E-mail: info@sfm-foundation.org
Web: www.sfmic.com

Summary To provide financial assistance to residents of Minnesota and Wisconsin whose parent was injured or killed in a work-related accident and who are interested in attending college, preferably in those state.

Eligibility This program is open to residents of Minnesota and Wisconsin between 16 and 25 years of age who are high school students, GED recipients, or high school graduates. Applicants must be the natural, adopted, or stepchild of a worker injured or killed in a work-related accident during the course and scope of employment with a Minnesota- or Wisconsin-based employer and entitled to receive benefits under the Minnesota Workers' Compensation Act or Worker's Compensation Act of Wisconsin. They must be planning to work on an associate or bachelor's degree or a certificate or license from any accredited school; preference is given to students attending institutions within the Minnesota State Colleges and Universities system or the University of Wisconsin system. Financial need is considered in the selection process.

Financial data Stipends range from $1,000 to $5,000 per year. Funds are paid to the recipient's school.

Duration 1 year; may be renewed, provided the recipient maintains a GPA of 2.0 or higher.

Number awarded Varies each year.

Deadline March of each year.

[1198]
SIBLING CONTINUING EDUCATION SCHOLARSHIPS

Hemophilia Federation of America
Attn: Scholarship Committee
210 Seventh Street, S.E., Suite 200B
Washington, DC 20003
(202) 675-6984   Toll Free: (800) 230-9797
Fax: (202) 675-6983   E-mail: info@hemophiliafed.org
Web: hemophiliafed.org

Summary To provide financial assistance for college to siblings of people with a blood clotting disorder.

Eligibility This program is open to siblings of people who have a blood clotting disorder. Applicants must be attending or planning to attend an accredited 2- or 4-year college, university, or trade school in the United States. Along with their application, they must submit a 1-page essay on their goals and aspirations and how the blood clotting community has played a part in their lives. Financial need is also considered in the selection process.

Financial data The stipend is $1,500 per year.

Duration 1 year; may be renewed.

Number awarded 1 each year.

Deadline April of each year.

[1199]
SOUTH CAROLINA TUITION PROGRAM FOR CHILDREN OF CERTAIN WAR VETERANS

South Carolina Office of Veterans Affairs
c/o VA Regional Office Building
6437 Garners Ferry Road, Suite 1126
Columbia, SC 29209
(803) 647-2434   Fax: (803) 647-2312
E-mail: va@oepp.sc.gov
Web: www.govoepp.state.sc.us/va/benefits.html

Summary To provide free college tuition to the children of disabled and other South Carolina veterans.

Eligibility This program is open to the children of war time veterans who were legal residents of South Carolina both at the time of entry into military or naval service and during service, or who have been residents of South Carolina for at least 1 year. Veteran parents must 1) be permanently and totally disabled as determined by the U.S. Department of Veterans Affairs; 2) have been a prisoner of war; 3) have been killed in action; 4) have died from other causes while in service; 5) have died of a disease or disability resulting from service; 6) be currently missing in action; 7) have received the Congressional Medal of Honor; 8) have received the Purple Heart Medal from wounds received in combat; or 9) now be deceased but qualified under categories 1 or 2 above. The veteran's child must be 26 years of age or younger and working on an undergraduate degree.

Financial data Children who qualify are eligible for free tuition at any South Carolina state-supported college, university, or postsecondary technical education institution. The waiver applies to tuition only. The costs of room and board, certain fees, and books are not covered.

Duration Students are eligible to receive this support as long as they are younger than 26 years of age and working on an undergraduate degree.

Number awarded Varies each year.

Deadline Deadline not specified.

[1200]
SOUTHERN CALIFORNIA AND NEVADA CHAPTER MS SOCIETY SCHOLARSHIP PROGRAM

National Multiple Sclerosis Society-Southern California
and Nevada Chapter
2400 South Sepulveda Boulevard, Suite 115
Los Angeles, CA 90064
(310) 479-4456   Fax: (310) 479-4436
Web: was.nationalmssociety.org

Summary To provide financial assistance to high school seniors and graduates from southern California and Nevada who have multiple sclerosis (MS) or have a parent with MS and are planning to attend college in any state.

Eligibility This program is open to graduating high school seniors, recent graduates, and GED recipients from southern California and Nevada who have MS or a parent who has MS. Applicants must be planning to enroll as an entering undergraduate student at a 2- or 4-year college, university, or vocational/technical school in the United States on at least a half-time basis. Along with their application, they must submit an essay on the impact MS has had on their lives. Selection is based on that essay, academic record, leadership and participation in school or community activities, work experience, goals and aspirations, an outside appraisal, special circumstances, and financial need. U.S. citizenship or permanent resident status is required.

Financial data Stipends range from $1,000 to $3,000.

Duration 1 year.

Number awarded Varies each year; recently, 26 of these scholarships were awarded.

Deadline January of each year.

[1201]
STEVEN M. PEREZ FOUNDATION SCHOLARSHIPS

Steven M. Perez Foundation
P.O. Box 955
Melville, NY 11747
(631) 367-9016   Fax: (631) 367-3848
E-mail: info@smpfoundation.org
Web: www.smpfoundation.org

Summary To provide financial assistance for college to high school seniors who have survived leukemia or lost a family member to cancer or a related disease.

Eligibility This program is open to graduating high school seniors who have survived leukemia or who have lost a parent or sibling to cancer or a related disease. Applicants must be planning to attend a college in any state. Along with their application, they must submit medical certification, a recommendation from a counselor, and an essay describing their connection to leukemia.

Financial data Stipend amounts vary; recently, they averaged approximately $1,450.

Duration 1 year.

Number awarded Varies each year; recently, 17 of these scholarships were awarded.

Deadline April of each year.

[1202]
SUPERSIBS! SCHOLARSHIPS

SuperSibs!
Attn: Scholarship Committee
660 North First Bank Drive
Palatine, IL 60067
(847) 462-4SIB   Toll Free: (888) 417-4704
Fax: (847) 984-9292   E-mail: info@supersibs.org
Web: supersibs.org

Summary To provide financial assistance for college to siblings of children with cancer.

Eligibility This program is open to seniors graduating from high schools in the United States, Puerto Rico, or the Virgin Islands who have a GPA of 2.0 or higher. Applicants must be the siblings of children who have or have had cancer. They must be planning to enroll full time at an accredited college, university, or vocational institution in the following fall. Half-siblings and stepsiblings who reside in the same home as the cancer patient are also eligible. Along with their application, they must submit an essay, up to 1,000 words, on 1 of the following: 1) what they learned from their personal "sibling journey;" 2) how the experience as the sibling of a brother or sister with cancer may impact their future; or 3) the advice they can share with other siblings living this journey. Financial need is not considered in the selection process.

Financial data The stipend is $1,000.

Duration 1 year.

Number awarded Varies each year; recently, 10 of these scholarships were awarded.

Deadline January of each year.

[1203]
SURVIVORS' AND DEPENDENTS' EDUCATIONAL ASSISTANCE PROGRAM

Department of Veterans Affairs
Attn: Veterans Benefits Administration
810 Vermont Avenue, N.W.
Washington, DC 20420
(202) 418-4343   Toll Free: (888) GI-BILL1
Web: www.gibill.va.gov

Summary To provide financial assistance for undergraduate or graduate study to 1) children and spouses of deceased and disabled veterans, MIAs, and POWs and 2) children and spouses who have their own disabilities.

Eligibility Eligible for this assistance are spouses and children of 1) veterans who died or are permanently and totally disabled as the result of active service in the armed forces; 2) veterans who died from any cause while rated permanently and totally disabled from a service-connected disability; 3) service members listed as missing in action or captured in the line of duty by a hostile force; 4) service members listed as forcibly detained or interned by a foreign government or power; and 5) service members who are hospitalized or receiving outpatient treatment for a service-connected permanent and total disability and are likely to be discharged for that disability. Children must be between 18 and 26 years of age, although extensions may be granted. Spouses and children over 14 years of age with physical or mental disabilities are also eligible.

Financial data Monthly stipends for study at an academic institution are $957 for full time, $718 for three-quarter time, or $476 for half-time. Other rates apply for apprenticeship and on-the-job training, farm cooperative training, and special restorative training.

Duration Up to 45 months (or the equivalent in part-time training). Spouses must complete their training within 10 years of the date they are first found eligible. For spouses of service members who died on active duty, benefits end 20 years from the date of death.

Additional data Benefits may be used to work on associate, bachelor's, or graduate degrees at colleges and universities, including independent study, cooperative training, and study abroad programs. Courses leading to a certificate or diploma from business, technical, or vocational schools may also be taken. Other eligible programs include apprenticeships, on-the-job training programs, farm cooperative courses, and correspondence courses (for spouses only). Remedial, deficiency, and refresher courses may be approved under certain circumstances.

Number awarded Varies each year.

Deadline Applications may be submitted at any time.

[1204]
SUSAN G. KOMEN BREAST CANCER FOUNDATION COLLEGE SCHOLARSHIP AWARDS

Susan G. Komen Breast Cancer Foundation
Attn: Scholarship Program Office
5005 LBJ Freeway, Suite 250
Dallas, TX 75244
(972) 855-1616   Toll Free: (877) GO-KOMEN
Fax: (972) 855-1605
E-mail: collegescholarships@komen.org
Web: ww5.komen.org

Summary To provide financial assistance for college to high school seniors and college students who lost a parent to breast cancer or are breast cancer survivors.

Eligibility This program is open to high school seniors and college freshmen, sophomores, and juniors who have lost a parent to breast cancer or are a breast cancer survivor diagnosed at 25 years of age or younger. Applicants must be under 25 years of age, be U.S. citizens or permanent residents, have a high school and/or college GPA of 2.8 or higher, and be enrolled or planning to enroll full time at a state-supported college or university in the state where they permanently reside. Along with their application, they must submit 2 essays of 500 words each on 1) how breast cancer has changed them, and 2) how their education will help them achieve their career objectives and personal goals. Selection is based on the essay, academic achievements or records, community involvement, letters of reference, and financial need.

Financial data Stipends up to $10,000 per year are available. Funds may be used for tuition, books, fees, and on-campus room and board.

Duration 4 years, provided the recipient remains enrolled full time and makes reasonable progress toward completion of a baccalaureate degree.

Number awarded 5 each year.

Deadline January of each year.

[1205]
SUSAN STEIN SCHOLARSHIP

American College of Nurse-Midwives
Attn: ACNM Foundation, Inc.
8403 Colesville Road, Suite 1550
Silver Spring, MD 20910-6374
(240) 485-1850   Fax: (240) 485-1818
E-mail: fdn@acnm.org
Web: www.midwife.org

Summary To provide financial assistance for midwifery education to student members of the American College of Nurse-Midwives (ACNM) who have had a personal experience with breast cancer.

Eligibility This program is open to ACNM members who are currently enrolled in an accredited basic midwife education program and have successfully completed 1 academic or clinical semester/quarter or clinical module. Applicants must have had or currently have a personal experience with breast cancer, either their own or a family member's. Along with their application, they must submit a 150-word essay on their midwifery career plans; a 100-word essay on their intended future participation in ACNM activities; and a 300-word essay on the effect of breast cancer in themselves or a close family member on their choice of midwifery. Selection is based primarily on the quality of the application, although leadership, financial need, academics, and personal goals may also be considered.

Financial data The stipend is $3,000.

Duration 1 year.

Additional data This program was established in 2010.

Number awarded 1 each year.

Deadline March of each year.

[1206]
TEENS FOR ALZHEIMER'S AWARENESS COLLEGE SCHOLARSHIP

Alzheimer's Foundation of America
Attn: AFA Teens
322 Eighth Avenue, Seventh Floor
New York, NY 10001
Toll Free: (866) 232-8484
Web: www.afateens.org/about_new.html

Summary To recognize and reward, with college scholarships, high school seniors who submit outstanding essays on the impact of Alzheimer's Disease on their life.

Eligibility The competition is open to seniors currently enrolled at a public, independent, parochial, military, home-school, or other high school in the United States. Applicants must be planning to enter an accredited 4-year college or university within 12 months. They must submit an essay of 1,200 to 1,500 words on 1) how Alzheimer's Disease has changed or impacted their life; and 2) what they have learned about themselves, their family, and/or their community in the face of coping with Alzheimer's Disease. They must also submit a 200-word autobiography, a high school transcript, and documentation of U.S. citizenship or permanent resident status. Financial need is not considered in the selection process.

Financial data Awards are a $5,000 college scholarship for the winner, a $500 award for the first runner-up, and a $250 award for the second runner-up.

Duration The awards are presented annually.

Number awarded 3 awards (of which 1 is intended as a college scholarship) are awarded each year.

Deadline February of each year.

[1207]
TENNESSEE DEPENDENT CHILDREN SCHOLARSHIP

Tennessee Student Assistance Corporation
Parkway Towers
404 James Robertson Parkway, Suite 1510
Nashville, TN 37243-0820
(615) 741-1346   Toll Free: (800) 342-1663
Fax: (615) 741-6101   E-mail: TSAC.Aidinfo@tn.gov
Web: www.tn.gov

Summary To provide financial assistance to the dependent children of disabled or deceased Tennessee law enforcement officers, fire fighters, or emergency medical service technicians who plan to attend college in the state.

Eligibility This program is open to Tennessee residents who are the dependent children of a Tennessee law enforcement officer, fire fighter, or emergency medical service technician who was killed or totally and permanently disabled in the line of duty. Applicants must be enrolled or accepted for enrollment as a full-time undergraduate student at a college or university in Tennessee.

Financial data The award covers tuition and fees, books, supplies, and room and board, minus any other financial aid for which the student is eligible.

Duration 1 year; may be renewed for up to 3 additional years or until completion of a program of study.

Additional data This program was established in 1990.

Number awarded Varies each year; recently, 19 students received $77,786 in support from this program.

Deadline July of each year.

[1208]
TEXAS CHILDREN OF DISABLED OR DECEASED FIREMEN, PEACE OFFICERS, GAME WARDENS, AND EMPLOYEES OF CORRECTIONAL INSTITUTIONS EXEMPTION PROGRAM

Texas Higher Education Coordinating Board
Attn: Grants and Special Programs
1200 East Anderson Lane
P.O. Box 12788
Austin, TX 78711-2788
(512) 427-6340   Toll Free: (800) 242-3062
Fax: (512) 427-6420
E-mail: grantinfo@thecb.state.tx.us
Web: www.collegeforalltexans.com

Summary To provide educational assistance to the children of disabled or deceased Texas fire fighters, peace officers, game wardens, and correctional employees.

Eligibility Eligible are children of Texas paid or volunteer fire fighters; paid municipal, county, or state peace officers; custodial employees of the Department of Corrections; or game wardens. The parent must have suffered an injury in the line of duty, resulting in disability or death. Applicants must be under 21 years of age.

Financial data Eligible students are exempted from the payment of all dues, fees, and tuition charges at publicly-supported colleges and universities in Texas.

Duration Support is provided for up to 120 semester credit hours of undergraduate study or until the recipient reaches 26 years of age, whichever comes first.

Number awarded Varies each year; recently, 140 students received support through this program.

Deadline Deadline not specified.

[1209]
TEXAS MUTUAL SCHOLARSHIP PROGRAM

Texas Mutual Insurance Company
Attn: Office of the President
6210 East Highway 290
Austin, TX 78723-1098
(512) 224-3820   Toll Free: (800) 859-5995, ext. 3820
Fax: (512) 224-3889   TDD: (800) 853-5339
E-mail: information@texasmutual.com
Web: www.texasmutual.com/workers/scholarship.shtm

Summary To provide money for college to workers and their families covered by workers' compensation in Texas.

Eligibility This program is open to 1) employees who qualify for lifetime income benefits as a result of injuries suffered on the job as covered by the Texas Workers' Compensation Act; 2) unmarried children and spouses of injured workers; and 3) unmarried children and unremarried spouses of employees who died as a result of a work-related injury. Workers must be covered by the Texas Mutual Insurance Company, formerly the Texas Workers' Compensation Insurance Fund. Children must be between 16 and 25 years of age. Surviving spouses must still be eligible for workers' compensation benefits. Financial need is considered in the selection process.

Financial data Scholarships are intended to cover normal undergraduate, technical, or vocational school tuition and fees, to a maximum of $4,000 per semester. Those funds are paid directly to the college or vocational school. The cost of course-related books and fees are also reimbursed, up to a maximum of $500 per semester. Those funds are paid directly to the student.

Duration 1 year; may be renewed if the recipient maintains a GPA of 2.5 or higher.

Number awarded Varies each year.

Deadline Applications may be submitted at any time.

[1210]
THROUGH THE LOOKING GLASS SCHOLARSHIPS

Through the Looking Glass
3075 Adeline Street, Suite 120
Berkeley, CA 94703
(510) 848-1112   Toll Free: (800) 644-2666
Fax: (510) 848-4445   TDD: (510) 848-1005
E-mail: scholarships@lookingglass.org
Web: lookingglass.org/announcements/scholarships

Summary To provide financial assistance for college to high school seniors who have a parent with a disability.

Eligibility This program is open to graduating high school seniors and full-time college students who are 21 years of age or younger. Applicants must have at least 1 parent who has a physical, sensory, intellectual, medical, or mental health disability. Along with their application, they must submit a 3-page essay describing the experience of growing up with a parent with a disability. Selection is based on that essay, academic performance, community service, and letters of recommendation; financial need is considered for some of the scholarships.

Financial data The stipend is $1,000.

Duration 1 year.

Number awarded 15 each year, of which 5 are awarded to students with extreme financial need.

Deadline March of each year.

[1211]
TOBY WRIGHT SCHOLARSHIP FUND

Workers' Compensation Association of New Mexico
Attn: Brock Carter
3207 Matthew Avenue, N.E., Suite A
Albuquerque, NM 87107
(505) 881-1112   Toll Free: (800) 640-0724
E-mail: brock@safetycounseling.com
Web: www.wcaofnm.com

Summary To provide financial assistance for college to residents of New Mexico whose parent was permanently disabled or killed in an employment-related accident.

Eligibility This program is open to residents of New Mexico between 16 and 25 years of age who are attending or planning to attend a college, university, or trade school in the state. Applicants must have a parent who was permanently or catastrophically injured or killed in an employment-related accident that resulted in a New Mexico workers' compensation claim. The parent's death or injury

must have resulted in a substantial decline in the family income.

Financial data A stipend is awarded (amount not specified). Funds may be used for tuition, books, housing, meals, and course fees.

Duration 1 semester or quarter; may be renewed if the recipient maintains a GPA of 2.5 or higher and full-time enrollment.

Number awarded Varies each year; recently, 8 of these scholarships were awarded.

Deadline Deadline not specified.

[1212]
TONY AND JAN VIESSMAN MEMORIAL SCHOLARSHIPS

Epilepsy Foundation of Missouri and Kansas
c/o Julie Viessman MacCash
10698 Lakemont Drive
Rolla, MO 65401
Web: epilepsyfoundation.ning.com

Summary To provide funding to residents of any state who have epilepsy or are caring for someone who does and want to attend college or graduate school.

Eligibility This program is open to residents of any state who are under a physician's care for epilepsy or are the caretaker for a person living with epilepsy. Applicants may be 1) high school seniors planning to attend a technical school, community college, or 4-year college or university; 2) freshmen, sophomores, or juniors at 1 of those institutions; 3) college seniors planning to enroll in graduate school; or 4) adults interested in working on a college degree. Along with their application, they must submit a 500-word essay on 1 of the following topics: 1) what the youth of today should focus on to improve the lives of others; 2) why they think it is important for high school graduates to further their education; or 3) the current event, from their community or around the glove, that they find most interesting and why. They must also submit a 500-word essay on how they have overcome, or are working to overcome, the challenges that epilepsy presents.

Financial data The stipend is $1,000.

Duration 1 year.

Number awarded 4 each year.

Deadline March of each year.

[1213]
TRANSPLANT RECIPIENTS INTERNATIONAL ORGANIZATION SCHOLARSHIPS

Transplant Recipients International Organization, Inc.
Attn: Scholarship Committee
2100 M Street, N.W., Suite 170-353
Washington, DC 20037-1233
(202) 293-0980   Toll Free: (800) TRIO-386
E-mail: info@trioweb.org
Web: www.trioweb.org

Summary To provide financial assistance for college to members of the Transplant Recipients International Organization (TRIO) and their families.

Eligibility This program is open to TRIO members and their immediate family who are solid organ or bone marrow candidates, recipients, donors, or their immediate family members. Applicants must be attending or planning to attend an accredited college, university, or trade/technical certificate program. They must have a cumulative GPA of 2.5 or higher and be able to demonstrate financial need. Along with their application, they must submit a 500-word essay on their personal history and educational and career ambitions and a statement on how transplantation has affected their life.

Financial data The stipend is $1,000.

Duration 1 year; nonrenewable.

Number awarded Several each year. Since the program began 16 years ago, it has awarded 108 scholarships.

Deadline June of each year.

[1214]
TROY BARBOZA EDUCATIONAL FUND

Hawai'i Community Foundation
Attn: Scholarship Department
827 Fort Street Mall
Honolulu, HI 96813
(808) 537-6333   Toll Free: (888) 731-3863
Fax: (808) 521-6286
E-mail: scholarships@hcf-hawaii.org
Web: www.hawaiicommunityfoundation.org/scholarships

Summary To provide financial assistance to disabled public employees in Hawaii or their dependents who plan to attend college in any state.

Eligibility This program is open to 1) disabled public employees in Hawaii who were injured in the line of duty; 2) dependents or other immediate family members of public employees in Hawaii who were disabled or killed in the line of duty; and 3) private citizens in Hawaii who have performed a heroic act for the protection and welfare of others. The public employee must work or have worked in a job where lives are risked for the protection and safety of others. The injury must have left the employee incapacitated or incapable or continuing in his or her profession. For private citizens, the heroic act must have occurred after October 21, 1986. Applicants must submit a short statement describing their course of study, career goals, outstanding attributes, talents, community service, family circumstances, and any other relevant information. Financial need is considered in the selection process.

Financial data The amount awarded varies, depending upon the needs of the recipient and the funds available; recently, the average value of each of the scholarships awarded by the foundation was more than $2,000.

Duration 1 year; scholarships for employees and their dependents may be renewed; scholarships for private citizens who have performed a heroic act are nonrenewable.

Additional data This program was established in 1991.

Number awarded 1 or more each year.

Deadline February of each year.

[1215]
UCB FAMILY EPILEPSY SCHOLARSHIP PROGRAM

UCB, Inc.
Family Scholarship Program
c/o Hudson Medical Communications
200 White Plains Road, Second Floor
Tarrytown, NY 10591
Toll Free: (866) 825-1920
E-mail: UCBScholarship@hudsongloballlc.com
Web: www.ucbepilepsyscholarship.com

Summary To provide financial assistance for college or graduate school to epilepsy patients and their family members and caregivers.

Eligibility This program is open to epilepsy patients and their family members and caregivers. Applicants must be working on or planning to work on an undergraduate or graduate degree at an institution of higher education in the United States. They must be able to demonstrate academic achievement, a record of participation in activities outside of school, and service as a role model. Along with their application, they must submit a 1-page essay explaining why they should be selected for the scholarship, how epilepsy has impacted their life either as a patient or as a family member or caregiver, and how they will benefit from the scholarship. U.S. citizenship or permanent resident status is required.

Financial data The stipend is $5,000.

Duration 1 year; nonrenewable.

Additional data This program, previously known as the Keppra Family Epilepsy Scholarship Program, was established in 2004.

Number awarded 30 each year.

Deadline April of each year.

[1216]
UCB FAMILY RA SCHOLARSHIP PROGRAM

UCB, Inc.
c/o Summit Medical Communications
1421 East Broad Street, Suite 340
Fuquay-Varina, NC 27526
(919) 567-7590   Toll Free: (888) 854-4996
Fax: (919) 567-7591
E-mail: ucbrascholarship@summitmedcomm.com
Web: www.reachbeyondra.com

Summary To provide financial assistance to undergraduate and graduate students who have rheumatoid arthritis (RA) and their families.

Eligibility This program is open to students who are working on or planning to work on an associate, undergraduate, or graduate degree or are enrolled in a trade school educational program. Applicants must have been diagnosed with RA or be an immediate family member (parent, spouse, child, or sibling) of a person with RA. They may be of any age. Along with their application, they must submit an essay of 1 to 2 pages describing how they are living beyond the boundaries of RA to demonstrate academic ambition and personal achievement and how the scholarship would impact their life.

Financial data   Stipends range up to $5,000.

Duration   1 year; nonrenewable.

Additional data   This program began on a pilot basis in 2008.

Number awarded   30 each year.

Deadline   March of each year.

[1217]
UPPER MIDWEST CHAPTER MS SOCIETY SCHOLARSHIP PROGRAM

National Multiple Sclerosis Society-Upper Midwest
  Chapter
Attn: Scholarship Program
200 12th Avenue South
Minneapolis, MN 55415
(612) 335-7928   Toll Free: (800) 582-5296
Fax: (612) 335-7997
E-mail: shannon.wolkerstorfer@nmss.org
Web: was.nationalmssociety.org

Summary   To provide financial assistance to high school seniors and graduates from Iowa, Minnesota, and North and South Dakota who have multiple sclerosis (MS) or have a parent with MS and are planning to attend college in any state.

Eligibility   This program is open to graduating high school seniors, recent graduates, and GED recipients from Iowa, Minnesota, North Dakota, and South Dakota who have MS or a parent who has MS. Applicants must be planning to enroll as a first-time student at a 2- or 4-year college, university, or vocational/technical school in the United States on at least a half-time basis. Along with their application, they must submit an essay on the impact MS has had on their lives. Selection is based on that essay, academic record, leadership and participation in school or community activities, work experience, goals and aspirations, an outside appraisal, special circumstances, and financial need. U.S. citizenship or permanent resident status is required.

Financial data   Stipends average $2,000.

Duration   1 year.

Number awarded   Varies each year; recently, 54 of these scholarships, worth $98,500, were awarded.

Deadline   January of each year.

[1218]
UTAH HEMOPHILIA FOUNDATION SCHOLARSHIPS

Utah Hemophilia Foundation
772 East 3300 South, Suite 210
Salt Lake City, UT 84106
(801) 484-0325   Toll Free: (877) INFO-VWD
Fax: (801) 746-2488
E-mail: western@hemophiliautah.org
Web: www.hemophiliautah.org

Summary   To provide financial assistance for attendance at a college in any state to residents of Utah who have a bleeding disorder and their families.

Eligibility   This program is open to people in Utah with bleeding disorders and to their spouses, children, and par-

ents. Applicants must be members of the bleeding disorders community served by the Utah Hemophilia Foundation and/or the Intermountain Hemophilia and Thrombosis Center in Salt Lake City. They must be attending or planning to attend a college, university, trade school, or technical program in any state. Along with their application, they must submit essays on 1) where they see themselves in 10 years and how their education will impact their future dealings with a bleeding disorder; and 2) a quality they possess that allows them to advance the interests of Utah's bleeding disorders community.

Financial data   Stipends range from $100 to $1,500.

Duration   1 year.

Additional data   This program includes the Robert Price Memorial Scholarship.

Number awarded   Varies each year.

Deadline   May of each year.

[1219]
UTAH-SOUTHERN IDAHO CHAPTER MS SOCIETY SCHOLARSHIP PROGRAM

National Multiple Sclerosis Society-Utah-Southern
  Idaho Chapter
2400 South Sepulveda Boulevard, Suite 115
Los Angeles, CA 90064
(310) 479-4456   Fax: (310) 479-4436
Web: was.nationalmssociety.org

Summary   To provide financial assistance to high school seniors and graduates from southern Idaho and Utah who have multiple sclerosis (MS) or have a parent with MS and are planning to attend college in any state.

Eligibility   This program is open to graduating high school seniors, recent graduates, and GED recipients from southern Idaho and Utah who have MS or a parent who has MS. Applicants must be planning to enroll as an entering undergraduate student at a 2- or 4-year college, university, or vocational/technical school in the United States on at least a half-time basis. Along with their application, they must submit an essay on the impact MS has had on their lives. Selection is based on that essay, academic record, leadership and participation in school or community activities, work experience, goals and aspirations, an outside appraisal, special circumstances, and financial need. U.S. citizenship or permanent resident status is required.

Financial data   Stipends range from $1,000 to $5,000.

Duration   1 year.

Number awarded   Varies each year; recently, 11 of these scholarships were awarded: 1 at $5,000, 1 at $3,000, 2 at $2,500, 1 at $1,500, and 6 at $1,000.

Deadline   January of each year.

[1220]
VERA YIP MEMORIAL SCHOLARSHIP

Ulman Cancer Fund for Young Adults
Attn: Scholarship Committee
10440 Little Patuxent Parkway, Suite G1
Columbia, MD 21044
(410) 964-0202   Toll Free: (888) 393-FUND
Fax: (410) 964-0402
E-mail: scholarship@ulmanfund.org
Web: www.ulmanfund.org/scholarship.aspx

Summary To provide money for college or graduate school to students who have cancer or have lost a parent with cancer.

Eligibility This program is open to students who have or have lost a parent or guardian to cancer. Applicants must be 35 years of age or younger and attending, or planning to attend, a 2- or 4-year college, university, or vocational program to work on an undergraduate or graduate degree. The parent or guardian must have been first diagnosed with cancer after the applicant was 15 years of age. Along with their application, they must submit an essay of at least 1,000 words on how their parent's cancer experience has impacted their outlook on life and the legacy that they desire to leave behind. This award is presented to the applicant who best demonstrates the qualities of Vera Yip of courage, determination, motivation, and dedication.

Financial data The stipend is $2,500. Funds are paid directly to the educational institution.

Duration 1 year; nonrenewable.

Additional data Recipients must agree to complete 40 hours of community service.

Number awarded 1 each year.

Deadline March of each year.

[1221]
VIRGINIA ELECTRONIC SYSTEMS ASSOCIATION YOUTH SCHOLARSHIP PROGRAM

Virginia Electronic Systems Association
Attn: Youth Scholarship Program
225 North Washington Street, Suite 186
Ashland, VA 23005
Toll Free: (800) 538-2322
Web: www.vbfaa.org

Summary To provide financial assistance to high school seniors in Virginia who are the children of disabled and other active-duty law enforcement and fire service personnel and interested in attending college in any state.

Eligibility This program is open to seniors graduating from high schools in Virginia who have been accepted at an accredited college or university in any state. Applicants must have a father, mother, or legal guardian who is a law enforcement employee (including emergency dispatchers and EMS personnel) or active-duty or volunteer fire service employee; children of those employees who were killed or disabled while on duty after at least 5 years of service or who are retired after at least 10 years of service are also eligible. Along with their application, they must

submit an essay of 500 to 750 words on how their parent or guardian helps secure our community. Selection is based on that essay (25 points), grade average (25 points), SAT scores (25 points), and academic prizes, awards, school and outside extracurricular activities, and hobbies (25 points); financial need is not considered.

Financial data The stipend is $500 for each regional winner. The state winner receives an additional $1,000.

Duration The awards are presented annually.

Additional data The state winner is entered in the national competition of the Electronic Security Association (formerly the National Burglar & Fire Alarm Association). The Virginia Electronic Systems Association was formerly the Virginia Burglar & Fire Alarm Association.

Number awarded 4 winners (1 in each region) are selected; of those, 1 is selected as the state winner.

Deadline April of each year.

[1222]
VIRGINIA MILITARY SURVIVORS AND DEPENDENTS EDUCATION PROGRAM

Virginia Department of Veterans Services
270 Franklin Road, Room 810
Roanoke, VA 24011-2215
(540) 597-1730   Fax: (540) 857-7573
Web: www.dvs.virginia.gov/veterans-benefits.shtml

Summary To provide funding to the children and spouses of disabled and other Virginia veterans or service personnel.

Eligibility This program is open to residents of Virginia whose parent or spouse served in the U.S. armed forces (including the Reserves, the Virginia National Guard, or the Virginia National Guard Reserves) during any armed conflict subsequent to December 6, 1941, as a result of a terrorist act, during military operations against terrorism, or on a peacekeeping mission. The veterans must have been killed, missing in action, taken prisoner of war, or become at least 90% disabled as a result of such service. Applicants must have been accepted at a public college or university in Virginia as an undergraduate or graduate student. Children must be between 16 and 29 years of age; there are no age restrictions for spouses. The veteran must have been a resident of Virginia at the time of entry into active military service or for at least 5 consecutive years immediately prior to the date of application or death. Surviving spouses must have been residents of Virginia for at least 5 years prior to marrying the veteran or for at least 5 years immediately prior to the date on which the application was submitted.

Financial data The program provides 1) waiver of tuition and all required fees at public institutions of higher education in Virginia; and 2) a stipend up to $1,500 per year to offset the costs of room, board, books, and supplies at those institutions. If more students qualify, the stipend is reduced; recently, it was $675 per semester ($1,350 per year) for full-time enrollment, $450 per semester for enrollment less than full-time but at least half-time, or $225 per semester for enrollment less than half-time.

Duration   Entitlement lasts 36 months (4 years).

Additional data   Individuals entitled to this benefit may use it to pursue any vocational, technical, undergraduate, or graduate program of instruction. Generally, programs listed in the academic catalogs of state-supported institutions are acceptable, provided they have a clearly-defined educational objective (such as a certificate, diploma, or degree). This program was formerly known as the Virginia War Orphans Education Program.

Number awarded   Varies each year; recently, funding allowed for a total of 667 stipends at $1,500, but 740 students actually qualified and received a reduced stipend.

Deadline   Applications may be submitted at any time, but they must be received at least 30 days prior to the start of the term.

[1223]
WISCONSIN CHAPTER MS SOCIETY SCHOLARSHIP PROGRAM

National Multiple Sclerosis Society-Wisconsin Chapter
Attn: Scholarship Program
1120 James Drive, Suite A
Hartland, WI 53029
(262) 369-4420   Toll Free: (800) 242-3358 (within WI)
Fax: (262) 369-4410   E-mail: info.wisMS@nmss.org
Web: was.nationalmssociety.org

Summary   To provide financial assistance to high school seniors and graduates from Wisconsin who have multiple sclerosis (MS) or have a parent with MS and are planning to attend college in any state.

Eligibility   This program is open to graduating high school seniors, recent graduates, and GED recipients from Wisconsin who have MS or a parent who has MS. Applicants must be planning to enroll as a first-time student at a 2- or 4-year college, university, or vocational/technical school in the United States on at least a half-time basis. Along with their application, they must submit an essay on the impact MS has had on their lives. Selection is based on that essay, academic record, leadership and participation in school or community activities, work experience, goals and aspirations, an outside appraisal, special circumstances, and financial need. U.S. citizenship or permanent resident status is required.

Financial data   Stipends average $1,500.

Duration   1 year.

Number awarded   Varies each year; recently, 30 of these scholarships were awarded.

Deadline   January of each year.

[1224]
WISCONSIN G.I. BILL TUITION REMISSION PROGRAM

Wisconsin Department of Veterans Affairs
201 West Washington Avenue
P.O. Box 7843
Madison, WI 53707-7843
(608) 266-1311   Toll Free: (800) WIS-VETS
Fax: (608) 267-0403
E-mail: WDVAInfo@dva.state.wi.us
Web: www.dva.state.wi.us/Ben_education.asp

Summary   To provide financial assistance for college or graduate school to disabled and other Wisconsin veterans and their dependents.

Eligibility   This program is open to current residents of Wisconsin who 1) were residents of the state when they entered or reentered active duty in the U.S. armed forces, or 2) have moved to the state and have been residents for any consecutive 12-month period after entry or reentry into service. Applicants must have served on active duty for at least 2 continuous years or for at least 90 days during specified wartime periods. Also eligible are 1) qualifying children and unremarried surviving spouses of Wisconsin veterans who died in the line of duty or as the direct result of a service-connected disability; and 2) children and spouses of Wisconsin veterans who have a service-connected disability rated by the U.S. Department of Veterans Affairs as 30% or greater. Children must be between 17 and 25 years of age (regardless of the date of the veteran's death or initial disability rating) and be a Wisconsin resident for tuition purposes. Spouses remain eligible for 10 years following the date of the veteran's death or initial disability rating; they must be Wisconsin residents for tuition purposes but they may enroll full or part time. Students may attend any institution, center, or school within the University of Wisconsin (UW) System or the Wisconsin Technical College System (WCTS). There are no income limits, delimiting periods following military service during which the benefit must be used, or limits on the level of study (e.g., vocational, undergraduate, professional, or graduate).

Financial data   Veterans who qualify as a Wisconsin resident for tuition purposes are eligible for a remission of 100% of standard academic fees and segregated fees at a UW campus or 100% of program and material fees at a WCTS institution. Veterans who qualify as a Wisconsin veteran for purposes of this program but for other reasons fail to meet the definition of a Wisconsin resident for tuition purposes at the UW system are eligible for a remission of 100% of non-resident fees. Spouses and children of deceased or disabled veterans are entitled to a remission of 100% of tuition and fees at a UW or WCTS institution.

Duration   Up to 8 semesters or 128 credits, whichever is greater.

Additional data   This program was established in 2005 as a replacement for Wisconsin Tuition and Fee Reimbursement Grants.

Number awarded Varies each year.

Deadline Applications must be submitted within 14 days from the office start of the academic term: in October for fall, March for spring, or June for summer.

Fellowships

[1225]
ALABAMA G.I. DEPENDENTS' SCHOLARSHIP PROGRAM

Alabama Department of Veterans Affairs
770 Washington Avenue, Suite 470
Montgomery, AL 36102-1509
(334) 242-5077   Fax: (334) 242-5102
E-mail: willie.moore@va.state.al.us
Web: www.va.state.al.us/scholarship.htm

Summary To provide educational benefits for college or graduate school to the dependents of disabled, deceased, and other Alabama veterans.

Eligibility This program is open to children, spouses, and unremarried widow(er)s of veterans who are currently rated as 20% or more service-connected disabled or were so rated at time of death, were a former prisoner of war, have been declared missing in action, died as the result of a service-connected disability, or died while on active military duty in the line of duty. The veteran must have been a permanent civilian resident of Alabama for at least 1 year prior to entering active military service and served honorably for at least 90 days during war time (or less, in case of death or service-connected disability). Veterans who were not Alabama residents at the time of entering active military service may also qualify if they have a 100% disability and were permanent residents of Alabama for at least 5 years prior to filing the application for this program or prior to death, if deceased. Children and stepchildren must be under the age of 26, but spouses and widow(er)s may be of any age. Spouses cease to be eligible if they become divorced from the qualifying veteran. Widow(er)s cease to be eligible if they remarry.

Financial data Eligible dependents may attend any state-supported Alabama institution of higher learning or enroll in a prescribed course of study at any Alabama state-supported trade school without payment of any tuition, book fees, or laboratory charges.

Duration This is an entitlement program for 5 years of full-time undergraduate or graduate study or part-time equivalent for all qualifying children and for spouses and unremarried widow(er)s who veteran spouse is or was rated 100% disabled or meets other qualifying requirements. Spouses and unremarried widow(er)s whose veteran spouse is or was rated between 20% and 90% disabled may attend only 3 standard academic years.

Additional data Benefits for children, spouses, and unremarried widow(er)s are available in addition to federal government benefits. Assistance is not provided for non-

credit courses, placement testing, GED preparation, continuing educational courses, pre-technical courses, or state board examinations.

Number awarded Varies each year.

Deadline Applications may be submitted at any time.

[1226]
BERNICE MCNAMARA MEMORIAL SCHOLARSHIP

Ulman Cancer Fund for Young Adults
Attn: Scholarship Committee
10440 Little Patuxent Parkway, Suite G1
Columbia, MD 21044
(410) 964-0202   Toll Free: (888) 393-FUND
Fax: (410) 964-0402
E-mail: scholarship@ulmanfund.org
Web: www.ulmanfund.org/scholarship.aspx

Summary To provide money for college or graduate school to students who have or have lost a parent with cancer.

Eligibility This program is open to students who have or have lost a parent or guardian to cancer. Applicants must be 35 years of age or younger and attending, or planning to attend, a 2- or 4-year college, university, or vocational program to work on an undergraduate or graduate degree. The parent or guardian must have been first diagnosed with cancer after the applicant was 15 years of age. Along with their application, they must submit an essay of at least 1,000 words on how their parent's cancer experience has impacted their outlook on life and the legacy that they desire to leave behind. Selection is based on demonstrated dedication to community service, commitment to educational and professional goals, use of their cancer experience to impact the lives of other young adults affected by cancer, medical hardship, and financial need.

Financial data The stipend is $2,500. Funds are paid directly to the educational institution.

Duration 1 year; nonrenewable.

Additional data Recipients must agree to complete 40 hours of community service.

Number awarded 1 each year.

Deadline March of each year.

[1227]
BRYON RIESCH SCHOLARSHIPS

Bryon Riesch Paralysis Foundation
P.O. Box 1388
Waukesha, WI 53187-1388
(262) 547-2083   E-mail: briesch@brpf.org
Web: www.brpf.org/Grants/ApplicationScholarships.html

Summary To provide financial assistance to undergraduate and graduate students who have a neurological disability or the children of people with such a disability.

Eligibility This program is open to students entering or enrolled at a 2- or 4-year college or university as an undergraduate or graduate student. Applicants must have a neurological disability or be the child of a person with such a disability. They must have a GPA of 2.5 or higher in high school or college. Along with their application, they must submit a 200-word essay on why they deserve the scholarship, a statement of their 5- and 10-year goals, and a list of work experience. Financial need is not considered.

Financial data   Stipends range from $1,000 to $2,000.

Duration   1 year; may be renewed.

Number awarded   Varies each semester; recently, 5 scholarships (all at $1,000) were awarded for the fall semester and 3 (including 1 at $2,000 and 2 at $1,000) were awarded for the spring semester.

Deadline   May of each year for fall semester; December of each year for spring semester.

[1228]
DISABLED AMERICAN VETERANS AUXILIARY NATIONAL EDUCATION SCHOLARSHIP FUND

Disabled American Veterans Auxiliary
Attn: National Education Scholarship Fund
3725 Alexandria Pike
Cold Spring, KY 41076
(859) 441-7300   Toll Free: (877) 426-2838, ext. 4020
Fax: (859) 442-2095   E-mail: dava@davmail.org
Web: auxiliary.dav.org/membership/Programs.aspx

Summary   To provide financial assistance to members of the Disabled American Veterans (DAV) Auxiliary who are interested in attending college or graduate school.

Eligibility   This program is open to paid life members of the auxiliary who are attending or planning to attend a college, university, or vocational school as a full- or part-time student. Applicants must be at least seniors in high school, but there is no maximum age limit. Selection is based on academic achievement; participation in DAV activities; participation in other activities for veterans in their school, community, or elsewhere; volunteer work; membership in clubs or organizations; honors and awards; academic goals; and financial need.

Financial data   Stipends are $1,500 per year for full-time students or $750 per year for part-time students.

Duration   1 year; renewable up to 4 more years, provided the recipient maintains a GPA of 2.5 or higher.

Additional data   Membership in the DAV Auxiliary is available to extended family members of veterans eligible for membership in Disabled American Veterans (i.e., any man or woman who served in the armed forces during a period of war or under conditions simulating war and was wounded, disabled to any degree, or left with long-term illness as a result of military service and was discharged or retired from military service under honorable conditions). This program was established in September 2010 as a replacement for the educational loan program that the DAV Auxiliary operated from 1931 until August 2010.

Number awarded   Varies each year.

Deadline   March of each year.

[1229]
EDWARD T. CONROY MEMORIAL SCHOLARSHIP PROGRAM

Maryland Higher Education Commission
Attn: Office of Student Financial Assistance
6 North Liberty Street, Ground Suite
Baltimore, MD 21201
(410) 767-3300   Toll Free: (800) 974-0203
Fax: (410) 332-0250   TDD: (800) 735-2258
E-mail: osfamail@mhec.state.md.us
Web: www.mhec.state.md.us

Summary   To provide financial assistance for college or graduate school in Maryland to children and spouses of victims of the September 11, 2001 terrorist attacks and specified categories of veterans, public safety employees, and their children or spouses.

Eligibility   This program is open to entering and continuing undergraduate and graduate students in the following categories: 1) children and surviving spouses of victims of the September 11, 2001 terrorist attacks who died in the World Trade Center in New York City, in the Pentagon in Virginia, or on United Airlines Flight 93 in Pennsylvania; 2) veterans who have, as a direct result of military service, a disability of 25% or greater and have exhausted or are no longer eligible for federal veterans' educational benefits; 3) children of armed forces members whose death or 100% disability was directly caused by military service; 4) POW/MIA veterans of the Vietnam Conflict and their children; 5) state or local public safety officers or volunteers who became 100% disabled in the line of duty; and 6) children and unremarried surviving spouses of state or local public safety employees or volunteers who died or became 100% disabled in the line of duty. The parent, spouse, veteran, POW, or public safety officer or volunteer must have been a resident of Maryland at the time of death or when declared disabled. Financial need is not considered.

Financial data   The amount awarded is equal to tuition and fees at a Maryland postsecondary institution, up to $19,000, for children and spouses of the September 11 terrorist attacks or $9,000 for all other recipients.

Duration   Up to 5 years of full-time study or 8 years of part-time study.

Additional data   Recipients must enroll at a 2- or 4-year Maryland college or university as a full-time or part-time degree-seeking undergraduate or graduate student or attend a private career school.

Number awarded   Varies each year.

Deadline   July of each year.

[1230]
GEORGE AND LINDA PRICE SCHOLARSHIP

Hemophilia Association of the Capital Area
10560 Main Street, Suite 419
Fairfax, VA 22030-7182
(703) 352-7641   Fax: (540) 427-6589
E-mail: admin@hacacares.org
Web: www.hacacares.org

Summary To provide financial assistance to individuals with bleeding disorders and their families who are members of the Hemophilia Association of the Capital Area (HACA) and interested in attending college or graduate school in any state.

Eligibility This program is open to residents of northern Virginia, Montgomery and Prince George's County in Maryland, and Washington, D.C. who have a bleeding disorder and their siblings and parents. Applicants must be members of HACA. They must be 1) high school seniors or graduates who have not yet attended college; 2) full-time freshmen, sophomores, or juniors at a college, university, or vocational/technical school in any state; or 3) college seniors planning to attend graduate school and students already enrolled at a graduate school in any state. Along with their application, they must submit a 500-word essay on what they have done to contribute to the bleeding disorders community and how they plan to contribute to that community in the future. Financial need is not considered.

Financial data The stipend is $2,500.

Duration 1 year; recipients may reapply.

Number awarded 2 each year.

Deadline April of each year.

[1231]
GEORGIA COUNCIL OF THE BLIND SCHOLARSHIPS

Georgia Council of the Blind
850 Gaines School Road
Athens, GA 30605
(706) 208-7132   Toll Free: (888) 519-3988
E-mail: gcbfyi@yahoo.com
Web: www.georgiacounciloftheblind.org

Summary To provide funding to students in Georgia who plan to attend college or graduate school in any state and are either legally blind or have legally blind parents.

Eligibility This program is open to residents of Georgia who are either 1) legally blind students, or 2) sighted students financially dependent on legally blind parents. Applicants must be enrolled or accepted for enrollment at a vocational/technical school, a 2- or 4-year college, or a master's or doctoral program in any state. All fields of study are eligible. Selection is based on academic transcripts, 2 letters of recommendation, a 1-page typed statement of the applicant's educational goals, an audio cassette recording of the applicant reading the goals statement, extracurricular activities, and financial need.

Financial data Stipends range up to $1,000 per year.

Duration 1 year; recipients may reapply.

Additional data This program began in 1988.

Number awarded 1 or more each year.

Deadline June of each year.

[1232]
HARVEY PICKER HORIZON SCHOLARSHIPS

Maine Employers' Mutual Insurance Company
Attn: MEMIC Education Fund
261 Commercial Street
P.O. Box 11409
Portland, ME 04104
(207) 791-3300   Toll Free: (800) 660-1306
Fax: (207) 791-3336   E-mail: mbourque@memic.com
Web: www.memic.com

Summary To provide financial assistance to Maine residents whose parent or spouse was killed or permanently disabled in a work-related accident and who are interested in attending college or graduate school in any state.

Eligibility This program is open to Maine residents who are the child or spouse of a worker killed or permanently disabled as the result of a work-related injury. The worker must have been insured through the sponsor at the time of the workplace injury. Applicants must be attending or planning to attend an accredited college or university in any state as an undergraduate or graduate student. They must submit a personal statement describing the impact of the workplace injury on their life. Selection is based on financial need, academic performance, community involvement, other life experiences, and future promise.

Financial data Stipends range up to $5,000, depending on the need of the recipient. Funds are paid directly to the recipient's institution.

Duration 1 year; may be renewed.

Additional data The Maine Employers' Mutual Insurance Company (MEMIC) began in 1993 as the result of reforms in Maine's workers' compensation laws. It is currently the largest workers' compensation insurance company in the state. It established this scholarship in 2001.

Number awarded 1 or more each year.

Deadline April of each year.

[1233]
HOPE FOR THE WARRIORS SPOUSE/ CAREGIVER SCHOLARSHIPS

Hope for the Warriors
Attn: Spouse/Caregiver Scholarships Director
1011 South MacDill Avenue, Suite 812
Tampa, FL 33629
Toll Free: (877) 246-7349
E-mail: scholarship@hopeforthewarriors.org
Web: www.hopeforthewarriors.org/spouse.html

Summary To provide money for college or graduate school to the spouses and caregivers of wounded or deceased military personnel or veterans.

Eligibility This program is open to spouses and caregivers of current and former service members who were wounded or killed in the line of duty since September 11, 2001. Applicants must be enrolled or planning to enroll full or part time at an accredited college, university, or trade school to work on a bachelor's degree, master's degree, or vocational certification. They must have a high school GPA of 2.6 or higher or a GED score of 650 or higher. Along with their application, they must submit a 500-word essay on how their life has been impacted by the Global War on Terror and how that impact played a role in their pursuit of higher education. Selection is based on that essay, academic achievement, goals, and recommendations.

Financial data The stipend is $5,000 or $1,250.

Duration 1 year; renewable up to 3 more years.

Additional data This program includes the following named scholarships: the Shannon Maxwell Award, the Bonnie Amos Award, the Karin Dickerson Award, the Robin Kelleher-New Beginnings Award, and the Sidney Popkin Memorial Scholarship.

Number awarded 4 at $5,000 and 1 at $1,250.

Deadline March of each year.

[1234]
ILLINOIS GRANT PROGRAM FOR DEPENDENTS OF POLICE OR FIRE OFFICERS

Illinois Student Assistance Commission
Attn: Scholarship and Grant Services
1755 Lake Cook Road
Deerfield, IL 60015-5209
(847) 948-8550   Toll Free: (800) 899-ISAC
Fax: (847) 831-8549   TDD: (800) 526-0844
E-mail: isac.studentservices@isac.illinois.gov
Web: www.collegeilllinois.org

Summary To provide funding to the children or spouses of disabled or deceased Illinois police or fire officers who plan to attend college or graduate school in the state.

Eligibility This program is open to the spouses and children of Illinois police and fire officers who were at least 90% disabled or killed in the line of duty. Applicants must be enrolled at least a half-time in either undergraduate or graduate study at an approved Illinois public or private 2- or 4-year college, university, or hospital school. They need not be Illinois residents. U.S. citizenship or eligible noncitizen status is required.

Financial data The grants provide full payment of tuition and mandatory fees at approved public colleges in Illinois or an equivalent amount at private colleges.

Duration Up to 8 academic semesters or 12 academic quarters of study.

Number awarded Varies each year.

Deadline September of each year for the academic year; February of each year for spring semester or winter or spring quarter; June of each year for summer term.

[1235]
INDIANA CHILD OF VETERAN AND PUBLIC SAFETY OFFICER SUPPLEMENTAL GRANT PROGRAM

State Student Assistance Commission of Indiana
Attn: Grants and Scholarships
W462 Indiana Government Center South
402 West Washington Street
Indianapolis, IN 46204
(317) 232-2355   Toll Free: (888) 528-4719 (within IN)
Fax: (317) 232-3260   E-mail: grants@ssaci.in.gov
Web: www.in.gov/ssaci/2338.htm

Summary To provide financial assistance to residents of Indiana who are the children or spouses of specified categories of deceased or disabled veterans or public safety officers and interested in attending college or graduate school in the state.

Eligibility This program is open to 1) children of deceased or disabled Indiana veterans, children of Purple Heart recipients, and children of Vietnam War veterans who were listed as POW or MIA; 2) children and spouses of members of the Indiana National Guard who suffered a service-connected death while serving on state active duty; 3) Indiana veterans who received a Purple Heart; 4) current and former students at the Indiana Soldiers' and Sailors' Children's Home (Morton Memorial High School); and 5) children and spouses of Indiana police officers, fire fighters, or emergency medical technicians killed in the line of duty or Indiana state police troopers permanently and totally disabled in the line of duty. The veterans and National Guard portions of this program are open to Indiana residents who are the natural or adopted children or spouses of veterans who served in the active-duty U.S. armed forces during a period of war time.

Financial data Qualified applicants receive a 100% remission of tuition and all mandatory fees for undergraduate or graduate work at state-supported postsecondary schools and universities in Indiana. Support is not provided for such fees as room and board.

Duration Up to 124 semester hours of study.

Additional data The veterans portion of this program is administered by the Indiana Department of Veterans' Affairs. The National Guard portion of this program is administered by Joint Forces Headquarters.

Number awarded Varies each year.

Deadline Applications must be submitted at least 30 days before the start of the college term.

[1236]
JAMES DOYLE CASE MEMORIAL SCHOLARSHIPS

Mississippi Council of the Blind
c/o Kenneth Maddox
217 Taylor Street
Jackson, MS 39216
Web: www.acb.org/mcb

Summary To provide financial assistance to legally blind residents of Mississippi and their children who plan to attend college or graduate school in any state.

Eligibility This program is open to residents of Mississippi who are legally blind or the children of at least 1 legally blind parent. Applicants must be enrolled or accepted for enrollment in an undergraduate or graduate program in any state and carrying or planning to carry at least 12 academic hours. Along with their application, they must submit a 2-page autobiographical sketch, transcripts, standardized test scores (ACT or SAT for undergraduates; GRE, MCAT, LSAT, etc. for graduate students), 2 letters of recommendation, proof of acceptance from a postsecondary school, and verification of blindness of the qualifying person (applicant or parent).

Financial data The stipend is $1,500 per year.
Duration 4 years.
Number awarded 2 each year.
Deadline February of each year.

[1237]
KATHERN F. GRUBER SCHOLARSHIPS

Blinded Veterans Association
477 H Street, N.W.
Washington, DC 20001-2694
(202) 371-8880   Toll Free: (800) 669-7079
Fax: (202) 371-8258   E-mail: bva@bva.org
Web: www.bva.org/services.html

Summary To provide funding for undergraduate or graduate study to spouses and children of blinded veterans.

Eligibility This program is open to dependent children and spouses of blinded veterans of the U.S. armed forces. The veteran must be legally blind; the blindness may be either service connected or nonservice connected. Applicants must have been accepted or be currently enrolled as a full-time student in an undergraduate or graduate program at an accredited institution of higher learning. Along with their application, they must submit a 300-word essay on their career goals and aspirations. Financial need is not considered in the selection process.

Financial data The stipend is $2,000; funds are intended to cover the student's expenses, including tuition, academic fees, books, dormitory fees, and cafeteria fees. Funds are paid directly to the recipient's school.

Duration 1 year; recipients may reapply for up to 3 additional years.

Number awarded 6 each year.
Deadline April of each year.

[1238]
KIDS' CHANCE OF INDIANA SCHOLARSHIP PROGRAM

Kids' Chance of Indiana, Inc.
Attn: President
721 East Broadway
Fortville, IN 46040
(317) 485-0043, ext. 123   Fax: (317) 485-4299
E-mail: ngath@fdgtlaborlaw.com
Web: www.kidschancein.org/scholarship.html

Summary To provide financial assistance to Indiana residents whose parent was killed or permanently disabled in a work-related accident and who are interested in attending college or graduate school in any state.

Eligibility This program is open to Indiana residents between 16 and 25 years of age who are the children of workers fatally or catastrophically injured as a result of a work-related accident or occupational disease. The death or injury must be compensable by the Workers' Compensation Board of the state of Indiana and must have resulted in a substantial decline in the family's income that is likely to impede the student's pursuit of his or her educational objectives. Applicants must be attending or planning to attend a trade/vocational school, industrial/com-

mercial training institution, junior/community college, 4-year college or university, or graduate school in any state. Financial need is considered in the selection process.

Financial data Stipends range up to $3,000 per year. Funds may be used for tuition and fees, books, room and board, and utilities.

Duration 1 year; may be renewed.
Number awarded Varies each year.
Deadline Deadline not specified.

[1239]
KIDS' CHANCE OF OHIO SCHOLARSHIPS

Kids' Chance of Ohio
Attn: Executive Director
52 East Gay Street
P.O. Box 1008
Columbus, OH 43216-1008
(614) 464-6410   E-mail: raminor@vssp.com
Web: www.kidschanceohio.org/scholarshipprogram.html

Summary To provide financial assistance for undergraduate or graduate study in any state to children of Ohio employees who were killed or disabled as a result of a work-related injury or occupational disease.

Eligibility This program is open to the children between 16 and 25 years of age of employees who have been declared to be permanently and totally disabled or who were fatally injured as a result of a work-related injury or occupational disease. The death, injury, or illness must have occurred as a result of work activities performed for an Ohio employer covered by the Ohio workers' compensation law, although neither the student nor the parent is required to be an Ohio resident. The injury or death must have resulted in a decline in the family's income. Applicants must be attending or planning to attend a college, university, community college, trade/vocational school, industrial/commercial training institute, or graduate school in any state.

Financial data The stipend depends on the need of the recipient, to a maximum of $5,000 per year. Funds may be used for payment of tuition, fees, books, room, and board.

Duration 1 year; recipients may reapply.
Number awarded Varies each year.
Deadline Applications must be submitted at least 1 month prior to the beginning of the semester or quarter.

[1240]
KIDS' CHANCE OF SOUTH CAROLINA SCHOLARSHIPS

Kids' Chance of South Carolina
P.O. Box 2957
Georgetown, SC 29442-2957
(843) 546-5837   E-mail: info@kidschancesc.org
Web: www.kidschancesc.org/scholarship-information

Summary To provide financial assistance to South Carolina residents whose parent was killed or permanently disabled in a work-related accident and who are interested in attending college or graduate school in any state.

Eligibility This program is open to South Carolina residents between 16 and 25 years of age who are the children of workers fatally or catastrophically injured as a result of a work-related accident or occupational disease. Applicants must be attending or planning to attend a trade school, vocational school, community or junior college, 4-year college or university, or graduate school in any state. They must have a GPA of 2.0 or higher. The work-related injury or occupational disease from which their parent suffers or died must be compensable by the Workers' Compensation Board of the state of South Carolina and must have resulted in a substantial decline in the family's income that is likely to interfere with the student's pursuit of his or her educational objectives.

Financial data Stipends range up to $3,000 per semester ($6,000 per year). Funds may be used for tuition and fees, books, room and board, and utilities.

Duration 1 semester; may be renewed up to 7 additional semesters, provided the recipient maintains a GPA of 2.5 or higher.

Number awarded Varies each year; recently, 11 of these scholarships were awarded.

Deadline Applications must be submitted 1 month before the beginning of the semester, or July for the fall semester and December for the spring semester.

[1241]
LISA HIGGINS-HUSSMAN FOUNDATION SCHOLARSHIP

Ulman Cancer Fund for Young Adults
Attn: Scholarship Committee
10440 Little Patuxent Parkway, Suite G1
Columbia, MD 21044
(410) 964-0202   Toll Free: (888) 393-FUND
Fax: (410) 964-0402
E-mail: scholarship@ulmanfund.org
Web: www.ulmanfund.org/scholarship.aspx

Summary To provide financial assistance for college or graduate school to students from Washington, D.C., Maryland, or Virginia who have been diagnosed with cancer or have or have lost a family member with cancer.

Eligibility This program is open to students who 1) have been diagnosed with cancer; 2) have a parent, sibling, or guardian living with cancer; or 3) have lost a parent, sibling, or guardian to cancer. Applicants must be residents of Washington, D.C., Maryland, or Virginia or attending college there. They must be 35 years of age or younger and attending, or planning to attend, a 2- or 4-year college, university, or vocational program to work on an undergraduate or graduate degree. The first diagnosis of cancer (whether of the applicant, a parent, a sibling, or a guardian) must have occurred after the applicant was 15 years of age. Along with their application, they must submit an essay of at least 1,000 words on how the cancer experience has impacted their outlook on life and the legacy that they desire to leave behind. Selection is based on demonstrated dedication to community service, commitment to educational and professional goals, use of their cancer experience to impact the lives of other young adults affected by cancer, medical hardship, and financial need.

Financial data The stipend is $2,500. Funds are paid directly to the educational institution.

Duration 1 year.

Additional data Recipients must agree to complete 40 hours of community service.

Number awarded 1 each year.

Deadline March of each year.

[1242]
LPA SCHOLARSHIPS

Little People of America, Inc.
Attn: Vice President of Programs
250 El Camino Real, Suite 201
Tustin, CA 92780
(714) 368-3689   Toll Free: (888) LPA-2001
Fax: (714) 368-3367   E-mail: info@lpaonline.org
Web: www.lpaonline.org/mc/page.do?sitePageID=49367

Summary To provide financial assistance for college or graduate school to members of the Little People of America (LPA), to their families, and (in limited cases) to others.

Eligibility This program is open to members of LPA (limited to people who, for medical reasons, are 4 feet 10 inches or under in height). Applicants must be high school seniors or students attending college, vocational school, or graduate school. Along with their application, they must submit a 500-word personal statement that explains their reasons for applying for a scholarship, their plans for the future, how they intend to be of service to LPA after graduation, and any other relevant information about themselves, their family, their background, and their educational achievements. Financial need is also considered in the selection process. If sufficient funds are available after all LPA members have been served, scholarships may also be given, first, to immediate family members of dwarfs who are also paid members of LPA, and, second, to people with dwarfism who are not members of LPA.

Financial data Stipends range from $250 to $1,000.

Duration 1 year; awards are limited to 2 for undergraduate study and 1 for graduate study.

Number awarded Varies; generally between 5 and 10 each year.

Deadline April of each year.

[1243]
MAINE VETERANS DEPENDENTS EDUCATIONAL BENEFITS

Bureau of Veterans' Services
117 State House Station
Augusta, ME 04333-0117
(207) 430-6035 Toll Free: (800) 345-0116 (within ME)
Fax: (207) 626-4471   E-mail: mainebvs@maine.gov
Web: www.maine.gov

Summary To provide financial assistance for undergraduate or graduate education to dependents of disabled and other Maine veterans.

Eligibility Applicants for these benefits must be children (high school seniors or graduates under 22 years of age), non-divorced spouses, or unremarried widow(er)s of veterans who meet 1 or more of the following requirements: 1) living and determined to have a total permanent disability resulting from a service-connected cause; 2) killed in action; 3) died from a service-connected disability; 4) died while totally and permanently disabled due to a service-connected disability but whose death was not related to the service-connected disability; or 5) a member of the armed forces on active duty who has been listed for more than 90 days as missing in action, captured, forcibly detained, or interned in the line of duty by a foreign government or power. The veteran parent must have been a resident of Maine at the time of entry into service or a resident of Maine for 5 years preceding application for these benefits. Children may be working on an associate or bachelor's degree. Spouses, widows, and widowers may work on an associate, bachelor's, or master's degree.

Financial data Recipients are given free tuition at institutions of higher education supported by the state.

Duration Children may receive up to 8 semesters of support; they have 6 years from the date of first entrance to complete those 8 semesters. Continuation in the program is based on their earning a GPA of 2.0 or higher each semester. Spouses are entitled to receive up to 120 credit hours of educational benefits and have 10 years from the date of first entrance to complete their program.

Additional data College preparatory schooling and correspondence courses are not supported.

Number awarded Varies each year.

Deadline Deadline not specified.

[1244]
MARILYN YETSO MEMORIAL SCHOLARSHIP

Ulman Cancer Fund for Young Adults
Attn: Scholarship Committee
10440 Little Patuxent Parkway, Suite G1
Columbia, MD 21044
(410) 964-0202   Toll Free: (888) 393-FUND
Fax: (410) 964-0402
E-mail: scholarship@ulmanfund.org
Web: www.ulmanfund.org/scholarship.aspx

Summary To provide funding for college or graduate school to students who have or have lost a parent to cancer.

Eligibility This program is open to students who have or have lost a parent or guardian to cancer. Applicants must be 35 years of age or younger and attending, or planning to attend, a 2- or 4-year college, university, or vocational program to work on an undergraduate or graduate degree. The parent or guardian must have been first diagnosed with cancer after the applicant was 15 years of age. Along with their application, they must submit an essay of at least 1,000 words on how their parent's cancer experience has impacted their outlook on life and the legacy that they desire to leave behind. Selection is based on demonstrated dedication to community service, commitment to educational and professional goals, use of their cancer experience to impact the lives of other young adults affected by cancer, medical hardship, and financial need.

Financial data The stipend is $2,500. Funds are paid directly to the educational institution.

Duration 1 year.

Additional data These scholarships were first awarded in 2002. Recipients must agree to complete 40 hours of community service.

Number awarded 1 each year.

Deadline March of each year.

[1245]
MINNESOTA G.I. BILL PROGRAM

Minnesota Office of Higher Education
Attn: Manager of State Financial Aid Programs
1450 Energy Park Drive, Suite 350
St. Paul, MN 55108-5227
(651) 642-0567   Toll Free: (800) 657-3866
Fax: (651) 642-0675   TDD: (800) 627-3529
E-mail: info@ohe.state.mn.us
Web: www.ohe.state.mn.us/mPg.cfm?pageID=891

Summary To provide financial assistance for college or graduate school in the state to residents of Minnesota who served in the military after September 11, 2001 and the families of deceased or disabled military personnel.

Eligibility This program is open to residents of Minnesota enrolled at colleges and universities in the state as undergraduate or graduate students. Applicants must be 1) a veteran who is serving or has served honorably in a branch of the U.S. armed forces at any time on or after September 11, 2001; 2) a non-veteran who has served honorably for a total of 5 years or more cumulatively as a member of the Minnesota National Guard or other active or Reserve component of the U.S. armed forces, and any part of that service occurred on or after September 11, 2001; or 3) a surviving child or spouse of a person who has served in the military at any time on or after September 11, 2001 and who has died or has a total and permanent disability as a result of that military service. Financial need is also considered in the selection process.

Financial data The stipend is $1,000 per semester for full-time study or $500 per semester for part-time study. The maximum award is $3,000 per fiscal year or $10,000 per lifetime.

Duration 1 year; may be renewed, provided the recipient continues to make satisfactory academic progress.

Additional data This program was established by the Minnesota Legislature in 2007.

Number awarded Varies each year.

Deadline Deadline not specified.

[1246]
NORTH CAROLINA BAR ASSOCIATION SCHOLARSHIPS

North Carolina Bar Association
Attn: Young Lawyers Division Scholarship Committee
8000 Weston Parkway
P.O. Box 3688
Cary, NC 27519-3688
(919) 677-0561   Toll Free: (800) 662-7407
Fax: (919) 677-0761   E-mail: jterrell@ncbar.org
Web: younglawyers.ncbar.org

Summary   To provide financial assistance for college or graduate school to the children of disabled or deceased law enforcement officers in North Carolina.

Eligibility   This program is open to the natural or adopted children of North Carolina law enforcement officers who were permanently disabled or killed in the line of duty. Applicants must be younger than 27 years of age and enrolled or planning to enroll full time at an accredited institution of higher learning (including community colleges, trade schools, colleges, universities, and graduate programs) in North Carolina. Selection is based on academic performance and financial need.

Financial data   The stipend is $2,000 per year.

Duration   Up to 4 years.

Number awarded   Varies each year; recently, 17 of these scholarships were awarded.

Deadline   March of each year.

[1247]
OREGON DECEASED OR DISABLED PUBLIC SAFETY OFFICER GRANT PROGRAM

Oregon Student Access Commission
Attn: Public Programs
1500 Valley River Drive, Suite 100
Eugene, OR 97401-2130
(541) 687-7443   Toll Free: (800) 452-8807, ext. 7443
Fax: (541) 687-7414   TDD: (800) 735-2900
E-mail: awardinfo@osac.state.or.us
Web: www.oregonstudentaid.gov/ddpso-grant.aspx

Summary   To provide financial assistance for college or graduate school in the state to the children of disabled or deceased Oregon public safety officers.

Eligibility   This program is open to the natural, adopted, or stepchildren of Oregon public safety officers (fire fighters, state fire marshals, chief deputy fire marshals, deputy state fire marshals, police chiefs, police officers, sheriffs, deputy sheriffs, county adult parole and probation officers, correction officers, and investigators of the Criminal Justice Division of the Department of Justice) who, in the line of duty, were killed or disabled. Applicants must be enrolled or planning to enroll as a full-time undergraduate student at a public or private college or university in Oregon. Children of deceased officers are also eligible for graduate study. Financial need must be demonstrated.

Financial data   At a public 2- or 4-year college, the amount of the award is equal to the cost of tuition and fees. At a private college, the award is equal to the cost of tuition and fees at the University of Oregon.

Duration   1 year; may be renewed for up to 3 additional years of undergraduate study, if the student maintains satisfactory academic progress and demonstrates continued financial need. Children of deceased public safety officers may receive support for 12 quarters of graduate study.

Number awarded   Varies each year.

Deadline   Deadline not specified.

[1248]
OREGON OCCUPATIONAL SAFETY AND HEALTH DIVISION WORKERS MEMORIAL SCHOLARSHIPS

Oregon Student Access Commission
Attn: Grants and Scholarships Division
1500 Valley River Drive, Suite 100
Eugene, OR 97401-2146
(541) 687-7395   Toll Free: (800) 452-8807, ext. 7395
Fax: (541) 687-7414   TDD: (800) 735-2900
E-mail: awardinfo@osac.state.or.us
Web: www.oregonstudentaid.gov/scholarships.aspx

Summary   To provide funding to children and spouses of disabled or deceased workers in Oregon who are interested in attending college or graduate school.

Eligibility   This program is open to residents of Oregon who are U.S. citizens or permanent residents. Applicants must be high school seniors or graduates who 1) are dependents or spouses of an Oregon worker who has suffered permanent total disability on the job; or 2) are receiving, or have received, fatality benefits as dependents or spouses of a worker fatally injured in Oregon. They may be attending a college or graduate school in any state. Along with their application, they must submit an essay of up to 500 words on how the injury or death of their parent or spouse has affected or influenced their decision to further their education. Financial need is not required, but it is considered in the selection process.

Financial data   Stipends range up to $1,000.

Duration   1 year.

Additional data   This program, started in 1991, is sponsored by the Oregon Occupational Safety and Health Division of the Department of Consumer Services.

Number awarded   Varies each year; recently, 7 of these scholarships were awarded.

Deadline   February of each year.

[1249]
PARENT PUBLIC POLICY FELLOWSHIP PROGRAM

Joseph P. Kennedy, Jr. Foundation
Attn: Executive Director
1133 19th Street, N.W., 12th Floor
Washington, DC 20036-3604
(202) 393-1240   Fax: (202) 824-0351
E-mail: eidelman@jpkf.org
Web: www.jpkf.org/Interest_Areas/Fellowship.html

Summary   To provide a public policy fellowship opportunity in Washington, D.C. to the parents of persons with intellectual disabilities.

Eligibility This program is open to the parents of persons with intellectual disabilities who live in the United States. They must be interested in participating in an intensive public policy fellowship in Washington, D.C. Applicants should have experience in state or national-level advocacy for persons with intellectual and developmental disabilities and their families; health care, mental health care, education, employment, child care, child welfare, law, community organizing, housing, or development of inclusive community supports and services for people with intellectual and developmental disabilities; development of training programs for people with disabilities, families and communities, and/or for the professionals who work with them; and development or improvements of family support services, programs focused on increasing individual's control of resources and decisions impacting their lives, technology in support of people with intellectual and developmental disabilities, and any other area of focus important to those Americans. Salaried experience in the field is not a requirement. They should submit a 2- to 4-page letter stating their interests and accomplishments to date and what they hope to do with the knowledge and experience gained from the fellowship, a resume or summary of their involvement in the field, and at least 3 letters of support.

Financial data The program provides a stipend of $75,000 and a relocation allowance.

Duration 1 year, beginning in January.

Additional data This program was established in 1995. During the fellowship year, participants learn how legislation is initiated, developed, and passed by Congress. They work on the staff of a member of Congress, a Congressional committee, or a federal department. The expectation is that fellows will become future leaders in the field of disabilities and return home, after their year in Washington, to make significant contributions to policy and program development in their home state.

Number awarded 1 each year.

Deadline March of each year.

[1250]
PERLITA LIWANAG MEMORIAL SCHOLARSHIP

Ulman Cancer Fund for Young Adults
Attn: Scholarship Committee
10440 Little Patuxent Parkway, Suite G1
Columbia, MD 21044
(410) 964-0202   Toll Free: (888) 393-FUND
Fax: (410) 964-0402
E-mail: scholarship@ulmanfund.org
Web: www.ulmanfund.org/scholarship.aspx

Summary To provide financial assistance for college or graduate school to students from Washington, D.C., Maryland, or Virginia who have been diagnosed with cancer or have or have lost a family member with cancer.

Eligibility This program is open to students who 1) have been diagnosed with cancer; 2) have a parent, sibling, or guardian living with cancer; or 3) have lost a parent, sibling, or guardian to cancer. Applicants must be residents of Washington, D.C., Maryland, or Virginia or attending college there. They must be 35 years of age or younger and attending, or planning to attend, a 2- or 4-year college, university, or vocational program to work on an undergraduate or graduate degree. The first diagnosis of cancer (whether of the applicant, a parent, a sibling, or a guardian) must have occurred after the applicant was 15 years of age. Along with their application, they must submit an essay of at least 1,000 words on how the cancer experience has impacted their outlook on life and the legacy that they desire to leave behind. Selection is based on demonstrated dedication to community service, commitment to educational and professional goals, use of their cancer experience to impact the lives of other young adults affected by cancer, medical hardship, and financial need.

Financial data The stipend is $2,500. Funds are paid directly to the educational institution.

Duration 1 year.

Additional data These scholarships were first awarded in 2011. Recipients must agree to complete 40 hours of community service.

Number awarded 1 each year.

Deadline March of each year.

[1251]
SEPTEMBER 11 MEMORIAL SCHOLARSHIPS

United Methodist Higher Education Foundation
Attn: Scholarships Administrator
60 Music Square East, Suite 350
P.O. Box 340005
Nashville, TN 37203-0005
(615) 649-3990   Toll Free: (800) 811-8110
Fax: (615) 649-3980
E-mail: umhefscholarships@umhef.org
Web: www.umhef.org

Summary To provide financial assistance to Methodists and undergraduate and graduate students at Methodist institutions whose parent or guardian was disabled or killed in the terrorist attacks on September 11, 2001.

Eligibility This program is open to 1) students attending a United Methodist-related college or university in the United States, and 2) United Methodist students attending a higher education institution in the United States. All applicants must have lost a parent or guardian or had a parent or guardian disabled as a result of the September 11, 2001 terrorist attacks. They must be enrolled as full-time undergraduate or graduate students and be able to demonstrate financial need. U.S. citizenship or permanent resident status is required.

Financial data The stipend depends on the number of applicants.

Duration 1 year; may be renewed as long as the recipients maintain satisfactory academic progress as defined by their institution.

Number awarded Varies each year; a total of $30,000 is available for this program.

Deadline Applications may be submitted at any time.

[1252]
SURVIVORS' AND DEPENDENTS' EDUCATIONAL ASSISTANCE PROGRAM

Department of Veterans Affairs
Attn: Veterans Benefits Administration
810 Vermont Avenue, N.W.
Washington, DC 20420
(202) 418-4343   Toll Free: (888) GI-BILL1
Web: www.gibill.va.gov

Summary To provide financial assistance for undergraduate or graduate study to 1) children and spouses of deceased and disabled veterans, MIAs, and POWs and 2) children and spouses who have their own disabilities.

Eligibility Eligible for this assistance are spouses and children of 1) veterans who died or are permanently and totally disabled as the result of active service in the armed forces; 2) veterans who died from any cause while rated permanently and totally disabled from a service-connected disability; 3) service members listed as missing in action or captured in the line of duty by a hostile force; 4) service members listed as forcibly detained or interned by a foreign government or power; and 5) service members who are hospitalized or receiving outpatient treatment for a service-connected permanent and total disability and are likely to be discharged for that disability. Children must be between 18 and 26 years of age, although extensions may be granted. Spouses and children over 14 years of age with physical or mental disabilities are also eligible.

Financial data Monthly stipends for study at an academic institution are $957 for full time, $718 for three-quarter time, or $476 for half-time. Other rates apply for apprenticeship and on-the-job training, farm cooperative training, and special restorative training.

Duration Up to 45 months (or the equivalent in part-time training). Spouses must complete their training within 10 years of the date they are first found eligible. For spouses of service members who died on active duty, benefits end 20 years from the date of death.

Additional data Benefits may be used to work on associate, bachelor's, or graduate degrees at colleges and universities, including independent study, cooperative training, and study abroad programs. Courses leading to a certificate or diploma from business, technical, or vocational schools may also be taken. Other eligible programs include apprenticeships, on-the-job training programs, farm cooperative courses, and correspondence courses (for spouses only). Remedial, deficiency, and refresher courses may be approved under certain circumstances.

Number awarded Varies each year.

Deadline Applications may be submitted at any time.

[1253]
SUSAN STEIN SCHOLARSHIP

American College of Nurse-Midwives
Attn: ACNM Foundation, Inc.
8403 Colesville Road, Suite 1550
Silver Spring, MD 20910-6374
(240) 485-1850   Fax: (240) 485-1818
E-mail: fdn@acnm.org
Web: www.midwife.org

Summary To provide financial assistance for midwifery education to student members of the American College of Nurse-Midwives (ACNM) who have had a personal experience with breast cancer.

Eligibility This program is open to ACNM members who are currently enrolled in an accredited basic midwife education program and have successfully completed 1 academic or clinical semester/quarter or clinical module. Applicants must have had or currently have a personal experience with breast cancer, either their own or a family member's. Along with their application, they must submit a 150-word essay on their midwifery career plans; a 100-word essay on their intended future participation in ACNM activities; and a 300-word essay on the effect of breast cancer in themselves or a close family member on their choice of midwifery. Selection is based primarily on the quality of the application, although leadership, financial need, academics, and personal goals may also be considered.

Financial data The stipend is $3,000.

Duration 1 year.

Additional data This program was established in 2010.

Number awarded 1 each year.

Deadline March of each year.

[1254]
TONY AND JAN VIESSMAN MEMORIAL SCHOLARSHIPS

Epilepsy Foundation of Missouri and Kansas
c/o Julie Viessman MacCash
10698 Lakemont Drive
Rolla, MO 65401
Web: epilepsyfoundation.ning.com

Summary To provide funding to residents of any state who have epilepsy or are caring for someone who does and want to attend college or graduate school.

Eligibility This program is open to residents of any state who are under a physician's care for epilepsy or are the caretaker for a person living with epilepsy. Applicants may be 1) high school seniors planning to attend a technical school, community college, or 4-year college or university; 2) freshmen, sophomores, or juniors at 1 of those institutions; 3) college seniors planning to enroll in graduate school; or 4) adults interested in working on a college degree. Along with their application, they must submit a 500-word essay on 1 of the following topics: 1) what the youth of today should focus on to improve the lives of others; 2) why they think it is important for high school graduates to further their education; or 3) the current event, from their community or around the glove, that they find most interesting and why. They must also submit a 500-word essay on how they have overcome, or are working to overcome, the challenges that epilepsy presents.

Financial data The stipend is $1,000.

Duration 1 year.

Number awarded 4 each year.

Deadline March of each year.

[1255]
UCB FAMILY EPILEPSY SCHOLARSHIP PROGRAM

UCB, Inc.
Family Scholarship Program
c/o Hudson Medical Communications
200 White Plains Road, Second Floor
Tarrytown, NY 10591
Toll Free: (866) 825-1920
E-mail: UCBScholarship@hudsongloballlc.com
Web: www.ucbepilepsyscholarship.com

Summary To provide financial assistance for college or graduate school to epilepsy patients and their family members and caregivers.

Eligibility This program is open to epilepsy patients and their family members and caregivers. Applicants must be working on or planning to work on an undergraduate or graduate degree at an institution of higher education in the United States. They must be able to demonstrate academic achievement, a record of participation in activities outside of school, and service as a role model. Along with their application, they must submit a 1-page essay explaining why they should be selected for the scholarship, how epilepsy has impacted their life either as a patient or as a family member or caregiver, and how they will benefit from the scholarship. U.S. citizenship or permanent resident status is required.

Financial data The stipend is $5,000.

Duration 1 year; nonrenewable.

Additional data This program, previously known as the Keppra Family Epilepsy Scholarship Program, was established in 2004.

Number awarded 30 each year.

Deadline April of each year.

[1256]
UCB FAMILY RA SCHOLARSHIP PROGRAM

UCB, Inc.
c/o Summit Medical Communications
1421 East Broad Street, Suite 340
Fuquay-Varina, NC 27526
(919) 567-7590   Toll Free: (888) 854-4996
Fax: (919) 567-7591
E-mail: ucbrascholarship@summitmedcomm.com
Web: www.reachbeyondra.com

Summary To provide financial assistance to undergraduate and graduate students who have rheumatoid arthritis (RA) and their families.

Eligibility This program is open to students who are working on or planning to work on an associate, undergraduate, or graduate degree or are enrolled in a trade

school educational program. Applicants must have been diagnosed with RA or be an immediate family member (parent, spouse, child, or sibling) of a person with RA. They may be of any age. Along with their application, they must submit an essay of 1 to 2 pages describing how they are living beyond the boundaries of RA to demonstrate academic ambition and personal achievement and how the scholarship would impact their life.

Financial data Stipends range up to $5,000.

Duration 1 year; nonrenewable.

Additional data This program began on a pilot basis in 2008.

Number awarded 30 each year.

Deadline March of each year.

[1257]
VERA YIP MEMORIAL SCHOLARSHIP

Ulman Cancer Fund for Young Adults
Attn: Scholarship Committee
10440 Little Patuxent Parkway, Suite G1
Columbia, MD 21044
(410) 964-0202   Toll Free: (888) 393-FUND
Fax: (410) 964-0402
E-mail: scholarship@ulmanfund.org
Web: www.ulmanfund.org/scholarship.aspx

Summary To provide money for college or graduate school to students who have cancer or have lost a parent with cancer.

Eligibility This program is open to students who have or have lost a parent or guardian to cancer. Applicants must be 35 years of age or younger and attending, or planning to attend, a 2- or 4-year college, university, or vocational program to work on an undergraduate or graduate degree. The parent or guardian must have been first diagnosed with cancer after the applicant was 15 years of age. Along with their application, they must submit an essay of at least 1,000 words on how their parent's cancer experience has impacted their outlook on life and the legacy that they desire to leave behind. This award is presented to the applicant who best demonstrates the qualities of Vera Yip of courage, determination, motivation, and dedication.

Financial data The stipend is $2,500. Funds are paid directly to the educational institution.

Duration 1 year; nonrenewable.

Additional data Recipients must agree to complete 40 hours of community service.

Number awarded 1 each year.

Deadline March of each year.

[1258]
VIRGINIA MILITARY SURVIVORS AND DEPENDENTS EDUCATION PROGRAM

Virginia Department of Veterans Services
270 Franklin Road, Room 810
Roanoke, VA 24011-2215
(540) 597-1730   Fax: (540) 857-7573
Web: www.dvs.virginia.gov/veterans-benefits.shtml

Summary To provide funding to the children and spouses of disabled and other Virginia veterans or service personnel.

Eligibility This program is open to residents of Virginia whose parent or spouse served in the U.S. armed forces (including the Reserves, the Virginia National Guard, or the Virginia National Guard Reserves) during any armed conflict subsequent to December 6, 1941, as a result of a terrorist act, during military operations against terrorism, or on a peacekeeping mission. The veterans must have been killed, missing in action, taken prisoner of war, or become at least 90% disabled as a result of such service. Applicants must have been accepted at a public college or university in Virginia as an undergraduate or graduate student. Children must be between 16 and 29 years of age; there are no age restrictions for spouses. The veteran must have been a resident of Virginia at the time of entry into active military service or for at least 5 consecutive years immediately prior to the date of application or death. Surviving spouses must have been residents of Virginia for at least 5 years prior to marrying the veteran or for at least 5 years immediately prior to the date on which the application was submitted.

Financial data The program provides 1) waiver of tuition and all required fees at public institutions of higher education in Virginia; and 2) a stipend up to $1,500 per year to offset the costs of room, board, books, and supplies at those institutions. If more students qualify, the stipend is reduced; recently, it was $675 per semester ($1,350 per year) for full-time enrollment, $450 per semester for enrollment less than full-time but at least half-time, or $225 per semester for enrollment less than half-time.

Duration Entitlement lasts 36 months (4 years).

Additional data Individuals entitled to this benefit may use it to pursue any vocational, technical, undergraduate, or graduate program of instruction. Generally, programs listed in the academic catalogs of state-supported institutions are acceptable, provided they have a clearly-defined educational objective (such as a certificate, diploma, or degree). This program was formerly known as the Virginia War Orphans Education Program.

Number awarded Varies each year; recently, funding allowed for a total of 667 stipends at $1,500, but 740 students actually qualified and received a reduced stipend.

Deadline Applications may be submitted at any time, but they must be received at least 30 days prior to the start of the term.

[1259]
WISCONSIN G.I. BILL TUITION REMISSION PROGRAM

Wisconsin Department of Veterans Affairs
201 West Washington Avenue
P.O. Box 7843
Madison, WI 53707-7843
(608) 266-1311   Toll Free: (800) WIS-VETS
Fax: (608) 267-0403
E-mail: WDVAInfo@dva.state.wi.us
Web: www.dva.state.wi.us/Ben_education.asp

Summary To provide financial assistance for college or graduate school to disabled and other Wisconsin veterans and their dependents.

Eligibility This program is open to current residents of Wisconsin who 1) were residents of the state when they entered or reentered active duty in the U.S. armed forces, or 2) have moved to the state and have been residents for any consecutive 12-month period after entry or reentry into service. Applicants must have served on active duty for at least 2 continuous years or for at least 90 days during specified wartime periods. Also eligible are 1) qualifying children and unremarried surviving spouses of Wisconsin veterans who died in the line of duty or as the direct result of a service-connected disability; and 2) children and spouses of Wisconsin veterans who have a service-connected disability rated by the U.S. Department of Veterans Affairs as 30% or greater. Children must be between 17 and 25 years of age (regardless of the date of the veteran's death or initial disability rating) and be a Wisconsin resident for tuition purposes. Spouses remain eligible for 10 years following the date of the veteran's death or initial disability rating; they must be Wisconsin residents for tuition purposes but they may enroll full or part time. Students may attend any institution, center, or school within the University of Wisconsin (UW) System or the Wisconsin Technical College System (WCTS). There are no income limits, delimiting periods following military service during which the benefit must be used, or limits on the level of study (e.g., vocational, undergraduate, professional, or graduate).

Financial data Veterans who qualify as a Wisconsin resident for tuition purposes are eligible for a remission of 100% of standard academic fees and segregated fees at a UW campus or 100% of program and material fees at a WCTS institution. Veterans who qualify as a Wisconsin veteran for purposes of this program but for other reasons fail to meet the definition of a Wisconsin resident for tuition purposes at the UW system are eligible for a remission of 100% of non-resident fees. Spouses and children of deceased or disabled veterans are entitled to a remission of 100% of tuition and fees at a UW or WCTS institution.

Duration Up to 8 semesters or 128 credits, whichever is greater.

Additional data This program was established in 2005 as a replacement for Wisconsin Tuition and Fee Reimbursement Grants.

Number awarded Varies each year.

Deadline Applications must be submitted within 14 days from the office start of the academic term: in October for fall, March for spring, or June for summer.

Grants-in-Aid

[1260]
AIR FORCE AID SOCIETY RESPITE CARE

Air Force Aid Society
Attn: Financial Assistance Department
241 18th Street South, Suite 202
Arlington, VA 22202-3409
(703) 607-3072, ext. 51   Toll Free: (800) 769-8951
Fax: (703) 607-3022
Web: www.afas.org

Summary   To provide financial assistance to Air Force personnel and their families who have a family member with special needs.

Eligibility   This program is open to active-duty Air Force members and their families who are responsible for 24 hour a day care for an ill or disabled family member (child, spouse, or parent) living in the household. Applicants must be referred by the Exceptional Family Member Program (EFMP) or the Family Advocacy Office. Selection is based on need, both financial need and the need of the family for respite time.

Financial data   Assistance is provided as a grant that depends on the needs of the family.

Number awarded   Varies each year.

Deadline   Applications may be submitted at any time.

[1261]
ALABAMA AD VALOREM TAX EXEMPTION FOR SPECIALLY ADAPTED HOUSES

Alabama Department of Revenue
Attn: Property Tax Division
Gordon Persons Building
50 North Ripley Street, Room 4126
P.O. Box 327210
Montgomery, AL 36132-7210
(334) 242-1525
Web: www.ador.state.al.us

Summary   To provide a property tax exemption to the owners of specially adapted housing (housing adapted for disabled veterans) in Alabama.

Eligibility   The home of any veteran which is or was acquired pursuant to the provisions of Public Law 702, 80th Congress (specially adapted housing grants for veterans) as amended (38 USC) will be exempted from ad valorem taxation if the house is owned and occupied by the veteran or the veteran's unremarried widow(er).

Financial data   Qualifying houses are exempt from all ad valorem taxation.

Duration   This exemption continues as long as the qualifying veteran or the unremarried widow(er) resides in the house.

Number awarded   Varies each year.

Deadline   Deadline not specified.

[1262]
ALABAMA MILITARY RETIREE INCOME TAX EXEMPTION

Alabama Department of Revenue
Attn: Income Tax Division
Gordon Persons Building
50 North Ripley Street, Room 4212
P.O. Box 327410
Montgomery, AL 36132-7410
(334) 242-1105   Fax: (334) 242-0064
E-mail: erohelpdesk@revenue.state.al.us
Web: www.ador.state.al.us

Summary   To exempt a portion of the income of disabled and other veterans and their survivors from taxation in Alabama.

Eligibility   Eligible are Alabama recipients of regular military retired pay or military survivors benefits. Recipients of benefits paid by the U.S. Department of Veterans Affairs (including disability retirement payments) are also eligible for this exemption.

Financial data   All income received as military retired pay, veterans' disability payment, or military survivors benefits is exempt from state, county, or municipal income taxation.

Duration   The exemption continues as long as the recipient resides in Alabama.

Deadline   Deadline not specified.

[1263]
ALEXANDER GRAHAM BELL ASSOCIATION PARENT-INFANT FINANCIAL AID PROGRAM

Alexander Graham Bell Association for the Deaf and
   Hard of Hearing
Attn: Financial Aid Coordinator
3417 Volta Place, N.W.
Washington, DC 20007-2778
(202) 337-5220   Fax: (202) 337-8314
TDD: (202) 337-5221   E-mail: financialaid@agbell.org
Web: nc.agbell.org/page.aspx?pid=499

Summary   To provide financial aid to the parents of young children with moderate to profound hearing loss who need assistance to cover expenses associated with early intervention services.

Eligibility   Applicants must be parents or guardians of children less than 3 years of age who have been diagnosed as having a moderate to profound bilateral hearing loss or auditory neuropathy. Children with cochlear implants are eligible, but those with unilateral hearing loss are not. Spoken communication must be the child's primary mode of communication. The family must be able to demonstrate financial need. Residents of Canada, the United States, and its territories are eligible.

Financial data   The amount awarded depends on the needs of the child; most awards range from $300 to $2,000 per year.

Duration   1 year.

Number awarded   Varies each year.

Deadline   September of each year.

[1264]
ANDRE SOBEL GRANTS

André Sobel River of Life Foundation
Attn: Awards
8581 Santa Monica Boulevard, Suite 80
P.O. Box 361640
Los Angeles, CA 90036
(310) 276-7111   Fax: (310) 276-0244
E-mail: info@andreriveroflife.org
Web: andreriveroflife.org/our-story/what-we-do

Summary To provide assistance to single mothers who have a child with a life-threatening illness.

Eligibility This assistance is available to single mothers who have a child experiencing a life-threatening medical crisis. They must have exhausted all other sources of support and need assistance for such purposes as household expenses, groceries, utilities, transportation, medical expenses, housing, or burial expenses. Grants are available from the Everyday Needs Assistance Fund (sponsored by the Genentech Foundation) for single-parent families of children undergoing treatment for cancer and the Compassion Can't Wait Fund for single-parent families of children with any catastrophic diagnosis.

Financial data Grants depend on the need of the recipient. Recently, single grants ranged up to $2,204 and total assistance ranged up to $14,475 for an individual.

Duration Grants are awarded as needed and may be repeated.

Additional data This foundation made its first grant in 2000.

Number awarded Varies each year; since the program was established, it has awarded more than $4 million in assistance to 11,300 family members.

Deadline Applications may be submitted at any time.

[1265]
ARKANSAS DISABLED VETERANS PROPERTY TAX EXEMPTION

Arkansas Assessment Coordination Department
1614 West Third Street
Little Rock, AR 72201-1815
(501) 324-9240   Fax: (501) 324-9242
E-mail: dasbury@acd.state.ar.us
Web: www.arkansas.gov/acd

Summary To exempt from taxation the property owned by blind or disabled veterans, surviving spouses, and minor dependent children in Arkansas.

Eligibility This program is open to disabled veterans in Arkansas who have been awarded special monthly compensation by the U.S. Department of Veterans Affairs and who have 1) the loss of or the loss of use of 1 or more limbs, 2) total blindness in 1 or both eyes, or 3) total and permanent disability. The benefit also extends to veterans' unremarried surviving spouses and their minor children.

Financial data Qualifying veterans (or their unremarried widows or dependent children) are exempt from payment of all state taxes on their homestead and personal property.

Duration This exemption continues as long as the qualifying veteran (or dependent) resides in Arkansas.

Number awarded Varies each year.

Deadline Applications may be submitted at any time.

[1266]
ARKANSAS INCOME TAX CREDIT FOR PHENYLKETONURIA DISORDER

Arkansas Department of Finance and Administration
Attn: Office of Income Tax Administration
Joel Ledbetter Building, Room 2300
1816 West Seventh Street
P.O. Box 3628
Little Rock, AR 72203-3628
(501) 682-1100   Fax: (501) 682-7692
E-mail: individual.income@dfa.arkansas.gov
Web: www.dfa.arkansas.gov

Summary To provide a state income tax credit for taxpayers in Arkansas who have a child with phenylketonuria (PKU) disorder or other metabolic disorders.

Eligibility This income tax credit is available to Arkansas individuals and families with a dependent child or children with PKU, galactosemia, organic acidemias, or disorders of amino acid metabolism. Taxpayers must have expenses incurred for the purchase of medically necessary foods and low protein modified food products.

Financial data The maximum state income tax credit is $2,400.

Duration The certificate that qualifies the taxpayer for this credit (AR1113) must be attached to the taxpayer's individual income tax return annually. Any unused credit amount may be carried forward for an additional 2 years.

Additional data The Arkansas legislature established this credit in 1999.

Number awarded Varies each year.

Deadline Deadline not specified.

[1267]
ARKANSAS INCOME TAX EXEMPTIONS FOR RETIREMENT AND DISABILITY PAY

Arkansas Department of Finance and Administration
Attn: Office of Income Tax Administration
Joel Ledbetter Building, Room 2300
1816 West Seventh Street
P.O. Box 3628
Little Rock, AR 72203-3628
(501) 682-1100   Fax: (501) 682-7692
E-mail: individual.income@dfa.arkansas.gov
Web: www.dfa.arkansas.gov

Summary To exempt a portion of the income from retirement or disability plans from state income taxes in Arkansas.

Eligibility Eligible are residents of Arkansas receiving income from retirement or disability plans. Surviving spouses also qualify for the exemption.

Financial data Exempt from state income taxation is the first $6,000 in disability pay, retired pay, or survivors benefits. Any resident who receives both military retirement or disability pay and other retirement or disability benefits is entitled to only a single $6,000 deduction. Surviving spouses are also limited to a single $6,000 exemption. Military retirees may adjust their figures if the payment includes survivor's benefit payments; the amount of adjustment must be listed on the income statement, and supporting documentation must be submitted with the return.

Duration The exemption continues as long as the recipient resides in Arkansas.

Deadline Deadline not specified.

[1268]
BOBBE AND JERRY MARCUS RESPITE CARE GRANT PROGRAM

ALS Association-DC/Maryland/Virginia Chapter
Attn: Director of Patient Services
7507 Standish Place
Rockville, MD 20855
(301) 978-9855
Fax: (301) 978-9854
Web: webdc.alsa.org
Toll Free: (866) FITE-ALS
E-mail: info@ALSinfo.org

Summary To provide funding for respite care to Amyotrophic Lateral Sclerosis (ALS) caregivers in Maryland, Virginia, and Washington, D.C.

Eligibility This assistance is available to residents of Maryland, Virginia, and Washington, D.C. who have a confirmed diagnosis of ALS and their family caregivers. Applicants must be registered with the local chapter of the ALS Association. They must be seeking funding to allow the caregiver some regular interval of renewal: for business or social activities, a weekend getaway, or even to sleep on occasion through the night. A professional service will provide needed care.

Financial data Grants provide up to $1,250 per family per year.

Duration 1 year; may be renewed.

Number awarded Varies each year.

Deadline Applications may be submitted at any time.

[1269]
CALIFORNIA DISABLED VETERAN EXEMPTION FROM THE IN LIEU TAX FEE FOR A MANUFACTURED HOME OR MOBILEHOME

Department of Housing and Community Development
Attn: Registration and Titling
1800 Third Street
P.O. Box 2111
Sacramento, CA 95812-2111
(916) 323-9224
Web: www.hcd.ca.gov
Toll Free: (800) 952-8356

Summary To provide a special property tax exemption to blind or disabled California veterans and/or their spouses who own and occupy a mobile home.

Eligibility This program is open to disabled veterans and/or their spouses in California who have a manufactured home or mobile home as their principal place of residence. Veterans must be disabled as a result of injury or disease incurred in military service and have been a resident of California 1) at the time of entry into the service

and be blind, or have lost the use of 1 or more limbs, or be totally disabled; 2) on November 7, 1972 and be blind in both eyes, or have lost the use of 2 or more limbs; or 3) on January 1, 1975 and be totally disabled. The spouses and unremarried surviving spouses of those disabled veterans are also eligible.

Financial data The exemption applies to the first $20,000 of the assessed market value of the manufactured home or mobile home. Veterans and/or spouses whose income falls below a specified level are entitled to an additional $10,000 exemption. The amount of the exemption is 100% if the home is owned by a veteran only, a veteran and spouse, or a spouse only; 50% if owned by a veteran and another person other than a spouse or by a spouse and another person other than the veteran; 67% if owned by a veteran, the spouse, and another person; 34% if owned by a veteran and 2 other people other than a spouse or by a spouse and 2 other people; 50% if owned by a veteran, the spouse, and 2 other people; or 25% if owned by a veteran and 3 other people or by a spouse and 3 other people.

Duration The exemption is available annually as long as the applicant meets all requirements.

Number awarded Varies each year.

Deadline Deadline not specified.

[1270]
CALIFORNIA PROPERTY TAX EXEMPTIONS FOR VETERANS

California Department of Veterans Affairs
Attn: Division of Veterans Services
1227 O Street, Room 101
P.O. Box 942895
Sacramento, CA 94295
(916) 653-2573
Fax: (916) 653-2563
Web: www.cdva.ca.gov/VetServices/Benefits.aspx
Toll Free: (877) 741-8532
TDD: (800) 324-5966

Summary To exempt a portion of the property of blind or disabled veterans in California and their spouses from taxation.

Eligibility This exemption is available to homeowners in California who are wartime veterans in receipt of service-connected disability compensation that is 1) at the totally disabled rate, 2) for loss or loss of use of 2 or more limbs, or 3) for blindness. Unremarried surviving spouses, including registered domestic partners, of veterans who are in receipt of service-connected death benefits are also eligible.

Financial data For veterans and spouses whose total household income from all sources is greater than $51,669 per year, up to $115,060 of the assessed value of a home is exempt from taxation. For veterans and spouses whose total household income from all sources is less than $51,669 per year, up to $172,592 of the assessed value of a home is exempt from taxation.

Duration The exemption is available as long as the veteran or spouse owns a home in California.

Additional data Information is available from the local county assessor's office in each California county.

Number awarded Varies each year.

Deadline Applications may be submitted at any time.

[1271]
CARNEGIE FUND FOR AUTHORS GRANTS-IN-AID

Carnegie Fund for Authors
c/o W.L. Rothenberg
One Old Country Road, Suite 113
Carle Place, NY 11514
(516) 877-2141   Fax: (516) 743-6595

Summary To provide emergency financial assistance to authors or their family members who have experienced an illness or injury.

Eligibility Authors who have had at least 1 book published are eligible to apply for financial assistance if they or their spouses/dependents have suffered financial problems because of an injury or illness. To qualify for assistance, the author's book must have earned reader acceptance and should have been listed in a standard reference book (e.g., *Books in Print*). Authors whose books have not been listed in a standard source must submit a copy of the qualifying publication when applying.

Financial data The amount awarded ranges from $500 to $1,500, depending upon the needs of the recipient.

Duration This is a 1-time award.

Number awarded Varies each year.

Deadline Applications may be submitted at any time.

[1272]
CHILDREN OF FALLEN SOLDIERS RELIEF FUND FINANCIAL ASSISTANCE GRANTS

Children of Fallen Soldiers Relief Fund
P.O. Box 3968
Gaithersburg, MD 20885-3968
(301) 685-3421   Toll Free: (866) 96-CFSRF
Fax: (301) 630-0592   E-mail: grants@cfsrf.org
Web: www.cfsrf.org

Summary To provide personal financial assistance to veterans severely disabled during service in Iraq or Afghanistan and to the families of military personnel killed or severely disabled in those countries.

Eligibility This program is open to 1) veterans severely disabled as a result of service in Operation Iraqi Freedom or Operation Enduring Freedom; and 2) the spouses and children of military personnel killed or severely disabled during that service. Applicants must submit a 1-page statement describing their reason for requesting funds, the amount requested, the specified purpose to which the funds will be applied, a breakdown of monthly income and expenses, 2 recent months of bank statements, and current bills that are in arrears.

Financial data Grants have ranged from $1,650 to $16,916, depending on the need of the recipient.

Duration These are 1-time grants.

Additional data This organization was founded in 2003.

Number awarded Varies each year; since the organization was founded, it has awarded 18 of these financial assistance grants.

Deadline Applications may be submitted at any time.

[1273]
CHILDREN'S LEUKEMIA RESEARCH ASSOCIATION PATIENT AID GRANTS

Children's Leukemia Research Association, Inc.
Attn: Patient Aid Department
585 Stewart Avenue, Suite 18
Garden City, NY 11530
(516) 222-1944   Fax: (516) 222-0457
E-mail: info@childrensleukemia.org
Web: www.childrensleukemia.org/patientaid.html

Summary To provide financial assistance to leukemia patients and their families.

Eligibility This assistance is available to leukemia patients and their families. Applicants must be seeking support for laboratory fees associated with leukemia, x-ray therapy treatment or chemotherapy treatment of leukemia, or leukemia drugs. They must submit a letter of diagnosis from the attending physician.

Financial data Grant support ranges up to $3,000 per year.

Additional data The sponsoring organization is also known as the National Leukemia Research Association, Inc.

Number awarded Varies each year.

Deadline Applications may be submitted at any time.

[1274]
CLAYTON DABNEY FOUNDATION FOR KIDS WITH CANCER GRANTS

Clayton Dabney Foundation for Kids with Cancer
6500 Greenville Avenue, Suite 342
Dallas, TX 75206
(214) 361-2600   Fax: (214) 217-5199
E-mail: admin@claytondabney.org
Web: www.claytondabney.org

Summary To provide assistance to families whose child is in the terminal stage of cancer.

Eligibility This assistance is available to families who have a child younger than 18 years of age whose cancer has progressed to a terminal stage. Families of children younger than 21 years of age who were diagnosed before turning 18 and are still being treated in pediatric oncology are also eligible. The family must demonstrate financial need, although that includes middle-income families where both parents are working though unable to take time off because they are working so hard to cover all of the family expenses and medical bills. Applications must be initiated by a licensed representative (case worker, child life specialist, nurse, or doctor) from a recognized organization or agency (hospital, hospice care, social work, or volunteer group).

Financial data Assistance is generally limited to $2,000 per family.

Number awarded Varies each year.

Deadline Applications may be submitted at any time.

[1275]
COAL MINERS BLACK LUNG BENEFITS

Department of Labor
Employment Standards Administration
Office of Workers' Compensation Programs
Attn: Division of Coal Mine Workers' Compensation
200 Constitution Avenue, N.W., Room C3520
Washington, DC 20210
(202) 693-0046   Toll Free: (800) 638-7072
TDD: (800) 326-2577
Web: www.dol.gov/dol/topic/workcomp/index.htm

Summary To provide monthly benefits to coal miners who are disabled because of pneumoconiosis (black lung disease) and to their surviving dependents.

Eligibility Present and former coal miners (including certain transportation and construction workers who were exposed to coal mine dust) and their surviving dependents, including surviving spouses, orphaned children, and totally dependent parents, brothers, and sisters, may file claims if they are totally disabled.

Financial data Benefit amounts vary; recently; the basic monthly benefit was $625 for a single totally disabled miner or surviving spouse, $938 per month for a claimant with 1 dependent, $1,094 per month for a claimant with 2 dependents, or $1,251 per month for a claimant with 3 or more dependents. Benefit payments are reduced by the amounts received for pneumoconiosis under state workers' compensation awards and by excess earnings.

Duration Benefits are paid as long as the miner is unable to work in the mines or until the miner dies.

Number awarded Varies; recently, 7,699 miners, 21,913 surviving spouses, 1,214 other eligible persons, 5,726 dependents of miners, 723 dependents of surviving spouses, and 122 dependents of other eligible persons received benefits from this program.

Deadline Deadline not specified.

[1276]
COLORADO PROPERTY TAX EXEMPTION FOR DISABLED VETERANS

Division of Veterans Affairs
1355 South Colorado Boulevard, Building C, Suite 113
Denver, CO 80220
(303) 343-1268   Fax: (303) 343-7238
Web: www.dmva.state.co.us/page/va/prop_tax

Summary To provide a partial exemption of taxes on property owned by disabled veterans or their spouses in Colorado.

Eligibility This exemption is open to veterans who reside in Colorado and have been rated 100% permanent and total service-connected disabled by the U.S. Department of Veterans Affairs. Applicants must have been honorably discharged and must own property in Colorado which they use as their primary residence. The exemption also applies to members of the National Guard or Reserves who sustained their injury during a period in which they were called to active duty, property owned by a veteran's spouse if both occupy the property as their primary residence, and property owned by a trust or other legal entity if the veteran or spouse is a major of the trust or other legal entity, the property was transferred solely for estate planning purposes, and the veteran or spouse would otherwise be the owner of record.

Financial data For qualifying veterans, 50% of the first $200,000 of actual value of the primary residence is exempted from taxes.

Duration The exemption continues as long as the veteran resides in the property.

Additional data This program was approved by Colorado voters in 2006.

Number awarded Varies each year.

Deadline Applications must be submitted by June of the year for which the exemption is requested.

[1277]
CONNECTICUT REAL ESTATE TAX EXEMPTION FOR DISABLED VETERANS

Office of Policy and Management
Attn: Intergovernmental Policy Division
450 Capitol Avenue
Hartford, CT 06106-1308
(860) 418-6278   Toll Free: (800) 286-2214 (within CT)
Fax: (860) 418-6493   TDD: (860) 418-6456
E-mail: leeann.graham@ct.gov
Web: www.ct.gov

Summary To exempt disabled or blind Connecticut veterans and their surviving spouses from the payment of a portion of their local property taxes.

Eligibility There are 2 categories of Connecticut veterans who qualify for exemptions from their dwelling house and the lot on which it is located: 1) those with major service-connected disabilities (paraplegia or osteochondritis resulting in permanent loss of the use of both legs or permanent paralysis of both legs and lower parts of the body; hemiplegia with permanent paralysis of 1 leg and 1 arm or either side of the body resulting from injury to the spinal cord, skeletal structure, or brain, or from disease of the spinal cord not resulting from syphilis; total blindness; amputation of both arms, both legs, both hands or both feet, or the combination of a hand and a foot; sustained through enemy action or resulting from an accident occurring or disease contracted in such active service) and 2) those with less severe disabilities (loss of use of 1 arm or 1 leg because of service-connected injuries). Surviving unremarried spouses of eligible deceased veterans are entitled to the same exemption as would have been granted to the veteran, as long as they continue to be the legal owner/occupier of the exempted residence. An additional exemption is available to veterans and spouses whose total adjusted gross income is less than $32,300 if unmarried or $39,500 if married. If the veteran is rated as 100% disabled by the U.S. Department of Veterans Affairs (VA), the maximum income levels are $18,000 if unmarried or $21,000 if married.

Financial data Veterans in the first category receive an exemption from local property taxation of $10,000 of assessed valuation. Veterans in the second category receive exemptions of $5,000 of assessed valuation. For veterans whose income is less than the specified levels, additional exemptions of $20,000 for the first category or $10,000 for the second category are available from municipalities that choose to participate. For veterans whose income exceeds the specified levels, the additional exemption from participating municipalities is $5,000 for the first category or $2,500 for the second category. Connecticut municipalities may also elect to exempt from taxation specially adapted housing acquired or modified by a veteran under the provisions of Section 801 of Title 38 of the United States Code.

Duration 1 year; exemptions continue as long as the eligible resident (or surviving spouse) owns/occupies the primary residence and lives in Connecticut.

Number awarded Varies each year; recently, a total of 19,669 veterans received property tax exemptions through this and other programs in Connecticut.

Deadline Applications for the additional municipality exemption must be submitted to the assessor's office of the town or residence by September of every other year.

[1278]
CONNECTICUT VETERANS' ADDITIONAL EXEMPTION TAX RELIEF PROGRAM

Office of Policy and Management
Attn: Intergovernmental Policy Division
450 Capitol Avenue
Hartford, CT 06106-1308
(860) 418-6278   Toll Free: (800) 286-2214 (within CT)
Fax: (860) 418-6493   TDD: (860) 418-6456
E-mail: leeann.graham@ct.gov
Web: www.ct.gov

Summary To exempt disabled veterans and their surviving spouses who are residents of Connecticut from a portion of their personal property taxes.

Eligibility Eligible to apply for this exemption are Connecticut veterans who are rated as disabled by the U.S. Department of Veterans Affairs (VA). Unremarried surviving spouses of qualified veterans are also eligible. An additional exemption may be available to veterans and spouses whose total adjusted gross income is less than $32,300 if unmarried or $39,500 if married. If the veteran is rated as 100% disabled by the U.S. Department of Veterans Affairs (VA), the maximum income levels are $18,000 if unmarried or $21,000 if married.

Financial data The amount of the exemption depends on the level of the VA disability rating: for 10% to 25%, it is $1,500; for more than 25% to 50%, $2,000; for more than 50% to 75%, $2,500; for more than 75% and for veterans older than 65 years of age with any level of disability, $3,000. Municipalities may elect to provide an additional exemption, equal to twice the amount provided, to veterans and spouses whose income is less than the qualifying level. For veterans and spouses who do not meet the income requirement, the additional exemption from partic-

ipating municipalities is equal to 50% of the basic state exemption.

Duration 1 year; exemptions continue as long as the eligible resident lives in Connecticut.

Number awarded Varies each year; recently, a total of 19,669 veterans received property tax exemptions through this and other programs in Connecticut.

Deadline Applications for the additional municipality exemption must be submitted to the assessor's office of the town of residence by September of every other year.

[1279]
DAVE MADEIROS CREATIVE ARTS SCHOLARSHIP

Factor Foundation of America
Attn: Scholarship Committee
P.O. Box 812542
Boca Raton, FL 33481-2542
(561) 504-6531
E-mail: kmadeiros@factorfoundation.org
Web: www.factorfoundation.org/programs.htm

Summary To provide financial assistance for artistic or sports activities to young people with a bleeding disorder and their siblings.

Eligibility This program is open to children between 5 and 17 years of age who have a bleeding disorder or are the sibling of such a person. Applicants must be interested in taking musical lessons, joining a sports team, taking drawing lessons, taking a drama class, taking a private sports class, etc. They must be recommended by a local hemophilia chapter, physician, and/or hemophilia treatment center. Parents must submit an application that includes a 500-word essay on their desire for their child to take part in a creative art and how that experience will benefit him or her, 2 letters of reference, and documentation of financial need.

Financial data The stipend is $1,000.

Duration 1 year; recipients may reapply.

Additional data This program began in 2006.

Number awarded At least 1 each year.

Deadline June of each year.

[1280]
DEATH PENSION FOR SURVIVORS OF VETERANS

Department of Veterans Affairs
Attn: Veterans Benefits Administration
810 Vermont Avenue, N.W.
Washington, DC 20420
(202) 418-4343   Toll Free: (800) 827-1000
Web: www.vba.va.gov/bln/21/pension/spousepen.htm

Summary To provide pensions to disabled and other spouses and children of deceased veterans with wartime service.

Eligibility This program is open to surviving spouses and unmarried children of deceased veterans who were discharged under conditions other than dishonorable and who had at least 90 days of active military service, at least 1 day of which was during a period of war. Veterans who enlisted after September 7, 1980 generally had to have served at least 24 months or the full period for which they were called to active duty. The countable income of spouses and children must be below specified limits.

Financial data Currently, the maximum annual pension rate is $8,219 for a surviving spouse without dependent children or $10,759 for a surviving spouse with 1 dependent child. Other rates apply to surviving spouses in need of regular aid and attendance, surviving spouses permanently housebound without dependent children, and surviving children who are living alone.

Duration For surviving spouse: until remarriage. For surviving unmarried child: until the age of 18, or 23 if attending a VA-approved school. For surviving child with disability: as long as the condition exists or until marriage.

Number awarded Varies each year.

Deadline Applications may be submitted at any time.

[1281]
FALLEN PATRIOT FUND GRANTS

Fallen Patriot Fund
c/o Bank of America Private Bank
TX1-492-19-09
P.O. Box 832409
Dallas, TX 75283-2409
(214) 658-7125   Fax: (214) 696-6310
E-mail: info@fallenpatriotfund.org
Web: www.fallenpatriotfund.org

Summary To provide personal financial assistance to veterans disabled as a result of combat in Iraq and to spouses and children of military personnel injured or killed in action in Iraq.

Eligibility This program is open to 1) veterans who were wounded in combat in support of Operation Iraqi Free, have been medically discharged from military service, received a disability rating from the U.S. Department of Veterans Affairs of 75% or greater, and can demonstrate dire financial hardship; 2) spouses of military personnel injured or killed in action in support of Operation Iraqi Freedom who can demonstrate dire financial hardship; and 3) children under 18 years of age of military personnel injured or killed in action in support of Operation Iraqi Freedom. Applicants who are currently enrolled as full-time undergraduate or vocational school students must demonstrate that all funds will be used to meet basic living expenses, not educational expenses. Graduate students, spouses who have received SGLI life insurance benefits, parents of military personnel injured or killed in action in support of Operation Iraqi Freedom, children over 18 years of age, and children or spouses of deceased military personnel whose death was a result of suicide are all ineligible. All applicants must state the nature of their financial hardship and how the money will be spent if a grant is provided.

Financial data The maximum grant is $3,000.

Duration Each disabled veteran or surviving spouse is limited to a total of 3 separate grants.

Additional data This program was established by the Mark Cuban Foundation.

Number awarded Varies each year; since the program was established, it has awarded more than $4.8 million in grants.

Deadline Applications may be submitted at any time.

[1282]
FEDERAL INCOME TAX CREDIT FOR ADOPTION EXPENSES

Internal Revenue Service
1111 Constitution Avenue, N.W.
Washington, DC 20224
Toll Free: (800) TAX-FORM
Web: www.irs.gov

Summary To provide a credit against federal income taxes to people who adopt children, especially special needs children.

Eligibility This credit is available to people who, during the preceding year, adopted a U.S. citizen who was either a child under 18 years of age or a disabled person unable to care for himself or herself. Different rules apply for adopting a child classified as having special needs. To qualify as a special needs child, the state in which the adoptee resides must have determined that the child cannot or should not be returned to his or her parents' home and probably will not be adopted unless assistance is provided to the adoptive parents. Factors used by states to make that determination include: 1) the child's ethnic background and age; 2) whether the child is a member of a minority or sibling group; and 3) whether the child has a medical condition or a physical, mental, or emotional handicap. This credit is not available to taxpayers whose modified adjusted gross income is greater than $225,210.

Financial data Taxpayers may utilize qualified adoption expenses as a credit against their federal income taxes, to a maximum of $13,360. Taxpayers who adopt a special needs child are entitled to the full credit of $13,360, regardless of their actual adoption expenses. The amount of the credit is reduced for taxpayers whose modified adjusted gross income is greater than $185,210 but less than $225,210.

Duration This credit is available for each qualifying child who is adopted.

Number awarded Varies each year.

Deadline This credit is taken on the qualifying taxpayers' federal income tax return, which is due in April of each year.

[1283]
FEDERAL INCOME TAX DEDUCTION FOR CHILD AND DEPENDENT CARE EXPENSES

Internal Revenue Service
1111 Constitution Avenue, N.W.
Washington, DC 20224
Toll Free: (800) TAX-FORM
Web: www.irs.gov

Summary To provide a federal income tax credit for a portion of the expenses of caring for a child or disabled dependent.

Eligibility Eligible for this credit are U.S. citizens or residents who have earned income and who live with a qualifying dependent who is either 1) under the age of 13; 2) a spouse who is physically or mentally unable to care for himself or herself; or 3) another dependent who is physically or mentally unable to care for himself or herself and for whom the taxpayer can claim an exemption. Qualifying expenses include amounts paid for household services and care of the dependent while the taxpayer worked or looked for work.

Financial data A percentage of the qualifying expenses in excess of $3,000 for 1 dependent or $6,000 for 2 or more dependents is applied as a credit against taxes; the percentage depends on the adjusted gross income of the taxpayer, ranging from 35% for incomes less than $15,000 to 20% for incomes greater than $43,000. The maximum credit is $5,000 or $2,500 if married filing separately.

Duration 1 year; taxpayers must reapply each year.

Number awarded Varies each year.

Deadline This credit is applied to the qualifying tax filers' federal income tax return, which is due in April of each year.

[1284]
FIRST HAND FOUNDATION GRANTS

First Hand Foundation
Attn: Case Manager
2800 Rockcreek Parkway
Kansas City, MO 64117
(816) 201-1569   Fax: (816) 571-1569
E-mail: Firsthandfoundation@cerner.com
Web: applications.cerner.com/firsthand

Summary To provide financial assistance to the families of children who have specific health care needs.

Eligibility Any person (family member, friend, social worker, health provider) may submit an application on behalf of a child under 18 years of age who has a specific health care need not covered by other resources (insurance, state aid, charitable organization, or the child's family). Applicants must be seeking funding to assist the child's family with 1) treatment expenses associated with clinical procedures, medicine, therapy, or prostheses; 2) equipment expenses associated with wheelchairs, assistive technology equipment, hearing aids, or care devices; 3) displacement expenses associated with families of seriously ill children who must travel away from their home during treatment, such as food, lodging, gas, parking, and transportation; or 4) vehicle modifications for expenses associated with lifts, ramps, and transfer boards. Funding is not available for home modification projects; alternative or experimental drugs, treatment, or therapy where there is significant controversy in the medical community with respect to specific treatment; wheelchair accessible van purchases; nonprofit organizational grants; or debt reduction. Children must be under the care of a pediatrician and the grant request must be clinically relevant to the health of the child. Treatment and equipment grants are limited to families with incomes less than $20,000 for a family with multiple children or $25,000 for single-child families, dis-placement grants to those with incomes less than $45,000, and vehicle modification grants to those with incomes less than $35,000.

Financial data The grant depends on the need of the child's family. For treatment and equipment grants, grants are based on the number of dependent children in the family. Maximum displacement grants are $1,000 for families with incomes less than $19,000, $750 for families with incomes from $19,001 to $30,000, or $500 for families with incomes from $30,001 to $45,000. Maximum vehicle modification grants are $2,500 from families with incomes less than $25,000 or $1,250 for families with incomes from $25,000 to $35,000.

Duration These are 1-time grants.

Additional data This foundation was established in 1995 with support from Cerner Corporation, its associates, its business partners, and friends.

Number awarded Varies each year; since its establishment, the program has provided more than $16 million to assist 146,000 children in 76 countries around the world.

Deadline Applications may be submitted at any time.

[1285]
FLEETWOOD MEMORIAL FOUNDATION GRANTS

Fleetwood Memorial Foundation
501 South Fielder Road
Arlington, TX 76013
(817) 825-6699   Fax: (817) 542-0839
E-mail: fleetwood@fleetwoodmemorial.org
Web: www.fleetwoodmemorial.org/form.php

Summary To provide no-strings-attached grants to injured law enforcement or fire protection personnel in Texas or to the families of deceased or disabled personnel.

Eligibility Open to certified Texas law enforcement or fire protection personnel who have been injured in the performance of their duties or to the families of personnel who were killed or permanently disabled in the performance of their duties. For the purposes of this program, "line of duty" does not automatically mean "on duty;" for example, no injuries considered Section V or strains during normal exercise, automobile accidents while going to lunch, etc. are viewed as "line of duty" by this program.

Financial data These grants, of varying amounts, are designed to provide immediate financial relief to meet unexpected expenses until insurance or more permanent sources of funds can be arranged. Grants may be used to re-educate qualified personnel if they are unable to return to their normal duties after an accident. Educational funds are also available to the dependent children of deceased or disabled peace and fire personnel as long as they attend a public junior or senior college in Texas. Those funds are intended to provide support for housing and other needs not covered by funding from the Texas Higher Education Coordinating Board.

Duration These are 1-time grants.

Number awarded Since its inception in 1974, the foundation has provided more than 500 grants to qualified recipients, totaling nearly $2 million.

Deadline Applications may be submitted at any time.

[1286]
FLORIDA SERVICE-CONNECTED TOTAL AND PERMANENT DISABILITY PROPERTY TAX EXEMPTION

Florida Department of Revenue
Attn: Taxpayer Services
5050 West Tennessee Street
Tallahassee, FL 32399-0100
(850) 617-8600   Toll Free: (800) 352-3671
E-mail: EMailDOR@dor.state.fl.us
Web: www.myflorida.com

Summary To exempt from property taxation real estate owned by disabled veterans and their surviving spouses.

Eligibility This exemption is available to Florida residents who have real estate that they own and use as a homestead. Applicants must be honorably-discharged veterans who have a total and permanent disability or require a wheelchair for mobility as a result of their military service. Under certain circumstances, the benefit of this exemption can carry over to a surviving spouse.

Financial data All real estate used and owned as a homestead, less any portion used for commercial purposes, is exempt from taxation.

Duration The exemption applies as long as the taxpayer owns the property in Florida.

Additional data Initial applications should be made in person at the appropriate county property appraiser's office.

Number awarded Varies each year.

Deadline Applications must be submitted by February of the year for which the exemption is sought.

[1287]
GEORGIA HOMESTEAD TAX EXEMPTION FOR DISABLED VETERANS

Georgia Department of Revenue
Attn: Property Tax Division
4245 International Parkway, Suite A
Hapeville, GA 30354-3918
(404) 968-0707   Fax: (404) 968-0778
E-mail: Local.Government.Services@dor.ga.gov
Web: etax.dor.ga.gov

Summary To exempt from property taxation a portion of the value of homesteads owned by disabled veterans in Georgia and their families.

Eligibility This program is open to residents of Georgia who qualify as a 100% disabled veteran under any of several provisions of state law. Surviving spouses and minor children are also eligible. Applicants must actually occupy a homestead and use it as their legal residence for all purposes.

Financial data The first $50,000 of assessed valuation of the homestead owned by disabled veterans or their family members is exempt from property taxes for state, county, municipal, and school purposes.

Duration The exemption remains in effect as long as the veteran or family member owns and resides in the homestead.

Number awarded Varies each year.

Deadline Applications must be filed with local tax officials by February of each year.

[1288]
GRANTS FOR ACCESSIBILITY

Corporation for Independent Living
157 Charter Oak Avenue, Third Floor
Hartford, CT 06106
(860) 563-6011   Fax: (860) 563-2562
E-mail: access@cilhomes.org
Web: www.cilhomes.org/accessolutions.html

Summary To provide grants to low- or moderate-income residents of Connecticut who have a disability (as well as their parents) and need to modify their existing housing.

Eligibility Eligible to participate in this program are Connecticut residents who have a specified disability: people in wheelchairs, the deaf or hearing impaired, the blind or visually impaired, and people who have multiple sclerosis, cerebral palsy, traumatic brain injury, or any other physical disability). Applicants must own their homes and have a total household income at or below 80% of median income. Also eligible are homeowner parents of a child who is physically disabled and tenants who have the landlord's written consent to make accessibility renovations. Applicants must have total household income that is less than 80% of the state median. Grant funds may be used to purchase and install fixtures and improvements required to improve accessibility and/or usability of a residential dwelling in Connecticut.

Financial data Grants range from $5,000 to $50,000. Initially, a full lien is placed against the recipient's home. Total lien amounts are reduced automatically by 10% every year. At the end of 10 years, the grant is forgiven in full and the lien is removed.

Additional data Funding for this program, which began in 1984, is provided by the Connecticut Department of Economic and Community Development.

Number awarded Varies each year. Since the program began, more than 1,500 individuals have received grants.

Deadline Applications may be submitted at any time.

[1289]
GREYHOUND SERVICES FOR CUSTOMERS WITH DISABILITIES

Greyhound Lines, Inc.
Attn: ADA Compliance Office
P.O. Box 660362
Dallas, TX 75266-0362
Toll Free: (800) 752-4841   TDD: (800) 345-3109
Web: www.greyhound.com

Summary To underwrite the cost of companions or assistants who accompany persons with disabilities traveling on Greyhound buses.

Eligibility This program is available to any person with a disability who requires assistance with personal hygiene, eating, medications, or while the bus is in motion. Proof of disability is not required. The personal care attendant (PCA) must be at least 12 years of age and capable of providing the necessary assistance.

Financial data The PCA is entitled to purchase a ticket at a 50% discount.

Duration The benefits of this program continue as long as the person with a disability needs a companion for physical assistance in bus travel.

Additional data Greyhound carries all wheelchairs, including battery operated ones, and certain other aids and devices for travelers with disabilities as baggage without cost. It also provides priority boarding, assistance with connections, special terminal seating, and any other required assistance. Travelers with disabilities who wish to travel alone must make arrangements with Greyhound at least 48 hours in advance of departure for any special assistance they will require enroute. Requests for a PCA ticket must be made at least 24 hours prior to a customer's time of departure. The traveler with a disability and PCA must stay together the entire trip and the PCA must assist the disabled person enroute and in boarding and alighting.

Number awarded There is no limit; all eligible travelers are granted discounted fares for PCAs without additional cost.

Deadline Deadline not specified.

[1290]
HACA FAMILY ASSISTANCE PROGRAM

Hemophilia Association of the Capital Area
10560 Main Street, Suite 419
Fairfax, VA 22030-7182
(703) 352-7641   Fax: (540) 427-6589
E-mail: admin@hacacares.org
Web: www.hacacares.org

Summary To provide emergency financial aid to individuals with bleeding disorders and their families in the Washington, D.C. area.

Eligibility This program is open to 1) residents of northern Virginia, Montgomery and Prince George's County in Maryland, and Washington, D.C.; and 2) people who receive treatment for bleeding disorders at Children's National Medical Center or Georgetown University Hospital in Washington, D.C. Also eligible are parents and caregivers of people living in their home who have a bleeding disorder relevant to the mission of the Hemophilia Association of the Capital Area (HACA). Applicants must be able to demonstrate need for assistance for 1) uncovered medical bills associated with the diagnosis and treatment of a bleeding disorder and any complications from that; or 2) basic living expense emergencies.

Financial data The amount of the assistance depends on the need of the grantee.

Duration Assistance is provided only once per calendar year.

Number awarded Varies each year.

Deadline Applications may be submitted at any time.

[1291]
HAWAII CHILDREN'S CANCER FOUNDATION FAMILY ASSISTANCE PROGRAM

Hawaii Children's Cancer Foundation
1814 Liliha Street
Honolulu, HI 96817
(808) 528-5161   Toll Free: (866) 443-HCCF (within HI)
Fax: (808) 521-4689   E-mail: info@hccf.org
Web: www.hccf.org/family-support

Summary To provide funding to families in Hawaii who have a child with cancer.

Eligibility This program is open to families in Hawaii who need assistance for a child who has or had cancer that was diagnosed before the age of 25 years. Support is available for payment of treatment bills, travel to treatment, medical supplies, prescriptions and medications, or other costs related to cancer.

Financial data Grants up to $4,000 per family are available for the first year of treatment and up to $2,000 per family for subsequent years of treatment. Funds are provided only for costs not covered by health insurance or other assistance programs.

Duration Grants are provided on an annual basis as long as the need continues.

Additional data This foundation was established in 1991.

Number awarded Varies each year; recently, 85 families received approximately $250,000 from this program.

Deadline Deadline not specified.

[1292]
HAWAII PROPERTY TAX EXEMPTIONS FOR DISABLED VETERANS

Office of Veterans Services
Attn: Veterans Services Coordinator
459 Patterson Road
E-Wing, Room 1-A103
Honolulu, HI 96819-1522
(808) 433-0420   Fax: (808) 433-0385
E-mail: ovs@ovs.hawaii.gov
Web: hawaii.gov

Summary To exempt the homes of disabled veterans and surviving spouses in Hawaii from real estate taxation.

Eligibility This program is open to totally disabled veterans in Hawaii and their surviving spouses.

Financial data The real property owned and occupied as a home is exempt from taxation.

Duration The exemption applies as long as the disabled veteran or his/her widow(er) resides in Hawaii.

Deadline Deadline not specified.

[1293]
HEMOPHILIA FOUNDATION OF ILLINOIS FINANCIAL ASSISTANCE PROGRAM

Hemophilia Foundation of Illinois
Attn: Executive Director
210 South DesPlaines
Chicago, IL 60661-5500
(312) 427-1495   E-mail: brobinson@hfi-il.org
Web: www.hemophiliaillinois.org/services.htm

Summary To provide financial assistance for personal and other needs to residents of Illinois who have a bleeding disorder and their families.

Eligibility This program is open to residents of Illinois who have a bleeding disorder and their families. Applicants must have exhausted all other resources and still need funds to pay for housing or rent, utilities, funeral expenses, or other needs such as those caused by fire or flood. Along with their application, they must submit copies of supporting documents, such as rent bills, mortgage statements, actual utility bills, and proof of medical premium payments or funeral director bills.

Financial data The amount of the assistance depends on the need of the applicant and the availability of funds. This program is intended to provide funding of last resort.

Duration Each family may be awarded 1 grant within a 12-month period. They may apply for a renewal grant, but after a family has been granted assistance for a third year in a row, they are ineligible for funding the following year in all categories except funeral expense.

Number awarded Varies each year.

Deadline Applications may be submitted at any time.

[1294]
HOPE FOR THE WARRIORS IMMEDIATE NEEDS GRANTS

Hope for the Warriors
Attn: Immediate Needs
1335 Western Boulevard, Suite E
Jacksonville, NC 28546-5539
(910) 938-1817   Toll Free: (877) 246-7349
E-mail: imn@hopeforthewarriors.org
Web: www.hopeforthewarriors.org/immneeds.html

Summary To provide funding for immediate needs to disabled military personnel, veterans, and their families.

Eligibility This assistance is available to wounded service members and their families. Applicants must need assistance to meet such immediate needs as travel to bedside where the government does not provide assistance, rental cars, lodging, groceries, gas, furniture, child care, essentials of daily living (e.g., rent and utilities), or items that assist and/or supplement programs at military treatment facilities and Veterans Administration polytrauma units.

Financial data The amount of the grant depends on the need of the recipient. Payment is always made to a third party.

Duration Applicants may apply once a year.

Number awarded Varies each year.

Deadline Applications may be submitted at any time.

[1295]
IDAHO INCOME TAX EXEMPTION FOR MAINTAINING A HOME FOR THE DEVELOPMENTALLY DISABLED

Idaho State Tax Commission
Attn: Public Information Office
800 Park Boulevard, Plaza IV
P.O. Box 36
Boise, ID 83722-0410
(208) 334-7660   Toll Free: (800) 972-7660
TDD: (800) 377-3529
Web: tax.idaho.gov/i-1039.cfm

Summary To exempt from state taxation a portion of the income of residents of Idaho who maintain a home for a family member, including themselves and their spouses, who is developmentally disabled.

Eligibility Individuals in Idaho who maintain a household that includes a developmentally disabled person (of any age) are eligible for this program if they provide at least half of the support of the developmentally disabled family member. The taxpayer and spouse may be included as a member of the family. Developmental disability is defined as a chronic disability that 1) is attributable to an impairment such as mental retardation, cerebral palsy, epilepsy, autism, or related condition; 2) results in substantial functional limitation in 3 or more of the following areas of life activity: self-care, receptive and expressive language, learning, mobility, self-direction, capacity for independent living, or economic self-sufficiency; and 3) reflects the need for a combination and sequence of special, interdisciplinary or generic care, treatment, or other services that are of lifelong or extended duration and individually planned and coordinated.

Financial data The amount of the deduction is $1,000 for each developmentally disabled family member, up to a maximum of $3,000.

Duration Application for the deduction must be submitted each year.

Additional data This deduction also applies to taxpayers maintaining a home for a family member who is 65 years of age or older. Taxpayers who do not claim the $1,000 deduction may be able to claim a tax credit of $100 for each member of the family who is developmentally disabled or elderly, to a maximum of 3 members.

Number awarded Varies each year.

Deadline April of each year.

[1296]
IDAHO RETIREMENT BENEFITS DEDUCTION

Idaho State Tax Commission
Attn: Public Information Office
800 Park Boulevard, Plaza IV
P.O. Box 36
Boise, ID 83722-0410
(208) 334-7660   Toll Free: (800) 972-7660
TDD: (800) 377-3529
Web: tax.idaho.gov/i-1039.cfm

Summary To deduct the retirement and disability income of certain residents from state income tax in Idaho.

Eligibility Eligible for this deduction are full-year residents of Idaho who are age 65 or older, or disabled and age 62 and older, and who are receiving the following annuities and benefits: 1) retirement annuities paid by the United States to a retired civil service employee or the unremarried widow of the employee; 2) retirement benefits paid from the firemen's retirement fund of the state of Idaho to a retired fireman or the unremarried widow of a retired fireman; 3) retirement benefits paid from the policeman's retirement fund of a city within Idaho to a retired policeman or the unremarried widow of a retired policeman; or 4) retirement benefits paid by the United States to a retired member of the U.S. military service or the unremarried widow of those veterans.

Financial data The amount of retirement or disability benefits may be deducted from taxable state income in Idaho, to a maximum deduction of $41,814 for married couples or $27,876 for single persons.

Duration 1 year; must reapply each year.

Number awarded Varies each year.

Deadline April of each year.

[1297]
IDAHO WAR VETERAN'S EMERGENCY GRANT PROGRAM

Idaho Division of Veterans Services
Attn: Office of Veterans Advocacy
444 Fort Street
Boise, ID 83702
(208) 577-2300   Fax: (208) 577-2333
E-mail: info@veterans.idaho.gov
Web: www.veterans.idaho.gov/Veterans_Advocacy.aspx

Summary To provide emergency assistance to disabled veterans, wartime veterans, and their families in Idaho.

Eligibility Eligible for these grants are veterans who had at least 90 days of honorable wartime military service and entered the military from Idaho or lived within the state for at least 5 years. Veterans with a service-connected disability are eligible with earlier separation. Surviving spouses and dependent children are also eligible. Applicants must be current residents of Idaho in need of assistance because of a major catastrophe (e.g., natural disaster or death of a spouse or child), loss of job because of a disability, or other extreme financial emergency (e.g., cut-off notice from a utility company, eviction notice from a landlord, arrears payment notice from the lien holder of a home).

Financial data The maximum amount available under this program is $1,000, issued in small incremental grants.

Duration The limit of $1,000 applies for the lifetime of each veteran or his/her family.

Additional data This program was established by the Idaho legislature in lieu of granting a wartime bonus to Idaho veterans.

Number awarded Varies each year.

Deadline Deadline not specified.

[1298]
ILLINOIS DISABLED VETERANS' HOMESTEAD EXEMPTION

Illinois Department of Revenue
101 West Jefferson Street
P.O. Box 19044
Springfield, IL 62794-9044
(217) 782-3336   Toll Free: (800) 732-8866
TDD: (800) 544-5304
Web: www.revenue.state.il.us

Summary To exempt a portion of the value of specially adapted housing owned by disabled veterans and their spouses in Illinois for purposes of property taxation.

Eligibility This exemption applies to housing owned and used by disabled veterans and their unmarried surviving spouses. The housing must have been purchased or constructed with funds provided by the U.S. Department of Veterans Affairs (VA) as part of a program of specially adapted housing for disabled veterans. The exemption is also available to disabled veterans and spouses who live in mobile homes. They may not utilize this exemption and either the Disabled Persons' Homestead Exemption or the Disabled Veterans Standard Homestead Exemption.

Financial data The exemption provides a reduction of $70,000 in the assessed value of the homestead.

Duration Veterans must file an annual application to continue to receive this exemption.

Deadline Deadline not specified.

[1299]
INDIANA PROPERTY TAX DEDUCTIONS FOR DISABLED VETERANS

Department of Local Government Finance
Indiana Government Center North, Room N1058(B)
100 North Senate Avenue
Indianapolis, IN 46201
(317) 232-3777   Fax: (317) 232-8779
E-mail: PropertyTaxInfo@dlgf.in.gov
Web: www.in.gov/dlgf

Summary To exempt disabled Indiana veterans and their spouses from a portion of their property taxes.

Eligibility This program is open to the following categories of veterans who are residents of Indiana: 1) served honorably at least 90 days and are either totally disabled (the disability does not need to be service connected) or are at least 62 years of age and have at least a 10% service-connected disability; 2) served honorably during war time and have at least a 10% service-connected disability; or 3) served honorably during war time and either have a 100% service-connected disability or are at least 62 years of age and have at least a 10% service-connected disability. A statutory disability rating for pulmonary tuberculosis does not qualify. A disability incurred during Initial Active Duty for Training (IADT) with the National Guard or Reserves is eligible only if the disability occurred from an event during the period of active duty and that duty was performed during wartime. Surviving spouses of those 3 categories of veterans are also eligible.

Financial data Property tax exemptions are $12,480 for veterans and spouses in the first category (only if the assessed value of the combined real and personal property owned by the veteran or spouse does not exceed $143,160), $24,960 in the second category, or $37,440 in the third category; there is no limit on the value of the property owned by a surviving spouse).

Duration 1 year; may be renewed as long as the eligible veteran or surviving unremarried spouse owns and occupies the primary residence in Indiana.

Number awarded Varies each year.

Deadline Applications must be submitted no later than May of each year.

[1300]
INJURED MARINE SEMPER FI GRANTS

Injured Marine Semper Fi Fund
c/o Wounded Warrior Center
Building H49
P.O. Box 555193
Camp Pendleton, CA 92055-5193
(760) 725-3680   Fax: (760) 725-3685
E-mail: info@semperfifund.org
Web: semperfifund.org/assistance

Summary To provide supplemental assistance to Marines injured in combat and their families.

Eligibility This program is open to Marines injured in post-9/11 combat operations or facing a life-threatening illness and their families. Members of the Army, Air Force, Coast Guard, and Navy who served in support of Marine forces are also eligible. Applicants must need financial assistance to deal with such needs as family support (e.g., travel and lodging, costs of hospitalization and rehabilitation, mortgages, car payments, utilities, grocery bills), adaptive housing support, adaptive transportation, or specialized and adaptive equipment.

Financial data Funds are available for such expenses as child care, travel expenses for families, and other necessities. Assistance is also available for the purchase of adaptive transportation, home modifications, and specialized equipment such as wheelchairs, audio/visual equipment for the blind, and software for traumatic brain injuries.

Duration Grants are provided as needed.

Additional data This fund was established in 2004 by a small group of Marine Corps spouses.

Number awarded Varies each year. Since this program was established, it has awarded more than 38,000 grants worth more than $57 million.

Deadline Applications may be submitted at any time.

[1301]
IOWA INCOME TAX DEDUCTION OF EXPENSES INCURRED FOR CARE OF A DISABLED RELATIVE

Iowa Department of Revenue
Attn: Taxpayer Services
Hoover State Office Building
1305 East Walnut
P.O. Box 10457
Des Moines, IA 50306-0457
(515) 281-3114   Toll Free: (800) 367-3388 (within IA)
Fax: (515) 242-6487   E-mail: idr@iowa.gov
Web: www.iowa.gov/tax

Summary To deduct the cost of caring for a disabled relative from taxable income of Iowa residents.

Eligibility This deduction applies to the expenses incurred in caring for a disabled relative in the home of an Iowa resident. The expenses must be for the care of a grandchild, child, parent, or grandparent. The disabled person must be unable, by reason of physical or mental disability, to live independently and must be receiving or be eligible to receive medical assistance benefits through Social Security. Only expenses that are not reimbursed can be claimed. An itemized list of expenses must be included with the income tax return.

Financial data Expenses up to $5,000 per year may be deducted from the taxable income of a qualifying resident.

Duration The deduction continues as long as the recipient remains a resident of Iowa for state income tax purposes and incurs expenses to care for a disabled relative.

Number awarded Varies each year.

Deadline Deadline not specified.

[1302]
IOWA PENSION/RETIREMENT INCOME EXCLUSION

Iowa Department of Revenue
Attn: Taxpayer Services
Hoover State Office Building
1305 East Walnut
P.O. Box 10457
Des Moines, IA 50306-0457
(515) 281-3114   Toll Free: (800) 367-3388 (within IA)
Fax: (515) 242-6487   E-mail: idr@iowa.gov
Web: www.iowa.gov/tax

Summary To exempt a portion of the income received by disabled and other retirees in Iowa, as well as their surviving spouses, from state taxation.

Eligibility This exemption applies to the retirement income of residents of Iowa who are 1) 55 years of age or older, 2) disabled, or 3) a surviving spouse or a survivor having an insurable interest in an individual who would have qualified from the exclusion on the basis of age or disability.

Financial data For joint filers, the exclusion is the lesser of $12,000 or the taxable amount of the retirement income; for all other statuses of filers, each eligible taxpayer can claim as an exemption the lesser of $6,000 or the taxable amount of the retirement income.

Duration The exemption continues as long as the recipient remains a resident of Iowa for state income tax purposes.

Number awarded Varies each year.

Deadline Deadline not specified.

[1303]
JACK NORTON FAMILY RESPITE CARE PROGRAM

ALS Association-MN/ND/SD Chapter
Attn: Patient Services Coordinator
333 North Washington Avenue, Suite 105
Minneapolis, MN 55401
(612) 672-0484   Toll Free: (888) 672-0484
Fax: (612) 672-9110   E-mail: anne@alsmn.org
Web: webmn.alsa.org

Summary To provide funding for respite care to residents of the upper Midwest who are a Person with Amyotrophic Lateral Sclerosis (PALS) or family member.

Eligibility This assistance is available to any PALS or family member living in Minnesota, North Dakota, eastern South Dakota, or Superior, Wisconsin. The family caregiver must be living with and caring for a PALS on a full-time basis.

Financial data The program provides funding to pay for a family caregiver to assist in caring for the PALS.

Duration Funding is provided for 18 hours a month.

Additional data The Minnesota Chapter of the ALS Association arranges with an appropriate licensed home care agency to provide the respite care.

Number awarded Varies each year.

Deadline Applications may be submitted at any time.

[1304]
KANSAS DISABLED ACCESS INCOME TAX CREDIT

Kansas Department of Revenue
Attn: Taxpayer Assistance Center
Robert B. Docking State Office Building
915 S.W. Harrison Street
Topeka, KS 66612-1712
(785) 368-8222   Toll Free: (877) 526-7738
Fax: (785) 291-3614   TDD: (785) 296-6461
Web: www.ksrevenue.org/taxcredits-disabled.htm

Summary To provide an income tax credit to individual and business taxpayers in Kansas who incur certain expenditures to make their property accessible to people with disabilities.

Eligibility This credit is available to state income taxpayers in Kansas who make buildings or facilities accessible and usable by persons with disabilities in conformity with the Americans with Disabilities Act of 1990. The credit applies to the taxpayer's principal dwelling or the principal dwelling of a lineal ascendant or descendant, including construction of a small barrier-free living unit attached to the principal dwelling. The only expenditures that qualify for this credit are those that are specifically intended to 1) make an existing facility accessible to people with disabilities; 2) remove existing architectural barri-

ers; or 3) modify or adapt an existing facility or piece of equipment in order to employ people with disabilities.

Financial data For individuals, the amount of the credit depends on adjusted gross income and the amount of the expenditure, ranging from 100% of the expenditure for incomes less than $25,000, to 50% for incomes greater than $45,000 but less than $55,000; persons with incomes greater than $55,000 do not qualify for the credit; the maximum individual credit is $9,000. For businesses, the credit is 50% of the amount of the expenditure, to a maximum of $10,000.

Duration This is a 1-time credit.

Number awarded Varies each year.

Deadline Claims are filed with the state income tax return, due in April.

[1305]
LIVING BREATH FOUNDATION FINANCIAL AID GRANTS

Living Breath Foundation
2031 Marsala Circle
Monterey, CA 93940
(831) 392-5285
E-mail: LivingBreathFoundation@gmail.com
Web: thelivingbreathfoundation.com/aid.html

Summary To provide funding to individuals who have cystic fibrosis and their families for assistance with expenses related to the disease.

Eligibility This program is open to U.S. residents who have cystic fibrosis and members of their families. Applicants must document a need for assistance in payment of bills from hospitals, doctors, or pharmacies; rent or utility bills; hotel expenses incurred while a child or spouse is in the hospital; or unreimbursed medical equipment. They must submit a 1- to 2-paragraph statement explaining why they need financial assistance at this time and how the foundation can provide that.

Financial data Grants depend on the recipient's needs.

Duration These are 1-time grants.

Additional data This foundation started in 2008.

Number awarded Varies each year.

Deadline Applications may be submitted at any time.

[1306]
LONGSHORE AND HARBOR WORKERS' COMPENSATION PROGRAM

Department of Labor
Employment Standards Administration
Office of Workers' Compensation Programs
Attn: Division of Longshore and Harbor Workers'
    Compensation
200 Constitution Avenue, N.W., Room C4315
Washington, DC 20210
(202) 693-0038   Toll Free: (800) 638-7072
Fax: (202) 693-1380   TDD: (800) 326-2577
Web: www.dol.gov/dol/topic/workcomp/index.htm

Summary To provide benefits to maritime workers disabled or killed during the course of employment and to their spouses.

Eligibility This program is open to longshoremen, harbor workers, and other maritime workers who are injured during the course of employment; by extension, various other classes of private industry workers (including workers engaged in the extraction of natural resources on the outer continental shelf, employees of defense contractors overseas, and employees at post exchanges on military bases) are also eligible if they become disabled for work-related causes. In addition, survivor benefits are provided if the work-related injury causes the employee's death.

Financial data The compensation for disability is 66 2/3% of the employee's average weekly wage, with a minimum of 50% of the national average weekly wage (NAWW) and a maximum of 200% of the NAWW. In a recent year, the Department of Labor calculated the NAWW as $647.60, so the minimum weekly disability payment was $323.80 and the maximum was $1,295.20. Death benefits are equivalent to the average weekly wage of the deceased employee, with a minimum equivalent to 100% of the NAWW and a maximum equivalent to 200% of the NAWW.

Duration Benefits are paid as long as the worker remains disabled; death benefits are paid for the life of the qualified survivor.

Additional data This program also provides medical benefits and rehabilitation services to qualifying longshoremen, harbor workers, and other workers.

Number awarded Varies; more than 15,000 maritime workers recently received compensation and medical benefits through this program.

Deadline Deadline not specified.

[1307]
LUNG TRANSPLANT GRANT PROGRAM

Boomer Esiason Foundation
c/o Jerry Cahill
483 Tenth Avenue, Suite 300
New York, NY 10018
(646) 292-7930   Fax: (646) 292-7945
E-mail: jcahill@esiason.org
Web: esiason.org/thriving-with-cf/transplant-grants.php

Summary To provide funding for travel and relocation costs during lung transplants to families of patients who have cystic fibrosis (CF).

Eligibility This program is open to families of CF patients who have lung transplants. Applicants must need funds to pay for expenses not covered by their insurance, including, but not limited to, 1) patient and family transportation costs for evaluation, surgery, and post-transplant clinic visits; and 2) housing, food, and living expenses associated with relocation to the transplant site. Along with their application, they must provide a letter from a social worker verifying that the patient has CF and needs assistance and a detailed cost breakdown specifying how the requested funds will be allocated.

Financial data Grants cover qualified expenses.

Duration These are 1-time grants.

Number awarded Varies each year. Recently, more than $100,000 in grants were awarded.

Deadline Applications may be submitted at any time.

[1308]
MAINE PROPERTY TAX EXEMPTIONS FOR VETERANS

Maine Revenue Services
Attn: Property Tax Division
P.O. Box 9106
Augusta, ME 04332-9106
(207) 287-2013   Fax: (207) 287-6396
E-mail: prop.tax@maine.gov
Web: www.maine.gov

Summary To exempt the estates of disabled Maine veterans and selected family members from property taxation.

Eligibility Eligible for this program are veterans who served during World War I, World War II, the Korean campaign, the Vietnam war, the Persian Gulf war, or other recognized service periods, are legal residents of Maine, and are either older than 62 years of age or are receiving a pension or compensation from the U.S. government for total disability (whether service connected or not). Vietnam veterans must have served 180 days on active duty unless discharged earlier for a service-connected disability. The exemption also includes 1) property held in joint tenancy with the veterans' spouses, and 2) property of unremarried widow(er)s, minor children, and parents of deceased veterans, if those dependents are receiving a pension or compensation from the U.S. government.

Financial data Estates of disabled veterans and eligible dependents, including both real and personal property, are exempt up to $6,000 of just valuation. For veterans and dependents who served in war time prior to World War II, estates up to $7,000 are exempt.

Duration Veterans, spouses, unremarried widow(er)s, and mothers are eligible for this exemption throughout their lifetimes; minor children of veterans are eligible until they reach the age of 18.

Number awarded Varies each year.

Deadline When an eligible person first submits an application, the proof of entitlement must reach the assessors of the local municipality prior to the end of March. Once eligibility has been established, notification need not be repeated in subsequent years.

[1309]
MAINE TAX EXEMPTION FOR SPECIALLY ADAPTED HOUSING UNITS

Maine Revenue Services
Attn: Property Tax Division
P.O. Box 9106
Augusta, ME 04332-9106
(207) 287-2013   Fax: (207) 287-6396
E-mail: prop.tax@maine.gov
Web: www.maine.gov

Summary To exempt the specially adapted housing units of paraplegic veterans or their surviving spouses from taxation in Maine.

Eligibility Veterans who served in the U.S. armed forces during any federally-recognized war period, are legal residents of Maine, are paraplegic veterans within the meaning of U.S. statutes, and have received a grant from the U.S. government for specially adapted housing are eligible. The exemption also applies to property held in joint tenancy with the veteran's spouse and to the specially adapted housing of unremarried widow(er)s of eligible veterans.

Financial data Estates of paraplegic veterans are exempt up to $50,000 of just valuation for a specially adapted housing unit.

Duration The exemption is valid for the lifetime of the paraplegic veteran or unremarried widow(er).

Number awarded Varies each year.

Deadline When an eligible person first submits an application, the proof of entitlement must reach the assessors of the local municipality prior to the end of March. Once eligibility has been established, notification need not be repeated in subsequent years.

[1310]
MARYLAND INCOME TAX ADJUSTMENTS FOR ADOPTING SPECIAL NEEDS CHILDREN

Comptroller of Maryland
Attn: Revenue Administration Division
80 Calvert Street
Annapolis, MD 21411
(410) 260-7980
Toll Free: (800) MD-TAXES (within MD)
Fax: (410) 974-3456   TDD: (410) 260-7157
E-mail: taxhelp@comp.state.md.us
Web: individuals.marylandtaxes.com

Summary To reduce the reportable taxable income of Maryland residents who adopt special needs (particularly disabled) children.

Eligibility Residents of Maryland who adopt disabled and other special needs children through a public or non-profit adoption agency are eligible for this program.

Financial data Eligible parents are permitted to reduce their reportable taxable income to cover the amount expended for filing fees, attorney's fees, and travel costs incurred in connection with the adoption of a qualifying child, up to a maximum of $6,000 (up to $5,000 for parents who adopt a child without special needs).

Duration This is a 1-time deduction.

Deadline Deadline not specified.

[1311]
MARYLAND PENSION EXCLUSION FOR DISABLED AND ELDERLY RESIDENTS

Comptroller of Maryland
Attn: Revenue Administration Division
80 Calvert Street
Annapolis, MD 21411
(410) 260-7980
Toll Free: (800) MD-TAXES (within MD)
Fax: (410) 974-3456   TDD: (410) 260-7157
E-mail: taxhelp@comp.state.md.us
Web: individuals.marylandtaxes.com

Summary To exempt a portion of the income of disabled and elderly residents (and selected spouses) from state income taxation in Maryland.

Eligibility Eligible are Maryland residents who receive income from a pension, annuity, or endowment from an employee retirement system and who are at least 65 years of age or classified as totally disabled; spouses of disabled persons also qualify. The disability must be a mental or physical impairment that prevents the person from engaging in gainful activity and that is expected to be of long, continuing, or indefinite duration (or to result in death).

Financial data Persons with disabilities, who have a spouse who is totally disabled, or who are 65 years of age or older may exclude from state taxation up to $26,300 of income received as a pension, annuity, or endowment.

Duration The exemption continues as long as the recipient resides in Maryland.

Deadline Deadline not specified.

[1312]
MARYLAND PROPERTY TAX EXEMPTION FOR BLIND PERSONS

Maryland Department of Assessments and Taxation
Attn: Property Taxes
301 West Preston Street
Baltimore, MD 21201-2395
(410) 767-1184   Toll Free: (888) 246-5941
TDD: (800) 735-2258
Web: www.dat.state.md.us/sdatweb/exempt.html

Summary To exempt the homes of blind people and their surviving spouses from property taxation in Maryland.

Eligibility This exemption is available to residents of Maryland who have a central visual acuity of 20/200 or less in the better eye. Applicants must own a dwelling house in Maryland. Surviving spouses of deceased blind people are also eligible for the exemption.

Financial data The dwelling houses of eligible blind people and their surviving spouses is exempt from $15,000 of assessment on their dwelling house for purposes of real property taxes.

Duration The exemption is available as long as the blind person or surviving spouse owns the dwelling house in Maryland.

Number awarded Varies each year.

Deadline Applications may be submitted at any time.

[1313]
MARYLAND PROPERTY TAX EXEMPTION FOR DISABLED VETERANS AND SURVIVING SPOUSES

Maryland Department of Assessments and Taxation
Attn: Property Taxes
301 West Preston Street
Baltimore, MD 21201-2395
(410) 767-1184   Toll Free: (888) 246-5941
TDD: (800) 735-2258
Web: www.dat.state.md.us/sdatweb/exempt.html

Summary To exempt the homes of disabled veterans and their surviving spouses from property taxation in Maryland.

Eligibility This exemption is available to armed services veterans with a permanent service-connected disability rated 100% by the U.S. Department of Veterans Affairs who own a dwelling house in Maryland. Unremarried surviving spouses are also eligible.

Financial data The dwelling houses of eligible veterans and surviving spouses are exempt from real property taxes.

Duration The exemption is available as long as the veteran or surviving spouse owns the dwelling house in Maryland.

Number awarded Varies each year.

Deadline Applications may be submitted at any time.

[1314]
MASSACHUSETTS INCOME TAX DEDUCTION FOR CARE OF ELDERLY DEPENDENTS WITH DISABILITIES

Massachusetts Department of Revenue
Attn: Personal Income Tax
P.O. Box 7010
Boston, MA 02204
(617) 887-MDOR
Toll Free: (800) 392-6089 (within MA)
Fax: (617) 887-1900
Web: www.mass.gov

Summary To provide a deduction for the care of elderly dependents from state income taxation in Massachusetts.

Eligibility Eligible for this deduction are residents of Massachusetts who can document expenses for the care of a dependent over 65 years of age who has a disability. The disabled person may not be the resident or the spouse. Married taxpayers filing separately are not eligible for this deduction.

Financial data Up to $3,600 for the care of 1 person or up to $7,200 for the care of 2 or more persons may be deducted from income for state taxation purposes.

Duration The benefit continues as long as the taxpayer provides for the care of a dependent with a disability.

Number awarded Varies each year.

Deadline Deadline not specified.

[1315]
MASSACHUSETTS INCOME TAX DEDUCTION FOR EMPLOYMENT-RELATED CARE OF FAMILY MEMBERS WITH DISABILITIES

Massachusetts Department of Revenue
Attn: Personal Income Tax
P.O. Box 7010
Boston, MA 02204
(617) 887-MDOR
Toll Free: (800) 392-6089 (within MA)
Fax: (617) 887-1900
Web: www.mass.gov

Summary To exempt employment-related expenses for the care of disabled children and spouses from state income taxation in Massachusetts.

Eligibility Eligible for this deduction are residents of Massachusetts who can document employment-related expenses for the care of a child or spouse with a disability. Married taxpayers filing separately are not eligible for this deduction.

Financial data Up to $4,800 for the care of 1 person or up to $9,600 for the care of 2 or more persons may be deducted from income for state taxation purposes.

Duration The benefit continues as long as the taxpayer provides for the care of a child or spouse with a disability.

Number awarded Varies each year.

Deadline Deadline not specified.

[1316]
MASSACHUSETTS PROPERTY TAX EXEMPTION FOR VETERANS AND THEIR FAMILIES

Massachusetts Department of Revenue
Attn: Division of Local Services
100 Cambridge Street
Boston, MA 02114
(617) 626-2386   Fax: (617) 626-2330
Web: www.mass.gov/dor/all-taxes/excise-and-property

Summary To provide a property tax exemption to blind, disabled, and other veterans (and their families) in Massachusetts.

Eligibility This program is open to veterans who are residents of Massachusetts, were residents for at least 6 months prior to entering the service, have been residents for at least 5 consecutive years, and are occupying property as their domicile. Applicants must have an ownership interest in the domicile that ranges from $2,000 to $10,000, depending on the category of exemption. Veterans must have been discharged under conditions other than dishonorable. Several categories of veterans and their families qualify: 1) veterans who have a service-connected disability rating of 10% or more; veterans who have been awarded the Purple Heart; Gold Star mothers and fathers; and surviving spouses of eligible veterans who do not remarry; 2) veterans who suffered, in the line of duty, the loss or permanent loss of use of 1 foot, 1 hand, or 1 eye; veterans who received the Congressional Medal of Honor, Distinguished Service Cross, Navy Cross, or Air Force Cross; and their spouses or surviving spouses; 3) veterans who suffered, in the line of duty, the loss or permanent loss of use of both feet, both hands, or both eyes; and their spouses or surviving spouses; 4) veterans who suffered total disability in the line of duty and received assistance in acquiring specially adapted housing, which they own and occupy as their domicile; and their spouses or surviving spouses; 5) unremarried surviving spouses of military personnel who died due to injury or disease from being in a combat zone, or are missing and presumed dead due to combat; 6) veterans who suffered total disability in the line of duty and are incapable of working; and their spouses or surviving spouses; and 7) veterans who are certified by the Veterans Administration as paraplegic and their surviving spouses.

Financial data   Qualified veterans and family members are entitled to an annual exemption from their taxes for the different categories: 1), $400; 2), $750; 3), $1,250; 4), $1,500; 5), total exemption for 5 years after death, and up to $2,500 after 5 years; 6), $1,000; or 7), total.

Duration   The exemptions are provided each year that the veteran or unremarried surviving spouse lives in Massachusetts and owns the property as a domicile.

Additional data   Applications are available from local assessor's offices.

Number awarded   Varies each year.

Deadline   Applications must be filed with the local assessor by December of each year.

[1317]
MICHIGAN HOMESTEAD PROPERTY TAX CREDIT FOR VETERANS AND BLIND PEOPLE

Michigan Department of Treasury
Attn: Homestead Exemption
Treasury Building
430 West Allegan Street
Lansing, MI 48922
(517) 636-4486   TDD: (800) 649-3777
E-mail: treasIndTax@michigan.gov
Web: www.michigan.gov/taxes

Summary   To provide an income tax credit to disabled and other veterans, military personnel, their spouses, blind people, and their surviving spouses in Michigan.

Eligibility   Eligible to apply are residents of Michigan who are 1) blind and own their homestead; 2) a veteran with a service-connected disability or his/her surviving spouse; 3) a surviving spouse of a veteran deceased in service; 4) a pensioned veteran, a surviving spouse of those veterans, or an active military member, all of whose household income is less than $7,500; or 5) a surviving spouse of a non-disabled or non-pensioned veteran of the Korean War, World War II, or World War I whose household income is less than $7,500. All applicants must own or rent a home in Michigan, have been a Michigan resident for at least 6 months during the year in which application is made, and fall within qualifying income levels (up to $82,650 in household income).

Financial data   The maximum credit, applied to state income taxes, is $1,200. The exact amount varies. For homeowners, the credit depends on the state equalized value of the homestead and on an allowance for filing category. For renters, 20% of the rent is considered property tax eligible for credit.

Duration   1 year; eligibility must be established each year.

Number awarded   Varies each year.

Deadline   April of each year.

[1318]
MICHIGAN HOMESTEAD PROPERTY TAX EXEMPTION FOR SPECIALLY ADAPTED HOUSING

Michigan Department of Treasury
Attn: Homestead Exemption
Treasury Building
430 West Allegan Street
Lansing, MI 48922
(517) 373-3200   TDD: (800) 649-3777
E-mail: treasPtd2@michigan.gov
Web: www.michigan.gov/taxes

Summary   To exempt specially adapted housing occupied as homesteads by disabled veterans and their unremarried spouses from property taxation in Michigan.

Eligibility   This exemption is available to Michigan residents who are disabled veterans living in specially adapted housing that they acquired with financial assistance from the U.S. Department of Veterans Affairs (VA). If the veteran has died, the exemption continues for the unremarried surviving spouse.

Financial data   All taxes on qualified housing are cancelled.

Duration   This exemption continues as long as the disabled veteran or unremarried surviving spouse owns the property in Michigan and, in the case of surviving spouses, remains unmarried.

Number awarded   Varies each year.

Deadline   Deadline not specified.

[1319]
MICHIGAN VETERANS TRUST FUND EMERGENCY GRANTS

Department of Military and Veterans Affairs
Attn: Michigan Veterans Trust Fund
2500 South Washington Avenue
Lansing, MI 48913-5101
(517) 373-3130   E-mail: dutchera@michigan.gov
Web: www.michigan.gov

Summary   To provide temporary financial assistance to disabled and other Michigan veterans and their families who are facing personal emergencies.

Eligibility   Eligible for this assistance are veterans and their families residing in Michigan who are temporarily unable to provide the basic necessities of life. Support is not provided for long-term problems or chronic financial difficulties. The qualifying veteran must have been discharged under honorable conditions with at least 180 days of active wartime service or have been separated as a result of a physical or mental disability incurred in the line of duty.

Financial data No statutory limit exists on the amount of assistance that may be provided; a local board in each Michigan county determines if the applicant is genuinely needy and the amount of assistance to be awarded.

Duration This assistance is provided to meet temporary needs only.

Number awarded Varies each year.

Deadline Applications may be submitted at any time.

[1320]
MINNESOTA MARKET VALUE EXCLUSION FOR DISABLED VETERANS

Minnesota Department of Revenue
Attn: Property Tax Division
600 North Robert Street
Mail Station 3340
St. Paul, MN 55146-3340
(651) 556-6087
Web: www.taxes.state.mn.us

Summary To exclude from property taxation a portion of the value of homesteads owned by disabled veterans, family caregivers, and surviving spouses in Minnesota.

Eligibility This exclusion is available to owners of homesteads in Minnesota who are veterans who have a service-connected disability rated at least at 70% by the U.S. Department of Veterans Affairs. If a disabled veteran has died (or was killed in action without becoming disabled), the surviving spouse is eligible for the exclusion. If a veteran meets the disability qualification but does not own homestead property, the homestead of the veteran's primary family caregiver, if any, is eligible for the exclusion for that veteran.

Financial data For veterans with a service-connected of 70% or more (and their surviving spouses or primary family caregivers), $150,000 of the market value of the homestead is excluded from property taxation. For veterans with a total (100%) and permanent service-connected disability (and their surviving spouses or primary family caregivers), $300,000 of the market value of the homestead is excluded from property taxation.

Duration This exclusion is available as long as the veteran, surviving spouse, or primary family caregiver owns the homestead and meets the eligibility requirements.

Additional data This exclusion was established by the Minnesota legislature for veterans in 2008 and expanded to included surviving spouses and primary family caregivers in 2011.

Deadline Applications must be submitted by June of each year.

[1321]
MINNESOTA STATE SOLDIERS ASSISTANCE PROGRAM

Minnesota Department of Veterans Affairs
Veterans Service Building
20 West 12th Street, Room 206C
St. Paul, MN 55155-2006
(651) 757-1556   Toll Free: (888) LINK-VET
Fax: (651) 296-3954
E-mail: kathy.schwartz@state.mn.us
Web: www.mdva.state.mn.us/SSAP/index.htm

Summary To provide emergency financial assistance to disabled veterans and their families in Minnesota.

Eligibility This assistance is available to veterans who are unable to work because of a temporary disability (from service-connected or other causes). Their dependents and survivors are also eligible. Applicants must also meet income and asset guidelines and be residents of Minnesota.

Financial data The maximum grant is $1,500. Funds may be used to pay for food and shelter, utility bills, and emergency medical treatment (including optical and dental benefits).

Duration This is a short-term program, with benefits payable up to 6 months only. If the veteran's disability is expected to be long term in nature or permanent, the department may continue to provide assistance while application is made for long-term benefits, such as Social Security disability or retirement benefits.

Number awarded Varies each year. A total of $1.4 million is available for this program annually.

Deadline Applications may be submitted at any time.

[1322]
MISSISSIPPI INCOME TAX EXEMPTION FOR THE BLIND

Mississippi Department of Revenue
Attn: Individual Income Tax Division
P.O. Box 1033
Jackson, MS 39215-1033
(601) 923-7089   Fax: (601) 923-7039
Web: www.dor.ms.gov/taxareas/individ/main.htm

Summary To exempt a portion of the income of blind people and their spouses from state income tax liability in Mississippi.

Eligibility Eligible for this exemption are residents of Mississippi who have been declared legally blind and their spouses.

Financial data The exemption is $1,500.

Duration The exemption continues as long as the blind person resides in Mississippi.

Number awarded Varies each year.

Deadline The exemption must be requested on the resident's state income tax return, which is due in April.

[1323]
MISSOURI SENIOR CITIZEN, DISABLED VETERAN, AND DISABLED PERSON PROPERTY TAX CREDIT CLAIM

Missouri Department of Revenue
Attn: Taxation Division
301 West High Street, Room 330
P.O. Box 2800
Jefferson City, MO 65105-2800
(573) 751-3505   Toll Free: (800) 877-6881
Fax: (573) 751-2195   TDD: (800) 735-2966
E-mail: PropertyTaxCredit@dor.mo.gov
Web: dor.mo.gov/personal

Summary To provide a property tax credit to low-income disabled veterans, senior citizens, and other persons with disabilities or their spouses in Missouri.

Eligibility This program is open to residents of Missouri (or their spouses) whose net household income does not exceed certain limits ($27,500 per year if they rented or did not own and occupy their home for the entire year, $30,000 if they owned and occupied their home for the entire year) and have paid property tax or rent on their homestead during the tax year. Applicants must be 1) 65 years of age or older, 2) classified by the U.S. Department of Veterans Affairs as a 100% service-connected disabled veteran, 3) 60 years of age or older and receiving surviving spouse Society Security benefits, or 4) 100% disabled.

Financial data The tax credit depends on the claimant's income and amount paid in property taxes or rent, up to a maximum of $1,100 per year for property tax or $750 per year for rent.

Duration The tax credit is available annually.

Number awarded Varies each year.

Deadline Eligible veterans, people with disabilities, and senior citizens may claim this credit when they file their state income tax return, in April of each year.

[1324]
MISSOURI SPECIAL NEEDS ADOPTION TAX CREDIT

Missouri Department of Revenue
Attn: Taxation Division
301 West High Street, Room 330
P.O. Box 2200
Jefferson City, MO 65105-2200
(573) 751-3505   Toll Free: (800) 877-6881
Fax: (573) 751-2195   TDD: (800) 735-2966
E-mail: taxcredit@dor.mo.gov
Web: dor.mo.gov/taxcredit/atc.php

Summary To provide an income tax credit to residents of Missouri who adopt a child with special needs.

Eligibility This credit is available to residents of Missouri who adopt a child that has special needs, i.e., a child for whom it has been determined by the Department of Social Services, a child-placing agency licensed by the state, or a court of competent jurisdiction to have a specific factor or condition (e.g., ethnic background, age, membership in a minority or sibling group, medical condition, handicap) that makes it difficult to place the child with

adoptive parents. Applicants must have incurred nonrecurring adoption expenses, such as reasonable and necessary adoption fees, court costs, attorney fees, and other expenses that are directly related to the adoption of a special needs child and are not in violation of federal, state, or local laws.

Financial data Qualifying taxpayers may claim up to $10,000 per child for nonrecurring adoption expenses. The full credit may be claimed when the adoption is final, or a claim for 50% of the credit may be made when the child is placed in the home and the remaining 50% may be claimed when the adoption is final.

Duration This credit is available for a total of 5 consecutive years, beginning when the credit is first taken or the adoption is final, whichever occurs first.

Number awarded Varies each year.

Deadline The credit must be claimed by April of each year.

[1325]
MONTANA DISABLED AMERICAN VETERAN PROPERTY TAX BENEFIT

Montana Department of Revenue
Attn: Property Tax
125 North Roberts, Third Floor
P.O. Box 5805
Helena, MT 59604-5805
(406) 444-6900   Toll Free: (866) 859-2254
Fax: (406) 444-1505   TDD: (406) 444-2830
Web: mt.gov/revenue

Summary To reduce the property tax rate in Montana for disabled veterans and their surviving spouses.

Eligibility This benefit is available to residents of Montana who own and occupy property in the state. Applicants must have been honorably discharged from active service in the armed forces and be currently rated 100% disabled or compensated at the 100% disabled rate because of a service-connected disability. They must have an adjusted gross income less than $53,867 if married or $46,685 if single. Also eligible are unremarried surviving spouses with an adjusted gross income less than $40,700 whose spouse was a veteran with a 100% service-connected disability or compensation at the 100% disabled rate at the time of death, died while on active duty, or died of a service-connected disability.

Financial data Qualifying veterans and surviving spouses are entitled to a reduction in local property taxes on their residence, 1 attached or detached garage, and up to 1 acre of land. The amount of the reduction depends on the status of the applicant (married, single, or surviving spouse) and adjusted gross income, but ranges from 50% to 100%.

Duration The reduction continues as long as the recipient resides in Montana and owns and occupies property used as a primary residence.

Number awarded Varies each year.

Deadline Applications must be filed with the local Department of Revenue Office by April of each year.

[1326]
MONTANA DISABLED DEPENDENT CHILDREN TAX EXEMPTION

Montana Department of Revenue
Attn: Individual Income Tax
125 North Roberts, Third Floor
P.O. Box 5805
Helena, MT 59604-5805
(406) 444-6900   Toll Free: (866) 859-2254
Fax: (406) 444-6642   TDD: (406) 444-2830
Web: mt.gov/revenue

Summary   To provide a state income tax exemption to the parents of disabled children in Montana.

Eligibility   Eligible are all persons considered Montana residents for purposes of state income taxation who have a disabled child claimed as a regular dependent. The child must be certified by a physician as having a permanent disability to 50% or more of the body as a whole; deafness and blindness do not meet this requirement.

Financial data   Parents may claim an additional exemption of $2,190 for each child with a disability reported as a dependent.

Duration   The exemption continues as long as the recipient resides in Montana with a dependent child with a disability.

Deadline   Deadline not specified.

[1327]
MONTANA INCOME TAX EXEMPTION FOR THE BLIND

Montana Department of Revenue
Attn: Individual Income Tax
125 North Roberts, Third Floor
P.O. Box 5805
Helena, MT 59604-5805
(406) 444-6900   Toll Free: (866) 859-2254
Fax: (406) 444-6642   TDD: (406) 444-2830
Web: mt.gov/revenue

Summary   To provide a state income tax exemption to blind residents of Montana and their spouses.

Eligibility   Eligible are all persons considered Montana residents for purposes of state income taxation who are blind or whose spouse is blind.

Financial data   Blind people and their spouses may claim an additional exemption of $2,190 from their income for state taxation purposes.

Duration   The exemption continues as long as the recipient resides in Montana.

Deadline   Deadline not specified.

[1328]
MUSICIANS FOUNDATION FINANCIAL ASSISTANCE

Musicians Foundation, Inc.
875 Sixth Avenue, Suite 2303
New York, NY 10001
(212) 239-9137   Fax: (212) 239-9138
E-mail: info@musiciansfoundation.org
Web: www.musiciansfoundation.org

Summary   To provide emergency assistance to disabled and other professional musicians (and their family members) who need assistance for living, medical, or related expenses.

Eligibility   Eligible to apply for this assistance are professional musicians who are working in the United States, regardless of their genre. Applicants must need financial assistance because of their age, illness, disability, or other misfortune. Their family members may also apply.

Financial data   The amount awarded varies, depending upon the needs of the recipient. Funds are to be used to meet current living, medical, and related costs.

Duration   These are generally 1-time awards.

Additional data   This foundation was incorporated in 1914. The foundation does not award scholarships, loans, or composition grants.

Number awarded   Varies each year.

Deadline   Applications may be submitted at any time.

[1329]
NATIONAL VACCINE INJURY COMPENSATION PROGRAM

Health Resources and Services Administration
Bureau of Health Professions
Attn: Division of Vaccine Injury Compensation
5600 Fishers Lane, Room 11C-26
Rockville, MD 20857
(301) 443-2703   Toll Free: (800) 338-2382
Fax: (301) 443-3354   E-mail: jceresa@hrsa.gov
Web: www.hrsa.gov/vaccinecompensation

Summary   To provide compensate individuals and/or the family of those individuals who became injured or died as a result of adverse vaccine or toxoid reactions for vaccines administered after October 1, 1988.

Eligibility   The vaccines and toxoids covered under the compensation law are: diphtheria and tetanus toxoids and pertussis vaccine (DTP); measles, mumps, and rubella (MMR); oral poliovirus vaccine (OPV) and inactivated poliovirus vaccine (IPV); hepatitis A vaccine; hepatitis B vaccine; haemophilus influenza type b vaccine; human papillomavirus; influenza (TIV or LAIV); varicella vaccine; rotavirus vaccine; and pneumococcal conjugate vaccines. No petition may be filed under this program if a civil action is pending for damages related to the vaccine injury or if damages were awarded by a court or in a settlement of a civil action against the vaccine manufacturer or administrator. Applicants must file a petition with the U.S. Court of Federal Claims. In the case of an injury, the effects must have continued at least 6 months after vaccine administration and the claim must be filed within 36 months after the first symptoms appeared. In the case of a death, the claim must be filed within 24 months of the death and within 48 months after the onset of the vaccine-related injury from which the death occurred. Medical documentation must be provided. The court will make a decision based on the individual's health prior to administering the vaccine, the type of vaccine and date given, and the date of onset and extent of injury occurring after receiving the vaccine.

Financial data For vaccine-related injury, the program provides reasonable compensation for past and future unreimbursable medical, custodial care, and/or rehabilitation costs; $250,000 maximum for actual and projected pain and suffering and/or emotional distress; lost earnings; and reasonable attorneys' fees and costs. For vaccine-related death, the program provides $250,000 compensation to the estate of the deceased and reasonable attorneys' fees and costs.

Duration Benefits can be awarded for the recipient's lifetime.

Additional data This program, begun in 1988, is jointly administered by the U.S. Department of Health and Human Services, Court of Federal Claims, and Department of Justice. Information on the rules of the court, including requirements for filing a petition, is available from Court of Federal Claims. The deadline has passed for filing claims for conditions that resulted from a vaccine administered prior to October 1, 1988 (the effective date of the National Childhood Vaccine Injury Act).

Number awarded Varies each year. Recently, the program awarded nearly $218 million to 250 patients.

Deadline In the case of a disability/injury, the residual effects or complications must have continued for at least 6 months after the vaccine was administered before a petition can be filed. In addition, in the case of a disability/injury, the claim must be filed within 36 months after the first symptoms appear. In the case of death, the claim must be filed within 24 months of the death and within 48 months after the appearance of the first symptoms of the disability/injury from which the death occurred.

[1330]
NCCS FINANCIAL ASSISTANCE

National Children's Cancer Society
Attn: Patient and Family Services
One South Memorial Drive, Suite 800
St. Louis, MO 63102
(314) 241-1600   Toll Free: (800) 532-6459
Fax: (314) 735-2014
E-mail: SSchuetz@children-cancer.org
Web: www.thenccs.org/assist

Summary To provide funding for expenses related to cancer or brain tumors to children with cancer (or their families).

Eligibility This assistance is available to children (under 18 years of age) who have a pediatric cancer or a high grade or anaplastic brain tumor. Applicants must be facing medical and non-medical expenses related to treatment, including meals during treatment, health insurance premiums, medical expenses not covered by insurance, lodging during treatment, and transportation during treatment. Families with liquid assets in excess of $5,000 may be asked to partially or completely "spend down" those assets prior to receiving this assistance. Children must be U.S. citizens or permanent residents who have maintained been in the United States for at least 12 consecutive months.

Financial data Assistance depends on the recipient's need.

Duration Assistance may be provided for up to 2 months; if continuing support is still required, a request for renewal may be submitted by a hospital professional.

Number awarded Varies each year.

Deadline Applications may be submitted at any time.

[1331]
NEBRASKA HOMESTEAD EXEMPTION

Nebraska Department of Revenue
301 Centennial Mall South
P.O. Box 94818
Lincoln, NE 68509-4818
(402) 471-5729
Toll Free: (800) 742-7474 (within NE and IA)
Web: www.revenue.ne.gov/PAD/homestead.html

Summary To exempt the property of Nebraska residents who are elderly, disabled, or veterans and their widow(er)s from a portion of taxation.

Eligibility This exemption is available to 3 categories of Nebraska residents: the elderly, certain people with disabilities, and certain disabled veterans and their widow(er)s. Elderly people are those 65 years of age or older who own a homestead with a value less than $95,000 or 200% of their county's average assessed value of single family residential property, whichever is greater. Disabled people are those who 1) have a permanent physical disability and have lost all mobility such as to preclude locomotion without the regular use of a mechanical aid or prosthesis; 2) have undergone amputation of both arms above the elbow, or 3) have a permanent partial disability of both arms in excess of 75%. They must own a homestead with a value less than $110,000 or 225% of their county's average assessed value of single family residential property, whichever is greater. Veterans are those who served on active duty in the U.S. armed forces (or a government allied with the United States) during specified periods of war and received an honorable discharge. They must 1) be drawing compensation from the U.S. Department of Veterans Affairs (VA) because of a 100% service-connected disability; 2) be totally disabled by a nonservice-connected illness or accident; or 3) own a home that is substantially contributed to by VA. Also eligible are unremarried widow(er)s of veterans who died because of a service-connected disability, whose death while on active duty was service-connected, who died while on active duty during war time, or who drew compensation from VA because of a 100% service-connected disability The homestead maximum value is $110,000 or 225% of the county's average assessed value of single family residential property, whichever is greater. Elderly people must have a household income less than $31,801 if single or $37,401 if married. Disabled persons, veterans, and widow(er)s (except veterans and widow(er)s who own a home that is substantially contributed to by the VA) must have a household income less than $34,901 if single or $40,301 if married.

Financial data Exemptions depend on the income of the applicant, ranging from 25% to 100% of the value of the homestead. For the elderly, the maximum exemption is the taxable value of the homestead up to $40,000 or 100% of the county's average assessed value of single family residential property, whichever is greater. For disabled people and veterans, the maximum exemption is the taxable value of the homestead up to $50,000 or 120% of the county's average assessed value of single family residential property, whichever is greater. For veterans and widow(er)s whose home was substantially contributed to by the VA, the homestead is 100% exempt regardless of the value of the homestead or the income of the owner.

Duration The exemption is provided as long as the qualifying homestead owner resides in Nebraska.

Number awarded Varies each year.

Deadline Applications must be filed by June of each year.

[1332]
NEVADA DISABLED VETERAN'S TAX EXEMPTION

Nevada Office of Veterans Services
Attn: Executive Director
5460 Reno Corporate Drive
Reno, NV 89511
(775) 688-1653   Toll Free: (866) 630-8387
Fax: (775) 688-1656
Web: veterans.nv.gov/veteran_benefits.html

Summary To exempt from taxation in Nevada a portion of the property owned by disabled veterans or their surviving spouses.

Eligibility This program is open to veterans who are residents of Nevada and have incurred a service-connected disability of 60% or more. Applicants must have received an honorable separation from military service. The widow(er) of a disabled veteran, who was eligible at the time of death, may also be eligible for this benefit.

Financial data Veterans and widow(er)s are entitled to exempt from taxation a portion of their property's assessed value. The amount depends on the extent of the disability and the year filed; it ranges from $6,250 to $20,000 and doubles over a 4-year period.

Duration Disabled veterans and their widow(er)s are entitled to this exemption as long as they live in Nevada.

Additional data Disabled veterans and widow(er)s are able to split their exemption between vehicle taxes and/or property taxes. Further information is available at local county assessors' offices.

Number awarded Varies each year.

Deadline Deadline not specified.

[1333]
NEW HAMPSHIRE PROPERTY TAX EXEMPTION FOR CERTAIN DISABLED VETERANS

New Hampshire Department of Revenue
  Administration
109 Pleasant Street
Concord, NH 03301
(603) 271-2191   Fax: (603) 271-6121
TDD: (800) 735-2964
Web: revenue.nh.gov

Summary To exempt from taxation certain property owned by New Hampshire blind and other disabled veterans or their surviving spouses.

Eligibility Eligible for this exemption are New Hampshire residents who are honorably discharged veterans with a total and permanent service-connected disability that involves double amputation of the upper or lower extremities or any combination thereof, paraplegia, or blindness of both eyes with visual acuity of 5/200 or less. Applicants or their surviving spouses must own a specially adapted homestead that has been acquired with the assistance of the U.S. Department of Veterans Affairs.

Financial data Qualifying disabled veterans and surviving spouses are exempt from all taxation on their specially adapted homestead.

Duration 1 year; once the credit has been approved, it is automatically renewed as long as the qualifying person owns the same residence in New Hampshire.

Number awarded Varies each year.

Deadline The original application for a permanent tax credit must be submitted by April.

[1334]
NEW HAMPSHIRE SERVICE-CONNECTED TOTAL AND PERMANENT DISABILITY TAX CREDIT

New Hampshire Department of Revenue
  Administration
109 Pleasant Street
Concord, NH 03301
(603) 271-2191   Fax: (603) 271-6121
TDD: (800) 735-2964
Web: revenue.nh.gov

Summary To provide property tax credits in New Hampshire to disabled veterans or their surviving spouses.

Eligibility Eligible for this tax credit are honorably discharged veterans residing in New Hampshire who 1) have a total and permanent service-connected disability, or 2) are a double amputee or paraplegic because of a service-connected disability. Unremarried surviving spouses of qualified veterans are also eligible.

Financial data Qualifying disabled veterans and surviving spouses receive an annual credit of $700 for property taxes on residential property. In addition, individual towns in New Hampshire may adopt a local option to increase the dollar amount credited to disabled veterans, to a maximum of $2,000.

Duration 1 year; once the credit has been approved, it is automatically renewed for as long as the qualifying person owns the same residence in New Hampshire.

Number awarded Varies each year.

Deadline The original application for a permanent tax credit must be submitted by April.

[1335]
NEW JERSEY PROPERTY TAX EXEMPTION FOR DISABLED VETERANS OR SURVIVING SPOUSES

New Jersey Division of Taxation
Attn: Technical Information Branch
50 Barrack Street
P.O. Box 281
Trenton, NJ 08695-0281
(609) 292-6400   Toll Free: (800) 323-4400
TDD: (800) 286-6613   E-mail: taxation@tax.state.nj.us
Web: www.state.nj.us/treasury/taxation/otherptr.shtml

Summary To provide a real estate tax exemption to New Jersey veterans with disabilities and certain surviving widow(er)s.

Eligibility This exemption is available to New Jersey residents who have been honorably discharged with active wartime service in the U.S. armed forces and have been certified by the U.S. Department of Veterans Affairs as totally and permanently disabled as a result of wartime service-connected conditions. Unremarried surviving spouses and civil union partners of eligible disabled veterans or of certain wartime servicepersons who died on active duty are also entitled to this exemption. Applicants must be the full owner of and a permanent resident in the dwelling house for which the exemption is claimed.

Financial data A 100% exemption from locally-levied real estate taxes is provided.

Duration 1 year; the exemption continues as long as the eligible veteran remains a resident of New Jersey.

Additional data This program is administered by the local tax assessor or collector. Veterans who are denied exemptions have the right to appeal the decision to their county and state governments.

Number awarded Varies each year.

Deadline Applications may be submitted at any time.

[1336]
NEW MEXICO DISABLED VETERAN PROPERTY TAX EXEMPTION

New Mexico Department of Veterans' Services
Attn: Benefits Division
407 Galisteo Street, Room 142
P.O. Box 2324
Santa Fe, NM 87504-2324
(505) 827-6374   Toll Free: (866) 433-VETS
Fax: (505) 827-6372
E-mail: alan.martinez@state.nm.us
Web: www.dvs.state.nm.us/benefits.html

Summary To exempt disabled veterans and their spouses from payment of property taxes in New Mexico.

Eligibility This exemption is available to veterans who are rated 100% service-connected disabled by the U.S. Department of Veterans Affairs, are residents of New Mexico, and own a primary residence in the state. Also eligible are qualifying veterans' unremarried surviving spouses, if they are New Mexico residents and continue to own the residence.

Financial data Veterans and surviving spouses are exempt from payment of property taxes in New Mexico.

Duration 1 year; continues until the qualifying veteran or spouse no longer live in the residence.

Number awarded Varies each year.

Deadline Deadline not specified.

[1337]
NEW MEXICO INCOME TAX DEDUCTION FOR THE ADOPTION OF A SPECIAL NEEDS CHILD

New Mexico Taxation and Revenue Department
Attn: Personal Income Tax Division
1100 South St. Francis Drive
P.O. Box 25122
Santa Fe, NM 87504-5122
(505) 827-0700
Web: www.tax.newmexico.gov

Summary To provide income tax exemptions to residents of New Mexico who adopt a special needs child.

Eligibility Residents of New Mexico who have adopted a child defined as "difficult to place" on or after January 1 of the tax year are eligible to claim a deduction for that child (and each special needs adopted child) who is under 18 years of age. The classification of children as "difficult to place" may be based on a physical or mental handicap or emotional disturbance that is at least moderately disabling. A copy of the certification issued by the New Mexico Human Services Department must be attached to the resident's tax form for each child for whom a deduction is claimed.

Financial data The deduction is $500 if the resident is married and filing separately or $1,000 if single, head of household, or married and filing jointly.

Duration The deduction continues as long as the qualifying resident remains in the state.

Number awarded Varies each year.

Deadline The qualifying resident claims the deduction on the New Mexico state income tax return, which is due in April.

[1338]
NEW MEXICO TAX EXEMPTION FOR THE BLIND AND ELDERLY

New Mexico Taxation and Revenue Department
Attn: Personal Income Tax Division
1100 South St. Francis Drive
P.O. Box 25122
Santa Fe, NM 87504-5122
(505) 827-0700
Web: www.tax.newmexico.gov

Summary To exempt a portion of the income of New Mexico residents who are blind or over the age of 65, and their surviving spouses, from state income tax liability.

Eligibility This exemption is available to residents of New Mexico who are 65 years of age or older or who are blind.

Financial data The income exemption ranges from $1,000 to $8,000, depending on filing status and income. The maximum income that still qualifies for an exemption is $25,500 for married individuals filing separate returns, $51,000 for heads of household, surviving spouses, and married individuals filing joint returns, or $28,500 for single individuals.

Duration The exemption continues as long as the qualifying resident remains in the state.

Number awarded Varies each year.

Deadline The qualifying resident claims the exemption on the New Mexico state income tax return, which is due in April.

[1339]
NEW YORK ALTERNATIVE PROPERTY TAX EXEMPTIONS FOR VETERANS

New York State Department of Taxation and Finance
Attn: Office of Real Property Tax Services
W.A. Harriman Campus
Building 8, Sixth Floor
Albany, NY 12227
(518) 486-4403   Fax: (518) 486-7754
Web: www.orps.state.ny.us

Summary To provide disabled and other wartime veterans and their spouses who are residents of New York with a partial exemption from property taxes.

Eligibility This program is open to veterans who served during specified periods of war time. Applicants must have been discharged under honorable conditions; additional benefits are available to those who served in a combat zone and to those who have a service-connected disability. The legal title to the property must be in the name of the veteran or the spouse of the veteran or both, or the unremarried surviving spouse of a deceased veteran. The property must be used exclusively for residential purposes. This program is only available in counties, cities, towns, and villages in New York that have opted to participate.

Financial data This program provides an exemption of 15% of the assessed valuation of the property, to a basic maximum of $12,000 per year; local governments may opt for reduced maximums of $9,000 or $6,000, or for increased maximums of $15,000 to $36,000. For combat-zone veterans, an additional 10% of the assessed valuation is exempt, to a basic maximum of $8,000 per year; local governments may opt for a reduced maximum of $6,000 or $4,000, or for increased maximums of $10,000 to $24,000. For disabled veterans, the exemption is the percentage of assessed value equal to half of the service-connected disability rating, to a basic maximum of $40,000 per year; local governments may opt for a reduced maximum of $30,000 or $20,000, or for increased

maximums of $50,000 to $120,000. At its option, New York City and other high appreciation municipalities may use the following increased maximum exemptions: war veteran, $54,000; combat-zone veteran, $36,000; disabled veteran, $180,000.

Duration This exemption is available annually.

Number awarded Varies each year.

Deadline Applications must be filed with the local assessor by "taxable status date;" in most towns, that is the end of February.

[1340]
NEW YORK COLD WAR VETERANS PROPERTY TAX EXEMPTIONS

New York State Department of Taxation and Finance
Attn: Office of Real Property Tax Services
W.A. Harriman Campus
Building 8, Sixth Floor
Albany, NY 12227
(518) 486-4403   Fax: (518) 486-7754
Web: www.orps.state.ny.us

Summary To provide disabled and other New York veterans who served during the Cold War and their spouses with a partial exemption from property taxes.

Eligibility This program is open to veterans who served during the Cold War, defined as September 2, 1945 to December 26, 1991. Applicants must have been discharged under honorable conditions; additional benefits are available to those who have a service-connected disability. The legal title to the property must be in the name of the veteran or the spouse of the veteran or both, or the unremarried surviving spouse of a deceased veteran. The property must be used exclusively for residential purposes. This program is only available in counties, cities, towns, and villages in New York that have opted to participate.

Financial data Local governments may opt to grant exemptions of 15% or 10%. For the 15% option, the basic maximum exemption is $12,000 per year; local governments may opt for reduced maximums of $9,000 or $6,000, or for increased maximums of $15,000 to $36,000. For the 10% option, the basic maximum exemption is $8,000 per year; local governments may opt for a reduced maximum of $6,000 or $4,000, or for increased maximums of $10,000 to $24,000. For disabled veterans, the exemption is the percentage of assessed value equal to half of the service-connected disability rating, to a basic maximum of $40,000 per year; local governments may opt for a reduced maximum of $30,000 or $20,000, or for increased maximums of $50,000 to $120,000. At its option, New York City and other high appreciation municipalities may use the following increased maximum exemptions: 15% option, $54,000; 10% option, $36,000; disabled veteran, $180,000.

Duration This exemption is available annually.

Number awarded Varies each year.

Deadline Applications must be filed with the local assessor by "taxable status date;" in most towns, that is the end of February.

[1341]
NEW YORK "ELIGIBLE FUNDS" PROPERTY TAX EXEMPTIONS FOR VETERANS

New York State Department of Taxation and Finance
Attn: Office of Real Property Tax Services
W.A. Harriman Campus
Building 8, Sixth Floor
Albany, NY 12227
(518) 486-4403   Fax: (518) 486-7754
Web: www.orps.state.ny.us

Summary To provide a partial exemption from property taxes to disabled and other veterans and their surviving spouses who are residents of New York.

Eligibility This program is open to veterans who have purchased properties in New York with such income as retirement pay, disability compensation, or death gratuities (referred to as "eligible funds"). Specially adapted homes of paraplegics, or the homes of their widowed spouses, are also covered.

Financial data This exemption reduces the property's assessed value to the extent that "eligible funds" were used in the purchase, generally to a maximum of $5,000. It is applicable to general municipal taxes but not to school taxes or special district levies.

Duration This exemption is available annually.

Number awarded Varies each year.

Deadline Applications must be filed with the local assessor by "taxable status date;" in most towns, that is the end of February.

[1342]
NEW YORK STATE BLIND ANNUITY

New York State Division of Veterans' Affairs
5 Empire State Plaza, Suite 2836
Albany, NY 12223-1551
(518) 486-3602
Toll Free: (888) VETS-NYS (within NY)
Fax: (518) 473-0379 E-mail: dvainfo@veterans.ny.gov
Web: veterans.ny.gov/state-benefits.html

Summary To provide an annuity to blind wartime veterans and their surviving spouses in New York.

Eligibility This benefit is available to veterans who served on active duty during specified periods of war. Applicants must 1) meet the New York standards of blindness; 2) have received an honorable or general discharge, or a discharge other than for dishonorable service; and 3) be now, and continue to be, residents of and continuously domiciled in New York. The annuity is also payable to unremarried spouses of deceased veterans who were receiving annuity payments (or were eligible to do so) at the time of their death, and are residents of and continuously domiciled in New York.

Financial data The annuity is currently $1,220.76 per year.

Number awarded Varies each year.

Deadline Deadline not specified.

[1343]
NORTH CAROLINA INCOME TAX CREDIT FOR CHILDREN WITH DISABILITIES WHO REQUIRE SPECIAL EDUCATION

North Carolina Department of Revenue
Attn: Individual Income Tax
501 North Wilmington Street
P.O. Box 25000
Raleigh, NC 27640-0100
(919) 733-4684
Web: www.dornc.com/taxes/individuals

Summary To provide a tax credit to residents of North Carolina who pay for special education for a dependent child.

Eligibility This credit is available to residents of North Carolina who pay tuition for special education and related services expenses for an eligible dependent child. The child must be enrolled in grades K-12 in a nonpublic or public school in North Carolina that charges tuition. The child must have a disability that requires special education or related services on a daily basis.

Financial data Taxpayers with eligible children are entitled to a credit equal to the amount they pay for special education or $3,000, whichever is less.

Duration The credit is available as long as the child resides in North Carolina and requires special education.

Additional data This credit was first available for the 2011 tax year.

Number awarded Varies each year.

Deadline Deadline not specified.

[1344]
NORTH DAKOTA PROPERTY TAX CREDIT FOR DISABLED VETERANS

Office of State Tax Commissioner
State Capitol Building
600 East Boulevard Avenue, Department 127
Bismarck, ND 58505-0599
(701) 328-7088   Toll Free: (877) 328-7088
Fax: (701) 328-3700   TDD: (800) 366-6888
E-mail: taxinfo@state.nd.us
Web: www.nd.gov/tax/property

Summary To provide property tax credits to disabled North Dakota veterans and their surviving spouses.

Eligibility This property tax credit is available to honorably-discharged veterans who have more than a 50% service-connected disability as certified by the U.S. Department of Veterans Affairs. Applicants must own and occupy a homestead according to state law. Unremarried surviving spouses are also eligible. If a disabled veteran co-owns the property with someone other than a spouse, the credit is limited to the disabled veteran's interest in the fixtures, buildings, and improvements of the homestead.

Financial data The credit is applied against the first $120,000 of true and full valuation of the fixtures, buildings, and improvements of the homestead, to a maximum amount calculated by multiplying $120,000 by the percentage of the disabled veteran's disability compensation rating for service-connected disabilities.

Duration 1 year; renewable as long as qualified individuals continue to reside in North Dakota and live in their homes.

Number awarded Varies each year.

Deadline Applications may be submitted to the county auditor at any time.

[1345]
NORTH DAKOTA PROPERTY TAX EXEMPTION FOR DISABLED PERSONS CONFINED TO A WHEELCHAIR

Office of State Tax Commissioner
State Capitol Building
600 East Boulevard Avenue, Department 127
Bismarck, ND 58505-0599
(701) 328-7088   Toll Free: (877) 328-7088
Fax: (701) 328-3700   TDD: (800) 366-6888
E-mail: taxinfo@state.nd.us
Web: www.nd.gov/tax/property

Summary To provide partial tax exemption in North Dakota to persons permanently confined to the use of a wheelchair and their spouses.

Eligibility Persons permanently confined to the use of a wheelchair are those who cannot walk with the assistance of crutches or any other device and will never be able to do so; this must be certified by a physician selected by a local governing board. The property must be owned and occupied as a homestead according to state law. The homestead may be owned by the spouse or jointly owned by the disabled person and spouse provided both reside on the homestead. Qualified residents and, if deceased, their unremarried surviving spouses are entitled to this exemption. Income and assets are not considered in determining eligibility for the exemption.

Financial data The maximum benefit may not exceed $3,600 taxable value, because a homestead is limited to $80,000 market value.

Duration The exemption continues as long as the homestead in North Dakota is owned by the disabled person and/or the spouse.

Additional data The exemption does not apply to special assessments levied upon the homestead.

Number awarded Varies each year.

Deadline Deadline not specified.

[1346]
NORTH DAKOTA PROPERTY TAX EXEMPTION FOR THE BLIND

Office of State Tax Commissioner
State Capitol Building
600 East Boulevard Avenue, Department 127
Bismarck, ND 58505-0599
(701) 328-7088   Toll Free: (877) 328-7088
Fax: (701) 328-3700   TDD: (800) 366-6888
E-mail: taxinfo@state.nd.us
Web: www.nd.gov/tax/property

Summary To provide partial tax exemption in North Dakota to blind persons and their spouses.

Eligibility Blind persons are defined as those who are totally blind, who have visual acuity of not more than 20/200 in the better eye with correction, or whose vision is limited in field so that the widest diameter subtends an angle no greater than 20 degrees. Eligible for this exemption is property that is owned by a blind person, by the spouse of a blind person, or jointly by a blind person and a spouse. The property that is exempt includes the entire building classified as residential, and owned and occupied as a residence by a person who qualifies, as long as the building contains no more than 2 apartments or rental units that are leased.

Financial data The exemption applies to all or any part of fixtures, building, and improvements upon any nonfarmland up to a taxable valuation of $7,200.

Duration The exemption continues as long as the blind person resides in the home in North Dakota.

Number awarded Varies each year.

Deadline Deadline not specified.

[1347]
NORTH DAKOTA PROPERTY TAX EXEMPTION FOR VETERANS WHO LIVE IN SPECIALLY ADAPTED HOUSING

Office of State Tax Commissioner
State Capitol Building
600 East Boulevard Avenue, Department 127
Bismarck, ND 58505-0599
(701) 328-7088   Toll Free: (877) 328-7088
Fax: (701) 328-3700   TDD: (800) 366-6888
E-mail: taxinfo@state.nd.us
Web: www.nd.gov/tax/property

Summary To provide property tax exemptions to North Dakota veterans and their surviving spouses who have been awarded specially adapted housing.

Eligibility This exemption is available to paraplegic disabled veterans of the U.S. armed forces or any veteran who has been awarded specially adapted housing by the U.S. Department of Veterans Affairs. The paraplegic disability does not have to be service connected. The unremarried surviving spouses of such deceased veterans are also eligible. Income and assets are not considered in determining eligibility for the exemption.

Financial data The maximum benefit may not exceed $5,400 taxable value, because the exemption is limited to the first $120,000 of true and full value of fixtures, buildings, and improvements.

Duration 1 year; renewable as long as qualified individuals reside in North Dakota and live in their homes.

Number awarded Varies each year.

Deadline Applications may be submitted to the county auditor at any time.

[1348]
OHIO HOMESTEAD EXEMPTION FOR SENIOR CITIZENS, DISABLED PERSONS AND SURVIVING SPOUSES

Ohio Department of Taxation
Attn: Tax Equalization Division
P.O. Box 530
Columbus, OH 43216-0530
(614) 466-5744   Toll Free: (800) 282-1780 (within OH)
Fax: (614) 752-9822
Web: tax.ohio.gov

Summary To exempt a portion of the value of homesteads owned by senior citizens and disabled persons (and their surviving spouses) from property taxation in Ohio.

Eligibility This exemption is available to residents of Ohio who are 65 years of age or older or who have a total and permanent disability. Applicants must own and occupy their home as their principal place of residence. Surviving spouses of persons who were receiving the exemption at the time of their death are also eligible if they were at least 59 years of age on the date of the decedent's death. There is no income limitation.

Financial data Qualifying homeowners may exempt up to $25,000 from the assessed value of their home for purposes of property taxation.

Duration The exemption is available as long as the recipient resides in Ohio and owns his or her home.

Number awarded Varies each year.

Deadline Applications must be submitted to the county auditor by May of each year.

[1349]
OHIO VETERANS' FINANCIAL ASSISTANCE

Ohio Department of Veterans Services
77 South High Street, Seventh Floor
Columbus, OH 43215
(614) 644-0898   Toll Free: (888) DVS-OHIO
Fax: (614) 728-9498   E-mail: ohiovet@dvs.ohio.gov
Web: dvs.ohio.gov

Summary To provide emergency aid to Ohio veterans, military personnel, and their dependents who, because of disability or disaster, are in financial need.

Eligibility This assistance is available to veterans and active-duty members of the U.S. armed forces, as well as their spouses, surviving spouses, dependent parents, minor children, and wards. Applicants must have been residents of the Ohio county in which they are applying for at least 3 months. They must be able to demonstrate need for relief because of sickness, accident, or destitution.

Financial data The amount granted varies, depending on the needs of the recipient.

Duration These are emergency funds only and are not designed to be a recurring source of income.

Additional data These grants are made by the various county veterans services offices in Ohio.

Number awarded Varies each year.

Deadline Applications may be submitted at any time.

[1350]
OKLAHOMA FINANCIAL ASSISTANCE PROGRAM

Oklahoma Department of Veterans Affairs
Veterans Memorial Building
2311 North Central Avenue
P.O. Box 53067
Oklahoma City, OK 73152
(405) 521-3684   Fax: (405) 521-6533
E-mail: mspear@odva.state.ok.us
Web: www.ok.gov

Summary To provide emergency aid to Oklahoma veterans and their families who, because of disability or disaster, are in financial need.

Eligibility This program is open to veterans with at least 90 days of wartime service (unless discharged earlier because of a service-connected disability) and an honorable discharge who are current residents of Oklahoma and have resided in the state for at least 1 year immediately preceding the date of application. Applicants must be seeking assistance because of an interruption or loss of job and income resulting from illness, injury, or disaster (such as loss of home due to fire, floor, or storm). Widow(er)s and minor children may also qualify for the benefit.

Financial data The amount of the grant depends on the need of the recipient.

Duration The grant is available only on a 1-time basis.

Additional data No financial assistance will be granted when regular monetary benefits are being received from other state agencies. The funds cannot be used for old debts, car payments, or medical expenses.

Number awarded Varies each year.

Deadline Applications must be submitted to the local post or chapter of a veterans services organization for initial approval or disapproval. They may be submitted at any time during the year.

[1351]
OKLAHOMA INCOME TAX EXEMPTION FOR THE BLIND

Oklahoma Tax Commission
Attn: Income Tax
2501 North Lincoln Boulevard
Oklahoma City, OK 73194-0009
(405) 521-3160   Toll Free: (800) 522-8165 (within OK)
Fax: (405) 522-0063   E-mail: otcmaster@tax.ok.gov
Web: www.tax.ok.gov/incometax.html

Summary To exempt a portion of the income of blind people and their spouses in Oklahoma from state taxation.

Eligibility This exemption is available to residents of Oklahoma and their spouses who are legally blind.

Financial data Each qualifying resident is entitled to claim an additional exemption of $1,000.

Duration The exemption is available as long as the recipient resides in Oklahoma.

Deadline Deadline not specified.

[1352]
OKLAHOMA PROPERTY TAX EXEMPTION FOR DISABLED VETERANS

Oklahoma Tax Commission
Attn: Ad Valorem Division
2501 North Lincoln Boulevard
P.O. Box 269060
Oklahoma City, OK 73126-9060
(405) 319-8200   Toll Free: (800) 522-8165 (within OK)
Fax: (405) 522-0166   E-mail: otcmaster@tax.ok.gov
Web: www.tax.ok.gov/adval.html

Summary   To exempt the property of disabled veterans and their surviving spouses from taxation in Oklahoma.

Eligibility   This program is available to Oklahoma residents who are veterans honorably discharged from a branch of the armed forces or the Oklahoma National Guard. Applicants must have a 100% permanent disability sustained through military action or accident or resulting from a disease contracted while in active service; the disability must be certified by the U.S. Department of Veterans Affairs. They must own property that qualifies for the Oklahoma homestead exemption. Surviving spouses of qualified veterans are also eligible.

Financial data   Qualified veterans and surviving spouses are eligible for exemption of the taxes on the full fair cash value of their homestead.

Duration   The exemption is available as long as the veteran or surviving spouse resides in Oklahoma and owns a qualifying homestead.

Additional data   This exemption was first available in 2006.

Deadline   Deadline not specified.

[1353]
OPERATION FAMILY FUND FINANCIAL ASSISTANCE

Operation Family Fund
P.O. Box 837
Ridgecrest, CA 93556
(760) 793-0053   Fax: (888) 851-1456
E-mail: support@operatonfamilyfund.org
Web: operationfamilyfund.org

Summary   To provide personal assistance to military and civilian personnel and the families of those personnel who died or were severely disabled as a result of service as a result of the Global War on Terror.

Eligibility   This assistance is available to military and civilian personnel and their families who died or were severely disabled as a result of Operations Enduring or Iraqi Freedom, either domestically or abroad. Civilians must have been serving officially as an employee of the U.S. government or contractor to the U.S. government. Applicants must be seeking funding for such short- and long-term living needs as food; rent or utilities; emergency transportation; vehicle repair; funeral expenses; medical and dental expenses; assistance with a home, rental, lease, or purchase; home improvements; or assistance with the purchase, rent, or lease of a vehicle. Grants are approved to applicants in the following priority order: 1)

member injured because of a hostile action and have a Department of Veterans Affairs (VA) disability rating of 50% or higher; 2) member injured because of an accident while serving in Iraq or Afghanistan and have a VA disability rating of 50% or higher; 3) member who has post-traumatic stress disorder with a VA disability rating of 50% or higher as a result of serving in Iraq or Afghanistan; 4) member who has other service-connected injuries caused in support of the Global War on Terror and a VA disability rating of 50% or higher; 5) member in any of the prior categories but still in the medical board process with a pending VA disability rating; 6) child (under 22 years of age) and/or spouse of a military member killed in action who did not receive government death benefit or SGLA; and 7) second requests.

Financial data   Most grants are at least $1,000 but less than $10,000.

Duration   These are 1-time grants; renewals may be approved if funding is available.

Number awarded   Varies each year; since this organization began, it has awarded more than 385 grants.

Deadline   Applications may be submitted at any time.

[1354]
OPERATION HOMEFRONT GRANTS

Operation Homefront
8930 Fourwinds Drive, Suite 340
San Antonio, TX 78239
(210) 659-7756   Toll Free: (800) 722-6098
Fax: (210) 566-7544
Web: www.operationhomefront.net

Summary   To provide assistance to military families and wounded personnel who face financial difficulties related to service.

Eligibility   This program is open to 1) veterans who are disabled as a result of service-connected injuries and their families; and 2) other military families who face financial needs because of the hardships associated with military service. Examples of financial needs include food assistance, auto repair, moving assistance, transitional family housing, vision care, child and dependent care, critical baby needs, travel and transportation, home repair, and essential home items.

Financial data   The amounts of the grants vary, depending on the need of the applicant. Recently, average grants were $100 to families for critical baby items, $161 for food assistance, $300 to assist in paying utilities, or $1,117 to help with rent or mortgage payments.

Duration   This are 1-time grants.

Additional data   This program began in 2002.

Number awarded   Varies each year; since the foundation was established, it has awarded $128 million to support more than 400,000 families and personnel.

Deadline   Applications may be submitted at any time.

[1355]
OPERATION SECOND CHANCE FAMILY ASSISTANCE GRANTS

Operation Second Chance
Attn: President
22708 Birchcrest Lane
P.O. Box 461
Clarksburg, MD 20871
Toll Free: (888) OSC-4VET
E-mail: assistance@operationsecondchance.org
Web: www.operationsecondchance.org

Summary　To provide assistance for payment of ordinary living expenses to disabled veterans and military personnel and their families.

Eligibility　This assistance is available to disabled veterans and military personnel who are within 18 months of their injury or are currently receiving care at a military health care facility and have an expected or adjudicated disability rating of 70% or higher. Their family members are also eligible. Applicants must be seeking funding for payment of rent or mortgages, utility bills, child care during illness or injury, or housing and/or airfare for a family member to assist an injured or recovering member.

Financial data　The amount of the grant depends on the need of the recipient.

Duration　These are 1-time grants.

Number awarded　Varies each year.

Deadline　Applications may be submitted at any time.

[1356]
OREGON PROPERTY TAX EXEMPTION FOR VETERANS WITH DISABILITIES AND THEIR SPOUSES

Oregon Department of Revenue
Attn: Property Tax Division
Revenue Building
955 Center Street, N.E.
Salem, OR 97310-2555
(503) 378-4988　Toll Free: (800) 356-4222 (within OR)
Fax: (503) 945-8738
TDD: (800) 886-7204 (within OR)
Web: www.oregon.gov/DOR/PTD/exemptions.shtml

Summary　To exempt disabled Oregon veterans and their spouses from a portion of their property taxes.

Eligibility　Qualifying veterans are those who received a discharge or release under honorable conditions after service of either 1) 90 consecutive days during World War I, World War II, or the Korean Conflict; or 2) 210 consecutive days after January 31, 1955. Eligible individuals must meet 1 of these conditions: 1) a war veteran who is officially certified by the U.S. Department of Veterans Affairs (VA) or any branch of the U.S. armed forces as having disabilities of 40% or more; 2) a war veteran who is certified each year by a licensed physician as being 40% or more disabled and has total gross income that is less than 185% of the federal poverty level; or 3) a war veteran's surviving spouse who has not remarried, even if the veteran's spouse was not disabled or did not take advantage of the exemption if disabled. Recipients of this exemption must own and live on a property in Oregon.

Financial data　The exemption is $17,911 of the homestead property's real market value.

Duration　1 year; may be renewed as long as the eligible veteran or surviving unremarried spouse owns and occupies the primary residence.

Number awarded　Varies each year.

Deadline　This exemption is not automatic. Applications must be submitted by March of each year.

[1357]
OREGON PROPERTY TAX EXEMPTION FOR VETERANS WITH SERVICE-CONNECTED DISABILITIES AND THEIR SPOUSES

Oregon Department of Revenue
Attn: Property Tax Division
Revenue Building
955 Center Street, N.E.
Salem, OR 97310-2555
(503) 378-4988　Toll Free: (800) 356-4222 (within OR)
Fax: (503) 945-8738
TDD: (800) 886-7204 (within OR)
Web: www.oregon.gov/DOR/PTD/exemptions.shtml

Summary　To exempt Oregon veterans with service-connected disabilities and their spouses from a portion of their property taxes.

Eligibility　Qualifying veterans are those who received a discharge or release under honorable conditions after service of either 1) 90 consecutive days during World War I, World War II, or the Korean Conflict; or 2) 210 consecutive days after January 31, 1955. Eligible individuals must meet 1 of these conditions: 1) a war veteran who is certified by the U.S. Department of Veterans Affairs (VA) or any branch of the U.S. armed forces as having service-connected disabilities of 40% or more; or 2) a surviving spouse of a war veteran who died because of service-connected injury or illness or who received at least 1 year of this exemption. Recipients of this exemption must own and live on a property in Oregon.

Financial data　The exemption is $21,493 of the homestead property's real market value.

Duration　1 year; may be renewed as long as the eligible veterans or surviving spouse owns and occupies the primary residence.

Number awarded　Varies each year.

Deadline　This exemption is not automatic. Applications must be submitted by March of each year.

[1358]
PENNSYLVANIA DISABLED VETERANS REAL ESTATE TAX EXEMPTION

Office of the Deputy Adjutant General for Veterans
　Affairs
Building S-0-47, FTIG
Annville, PA 17003-5002
(717) 865-8907
Toll Free: (800) 54 PA VET (within PA)
Fax: (717) 861-8589　　　E-mail: RA-VA-Info@pa.gov
Web: www.dmva.state.pa.us

Summary　To exempt blind and disabled Pennsylvania veterans and their unremarried surviving spouses from all state real estate taxes.

Eligibility　Eligible to apply for this exemption are honorably-discharged veterans who are residents of Pennsylvania and who are blind, paraplegic, or 100% disabled from a service-connected disability sustained during wartime military service. The dwelling must be owned by the veteran solely or jointly with a spouse, and financial need for the exemption must be determined by the State Veterans' Commission. Veterans whose income is less than $81,340 per year are presumed to have financial need; veterans with income greater than $81,340 must document need. Upon the death of the veteran, the tax exemption passes on to the veteran's unremarried surviving spouse.

Financial data　This program exempts the principal residence (and the land on which it stands) from all real estate taxes.

Duration　The exemption continues as long as the eligible veteran or unremarried widow resides in Pennsylvania.

Number awarded　Varies each year.

Deadline　Deadline not specified.

[1359]
PRESCHOOL FINANCIAL AID PROGRAM

Alexander Graham Bell Association for the Deaf and
　Hard of Hearing
Attn: Financial Aid Coordinator
3417 Volta Place, N.W.
Washington, DC 20007-2778
(202) 337-5220　　　　　　Fax: (202) 337-8314
TDD: (202) 337-5221　E-mail: financialaid@agbell.org
Web: nc.agbell.org/page.aspx?pid=497

Summary　To provide financial aid to the parents of preschool children with moderate to profound hearing loss who need assistance to cover expenses associated with early intervention services.

Eligibility　Applicants must be parents or guardians of children between 4 and 6 years of age who have been diagnosed as having a moderate to profound bilateral hearing loss or auditory neuropathy. Children with cochlear implants are eligible, but those with unilateral hearing loss are not. Spoken communication must be the child's primary mode of communication. The family must be able to demonstrate financial need. Residents of Canada, the United States, and its territories are eligible.

Financial data　The amount awarded depends on the needs of the child; most grants range from $275 to $1,100 per year.

Duration　1 year; may be renewed upon reapplication, but preference is given to new applicants who are just enrolling their child in preschool.

Number awarded　Varies each year.

Deadline　July of each year.

[1360]
RAILROAD RETIREMENT DISABILITY ANNUITY

Railroad Retirement Board
Attn: Office of Public Affairs
844 North Rush Street
Chicago, IL 60611-2092
(312) 751-4777　　　　　Toll Free: (877) 772-5772
Fax: (312) 751-7154　　　TDD: (312) 751-4701
Web: www.rrb.gov

Summary　To provide an annuity to railroad workers with disabilities and their families.

Eligibility　The Railroad Retirement Board provides annuities for 2 types of disability. Eligible for total disability are regular employees of companies covered by the Railroad Retirement Act (railroads engaged in interstate commerce and certain of their subsidiaries, railroad associations, and national railway labor organizations) who are totally disabled for all regular work and have at least 10 years of creditable railroad service; credit for a month of railroad service is given for every month in which an employee had some compensated service for at least 1 day, but the 120 service months need not be consecutive. The other type of disability, occupational disability, is available to employees who have at least 20 years of service, or who are 60 years of age or older and have at least 10 years of service, and are permanently disabled from their regular railroad occupation. Survivor benefits are available to widows, widowers, unmarried children, and, in certain cases, parents, remarried widow(er)s, grandchildren, and surviving divorced spouses. For widow(er)s of workers with disabilities, annuities are payable at the age of 60; widow(er)s who are permanently and totally disabled are eligible if they are between the ages of 50 and 59 and the disability began within 7 years after the employee's death; widow(er)s of any age are eligible if they are caring for a child of the deceased employee under the age of 18 or a child with a disability of any age who became disabled before age 22. Unmarried children (or grandchildren if both parents are deceased) are eligible for survivor benefits if they are under the age of 18, or are still enrolled full time in an elementary or secondary school, or become totally and permanently disabled before age 22. Parents over the age of 60 who were dependent on the employee for at least half of the parent's support also qualify for survivor benefits. Surviving divorced spouses qualify if they were married to the employee for at least 10 years and are 60 years of age or older (50 or older if disabled), or if they are still caring for a child of the employee under 16 years of age or disabled. Remarried widow(er)s retain eligibility if they remarry after age 60 (after age 50 if disabled).

Financial data Benefits are based on months of service and earnings credits. Recently, the average monthly annuity paid to employees retired with disabilities was $2,221, for spouses and divorced spouses it was $817, for disabled widows and widowers it was $1,108, for widowed mothers and fathers it was $1,653, for remarried widows and widowers it was $896, for divorced widows and widowers it was $880, and for children it was $937.

Duration Disability annuities are paid until the employee dies or recovers from the disability; survivor annuities are paid until death or, in the case of able-bodied children, until age 18 or graduation from high school.

Additional data Employees who are disabled from their regular railroad occupation may work in another job and earn up to $700 per month or $8,400 per year without loss of any railroad retirement disability benefits. A 5-month waiting period beginning with the month after the month of the onset of disability is required before disability annuity payments can begin.

Number awarded Varies each year; recently, the number of employees retired with disabilities was 83,517, and disabled widows and widowers 4,251.

Deadline Deadline not specified.

[1361]
RUTH BILLOW MEMORIAL PERSONAL AID

Delta Gamma Foundation
Attn: Director, Service for Sight
3250 Riverside Drive
P.O. Box 21397
Columbus, OH 43221-0397
(614) 481-8169   Toll Free: (800) 644-5414
Fax: (614) 481-0133
E-mail: fngrants@deltagamma.org
Web: www.deltagamma.org

Summary To provide financial assistance to members of Delta Gamma sorority who are in need because of their visual impairment or that of a family member.

Eligibility This program is open to members of the sorority who require assistance 1) in order to restore or retain their sight; or 2) because of their responsibilities directly related to dependents who are blind or visually impaired. Applicants must be residents of the United States or Canada.

Financial data The amount awarded varies, depending upon individual circumstances.

Duration 1 year or more.

Number awarded Varies each year.

Deadline Applications may be submitted at any time.

[1362]
SOCIAL SECURITY DISABILITY INSURANCE (SSDI) BENEFITS

Social Security Administration
6401 Security Boulevard
Baltimore, MD 21235-0001
(410) 594-1234   Toll Free: (800) 772-1213
TDD: (800) 325-0778
Web: www.ssa.gov

Summary To provide monthly benefits to workers and their families if the worker becomes disabled or blind.

Eligibility This program defines disabled people as those who are unable to do any kind of work for which they are suited and whose disability has lasted or is expected to last for at least a year or to result in death. Blind people qualify if their vision cannot be corrected to better than 20/200 in their better eye or if their visual field is 20 degrees or less, even with corrective lenses. Family members who are eligible include 1) unmarried children, including adopted children and, in some cases, stepchildren and grandchildren who are under 18 years of age (19 if still in high school full time); 2) unmarried children, over 18 years of age, if they have a disability that started before age 22; and 3) spouses who are 62 years of age or older, or of any age if caring for a child of the disabled worker who is under 16 years of age or disabled. For deceased workers, disabled widow(er)s 50 years of age or older are also eligible. Applicants must also have worked long enough and recently enough under Social Security in order to qualify. Workers who become disabled before the age of 24 need 6 credits in the 3-year period ending when the disability begins; workers who become disabled between the ages of 24 and 31 must have credit for having worked half the time between the age of 21 and the date of disability; workers 31 years of age or older at the time of disability must have earned as many total credits as needed for retirement (from 20 credits if disabled at age 31 through 42 to 40 credits if disabled at age 62 or older) and must have earned at least 20 of the credits in the 10 years immediately before becoming disabled. An exception applies to blind workers who need no recent credit but may have earned the required credit any time after 1936.

Financial data The amount of the monthly benefit depends on several factors, including the worker's age at the time of disability, the number of dependents, and the amount of earnings on which Social Security taxes have been paid. Recently, the average monthly benefit was $1,110.70 for disabled workers, $298.60 for spouses of disabled workers, and $330.70 for children of disabled workers.

Duration For a disabled or blind person, whether a worker, widow, widower, surviving divorced spouse, or person over the age of 18 who became disabled before the age of 22, monthly benefits continue until the person is no longer disabled or dies. For a dependent spouse, benefits are paid until the worker is no longer disabled or dies. For a dependent child, the benefits continue until the child marries or reaches the age of 18 (19 if still enrolled as a full-time high school student).

Additional data Disabled workers may test their ability to return to work for a trial work period of up to 9 months, during which time they receive full SSDI benefits. At the end of that period, a decision is made as to whether or not they are able to engage in substantial gainful activity. Persons who find that they cannot continue substantial gainful employment continue to receive SSDI benefits without interruption. Persons who can engage in substantial gainful activity receive benefits for an additional 3 months after which payments cease. Several factors are considered to determine if the person can engage in substantial gainful employment, but the most important is income; for disabled people the amount is $1,000 a month gross wages and for blind people the income is $1,640 monthly.

Number awarded Varies; recently, approximately 8,630,000 disabled workers were receiving SSDI monthly benefits, along with 163,000 spouses and 1,897,000 children.

Deadline Deadline not specified.

[1363]
SOUTH CAROLINA DISABLED PERSON PROPERTY TAX EXEMPTION

South Carolina Department of Revenue
Attn: Property Division
301 Gervais Street
P.O. Box 125
Columbia, SC 29214
(803) 898-5480   Fax: (803) 898-5822
Web: www.sctax.org

Summary To exempt the home of disabled residents of South Carolina and their surviving spouses from property taxation.

Eligibility Eligible for this exemption are residents of South Carolina who are defined as paraplegic or hemiplegic and own a dwelling house that is their domicile. The exemption is allowed to the surviving spouse of the person as long as the spouse does not remarry, resides in the dwelling, and obtains the fee or a life estate in the dwelling. Paraplegic or hemiplegic includes a person with Parkinson's Disease, multiple sclerosis, or amyotrophic lateral sclerosis that has caused the same ambulatory difficulties as a person with paraparesis or hemiparesis. Surviving spouses of those persons are also eligible for this exemption as long as they remain unmarried.

Financial data The exemption applies to all taxes on 1 house and a lot (not to exceed 1 acre).

Duration The exemption extends as long as the person with a disability or the surviving spouse resides in the house.

Number awarded Varies each year.

Deadline Applications may be submitted at any time.

[1364]
SOUTH CAROLINA HOMESTEAD EXEMPTION PROGRAM

South Carolina Department of Revenue
301 Gervais Street
P.O. Box 125
Columbia, SC 29214
(803) 898-5680   Toll Free: (800) 763-1295
Fax: (803) 898-5822   E-mail: MillerC@sctax.org
Web: www.sctax.org

Summary To provide a homestead exemption to South Carolina residents who are elderly, disabled, or blind, and their widow(er)s.

Eligibility Legal residents of South Carolina who own a house or mobile home are eligible for this exemption if they are 65 years of age or older, totally and permanently disabled, or legally blind. Spouses of deceased persons who were eligible also qualify to receive the exemption as long as they remain unmarried.

Financial data The first $50,000 of the fair market value of the qualified applicant's home is exempted from property taxes. The exemption is from county, municipal, school, and special assessment real estate property taxes.

Duration The exemption continues as long as the homeowners live in their primary residence in South Carolina.

Additional data This program, established in 1972, is administered by county auditors.

Number awarded Varies each year.

Deadline Persons applying for this exemption for the first time must do so prior to July of each year; subsequently, no re-application is necessary unless the title or use of the property changes.

[1365]
SOUTH CAROLINA INCOME TAX EXEMPTION FOR THE ADOPTION OF A SPECIAL NEEDS CHILD

South Carolina Department of Revenue
301 Gervais Street
P.O. Box 125
Columbia, SC 29214
(803) 898-5000   Toll Free: (800) 763-1295
Fax: (803) 898-5822
Web: www.sctax.org

Summary To provide income tax exemptions to residents of South Carolina who adopt a special needs child.

Eligibility South Carolina residents who adopt a special needs child and provide the child's chief financial support are eligible for this exemption. For the purposes of the program, "special needs" is defined as a child with disabilities (physical, mental, or emotional), ethnic minority status, sibling group membership, medical condition, or age status that makes unassisted adoption unlikely. The child must be under the age of 21 or be incapable of self-support because of mental or physical disabilities to qualify for the program.

Financial data Eligible parents receive a $2,000 per year state income tax exemption.

Duration This exemption continues as long as the dependent is under 21 years of age, unless the child is regularly enrolled in an accredited school or college or is incapable of self-support because of mental or physical disabilities.

Additional data The entire deduction is allowed for a taxable year, even if the special needs child does not survive for the entire year. The program was started in 1985.

Number awarded Varies each year.

Deadline The exemption is filed on the parent's state income tax form each year, due in April.

[1366]
SOUTH CAROLINA PROPERTY TAX EXEMPTION FOR DISABLED VETERANS, LAW ENFORCEMENT OFFICERS, AND FIREFIGHTERS

South Carolina Department of Revenue
Attn: Property Division
301 Gervais Street
P.O. Box 125
Columbia, SC 29214
(803) 898-5480   Fax: (803) 898-5822
Web: www.sctax.org

Summary To exempt the residence of disabled South Carolina veterans, law enforcement officers, fire fighters, their unremarried widow(er)s, and others from property taxation.

Eligibility This exemption is available to owners of homes in South Carolina who are veterans of the U.S. armed forces, former law enforcement officers, or former fire fighters (including volunteer fire fighters). Applicants must be permanently and totally disabled from service-connected causes. The exemption is also available to qualified surviving spouses (defined to include unremarried spouses of disabled veterans, law enforcement officers, and fire fighters, as well as surviving spouses of service members killed in the line of duty, law enforcement officers who died in the line of duty, and fire fighters who died in the line of duty).

Financial data The exemption applies to all taxes on 1 house and a lot (not to exceed 1 acre).

Duration The exemption extends as long as the veteran, law enforcement officer, or fire fighter resides in the house, or as long as the spouse of a deceased veteran, service member, law enforcement officer, or fire fighter remains unremarried and resides in the original house or a single new dwelling.

Number awarded Varies each year.

Deadline Applications may be submitted at any time.

[1367]
SOUTH DAKOTA PROPERTY TAX EXEMPTION FOR PARAPLEGIC VETERANS

South Dakota Department of Revenue and Regulation
Attn: Property Tax Division
445 East Capitol Avenue
Pierre, SD 57501-3185
(605) 773-3311   Toll Free: (800) TAX-9188
Fax: (605) 773-6729   E-mail: PropTaxIn@state.sd.us
Web: www.state.sd.us

Summary To exempt from property taxation the homes of paraplegic veterans in South Dakota and their widow(er)s.

Eligibility This benefit is available to residents of South Dakota who are 1) paraplegic veterans, 2) veterans with loss or loss of use of both lower extremities, or 3) unremarried widows or widowers of such veterans. Applicants must own and occupy a dwelling (including the house, garage, and up to 1 acre on which the building is located) that is specifically designed for wheelchair use within the

structure. The veteran's injury does not have to be service connected.

Financial data Qualified dwellings are exempt from property taxation in South Dakota.

Duration The exemption applies as long as the dwelling is owned and occupied by the disabled veteran or widow(er).

Number awarded Varies each year.

Deadline Deadline not specified.

[1368]
SOUTH DAKOTA PROPERTY TAX REDUCTION FOR PARAPLEGICS

South Dakota Department of Revenue and Regulation
Attn: Property Tax Division
445 East Capitol Avenue
Pierre, SD 57501-3185
(605) 773-3311   Toll Free: (800) TAX-9188
Fax: (605) 773-6729   E-mail: PropTaxIn@state.sd.us
Web: www.state.sd.us

Summary To provide a reduction in property taxes on the homes of people with disabilities in South Dakota and their widow(er)s.

Eligibility This benefit is available to residents of South Dakota who are 1) paraplegic individuals, 2) individuals with loss or loss of use of both lower extremities, or 3) unremarried widows or widowers of such individuals. Applicants must own and occupy a dwelling (including the house, garage, and up to 1 acre on which the building is located) that is specifically designed for wheelchair use within the structure. They must have a federal adjusted income of less than $8,000 if they live in a single-member household or less than $12,000 if they live in a multiple-member household.

Financial data The reduction depends on the federal adjusted gross income of the applicant. For single-member households, the reduction is 100% if the income is less than $5,000, 75% if the income is between $5,000 and $6,000, 50% if the income is between $6,000 and $7,000, or 25% if the income is between $7,000 and $8,000. For multiple-member household, the reduction is 100% if the income is less than $9,000, 75% if the income is between $9,000 and $10,000, 50% if the income is between $10,000 and $11,000, or 25% if the income is between $11,000 and $12,000.

Duration The reduction applies as long as the dwelling is owned and occupied by the disabled person or widow(er).

Number awarded Varies each year.

Deadline Deadline not specified.

[1369]
TENNESSEE PROPERTY TAX RELIEF FOR DISABLED VETERANS AND THEIR SPOUSES

Tennessee Comptroller of the Treasury
Attn: Property Tax Relief Program
James K. Polk State Office Building
505 Deaderick Street, Room 1700
Nashville, TN 37243-1402
(615) 747-8858   Fax: (615) 532-3866
E-mail: kim.darden@cot.tn.gov
Web: www.comptroller1.state.tn.us/pa/patxr.asp

Summary   To provide property tax relief to blind and disabled veterans and their spouses in Tennessee.

Eligibility   This exemption is offered to veterans or their surviving unremarried spouses who are residents of Tennessee and own and live in their home in the state. The veteran must have served in the U.S. armed forces and 1) have acquired, as a result of such service, a disability from paraplegia, permanent paralysis of both legs and lower part of the body resulting from traumatic injury, disease to the spinal cord or brain, legal blindness, or loss or loss of use of both legs or arms from any service-connected cause; 2) have been rated by the U.S. Department of Veterans Affairs (VA) as 100% permanently disabled as a result of service as a prisoner of war for at least 5 months; or 3) have been rated by the VA as 100% permanently and totally disabled from any other service-connected cause. Unremarried spouses of deceased veterans are also eligible if 1) the veteran was receiving tax relief as a disabled veteran before death; 2) death resulted from a service-connected, combat-related cause, or killed in action; or 3) death resulted from being deployed, away from any home base of training, and in support of combat operations.

Financial data   The amount of the relief depends on the property assessment and the tax rate in the city or county where the beneficiary lives. The maximum market value on which tax relief is calculated is $175,000.

Duration   1 year; may be renewed as long as the eligible veteran or surviving unremarried spouse owns and occupies the primary residence.

Number awarded   Varies each year.

Deadline   Deadline not specified.

[1370]
TEXAS PROPERTY TAX EXEMPTION FOR DISABLED VETERANS AND THEIR FAMILIES

Texas Veterans Commission
P.O. Box 12277
Austin, TX 78711-2277
(512) 463-5538
Toll Free: (800) 252-VETS (within TX)
Fax: (512) 475-2395   E-mail: info@tvc.state.tx.us
Web: texas-veterans.com/claims/property-tax-exemption

Summary   To extend property tax exemptions on the appraised value of their property to blind, disabled, and other Texas veterans and their surviving family members.

Eligibility   Eligible veterans must be Texas residents rated at least 10% service-connected disabled. Surviving

spouses and children of eligible veterans are also covered by this program.

Financial data   For veterans in Texas whose disability is rated as 10% through 29%, the first $5,000 of the appraised property value is exempt from taxation; veterans rated as 30% through 49% disabled are exempt from the first $7,500 of appraised value; those with a 50% through 69% disability are exempt from the first $10,000 of appraised value; the exemption applies to the first $12,000 of appraised value for veterans with disabilities rated as 70% to 99%; veterans rated as 100% disabled are exempt from 100% of the appraised value of their property. A veteran whose disability is 10% or more and who is 65 years or older is entitled to exemption of the first $12,000 of appraised property value. A veteran whose disability consists of the loss of use of 1 or more limbs, total blindness in 1 or both eyes, or paraplegia is exempt from the first $12,000 of the appraised value. The unremarried surviving spouse of a deceased veteran who died on active duty and who, at the time of death had a compensable disability and was entitled to an exemption, is entitled to the same exemption. The surviving spouse of a person who died on active duty is entitled to exemption of the first $5,000 of appraised value of the spouse's property; they are also eligible for the 100% exemption. A surviving child of a person who dies on active duty is entitled to exemption of the first $5,000 of appraised value of the child's property, as long as the child is unmarried and under 21 years of age.

Duration   1 year; may be renewed as long as the eligible veteran (or unremarried surviving spouse or child) owns and occupies the primary residence in Texas.

Additional data   This program is administered at the local level by the various taxing authorities.

Number awarded   Varies each year.

Deadline   April of each year.

[1371]
THE 9-11 HELPAMERICA FOUNDATION ASSISTANCE

The 9-11 HelpAmerica Foundation
14147 Hawthorne Boulevard
Hawthorne, CA 90250
(310) 355-0266
Web: www.911helpamerica.com

Summary   To provide support to veterans wounded in Iraq or Afghanistan and to families of veterans and military personnel wounded or killed in combat.

Eligibility   This assistance is available to 1) veterans disabled as a result of service in Operation Iraqi Freedom or Operation Enduring Freedom; and 2) families of veterans and military personnel injured or killed in those operations. Applicants must need general financial assistance to help meet special circumstances, especially those associated with the death or disability of the veteran or military service member.

Financial data   The amount of the support depends on the need of the recipient.

Duration   Support is provided for up to 18 months.

Additional data This foundation was established in October, 2001.

Number awarded Varies; in a recent year, 20 disabled veterans or survivors received support from this foundation.

Deadline Applications may be submitted at any time.

[1372]
THOMARA LATIMER CANCER FOUNDATION GRANTS

Thomara Latimer Cancer Foundation
Attn: Cancer Funding Committee
Franklin Plaza Center
29193 Northeastern Highway, Suite 528
Southfield, MI 48034-1006
(248) 557-2346   Fax: (248) 557-8063
E-mail: funding@thomlatimercares.org
Web: www.thomlatimercares.org

Summary To provide funding to cancer patients and family members who are unable to meet expenses.

Eligibility This program is open to cancer patients and family members who, after a thorough investigation of other resources, are unable to meet expenses that are causing a financial burden. Applicants must be seeking funding for homecare assistance (including child care); medication or treatment not covered by insurance (including alternative care, family lodging for out-of-town treatment); transportation to and from treatment, physician, support facilities; special needs funds for wigs or head coverings for diagnosis or treatment related to hair loss; or assistance with final arrangements.

Financial data Grant amounts depend on the availability of funds.

Duration These are 1-time grants.

Number awarded Varies each year.

Deadline Applications may be submitted at any time.

[1373]
UNITEDHEALTHCARE CHILDREN'S FOUNDATION GRANTS

UnitedHealthCare Children's Foundation
MN012-S286
P.O. Box 41
Minneapolis, MN 55440-0041
(952) 992-4459
Web: www.uhccf.org

Summary To provide funding to parents of children who have medical needs not covered by commercial health insurance.

Eligibility This program is open to families who have children with medical needs not covered or not fully covered by their commercial health benefit plan. Children must be 16 years of age or younger and the family income must be less than $50,000 for a family of 2, rising to $125,000 for a family of 5 or more. Funding is not provided for alternative treatments (e.g., neuro-feedback, social skills therapy); dental or orthodontic treatment; drugs not licensed by the Food and Drug Administration; personal care, comfort, and convenience (e.g., camps, home

improvements, vehicles); procedures and treatments (e.g., biofeedback, biomedical consultations, heavy metal toxicity testing, hyperbaric oxygen treatment, herbal testing); reproduction (e.g., infertility, pregnancy, birthing); or other exclusions (e.g., burial costs, clinical trials).

Financial data Grants are limited to $5,000 within a 12-month period or 85% of the fund balance, whichever is less. Awards to a single individual are limited to a lifetime maximum of $10,000. Funds are paid directly to a health professional.

Duration These are 1-time grants that may be renewed until the lifetime maximum limit is reached.

Additional data This program began in 2000.

Number awarded Varies each year; since the program began, it has awarded more than $1 million to more than 400 families.

Deadline Applications may be submitted at any time.

[1374]
UTAH BLIND PROPERTY TAX EXEMPTION

Utah State Tax Commission
Attn: Property Tax Division
210 North 1950 West
Salt Lake City, UT 84134
(801) 297-3600   Toll Free: (800) 662-4335, ext. 3600
Fax: (801) 297-3699   TDD: (801) 297-2020
E-mail: propertytax@utah.gov
Web: propertytax.utah.gov

Summary To exempt from taxation a portion of the real and tangible property of blind people and their families in Utah.

Eligibility This exemption is available to legally blind property owners in Utah, along with their unremarried surviving spouses or minor orphans. First-year applications must be accompanied by a signed statement from an ophthalmologist and, if appropriate, a death certificate.

Financial data The first $11,500 of the taxable value of real and tangible personal property is exempt from taxation.

Duration The exemption is available each year the beneficiary owns property in Utah.

Number awarded Varies each year.

Deadline Applications must be submitted by August of each year.

[1375]
UTAH DISABLED VETERAN PROPERTY TAX ABATEMENT

Utah Department of Veteran's Affairs
Attn: Director
550 Foothill Boulevard, Room 202
Salt Lake City, UT 84108
(801) 326-2372   Toll Free: (800) 894-9497 (within UT)
Fax: (801) 326-2369   E-mail: veterans@utah.gov
Web: veterans.utah.gov

Summary To exempt a portion of the property of disabled veterans and their families in Utah from taxation.

Eligibility This program is available to residents of Utah who are disabled veterans or their unremarried widow(er)s or minor orphans. The disability must be at least 10% and incurred as the result of injuries in the line of duty.

Financial data The exemption is based on the disability rating of the veteran, to a maximum of $232,312 for a 100% disability. The exemption for veterans with lesser disabilities is equal to $232,312 times the percentage of their disability.

Duration This benefit is available as long as the disabled veteran or family members reside in Utah.

Deadline Tax exemption applications must be filed with the county government of residence by August of the initial year; once eligibility has been established, reapplication is not required.

[1376]
UTAH VETERAN'S PROPERTY TAX EXEMPTION

Utah State Tax Commission
Attn: Property Tax Division
210 North 1950 West
Salt Lake City, UT 84134
(801) 297-3600   Toll Free: (800) 662-4335, ext. 3600
Fax: (801) 297-7699   TDD: (801) 297-2020
E-mail: propertytax@utah.gov
Web: propertytax.utah.gov

Summary To exempt from taxation a portion of the real and tangible property of disabled veterans and their families in Utah.

Eligibility This exemption is available to property owners in Utah who are veterans with a disability of at least 10% incurred in the line of duty, along with their unremarried surviving spouses or minor orphans. First year applications must be accompanied by proof of military service and proof of disability or death.

Financial data Veterans with a 100% disability are entitled to a full current-year exemption (recently, that was $237,949). Veterans with disabilities rated at a smaller percentage are entitled to that percentage of the current year exemption amount. Survivors are entitled to the same percentage as if the veteran were still living.

Duration The exemption is available each year the beneficiary owns property in Utah.

Number awarded Varies each year.

Deadline Applications must be submitted by August of each year.

[1377]
VERMONT PROPERTY TAX EXEMPTION FOR DISABLED VETERANS

Vermont Department of Taxes
Attn: Property Valuation and Review Division
P.O. Box 1577
Montpelier, VT 05601-1577
(802) 828-2865   Toll Free: (866) 828-2865 (within VT)
Fax: (802) 828-2824
Web: www.state.vt.us/tax/pvrmilitary.shtml

Summary To exempt disabled Vermont veterans and their dependents from the payment of at least a portion of the state's property tax.

Eligibility Entitled to a property tax exemption are veterans of any war (or their spouses, widow(er)s, or children) who are receiving wartime disability compensation for at least a 50% disability, wartime death compensation, wartime dependence and indemnity compensation, or pension for disability paid through any military department or the Department of Veterans Affairs. Unremarried widow(er)s of previously qualified veterans are also entitled to the exemption whether or not they are receiving government compensation or a pension.

Financial data Up to $10,000 of the assessed value of real and personal property belonging to eligible veterans or their unremarried widow(er)s is exempt from taxation; individual towns may increase the exemption to as much as $40,000.

Duration 1 year; may be renewed as long as the eligible veteran or widow(er) continues to be the owner/occupant of the residence and lives in Vermont.

Additional data Only 1 exemption may be allowed on a property.

Number awarded Varies each year.

Deadline April of each year.

[1378]
VIRGINIA LIVABLE HOME TAX CREDIT

Virginia Department of Taxation
Attn: Tax Credit Unit
1957 Westmoreland Street
P.O. Box 715
Richmond, VA 23218-0715
(804) 786-2992   Fax: (804) 786-2800
Web: www.tax.virginia.gov

Summary To provide an income tax credit to residents of Virginia who wish to install accessibility features in a home to accommodate disabled individuals.

Eligibility This credit is available to residents of Virginia who either 1) purchase a new residence that has universal visibility or accessibility features, or 2) retrofit a residence to improve accessibility or provide universal visitability. New residences must include the 3 features of universal visitability (at least 1 zero-step entrance, an accessible bathroom on the same floor as the zero-step entrance, and doors with at least 32 inches of clear width and hallways of at least 36 inches of clear width to the accessible bathroom and eating area). Retrofitting of an existing residential unit must include at least 1 accessibility feature, lifts, or elevators and meet the requirements of an existing standard or provide sensory modifications.

Financial data The credit is $5,000 for the purchase of a new residence or 50% of the cost of retrofitting activities, up to $5,000.

Additional data This program was formerly known as the Virginia Home Accessibility Features for the Disabled Credit.

Number awarded Varies each year. The Department of Taxation is allowed to grant up to $1 million in these credits each year; if the total amount of applications for credits exceeds that sum, the Virginia Department of Housing and Community Development prorates the amounts of credits among the eligible applicants.

Deadline Applications must be submitted by February of each year.

[1379]
WASHINGTON PROPERTY TAX ASSISTANCE PROGRAM FOR WIDOWS OR WIDOWERS OF VETERANS

Washington State Department of Revenue
Attn: Property Tax Division
P.O. Box 47471
Olympia, WA 98504-7471
(360) 534-1410   Toll Free: (800) 647-7706
TDD: (360) 705-6718
Web: dor.wa.gov

Summary To exempt from taxation in Washington a portion of the assessed valuation of property owned by senior citizens or people with disabilities who are widow(er)s of veterans.

Eligibility This exemption is available to residents of Washington who are either 62 years of age or older or who have a disability that prevents them from being gainfully employed and is expected to last for at least 12 months. Applicants must be the unmarried widow or widower of a veteran who 1) died as a result of a service-connected disability; 2) was 100% disabled for 10 years prior to his or her death; 3) was a former prisoner of war and rated as 100% disabled for at least 1 year prior to death; or 4) died in active duty or in active training status. They must own property that they use as their principal home for at least 6 months of the year; mobile homes may qualify as a residence even if its owner does not own the land where it is located. Their annual disposable income may not exceed $40,000 per year.

Financial data The exemption is $100,000 of the home's assessed value if disposable income is $30,000 or less, $75,000 if disposable income is $30,001 to $35,000, or $50,000 if disposable income is $35,001 to $40,000.

Duration The exemption is available as long as the widow or widower meets the eligibility requirements.

Additional data This program offered assistance beginning with the 2006 tax year.

Number awarded Varies each year.

Deadline 30 days before taxes are due.

[1380]
WASHINGTON PROPERTY TAX EXEMPTIONS FOR SENIOR CITIZENS AND DISABLED PERSONS

Washington State Department of Revenue
Attn: Property Tax Division
P.O. Box 47471
Olympia, WA 98504-7471
(360) 534-1410   Toll Free: (800) 647-7706
TDD: (360) 705-6718
Web: dor.wa.gov

Summary To exempt a portion of the property owned by senior citizens and people with disabilities, including their surviving spouses, from taxation in Washington.

Eligibility This exemption is available to residents of Washington who are 1) unable to work because of a disability, 2) veterans with a 100% service-connected disability, 3) at least 61 years of age, or 4) a surviving spouse at least 57 years of age of a person who was approved for this exemption. Applicants must own property that they use as their principal home for at least 6 months of the year; mobile homes may qualify as a residence even if its owner does not own the land where it is located. Their annual disposable income may not exceed $35,000 per year.

Financial data Property owners whose annual income is $25,000 or less are exempt from regular property taxes on the first $60,000 or 60% of their home's assessed value, whichever is greater. Property owners whose annual income is between $25,001 and $30,000 are exempt from regular property taxes on $50,000 or 35% of the assessed value, whichever is greater, not to exceed $70,000 or the assessed value. Property owners whose annual income is $35,000 or less are exempt from all levies that have been approved by voters in excess of regular property taxes.

Duration The exemption is available as long as the property owner meets the eligibility requirements.

Number awarded Varies each year.

Deadline Applications for each year are due by December of the preceding year.

[1381]
WEST VIRGINIA SENIOR CITIZEN OR DISABILITY INCOME TAX EXEMPTION

West Virginia State Tax Department
Attn: Taxpayer Services Division
P.O. Box 3784
Charleston, WV 25337-3784
(304) 558-3333 Toll Free: (800) 982-8297 (within WV)
Fax: (304) 558-3269   TDD: (800) 282-9833
Web: www.wva.state.wv.us/wvtax/default.aspx

Summary To provide income tax exemptions for West Virginia residents with disabilities and their surviving spouses.

Eligibility Residents of West Virginia who are totally and permanently disabled (or 65 years of age or older) are eligible for this income tax exemption. Surviving spouses of eligible residents are also entitled to the exemption.

Financial data Qualifying taxpayers may deduct from state income taxation up to $8,000 for a single return or a maximum of $8,000 per person for a joint return.

Duration The exemption continues as long as the eligible resident (or his/her spouse) remains a resident of West Virginia.

Deadline Deadline not specified.

[1382]
WISCONSIN VETERANS AND SURVIVING SPOUSES PROPERTY TAX CREDIT

Wisconsin Department of Revenue
Attn: Homestead Credit
2135 Rimrock Road
P.O. Box 34
Madison, WI 53786-0001
(608) 266-8641   Fax: (608) 267-1030
E-mail: homestd@revenue.wi.gov
Web: www.revenue.wi.gov/individuals/military.html

Summary To provide an income tax credit to disabled Wisconsin veterans and their surviving spouses equal to the amount of property taxes they pay.

Eligibility This credit is available to Wisconsin veterans who served on active duty under honorable conditions in the U.S. armed forces and have resided in Wisconsin for any consecutive 5-year period after entry into active duty. Applicants must have either a service-connected disability rating of 100% or a 100% disability rating based on individual unemployability. Also eligible are unremarried surviving spouses of such disabled veterans and of members of the National Guard or a Reserve component of the U.S. armed forces who were residents of Wisconsin and died in the line of duty while on active or inactive duty for training purposes.

Financial data Eligible veterans and surviving spouses are entitled to an income tax credit equal to the amount of property taxes they pay on their principal residence.

Duration The credit is available as long as the recipient resides in Wisconsin.

Number awarded Varies each year.

Deadline Income tax returns must be filed by April of each year.

[1383]
WYOMING VETERANS PROPERTY TAX EXEMPTION

Wyoming Department of Revenue
Attn: Property Tax Relief Program
122 West 25th Street, Second Floor West
Cheyenne, WY 82002-0110
(307) 777-7320   Fax: (307) 777-7527
E-mail: DirectorOfRevenue@wy.gov
Web: revenue.state.wy.us

Summary To provide a partial tax exemption on the property owned by disabled and other veterans and their surviving spouses in Wyoming.

Eligibility This program is open to honorably-discharged veterans who were Wyoming residents at the time they entered military service and have resided in Wyoming for 3 years prior to applying for this exemption. Applicants must have served during specified periods of war time or have received an armed forces expeditionary medal or other authorized service or campaign medal for service in an armed conflict in a foreign country. Surviving spouses of qualified veterans are also eligible. The exemption applies to county fees only, not state fees.

Financial data Veterans and spouses may exempt $3,000 in assessed value of property from taxation per year. Disabled veterans are entitled to additional exemptions that depend on the level of their disability, to a maximum of $2,000 for a 100% disability.

Duration Veterans and spouses are entitled to use these exemptions as long as they reside in Wyoming and own the property as their principal residence.

Number awarded Varies each year.

Deadline Applicants must advise their county assessor of their intent to use the exemption by May of each year.

Indexes

Program Title Index

If you know the name of a particular funding program and want to find out where it is covered in the directory, use the Program Title Index. Here, program titles are arranged alphabetically, word by word. To assist you in your search, every program is listed by all its known names or abbreviations. In addition, we've used a two-character alphabetical code (within parentheses) to help you determine if the program falls within your scope of interest. The first character (capitalized) in the code identifies the program focus: A = Any Disability; V = Visual Disabilities; H = Hearing Disabilities; P = Physical/Orthopedic; O = Other Disabilities/Disorders; F = Families of the Disabled. The second character (lower-cased) identifies funding type: s = scholarships; f = fellowships; g = grants-in-aid. Here's how the code works: if a program is followed by (H–f) 281, the program is described in the Hearing Disabilities chapter, in the fellowships section, in entry 281. If the same program title is followed by another entry number—for example, (F–g) 1284—the program is also described in the Families of the Disabled chapter, under grants-in-aid, in entry 1284. Remember: the numbers cited here refer to program entry numbers, not to page numbers in the book.

A—Any Disability	V—Visual	H—Hearing	P—Physical/Orthopedic	O—Other Disabilities	F—Families
s—scholarships			f—fellowships		g—grants-in-aid

443

A—Any Disability	V—Visual	H—Hearing	P—Physical/Orthopedic	O—Other Disabilities	F—Families
s—scholarships			f—fellowships		g—grants-in-aid

A—Any Disability   V—Visual   H—Hearing   P—Physical/Orthopedic   O—Other Disabilities   F—Families

s—scholarships   f—fellowships   g—grants-in-aid

A—Any Disability	V—Visual	H—Hearing	P—Physical/Orthopedic	O—Other Disabilities	F—Families
s—scholarships			f—fellowships		g—grants-in-aid

Herter Memorial Scholarship. *See* Christian A. Herter Memorial Scholarship, entry (A—s) 15

Higgins-Hussman Foundation Memorial Scholarship. *See* Lisa Higgins-Hussman Foundation Scholarship, entries (O—s) 854, (O—f) 955, (F—s) 1133, (F—f) 1241

High Plains Cancer Survivor Scholarships, (O—s) 825, (O—f) 952

Higher Education Assistance Program Scholarship, (P—s) 651, (O—s) 826

HIKE Fund Grants, (H—g) 625

Hissey College Scholarships. *See* Alexander Graham Bell College Scholarship Awards Program, entry (H—s) 590

Hiteshew Memorial Scholarships for Siblings. *See* Doug Hiteshew Memorial Scholarships for Siblings, entry (F—s) 1058

Hiteshew Memorial Scholarships for Students. *See* Doug Hiteshew Memorial Scholarships for Students, entry (O—s) 798

Hobson Scholarship. *See* Hemophilia Health Services Memorial Scholarships, entries (O—s) 823, (O—f) 951

Hofstetter Opportunity Grants. *See* Hank Hofstetter Opportunity Grants, entries (V—s) 364, (V—g) 536

Holly Elliott and Laurel Glass Scholarship Endowment, (V—f) 477, (H—f) 616

Honka Scholarships. *See* Emil A. Honka Scholarships, entries (V—s) 349, (V—f) 466

Hope for the Warriors Immediate Needs Grants, (A—g) 214, (F—g) 1294

Hope for the Warriors Spouse/Caregiver Scholarships, (F—s) 1089, (F—f) 1233

Horatio Alger National Scholarship Program, (A—s) 32

Horizon Scholarships. *See* Harvey Picker Horizon Scholarships, entries (F—s) 1084, (F—f) 1232

Howard E. May Memorial Scholarship. *See* National Federation of the Blind of Connecticut Scholarships, entries (V—s) 400, (V—f) 495

Howard Taylor Scholarship. *See* Eastern Amputee Golf Association Scholarship Award, entries (P—s) 646, (F—s) 1061

Huber Learning through Listening Awards. *See* Marion Huber Learning through Listening Awards, entry (O—s) 861

Huey and Angelina Wilson Nontraditional Scholarships, (O—s) 827, (F—s) 1090

Huey and Angelina Wilson Traditional Scholarships, (O—s) 828

Hugh S. Niles Memorial Scholarship. *See* Pennsylvania National Guard Scholarship Fund, entry (F—s) 1186

Hughes, '18 Fellowship. *See* Regina Olson Hughes, '18, Fellowship, entry (H—f) 620

Hunt Scholarship. *See* Alexander Graham Bell College Scholarship Awards Program, entry (H—s) 590

Hunter Memorial Scholarship. *See* Michael A. Hunter Memorial Scholarship, entries (O—s) 866, (F—s) 1144

Hurdus President's Award. *See* Syde Hurdus President's Award, entries (V—s) 436, (V—f) 515

Hylton and Ron Niederman Scholarships. *See* Mike Hylton and Ron Niederman Scholarships, entries (O—s) 870, (F—s) 1147

I

I. King Jordan, '70 Fellowship. *See* Gallaudet University Alumni Association Graduate Fellowship Fund, entry (H—f) 612

IADES Fellowship Award, (H—f) 617

Idaho Circuit Breaker Property Tax Reduction, (A—g) 215, (V—g) 538

Idaho Income Tax Deduction for the Blind and Their Widow(er)s, (V—g) 539

Idaho Income Tax Exemption for Maintaining a Home for the Developmentally Disabled, (O—g) 1002, (F—g) 1295

Idaho Minority and "At Risk" Student Scholarship, (A—s) 33

Idaho Public Safety Officer Dependent Scholarship, (F—s) 1091

Idaho Retirement Benefits Deduction, (A—g) 216, (F—g) 1296

Idaho War Veteran's Emergency Grant Program, (A—g) 217, (F—g) 1297

Illinois Children of Veterans Scholarships, (F—s) 1092

Illinois Disabled Persons' Homestead Exemption, (A—g) 218

Illinois Disabled Veterans' Homestead Exemption, (A—g) 219, (F—g) 1298

Illinois Disabled Veterans' Standard Homestead Exemption, (A—g) 220

Illinois Grant Program for Dependents of Correctional Officers, (F—s) 1093

Illinois Grant Program for Dependents of Police or Fire Officers, (F—s) 1094, (F—f) 1234

Illinois Income Tax Exemption for the Blind, (V—g) 540

Illinois Income Tax Subtraction for Government Retirees, (A—g) 221

Illinois MIA/POW Scholarship, (A—s) 34, (F—s) 1095

Ina Brudnick Scholarship Award, (O—s) 829

Incight Scholarships, (A—s) 35

Indiana Breast Cancer Legacy Scholarship Fund, (F—s) 1096

Indiana Child of Veteran and Public Safety Officer Supplemental Grant Program, (F—s) 1097, (F—f) 1235

Indiana Disability Retirement Income Tax Deduction, (A—g) 222

Indiana Income Tax Exemption for the Blind, (V—g) 541

Indiana Organ Procurement Organization Foundation Scholarships. *See* IOPO Foundation Scholarships, entries (O—s) 831, (F—s) 1099

Indiana Property Tax Deduction for Blind or Disabled Persons, (A—g) 223, (V—g) 542

Indiana Property Tax Deductions for Disabled Veterans, (A—g) 224, (F—g) 1299

Injured Marine Semper Fi Grants, (A—g) 225, (F—g) 1300

A—Any Disability	V—Visual	H—Hearing	P—Physical/Orthopedic	O—Other Disabilities	F—Families
s—scholarships			f—fellowships		g—grants-in-aid

A—Any Disability   **V—Visual**   **H—Hearing**   **P—Physical/Orthopedic**   **O—Other Disabilities**   **F—Families**
s—scholarships   **f—fellowships**   **g—grants-in-aid**

A—Any Disability   V—Visual   H—Hearing   P—Physical/Orthopedic   O—Other Disabilities   F—Families
s—scholarships   f—fellowships   g—grants-in-aid

A—Any Disability	V—Visual	H—Hearing	P—Physical/Orthopedic	O—Other Disabilities	F—Families
s—scholarships			f—fellowships		g—grants-in-aid

A—Any Disability	V—Visual	H—Hearing	P—Physical/Orthopedic	O—Other Disabilities	F—Families
s—scholarships			f—fellowships		g—grants-in-aid

A—Any Disability **V—Visual** **H—Hearing** **P—Physical/Orthopedic** **O—Other Disabilities** **F—Families**
s—scholarships **f—fellowships** **g—grants-in-aid**

A—Any Disability   V—Visual   H—Hearing   P—Physical/Orthopedic   O—Other Disabilities   F—Families

s—scholarships   f—fellowships   g—grants-in-aid

Paul Leimkuehler Memorial Scholarship. *See* Eastern Amputee Golf Association Scholarship Award, entries (P—s) 646, (F—s) 1061

Paul W. Airey Memorial Scholarship. *See* Chief Master Sergeants of the Air Force Scholarships, entries (A—s) 14, (F—s) 1041

Peace Officers Research Association of California Scholarships. *See* PORAC Scholarships, entry (A—s) 64

Pearl Scholarship Program. *See* Minnie Pearl Scholarship Program, entry (H—s) 601

Pediatric Brain Tumor Foundation Scholarship Program, (O—s) 889

Peggy Sherrell Memorial Scholarship, (O—s) 890

Peikoff, '29 Fellowship. *See* Gallaudet University Alumni Association Graduate Fellowship Fund, entry (H—f) 612

Pennsylvania Association of Medical Suppliers Scholarship, (A—s) 61

Pennsylvania Blind Veterans Pension, (V—g) 576

Pennsylvania Disabled Veterans Real Estate Tax Exemption, (A—g) 294, (V—g) 577, (P—g) 738, (F—g) 1358

Pennsylvania Educational Gratuity for Veterans' Dependents, (F—s) 1185

Pennsylvania National Guard Enlisted Association USAA Scholarship. *See* Pennsylvania National Guard Scholarship Fund, entry (F—s) 1186

Pennsylvania National Guard Scholarship Fund, (F—s) 1186

Pennsylvania Paralyzed Veterans Pension, (P—g) 739

Pequeno Memorial Scholarship. *See* Dakota Pequeno Memorial Scholarship, entry (O—s) 789

Perez Foundation Scholarships. *See* Steven M. Perez Foundation Scholarships, entries (O—s) 918, (F—s) 1201

Perkins Coie Diversity Student Fellowships, (A—f) 140

Perlita Liwanag Memorial Scholarship, (O—s) 891, (O—f) 961, (F—s) 1187, (F—f) 1250

Persina Scholarship. *See* National Press Club Scholarship for Journalism Diversity, entry (A—s) 52

Peter and Bruce Bidstrup Scholarship Fund, (O—s) 892

Peter Grunwald Scholarship. *See* National Federation of the Blind of Illinois Scholarships, entries (V—s) 402, (V—f) 496

Peter Lindh Scholarship, (V—s) 426, (V—f) 506

Phillips Award. *See* Jay and Rose Phillips Award, entry (P—f) 694

Phillips Caregiver Award. *See* Jay and Rose Phillips Award, entry (P—f) 694

Picker Horizon Scholarships. *See* Harvey Picker Horizon Scholarships, entries (F—s) 1084, (F—f) 1232

PinkRose Breast Cancer Scholarship, (F—s) 1188

Pinky Johnson Memorial Scholarship. *See* National Federation of the Blind of California Scholarships, entries (V—s) 398, (V—f) 494

Pinnacol Foundation Scholarship Program, (F—s) 1189

Pistilli Scholarships. *See* P.O. Pistilli Scholarships, entry (A—s) 63

P.J. Zuker, Jr. Memorial Scholarship. *See* ChairScholars Foundation National Scholarships, entry (P—s) 639

Plapinger Award. *See* Anna and Henry Plapinger Award, entry (H—f) 610

Playwright Discovery Award, (A—s) 62

P.O. Pistilli Scholarships, (A—s) 63

Popkin Memorial Scholarship. *See* Hope for the Warriors Spouse/Caregiver Scholarships, entries (F—s) 1089, (F—f) 1233

PORAC Scholarships, (A—s) 64

Postdoctoral Research Fellowships in Biology, (A—f) 141

Potts Scholarship. *See* Deanna Lynn Potts Scholarship, entry (O—s) 792

Poulson Family Scholarships, (V—s) 427, (V—f) 507

Powering Education Scholarships, (A—s) 65, (A—f) 142

Preschool Financial Aid Program, (H—g) 631, (F—g) 1359

Price Memorial Scholarship. *See* Utah Hemophilia Foundation Scholarships, entries (O—s) 932, (F—s) 1218

Price Scholarship. *See* George and Linda Price Scholarship, entries (O—s) 814, (O—f) 949, (F—s) 1075, (F—f) 1230

Professional Associates Program for Women and Minorities at Brookhaven National Laboratory, (A—f) 143

Professor Ulla Hedner Scholarships, (O—s) 893

Project Red Flag Academic Scholarship for Women with Bleeding Disorders. *See* Victory for Women Academic Scholarship for Women with Bleeding Disorders, entries (O—s) 935, (O—f) 979

Prows Memorial Scholarship. *See* Beverly Prows Memorial Scholarship, entries (V—s) 332, (V—f) 455

PVA Educational Scholarship Program, (P—s) 671, (F—s) 1190

Q

Qualls Memorial Scholarships. *See* Floyd Qualls Memorial Scholarships, entries (V—s) 356, (V—f) 470

Quarterly Grant Program of the Jim "Catfish" Hunter Chapter, (P—g) 740

Quigley Memorial Scholarship. *See* Rosemary Quigley Memorial Scholarship, entries (O—s) 900, (O—f) 963

Quinci Scholarships. *See* Salvatore E. Quinci Scholarships, entry (O—s) 903

R

Railroad Retirement Disability Annuity, (A—g) 295, (F—g) 1360

Ralph G. Norman Scholarships, (O—s) 894

Ray and Eileen Froncillo Scholarship. *See* Eastern Amputee Golf Association Scholarship Award, entries (P—s) 646, (F—s) 1061

A—Any Disability   V—Visual   H—Hearing   P—Physical/Orthopedic   O—Other Disabilities   F—Families

s—scholarships   f—fellowships   g—grants-in-aid

Reaching Out to Cancer Kids College Scholarship Program. *See* R.O.C.K. College Scholarship Program, entry (O—s) 899

Red Rose Scholarship, (V—s) 428

Reduced Tuition for Children and Spouses of South Dakota National Guardsmen Disabled or Deceased in the Line of Duty, (F—s) 1191

Reed Award. *See* Geological Society of America Graduate Student Research Grants, entry (A—f) 114

Reed Scholarship. *See* Eastern Amputee Golf Association Scholarship Award, entries (P—s) 646, (F—s) 1061

Reggie Johnson Memorial Scholarship. *See* Association of Blind Citizens Scholarships, entry (V—s) 330

Regina Olson Hughes, '18, Fellowship, (H—f) 620

RehabGYM Scholarship, (A—s) 66

Renee Feldman Scholarships, (F—s) 1192

Rennie Memorial Fund. *See* California Eastern Star Cancer Assistance, entry (O—g) 985

Renzi, USA (Ret.)/ManTech International Corporation Teacher's Scholarship. *See* MG Eugene C. Renzi, USA (Ret.)/ManTech International Corporation Teacher's Scholarship, entries (A—s) 46, (A—f) 127

Rhode Island Educational Benefits for Disabled American Veterans, (A—s) 67

Rhode Island Income Tax Deduction for the Blind, (V—g) 578

Richard Bennet of Maine Scholarship, (V—s) 429

Richard D. Kisling Scholarship. *See* Chief Master Sergeants of the Air Force Scholarships, entries (A—s) 14, (F—s) 1041

Richard E. Thorn Memorial Scholarship. *See* Pennsylvania National Guard Scholarship Fund, entry (F—s) 1186

Ricky Hobson Scholarship. *See* Hemophilia Health Services Memorial Scholarships, entries (O—s) 823, (O—f) 951

Riesch Scholarships. *See* Bryon Riesch Scholarships, entries (O—s) 776, (O—f) 942, (F—s) 1035, (F—f) 1227

Rimington Trophy Scholarship, (O—s) 895, (O—f) 962

Rise Scholarships, (O—s) 896

Rising Angus Star Youth Scholarship, (A—s) 68

Rising Star Scholarship of the Juvenile Diabetes Research Foundation, (O—s) 897

Ritch Dangel Memorial Scholarship. *See* Cystic Fibrosis Scholarships, entry (O—s) 788

Ritchie Learning Through Listening Award. *See* William L. Ritchie Learning Through Listening Award, entries (V—s) 448, (O—s) 937

R.L. Gillette Scholarships, (V—s) 430

Roadway Worker Memorial Scholarships, (F—s) 1193

Robert and Hazel Staley Memorial Scholarship, (V—s) 431, (V—f) 508

Robert Dole Scholarship Fund for Disabled Students, (P—s) 672, (O—s) 898

Robert Guthrie PKU Scholarship. *See* Guthrie-Koch PKU Scholarship, entry (O—s) 818

Robert H. Weitbrecht Scholarship. *See* Alexander Graham Bell College Scholarship Awards Program, entry (H—s) 590

Robert K. Fahnestock Memorial Award. *See* Geological Society of America Graduate Student Research Grants, entry (A—f) 114

Robert Price Memorial Scholarship. *See* Utah Hemophilia Foundation Scholarships, entries (O—s) 932, (F—s) 1218

Robin Kelleher-New Beginnings Award. *See* Hope for the Warriors Spouse/Caregiver Scholarships, entries (F—s) 1089, (F—f) 1233

Robyn Kimberly Meredith Multiple Sclerosis Memorial Scholarship, (F—s) 1194

R.O.C.K. College Scholarship Program, (O—s) 899

Roeder Assistive Technology Scholarship. *See* Joseph Roeder Assistive Technology Scholarship, entries (V—s) 377, (V—f) 481

Ron Niederman Scholarships. *See* Mike Hylton and Ron Niederman Scholarships, entries (O—s) 870, (F—s) 1147

Rose Phillips Award. *See* Jay and Rose Phillips Award, entry (P—f) 694

Rose Phillips Caregiver Award. *See* Jay and Rose Phillips Award, entry (P—f) 694

Rosemary Quigley Memorial Scholarship, (O—s) 900, (O—f) 963

Ross N. and Patricia Pangere Foundation Scholarships, (V—s) 432, (V—f) 509

Ross Research Fund Award. *See* Geological Society of America Graduate Student Research Grants, entry (A—f) 114

Roy Foundation Grants. *See* Travis Roy Foundation Grants, entry (P—g) 754

Roy Johnson Scholarships, (V—f) 510

Ruckes Scholarship. *See* Paul and Ellen Ruckes Scholarship, entries (V—s) 425, (V—f) 505

Rudolph Dillman Memorial Scholarship, (V—s) 433, (V—f) 511

Ruth Billow Memorial Education Fund. *See* Delta Gamma Foundation/Ruth Billow Memorial Education Fund, entries (V—s) 344, (V—f) 463

Ruth Billow Memorial Personal Aid, (V—g) 579, (F—g) 1361

Ruth L. Kirschstein National Research Service Awards for Individual Predoctoral Fellowships to Promote Diversity in Health-Related Research, (A—f) 144

Ruth Russell Memorial Grants. *See* Cynthia Ruth Russell Memorial Grants, entries (P—s) 643, (P—f) 692

Ryan Mullaly Second Chance Scholarships, (O—s) 901

S

S. Bradley Burson Memorial Scholarship. *See* Dr. S. Bradley Burson Memorial Scholarship, entries (V—s) 346, (V—f) 464

Sacks for CF Scholarships, (O—s) 902, (O—f) 964

Sad Sacks Nursing Scholarship, (F—s) 1195

A—Any Disability	V—Visual	H—Hearing	P—Physical/Orthopedic	O—Other Disabilities	F—Families
s—scholarships			f—fellowships		g—grants-in-aid

South Carolina Income Tax Exemption for the Adoption of a Special Needs Child, (F—g) 1365

South Carolina National Kidney Foundation Emergency Financial Assistance, (O—g) 1017

South Carolina Permanent Disability Retirement Income Tax Exclusion, (A—g) 300

South Carolina Property Tax Exemption for Disabled Veterans, Law Enforcement Officers, and Firefighters, (A—g) 301, (F—g) 1366

South Carolina Tuition Program for Children of Certain War Veterans, (F—s) 1199

South Dakota Property Tax Exemption for Paraplegic Veterans, (P—g) 743, (F—g) 1367

South Dakota Property Tax Reduction for Paraplegics, (P—g) 744, (F—g) 1368

South Dakota Reduced Tuition for Veterans, (A—s) 72

South Dakota Reduced Tuition for Visual Impairment, (V—s) 434, (V—f) 512

South Dakota Sales and Property Tax Refund for Senior and Disabled Citizens, (A—g) 302

Southern California and Nevada Chapter MS Society Scholarship Program, (P—s) 673, (F—s) 1200

Special Housing Adaptations Grants, (V—g) 583, (P—g) 745

Specially Adapted Housing Grants, (V—g) 584, (P—g) 746

Spibelt Athletic Scholarship, (O—s) 916

Spina Bifida Association of Alabama Advanced Education Scholarship Program, (P—s) 674, (P—f) 698

Spina Bifida Association of Central Indiana College Scholarship, (P—s) 675

Spina Bifida Association of Connecticut Scholarship Fund, (P—s) 676

Spina Bifida Association of Illinois Scholarships, (P—s) 677, (P—f) 699

Spina Bifida Association of North Texas Scholarship, (P—s) 678

Spina Bifida Association of Wisconsin Educational Scholarship in Memory of Mary Ann Potts, (P—s) 679, (P—f) 700

Spina Bifida Association One-Year Scholarship, (P—s) 680, (P—f) 701

Spina Bifida Program for Children of Veterans, (P—g) 747

SSDI Benefits. See Social Security Disability Insurance (SSDI) Benefits, entries (A—g) 298, (V—g) 581, (F—g) 1362

Staley Memorial Scholarship. See Robert and Hazel Staley Memorial Scholarship, entries (V—s) 431, (V—f) 508

Stan Beck Fellowship, (A—s) 73, (A—f) 149

Starr Endowed Scholarship. See Harry G. Starr Endowed Scholarship, entries (V—s) 365, (V—f) 474

State Vocational Rehabilitation Services Program, (A—s) 74, (A—f) 150

Stearns Fellowship Award. See Geological Society of America Graduate Student Research Grants, entry (A—f) 114

Stefano Scholarship Award. See Vincent Stefano Scholarship Award, entry (O—s) 936

Stein Scholarship. See Susan Stein Scholarship, entries (O—s) 921, (O—f) 972, (F—s) 1205, (F—f) 1253

Stephen T. Marchello Scholarships, (O—s) 917

Steve Fasteau Past Presidents' Scholarship, (A—s) 75, (A—f) 151

Steven M. Perez Foundation Scholarships, (O—s) 918, (F—s) 1201

Stineback Scholarship. See Hemophilia Health Services Memorial Scholarships, entries (O—s) 823, (O—f) 951

Stone Award. See Novo Nordisk Donnelly Awards, entry (O—s) 882

Strangio Education Scholarship. See Bonnie Strangio Education Scholarship, entries (O—s) 771, (O—f) 940

Streeter Memorial Scholarship. See Larry Streeter Memorial Scholarship, entries (V—s) 384, (V—f) 486

Stroud Scholarship. See NCTA Scholarships, entry (F—s) 1162

Stubblefield Foundation Scholarship. See Sarah Elizabeth Stubblefield Foundation Scholarship, entry (O—s) 904

Students with Disabilities Endowed Scholarships Honoring Elizabeth Daley Jeffords, (A—s) 76

SuperSibs! Scholarships, (F—s) 1202

Supplemental Security Income (SSI), (V—g) 585, (H—g) 634, (P—g) 748, (O—g) 1018

Supreme Emblem Club of the United States of America Grant-in-Aid Awards, (A—s) 77

Surviving and Moving Forward Grants and Scholarships. See SAMFund Grants and Scholarships, entries (O—f) 965, (O—g) 1015

Survivors' and Dependents' Educational Assistance Program, (A—s) 78, (A—f) 152, (F—s) 1203, (F—f) 1252

Susan Brown Transportation Program, (P—g) 749

Susan Bunch Memorial Scholarship, (O—s) 919, (O—f) 971

Susan G. Komen Breast Cancer Foundation College Scholarship Awards, (O—s) 920, (F—s) 1204

Susan Stein Scholarship, (O—s) 921, (O—f) 972, (F—s) 1205, (F—f) 1253

Susanna DeLaurentis Memorial Scholarships, (O—s) 922

Susquehanna Foundation for the Blind Trustees' Scholarship, (V—s) 435, (V—f) 513

Susquehanna Post-Graduate Scholarship, (V—f) 514

Sussman Trust Grants. See Otto Sussman Trust Grants, entries (A—s) 59, (A—f) 138

Sutton Scholarships. See Michael Bendix Sutton Scholarships, entry (O—s) 867

Swift Educational Trust Scholarships. See Knights of Columbus/Francis P. Matthews and John E. Swift Educational Trust Scholarships, entry (F—s) 1131

Swim With Mike, (A—s) 79

Syde Hurdus President's Award, (V—s) 436, (V—f) 515

Syle Memorial Fellowship for Seminary Studies. See Henry Syle Memorial Fellowship for Seminary Studies, entry (H—f) 615

A—Any Disability	V—Visual	H—Hearing	P—Physical/Orthopedic	O—Other Disabilities	F—Families
s—scholarships			f—fellowships		g—grants-in-aid

A—Any Disability	V—Visual	H—Hearing	P—Physical/Orthopedic	O—Other Disabilities	F—Families
s—scholarships			f—fellowships		g—grants-in-aid

Sponsoring Organization Index

The Sponsoring Organization Index makes it easy to identify agencies that offer financial aid to persons with disabilities and members of their families. In this index, sponsoring organizations are listed alphabetically, word by word. In addition, we've used a two-character alphabetical code (within parentheses) to help you identify which programs sponsored by these organizations fall within your scope of interest. The first character (capitalized) in the code identifies the program focus: A = Any Disability; V = Visual Disabilities; H = Hearing Disabilities; P = Physical/Orthopedic; O = Other Disabilities/Disorders; F = Families of the Disabled. The second character (lower-cased) identifies funding type: s = scholarships; f = fellowships; g = grants-in-aid. Here's how the code works: if a program is followed by (A–s) 28, the program is described in the Any Disability chapter, in the scholarships section, in entry 28. If that sponsoring organization's name is followed by another entry number—for example, (F–g) 1368—the same or a different program sponsored by that organization is described in the Families of the Disabled chapter, under grants-in-aid, in entry 1368. Remember: the numbers cited here refer to program entry numbers, not to page numbers in the book.

A—Any Disability	V—Visual	H—Hearing	P—Physical/Orthopedic	O—Other Disabilities	F—Families
s—scholarships			f—fellowships		g—grants-in-aid

A—Any Disability   V—Visual   H—Hearing   P—Physical/Orthopedic   O—Other Disabilities   F—Families
s—scholarships   f—fellowships   g—grants-in-aid

A—Any Disability	V—Visual	H—Hearing	P—Physical/Orthopedic	O—Other Disabilities	F—Families
s—scholarships			f—fellowships		g—grants-in-aid

Residency Index

Some programs listed in this book are restricted to residents of a particular state or region. Others are open to applicants wherever they might live. The Residency Index will help you pinpoint programs available only to residents in your area as well as programs that have no residency restrictions at all (these are listed under the term "United States"). To use this index, look up the geographic areas that apply to you (always check the listings under "United States"), jot down the entry numbers listed after the target groups and types of funding that interest you, and use those numbers to find the program descriptions in the directory. To help you in your search, we've provided some "see also" references in the index entries. Remember: the numbers cited here refer to program entry numbers, not to page numbers in the book.

A

Alabama
Any disability: **Grants-in-aid,** 164-168
Visual disabilities: **Grants-in-aid,** 520-522
Hearing disabilities: **Grants-in-aid,** 621
Physical/orthopedic disabilities: **Scholarships,** 674; **Fellowships,** 698
Other disabilities/disorders: **Scholarships,** 868
Families of the disabled: **Scholarships,** 1021-1022, 1130; **Fellowships,** 1225; **Grants-in-aid,** 1261-1262
See also United States

Alaska
Any disability: **Grants-in-aid,** 169
Physical/orthopedic disabilities: **Scholarships,** 650
Other disabilities/disorders: **Scholarships,** 817, 834
Families of the disabled: **Scholarships,** 1083
See also United States

Alexandria, Virginia
Visual disabilities: **Scholarships,** 448
Other disabilities/disorders: **Scholarships,** 937
See also Virginia

Anne Arundel County, Maryland
Visual disabilities: **Scholarships,** 448
Other disabilities/disorders: **Scholarships,** 937
See also Maryland

Arizona
Any disability: **Grants-in-aid,** 171
Visual disabilities: **Scholarships,** 397; **Fellowships,** 493; **Grants-in-aid,** 524
Other disabilities/disorders: **Scholarships,** 817, 892
Families of the disabled: **Scholarships,** 1113
See also United States

Arkansas
Any disability: **Scholarships,** 4; **Fellowships,** 97; **Grants-in-aid,** 172-175
Visual disabilities: **Scholarships,** 328, 333; **Grants-in-aid,** 525
Physical/orthopedic disabilities: **Grants-in-aid,** 707
Other disabilities/disorders: **Scholarships,** 868, 894
Families of the disabled: **Scholarships,** 1027-1028, 1114; **Grants-in-aid,** 1265-1267
See also United States

Arlington County, Virginia
Visual disabilities: **Scholarships,** 448
Other disabilities/disorders: **Scholarships,** 937
See also Virginia

C

California
Any disability: **Scholarships,** 5, 8-9, 16, 41, 60, 64, 75, 91; **Fellowships,** 100, 103, 151, 160; **Grants-in-aid,** 177-178, 256
Visual disabilities: **Scholarships,** 330, 335, 341, 398, 443; **Fellowships,** 457, 461, 494, 517; **Grants-in-aid,** 527-528
Hearing disabilities: **Scholarships,** 592
Physical/orthopedic disabilities: **Scholarships,** 638; **Fellowships,** 689; **Grants-in-aid,** 710, 719
Other disabilities/disorders: **Scholarships,** 777, 779, 795, 919; **Fellowships,** 943, 946, 971; **Grants-in-aid,** 985
Families of the disabled: **Scholarships,** 1036-1039, 1056; **Grants-in-aid,** 1269-1270
See also United States

California, southern
Physical/orthopedic disabilities: **Scholarships,** 673

Visual disabilities: **Scholarships,** 351, 382; **Fellowships,** 484; **Grants-in-aid,** 543-544
Hearing disabilities: **Grants-in-aid,** 626
Physical/orthopedic disabilities: **Scholarships,** 643, 662; **Fellowships,** 692
Other disabilities/disorders: **Scholarships,** 763, 787, 825; **Fellowships,** 952
Families of the disabled: **Scholarships,** 1023, 1146; **Grants-in-aid,** 1304
See also United States

Kentucky
Any disability: **Fellowships,** 98; **Grants-in-aid,** 232
Visual disabilities: **Scholarships,** 403
Physical/orthopedic disabilities: **Scholarships,** 681
Other disabilities/disorders: **Scholarships,** 868, 890, 910
Families of the disabled: **Scholarships,** 1110-1111, 1117
See also United States

Kentucky, eastern
Families of the disabled: **Scholarships,** 1194
See also Kentucky

L

Latin America. *See* Caribbean; Central America; Mexico

Lee County, Florida
Physical/orthopedic disabilities: **Scholarships,** 636
See also Florida

Loudoun County, Virginia
Visual disabilities: **Scholarships,** 448
Other disabilities/disorders: **Scholarships,** 937
See also Virginia

Louisiana
Any disability: **Grants-in-aid,** 234
Visual disabilities: **Scholarships,** 404
Physical/orthopedic disabilities: **Scholarships,** 660
Other disabilities/disorders: **Scholarships,** 827-828, 856, 868
Families of the disabled: **Scholarships,** 1090, 1118, 1134-1135
See also United States

M

Mahoning County, Ohio
Other disabilities/disorders: **Scholarships,** 925
See also Ohio

Maine
Any disability: **Scholarships,** 65; **Fellowships,** 142; **Grants-in-aid,** 235
Visual disabilities: **Scholarships,** 429; **Grants-in-aid,** 546-547
Physical/orthopedic disabilities: **Scholarships,** 646, 649, 657; **Grants-in-aid,** 705, 723
Other disabilities/disorders: **Scholarships,** 877
Families of the disabled: **Scholarships,** 1061, 1082, 1084, 1107, 1138, 1159; **Fellowships,** 1232, 1243; **Grants-in-aid,** 1308-1309
See also New England states; United States

Maryland
Any disability: **Scholarships,** 23, 43; **Fellowships,** 111; **Grants-in-aid,** 185, 236-237
Visual disabilities: **Scholarships,** 376; **Grants-in-aid,** 548-549
Hearing disabilities: **Scholarships,** 600; **Fellowships,** 619
Physical/orthopedic disabilities: **Scholarships,** 646; **Grants-in-aid,** 749
Other disabilities/disorders: **Scholarships,** 798, 854, 891; **Fellowships,** 955, 961
Families of the disabled: **Scholarships,** 1058, 1061-1062, 1119, 1133, 1187; **Fellowships,** 1229, 1241, 1250; **Grants-in-aid,** 1268, 1310-1313
See also United States

Massachusetts
Any disability: **Scholarships,** 15, 44; **Grants-in-aid,** 238-239
Visual disabilities: **Scholarships,** 330-331, 390; **Grants-in-aid,** 550-552
Physical/orthopedic disabilities: **Scholarships,** 646, 649, 683; **Fellowships,** 703; **Grants-in-aid,** 724
Other disabilities/disorders: **Scholarships,** 797
Families of the disabled: **Scholarships,** 1057, 1061, 1082; **Grants-in-aid,** 1314-1316
See also New England states; United States

Massachusetts, western
Other disabilities/disorders: **Scholarships,** 876
Families of the disabled: **Scholarships,** 1158
See also Massachusetts

Mexico
Any disability: **Scholarships,** 73; **Fellowships,** 114, 149
See also Foreign countries

Michigan
Any disability: **Scholarships,** 47, 69; **Fellowships,** 146; **Grants-in-aid,** 183, 241-244
Visual disabilities: **Scholarships,** 446; **Grants-in-aid,** 553-554
Hearing disabilities: **Grants-in-aid,** 627
Physical/orthopedic disabilities: **Grants-in-aid,** 725
Other disabilities/disorders: **Scholarships,** 789, 821, 923; **Fellowships,** 973; **Grants-in-aid,** 1001
Families of the disabled: **Scholarships,** 1085, 1145; **Grants-in-aid,** 1317-1319
See also United States

Minnesota
Any disability: **Scholarships,** 17; **Fellowships,** 119; **Grants-in-aid,** 245-247
Visual disabilities: **Scholarships,** 326, 405; **Fellowships,** 453
Physical/orthopedic disabilities: **Scholarships,** 656, 684; **Fellowships,** 694; **Grants-in-aid,** 718, 755
Other disabilities/disorders: **Scholarships,** 803, 822, 869
Families of the disabled: **Scholarships,** 1108, 1148, 1197, 1217; **Fellowships,** 1245; **Grants-in-aid,** 1303, 1320-1321
See also United States

Tenability Index

Some programs listed in this book can be used only in specific cities, counties, states, or regions. Others may be used anywhere in the United States (or even abroad). The Tenability Index will help you locate funding that is restricted to a specific area as well as funding that has no tenability restrictions (these are listed under the term "United States"). To use this index, look up the geographic areas where you'd like to go (always check the listings under "United States"), jot down the entry numbers listed after the target group and type of funding that applies to you, and use those numbers to find the program descriptions in the directory. To help you in your search, we've provided some "see also" references in the index entries. Remember: the numbers cited here refer to program entry numbers, not to page numbers in the book.

A

Alabama
Any disability: **Grants-in-aid,** 164-168
Visual disabilities: **Grants-in-aid,** 520-522
Hearing disabilities: **Grants-in-aid,** 621
Families of the disabled: **Scholarships,** 1021-1022; **Fellowships,** 1225; **Grants-in-aid,** 1261-1262
See also United States

Alaska
Any disability: **Grants-in-aid,** 169
See also United States

Alexandria, Virginia
Visual disabilities: **Scholarships,** 448
Other disabilities/disorders: **Scholarships,** 937
See also Virginia

Anne Arundel County, Maryland
Visual disabilities: **Scholarships,** 448
Other disabilities/disorders: **Scholarships,** 937
See also Maryland

Arizona
Any disability: **Grants-in-aid,** 171
Visual disabilities: **Grants-in-aid,** 524
Physical/orthopedic disabilities: **Scholarships,** 686; **Fellowships,** 704
Other disabilities/disorders: **Scholarships,** 892
See also United States

Arkansas
Any disability: **Grants-in-aid,** 172-175
Visual disabilities: **Grants-in-aid,** 525
Physical/orthopedic disabilities: **Grants-in-aid,** 707
Families of the disabled: **Scholarships,** 1027-1028; **Grants-in-aid,** 1265-1267
See also United States

Arlington County, Virginia
Visual disabilities: **Scholarships,** 448
Other disabilities/disorders: **Scholarships,** 937
See also Virginia

Atlanta, Georgia
Any disability: **Fellowships,** 121
See also Georgia

B

Berkeley, California
Any disability: **Fellowships,** 106, 155
See also California

Bloomington, Indiana
Any disability: **Fellowships,** 99
See also Indiana

Boston, Massachusetts
Any disability: **Fellowships,** 107
See also Massachusetts

Boulder, Colorado
Visual disabilities: **Scholarships,** 379
See also Colorado

Broomfield, Colorado
Any disability: **Fellowships,** 107
See also Colorado

C

California
Any disability: **Scholarships,** 5, 8, 16, 41, 60, 75, 91; **Fellowships,** 100, 103, 151, 160; **Grants-in-aid,** 177-178, 256
Visual disabilities: **Scholarships,** 341, 443; **Fellowships,** 461, 517; **Grants-in-aid,** 527-528
Physical/orthopedic disabilities: **Grants-in-aid,** 710

Physical/orthopedic disabilities: **Scholarships,** 638; **Fellowships,** 689
Other disabilities/disorders: **Scholarships,** 779, 823; **Fellowships,** 943, 951; **Grants-in-aid,** 1003
Families of the disabled: **Scholarships,** 1202
See also Caribbean; United States; United States possessions

R

Redwood Shores, California
Any disability: **Fellowships,** 121
See also California
Reston, Virginia
Any disability: **Fellowships,** 107
See also Virginia
Rhode Island
Any disability: **Scholarships,** 67
Visual disabilities: **Grants-in-aid,** 578
Physical/orthopedic disabilities: **Scholarships,** 646
Families of the disabled: **Scholarships,** 1061
See also United States
Riverside, California
Any disability: **Fellowships,** 155
See also California

S

San Diego, California
Any disability: **Fellowships,** 107, 155
See also California
San Francisco, California
Any disability: **Fellowships,** 107, 121, 155
See also California
Santa Barbara, California
Any disability: **Fellowships,** 155
See also California
Santa Cruz, California
Any disability: **Fellowships,** 155
See also California
Sarasota County, Florida
Any disability: **Fellowships,** 145
See also Florida
Seattle, Washington
Any disability: **Fellowships,** 107
See also Washington
South Carolina
Any disability: **Grants-in-aid,** 299-301
Visual disabilities: **Scholarships,** 414; **Grants-in-aid,** 582
Physical/orthopedic disabilities: **Scholarships,** 645; **Fellowships,** 693; **Grants-in-aid,** 742
Other disabilities/disorders: **Grants-in-aid,** 994, 1017
Families of the disabled: **Scholarships,** 1199; **Grants-in-aid,** 1363-1366
See also United States
South Dakota
Any disability: **Scholarships,** 72; **Fellowships,** 119; **Grants-in-aid,** 302

Visual disabilities: **Scholarships,** 434; **Fellowships,** 512
Physical/orthopedic disabilities: **Fellowships,** 694; **Grants-in-aid,** 743-744
Families of the disabled: **Scholarships,** 1191; **Grants-in-aid,** 1367-1368
See also United States
Stennis Space Center, Mississippi
Any disability: **Fellowships,** 117
See also Mississippi

T

Tennessee
Any disability: **Grants-in-aid,** 303-304
Visual disabilities: **Grants-in-aid,** 586-587
Physical/orthopedic disabilities: **Grants-in-aid,** 750-751
Other disabilities/disorders: **Scholarships,** 799
Families of the disabled: **Scholarships,** 1059, 1207; **Grants-in-aid,** 1369
See also United States
Texas
Any disability: **Scholarships,** 27, 80-81; **Fellowships,** 153; **Grants-in-aid,** 202, 305
Visual disabilities: **Scholarships,** 439; **Grants-in-aid,** 588
Hearing disabilities: **Scholarships,** 606
Physical/orthopedic disabilities: **Grants-in-aid,** 752
Other disabilities/disorders: **Scholarships,** 838; **Fellowships,** 953
Families of the disabled: **Scholarships,** 1065, 1069, 1208; **Grants-in-aid,** 1285, 1370
See also United States

U

United States
Any disability: **Scholarships,** 1-4, 6-7, 9, 11-15, 17, 19-21, 24-26, 28-30, 32, 35-38, 42, 45-47, 49-55, 57, 59, 61-64, 66, 68-71, 73-74, 76-79, 82, 84-90, 93-94; **Fellowships,** 95-97, 101-102, 104-105, 107-110, 112, 114-118, 121-141, 144-150, 152, 154, 156-159, 161; **Grants-in-aid,** 163, 170, 176, 179-182, 184, 188, 193, 196, 198-201, 208, 214, 225, 233, 240, 254-255, 278, 286-289, 295-298, 306-307, 311-312, 315, 322
Visual disabilities: **Scholarships,** 324-340, 342-349, 351-353, 355-363, 365, 367-378, 380-384, 386-389, 391-393, 395-404, 406-411, 413-417, 419-421, 423-426, 428-433, 435-438, 440-442, 444-447, 450; **Fellowships,** 451-460, 462-474, 476-486, 488-491, 493-499, 501-506, 508-509, 511, 513-516, 518-519; **Grants-in-aid,** 526, 533, 545, 579-581, 583-585
Hearing disabilities: **Scholarships,** 590-593, 595-599, 601-605, 607; **Fellowships,** 608-612, 614-618, 620; **Grants-in-aid,** 622-623, 625, 628, 631-634
Physical/orthopedic disabilities: **Scholarships,** 635, 637-642, 644-646, 648-650, 652-665, 667-680, 682-685, 687; **Fellowships,** 688-690, 693, 695-703; **Grants-in-aid,** 706, 708-709, 711, 715-717, 719-722, 726, 728, 733, 737, 741, 745-748, 753-754, 756

Subject Index

Use the Subject Index when you want to identify the subject focus of available funding programs. There are more than 250 different subject areas indexed in this directory (each subdivided by both disability group and funding type). To help you pinpoint your search, we've also included hundreds of "see" and "see also" references. In addition to looking for terms that represent your specific subject interest, be sure to check the "General programs" entry; hundreds of programs are listed there that can be used to support study, research, or other activities in *any* subject area (although the programs may be restricted in other ways). Remember: the numbers cited in this index refer to program entry numbers, not to page numbers in the book.

Calendar Index

Since most financial aid programs have specific deadline dates, some may have already closed by the time you begin to look for funding. You can use the Calendar Index to identify which programs are still open. To do that, check the type of funding sections and disability categories that apply to you, think about when you'll be able to complete your application forms, go to the appropriate months, jot down the entry numbers listed there, and use those numbers to find the program descriptions in the directory. Keep in mind that the numbers cited here refer to program entry numbers, not to page numbers in the book.

Scholarships

March: 759, 761, 765, 768, 770, 772, 775, 780, 783-784, 786, 788-790, 792, 797, 803, 807, 821, 824-825, 832, 838, 851, 854, 860-862, 866-867, 869, 872, 874, 883, 886, 888, 891, 894, 908, 911, 917, 921, 925-927, 933-934, 937, 939

April: 764, 767, 777-778, 793, 796, 798-802, 804-805, 814, 816, 820, 823, 826, 839-840, 847, 849, 870-871, 879-880, 882, 884, 899, 903-904, 906-907, 914, 918, 922, 931

May: 757, 766, 773, 776, 781-782, 787, 794, 806, 811, 822, 830, 835, 841, 844-846, 857-858, 863-864, 873, 876, 885, 890, 893, 897, 905, 910, 912, 916, 924, 932, 935-936

June: 771-772, 774, 791, 808, 810, 815, 827-828, 856, 878, 895, 900, 928-929

July: 829, 842-843, 859, 877, 901, 915

September: 772, 795, 836, 865, 919

October: 780, 818

November: 859

December: 758, 762, 772, 776, 785, 827-828, 856, 923

Any time: 884, 909

Deadline not specified: 779, 813, 833, 852, 875, 887, 892

Families of the Disabled:

January: 1047-1048, 1052, 1081-1083, 1129, 1134, 1142-1143, 1146, 1160, 1166, 1170, 1177-1178, 1200, 1202, 1204, 1217, 1219, 1223

February: 1026, 1064, 1073, 1093-1094, 1099, 1102, 1118, 1131, 1155, 1170-1171, 1175, 1182, 1193, 1195, 1206, 1214

March: 1023-1024, 1029, 1032-1033, 1041, 1044-1045, 1049, 1051, 1054, 1057, 1070, 1074, 1085-1086, 1088-1089, 1096, 1100-1101, 1106, 1112, 1132-1133, 1140-1141, 1144, 1156-1157, 1162, 1168-1169, 1181, 1187, 1189, 1197, 1205, 1210, 1212, 1216, 1220, 1224

April: 1031, 1053, 1055, 1058-1059, 1075, 1080, 1084, 1105, 1107, 1109, 1117, 1120-1121, 1124, 1130, 1136, 1147, 1167, 1174, 1184, 1192, 1198, 1201, 1215, 1221

May: 1027-1028, 1030, 1035, 1040, 1060, 1071, 1079, 1098, 1108, 1114, 1137, 1139, 1153, 1158, 1180, 1183, 1190, 1218

June: 1034, 1050, 1061, 1067, 1077, 1087, 1090, 1093-1094, 1104, 1152, 1163, 1165, 1176, 1183, 1186, 1213, 1224

July: 1062, 1072, 1078, 1125, 1159, 1183, 1207

August: 1154, 1183, 1188

September: 1076, 1093-1094, 1149

October: 1027-1028, 1063, 1117, 1121, 1224

November: 1071, 1103

December: 1035, 1063, 1090, 1125

Any time: 1021, 1025, 1039, 1042, 1066, 1069, 1150, 1171, 1194, 1196, 1203, 1209, 1222

Deadline not specified: 1022, 1036-1038, 1043, 1046, 1056, 1065, 1068, 1091-1092, 1095, 1097, 1110-1111, 1113, 1115-1116, 1119, 1122-1123, 1126-1128, 1135, 1138, 1145, 1148, 1151, 1161, 1164, 1172-1173, 1179, 1185, 1191, 1199, 1208, 1211

Fellowships

Any Disability:

January: 112, 114, 140, 145, 153, 158

February: 97, 104-105, 109, 115, 120, 129-131, 133, 137, 148, 154, 156

March: 95, 118, 127-128, 142, 161

April: 117, 125, 144

May: 101-102, 119, 146

June: 99, 104, 107, 122, 130-131, 133, 137, 148-149, 154, 159

July: 111, 138

August: 98, 121, 125, 135-136, 144

September: 100, 103, 108, 123, 139, 151, 160

October: 104, 109-110, 130-131, 133, 137, 141, 148, 154

November: 96, 106, 113, 116, 124, 147, 155

December: 125-126, 134, 144

Any time: 143, 152, 157

Deadline not specified: 132, 150

Visual Disabilities:

January: 466, 474, 482, 485, 513-516

February: 452, 454, 464-465, 467, 470-471, 475, 477-478, 502, 509, 519

March: 458-459, 483, 486, 490, 496-497, 500-501

April: 456, 462, 468, 473, 479, 491-492, 499, 504-505, 507, 511

May: 451, 484, 493, 510

June: 453, 457, 472, 508

July: 481, 518

August: 455, 460, 476, 480, 488, 503, 506

September: 494-495, 517

October: 469, 498

December: 460

Any time: 463

Deadline not specified: 461, 487, 489, 512

Hearing Disabilities:

February: 616

April: 608-609, 611-612, 614-615, 620

May: 613, 618-619

September: 617

Deadline not specified: 610

Physical/Orthopedic Disabilities:

January: 690

February: 691, 704

March: 692, 700-702

Grants-in-Aid